Heating, ventilating, air conditioning and refrigeration

CIBSE Guide B

Registered charity number 278104

ISBN 1 903287 58 8

Typeset by CIBSE Publications

Printed in Great Britain by Page Bros. (Norwich) Ltd., Norwich, Norfolk NR6 6SA

Note from the publisher

This publication is primarily intended to provide guidance to those responsible for the design, installation, commissioning, operation and maintenance of building services. It is not intended to be exhaustive or definitive and it will be necessary for users of the guidance given to exercise their own professional judgement when deciding whether to abide by or depart from it.

Foreword

During 2001 and 2002, a completely new edition of CIBSE Guide B was published in the form of five separate 'stand alone' books. In 2004, the decision was taken to produce Guide B as a single volume and this publication is the result.

The technical content of this volume is the same as the five separate sections, with only minor editing to correct errors and to remove obvious duplication between sections. Each section retains its own introduction, following a common format, which sets down a framework for making strategic design decisions. It has been necessary to renumber section headings, tables, equations and figures for consistency within the volume. A single, coherent index has been provided. In accordance with CIBSE policy, Guide B will be reviewed and the next edition will provide an opportunity to further integrate the sections and to provide a common introduction.

I wish to thank the authors and contributors to the sections, and the members of the Guide B Steering Committee and the section Steering Committees for generously contributing their time and expertise to this project. Finally, the Institution wishes to acknowledge the support provided by the Department of Trade and Industry in the preparation of sections 2 and 5.

Vic Crisp
Chairman, CIBSE Guide B Steering Committee

Guide B Steering Committee

Vic Crisp (Carbon Trust) (Chairman), Laurence Aston (AMEC), Hywel Davies (Consultant), Tim Dwyer (South Bank University), Peter Grigg (BRE Environment), Barry Hutt (Consultant), Steve Irving (Faber Maunsell), Alan C Watson (CIBSE) (Secretary)

Principal authors, contributors and acknowledgements

Section 1: Heating

Principal author
George Henderson

Guide B1 Steering Committee
Paul Compton (Chairman) (Colt International Ltd), Peter Koch, Nick Skemp (Nick Skemp Associates)

CIBSE Project Manager
Alan C Watson

Acknowledgements
Barrie Church (Global Energy Associates Ltd.), Howard Davies (Nordair), Hamworthy Heating Ltd., Roger Hitchin (BRE Ltd.), Barrie Huggins (Faber Maunsell), Institution of Gas Engineers and Managers, Vina Kukadia (BRE Ltd.), Tom McDonnell (Spirax-Sarco Engineering plc), Loveday Murley (National Society for Clean Air), David Murrell (BDP), Martin Ratcliffe (South Bank University)

Section 2: Ventilation and air conditioning

Principal authors
Nick Barnard (Faber Maunsell), Denice Jaunzens (BRE Ltd.)

Contributors
Mike Burton (Faber Maunsell), May Cassar (Bartlett School of Architecture), Richard Daniels (Department for Education and Skills; Architects and Building Branch), Hywel Davies (Hywel Davies Consultancy), Alan Fox (Faber Maunsell), Matthew Hignell (Faber Maunsell), Graham Millard (Faber Maunsell), Richard Pearce (Faber Maunsell), Iain Shaw (Faber Maunsell), Simon Steed (AMEC Design and Management Ltd.), Chris Twinn (Arup)

Guide B2 Steering Committee
Phil Jones (Chairman) (University of Cardiff School of Architecture and the Built

Environment), Wayne Aston (Willan Building Services Ltd.), Nick Barnard (Faber Maunsell), John Boxall (FBE Management Ltd.), May Cassar (Bartlett School of Architecture), Andrew Cripps (Buro Happold Consulting Engineers), Richard Daniels (Department for Education and Skills, Architects and Building Branch), Mike Duggan (Federation of Environmental Trade Associations), Paul Evans (FBE Management Ltd.), Les Fothergill (Department of the Environment, Food and Rural Affairs), George Henderson (W S Atkins plc, on behalf of the Department of Trade and Industry), Roger Hitchin (Building Research, Energy Conservation Unit), Denice Jaunzens (BRE Ltd.), Ted King (Department of the Environment, Food and Rural Affairs), Geoff Leventhall (consultant), Luke Neville (Brian Warwicker Partnership), Derrick Newson (consultant, representing the Heating and Ventilating Contractors' Association), Fergus Nicol (Oxford Brookes University), Nigel Pavey (F C Foreman Ltd.), Mike Price (Biddle Air Systems Ltd.), Mike Smith (Building Services Research and Information Association), Helen Sutcliffe (FBE Management Ltd.), Simon Steed (AMEC Design and Management Ltd.), Chris Twinn (Arup), Christine Wiech (Max Fordham & Partners), John Wright (Willan Building Services Ltd.)

CIBSE Project Manager
Hywel Davies

Acknowledgements
This section was funded in part by the Department of Trade and Industry under the Partners in Innovation Scheme (formerly known as the DETR Partners in Innovation Scheme) and the CIBSE Research Fund. It was also supported by the various organisations represented on the Guide B2 Steering Committee. This document is published with the consent of the DTI, but the views expressed are not necessarily accepted or endorsed by the Department.

Section 3: Ductwork

Principal author
John Armstrong

Guide B3 Steering Committee
Professor Phillip Jones (Chairman) (Cardiff University), Robert Kingsbury (EMCOR Drake & Scull), Peter Koch (Coventry University), Stephen Loyd (Building Services Research and Information Association)

Contributors
Steve Irving (Faber Maunsell), Professor Phillip Jones (Cardiff University), Robert Kingsbury (EMCOR Drake & Scull), Peter Koch (Coventry University), Stephen Loyd (Building Services Research and Information Association), Jim Murray (Senior Hargreaves)

CIBSE Project Manager
Alan C Watson

Section 4: Refrigeration and heat rejection

Principal author
David Butler (BRE)

Contributor
Alan J Cooper (consultant)

Guide B4 Steering Committee
James Fretwell (Chairman), David Butler (BRE), Tim Davies (HFM Consulting Engineers), Shakil Mughal (Airedale International Air Conditioning Ltd.), Derrick Newson (consultant), Robert Tozer (Waterman Gore plc)

CIBSE Project Manager
Alan C Watson

Acknowledgements
The Institution gratefully acknowledges the American Society of Heating, Refrigerating and Air-Conditioning Engineers and E .I. duPont de Nemours & Co. Inc. for permission to reproduce the pressure–enthalpy diagrams shown in Appendix 4.A2.

Section 5: Noise and vibration control for HVAC

Principal author
Dr Geoff Leventhall (Consultant)

Contributors

Peter Tucker (Eurovib (Acoustic Products) Ltd.) (section 5.11), Professor David Oldham (University of Liverpool) (Appendix 5.A2.4)

Guide B5 Steering Committee
Dr Geoff Leventhall (Chairman) (Consultant), Peter Tucker (Eurovib (Acoustic Products), Ltd.), Peter Bird (Bird Acoustics), Gary Hughes (formerly of AMEC Designs), Richard Galbraith (Sandy Brown Associates), Peter Hensen (Bickerdike Allen Partners), Mathew Ling (Building Research Establishment Ltd.), Mike Price (Biddle Air Systems Ltd.) Peter Allaway (Consultant)

Acknowledgements
This section was part funded by the Department of Trade and Industry under the Partners in Innovation Scheme and by the CIBSE Research Fund. This Guide is published with the consent of the DTI, but the views expressed are not necessarily accepted or endorsed by the Department.

CIBSE Project Manager
Hywel Davies

Editor

Ken Butcher

CIBSE Research Manager

Hywel Davies

CIBSE Publishing Manager

Jacqueline Balian

Contents

1 Heating

1.1 Introduction

This Guide starts by considering the strategic choices facing the heating system designer, including the requirements imposed by the intended use of the building, energy and environmental targets, legal requirements and possible interaction with other building services. The succeeding sections follow the various stages of design, as follows:

— detailed definition of requirements and the calculation of system loads

— characteristics and selection of systems

— characteristics and selection of system components and equipment

— characteristics of fuels and their requirements for storage

— commissioning and hand-over.

Section 1.2, which deals with strategic choices, is relatively broad ranging and discursive and is intended to be read from time to time as a reminder of the key decisions to be taken at the start of the design process. The latter sections are sub-divided by topic and are likely to be used for reference, as particular issues arise; they contain a range of useful details but also direct the reader to more specialised sources where appropriate, including other CIBSE publications and BS, EN, and ISO standards.

When using this Guide, the designer should firstly fully map the design process that is being undertaken. The process for each application will be unique, but will follow the general format:

— problem definition

— ideas generation

— analysis, and

— selection of the final solution.

This procedure is illustrated in Figure 1.1 in the form of a outline flowchart.

1.2 Strategic design decisions

1.2.1 General

In common with some other aspects of building services, the requirements placed upon the heating system depend crucially on the form and fabric of the building. It follows that the role of the building services engineer in heating system design is at its greatest when it begins at an early stage, when decisions about the fabric of the building can still be influenced. This allows options for heating to be assessed on an integrated basis that takes account of how the demand for heating is affected by building design as well as by the provision of heating. In other cases, especially in designing replacement heating systems for existing buildings, the scope for integrated design may be much more limited. In all cases, however, the designer should seek to optimise the overall design as far as is possible within the brief.

A successful heating system design will result in a system that can be installed and commissioned to deliver the indoor temperatures required by the client. When in operation, it should operate with high efficiency to minimise fuel costs and environmental emissions while meeting those requirements. It should also sustain its performance over its planned life with limited need for maintenance and replacement of components. Beyond operational and economic requirements, the designer must comply with legal requirements, including those relating to environmental impact and to health and safety.

1.2.2 Purposes of space heating systems

Heating systems in most buildings are principally required to maintain comfortable conditions for people working or living in the building. As the human body exchanges heat with its surroundings both by convection and by radiation, comfort depends on the temperature of both the air and the exposed surfaces surrounding it and on air movement. Dry resultant temperature, which combines air temperature and mean radiant temperature, has generally been used for assessing comfort. The predicted mean vote (PMV) index, as set out in the European Standard BS EN 7730[1], incorporates a range of factors contributing to thermal comfort. Methods for establishing comfort conditions are described in more detail in section 1.3.2 below.

In buildings (or parts of buildings) that are not normally occupied by people, heating may not be required to maintain comfort. However, it may be necessary to control temperature or humidity in order to protect the fabric of the building or its contents, e.g. from frost or condensation, or for processes carried out within the building. In either case, the specific requirements for each room or zone need to be established.

1.2.3 Site-related issues

The particular characteristics of the site need to be taken into account, including exposure, site access and connection to gas or heating mains. Exposure is taken into account in the calculation of heat loss (see section 1.3.3 below). The availability of mains gas or heat supplies is a key factor affecting the choice of fuel.

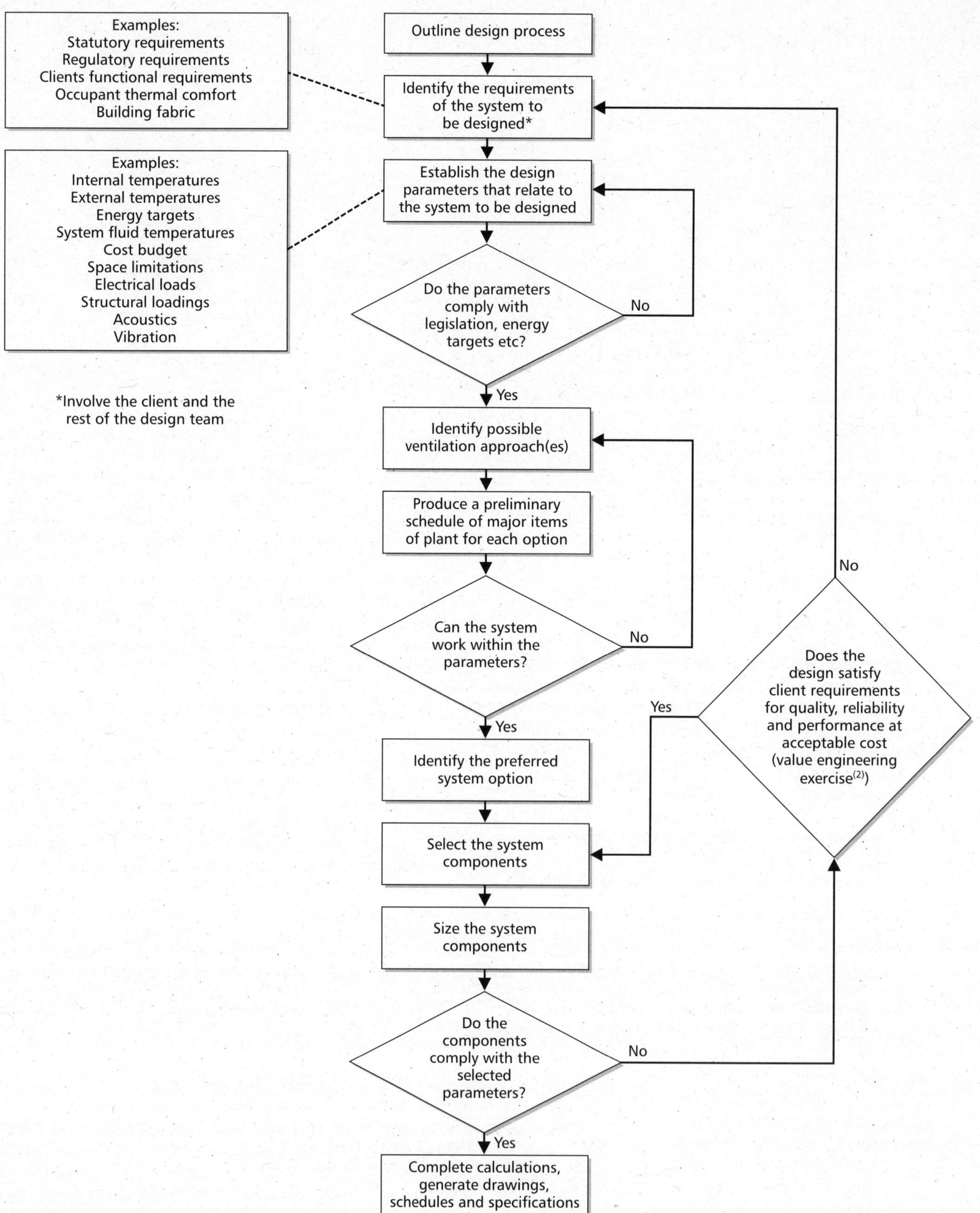

Figure 1.1 Outline design process; heating

The form and orientation of buildings can have a significant effect on demand for heating and cooling. If the building services designer is involved early enough in the design process, it will be possible to influence strategic decisions, e.g. to optimise the 'passive solar' contribution to energy requirements.

1.2.4 Legal, economic and general considerations

Various strands of legislation affect the design of heating systems. Aspects of the design and performance of heating systems are covered by building regulations aimed at the conservation of fuel and power[3–5] and ventilation[4–6]; and regulations implementing the EU Boiler Directive[7] set minimum efficiency levels for boilers. Heat producing appliances are also subject to regulations governing supply of combustion air, flues and chimneys, and emissions of gases and particles to the atmosphere[8], see section 1.5.5.1. Designers should also be aware of their obligations to comply with the Construction (Design and Management) Regulations[9,10] and the Health and Safety at Work Act[11].

Beyond strictly legal requirements, the client may wish to meet energy and environmental targets, which can depend strongly on heating system performance. These include:

— CIBSE *Building Energy Codes*[12] define a method for setting energy targets.

— Carbon performance rating/carbon intensity: although primarily intended as a means of showing compliance with Part L of the Building Regulations[3], 'carbon performance rating' (CPR) and 'carbon intensity' may be used more widely to define performance. CPR applies to the overall energy performance of office buildings with air conditioning and mechanical ventilation. Carbon intensity applies to heating systems generally.

— Broader ranging environmental assessments also take energy use into account, e.g. *Building Research Environmental Assessment Method*[13] (BREEAM) sets a series of best practice criteria against which aspects of the environmental performance of a building can be assessed. A good BREEAM rating also depends strongly on the performance of the heating system.

— Clients who own and manage social housing may also have 'affordable warmth' targets, which aim to ensure that low income households will not find their homes too expensive to heat. The UK government's *Standard Assessment Procedure for the Energy Rating of Dwellings*[14] (SAP) and the *National Home Energy Rating*[15] (NHER) are both methods for assessing the energy performance of dwellings.

Economic appraisal of different levels of insulation, heating systems, fuels, controls should be undertaken to show optimum levels of investment according to the client's own criteria, which may be based on a simple payback period, or a specified discount rate over a given lifetime. Public sector procurement policies may specifically require life cycle costing.

1.2.5 Interaction with building design, building fabric, services and facilities

As noted above, the earlier the heating system designer can be involved in the overall design process, the greater the scope for optimisation. The layout of the building, the size and orientation of windows, the extent and location of thermal mass within the building, and the levels of insulation of the building fabric can all have a significant effect on demand for heat. The airtightness of the building shell and the way in which the building is ventilated are also important. Buildings that are very well insulated and airtight may have no net heating demand when occupied, which requires heating systems to be designed principally for pre-heating prior to occupancy[16].

However, the designer is often faced with a situation in which there is little or no opportunity to influence important characteristics of the building that have a strong bearing on the heating system, particularly in the replacement of an existing heating system. For example, there may be constraints on the area and location of plant rooms, the space for and the routing of distribution networks. There may also be a requirement to interface with parts of an existing system, either for heating or ventilation. Where domestic hot water is required, a decision is required on whether it should be heated by the same system as the space heating or heated at the point of use.

1.2.6 Occupancy

When the building is to be occupied and what activities are to be carried out within it are key determinants of the heating system specification. Are the occupants sedentary or physically active? What heat gains are expected to arise from processes and occupancy, including associated equipment such as computers and office machinery? Do all areas of the building have similar requirements or are there areas with special requirements? These factors may determine or at least constrain the options available. The anticipated occupancy patterns may also influence the heating design at a later stage. Consideration should also be given to flexibility and adaptability of systems, taking account of possible re-allocation of floor space in the future.

1.2.7 Energy efficiency

The term 'energy efficiency' gained currency during the 1980s and is now widely used.

In general, the energy efficiency of a building can only be assessed in relative terms, either based on the previous performance of the same building or by comparison with other buildings. Thus the energy use of a building might be expressed in terms of annual energy use per square metre of floor area, and compared with benchmark levels for similar buildings. The result so obtained would depend on many physical factors including insulation, boiler efficiency, temperature, control systems, and the luminous efficacy of the lighting installations, but it would also depend on the way the occupants interacted with the building, particularly if it were naturally ventilated with openable windows.

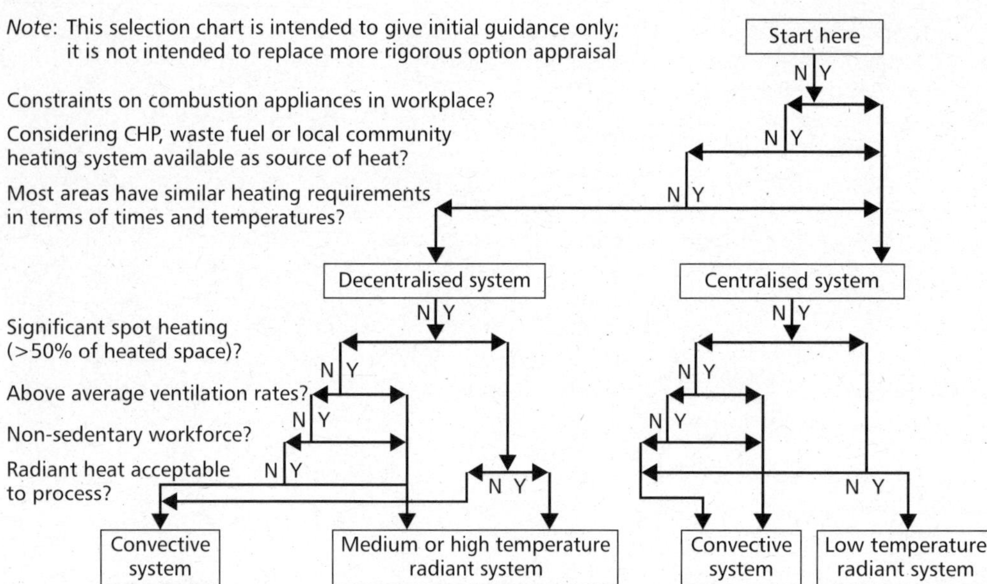

Figure 1.2 Selection chart: heating systems[17] (reproduced from EEBPP Good Practice Guide GPG303 by permission of the Energy Efficiency Best Practice Programme)

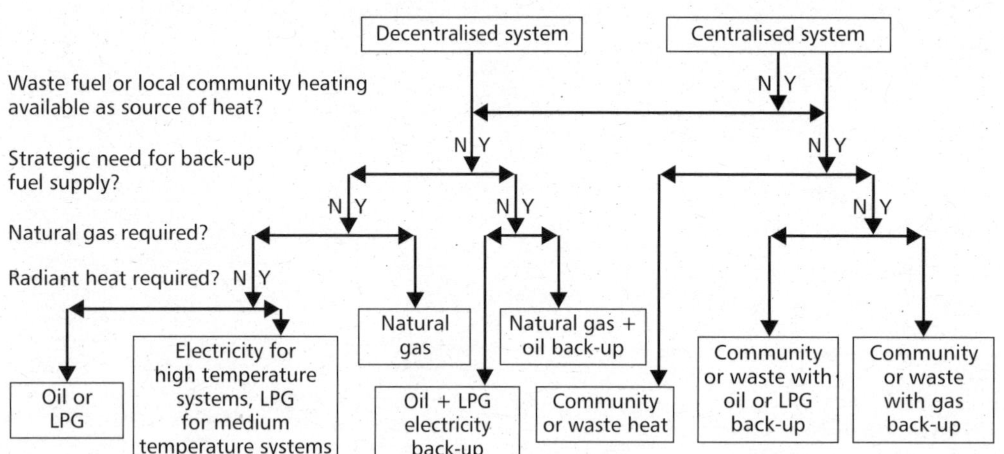

Figure 1.3 Selection chart: fuel[17] (reproduced from EEBPP Good Practice Guide GPG303 by permission of the Energy Efficiency Best Practice Programme)

The energy consumption of buildings is most readily measured in terms of 'delivered' energy, which may be read directly from meters or from records of fuels bought in bulk. Delivered energy fails to distinguish between electricity and fuel which has yet to be converted to heat. 'Primary' energy includes the overheads associated with production of fuels and with the generation and distribution of electricity. Comparisons of energy efficiency are therefore sometimes made on the basis of primary energy or on the emissions of 'greenhouse' gases, which also takes account of energy overheads. Fuel cost may also be used and has the advantage of being both more transparent and more relevant to non-technical building owners and occupants. In any event, it is meaningless to quote energy use in delivered energy obtained by adding electricity use to fuel use. Consequently, if comparisons are to be made in terms of delivered energy, electricity and fuel use must be quoted separately.

Clearly, the performance of the heating system has a major influence on energy efficiency, particularly in an existing building with relatively poor insulation. The designer has the opportunity to influence it through adopting an appropriate design strategy and choice of fuel, by specifying components with good energy performance, and by devising a control system that can accurately match output with occupant needs. Particular aspects of energy efficiency are dealt with in other sections of this Guide as they arise. The energy efficiency of heating and hot water systems is dealt with in detail in section 9 of CIBSE Guide F: *Energy efficiency in buildings*[17].

1.2.8 Making the strategic decisions

Each case must be considered on its own merits and rigorous option appraisal based on economic and environmental considerations should be undertaken. However, the flow charts shown in Figures 1.2 and 1.3 are offered as general guidance. They first appeared in Good Practice Guide GPG303[18], which was published under the government's Energy Efficiency Best Practice programme and was aimed specifically at industrial buildings, but they are considered to be generally applicable. Figure 1.2 refers to heating systems in general and Figure 1.3 to choice of fuel.

1.3 Design criteria

1.3.1 General

After taking the principal strategic decisions on which type of system to install, it is necessary to establish design criteria for the system in detail. Typically this starts by defining the indoor and outdoor climate requirements and the air change rates required to maintain satisfactory air quality. A heat balance calculation may then be used to determine the output required from the heating system under design condition, which in turn defines the heat output required in each room or zone of the building. This calculation may be done on a steady-state or dynamic basis. As the latter type of calculation can lead to extreme complexity, simplified methods have been devised to deal with dynamic effects, such as those described in CIBSE Guide A[19], section 5.6. Dynamic simulation methods using computers are necessary when dynamic responses need to be modelled in detail. In all cases, however, underlying principles are the same — the required output from the heating system is calculated from consideration of the outflow of heat under design conditions, whether static or dynamic.

1.3.2 Internal climate requirements

Indoor climate may be defined in terms of temperature, humidity and air movement. The heat balance of the human body is discussed in CIBSE Guide A, section 1.4. The human body exchanges heat with its surroundings through radiation and convection in about equal measure. Thus the perception of thermal comfort depends on the temperature of both the surrounding air and room surfaces. It also depends upon humidity and air movement. When defining temperature for heating under typical occupancy conditions, the generally accepted measure is the dry resultant temperature, given by:

$$t_c = \{t_{ai}\sqrt{(10\,v)} + t_r\}/\{1 + \sqrt{(10\,v)}\} \tag{1.1}$$

where t_c is the dry resultant temperature (°C), t_{ai} is the inside air temperature (°C), t_r is the mean radiant temperature (°C) and v is the mean air speed (m·s^{-1}).

For $v < 0.1$ m·s^{-1}:

$$t_c = (0.5\,t_{ai} + 0.5\,t_r) \tag{1.2}$$

As indoor air velocities are typically less than 0.1 m·s^{-1}, equation 1.2 generally applies.

Table 1.1 gives recommended winter dry resultant temperatures for a range of building types and activities. These are taken from CIBSE Guide A[19], section 1, and assume typical activity and clothing levels. Clients should be consulted to establish whether there any special requirements, such as non-typical levels of activity or clothing. Guide A, section 1, includes methods for adjusting the dry resultant temperature to take account of such requirements.

For buildings with moderate to good levels of insulation, which includes those constructed since insulation requirements were raised in the 1980s, the difference between air and mean radiant temperature is often small enough to be insignificant for the building as a whole. Nevertheless, it is important to identify situations where these temperatures differ appreciably since this may affect the output required from heating appliances. As a general rule, this difference is likely to be significant when spaces are heated non-uniformly or intermittently. For some appliances, e.g. fan heater units, the heat output depends only on the difference between air temperature and heating medium temperature. For other types of appliance, e.g. radiant panels, the emission is affected by the temperature of surrounding surfaces. Section 1.3.3.3 below deals with this subject in greater detail.

Temperature differences within the heated space may also affect the perception of thermal comfort. Vertical temperature differences are likely to arise from the buoyancy of warm air generated by convective heating. In general it is recommended that the vertical temperature difference should be no more than 3 K between head and feet. If air velocities are higher at floor level than across the upper part of the body, the gradient should be no more than 2 K·m^{-1}. Warm and cold floors may also cause discomfort to the feet. In general it is recommended that floor temperatures are maintained between 19 and 26 °C, but that may be increased to 29 °C for under-floor heating systems.

Asymmetric thermal radiation is a potential cause of thermal discomfort. It typically arises from:

— proximity to cold surfaces, such as windows

— proximity to hot surfaces, such as heat emitters, light sources and overhead radiant heaters

— exposure to solar radiation through windows.

CIBSE Guide A recommends that radiant temperature asymmetry should result in no more than 5% dissatisfaction, which corresponds approximately to vertical radiant asymmetry (for a warm ceiling) of less than 5 K and horizontal asymmetry (for a cool wall) of less than 10 K. The value for a cool ceiling is 14 K and for a warm wall is 23 K. It also gives recommended minimum comfortable distances from the centre of single glazed windows of different sizes.

In buildings that are heated but do not have full air conditioning, control of relative humidity is possible but unusual unless there is a specific process requirement. Even where humidity is not controlled, it is important to take account of the range of relative humidity that is likely to be encountered in the building, particularly in relation to surface temperatures and the possibility that condensation could occur under certain conditions.

Also, account should be taken of air movement, which can have a significant effect on the perception of comfort. Where the ventilation system is being designed simultaneously, good liaison between the respective design teams is essential to ensure that localised areas of discomfort are avoided through appropriate location of ventilation outlets and heat emitters, see section 2: *Ventilation and air conditioning*. For a building with an existing mechanical ventilation system, heating system design should also take account of the location of ventilation supply outlets and the air movements they produce.

The level of control achieved by the heating system directly affects occupant satisfaction with the indoor environment, see CIBSE Guide A, section 1.4.3.5. Although other factors also contribute to satisfaction (or dissatisfaction), the ability of the heating system and its controls to maintain dry resultant temperature close to design conditions is a necessary condition for satisfaction. Further guidance on comfort in naturally ventilated buildings may be found in CIBSE Applications Manual AM10: *Natural ventilation in non-domestic buildings*[20]. The effect of temperatures on office worker performance is addressed in CIBSE TM24: *Environmental factors affecting office worker performance*[21].

Close control of temperature is often impractical in industrial and warehouse buildings, in which temperature variations of ±3 K may be acceptable. Also, in such buildings the requirements of processes for temperature control may take precedence over human comfort.

Table 1.1 Recommended winter dry resultant temperatures for various buildings and activities[19]

Building/room type	Temperature / °C	Building/room type	Temperature / °C
Airport terminals		Hotels	
— baggage reclaim	12–19	— bathrooms	26–27
— check-in areas	18–20	— bedrooms	19–21
— customs areas	12–19	Ice rinks	12
— departure lounges	19–21	Laundries	
Banks, building societies and post offices		— commercial	16–19
— counters	19–21	— launderettes	16–18
— public areas	19–21	Law courts	19–21
Bars, lounges	20–22	Libraries	
Churches	19–21	— lending/reference rooms	19–21
Computer rooms	19–21	— reading rooms	22–23
Conference/board rooms	22–23	— store rooms	15
Drawing offices	19–21	Museums and art galleries	
Dwellings		— display	19–21
— bathrooms	26–27	— storage	19–21
— bedrooms	17–19	Offices	
— hall/stairs/landing	19–24	— executive	21–23
— kitchen	17–19	— general	21–23
— living rooms	20–23	— open plan	21–23
— toilets	19–21	Public assembly buildings	
Educational buildings		— auditoria	22–23
— lecture halls	19–21	— changing/dressing rooms	23–24
— seminar rooms	19–21	— circulation spaces	13–20
— teaching spaces	19–21	— foyers	13–20
Exhibition halls	19–21	Prison cells	19–21
Factories		Railway/coach stations	
— heavy work	11–14	— concourse (no seats)	12–19
— light work	16–19	— ticket office	18–20
— sedentary work	19–21	— waiting room	21–22
Fire/ambulance stations		Restaurants/dining rooms	22–24
— recreation rooms	20–22	Retail buildings	
— watch room	22–23	— shopping malls	19–24
Garages		— small shops, department stores	19–21
— servicing	16–19	— supermarkets	19–21
General building areas		Sports halls	
— corridors	19–21	— changing rooms	22–24
— entrance halls	19–21	— hall	13–16
— kitchens (commercial)	15–18	Squash courts	10–12
— toilets	19–21	Swimming pools	
— waiting areas/rooms	19–21	— changing rooms	23–24
Hospitals and health care		— pool halls	23–26
— bedheads/wards	22–24	Television studios	19–21
— circulation spaces (wards)	19–24		
— consulting/treatment rooms	22–24		
— nurses stations	19–22		
— operating theatres	17–19		

1.3.3 Design room and building heat loss calculation

1.3.3.1 Calculation principles

The first task is to estimate how much heat the system must provide to maintain the space at the required indoor temperature under the design external temperature conditions. Calculations are undertaken for each room or zone to allow the design heat loads to be assessed and for the individual heat emitters to be sized.

1.3.3.2 External design conditions

The external design temperature depends upon geographical location, height above sea level, exposure and thermal inertia of the building. The method recommended in Guide A is based on the thermal response characteristics of buildings and the risk that design temperatures are exceeded. The degree of risk may be decided between designer and client, taking account of the consequences for the building, its occupants and its contents when design conditions are exceeded.

CIBSE Guide A, section 2.3, gives guidance on the frequency and duration of extreme temperatures, including the 24- and 48-hour periods with an average below certain thresholds. It also gives data on the coincidence of low temperatures and high wind speeds. The information is available for a range of locations throughout the UK for which long term weather data are available.

The generally adopted external design temperature for buildings with low thermal inertia (capacity), see section 1.3.3.7, is that for which only one day on average in each heating season has a lower mean temperature. Similarly for buildings with high thermal inertia the design temperature selected is that for which only one two-day spell on average in each heating season has a lower mean temperature. Table 1.2 shows design temperatures derived on this basis for various location in the UK. In the absence of more localised information, data from the closest tabulated location may be used, decreased by 0.6 K for every 100 m by which the height above sea level of the site exceeds that of the location in the table. To determine design temperatures based on other levels of risk, see Guide A, section 2.3.

It is the mass in contact with the internal air which plays a dominant role in determining whether a particular structure should be judged to be of low or high thermal inertia. Where carpets and false ceilings are installed, they have the effect of increasing the speed of response of the zone, which makes it behave in a manner more akin to that of a structure of low thermal inertia. Practical guidance may be found in Barnard et al.[22] and in BRE Digest 454[23]. In critical cases, dynamic thermal modelling should be undertaken.

The thermal inertia of a building may be determined in terms of a thermal response factor, f_r, see Guide A, section 5.6.3. Guide A, section 2.3.1, suggests that for most buildings a 24-hour mean temperature is appropriate. However, a 48-hour mean temperature is more suitable for buildings with high thermal inertia (i.e. high thermal mass, low heat loss), with a response factor ≥ 6.

1.3.3.3 Relationship between dry resultant, environmental and air temperatures

As noted above, thermal comfort is best assessed in terms of dry resultant temperature, which depends on the combined effect of air and radiant temperature. However, steady-state heat loss calculations should be made using environmental temperature, which is the hypothetical temperature that determines the rate of heat flow into a room by both convection and radiation. For tightly built and well insulated buildings, differences between internal air temperature (t_{ai}), mean radiant temperature (t_r), dry resultant temperature (t_c) and environmental temperature (t_e) are usually small in relation to the other approximations involved in plant sizing and may be neglected under steady-state conditions. This will apply to buildings built to current Building Regulations with minimum winter ventilation. However, where U-values are higher, e.g. in old buildings, or where there is a high ventilation rate either by design or due to leaky construction, there may be significant differences.

An estimate of the air temperature required to achieve a particular dry resultant temperature can be made using equation 5.11 in CIBSE Guide A. The difference between air and dry resultant temperature is likely to be greater in a thermally massive building that is heated intermittently for short periods only, such as some church buildings. In such cases, radiant heating can quickly achieve comfortable conditions without having to raise the temperature of the structure. Radiant heating can also be effective in buildings that require high ventilation rates, especially when they have high ceilings, a situation that typically occurs in industrial buildings. In this case, comfort conditions can be achieved in working areas without having to heat large volumes of air at higher levels, typically by exploiting heat absorbed by the floor and re-radiated at low level.

Table 1.2 Suggested design temperatures for various UK locations

Location	Altitude (m)	Design temperature*/ °C	
		Low thermal inertia	High thermal inertia
Belfast (Aldegrove)	68	–3	–1.5
Birmingham (Elmdon)	96	–4.5	–3
Cardiff (Rhoose)	67	–3	–2
Edinburgh (Turnhouse)	35	–4	–2
Glasgow (Abbotsinch)	5	–4	–2
London (Heathrow)	25	–3	–2
Manchester (Ringway)	75	–4	–2
Plymouth (Mountbatten)	27	–1	0

* Based on the lowest average temperature over a 24- or 48-hour period likely to occur once per year on average (derived from histograms in Guide A, section 2.3)

1.3.3.4 Structural or fabric heat loss

Structural heat loss occurs by conduction of heat through those parts of the structure exposed to the outside air or adjacent to unheated areas, often referred to as the 'building envelope'. The heat loss through each external element of the building can be calculated from:

$$\phi_f = U A\,(t_{en} - t_{ao}) \qquad (1.3)$$

where ϕ_f is the heat loss through an external element of the building (W), U is the thermal transmittance of the building element (W·m^{-2}·K^{-1}), A is the area of the of building element (m$_2$), t_{en} is the indoor environmental temperature (°C) and t_{ao} is the outdoor temperature (°C).

Thermal bridges occur where cavities or insulation are crossed by components or materials with high thermal conductivity. They frequently occur around windows, doors and other wall openings through lintels, jambs and sills and can be particularly significant when a structural feature, such as a floor extending to a balcony, penetrates a wall. This type of thermal bridge may conveniently be treated as a linear feature, characterised by a heat loss per unit length.

Thermal bridging may also occur where layers in a construction are bridged by elements required for its structural integrity. Examples include mortar joints in masonry construction and joists in timber frame buildings. Tabulated U-values may already take account of some such effects but, where U-values are being calculated from the properties of the layers in a construction, it is essential that such bridging is taken into account, especially for highly insulated structures. Several methods exist for calculating the effects of bridging including the 'combined method' specified by BS EN ISO 6946[24] and required by Building Regulations Approved Documents L1 and L2[3]. Section 3 of CIBSE Guide A gives detailed information on thermal bridging and includes worked examples of the calculation required for both the methods referred to above. Other thermal bridging effects may be taken into account using the methods given in BS EN ISO 10211[25,26].

Heat losses through ground floors need to be treated differently from other losses as they are affected by the mass of earth beneath the floor and in thermal contact with it. A full analysis requires three-dimensional treatment and allowance for thermal storage effects but methods have been developed for producing an effective U-value for the whole floor. The standard for the calculation of U-values for ground floors and basements is BS EN ISO 13370[27]. The recommended method is described in detail in CIBSE Guide A, section 3; the following is a brief description of the method for solid ground floors in contact with the earth.

Table 1.3 gives U-values for solid ground floors on clay (thermal conductivity = 1.5 W·m^{-1}·K^{-1}), for a range of values of the ratio of the exposed floor perimeter p_f (m) and floor area A_f (m^2). The U-values are given as a function of the thermal resistance of the floor construction, R_f, where R_f = 0 for an uninsulated floor. CIBSE Guide A section 3 includes tables for soils having different conductivity and gives equations for calculating the U-values for other types of ground floors. Losses are predominantly from areas close to the perimeter and hence large floors have low average U-values. Therefore large floors may not require to be insulated to satisfy the Building Regulations. However, the mean value should not be applied uniformly to each ground floor zone and the heat losses should be calculated separately for individual perimeter rooms.

U-values for windows are normally quoted for the entire opening and therefore must include heat lost through both the frame and the glazing. Indicative U-values for typical glazing/frame combinations are given in Building Regulations Approved Documents L1 and L2[3]. For advanced glazing, incorporating low emissivity coatings and inert gas fillings, the performance of the frame can be significantly worse than that of the glazing. In such cases, U-values should be calculated individually using the methods given in BS EN ISO 10077[28] or reference made to manufacturers' certified U-values.

The rate of fabric heat loss for the whole building may be calculated by summing the losses calculated for each element. The area of each element may be based on either internal or external measurement; however, if internal measurements are used, they should be adjusted to take account of intermediate floors and party walls. Measurements used in calculations to show compliance with the Building Regulations should be based on overall internal dimensions for the whole building, including the thickness of party walls and floors.

U-values for typical constructions are given in Guide A, Appendix 3.A8. For other constructions the U-value must be calculated by summing the thermal resistances for the various elements. For each layer in a uniform plane, the thermal resistance is given by:

$$R_i = d / \lambda \tag{1.4}$$

Table 1.3 U-values for solid ground floors on clay soil

Ratio p_f/A_f	U-value (W·m^{-2}·K^{-1}) for stated thermal resistance of floor construction R_f (m^2·K·W^{-1})					
	0	0.5	1.0	1.5	2.0	2.5
0.05	0.13	0.11	0.10	0.09	0.08	0.08
0.10	0.22	0.18	0.16	0.14	0.13	0.12
0.15	0.30	0.24	0.21	0.18	0.17	0.15
0.20	0.37	0.29	0.25	0.22	0.19	0.18
0.25	0.44	0.34	0.28	0.24	0.22	0.19
0.30	0.49	0.38	0.31	0.27	0.23	0.21
0.35	0.55	0.41	0.34	0.29	0.25	0.22
0.40	0.60	0.44	0.36	0.30	0.26	0.23
0.45	0.65	0.47	0.38	0.32	0.27	0.23
0.50	0.70	0.50	0.40	0.33	0.28	0.24
0.55	0.74	0.52	0.41	0.34	0.28	0.25
0.60	0.78	0.55	0.43	0.35	0.29	0.25
0.65	0.82	0.57	0.44	0.35	0.30	0.26
0.70	0.86	0.59	0.45	0.36	0.30	0.26
0.75	0.89	0.61	0.46	0.37	0.31	0.27
0.80	0.93	0.62	0.47	0.37	0.32	0.27
0.85	0.96	0.64	0.47	0.38	0.32	0.28
0.90	0.99	0.65	0.48	0.39	0.32	0.28
0.95	1.02	0.66	0.49	0.39	0.33	0.28
1.00	1.05	0.68	0.50	0.40	0.33	0.28

where R_i is the thermal resistance of the element (m^2·K·W^{-1}), d is the thickness of the element (m) and λ is the thermal conductivity (W·m^{-1}·K^{-1}).

Values of thermal conductivity of the materials used in the various building elements can be obtained from manufacturers or from CIBSE Guide A, Appendix 3.A7. The thermal resistances of air gaps and surfaces should also be taken into account using the values given in CIBSE Guide A, Table 3.53.

The total thermal resistance of the element is calculated by adding up the thermal resistances of its layers:

$$R = R_{si} + R_1 + R_2 \cdots\cdots + R_a + R_{se} \tag{1.5}$$

where R_{si} is the internal surface resistance (m^2·K·W^{-1}), R_1, R_2 etc. are the thermal resistances of layers 1, 2 etc. (m^2·K·W^{-1}), R_a is the thermal resistance of the airspace (m^2·K·W^{-1}) and R_{se} is the external surface resistance (m^2·K·W^{-1}).

The U-value is the reciprocal of the thermal resistance:

$$U = 1 / R \tag{1.6}$$

Where adjacent rooms are to be maintained at the same temperature, there are neither heat losses nor heat gains either via the internal fabric or by internal air movement. However, where the design internal temperatures are not identical, heat losses between rooms should be taken into account in determining the heat requirements of each room.

1.3.3.5 Ventilation heat loss

Ventilation heat loss depends upon the rate at which air enters and leaves the building, the heat capacity of the air and the temperature difference between indoors and outdoors. The heat capacity of air is approximately constant under the conditions encountered in a building. The volume of air passing through the building depends upon the volume of the building and the air change rate, which is usually expressed in air changes per hour (h^{-1}). The ventilation heat loss rate of a room or building may be calculated by the formula:

$$\phi_v = q_m (h_{ai} - h_{ao}) \quad (1.7)$$

where ϕ_v is the heat loss due to ventilation (W), q_m is the mass flow rate of ventilation air ($kg{\cdot}s^{-1}$), h_{ai} is the enthalpy of the indoor air ($J{\cdot}kg^{-1}$) and h_{ao} is the enthalpy of the outdoor air ($J{\cdot}kg^{-1}$).

Where the moisture content of the air remains constant, only sensible heat needs to be considered so the ventilation heat loss can be given by:

$$\phi_v = q_m c_p (t_{ai} - t_{ao}) \quad (1.8)$$

where c_p is the specific heat capacity of air at constant pressure ($J{\cdot}kg^{-1}{\cdot}K^{-1}$), t_{ai} is the inside air temperature (°C) and t_{ao} is the outside air temperature (°C).

By convention, the conditions for the air are taken as the internal conditions, for which the density will not differ greatly from $\rho = 1.20\ kg{\cdot}m^{-3}$, and the specific heat capacity $c_p = 1.00\ kJ{\cdot}kg^{-1}{\cdot}K^{-1}$. This leads to the following simplifications:

$$\phi_v = 1.2\, q_v (t_{ai} - t_{ao}) \quad (1.9)$$

or:

$$\phi_v = (N\, V / 3)(t_{ai} - t_{ao}) \quad (1.10)$$

where ϕ_v is the heat loss due to ventilation (W), q_v is the volume flow rate of air ($litre{\cdot}s^{-1}$), t_{ai} is the inside air temperature (°C), t_{ao} the outside air temperature (°C), N is the number of air changes per hour (h^{-1}) and V is the volume of the room (m^3).

Ventilation heat losses may be divided into two distinct elements:

— purpose provided ventilation, either by mechanical or natural means

— air infiltration.

The amount of purpose-provided ventilation is decided according to how the building is to be used and occupied. In most buildings, ventilation is provided at a rate aimed at ensuring adequate air quality for building occupants but in some industrial buildings it must be based on matching process extract requirements. Mechanical ventilation is controlled, the design amount known, and the heat loss easily calculated. Ventilation requirements may be specified either in volume supply ($litre{\cdot}s^{-1}$) or in air changes per hour (h^{-1}). Recommended air supply rates for a range of buildings and building uses are given in CIBSE Guide A[19], section 1, extracts from which are given in Table 1.4. More detailed guidance on ventilation is given in section 2 *Ventilation and air conditioning*.

When heat recovery is installed, the net ventilation load becomes:

$$\phi_v = 1.2\, q_v (t_{a2} - t_{ao}) \quad (1.11)$$

or:

$$\phi_v = q_m (h_{a2} - h_{ao}) \quad (1.12)$$

Table 1.4 Recommended fresh air supply rates for selected buildings and uses[1]

Building/use	Air supply rate
Public and commercial buildings (general use)	8 $litre{\cdot}s^{-1}{\cdot}person^{-1}$
Hotel bathrooms	12 $litre{\cdot}s^{-1}{\cdot}person^{-1}$
Hospital operating theatres	650 to 1000 $m^3{\cdot}s^{-1}$
Toilets	>5 air changes per hour
Changing rooms	10 air changes per hour
Squash courts	4 air changes per hour
Ice rinks	3 air changes per hour
Swimming pool halls	15 $litre{\cdot}s^{-1}{\cdot}m^{-2}$ (of wet area)
Bedrooms and living rooms in dwellings	0.4 to 1 air changes per hour
Kitchens in dwellings	60 $litre{\cdot}s^{-1}$
Bathrooms in dwellings	15 $litre{\cdot}s^{-1}$

where t_{a2} is the extract air temperature after the heat recovery unit (°C) and h_{a2} is the extract air enthalpy after the heat recovery unit ($J{\cdot}kg^{-1}$).

Air infiltration is the unintentional leakage of air through a building due to imperfections in its fabric. The air leakage of the building can be measured using a fan pressurisation test, which provides a basis for estimating average infiltration rates. However, infiltration is uncontrolled and varies both with wind speed and the difference between indoor and outdoor temperature, the latter being particularly important in tall buildings. It is highly variable and difficult to predict and can therefore only be an estimate for which a suitable allowance is made in design. Methods for estimating infiltration rates are given in CIBSE Guide A[19], section 4. Table 1.5 gives empirical infiltration allowances for use in heat load calculations for existing buildings where pressurisation test results are not available. As air infiltration is related to surface area rather than volume, estimates based on air change rate tend to exaggerate infiltration losses for large buildings, which points to the need for measurement in those cases.

The air infiltration allowances given in Table 1.5 are applicable to single rooms or spaces and are appropriate for the estimation of room heat loads. The load on the central plant will be somewhat less (up to 50%) than the total of the individual room loads due to infiltration diversity.

Building Regulations Approved Document L2[3] recommends that air permeability measured in accordance with CIBSE TM23: *Testing buildings for air leakage*[29] should not be greater than 10 $m^3{\cdot}h^{-1}$ per m^2 of external surface area at a pressure of 50 Pa. It also states that pressurisation tests should be used to show compliance with the Regulations for buildings with a floor area of 1000 m^2 or more. For buildings of less than 1000 m^2, pressurisation testing may also be used, but a report by a competent person giving evidence of compliance based on design and construction details may be accepted as an alternative.

CIBSE TM23: *Testing buildings for air leakage*[29] describes the two different parameters currently used to quantify air leakage in buildings, i.e. air leakage index and air permeability. Both are measured using the same pressurisation technique, as described in TM23, and both are expressed in

Table 1.5 Recommended allowances for air infiltration for selected building types[19]

Building/room type	Air infiltration allowance / air changes·h^{-1}	Building/room type	Air infiltration allowance / air changes·h^{-1}
Art galleries and museums	1	Hospitals (continued):	
Assembly and lecture halls	0.5	— wards and patient areas	2
		— waiting rooms	1
Banking halls	1 to 1.5	Hotels:	
Bars	1	— bedrooms	1
Canteens and dining rooms	1	— public rooms	1
		— corridors	1.5
Churches and chapels	0.5 to 1	— foyers	1.5
Dining and banqueting halls	0.5	Laboratories	1
Exhibition halls	0.5	Law courts	1
Factories:		Libraries:	
— up to 300 m^3 volume	1.5 to 2.5	— reading rooms	0.5 to 0.7
— 300 m^3 to 3000 m^3	0.75 to 1.5	— stack rooms	0.5
— 3000 m^3 to 10,000 m^3	0.5 to 1.0	— storerooms	0.25
— over 10,000 m3	0.25 to 0.75	Offices:	
Fire stations	0.5 to 1	— private	1
		— general	1
Gymnasia	0.75	— storerooms	0.5
Houses, flats and hostels:		Police cells	5
— living rooms	1		
— bedrooms	0.5	Restaurants, cafes	1
— bed-sitting rooms	1	Schools, colleges:	
— bathrooms	2	— classrooms	2
— lavatories, cloakrooms	1.5	— lecture rooms	1
— service rooms	0.5	— studios	1
— staircases, corridors	1.5		
— entrance halls, foyers	1.5	Sports pavilion changing rooms	1
— public rooms	1	Swimming pools:	
Hospitals:		— changing rooms	0.5
— corridors	1	— pool hall	0.5
— offices	1	Warehouses:	
— operating theatres	0.5	— working and packing areas	0.5
— storerooms	0.5	— storage areas	0.2

terms of volume flow per hour (m^3·h^{-1}) of air supplied per m^2 of building envelope area. They differ in the definition of building envelope area to which they refer; the solid ground floor is excluded from the definition of envelope used for the air leakage index, but is included for air permeability. Air permeability is used in the Building Regulations and the European Standard BS EN 13829[30]. However, the air leakage index was used for most of the measurements used to produce the current database of results.

TM23 provides a simple method of estimation of air infiltration rate from the air permeability. This should be used with caution for calculation of heat losses since it currently applies only to houses and offices and does not include additional infiltration losses related to the building's use.

1.3.3.6 Calculation of design heat loss for rooms and buildings

The design heat loss for each zone or room is calculated by summing the fabric heat loss for each element and the ventilation heat loss, including an allowance for infiltration. The calculations are carried out under external conditions chosen as described in section 1.3.3.2:

$$\phi = \Sigma\,(\phi_f) + \phi_v \tag{1.13}$$

where ϕ is the total design heat loss (W), ϕ_f is the fabric heat loss (W) and ϕ_v is the ventilation heat loss (W).

Section 1.4.7 describes how the calculated heat loss may be used in sizing system components, including both heat emitters and boilers.

The recommended allowance for infiltration is important and may constitute a significant component of the total design heat loss. While this allowance should be used in full for sizing heat emitters, a diversity factor should be applied to it when sizing central plant. CIBSE Guide A[19], section 5.8.3.5, notes that infiltration of outdoor air only takes place on the windward side of a building at any one time, the flow on the leeward side being outwards. This suggests that a diversity factor of 0.5 should be applied to the infiltration heat loss in calculating total system load. The same section of Guide A gives overall diversity factors ranging from 0.7 to 1.0 for the total load in continuously heated buildings.

1.3.3.7 Thermal capacity

Thermal capacity (or thermal mass) denotes the capacity of building elements to store heat, which is an important determinant of its transient or dynamic temperature response. High thermal capacity is favoured when it is desirable to slow down the rate at which a building changes temperature, such as in reducing peak summertime temperatures caused by solar gains, thereby reducing peak cooling loads.

High thermal capacity reduces both the drop in temperature during periods when the building is not occupied and the rate at which it re-heats. When buildings are not occupied at weekends, then the effect of heating up from cold on a Monday morning needs to be considered; in this case a greater thermal capacity will require either a higher plant ratio or a longer pre-heat period. Full treatment of the effects of thermal capacity requires the use of dynamic modelling, as described in CIBSE A[19], section 5.6, or the use of a computer-based dynamic energy simulation. Simplified analysis can be undertaken using the concept of thermal admittance (Y-value), which is a measure of the rate of flow between the internal surfaces of a structure and the environmental temperature in the space it encloses, see section 1.4.7.

1.3.4 'Buildability', 'commissionability' and 'maintainability'

All design must take account of the environment in which the system will be installed, commissioned and operated, considering both safety and economy.

The Construction (Design and Management) Regulations 1994[9] (CDM Regulations) place an obligation on designers to ensure that systems they design and specify can be safely installed and maintained. The Regulations require that a designer must be competent and have the necessary skills and resources, including technical facilities. The designer of an installation or a piece of equipment that requires maintenance has a duty to carry out a risk assessment of the maintenance function. Where this assessment shows a hazard to the maintenance operative, the designer must reconsider the proposals and try to remove or mitigate the risk.

Apart from matters affecting safety, designers must take account of maintenance cost over the lifetime of the systems they specify. In particular, it is important to ensure that the client understands the maintenance requirements, including cost and the need for skills or capabilities. The CIBSE's *Guide to ownership, operation and maintenance of building services*[31] contains guidance on maintenance issues that need to be addressed by the building services designer.

Part L of the Building Regulations[3] requires the provision of a 'commissioning plan that shows that every system has been inspected and commissioned in an appropriate sequence'. This implies that the designer must consider which measurements are required for commissioning and provide the information required for making and using those measurements. Also, the system must be designed so that the necessary measurements and tests can be carried out, taking account of access to the equipment and the health and safety those making the measurements. Approved Document L2 states that one way of demonstrating compliance would be to follow the guidance given in CIBSE Commissioning Codes[32–36], in BSRIA Commissioning Guides[37–42] and by the Commissioning Specialists Association[43]. The guidance on balancing given in section 1.4.3.2 is also relevant to this requirement.

1.3.5 Energy efficiency targets

New buildings and buildings undergoing major refurbishment must comply with the requirements of Part L1 (dwellings) or Part L2 (buildings other then dwellings) of the Building Regulations[3] (or the equivalent regulations that apply in Scotland[44] and Northern Ireland[45]). These requirements may be expressed either in U-values or as energy targets, typically calculated in terms of energy use per year according to a closely specified procedure. For example, the Standard Assessment Procedure for the Energy Rating of Dwellings[14] (SAP) describes how such a calculation may be done for dwellings in order to comply with Part L. SAP is also used in other contexts, for example to assess or specify the performance of stocks of houses owned by local authorities and housing associations. The Building Regulations in the Republic of Ireland offer a heat energy rating as a way of showing compliance with energy requirements for dwellings. It should be remembered that the Building Regulations set minimum levels for energy efficiency and it may economic to improve upon those levels in individual cases.

Energy targets for non-domestic buildings include those described in CIBSE Building Energy Codes 1 and 2. Energy benchmarks have also been developed for certain types of buildings; for example, Energy Consumption Guide 19[46] (ECON 19) gives typical performance levels achieved in office buildings. A method for estimating consumption and comparing performance with the ECON 19 benchmarks is described in CIBSE TM22: *Energy assessment and reporting methodology*[47]. Building Regulations Approved Document L[3] includes a carbon performance rating (CPR) as one way of showing compliance with the Regulations for office buildings. The BRE Environmental Assessment Method[13] (BREEAM) includes a broad range of environmental impacts but energy use contributes significantly to its overall assessment.

See CIBSE Guide F: *Energy efficiency in buildings* for detailed guidance on energy efficiency.

1.3.6 Life cycle issues

The designer's decisions will have consequences that persist throughout the life of the equipment installed, including durability, availability of consumable items and spare parts, and maintenance requirements. Consideration should also be given to how the heating system could be adapted to changes of use of the building. The combined impact may be best assessed using the concept of life cycle costs, which are the combined capital and revenue costs of an item of plant or equipment throughout a defined lifetime.

The capital costs of a system include initial costs, replacement costs and residual or scrap value at the end of the useful life of the system. Future costs are typically discounted to their present value. Revenue costs include energy costs, maintenance costs and costs arising as a consequence of system failure.

Life cycle costing is covered by BS ISO 156861-1[48] and guidance is given by HM Treasury[49], the Construction Client's Forum[1], BRE[50] and the Royal Institution of Chartered Surveyors[51]. See also CIBSE's *Guide to ownership, operation and maintenance of building services*[31].

1.4 System selection

1.4.1 Choice of heating options

This section deals with the attributes of particular systems and sub-systems, and the factors that need to be taken into consideration in their specification and design.

1.4.1.1 Heat emitters

The general characteristics of heat emitters need to be considered, with particular emphasis on the balance between convective and radiative output appropriate to the requirements of the building and activities to be carried out within it. As noted in section 1.3, well insulated buildings tend to have only small differences between air and mean radiant temperatures when they are in a steady-state. Nevertheless there can be situations in which it is better to provide as much output as possible in either convective or radiant form. For example, radiant heating may be desirable in heavyweight buildings that are occupied intermittently, such as churches, or in buildings with high ceilings, where the heat can be better directed to fall directly on occupants without having to warm the fabric of the building. The characteristics of particular heat emitters are discussed in the following sections.

1.4.1.2 Location of heat emitters

As it is generally desirable to provide uniform temperatures throughout a room or zone, careful consideration should be given to the location of heat emitters. Their position can contribute to the problem of radiant asymmetry described in section 1.3.2, and can significantly affect the comfort of particular areas within a room. For example, it may be beneficial to locate emitters to counteract the radiative effects or down-draughts caused by cool surfaces. When single glazing is encountered, it is particularly important to locate radiators beneath windows, but it can still be desirable to do so with double glazing. It is best to locate heat sources on external walls if the walls are poorly insulated.

1.4.1.3 Distribution medium

The medium for distributing heat around the building needs also to be considered, taking account of requirements for heat emitters. Air and water are the commonest choices but steam is still used in many existing buildings and refrigerant fluids are used in heat pumps. Electricity is the most versatile medium for distribution as it can be converted to heat at any temperature required at any location. However, consideration of primary energy, CO_2 emissions and running cost tend to militate against the use of electricity. Gas and oil may also be distributed directly to individual heaters.

The choice of distribution medium must take account of the balance between radiant and convective output required. When air is used for distribution, the opportunity for radiant heat output is very limited but water and steam systems can be designed to give output that is either predominantly convective or with a significant radiative component. However, when highly directed radiant output is required then only infrared elements powered by electricity or directly fired by gas are applicable. The relative merits of various distribution media are described briefly in Table 1.6.

1.4.2 Energy efficiency

See section 1.2 above. The practical realisation of energy efficiency depends not only on the characteristics of the equipment installed but also on how it is controlled and integrated with other equipment. The following sections describe aspects of energy efficiency that need to be taken into account in heating system design.

1.4.2.1 Thermal insulation

For new buildings, satisfying the Building Regulations will ensure that the external fabric has a reasonable and cost-effective degree of insulation (but not necessarily the economic optimum), and that insulation is applied to hot water storage vessels and heating pipes that pass outside heated spaces.

In existing buildings, consideration should be given to improving the thermal resistance of the fabric, which can reduce the heat loss significantly. This can offer a number of advantages, including reduced load on the heating system, improved comfort and the elimination of condensation on the inner surfaces of external walls and ceilings. In general, decisions on whether or not to improve insulation should be made following an appraisal

Table 1.6 Characteristics of heat distribution media

Medium	Principal characteristics
Air	The main advantage of air is that no intermediate medium or heat exchanger is needed. The main disadvantage is the large volume of air required and the size of ductwork that results. This is due to the low density of air and the small temperature difference permissible between supply and return. High energy consumption required by fans can also be a disadvantage.
Low pressure hot water (LPHW)	LPHW systems operate at low pressures that can be generated by an open or sealed expansion vessel. They are generally recognised as simple to install and safe in operation but output is limited by system temperatures restricted to a maximum of about 85 °C.
Medium pressure hot water (MPHW)	Permits system temperatures up to 120 °C and a greater drop in water temperature around the system and thus smaller pipework. Only on a large system is this likely to be of advantage. This category includes pressurisation up to 5 bar absolute.
High pressure hot water (HPHW)	Even higher temperatures are possible in high pressure systems (up to 10 bar absolute), resulting in even greater temperature drops in the system, and thus even smaller pipework. Due to the inherent dangers, all pipework must be welded and to the standards applicable to steam pipework. This in unlikely to be a cost-effective choice except for the transportation of heat over long distances.
Steam	Exploits the latent heat of condensation to provide very high transfer capacity. Operates at high pressures, requiring high maintenance and water treatment. Principally used in hospitals and buildings with large kitchens or processes requiring steam.

of the costs and benefits, taking account both of running costs and the impact on capital costs of the heating system.

Where a new heating system is to be installed in an existing building, pipe and storage vessel insulation should meet the standards required by Parts L1/L2 of the Building Regulations[3]. This should apply when parts of an existing system are to be retained, constrained only by limited access to sections of existing pipework.

1.4.2.2 Reducing air infiltration

See section 1.3.3.5 above. Infiltration can contribute substantially to the heating load of the building and cause discomfort through the presence of draughts and cold areas. As for fabric insulation, the costs and benefits of measures to reduce infiltration should be appraised on a life-cycle basis, taking account of both running costs and capital costs.

1.4.2.3 Seasonal boiler efficiency

Boiler efficiency is the principal determinant of system efficiency in many heating systems. What matters is the average efficiency of the boiler under varying conditions throughout the year, known as 'seasonal efficiency'. This may differ significantly from the bench test boiler efficiency, although the latter may be a useful basis for comparison between boilers. Typical seasonal efficiencies for various types of boiler are given in Table 1.7. For domestic boilers, seasonal efficiencies may be obtained from the SEDBUK[52] database.

Many boilers have a lower efficiency when operating at part load, particularly in an on/off control mode, see Figure 1.4. Apart from the pre-heat period, a boiler spends most of its operating life at part load. This has led to the increased popularity of multiple boiler systems since, at 25% of design load, it is better to have 25% of a number of small boilers operating at full output, rather than one large boiler operating at 25% output.

Condensing boilers operate at peak efficiency when return water temperatures are low, which increases the extent to which condensation takes place. This can occur either at part or full load and depends principally on the characteristics of the system in which it is installed. Condensing boilers are particularly well suited to LPHW systems operating at low flow and return temperatures, such as under-floor heating. They may also be operated as lead boilers in multiple boiler systems.

Table 1.7 Typical seasonal efficiencies for various boiler types[12]

Boiler/system	Seasonal efficiency / %
Condensing boilers:	
— under-floor or warm water system	90
— standard size radiators, variable temperature circuit (weather compensation)	87
— standard fixed temperature emitters (83/72 °C flow/return)*	85
Non-condensing boilers:	
— modern high-efficiency non-condensing boilers	80–82
— good modern boiler design closely matched to demand	75
— typical good existing boiler	70
— typical existing oversized boiler (atmospheric, cast-iron sectional)	45–65

* Not permitted by current Building Regulations

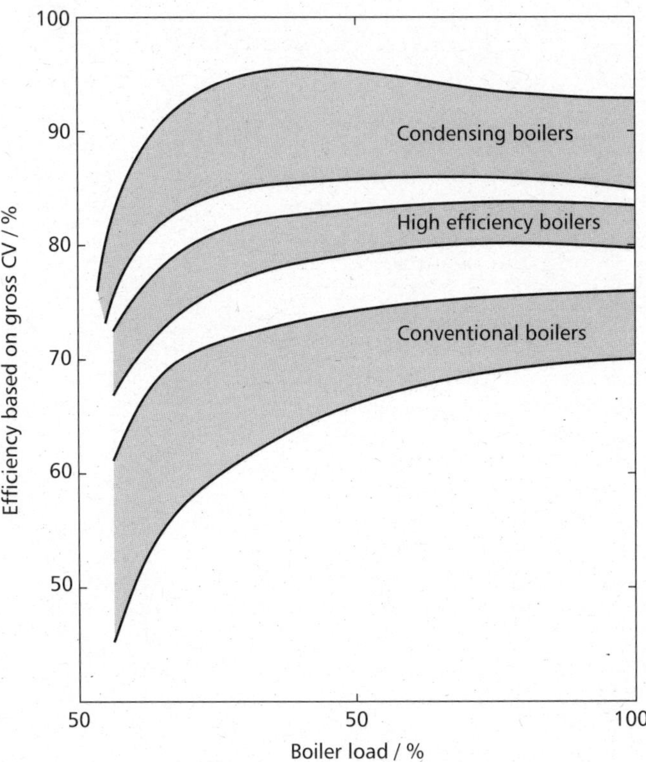

Figure 1.4 Typical seasonal LTHW boiler efficiencies at part load[53]

1.4.2.4 Efficiency of ancillary devices

Heating systems rely on a range of electrically powered equipment to make them function, including pumps, fans, dampers, electrically actuated valves, sensors and controllers. Of these, pumps and fans are likely to consume the most energy, but even low electrical consumption may be significant if it is by equipment that is on continuously. It is important to remember that the cost per kW·h of electricity is typically four times that of fuels used for heating, so it is important to avoid unnecessary electrical consumption.

For pumps and fans, what matters is the overall efficiency of the combined unit including the motor and the drive coupling. Fan and pump characteristics obtained from manufacturers should be used to design the system to operate around the point of maximum efficiency, taking account of both the efficiency of the motors and of the coupling to the pump or fan. Also, it is important that the drive ratios are selected to give a good match between the motor and the load characteristic of the equipment it is driving.

Pumping and fan energy consumption costs can be considerable and may be a significant proportion of total running costs in some heating systems. However, it may be possible to reduce running costs by specifying larger pipes or ductwork. Control system design can also have a significant impact on running costs. Pumps and fans should not be left running longer than necessary and multiple speed or variable speed drives should be considered where a wide flow range is required.

1.4.2.5 Controls

Heating system controls perform two distinct functions:

— they maintain the temperature conditions required within the building when it is occupied, including pre-heating to ensure that those conditions are met at the start of occupancy periods

— they ensure that the system itself operates safely and efficiently under all conditions.

The accuracy with which the specified temperatures are maintained and the length of the heating period both have a significant impact on energy efficiency and running costs. A poorly controlled system will lead to complaints when temperatures are low. The response may be raised set-points or extended pre-heat periods, both of which have the effect of increasing average temperatures and energy consumption. Controls which schedule system operation, such as boiler sequencing, can be equally important in their effect on energy efficiency, especially as the system may appear to function satisfactorily while operating at low efficiency.

1.4.2.6 Zoning

Rooms or areas within buildings may require to be heated to different temperatures or at different times, each requiring independent control. Where several rooms or areas of a building behave in a similar manner, they can be grouped together as a 'zone' and put on the same circuit and controller. For instance, all similar south-facing rooms of a building may experience identical solar gain changes and some parts of the building may have the same occupancy patterns. The thermal responses of different parts of a building need to be considered before assigning them to zones, so that all parts of the zone reach their design internal temperature together. A poor choice of zones can lead to some rooms being too hot and others too cool.

1.4.2.7 Ventilation heat recovery

A mechanical ventilation system increases overall power requirements but offers potential energy savings through better control of ventilation and the possibility of heat recovery. The most obvious saving is through limiting the operation of the system to times when it is required, which is usually only when the building is occupied. The extent to which savings are possible depends crucially on the air leakage performance of the building. In a leaky building, heat losses through infiltration may be comparable with those arising from ventilation. In an airtight building, the heat losses during the pre-heat period may be considerably reduced by leaving the ventilation off and adopting a smaller plant size ratio.

Ventilation heat recovery extracts heat from exhaust air for reuse within a building. It includes:

— 'air-to-air' heat recovery, in which heat is extracted from the exhaust air and transferred to the supply air using a heat exchanger or thermal wheel

— a heat pump, to extract heat from the exhaust air and transfer it to domestic hot water.

Air-to-air heat recovery is only possible where both supply air and exhaust air are ducted. High heat transfer efficiencies (up to 90%) can be achieved. Plate heat exchangers are favoured for use in houses and small commercial systems, while thermal wheels are typically used in large commercial buildings. Heat pipe systems offer very high heat efficiency and low running cost. Run-around coils may also be used and have the advantage that supply and exhaust air streams need not be adjacent to each other.

The benefits of the energy saved by heat recovery must take account of any additional electricity costs associated with the heat recovery system, including the effect of the additional pressure drop across the heat exchanger. Assessment of the benefits of heat recovery should also take account of the effect of infiltration, which may bypass the ventilation system to a large extent. The cost-effectiveness of heat recovery also depends on climate and is greatest when winters are severe.

Heat pumps transferring heat from exhaust ventilation air to heat domestic hot water have widely been used in apartment buildings in Scandinavia. The same principle has been successfully used in swimming pools.

1.4.3 Hydronic systems

Hydronic systems use hot water for transferring heat from the heat generator to the heat emitters. The most usual type of heat generator for hydronic systems is a 'boiler', misleadingly named as it must be designed to avoid boiling during operation. Hot water may also be generated by heat pumps, waste heat reclaimed from processes and by solar panels, the latter typically being used to produce domestic hot water in summer. Heat emitters take a variety of forms including panel radiators, natural and forced convectors, fan-coil units, and under-floor heating. Hydronic systems normally rely on pumps for circulation, although gravity circulation was favoured for systems designed before around 1950.

Hydronic systems offer considerable flexibility in type and location of emitters. The heat output available in radiant form is limited by the temperature of the circulation water but, for radiators and heated panels, can be sufficient to counteract the effect of cold radiation from badly insulated external surfaces. Convective output can be provided by enclosed units relying on either natural or forced air-convection. Flexibility of location is ensured by the small diameter of the circulation pipework and the wide variety of emitter sizes and types.

In addition to the sizing of emitters and boilers, the design of hydronic systems involves the hydraulic design of the circulation system to ensure that water reaches each emitter at the necessary flow rate and that the pressures around the system are maintained at appropriate levels. System static pressures may be controlled either by sealed expansion vessels or by hydrostatic pressure arising from the positioning of cisterns at atmospheric pressure above the highest point of the circulating system. Both cisterns and pressure vessels must cope with the water expansion that occurs as the system heats up from cold; the design of feed, expansion and venting is crucial to both the safety and correct operation of systems.

1.4.3.1 Operating temperatures for hydronic systems

The operating temperature of a hydronic heating system both determines its potential performance and affects its design. Systems are generally classified according to the temperature and static pressure at which they operate, see Table 1.8. Low pressure hot water (LPHW) systems may be either sealed or open to the atmosphere and use a variety of materials for the distribution pipework. Also, the operating temperature should be set low enough that

Table 1.8 Design water temperatures and pressures for hydronic heating systems

Category	System design water temperature / °C	Operating static pressure / bar (absolute)
Low pressure hot water (LPHW)	40 to 85	1 to 3
Medium pressure hot water (MPHW)	100 to 120	3 to 5
High pressure hot water (HPHW)	>120	5 to 10*

* Account must be taken of varying static pressure in a tall building

exposed heat emitters, such as panel radiators, do not present a burn hazard to building occupants. Medium and high pressure systems are favoured where a high heat output is required, such as in a fan coil system in a large building. High pressure systems are particularly favoured for distribution mains, from which secondary systems extract heat by heat exchangers for local circulation at lower temperatures.

LPHW systems are typically designed to operate with a maximum flow temperature of 82 °C and system temperature drop of 10 K. A minimum return temperature of 66 °C is specified by BS 5449[(54)] unless boilers are designed to cope with condensation or are of the electric storage type. For condensing boilers, a low return temperature may be used with the benefit of improved operating efficiency. It may also be noted that the larger the difference between flow and return temperatures $(t_1 - t_2)$, the smaller the mass flow required, which tends to reduce pipe sizes and pumping power. The heat flux is given by:

$$\phi = q_m c_p (t_1 - t_2) \qquad (1.14)$$

where ϕ is the heat flux (W), q_m is the mass flow rate (kg·s^{-1}), c_p is the specific heat capacity of the heat transfer fluid (J·kg^{-1}·K^{-1}), t_1 is the flow temperature (°C) and t_2 is the return temperature (°C).

Hence, the mass flow rate is given by:

$$q_m = \phi / [c_p (t_1 - t_2)] \qquad (1.15)$$

The efficiency of a condensing boiler is more strongly influenced by the return temperature, rather than the flow temperature, which ought to be a further encouragement to use large values of $(t_1 - t_2)$. However, a larger temperature difference lowers the mean water temperature of the emitter, which reduces specific output and requires larger surface area. The effect of flow rate and return temperature on heat output is explored more fully in section 1.5.1.1.

The relationship between emitter output and temperature is dealt with in section 1.5 and varies according to the type of emitter. In general, it may be noted that output tends to increase disproportionately as the difference between the mean system temperature and the room temperature increases. This favours the use of a high system temperature. However, other factors need to be considered which may favour a lower temperature, including the surface temperature of radiators, boiler operating efficiency and the characteristics of certain heat emitters. For example, underfloor heating is designed to operate with low system temperatures to keep floor surface temperatures below 29 °C.

1.4.3.2 System layout and design

Systems must be designed to match their specified design heat load, including domestic hot water provision where required, and to have controls capable of matching output to the full range of variation in load over a heating season. Separate circuits may be required to serve zones of the building with different heat requirements. In addition, there must be provision for hydraulic balancing of circuits and sub-circuits, and for filling, draining and venting of each part of the system.

Distribution systems may be broadly grouped into one-pipe and two-pipe categories. In one-pipe systems, radiators are effectively fed in series, and system temperature varies around the circuit. They have not been extensively used in the UK during the last half-century but are common throughout the countries of the former Soviet Union, East Europe and China. Control of one-pipe systems requires the use of by-passes and 3-port valves. Two-pipe systems operate at nominally the same temperature throughout the circuit but require good balancing for that condition to be achieved in practice. Control of two-pipe systems may employ either 2-port or 3-port valves to restrict flow to individual heat emitters.

Draft European Standard prEN 12828[(55)] deals with the design of hydronic heating systems with operating temperatures up to 105 °C and 1 MW design heat load. It covers heat supply, heat distribution, heat emitters, and control systems. BS 5449[(54)] describes systems specifically for use in domestic premises, although it contains much that is applicable to small systems in other buildings. Detailed guidance on the design of domestic systems is given in the HVCA's *Domestic Heating Design Guide*[(56)].

Hydraulic design

Hydraulic design needs to take account of the effect of water velocity on noise and erosion, and of the pressure and flow characteristics of the circulation pump. CIBSE Guide C[(57)], section 4.4, contains tables showing pressure loss against flow rate for common tube sizes and materials. Flow velocities may be determined by consideration of pressure drops per metre of pipe run (typically in the range of 100 to 350 Pa·m^{-1}). Alternatively, flow velocities may be considered directly, usually to be maintained in the range 0.75 to 1.5 m·s^{-1} for small-bore pipes (<50 mm diameter) and between 1.25 and 3 m·s^{-1} for larger pipes.

Pumps should be capable of delivering the maximum flow required by the circuit at the design pressure drop around the circuit of greatest resistance, commonly known as the index circuit. If variable speed pumping is to be used, the method of controlling pump speed should be clearly described and the pump should be sized to operate around an appropriate part of its operating range.

The location and sizing of control valves need to take account of pressure drops and flows around the circuit to ensure that they operate with sufficient valve authority, see section 1.5.1.5.

Balancing

The objective of balancing is to ensure that each emitter receives the flow required at the design temperature.

Balancing may be carried out most precisely by measuring and adjusting flow to individual parts of the circuit, but can also be carried out by observing temperatures throughout the system. Temperature-based balancing is commonly used on domestic systems but has the disadvantage that the adjustments must be made and checked when the system has reached a steady-state, which may take a considerable time.

It is important to take account of the need for balancing at the design stage, including the location of measuring stations around the system, the equipment needed to achieve balancing, and the procedures for carrying it out. Balancing by flow requires a provision for flow measurement and, in all cases, appropriate valves must be installed to control the flow to particular parts of the circuit. Balancing procedures, including a technical specification for commissioning the system, and the responsibilities of the various parties involved should be clearly identified at the outset. Flow measurement and regulating devices used for balancing are described in section 1.5.1.5.

The design of pipework systems can have a considerable effect on the ease with which balancing can be achieved. Reverse return circuits, which ensure that each load has a similar circuit length for its combined flow and return path, can eliminate much of the inequality of flow that might otherwise need to be rectified during balancing. Distribution manifolds and carefully selected pipe sizes can also assist with circuit balancing. It is important to avoid connecting loads with widely differing pressure drops and heat emitting characteristics (e.g. panel radiators and fan coil units) to the same sub-circuit.

Detailed guidance on commissioning may be found in CIBSE Commissioning Code W: *Water distribution systems*(36) and BSRIA Application Guide: *Commissioning of water systems in buildings*(39). Guidance for systems with variable speed and multiple pumps may be found in the BSRIA Application Guide: *Variable-flow water systems: Design, installation and commissioning guidance*(58).

1.4.3.3 Choice of heat source

The choice of heat source will depend on the options available. These are outlined below.

Boilers

Boilers are available in a large range of types and sizes and, unless they are connected to a community heating system (see *Community heating* (page 1-17)), almost all hydronic heating systems rely on one or more boilers. Boiler efficiency has improved markedly over the past two decades. Technical developments have included the use of new materials to reduce water content and exploit the condensing principle, gas-air modulation to improve combustion efficiency and modularisation to optimise system sizing. These developments have resulted in considerable improvements in performance at part load, with considerable benefit to seasonal efficiency.

Condensing boilers have efficiencies of up to 92% (gross calorific value) and are no longer much more expensive than other boilers. Neither are they so widely differentiated from non-condensing boilers in their performance, as the latter have improved considerably in their efficiency. Seasonal efficiency is the principal characteristic affecting the running cost of a boiler (or boiler system). In considering whole life cost, the lifetime of components should be taken into account.

'Combination' boilers provide an instantaneous supply of domestic hot water in addition to the usual boiler function. Their main advantage lies in the space they save, as they need no hot water storage cylinder or associated storage cistern. Also, they typically incorporate an expansion vessel for sealed operation, so that they need no plumbing in the loft space; this is particularly advantageous in flats where it may be difficult to obtain sufficient head from an open system. A further advantage is the elimination of heat losses from the hot water stored in the cylinder. Combination boilers have gained a large share of the market for boilers installed in housing over the past decade. However, the limitations of combination boilers should also be understood by both the installer and the client. The maximum flow rate at which hot water can be drawn is limited, especially over a prolonged period or when more than one point is being served simultaneously. Combination boilers are also susceptible to scaling by hard water, as the instantaneous water heating function requires the continual passage of water direct from the mains through a heat exchanger.

Heat pumps

Heat pumps have a number of different forms and exploit different sources of low grade heat. World wide, the heat pumps most widely used for heating are reversible air-to-air units that can also be used for cooling. Such units are typically found where there is significant need for cooling and the need for heating is limited. In the UK climate, electrically driven air-to-air heat pumps are not frequently installed solely to provide heating, which may be explained by the relatively high price of electricity in relation to gas. Heat pumps offer a particularly attractive option for heating when there is a suitably large source of low grade heat, such as a river, canal or an area of ground. Gas-fired ground source heat pumps currently being evaluated for use in housing as a boiler replacement are reported to have a seasonal coefficient of performance of around 1.4.

Solar panels

Solar water heating panels are widely used around the world to provide domestic hot water, particularly where sunshine is plentiful and fuel is relatively expensive, but are rarely used for space heating. In the UK climate, a domestic installation can typically provide hot water requirements for up to half the the annual hot water requirements, using either a separate pre-heat storage cylinder or a cylinder with two primary coils, one linked to the solar panel and the other to a boiler. Although technically successful, the economics of such systems are at best marginal in the UK when assessed against heat produced by a gas or oil boiler and they are rarely used in non-domestic buildings. Solar panels are also widely used for heating outdoor swimming pools in summer, for which they are more likely to be cost effective.

Community heating

If available, consideration should be given to utilising an existing supply of heat from a district or local heat supply ('community heating'). Heat supplied in this way may be of lower cost and may also have significantly lower environmental impact, especially if it is generated using combined heat and power (CHP) or makes use of heat from industrial processes or waste combustion. The low net CO_2 emissions from heat from such sources can contribute significantly to achieving an environmental target for a building. Detailed guidance on the evaluation and implementation of community heating may be found in *Guide to community heating and CHP*[59], published under the government's Energy Efficiency Best Practice programme.

Stand-alone CHP systems

Where there is no suitable existing supply of heat, the opportunity for using a stand-alone combined heat and power (CHP) unit should be evaluated. The case for using CHP depends on requirements both for heat and electricity, their diurnal and seasonal variability and the extent to which they occur simultaneously. The optimum CHP plant capacity for a single building needs to be determined by an economic assessment of a range of plant sizes and in general will result in only part of the load being met by CHP, the rest being met by a boiler. It is important to have a reasonable match between the generated output and electricity demand, as the value of the electricity generated tends to dominate the economic analysis; the optimum ratio of heat demand to power demand generally lies between 1.3:1 and 2:1. There may be opportunities for exporting electricity. The best price for exported electricity is likely to be obtained from consumers who can link directly to the system rather than from a public electricity supplier. Where standby power generation is required to reduce dependency of public supplies of electricity, it may be particularly advantageous to install a CHP unit, thereby avoiding the additional capital cost of a separate standby generator. CIBSE Applications Manual AM12: *Small-scale combined heat and power for buildings*[60], gives detailed guidance on the application of CHP in buildings.

1.4.3.4 Choice of heat emitter

Hydronic systems are capable of working with a wide variety of heat emitters, offering a high degree of flexibility in location, appearance and output characteristics. This section deals with some of the principal characteristics of emitters affecting their suitability for particular situations.

Radiators

Radiators, usually of pressed steel panel construction, are the most frequent choice of emitter. They are available in a wide variety of shapes, sizes and output ranges, making it possible to obtain a unit (or units) to match the heat requirements of almost any room or zone.

Despite their name, radiators for hydronic systems usually produce more than half their output by convection, often aided by fins added to increase their surface area. Details on the heat output available from radiators are given in section 1.5.1.1.

Natural convectors

Wall-mounted natural convectors may be used instead of radiators. They may also be used where there is insufficient space for mounting radiators, for example in base-board or trench heating configurations. The output from natural convectors varies considerably with design and manufacturer's data for individual emitter types should be used. Details of how the heat output from natural convectors varies with system temperature are given in section 1.5.1.1.

Fan coil heaters

Fan coil units produce high heat outputs from compact units using forced air circulation. Their output may be considered to be entirely convective and is approximately proportional to temperature difference. Where systems contain a mixture of natural and forced air appliances, the different output characteristics of the two types should be taken into account, particularly with regard to zoning for control systems.

Floor heating

Floor heating (also referred to as under-floor heating) uses the floor surface itself as a heat emitter. Heat may be supplied either by embedded electric heating elements or by the circulation of water as part of a hydronic system, involving appropriately spaced pipes positioned beneath the floor surface. The pipes may be embedded within the screed of a solid floor or laid in a carefully controlled configuration beneath a suspended floor surface. Insulation beneath the heating elements is clearly very important for good control of output and to avoid unnecessary heat loss.

The heat emission characteristics of floor heating differ considerably from those of radiator heating. Floor surface temperature is critical to comfort, as well as to heat output. The optimum floor temperature range for comfort lies between 21 and 28 °C depending on surface material, see Table 1.20 (page 1-30), so systems are normally designed to operate at no higher than 29 °C in occupied areas. Higher temperatures are acceptable in bathrooms and close to external walls with high heat loss, such as beneath full-length windows.

The design surface temperature is controlled by the spacing between pipes and the flow water temperature. It is also affected by floor construction, floor covering and the depth of the pipes beneath the floor surface; detailed design procedures are given by system manufacturers. In practice, systems are usually designed to operate at flow temperatures of between 40 and 50 °C, with a temperature drop of between 5 and 10 K across the system. Maximum heat output is limited by the maximum acceptable surface temperature to around 100 $W \cdot m^{-2}$ for occupied areas. The overall design of floor heating systems should be undertaken in accordance with the European Standard BS EN 1264[61]. See also section 1.5.1.1.

Floor heating may be used in conjunction with radiators, for example for the ground floor of a house with radiators on upper floors. Separate circuits are required is such cases, typically using a mixing valve to control the temperature of the under-floor circuit. Floor heating is best suited to well insulated buildings, in which it can provide all the required heating load.

1.4.3.5 Pumping and pipework

The hydraulic requirements for a system are derived from parameters such as system operating temperature and the heat output required from emitters, which affect pipework layout. The design also needs to take account of the effect of water velocity on noise and corrosion, and the pressure and flow characteristics required of the circulation pump. The key design decisions include:

- system pressures
- whether to use an open or a sealed pressurisation method
- which material to use for pipes
- the flow velocity to be used
- how the system is to be controlled
- filling and air removal arrangements
- pumping requirements, i.e. variable or fixed flow rate.

Details of the characteristics of pipework and pumps are dealt with in sections 1.5.1.3 and 1.5.1.4.

1.4.3.6 Energy storage

Energy storage may either be used to reduce peak loads or to take advantage of lower energy prices at certain times of day. Heat is stored using either solid cores or hot water vessels. The most common application of thermal storage is in dwellings, in which solid core storage is charged with heat at off-peak rates for a 7 or 8 hour period. Guidance for the design of such systems is contained in Electricity Association publication *Design of mixed storage heater/direct systems*[62].

Systems relying on hot water storage vessels are also available for use in dwellings. The three main types are as follows:

- *Combined primary storage units (CPSU)*: provide both space and water heating from within a single appliance, in which a burner heats a thermal store. The water in the thermal store is circulated to radiators to provide space heating, while a heat exchanger is used to transfer heat to incoming cold water at mains pressure to provide a supply of domestic hot water.
- *Integrated thermal stores*: also provide both space and water heating from within a single appliance. However, they differ from CPSUs in that a separate boiler is used to heat the primary water.
- *Hot-water-only thermal stores*: use thermal storage only for production of domestic hot water. As for the two types described above, the domestic hot water is provided by a heat exchanger working at mains pressure.

Also, some models of combination boiler contain a small thermal store to overcome the limitation on flow rates for domestic hot water, see section 1.4.3.3.

Thermal storage for larger buildings must rely on purpose-designed storage vessels with capacity and storage temperature optimised for the heat load. Other design parameters that must be considered are insulation of the storage vessel, arrangements for dealing with expansion and the control strategy for coupling the store to the rest of the system.

1.4.3.7 Domestic hot water

Whether or not to produce domestic hot water from the same system as space heating is a key decision to be taken before detailed design proceeds. In housing, where demand for hot water is a substantial proportion of the total heat load, a hydronic heating system is usually the most convenient and satisfactory means of producing hot water, using either a hot water storage cylinder or a combination boiler.

In buildings other than housing, the case for deriving domestic hot water from a hydronic heating system depends greatly on circumstances. The demand for hot water and the locations with the building where it is required will affect the relative costs of independent heat generation and connection to the space heating system. In general, independent hot water generation is the more economical choice when relatively small amounts of hot water are required at positions distant from the boiler. Circulating hot water circuits that require long pipe runs and operate for extended periods solely to provide hot water can waste large amounts of energy, particularly during summer months when no space heating is required. In commercial buildings, toilet areas are often best served by independent gas or electric water heaters.

1.4.3.8 Control for hydronic systems

Hydronic heating systems are capable of very close control over environmental conditions using a range of strategies. The choice of control system type will depend on the closeness of control required, the number of different zones that must be controlled independently and the times at which the building will be occupied and require heating. The design must also take account of the characteristics of both heat generators and emitters.

A typical control system for a hydronic heating system in a dwelling or small building consists of a programmer, which may incorporate a timeswitch or optimum start/stop functions, a room thermostat for each zone, motorised valves to control the flow to each zone and, if necessary, a frost protection thermostat. Where domestic hot water is also provided by the system, a thermostat and motorised valve to control the temperature of the hot water storage cylinder are also needed. Controls should be wired in such a way that the boiler operates only when a space heating or cylinder thermostat is calling for heat. Thermostatic radiator valves (TRVs) may be used to control individual rooms within a zone. Pump 'over-run' (i.e. delay in switching off a pump) may also be provided by the system or may be incorporated in the boiler controls.

Hydronic systems in larger buildings are likely to have more complex controls, including optimum start, and often incorporate weather compensation in which the system flow temperature is controlled in response to external temperature, according to a schedule derived for the building. Where there are multiple or modular boilers, sequence control is required for the boilers. Variable speed pumping may also be used. The pump speed is usually controlled to maintain a constant pressure differential across a point in the circuit as flow reduces in response to 2-port valve and TRV positions. Care is needed in the choice of valves used for control to ensure good 'valve authority', which means that they are sized appropriately in relation to the pressure drops around the circuit.

Comprehensive guidance on control system design is given in CIBSE Guide H[63] and the characteristics of control system components are given in section 1.5.1.5.

1.4.3.9 Water expansion

The density of water reduces significantly as temperature rises which results in significant expansion as a hydronic system warms up from cold. This must be accommodated without an excessive rise in system pressure. Table 1.9 shows the percentage expansion, calculated with reference to 4 °C at start-up for a range of operating temperatures using the expression:

$$(\Delta V / V_4) = (\rho_4 / \rho) - 1 \qquad (1.16)$$

where ΔV is the change in volume resulting from change in temperature (m^3), V_4 is the volume at 4 °C (m^3), ρ_4 is the density at 4 °C (kg·m^{-3}) and ρ is the density (kg·m^{-3}) at a given temperature.

Allowance may also be made for the expansion of the pipework, but this is small for most materials.

All hydronic systems must have provision for maintaining system operating pressure within a range that ensures safety and effective operation of the system. For low pressure systems this may be achieved by the use of a cistern positioned to maintain pressure by gravity, or by a sealed expansion vessel in which a volume of pressurised gas is separated from the primary water by a diaphragm. In both cases, the system must be able to cope with the expansion of the primary water as the system heats up from cold to its design temperature.

An open system, relying on hydrostatic pressurisation normally has separate feed and open safety vent pipes, with the latter positioned to provide an unrestricted path for the relief of pressure and the escape of steam if the boiler thermostat were to fail and the system overheat. The open safety vent pipe should rise continuously from its point of connection, contain no valves or restrictions and discharge downwards into the feed and expansion cistern. BS 5449[54] recommends that cistern capacity should be at least 5% of system volume to give an adequate margin of safety in operation.

Table 1.9 Percentage expansion of water heating up from 4 °C

Temperature (°C)	Expansion (%)
40	0.79
50	1.21
60	1.71
70	2.27
80	2.90
90	3.63
100	4.34
110	5.20
120	6.00
130	7.00
140	8.00
150	9.10
160	10.2
170	11.4
180	12.8
190	14.2
200	15.7

Sealed pressurisation equipment for low pressure systems consists of an expansion vessel complying with BS 4814[64], a pressure gauge, a means for filling, and a non-adjustable safety valve. Boilers fitted to sealed systems must be approved for the purpose by their manufacturer and must incorporate a high limit thermostat and a safety/pressure relief valve. The expansion vessel contains a diaphragm, which separates the system water from a volume of gas (air or nitrogen). When the system water expands, it enters the vessel, compressing the gas. The vessel must have sufficient volume to accommodate the change in system volume without an excessive increase in pressure. BS 7074[65] gives guidance on expansion vessel sizing, initial system pressure and safety valve settings. The expansion vessel should be connected to the return circuit just prior to the pump inlet.

A sealed system has the considerable advantage of eliminating the need for a feed and expansion cistern, placed at a suitable level, and the associated pipework. In housing, this can mean the elimination of pipework and cisterns in the roof space, reducing the risk of frost damage and condensation. A sealed system is also much less prone to corrosion since there is no opportunity for the introduction of air into the system under normal operation. An example calculation for sizing a sealed expansion vessel is given in Appendix 1.A1.1.

Medium and high pressure systems may use a variety of techniques to maintain working pressure:

- pressurisation by expansion of water, in which the expansion of the water in the system is itself used to charge a pressure vessel
- pressurisation by an elevated header tank
- gas pressurisation with a spill tank, in which a pressure cylinder is partly filled with water and partly with a gas (usually nitrogen)
- hydraulic pressurisation with spill tank, in which pressure is maintained by a continuously running pump.

1.4.4 Steam systems

1.4.4.1 Characteristics of steam systems

Steam systems use dry saturated steam to convey heat from the boiler to the point of use, where it is released by condensation. Control of heat output is generally by variation of the steam saturation pressure within the emitter. The resulting condensate is returned to the feed tank, where it becomes a valuable supply of hot feed-water for the boiler. The flow of steam is generated by the pressure drop that results from condensation. Condensate is returned to the lowest point in the circuit by gravity.

Steam offers great flexibility in application and is long established as a medium for heating in buildings. However, it is not frequently chosen as a medium for heating buildings when that is the sole requirement. This is because of more stringent safety requirements and more onerous maintenance requirements than are required for LTHW systems. It is much more likely to be appropriate when there are other requirements for steam, such as manufacturing processes or sterilisation. In such cases, steam may be the most satisfactory medium both for space heating and for domestic hot water generation. In many cases, it will be appropriate to use steam to generate hot water in a heat exchanger for distribution in a standard hydronic heating system.

1.4.4.2 Types of system/system design

Typical steam circuit

A typical steam circuit is shown in Figure 1.5, showing a main pipe carrying steam from the crown valve of the boiler and a second pipe returning condensate to the feed tank. Branch pipes connect individual pieces of equipment or loads to the mains. Condensate from the feed tank is returned to the boiler by the feed pump, which is controlled to maintain the water level in the boiler. Treated water is supplied to the feed tank as required to make up for losses incurred through leaks or venting.

Calculation of system loads

The heat requirement may be calculated in the same way as for a hydronic heating system. This may then be converted to a mass flow rate for steam at the design temperature and pressure using steam tables, see CIBSE Guide C[(57)], which give the specific enthalpy of evaporation in $kJ{\cdot}kg^{-1}$. A correction should be made for the dryness of the steam, which is typically around 95% and will increase the required mass flow rate pro rata.

Working pressure

The working pressure at which steam must be circulated depends upon:

— the pressure required where each piece of plant is connected

— the pressure drop along the distribution pipework due to resistance to flow

— pipe heat losses.

As steam at high pressure occupies less volume per unit of mass than steam at low pressure, smaller distribution pipework can be used to achieve a given mass flow rate. This leads to lower capital cost for the pipework and associated valves, flanges and pipe insulation. Higher pressure also offers the advantages of drier steam at the point of use and increased thermal storage in the boiler. The usual practice is to convey steam to the points of use at high pressure and to provide pressure reduction at the point of use.

Pipework sizing

Oversized pipework results in excessive capital costs, greater than necessary condensate formation, and poor steam quality. Undersized pipework causes excessive steam velocity and higher pressure drops, which can cause steam starvation at the point of use as well as a greater risk of erosion and noise. Pipe sizing may be carried out from consideration of the steam velocity required to match the loads around the circuit. In practice, limiting the velocity to between 15 and 25 $m{\cdot}s^{-1}$ will avoid excessive pressure drops and problems with noise and erosion. Velocities of up to 40 $m{\cdot}s^{-1}$ may be acceptable in large mains. Sizing may also be carried out from consideration of the steam pressure required at particular pieces of plant.

Pressure reducing sets

Steam distributed at a higher pressure than the equipment served requires pressure reduction. The main component in a pressure reducing set is the reducing valve, often a spring loaded diaphragm or bellows type. Simple direct acting reducing valves can be used where the load is small or remains fairly steady. For larger and varying loads a more elaborate, pilot-operated valve may be necessary.

To prevent water or dirt entering the reducing valve it is good practice to install a baffle-type separator and strainer upstream of the valve. Pressure gauges are usually fitted either side of the reducing valve to set the valve initially and to check its operation in use.

It is essential to fit a pressure relief or safety valve on the downstream side of the reducing valve. The relief valve and its discharge pipe must be sized and located to discharge

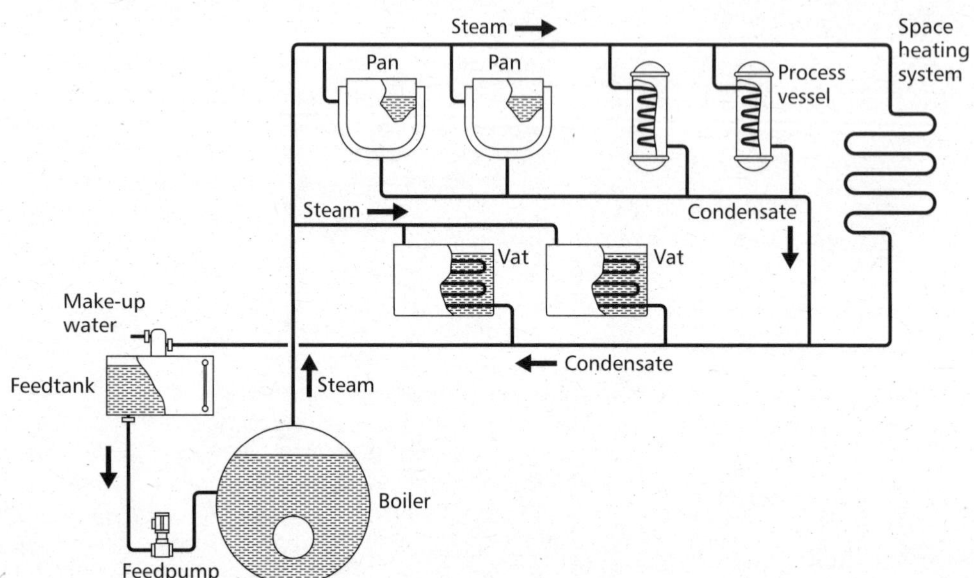

Figure 1.5 Typical steam circuit (courtesy of Spirax-Sarco Ltd)

steam safely at the upstream pressure for the maximum capacity of the reducing valve, should it fail wide open.

Steam trapping and air venting

Condensation occurs whenever heat is transferred to a load and it must be removed for return to the feed tank. The principal function of a steam trap is to discharge condensate while preventing the escape of dry steam. Air is present within steam supply pipes and steam equipment when the system is started and may also be introduced at other times in solution in the feed water. Air must be removed since it both reduces the capability of a steam system to supply heat and causes corrosion. Some types of steam traps are also designed to remove air and other non-condensing gases from systems. Specialised automatic air vents are fitted at remote points to achieve full air removal.

Condensation takes place in steam mains even when they are well insulated and provision must be made for drainage. Steam mains should be installed with a fall of not less than 100 mm in 10 m in the direction of steam flow, with collection points arranged as shown in Figure 1.6 using appropriate steam traps. Where possible, branch connections should be taken from the top of the main to avoid the entry of condensate. Low points in branch lines, such as those that occur in front of a control valve, will also accumulate condensate and need provision for trapping and drainage. Steam traps must be sized to remove condensate at the rate needed for cold start-up. A general rule of thumb is to size the condensate return system for twice the mean condensing rate at the operating differential pressure. The characteristics of steam traps and their suitability for particular applications are described in section 1.5.2.2.

Condensate handling

Effective condensate removal and return to the boiler is essential for steam systems to operate properly. As mentioned above, it is important to trap the steam main at low points along its length to ensure that dry steam is available at the point of use.

Temperature control of steam process equipment and heat exchangers is usually achieved by throttling the flow of steam. Consequently, steam pressure falls inside the exchanger. When the steam pressure inside the exchanger is equal to, or lower than the pressure at the outlet side of the steam trap, condensate will not flow. To prevent the exchanger from flooding with condensate it is necessary to locate the trap below the exchanger outlet to provide a hydrostatic head to enable condensate to pass through the trap by gravity, the outlet side of the trap normally being kept at atmospheric pressure. A vacuum breaker is often fitted at the steam inlet point of the heat exchanger to admit air in the event that steam pressure inside the exchanger falls below atmospheric pressure. If condensate is to return to the boiler feed tank through pipework at a higher level than the trap, as is usually the case, then the condensate must be pumped, see below.

Condensate pumping

A condensate pump set usually comprises an open vented vessel mounted above one or more electric motor pumps or pressure operated lifting pumps, the latter most often using steam but compressed air or other gas may also be used. Condensate from steam traps is piped to discharge into the receiver vessel by gravity.

Electric pumps are usually switched on and off by level controls in the receiver vessel. Special measures regarding electric pumps need to be taken with high pressure steam systems, where condensate temperatures can equal or exceed 100 °C.

Pressure operated pumps work by displacing a volume of collected condensate in the pump body. Check valves are fitted on the condensate inlet and outlet of the pump to ensure correct water flow. When the pump body is full of condensate from the receiver an internal mechanism opens the pressurising gas inlet valve. The condensate is pushed through the outlet check valve. At the end of the discharge stroke the mechanism closes the inlet valve and opens an exhaust valve. The 'used' pressurising gas within the pump body then vents either to atmosphere or to the space from which the condensate is being drained. When the pressures are equalised, more condensate can flow by gravity from the receiver into the pump body, and the cycle repeats.

Condensate return mains

There are essentially two types of condensate return: gravity and pumped. Traps draining a steam main or device that is always at full steam pressure can vertically lift condensate a limited distance before discharging into a gravity return main laid to fall towards the boiler feed tank. As mentioned above, traps draining heat exchange equipment normally discharge condensate by gravity into a vented receiver from where it is pumped into a separate return main. Gravity condensate return lines carry both condensate and incondensable gases, together with flash steam from the hot condensate. The pipework should be sufficiently large to convey all the liquid, gases and flash steam. An adequately sized pipeline is capable of accepting condensate discharged from traps with different upstream pressures. However, if the pipeline is too small, excessive velocities and pressure drops may arise, particularly where condensate at high pressure and temperature enters the line, giving off flash steam. Such situations often give rise to water-hammer.

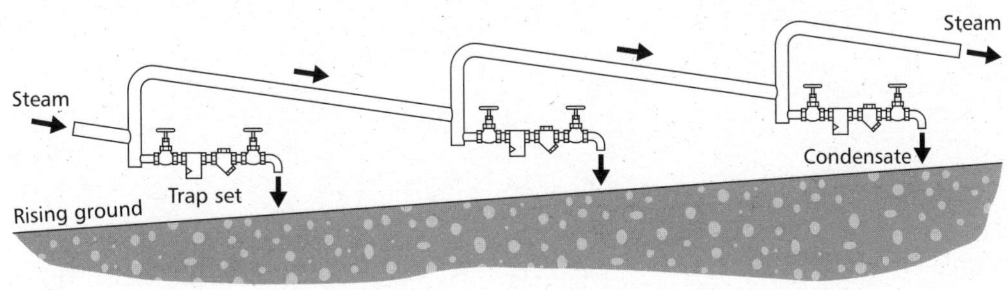

Figure 1.6 Steam main on rising ground showing drainage (courtesy of Spirax-Sarco Ltd)

Pumped condensate pipes carry only water and can be sized for higher velocities than gravity lines. Trap discharge pipes should not connect directly into pumped condensate pipelines. Flash steam released from additional condensate flowing into a flooded pipe will invariably result in water-hammer.

Safety

Every steam boiler must be fitted with a safety valve to protect it from excessive pressure. The safety valve must:

— have a total discharge capacity at least equal to the capacity of the boiler

— achieve full discharge capacity within 110% of the boiler design pressure

— have a minimum valve seat bore of 20 mm

— be set at a pressure no higher than the design pressure of the boiler and with an adequate margin above the normal working pressure of the boiler.

Boilers with a capacity of more than 3700 $kg \cdot h^{-1}$ must have at least two single safety valves or a one double safety valve. All boilers must also be fitted with:

— a stop valve (also known as a crown valve) to isolate the boiler from the plant

— at least one bottom blow-down valve to remove sediment

— a pressure gauge

— a water level indicator.

1.4.4.3 Guidance and standards

There are many standards and guidance documents relevant to steam systems, including the following:

— Statutory Instrument 1989 No. 2169, The Pressure Systems and Transportable Gas Containers Regulations 1989[(66)]: provides the legal framework for pressurised vessels.

— BS 1113[(67)]: covers the design and manufacture of water-tube steam generating plant

— BS 2790[(68)]: covers the design and manufacture of shell boilers of welded construction , including aspects such as stop valves

— BS 6759-1[(69)]: covers the specification of safety valves

— BS 759: Part 1[(70)]: covers valves, mountings and fittings for steam boilers above 1 bar gauge

— Health and Safety Executive PM60[(71)]: covers bottom blow-down

— BS 1780: Part 2[(72)]: cover pressure gauges

— BS 3463[(73)]: covers level indicators

— BS 806[(74)]: covers drainage of steam lines

— Health and Safety Executive PM5[(75)]: covers boiler operation.

1.4.5 Warm air systems

1.4.5.1 Characteristics of warm air heating

Warm air heating can be provided either by stand-alone heaters or distributed from central air-handling plant; in many cases the same plant is used for summertime cooling/ventilation. Almost all the heat output is provided in convective form so the room air temperature is usually greater than the dry resultant temperature. Warm air systems generally have a much faster response time than hydronic systems. For example, a typical factory warm air system will bring the space up to design temperature within 30 minutes. Warm air systems can cause excessive temperature stratification, with warm air tending to collect at ceiling level. This may be particularly unwelcome in buildings with high ceilings, although it can be overcome by the use of destratification systems.

Warm air systems may be used to provide full heating to a space or simply supply tempered 'make-up' air to balance the heat loss and air flow rate from exhaust ventilation systems. A slight excess air flow can be used to pressurise the heated space slightly and reduce cold draughts.

1.4.5.2 Layout and design

Warm air systems for housing are often based on stub ducts, radiating from a centrally located furnace. This minimises the length of ductwork required and simplifies installation. Systems used in larger houses, especially in North America, typically rely on long lengths of ductwork distributing heat from a furnace located in a basement. Systems for large commercial buildings are described in section 2. Such systems typically use ductwork, which may also provide ventilation air and cooling.

For industrial and warehouse buildings, heating is often provided by dedicated warm air heaters.

Most commonly a distributed system using individual warm air heaters rated at between about 20 kW and 300 kW is used. Efficiency is high at about 80% gross. Traditionally these heaters have been floor standing, oil or gas fired and of high output. This minimises initial cost and floor space requirements but provides fairly coarse control of conditions. Current practice typically uses suspended gas fired heaters, rated at up to 100 kW. These are quieter, avoid loss of floor space and provide better heat distribution.

It is necessary to use a de-stratification system (punkah fans or similar) to avoid excess heat loss through the roof and poor comfort at floor level due to temperature stratification, particularly when using suspended heaters. A well designed system can limit temperature differences arising from stratification to only a few degrees, even in buildings with high ceilings.

In tall industrial and warehouse buildings, specialist central plant warm air heating systems are also used. They typically rely on high-temperature, high-velocity primary air supply at high level, supplemented by induction of room air at discharge points to provide good air circulation and even temperatures in the occupied zone.

Electric warm air unit heaters are typically only used in restricted circumstances, such as air curtains at entrance doors, due to their relatively high running cost. Air curtains are described in BSRIA Application Guide AG2/97: *Air curtains — commercial applications*[76].

Direct fired (flueless) gas warm air heating is sometimes used due to its high efficiency (100% net, 92% gross). While this benefit makes it attractive, particularly if a high ventilation rate is needed, the dispersion of combustion gases into the heated space means that it must be used with care. In particular the ventilation requirements of BS 6230[77] should be met to ensure that CO_2 levels are kept low enough to avoid adverse effects on health and comfort.

Care should be taken to ensure that even these low levels of diluted products of combustion do not have adverse an effect on items stored in the heated space, such as premature yellowing of paper and some fabrics due to NO_x levels.

1.4.5.3 Control of warm air heating

For central plant providing heating and ventilation, the heating component generally places no extra demands on the control system, although care should be taken to ensure that the sensor locations accurately reflect zone temperatures in the heating mode.

For individual warm air heaters it is usual to provide a separate thermostat or sensor to control each heater although, exceptionally, up to four small heaters in one space may be controlled together. Time control is usually by simple time-switch, since the fast response of warm air heaters makes optimum start/stop of limited benefit

1.4.5.4 Restrictions on use

Flueless appliances may only be used in accordance with the requirements of the Building Regulations Part J[8]. Noise generated by warm air distribution may also restrict the use of warm air heating in some circumstances.

1.4.6 Radiant systems

1.4.6.1 Characteristics of radiant heating

In general, systems are considered to be radiant when more than 50% of their output is radiant, which corresponds broadly to those with emitter temperatures greater than 100 °C. This definition includes medium temperature systems, such as high pressure hydronic systems, steam systems and air heated tubes, which operate at temperatures up to 200 °C. High temperature radiant systems, such as those with electric radiant elements or gas heated plaques, produce a higher proportion of their output in radiant form and are particularly effective when heat output needs to be focussed and directed to specific locations.

Radiant heating is particularly useful in buildings with high air change rates or large volumes that do not require uniform heating throughout, e.g., factories, and intermittently heated buildings with high ceilings. The key characteristics of radiant heating are as follows:

— Heat transfer occurs by radiation directly on surfaces, including building occupants and the internal surfaces of buildings and fittings. The surrounding air need not be heated to the same temperature as would be required with convective heating.

— A rapid response can be achieved because the effect of the thermal inertia of the building is bypassed by direct radiation.

— After an initial warm-up period, radiant heating directed downwards towards floor level is augmented by re-radiation and convection from surfaces at the level occupied by people.

— Radiant asymmetry is a potential problem and may place restrictions on design.

Radiant heating can require less energy than convective heating because it enables comfort conditions to be achieved at lower air temperatures. As a general rule it is likely to have an advantage in this respect whenever ventilation heat losses exceed fabric heat losses. Further savings may be achieved when only some zones within a large open area require heating and local radiant temperature can be raised by well directed radiant heat. In such cases, large volumes of surrounding air may be left at much lower temperatures without a detrimental effect on dry resultant temperature in the working zones.

1.4.6.2 Layout and design of radiant heating systems

There are two basic approaches to radiant heating design:

— *Spot heating*: applies to the situation described in the preceding paragraph, in which the intention is to heat only a small part of a larger space. In such cases, comfort depends mainly on direct radiant output from the heaters and there is little effect on the overall air temperature in the building.

— *Total heating*: applies to situations in which the whole space must be heated to a uniform temperature.

Detailed guidance on the design of radiant heating systems is given in BSRIA Application Guide AG3/96: *Radiant heating*[78].

For spot heating, standard heat loss calculations are not appropriate for calculating the output required from emitters. Relatively high levels of irradiance are required to produce the necessary dry resultant temperature and it is necessary to determine the distribution of radiant energy within the space. To achieve this, it is necessary to know the directional characteristics of each heat emitter. For an air temperature of 15 °C, the maximum irradiance recommended[78] at floor level is 80 $W \cdot m^{-2}$, which places limitations on the mounting height of emitters. Total spherical irradiance at 1.8 m above floor level is recommended not to exceed 240 $W \cdot m^{-2}$. These figures are considered conservative for industrial heating applications and may be exceeded with caution. However, account should be taken of temperatures reached on surfaces close to heaters, for example on the tops of shelving. When considering the use of spot radiant heating, it is important to consider relative humidity of the air in the building. Contact between moist air and cold surfaces away from the heated areas may cause problems with condensation, particularly where flueless gas radiant heaters are used.

When designing for total radiant heating relying on low and medium temperature emitters, the procedure is similar to that required for other heating systems, involving consideration of fabric and ventilation heat loss and the calculation of total heat output required. Designs typically assume that air temperature will be around 3 °C below dry resultant temperature.

1.4.6.3 Control of radiant heating

The sensing of temperature for the control of radiant heating presents difficulties both in sensing dry resultant temperature and in finding an appropriate location for the sensor. A black-bulb thermometer needs to be located centrally in a zone to avoid influence by proximity to a wall. Hemispherical black-bulb sensors are available for wall mounting, but are often difficult to set in relation to perceived comfort conditions.

Air temperature sensors may be used to control radiant heating, particularly where total heating is provided. However, they tend to underestimate dry resultant temperature during warm up and cause waste of energy.

1.4.6.4 Restrictions of use of radiant heating

Physical restrictions on the mounting of radiant emitters apply. High temperature emitters must not be placed where they can come into contact with people or objects that cannot withstand the resulting surface temperatures. Also, the irradiance from emitters limits their proximity to working areas. Consequently, radiant heating may be considered unsuitable for use in buildings with low ceilings. Table 1.10 shows typical restrictions on mounting height for various types of radiant heat emitter.

Despite its obvious advantages for partially heated buildings, 'spot' radiant heating does not offer good control of temperature. It should not be considered, therefore, where close temperature control is required.

Table 1.10 Minimum heights for radiant heat emitters (source BSRIA AG 3/96[78])

Emitter type	Input rating / kW	Min. height / m
Gas radiant U-tube	13	3.0
	22	3.6
	38	4.3
Gas plaque heater	13.5	4.2
	27	7.0
Gas cone heater	12	3.6
Quartz tube heater	3	3.0
	6	4.5

1.4.7 Plant size ratio

1.4.7.1 Definition of plant size ratio

Heating systems are designed to meet the maximum steady-state load likely to be encountered under design conditions. However, additional capacity is needed to overcome thermal inertia so that the building may reach equilibrium in a reasonable time, particularly if the building is heated intermittently.

Plant size ratio (PSR) is defined as:

$$\text{PSR} = \frac{\text{installed heat emission}}{\text{design heat load}}$$

The design heat load used in the calculation of PSR is the heat loss from the space or building under conditions of external design temperature and internal design temperature. For the purpose of specifying the heating system this condition should be calculated for the time of peak steady state load. The time at which this occurs will depend on the building or space, its services and its occupancy. Peak load normally occurs under one of the following conditions:

- *during occupancy*: taking account of any reliable internal heat gains, fabric heat losses and all ventilation heat losses
- *before occupancy*: taking account of any permanent internal heat gains (but not those occurring only during occupied periods), fabric heat losses and all ventilation losses (unless ventilation systems operate during occupied periods only, in which case only infiltration losses are applicable).

1.4.7.2 Intermittent heating

Intermittent occupancy permits a reduction in internal temperature while the building is unoccupied and a consequent reduction in fuel consumption. It is important to note that the building continues to lose heat during the off period and requires additional heat to bring the building back up to temperature during the 'pre-heat' period prior to the next period of occupancy. For many buildings, the preheat period can constitute the major energy consumption of the building. The shaded area in Figure 1.7 represents the accumulated temperature reduction (in degree-hours), which is directly related to the energy saved by the system due to the reduction in space temperature during the period of non-occupancy. A building having low thermal inertia, which cools to a lower temperature when the heating system is off, will experience greater economy as a result of intermittent heating, than a building of high thermal inertia, see Figure 1.8. However, it should be noted that high thermal inertia is beneficial in that it enables better utilisation of heat gains.

The necessary plant size ratio required to reach design temperature for a particular building depends on the occupancy and heating pattern. For many buildings, the most demanding situation arises on Monday morning after being unoccupied during the weekend. If the system is shut off completely during the weekend, the building

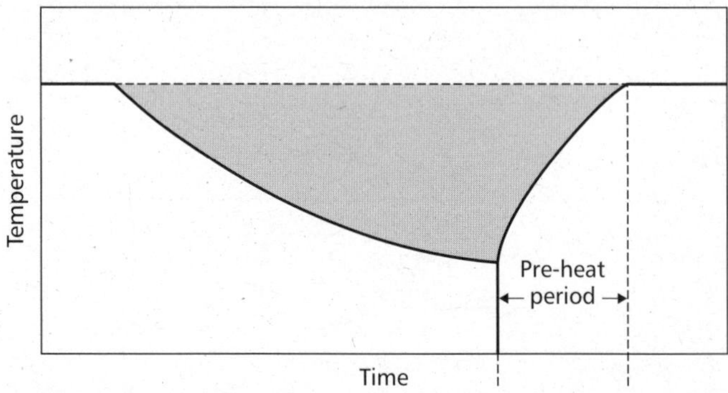

Figure 1.7 Temperature profile of a space during intermittent heating with the pre-heat period optimised to be as short as possible

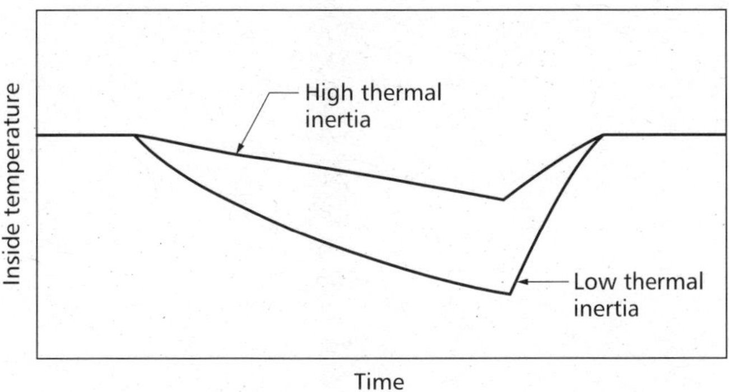

Figure 1.8 Profile of space temperature for buildings of high thermal inertia and low thermal inertia, each having the same plant size ratio

may have to be heated up from a room temperature little higher than the outside temperature. The heating system may also be operated at a set-back temperature when it is not occupied, in which case less energy is required to restore it to design temperature. It may also be observed from Figure 1.8 that a building with low thermal inertia heats up more quickly than one with high thermal inertia and therefore a lower plant size ratio may be employed.

1.4.7.3 Choice of plant size ratio

The shorter the pre-heat period, the greater is the saving in energy. This implies that the greater the plant size ratio, the greater the economy in energy consumption. However there are several disadvantages in over-sizing the heating system:

— greater capital cost

— more difficult to achieve stability of controls

— except during pre-heat, the plant will run at less than full load, generally leading to a lower seasonal efficiency.

The optimum plant size ratio is difficult to determine as it requires knowledge, or estimates, of:

— the occupancy pattern

— the thermal inertia or thermal response of the building areas

— the design internal temperature

— the minimum permissible internal temperature

— a record of the weather over a typical season

— the current fuel tariffs and estimates of future tariffs over the life of the system

— the capital and maintenance costs of different sizes of equipment.

Section 5 of CIBSE Guide A(19) deals with thermal response, including descriptions of steady-state and dynamic models. Fully functional dynamic models are too complex for hand calculation and in practice must be implemented through carefully developed and validated software. CIBSE Applications Manual AM11(79) gives guidance on the selection of suitable models. For complex buildings, it is recommended that plant size ratio be calculated using a dynamic simulation of the building and the plant.

For less complex buildings, CIBSE Guide A, section 5.8.3.3, describes a method of calculating plant size ratio based on the admittance procedure:

$$F_3 = \frac{24 f_r}{H f_r + (24 - H)} \tag{1.17}$$

where F_3 is the plant size ratio (or 'intermittency factor'), f_r is the thermal response factor (see equation 1.18) and H is the hours of plant operation (including preheat) (h).

The response factor may be calculated from:

$$f_r = \frac{\Sigma\,(A\,Y) + C_v}{\Sigma\,(A\,U) + C_v} \tag{1.18}$$

where f_r is the thermal response factor, $\Sigma\,(A\,Y)$ is the sum of the products of surface areas and their corresponding thermal admittances (W·K^{-1}), $\Sigma\,(A\,U)$ is the sum of the products of surface areas and their corresponding thermal transmittances over surfaces through which heat flow occurs (W·K^{-1}) and C_v is the ventilation heat loss coefficient (W·K^{-1}).

The ventilation heat loss coefficient is given by:

$$C_v = (c_p\,\rho\,N\,V) / 3600 \tag{1.19}$$

where c_p is the specific heat capacity of air ($\text{J·kg}^{-1}\text{·K}^{-1}$), ρ is the density of air (kg·m^{-3}), N is the number of air changes in the space (h^{-1}) and V is the room volume (m^3).

For air at ambient temperatures, $\rho \approx 1.20\ \text{kg·m}^{-3}$ and $c_p \approx 1000\ \text{J·kg}^{-1}\text{·K}^{-1}$, hence:

$$C_v \approx N\,V / 3 \tag{1.20}$$

Table 1.11 shows plant size ratios for a range of heating periods and thermal response factors. Structures with a response factor greater than 4 are referred to as slow response or 'heavyweight', and those with a response factor less than 4 as fast response or 'lightweight'. CIBSE Guide A recommends that when the calculation yields a result of less than 1.2, a plant size ratio of 1.2 should be used.

Plant sizing as described above is based on ensuring that the heating system is able to bring the building up to design temperature in the required time. A more comprehensive approach, including economic appraisal, is described in a paper by Day et al(80). This proposes a new method for calculating the pre-heat time required, which takes account of the plant capacity in relation to the mean temperature of the whole daily cycle. It goes on to optimise plant size by finding the minimum life cycle cost, taking account of both capital and running costs. The

Table 1.11 Plant size ratio calculated for different heating periods

Heating hours (including pre-heat period)	Thermal weight		
	Light ($f_r = 2$)	Medium ($f_r = 4$)	Heavy ($f_r = 8$)
6	1.6	—	—
7	1.5	—	—
8	1.5	2.0	—
9	1.5	1.9	—
10	1.4	1.8	2.0
11	1.4	1.7	1.9
12	1.3	1.6	1.8
13	1.3	1.5	1.7
14	1.3	1.5	1.6
15	1.2	1.4	1.5
16	1.2	1.3	1.4

paper also reports conclusions reached from applying the model to a large gas-fired system (750 kW), as follows:

— The greater the thermal capacity of the building, the smaller the optimal plant size ratio. In determining the effective thermal capacity of the building, as a general guide, the first 100 mm of the inner fabric skin should be taken into account.

— For the particular case studied, the optimum plant size ratio was found to be 1.63 but the economic savings which result from this choice do not vary significantly for plant size ratios of ±10% of the optimum.

— Plant size ratio >2.0 are not justified for most typical buildings.

— Smaller plants have higher values of marginal installed cost (£/extra kW), so the optimum plant size ratio will be lower.

In general, it may be observed that, unless rapid warm-up is essential, plant size ratio should be in the range 1.2 to 2.0. Optimum start control can ensure adequate pre-heat time in cold weather.

1.5 Plant and equipment

1.5.1 Equipment for hydronic systems

1.5.1.1 Heat emitters

Radiators and convectors

Both radiators and convectors emit heat by virtue of their surface temperatures being greater than the room air temperature and the mean radiant temperature of the surfaces surrounding them. In each case, heat is emitted by both radiation and convection. Even for a 'radiator', the convective component may be well over half the heat emission when fins are included either behind or between panels.

Manufacturers are obliged to quote the nominal output of the emitter under a standard method for testing as specified in BS EN 442-2[81].

The standard emission is under conditions of 'excess temperature' of 50 K, i.e:

$$\Delta T = (t_m - t_{ai}) = 50 \qquad (1.21)$$

where ΔT is the excess temperature (K), t_m is the mean water temperature within the emitter (°C) and t_{ai} is the temperature of the surrounding air (°C).

The test conditions require that the surrounding mean radiant temperature does not differ significantly from the surrounding air temperature. They also require that the inlet and outlet temperatures should be 75 °C and 65 °C respectively in surroundings at 20 °C. The designer is not obliged to adhere to these temperatures.

The 'water-side' of the heat exchange is given by:

$$\phi = q_m \, c_p \, (t_1 - t_2) \qquad (1.22)$$

where ϕ is the heat emission (W), q_m is the mass flow rate (kg·s^{-1}), c_p is the specific heat capacity of water (J·kg^{-1}·K^{-1}), t_1 is the inlet temperature (°C) and t_2 is the outlet temperature (°C).

The 'air-side' of the heat exchange is given by:

$$\phi = K_m \, \Delta T^n \qquad (1.23)$$

where K_m is a constant for a given height and design of emitter and n is an index.

The value of c_p for water varies slightly with temperature, see Table 1.12.

The effects of architectural features and surface finish on radiator output are summarised in Table 1.13. In general, it may be observed that heat output is reduced when airflow is restricted, such as by placing a shelf immediately above a radiator, or by an enclosure. It is also reduced by surface finishes with low emissivity, such as metallic paints or plating.

Radiator output is also affected by the form of connection to the system pipework. Testing is commonly done with top and bottom opposite end (TBOE) connections. Other forms of connection produce different outputs which may be corrected for by applying factors obtained from manufacturers.

Fan coil heaters

The characteristics of fan coil heaters are described in BS 4856[82], which gives test methods for heat output and air movement with and without attached ducting, and for noise levels without attached ducting. The heat output from fan coil heaters is approximately linear with the difference between system temperature and room air temperature, corresponding to n = 1.0 in equation 1.23.

The output from fan coil units is generally more sensitive to airflow problems than to water circulation and this should be borne in mind both at the design stage and when investigating problems. Other practical difficulties with fan coil units can arise from the use of copper tubing

Table 1.12 Values of specific heat capacity and density of water

Temperature / °C	Specific heat capacity c_p / kJ·kg^{-1}·K^{-1}	Density ρ / kg·m^{-3}
10	4.193	999.7
20	4.183	999.8
30	4.179	995.6
40	4.179	992.2
50	4.182	988.0
60	4.185	983.2
70	4.191	977.8
80	4.198	971.8
90	4.208	965.3
100	4.219	958.4
110	4.233	950.6
120	4.248	943.4
130	4.27	934.6
140	4.29	925.9
150	4.32	916.6
160	4.35	907.4
170	4.38	897.7
180	4.42	886.5
200	4.50	864.3

Table 1.13 Effects of finishes and architectural features on radiator output

Feature	Effect
Ordinary paint or enamel	No effect, irrespective of colour.
Metallic paint such as aluminium and bronze	Reduces radiant output by 50% or more and overall output by between 10 and 25%. Emission may be substantially restored by applying two coats of clear varnish.
Open fronted recess	Reduces output by 10%.
Encasement with front grille	Reduces output by 20% or more, depending on design.
Radiator shelf	Reduces output by 10%.
Fresh air inlet at rear with baffle at front	May increase output by up to 10%. This increase should not be taken into account when sizing radiator but should be allowed for in pipe and boiler sizing. A damper should always be fitted.
Distance of radiator from wall	A minimum distance of 25 mm is recommended. Below this emission may be reduced due to restriction of air-flow.
Height of radiator above floor	Little effect above a height of 100 mm. If radiators are mounted at high level, output will depend on temperature at that level and stratification may be increased.

in their fabrication, which can lead to corrosion if traces of sulphides remain following manufacture.

Variation of heat emitter output with system water temperature

The variation with mean water temperature depends upon the characteristics of the individual emitter. If correction factors are not given by the manufacturer, then reasonably accurate values can be obtained using equation 1.23 above.

BS EN 442-2 obliges the manufacturer to test the radiator at excess temperatures $\Delta T = 30$ K, 50 K and 60 K so as to determine the value of n. Thus if the test conditions are not precisely those specified, the experimental readings can be adjusted to correspond to the nominal conditions. The manufacturer is not obliged to publish the value of n but some manufacturers give data for both $\Delta T = 50$ K and $\Delta T = 60$ K. From such data it would be possible to deduce the value of n using:

$$n = \frac{\ln \phi_{60} / \phi_{50})}{\ln (60 / 50)} \tag{1.24}$$

where ϕ_{60} is the heat emission at 60 °C (W) and ϕ_{50} is the heat emission at 50 °C (W).

A value of $n = 1.24$ has been obtained from the quoted outputs of one manufacturer, but values of up to 1.33 may be encountered.

Then for any value of ΔT, the output can be determined from:

$$\phi = \phi_{50} (\Delta T / 50)^n \tag{1.25}$$

Variation of emitter heat output with water flow rate

Although a lower flow rate might cause a slight decrease in the water-side convection coefficient, this small increase in resistance is trivial in comparison with the overall resistance. Thus it is reasonable to consider that the overall heat transfer coefficient will remain constant. A reduction in the mass flow rate of the water has a greater effect on the mean water temperature and it is this that affects the heat emission.

One way of reducing emitter output and reducing pump power consumption is to reduce the pump speed, and hence the mass flow. The effect is considered here, assuming that the flow temperature t_1 remains constant. The mathematics involves equating the water-side and air-side heat transfer equations (equations 5.2 and 5.3). i.e:

$$q_m \, c_p \, (t_1 - t_2) = K_m \, \Delta T^n \tag{1.26}$$

The mean water temperature, $t_m = (t_1 + t_2) / 2$. Therefore, from equation 1.21:

$$\Delta T = \frac{(t_1 + t_2)}{2} - t_{ai} \tag{1.27}$$

Hence, substituting into equation 1.26:

$$q_m \, c_p \, (t_1 - t_2) = K_m \left[\frac{1}{2} \left(t_1 - t_2 \right) - t_{ai} \right]^n \tag{1.28}$$

Rearranging in terms of the unknown return temperature, t_2, gives:

$$t_2 = t_1 - \frac{K_m}{q_m \, c_p} \left[\frac{1}{2} \left(t_1 - t_2 \right) - t_{ai} \right]^n \tag{1.29}$$

Equation 1.29 contains t_2 on both sides of the equation. Once a starting value is inserted in the right hand side of the equation, the value of t_2 may be obtained by iteration. Equation 1.22 will then readily yield the heat output.

The example calculation in Appendix 1.A1.2 shows how to calculate the heat output for conditions other than nominal. Although shown for a change in flow rate only, the same technique could be used if using a different flow temperature, t_1.

Figure 1.9, which was obtained using the above method, shows the effect on emitter output for flow rates less than nominal. It can be seen that whatever the design value of water temperature drop $(t_1 - t_2)$, an appreciable reduction in water flow rate causes little reduction in heat output. Thus, except when full heat output is required (during the pre-heat period), there is no need for the pumps to run at full speed. Similarly it can be seen that increasing the flow above the design flow does not boost the heat output appreciably. A change in flow temperature from 75 °C to 65 °C does not make a significant difference to the shape of the curves.

Table 1.14 Heat emission from plane surfaces by radiation

Surface temp (°C)	Heat emission / $W \cdot m^{-2}$ for stated surface emissivity and enclosure mean radiant temperature (°C)																				
	Surface emissivity = 0.3							Surface emissivity = 0.6							Surface emissivity = 0.9						
	10	12.5	15	17.5	20	22.5	25	10	12.5	15	17.5	20	22.5	25	10	12.5	15	17.5	20	22.5	25
20	16	12	8.3	4.2	0	–4.3	–8.8	33	25	17	8.4	0	–8.7	–18	49	37	25	13	0	–13	–26
30	34	30	26	22	18	14	9.2	69	61	53	44	36	27	18	103	91	79	67	54	41	28
40	54	50	46	42	38	34	29	108	100	92	84	76	67	58	162	151	139	126	114	101	87
50	76	72	68	64	60	55	51	152	144	136	128	120	111	102	228	216	204	192	179	166	153
60	100	96	92	88	84	79	75	200	192	184	176	168	159	150	300	288	276	264	251	238	225
70	126	122	118	114	110	106	101	253	245	237	229	220	211	203	379	367	355	343	330	317	304
80	155	151	147	143	139	134	130	310	302	294	286	278	269	260	465	453	441	429	416	403	390
90	186	182	178	174	170	166	161	372	365	357	348	340	331	322	559	547	535	523	510	497	484
100	220	216	212	208	204	200	195	440	432	424	416	408	399	390	660	649	637	624	612	599	585
120	297	293	289	285	280	276	272	593	586	577	569	561	552	543	890	878	866	854	841	828	815
140	386	382	378	374	370	365	361	772	764	756	747	739	730	721	1160	1150	1130	1120	1110	1100	1080
160	489	485	481	477	473	468	464	978	970	962	954	945	936	928	1470	1450	1440	1430	1420	1400	1390

Table 1.15 Heat emission from plane surfaces by convection

Surface temp. (°C)	Heat emission / $W \cdot m^{-2}$ for stated direction and air temperature (°C)																				
	Horizontal looking down							Vertical							Horizontal looking up						
	10	12.5	15	17.5	20	22.5	25	10	12.5	15	17.5	20	22.5	25	10	12.5	15	17.5	20	22.5	25
20	11	7.9	4.8	2.0	0	–5.8	–14	30	20	12	4.7	0	–4.7	–12	36	25	14	5.8	0	–2.0	–4.8
30	27	23	19	15	11	7.9	4.8	75	63	51	40	30	20	12	91	77	62	49	36	25	14
40	45	40	36	31	27	23	19	129	115	101	88	75	63	51	157	140	123	107	91	77	62
50	64	59	54	50	45	40	36	189	174	158	144	129	115	101	230	211	192	174	157	140	123
60	85	80	75	69	64	59	54	255	238	221	205	189	174	158	309	289	269	249	230	211	192
70	107	101	96	90	85	80	75	324	307	289	272	255	238	221	394	372	351	330	309	289	269
80	130	124	118	112	107	101	96	398	379	361	342	324	307	289	484	461	438	416	394	372	351
90	153	147	141	135	130	124	118	476	456	436	417	398	379	361	578	554	530	507	484	461	438
100	177	171	165	159	153	147	141	556	536	516	495	476	456	436	675	651	626	602	578	554	530
120	228	222	215	209	202	196	190	726	705	683	661	640	619	598	882	856	829	803	777	751	726
140	281	274	267	261	254	248	241	907	884	861	838	816	793	771	1100	1070	1050	1020	990	963	936
160	336	329	322	315	308	301	295	1100	1070	1050	1020	1000	977	954	1330	1300	1270	1240	1220	1190	1160

Table 1.16 Heat emission from single horizontal steel pipes with a surface emissivity of 0.9 and freely exposed to ambient air at temperatures between 10 and 20 °C

Nominal pipe size / mm	Heat emission / W·m^{-2} for stated temperature difference between surface to surroundings / K																			
	40	45	50	55	60	65	70	75	80	100	120	140	160	180	200	220	240	260	280	300
15	42	48	55	62	69	77	84	92	100	135	173	215	261	311	366	425	490	560	635	717
20	51	59	67	75	84	93	103	112	122	164	211	262	318	380	447	520	600	686	780	881
25	62	71	81	92	102	114	125	137	149	200	257	320	389	465	547	637	735	842	957	1080
32	75	87	99	112	125	138	152	167	181	244	314	391	476	569	670	781	902	1030	1180	1330
40	84	98	111	125	140	155	170	186	203	273	352	438	534	638	753	878	1010	1160	1320	1500
50	106	118	135	152	169	188	206	226	246	331	427	532	648	776	916	1070	1240	1420	1620	1830
65	125	145	165	186	207	230	253	277	301	406	523	653	796	954	1130	1320	1520	1750	2000	2260
80	143	166	189	213	238	263	290	317	345	466	600	750	915	1100	1300	1510	1750	2010	2300	2610
100	179	207	236	266	297	329	362	396	431	582	750	937	1140	1370	1620	1900	2200	2530	2890	3280
125	214	247	281	317	354	392	432	473	515	696	897	1120	1370	1650	1950	2280	2650	3040	3480	3950
150	248	287	327	368	411	456	502	549	598	808	1040	1310	1600	1920	2270	2660	3090	3550	4060	4620
200	319	369	421	474	529	586	646	706	769	1040	1340	1680	2060	2480	2940	3450	4000	4610	5280	6010
250	389	449	512	577	644	714	786	860	937	1270	1640	2050	2520	3030	3600	4220	4900	5650	6470	7370
300	453	524	597	673	751	832	916	1000	1090	1480	1910	2400	2940	3540	4200	4930	5740	6620	7590	8650

Table 1.17 Heat emission from single horizontal copper pipes freely exposed to ambient air at temperatures of 20 °C

Nominal pipe size / mm	Heat emission / W·m^{-2} for stated surface finish and temperature difference between surface and surroundings / K																			
	Painted pipe ($\varepsilon = 0.95$)										Tarnished pipe ($\varepsilon = 0.5$)									
	40	45	50	55	60	65	70	75	80	100	40	45	50	55	60	65	70	80	90	100
8	18	21	24	27	30	33	37	40	43	58	15	17	20	22	25	27	30	33	36	48
10	22	25	29	32	36	40	44	48	52	70	18	21	24	27	30	33	36	39	43	57
15	31	36	41	46	51	57	62	68	74	99	25	29	33	37	41	46	50	55	60	80
22	43	49	56	63	71	78	86	94	103	138	34	39	45	51	56	62	69	75	81	109
28	53	61	69	78	87	97	106	116	126	170	42	48	55	62	69	76	84	91	99	133
35	64	74	84	95	106	117	129	141	153	206	50	58	66	74	83	92	101	110	120	160
42	75	86	98	111	124	137	151	165	179	242	58	67	77	86	96	107	117	128	139	186
54	93	107	122	138	154	171	188	205	223	301	72	83	94	106	119	131	144	158	171	230
76	125	145	165	186	208	230	253	277	302	407	95	110	126	142	158	175	192	210	229	306
108	171	197	225	253	283	313	345	377	411	554	128	148	169	190	212	235	258	282	307	412
133	205	237	270	305	340	377	415	454	494	668	153	177	201	227	253	280	308	337	366	492
159	240	278	317	357	399	442	486	532	579	783	178	205	234	264	294	326	358	392	426	572

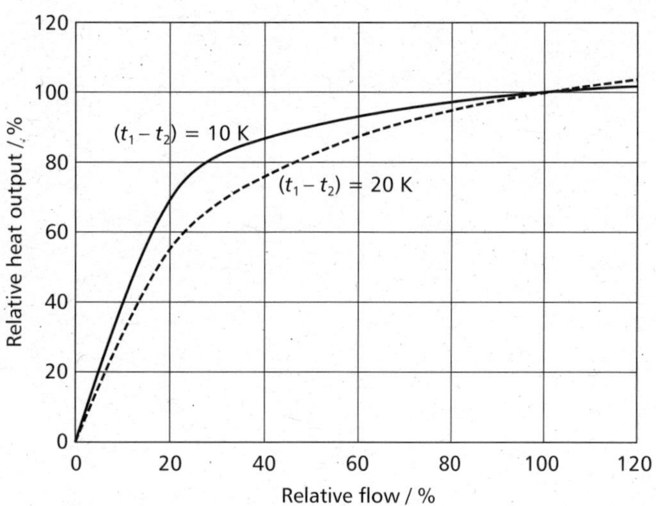

Figure 1.9 Heat emission of a radiator having $n = 1.25$ and $t_1 = 75$ °C for design values of $(t_1 - t_2) = 10$ K and 20 K.

Plane surfaces

Heat emitted from plane surfaces, e.g. panels or beams, may be estimated using Tables 1.14 and 1.15, which have been calculated using the data given in CIBSE Guide C(57), section 3.3.4. Radiative and convective outputs are given separately to assist where significant differences between air and mean radiant temperature are expected in heated areas. The convective output applies to draught-free conditions; significantly increased output may be available where there is air movement. For example, a local air movement velocity of 0.5 m·s^{-1} could be expected to increase convective output by around 35%. In practice, the heat output from a vertical surface varies with the height of the surface.

Heat emission from distribution pipework

Account needs to be taken of the heat emitted from distribution pipework when sizing both emitters and boilers. Large diameter pipes may also be used as heat emitters by design, but this is no longer common practice. Tables 1.16 and 1.17 give heat emissions per metre horizontal run for steel and copper pipes respectively. When pipes are installed vertically, heat emissions are different due to the differences in the boundary layer or air around the pipe surface. Table 1.18 gives correction factors for vertical pipes. When pipes are arranged in a horizontal bank, each pipe directly above another at close pitch, overall heat emission is reduced. Table 1.19 gives correction factors for such installations.

Heat emission from pipes and plane surfaces is covered in detail in CIBSE Guide C(57), section 3.3.

Heat emissions from room surfaces

Room surfaces may be designed to emit heat or, in other cases, heat emissions arising from surfaces may need to be taken into account as heat gains in the design of systems. Tables 1.14 and 1.15 may be used for this purpose.

Surface temperatures must be limited to a level that will not cause discomfort to building occupants, taking account of thermal gradients and asymmetrical thermal radiation, see section 1.3.2. CIBSE Guide A(19), section 1.4.3, notes that local discomfort of the feet can be caused by either high or low temperatures. For rooms in which occupants spend much of their time with bare feet (e.g. changing rooms and bathrooms), it is recommended that floor temperatures should lie within the ranges shown in Table 1.20. For rooms in which normal footware is expected to be worn, the optimal surface temperature for floors is 25 °C for sedentary occupants and 23 °C for standing or walking occupants. Flooring material is considered to be unimportant in these circumstances.

Table 1.18 Correction factors for for Tables 1.16 and 1.17 for heat emission from vertical pipes

Pipe size / mm	Correction factor
8	0.72
10	0.74
15	0.76
20	0.79
25	0.82
32	0.84
40	0.86
50	0.88
65	0.90
80	0.92
100	0.95
125	0.97
150	0.99
200	1.03
250	1.05
300	1.07

Table 1.19 Correction factors for Tables 1.16 and 1.17 for heat emission from horizontal pipes in banks

Number of pipes in bank	Correction factor
2	0.95
4	0.85
6	0.75
8	0.65

Table 1.20 Comfortable temperatures for barefoot occupants for typical floor surfaces

Material	Surface temp. range / °C
Textiles	21 to 28
Pine wood	21.5 to 28
Oak wood	24.5 to 28
Hard thermoplastic	24 to 28
Concrete	26 to 28

Floor heating

BS EN 1264(61) deals with floor heating. The general characteristics of floor heating are described in section 1.4.3.4 above. The floor surface itself is used as a heat emitter and heat is supplied by the circulation of water as part of a hydronic system, through appropriately spaced pipes positioned beneath the floor surface.

Much of the equipment required for floor heating systems is the same as that used for other hydronic heating systems. However, the heat emitting floor surfaces require careful design to produce the required surface temperatures and heat output. Surface temperature should not exceed 29 °C in general or 35 °C for peripheral areas, which are defined in BS EN 1264 as 'generally an area of 1 m maximum in width along exterior walls' and 'not an occupied area'.

BS EN 1264 gives the heat output available from the floor surface as:

$$\phi = 8.92\,(t_{fm} - t_i)^{1.1} \tag{1.30}$$

where ϕ is the heat output per unit area of floor (W·m^{-2}), t_{fm} is the average floor temperature (°C) and t_i is the room temperature (°C).

The limitation on surface temperature leads to a corresponding limitation on heat output. For a room temperature of 20 °C, the maximum output is around 100 W·m^{-2} in general and 175 W·m^{-2} at the periphery.

The designer's task is to ensure that the heat flow density at the floor surface is such as to maintain design surface temperatures. Calculations need to take account of the spacing and diameter of embedded pipes, the thickness and heat conductivity of the material between the pipes and the floor surface (including floor covering), and the properties of pipes and any heat conducting devices used to distribute heat within the floor material. BS EN 1264-2 gives procedures for systems with pipes embedded in the floor screed and those with pipes below the screed.

1.5.1.2 Heat sources

Boilers

Boilers intended for use in hydronic systems are available in a wide range of types, constructions and output ranges, and suitable for use with different fuels. Many standards and codes of practice relate to boilers, covering their construction, the combustion equipment required for each type of fuel, and their installation and commissioning. The recommendations of HSE Guidance Note PM5[(75)] should be followed in all cases.

(*a*) Cast iron sectional boilers

Boilers of this type are constructed out of sections joined by barrel nipples, with the number of sections selected to produce the required output. They are normally operated at pressures below 350 kPa and have outputs of up to 1500 kW. Where access is limited, the boiler may be delivered in sections and assembled on site. It is important that water flow be maintained at all times to meet the manufacturer's recommendations, including a period after shutdown to disperse residual heat. Boilers of this type are covered by BS 779[(83)].

(*b*) Low carbon steel sectional boilers

These are similar to cast iron boilers except that their sections are made of steel. Similar recommendations apply.

(*c*) Welded steel and reverse flow boilers

Welded steel and reverse flow boilers are fabricated from steel plate. The combustion chamber is pressurised and a 'blind' rear end reverses the burner discharge back over the flame, in counter-flow. The gases then pass through a circumferential ring of fire tubes around the combustion chamber. This arrangement achieves high efficiency and compactness. They are typically designed for a maximum working pressure of 450 kPa but can be designed to operate at up to 1 MPa, with outputs between 100 kW and 3 MW. Boilers of this type are covered by BS 855[(84)].

(*d*) Steel shell and fire-tube boilers

Steel shell and fire-tube boilers consist of a steel shell and a furnace tube connected to the rear combustion chamber, from which convection tubes are taken to provide two-pass or three-pass operation. Boilers of this type are suitable for pressures up to 1 MPa and are available with outputs up to 12 MW and are often used for steam applications (see also section 5.2). The relevant standard is BS 2790[(68)].

(*e*) Multiple or modular boilers

Multiple or modular boilers are designed to operate in installations in which the number of boilers firing is matched to the load on the system. The result is that the load on each boiler remains high even when the system load is low, leading to higher operating efficiency. Reliability is also improved, as the unavailability of a single boiler does not shut down the entire system. Multiple boilers are typically operated in parallel, under a sequence controller that detects the load on the system and brings individual boilers into the circuit as required. For circuits with two-port valves, where flow is progressively reduced as individual thermostats are satisfied, it is advantageous to use an additional primary circuit de-coupled from the load by a common header or buffer vessel. The use of a header allows flow through the boiler circuit to be unaffected by variations in flow to the load. Circuits connected to loads are operated from the header. The use of reverse return pipework is recommended for the boiler side of the header to ensure equal flows through all boilers. A circuit of this type is shown in Figure 1.10, incorporating a 4-module boiler system and two weather-compensated heating circuits.

(*f*) Condensing boilers

Condensing boilers differ from others in that they are designed to extract extra heat from the combustion gases by causing condensation of the water vapour in the flue gas. A drain to remove condensate is necessary. However, condensing operation cannot be achieved unless the return water temperature is low, typically below 55 °C; the lower the return temperature, the greater the condensation and the higher the efficiency. The materials of construction must be able to withstand the slightly acidic condensate; stainless steel is frequently used for these heat exchangers. Institution of Gas Engineers publication IGE UP/10[(85)] gives detailed advice on the use of stainless steel flues and plastic

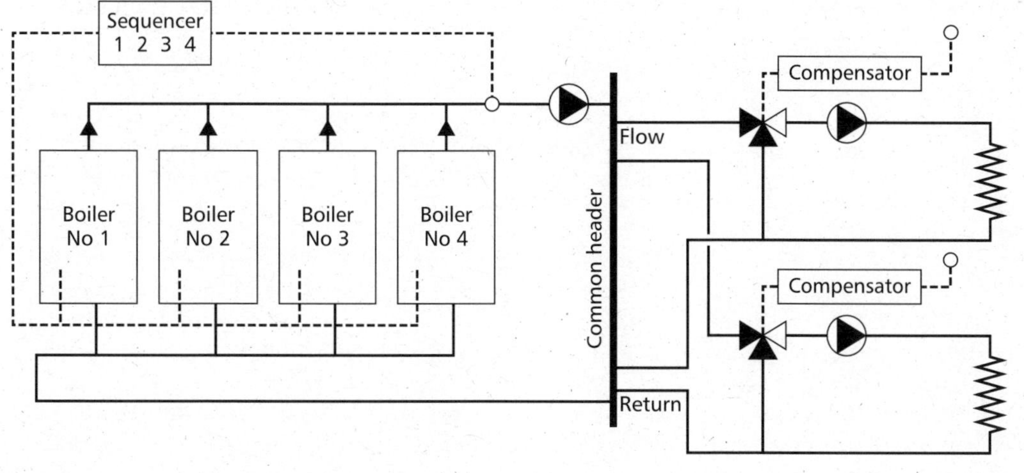

Figure 1.10 Multiple boiler circuit with header and reverse return circulation through boilers (courtesy of Hamworthy Heating Ltd)

condensate pipes. The relatively cool combustion gases lack buoyancy and it is usual to have additional fan power to drive them through the flue system. Condensing boilers should be used only with very low sulphur content fuels.

(*g*) Low water content boilers

Low water content boilers have compact heat exchangers designed for maximum surface area. Common materials for heat exchangers include aluminium, copper and stainless steel. Both natural and forced draught combustion types are available.

Good water circulation through the heat exchanger is essential during boiler operation and a means of flow sensing is usually required, interlocked with the burner.

Low water content boilers offer rapid heat-up and high efficiency coupled with compact size and light weight. However, life expectancy is usually significantly shorter than for cast iron or steel boilers with larger combustion chambers.

(*h*) Gas boilers

Gas boilers are available in a large range of types and sizes for use with both natural gas and liquefied petroleum gas (LPG). The properties of both types of gas are described in section 1.6. Modern appliances are designed and manufactured in compliance with European standards. Under UK gas safety legislation, all new appliances must display a CE mark of conformity; to install appliances not having the CE mark or to modify appliances displaying the mark may be unlawful. Strict requirements for gas safety apply similarly to forced draught and natural draught burners.

Appliance standards deal not only with construction but also cover efficiency and emissions to the atmosphere. However, standards cannot easily cover the quality of the installation, which is the responsibility of competent designers and installers. Guidance on installation is provided in IGE UP/10[85], which also includes information on ventilation and flues for appliances with a net output above 70 kW.

Gas boilers rely on various different types of burner:

— *Forced draught burners*: typically of the nozzle mix type in which gas and air are separately supplied right up to the burner head, where mixing takes place. The effectiveness of the combustion process relies on the design of the mixing head and the pressure of the air and gas at the head, particularly in achieving low emissions of nitrogen oxides (NO_x) and carbon monoxide (CO). Most burners are made to comply with BS EN 676[86]. It is rare today to see a burner with a separate pilot since most start at a low fire condition at the main burner. Air proving is essential with a 'no-air' check being made before the fan starts, to check that the proving switch/transistor is operational. The combustion system is normally purged with up to 5 volumes of air in order to remove any traces of gas or remaining products of combustion. The gas safety train to the main burner supply incorporates a low inlet pressure switch, a pressure regulator and two high quality safety shut off valves. Above 1200 kW there is a requirement for either a valve seat condition proving system or a double block and vent valve position proving.

  The turndown range of the burner from high to low depends on the individual manufacturer's designs and the required excess air levels from high to low fire. Many can operate over a range of more than 4 to 1.

  Some larger burners require higher pressures than are available from the gas supply system. In such cases, a gas pressure booster may be required, which is typically provided by a simple centrifugal fan. Overall safety requirements are covered by IGE UP/2[87]; they include a stainless steel flexible pipe either side of each booster and a pressure switch to cut off the booster at low line pressure.

  It is possible for forced draught burners to operate in dual fuel mode, using an additional nozzle for oil firing. Larger types of dual fuel burner may incorporate a rotary or spinning cup to atomise the oil but many simply rely on high oil pressures at the atomiser.

— *Pre-mix burners*: these differ from forced draught burners principally in that the air for combustion is mixed with the gas before it reaches the burner head. They produce very short intense flames that can work in very compact combustion chambers and, due to lower excess air levels, can achieve higher efficiencies. However, turndown is more restricted than with nozzle mix burners and is typically of the order of 1.5 or 2 to 1 on a single burner head. Larger turndowns are achieved by sequencing burner heads or bars within a single combustion chamber.

— *Natural draught (atmospheric) burners*: these are widely used on gas cookers and small boilers and are often described as 'Bunsen' type. The incoming gas at the injector induces combustion air with which it mixes before reaching the head. The amount of air induced is typically 40 to 50% of what is required and the remainder is drawn in by the combustion process itself. Because of its slow and staged mixing, the flame envelope is larger and requires a larger combustion chamber than forced draught and pre-mix burners. Some boilers of less than 45 kW still use thermo-electric flame safeguards to detect the loss of flame but fully automatic flame rectification and ignition are increasingly becoming standard.

— *Pulse combustion*: air is induced into the combustion system by means of Helmholtz effect. The rapid forward flow of the exploding combustion products within a strong chamber leaves a shock wave behind that induces the gas and air required for the next pulse, which ignites automatically. The cycle continues until the gas supply is turned off. Pulse combustion operates at high pressure and enables very small heat exchangers and flues to be used.

(*i*) Oil boilers

Burners for oil boilers almost always rely on atomisation, which is carried out mechanically. Oil of various grades is used for firing. Kerosene (Class C2) is commonly used in domestic boilers, gas oil (Class D) is most frequently used in larger heating installations, and fuel oil (Classes E, F and G) is used in some large installations. Guidance on oil boilers may be obtained from OFTEC[88,89].

— *Pressure jet burners*: most frequently used on smaller boilers, but can operate at outputs up to 4.5 MW. They consist of a fan to provide combustion air and to mix it with atomised droplets of oil produced by a nozzle fed at a high pressure from a fuel pump. Since effective atomisation depends on the flow of oil to the nozzle, the turn down ratio is limited to about 2:1. Modulation is correspondingly restricted and on/off operation is common.

— *Rotary burners*: normally used on larger boilers of the welded shell type, where fuel heavier than Grade D is burned. Atomisation is achieved by centrifugal action as oil is fed to a rotating cup, which throws droplets into an air stream produced by the primary combustion air fan. A secondary combustion air fan enables the burner to operate over a wide turn-down range, which may be up to 5:1. This type of burner can be readily adapted for dual fuel (gas/oil) operation. However, it is relatively noisy in operation and may require sound attenuation measures.

(*j*) Solid fuel boilers

Solid fuel burners are less flexible in use than those for gaseous or liquid fuels and consideration must be given at an early stage to arrangements for the storage and handling of fuel, the removal of ash and grit, flue gas cleaning and operation and maintenance of the boiler house. Also, it is necessary to design the system to ensure that heat can be safely dissipated when the boiler is shut down or the load sharply reduced.

— *Gravity feed burners*: suitable for use with outputs up to about 500 MW. Their rate of combustion may be controlled by modulating the fan supplying combustion air, giving a good turn-down ratio and a high thermal efficiency.

— *Underfeed stokers*: most commonly used for sectional and fabricated steel boilers operating at outputs up to 1.5 MW. The fuel is supplied through a tube using a screw, regulated to match the requirements of the furnace, and combustion air is controlled by a fan. Fuel types and grades may be restricted.

— *Coking stokers*: used with shell boilers rated at up to 4.5 MW. A ram pushes coal from a hopper into the boiler, where there is partial distillation of the volatile components of the coal. The fuel then travels forward into a moving grate where combustion is completed, relying on induced draught.

— *Chain grate stokers*: used in large shell boilers, with outputs of up to 10 MW. An endless chain grate feeds coal continuously into the boiler furnace, where combustion takes place with either forced or induced air supply.

— *Sprinkler stokers*: an air stream is used to convey coal to a fixed grate in shell boilers with outputs between 600 kW and 8.5 MW.

— *Fluidised bed systems*: these rely on fuel fed into a furnace bed consisting of particles of inert material that are continuously recycled. The mixture is fluidised by a flow of air large enough to hold the fuel in suspension while combustion takes place. This type of combustion is suitable for a wide range of coal types, including poor quality coal. It is well suited to automatic control and may be able to reduce acid gas emissions by the use of additives in the fuel bed.

Boiler selection

The following factors need to be taken into account in selecting a boiler for a particular application:

— output in relation to calculated system requirements, see section 1.4.7

— efficiency, particularly at part load, see section 1.4.2.3

— hydraulic pressure at which the boiler must operate

— system operating temperature: it is particularly important that return water be maintained above the minimum recommended by the manufacturer for non-condensing oil-fired boilers to avoid corrosion from acid condensation in the flue system

— flue gas conditions, to comply with emission requirements, see section 1.5.5

— corrosion and water treatment, taking account of the specific recommendations of the boiler manufacturer

— acoustic considerations, taking account of noise both inside and outside the boiler room

— floor temperature beneath the boiler: the temperature of a concrete floor should not be allowed to exceed 65 °C; this should not occur where the base of the boiler is water cooled, but may otherwise require a refractory hearth under the boiler

— space in the boiler house, especially with regard to access for maintenance

— access for initial installation and subsequent replacement.

District or local heat supplies

Where a supply of delivered heat is available, connection to the main may be either direct or indirect, via a heat exchanger. Direct connection is normally used in small heat distribution systems where heat is distributed at temperatures not exceeding 90 °C, e.g. using heat from a CHP unit based on an internal combustion engine.

For indirect connection, the role of the boiler is effectively assumed by a heat exchanger, either a non-storage shell and tube calorifier or, more commonly in recent years, a plate heat exchanger. This allows the distribution system within the building to be run at a temperature and pressure suitable for the building rather than for the heating main. The distribution network, controls and heat emitters in the building can effectively be the same as those used with a boiler.

When connecting to a heat distribution system, it is important to design the connection method and the secondary system so that water is returned to the system at as low a temperature as possible. This reduces flow rates and lowers network costs. It is recommended that the heat supply company should be allowed to review and comment on the design of the connection method and the heat distribution. Good Practice Guide 234: *Guide to community heating and CHP* [59], gives detailed guidance.

Small-scale combined heat and power (CHP)

Small-scale combined heat and power units may be used to replace part or all of the boiler capacity in buildings with a suitable electricity demand profile. CIBSE Applications Manual AM12[60] describes the main features of CHP plant and its integration into buildings. The CHP unit is typically used as the lead boiler in a multi-boiler system and sized to minimise life cycle costs, which may involve some dumping of heat. A computer program is available under the government's Energy Efficiency Best Practice programme for optimising the capacity of CHP units in certain types of buildings.

CHP systems based on reciprocating engines are available with electrical outputs ranging from 50 kW to 4500 kW. Small installations generally favour systems with spark ignition engines, fuelled by gas, including LPG, biogas and landfill gas, as well as natural gas. Larger installation may use diesel engines, fuelled by either gas or oil, or gas turbines. Gas turbines are favoured particularly when high grade heat is required for steam raising or when it is necessary to produce a high ratio of electricity to heat through operation in combined cycle mode.

Micro-CHP units, based on Stirling engines, are becoming available for installation as replacements for boilers in dwellings. Heat output must be around 10–20 kW to meet the heat load in a typical installation but electrical output is typically restricted to around 1 kW, to maximise the proportion of kW·h generated that can be used within the dwelling.

Heat may be recovered from various sources within CHP units, including the exhaust, the engine and oil cooling circuits and the after cooler. Figure 1.11 shows alternative schemes for heat recovery.

Heat pumps

Air source heat pumps may be used to extract heat either from outside air or from ventilation exhaust air. When outside air is used as a heat source, the coefficient of performance tends to decline as the air temperature drops. There can also be problems with icing of the heat exchanger where the outside air is of high humidity, which is frequently the case in the UK. This requires periodic defrosting, which is often achieved by temporary reversals of the heat pump and reduces the coefficient of performance (COP). Because of these factors, air-to-air heat pumps have a relatively low COP (in the range of 2.0 to 2.5) when used for heating in a typical UK climate. As COP declines with outside temperature, it is not economic to size air source heat pumps for the coldest conditions, and they often include electrical resistance coils for supplementary heating.

Ground or water source heat pumps extract heat from the ground or bodies of water, either at ambient temperature

Exhaust
Oil and jacket
AC
G
From load
To load
Heat rejection
Pressuriser
From load
To load
Heat rejection

Scheme A

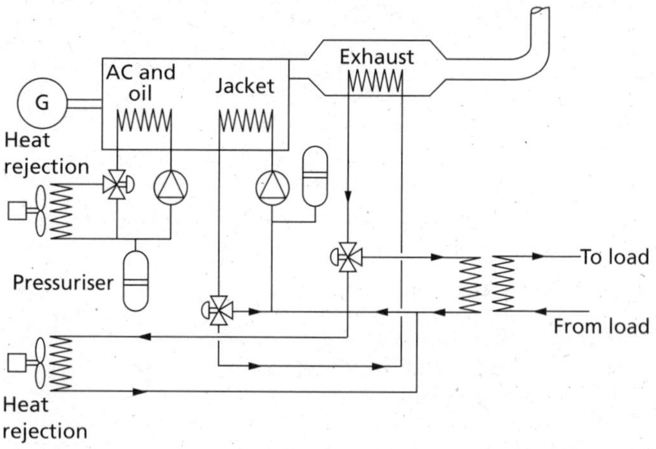

Scheme B

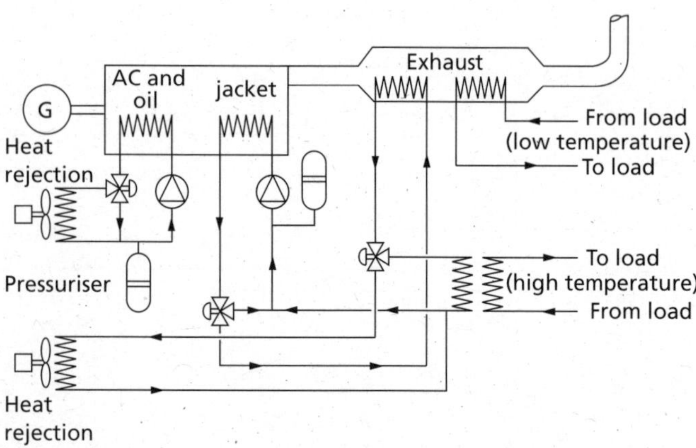

Scheme C

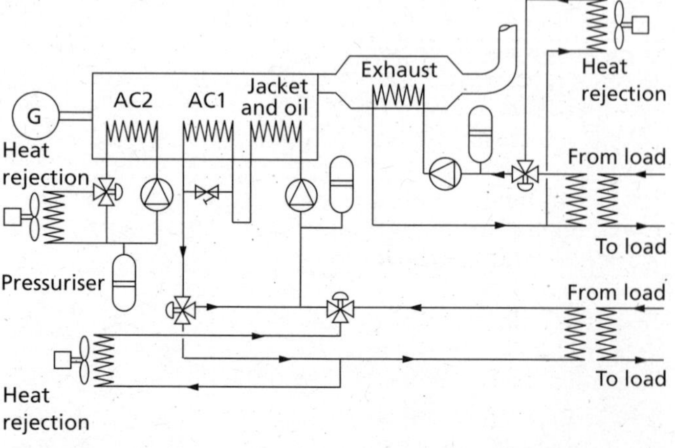

Scheme D

Figure 1.11 Schemes for heat extraction from CHP units [60]

or with temperature raised by the outflow of waste heat. They have the advantage over air source heat pumps that their heat source has much greater specific heat capacity and, provided it has sufficient mass, varies much less with outside temperature. Small ground source heat pumps have a seasonal COP of around 3.5 in a typical UK climate.

The COP figures given above are for electrically-driven vapour compression cycle heat pumps. Absorption cycle heat pumps have a much lower COP but have the advantage that they can be powered directly by gas. When used for heating, the COP obtainable in practice (typically 1.4) still offers a considerable advantage over a boiler. Domestic sized absorption heat pumps are currently being evaluated in field trials in the Netherlands; these are silent in operation and compact enough to be considered as a replacement for a boiler.

Most heat pumps used for heating in commercial buildings in the UK are reversible and can therefore provide cooling in summer at no additional capital cost.

The environmental advantages/disadvantages of heat pumps hinge on their coefficient of performance and the potential CO_2 emission of the fuel used to power them. Gas-fired heat pumps with a relatively low COP may therefore produce lower CO_2 emissions per unit of useful heat output than electrically driven units. For electricity drawn from the UK grid, a seasonal COP of around 2 is required to achieve lower emissions than would be obtained from a gas condensing boiler.

Solar water heating panels

Solar water heating panels are widely used around the world to provide domestic hot water, particularly where sunshine is plentiful and fuel is relatively expensive. In the UK, the great majority of installed systems are in dwellings.

The efficiency of solar collector panels depends on a number of factors[90], including the type of collector, the spectral response of the absorbing surface, the extent to which the panel is insulated and the temperature difference between the panel and the ambient air. It is conventional to show collector efficiency against the function:

$$[(t_{f,i} - t_a) / I_f] \; (\mathrm{K \cdot m^2 \cdot W^{-1}})$$

where $t_{f,i}$ and t_a are panel and ambient temperatures, respectively, (°C) and I_f is the intensity of the incident solar radiation ($\mathrm{W \cdot m^{-2}}$). Figure 1.12 shows the efficiency of some types of flat plate collectors in this format. This shows that, in general, the efficiency declines sharply as panel temperature increases above air temperature and that the surface finish of the collector is important. Evacuated tube collectors tend to be no more efficient at low temperature rises but are able to maintain their efficiency at high temperatures.

BS 5918[91] classifies the performance of solar collectors in terms of the ratio of collector heat loss ($\mathrm{W \cdot m^{-2} \cdot K^{-1}}$) to zero-loss collector efficiency. Typical values of this measure range from greater than 13 for unglazed collectors with no special coating to between 3 and 6 for vacuum insulated panels. The current generation of flat plate collectors with selective coatings generally lie in the range 3 to 5.

A typical solar water heating installation consists of one or more roof mounted panels, a hot water storage cylinder and a means of transferring heat from the panels to the cylinder. Very simple systems, used where sunshine is abundant, rely on gravity circulation but systems designed for a typical UK climate require a pumped primary circulation. BS 5918 gives guidance for the design and installation of such systems. Some systems used in the UK have separate storage cylinders for solar heated water, which can be kept at an intermediate temperature to maximise the amount of heat collected. Others rely on an additional heating coil in the main hot water cylinder, which is also heated by a central heating system or by an electric immersion heater. The circulation pump is usually controlled by a differential temperature sensor, which causes the pump to operate whenever the temperature of the collector exceeds the temperature of the stored water in the cylinder by a pre-set margin of 2 or 3 °C. Primary circuits often contain a water/glycol solution to avoid freezing.

The energy content of the hot water produced annually per unit area of solar water heating panel depends upon several factors, including the collector efficiency, storage volume and usage patterns. BS 5918 gives a method for sizing solar hot water systems for individual dwellings, taking account of climate, panel orientation and collector performance. It shows that the optimum panel orientation is just west of south but that there is little effect on output within 45° of the optimum. Optimum tilt for the UK is around 33° but there is little difference within ±15°, which includes most pitched roofs in the UK. Although individual household requirements vary considerably, a rule of thumb is that a house requires 2 to 4 m^2 of panel area, which will yield around a 1000 kW·h per year of heat and meet around half of annual hot water requirements. A set of European Standards dealing with solar heating systems has been developed[92–94].

Solar panels are also well suited to heating swimming pools. The low temperature required and the very large thermal capacity of the pool water makes it possible to achieve relatively high collector efficiency using simple unglazed panels. Typical installations in the UK (covered by BS 6785[95]) have a panel area of around half of the pool surface area and produce an average temperature rise above ambient air temperature of around 5 K provided the pool is covered at night or indoors.

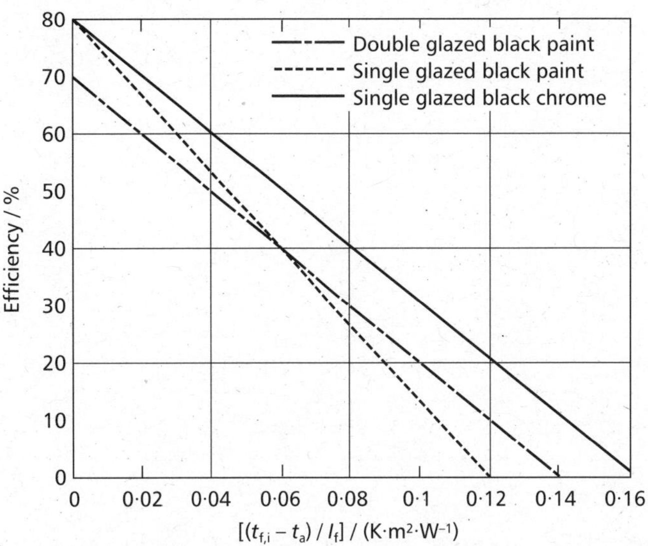

Figure 1.12 Efficiency of typical flat plate solar collectors

1.5.1.3 Pipework

The layout and sizing of pipework for hydronic heating systems is a vital aspect of system design. Once the emitters have been selected and the design flow and return temperatures decided, the circulation requirements in each part of the circuit can be determined. Pipe sizes for individual parts of each circuit may then be selected to give acceptable pressure drops and flow velocities. Consideration should also be given at this stage to the compatibility of emitters connected to particular circuits and to how the system can maintain balance as flow is restricted by control valves.

The designer has considerable flexibility in choosing appropriate pipe sizes. A larger pipe diameter reduces the friction pressure drop and hence the pump power needed to achieve the design circulation. Even a small increase in diameter can have a significant effect, as the pressure drop is approximately proportional to the fifth power of diameter for the same mass flow. An example is given in Appendix 1.A1.3.

The theoretical basis for calculating pressure drops in pipework is covered in detail in CIBSE Guide C[(57)], section 4, which also provides tables giving pressure drop per metre run for a range of pipe sizes and materials. Pipe sizes should ideally be selected to achieve minimum life cycle cost, taking account of both capital cost of pumps and pipework and the running cost to provide the pumping power required. In practice, the starting point for pipe sizing is usually based on flow velocity, ranging from <1 m·s^{-1} for small bore pipes to 3 m·s^{-1} for pipes with a diameter of greater than 50 mm. The tables in Guide C are banded to show flow velocity. Another approach is to size for a particular pressure drop per unit length, typically between 200 to 300 Pa·m^{-1}.

The tables in Guide C relevant to heating circuits are calculated for temperatures of 75 °C. When using water temperature temperatures lower than 75 °C, the pressure drop will be greater, due mainly to the higher viscosity. Table 1.21 gives the correction factor to be applied to the tabulated data, see equation 1.30 (page 1-30). The correction factor does not vary with diameter, though velocity does have a small effect.

$$\Delta p = C \, \Delta p_{75} \qquad (1.31)$$

where Δp is the corrected pressure drop (Pa), C is the correction factor and Δp_{75} is the tabulated pressure drop at 75 °C (Pa).

1.5.1.4 Pumps

Pump characteristics

Centrifugal pumps are well suited to providing the necessary circulation in hydronic heating systems. They operate by using the energy imparted by a rotating impeller fitted in a carefully designed casing; liquid enters near the centre of the impeller and leaves at higher velocity at its perimeter. A typical centrifugal pump characteristic is shown in Figure 1.13, in which it may be observed that maximum pressure is produced at zero flow and maximum flow at zero pressure.

Table 1.21 Values of correction factor C for water at different temperatures

Flow velocity / m·s^{-1}	Correction factor for stated water temperature / °C: 40	50	60	70	75
0.2	1.161	1.107	1.060	1.018	1.000
1.0	1.156	1.104	1.058	1.017	1.000
2.0	1.150	1.099	1.055	1.017	1.000
4.0	1.140	1.092	1.051	1.015	1.000

Centrifugal pumps have the following characteristics:

- flow varies directly with the speed of rotation of the impeller
- pressure varies as the square of the speed
- power absorbed varies with cube of the speed.

If the diameter of the impeller is changed, but speed of rotation kept constant:

- flow varies as the cube of the impeller diameter
- pressure varies as the square of the impeller diameter
- power absorbed varies as the fifth power of the impeller diameter.

The flow available from a centrifugal pump in a circuit depends upon the resistance characteristics of the circuit. Figure 1.13 shows a typical system curve superimposed on the performance curves of the pump. The flow obtained at a given pump speed can be determined from the point at which the pump and system curves intersect. A pump speed is selected which can provide the required flow at the pressure drop around the path of the circuit with the highest pressure drop, otherwise known as the 'index' circuit.

Variable speed pumping

Maximum flow and power are only required under design conditions in which all loads are calling for heat. As demand is satisfied, full flow is no longer required in parts of the circuit and pumping power can be reduced to match the system requirement at the time. The most effective method of controlling pump speed is by means of induction motors powered by variable frequency inverters; such a combination can maintain high efficiency over a wide range of speeds. Variable speed motors, which have a built-in inverter drive, are also available. Pump energy savings of 60–70% are possible, with payback times of around 2 years.

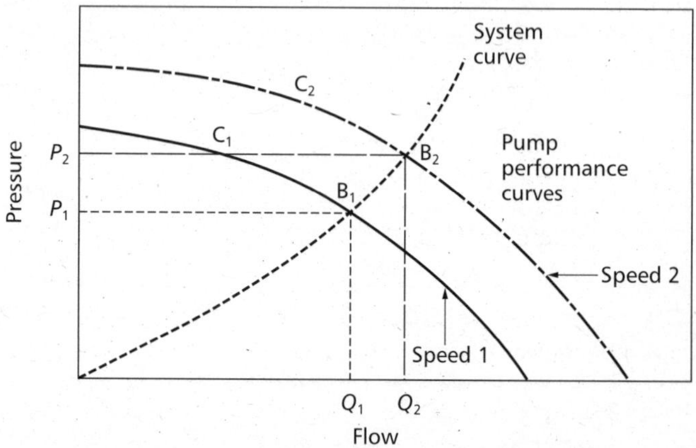

Figure 1.13 Performance curves for a centrifugal pump

The design of variable speed pumping systems needs to allow two-port control valves to close without causing unwanted flow or pressure variations in other parts of the circuit. The most common method of controlling pump speed is to maintain a constant pressure differential between two points in the index circuit. BSRIA Application Guide AG 14/99[96] describes procedures for the design of systems with variable speed pumping.

1.5.1.5 Controls

Section 1.4.3.8 describes the general principles of control and control functions applied to hydronic systems; this section describes the key components required to implement those functions. Control equipment may be broadly subdivided into sensors, actuators and processors, all linked by some form of network.

Sensors

Sensors may be broadly grouped into three types:

— *Analogue sensors*: the measured variable to be controlled is converted into a continuously variable signal, usually electrical. The signals produced are often very small and require signal conditioning, amplification or conversion to digital form before they can be fed to a processor or actuator. The signal conditioning may be remote from the sensing element or incorporated within the same unit. Standard signal levels for interfacing with controllers and actuators include 0 to 10 volts and 4 to 20 mA.

— *Status sensors*: an on/off signal is produced, depending on whether the variable is above or below a set point. They are frequently electromechanical devices, where a physical movement causes contacts to open or close. They exhibit hysteresis (a 'dead band') in operation, which must be overcome before they change state.

— *Intelligent sensors*: some element of processing is incorporated, as well as the basic sensor function.

Temperature sensors

Electromechanical thermostats are widely used for room temperature control. Higher accuracy and lower hysteresis may be obtained from resistance thermometers (platinum or nickel) or thermistors. If a fast response is required, thermocouples may be the best choice, particularly for temperature difference measurements. Section 3.1.3 of CIBSE Guide H[63] gives guidance on the selection of temperature sensors.

— *Thermostatic radiator valves*: an effective form of room temperature control when incorporated in a suitable overall control system. They provide autonomous local control by combining a wax-operated thermostat with a directly coupled valve.

— *Programmable room thermostats*: these combine the functions of a programmer (or time switch) and a thermostat and offer the possibility of different set points at different times of day or week; e.g. a lower set-back temperature at night to prevent excessive overnight cooling.

Humidity sensors

Humidity sensors are necessary when air conditioning or humidity control is provided in combination with the heating system. Heating in 'heritage' rooms may be controlled to prevent low relative humidity, when preservation takes precedence over visitor comfort. Simple mechanical humidity sensors (or hygrometers) are based on the expansion of a natural material or nylon as water is absorbed from the ambient air but these have poor accuracy and repeatability. More accurate measurements of relative humidity have traditionally been made with the wet and dry bulb hygrometer, but this device does not lend itself well to automatic operation.

For building services applications, the sensors most commonly used for automatic control rely on capacitive polymer film sensors, with the sensing element protected by a membrane or netting filter. The polymer film, which forms the dielectric within the capacitor, responds to relative humidity and affects the measured capacitance. Where accurate measurements are required (e.g., for calibration of other sensors), dewpoint measurements are recommended. Automatic dewpoint sensors are available but are too expensive for routine application.

Flow sensors

Flow measurement may be required during the commissioning of a heating system. Turbine flow meters and orifice plates may be used for this purpose provided suitable metering points have been incorporated in the system pipework. Where that is not the case, it may be possible to make non-intrusive measurements using ultrasonic flow meters. Flow switches, which give a status signal to indicate that flow is taking place, may also be used as part of a control system.

Balancing valves (Y-pattern), which incorporate a close-coupled orifice and a pair of pressure tappings, are available ready calibrated for use during commissioning. Unfortunately, the permanent inclusion of an orifice plate incurs an unnecessary permanent pressure drop and increased pumping power over the life of the installation.

Pressure sensors

The maintenance of design system pressure is important both for proper function and safe operation in hydronic heating systems, particularly in sealed systems and those operating at high pressure. Simple Bourdon gauges may be used to give a visual display and various pressure transducers are available for supplying signals to automatic control systems. Pressure operated switches are also available.

Actuators

Actuators are principally required in hydronic heating systems to operate valves that control the flow to various circuits and emitters. Apart from the built-in thermic actuators used in thermostatic control valves, electric motor and solenoid actuators are widely used with valves. The actuator may be fully modulating, where the position of the actuator is proportional to the control signal, or multi-state, where it can assume two or more fixed positions in response to a signal. Actuators often include a positional feedback signal, which may be analogue or status.

Pneumatic actuators were once very widely used in HVAC systems but have been largely supplanted by electrical types. However, they are often still used to operate large valves and in high pressure applications that require a motor with high torque. Where existing pneumatic systems are being upgraded to electronic control, it may be possible to retain pneumatic operation of actuators by using hybrid electro-pneumatic transducers.

Valves

Various valve types are shown in Figure 1.14. Two- and three-port valves are commonly used in heating circuits. Three-port valves may be of the mixing type, which has two inlet ports and one outlet, or the diverting type, which has one inlet port and two outlets. Correct application of three-port valves requires that account be taken of the direction of flow through each port. Small four-port valves are often used on fan coil units. However, they are essentially three-port valves with a built in bypass, which has flow and return connections into the valve and flow and return connections out.

Valve characteristic curves, which relate flow to actuator position, are very important to successful control system design. Figure 1.15 shows some typical valve characteristics. The way in which valve stem position can influence flow through the circuit it controls depends not only on the valve characteristic but also on how the pressure drop across the valve compares with that around the rest of the circuit. If the valve is too large, the resistance to flow will be dominated by the rest of the circuit except when the valve is near to its closed position and therefore the valve will have little effect over much of its range. If the valve is too small, it will cause a large pressure drop and require additional pumping pressure under normal operating conditions.

Valve performance is usually defined in terms of flow capacity K, defined by the relationship:

$$K = q_v / \sqrt{\Delta p} \qquad (1.32)$$

where K is the flow capacity ($m^3 \cdot h^{-1} \cdot bar^{-0.5}$), q_v is the volumetric flow rate ($m^3 \cdot h^{-1}$) and Δp is the pressure drop (bar).

The action of the valve in intermediate positions is best characterised in terms of relative valve capacity:

$$\alpha = (K_v / K_o) \times 100 \qquad (1.33)$$

where α is the percentage opening of the valve (%), K_v is the flow capacity for a particular valve position and K_o is the flow capacity in the fully open position.

The relationship between valve and circuit pressure drop is expressed in terms of valve authority, N_{des}, which is defined as:

$$N_{des} = \Delta p_{vo} / (\Delta p_{vo} + \Delta p_c) \qquad (1.34)$$

where N_{des} is the valve authority, Δp_{vo} is the pressure drop across the valve in fully open position at design flow (Pa) and Δp_c is the pressure drop across the rest of the circuit (Pa).

Valve selection is covered in detail in section 3.3.4 of CIBSE Guide H[(63)].

Compound valves, incorporating measurement and/or regulating functions, are available to assist commissioning and control. These include the following:

— *Double regulating valves*: incorporate a device that allows a pre-set position to be retained while also providing an isolating function.

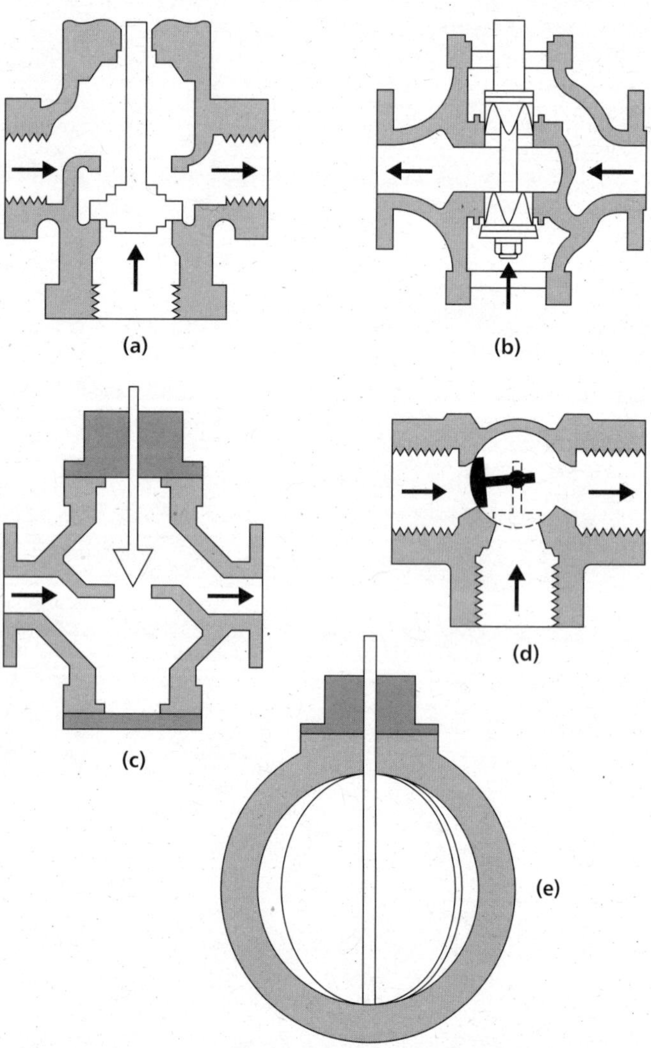

Figure 1.14 Common valve types: (*a*) plug and seat three-port mixing valve, single seat; (*b*) plug and seat three-port mixing valve, double seat; (*c*) two-part plug and seat valve; (*d*) rotary shoe valve; (*e*) butterfly valve

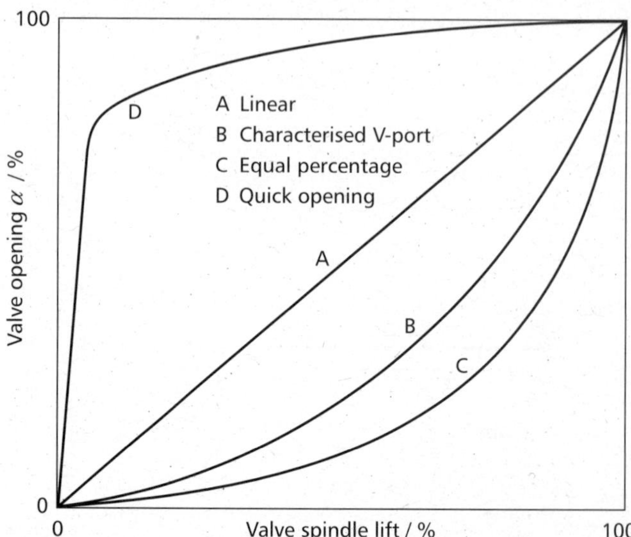

Figure 1.15 Typical valve characteristics

— *Variable orifice double regulating valves*: include tappings that allow the pressure drop across the valve to be measured

— *Fixed orifice double regulating valves*: incorporate an orifice plate with tappings to enable flow measurement; this type is also known as a 'commissioning set'

— *Constant flow regulators*: automatically control flow rate provided the differential pressure across the valve is maintained within certain limits

— *Differential pressure control valves*: maintain a constant pressure across a branch of a circuit.

Both constant flow regulators and differential pressure control valves may be used to assist in the commissioning of circuits.

1.5.2 Equipment for steam systems

1.5.2.1 Boilers

A steam boiler differs from a water circuit boiler in that it produces a phase change from water to steam, which introduces additional requirements for the control of both the pressure and the water level within the boiler. Also, as a pressurised vessel containing water and steam at above 100 °C, it requires greater attention to the maintenance of safety in operation.

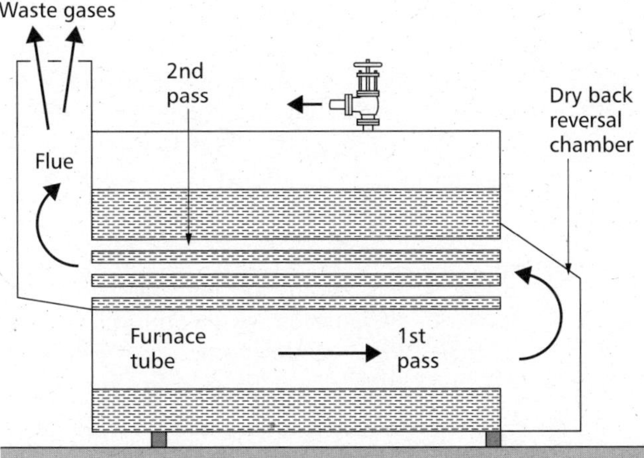

Figure 1.16 Two-pass dry back shell boiler (courtesy of Spirax-Sarco Ltd)

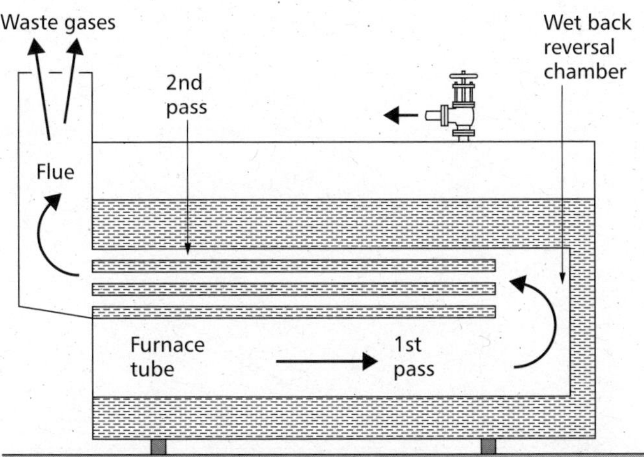

Figure 1.17 Two-pass wet back shell boiler (courtesy of Spirax-Sarco Ltd)

Steam boilers may be broadly classified into two types:

— *shell (or fire tube) boilers*

— *water tube boilers*.

Shell boilers operate by passing heated gases through tubes in the boiler. Figures 1.16 and 1.17 show typical shell boiler configurations for 'two-pass' operation, in which the heated gases from the furnace are reversed to flow through the boiler for a second pass to extract more heat. In the 'dry back' configuration, the flow is reversed by a refractory lined chamber; in the 'wet back' version the reversal chamber is contained entirely within the boiler, which improves the efficiency of heat transfer. Modern packaged boilers commonly use three passes to achieve high efficiency and compact dimensions. Shell boilers are covered by BS 2790[(68)].

Water tube boilers differ from shell boilers in that the heat source surrounds tubes circulating the boiler water, see Figure 1.18. They are able to operate at higher pressures than shell boilers because the tube diameters are much lower than those of the shell of a shell boiler, with corresponding reductions in the hoop stress. As shell boilers are limited in practice to pressures below 27 bar (gauge), or a steam temperature of 340 °C, water tube types tend to be used for applications requiring high pressure, high temperature or very large steam output. Water tube boilers are available in smaller sizes but offer no advantage over shell boilers for most commercial and industrial applications involving heating. Water tube boilers are covered by BS 1113[(67)].

Steam boiler output depends on operating conditions and is rated in three ways:

— 'from and at' rating

— kW rating

— boiler horse power (BoHP).

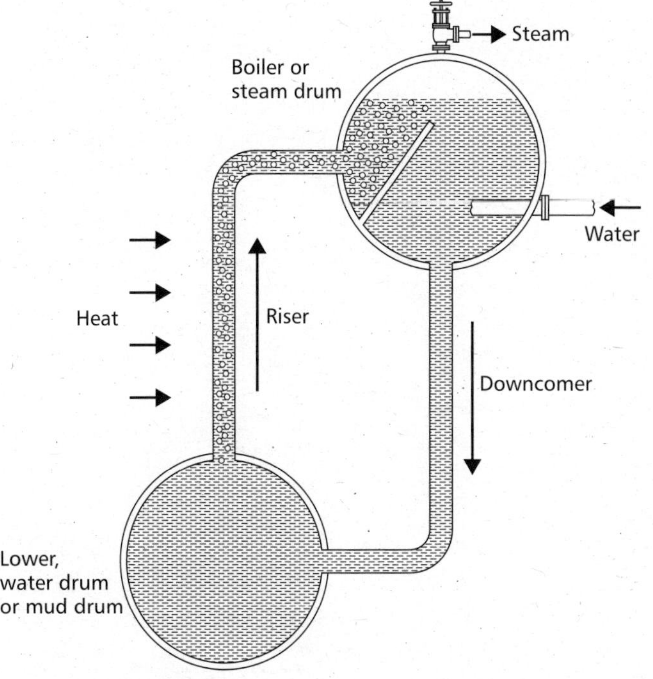

Figure 1.18 Riser-downcomer configuration of water tube steam boiler (courtesy of Spirax-Sarco Ltd)

The 'from and at' rating is based on the amount of steam (in kg) at 100 °C and atmospheric pressure that the boiler can generate in 1 hour from a feed water temperature of 100 °C. Under these conditions, each kilogram of water requires 2258 kJ of heat per hour to convert it to steam, which is equivalent to 627 W. In practice, boilers are operated under a range of conditions and the steam output under different conditions may be calculated using steam tables or estimated from the graph shown in Figure 1.19. 'From and at' ratings are widely used by manufacturers of shell boilers.

Some manufacturers give boiler ratings in kW. Steam output may be calculated from the difference between the specific enthalpy of the feed-water and the steam at the required pressure.

'Boiler horse power' tends to be used only in the USA, Australia and New Zealand and should not be confused with the imperial unit of power, which is approximately 746 W. In Australia and the USA, 1 BOHP is defined as the power required to evaporate 34.5 pounds of water per hour at 212 °F at atmospheric pressure. This is essentially the same form of definition as the 'from and at' rating, except that it is based on 34.5 lb instead on 1 kg; 1 BOHP is equivalent to 15.51 kg/hour. In New Zealand, BOHP is defined in terms of the heat transfer area of the boiler.

Boiler efficiency depends upon the design of the boiler and the conditions under which it is operated. Some boilers incorporate an 'economiser', which consists of an additional heat exchanger using exhaust gases to preheat the feed-water before it is returned to the boiler. However, economisers may not be used on boilers with on-off level controls. Efficiency in steam systems also depends on minimising heat losses from the boiler feed-tank, which should be well insulated to prevent heat losses.

Steam boilers must be fitted with appropriate safety devices. In the UK, these are currently covered by BS 759: Part 1[97]. Each boiler must have a name plate, with a serial number and model number which uniquely identifies it and its manufacturer and gives details of various tests to which it has been subjected. It must also be fitted with a safety valve to protect it from overpressure and the risk of explosion; in the UK, BS 6759[98] covers safety valves for steam boilers. Safety valves are also covered by section 8 of BS 2790[68], which relates to the design and manufacture of shell boilers of welded construction.

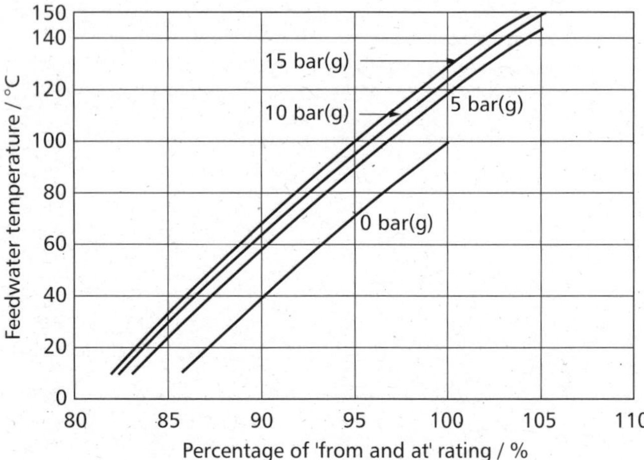

Figure 1.19 'From and at' variation with temperature (courtesy of Spirax-Sarco Ltd)

A typical safety valve is shown in Figure 1.20. Safety valves must be capable of discharging the full 'from and at 100 °C' capacity of the boiler within 110% of the design boiler pressure and be set at no higher than the design pressure. At least one safety valve is required for all boilers; boilers rated at more than 3700 kg·h^{-1} are required to have two single safety valves or one double safety valve. The discharge pipe from the safety valve must have no obstructions and be drained at the base to ensure that condensate cannot accumulate. Each boiler must also be fitted with a stop valve (or crown valve) to isolate it from the plant it serves. This should always be fully open or fully closed, and should not be used as a throttling valve.

Other safety equipment required by steam boilers includes:

- a feed check valve to prevent return flow from the boiler when the feed pump is not operating and flooding from the static head in the feed tank
- a bottom blow-down valve, which may be manual or automatic in operation
- a pressure indicator, which may be a simple Bourdon gauge with a dial of least 150 mm in diameter
- a gauge glass to show the level of water in the boiler (see Figure 1.21). In the UK, gauge glasses should comply with BS 3463[73].

1.5.2.2 Steam traps

Steam traps are used to drain condensate automatically from the system while preventing the escape of steam. They operate according to three main principles, as follows:

- *Thermostatic steam traps*: operate in response to change in temperature and open when condensate temperature falls below a pre-set threshold; they are available in various types suited to particular applications.
- *Mechanical or balanced pressure steam traps*: operate by sensing the difference in density between steam and condensate; they include 'ball float' and 'inverted bucket' types, which both operate by simple mechanical means.
- *Thermodynamic steam traps*: these are operated in part by the formation of flash steam from condensate; hot condensate released under pressure closes the trap when it evaporates.

The choice of steam traps for particular applications involves a number of considerations, including air venting, condensate removal (either continuous or intermittent),

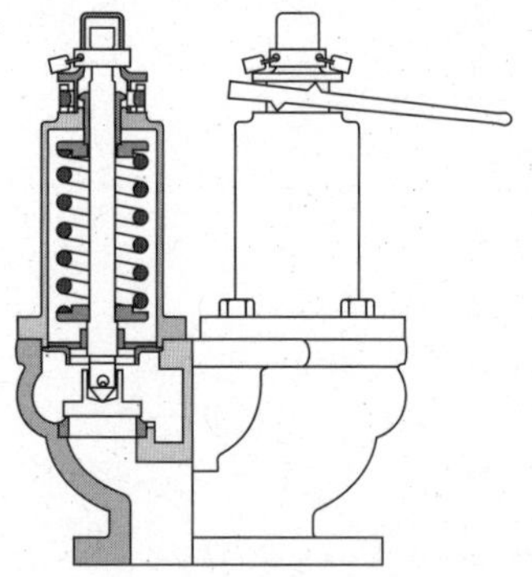

Figure 1.20 Typical steam boiler safety valve (courtesy of Spirax-Sarco Ltd)

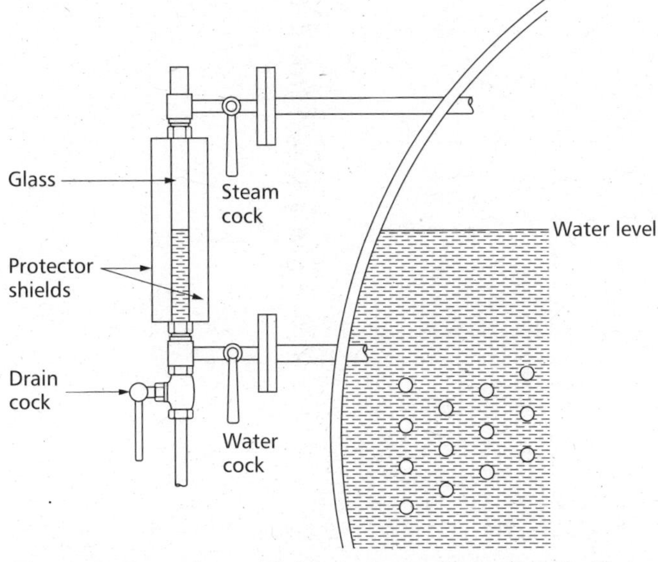

Figure 1.21 Gauge glass and fittings (courtesy of Spirax-Sarco Ltd)

capacity, thermal efficiency and reliability. The avoidance of water hammer may also depend upon the selection and positioning of traps, as the presence of water hammer may cause traps to fail. Dirt is another factor to be considered in trap selection; traps that operate intermittently with a blast action are less susceptible to dirt than those that depend on small orifices for their operation. Table 1.22 shows a range of steam traps, together with typical applications.

1.5.2.3 Air vents

Steam traps are capable of venting air from steam systems but separate air vents are fitted in certain situations, particularly at the end of a steam main. An automatic air vent typically consists of a thermostatically operated valve, see Table 1.22, items 7 and 8. It is best installed at a location where the temperature is low enough for steam to have condensed before reaching it, but where condensation does not collect. In practice this is typically at the top end of a 300 mm length of pipe arranged as a 'collecting bottle', which is left unlagged.

1.5.2.4 Feedwater equipment

A typical feedwater system is shown in Figure 1.22. The feed tank receives condensate returned from the system and treated water as required to make up losses from the system. The feed pump takes water from the feed tank and supplies it into the boiler at the rate required to maintain the water level in the boiler.

The treatment of make-up water is vital to the longevity, safe operation and efficiency of the system. In particular, it seeks to avoid scaling, corrosion and caustic embrittlement in boilers by removing dissolved and suspended solids and dissolved gases thereby keeping the pH value of the water within defined limits. Water softening, to remove scale-producing ions, may be carried out using (in ascending order of effectiveness) base-exchange methods, de-alkalisation, or de-mineralisation.

Table 1.22 Characteristics of steam traps and air vents

Type	Schematic	Notes
Float trap	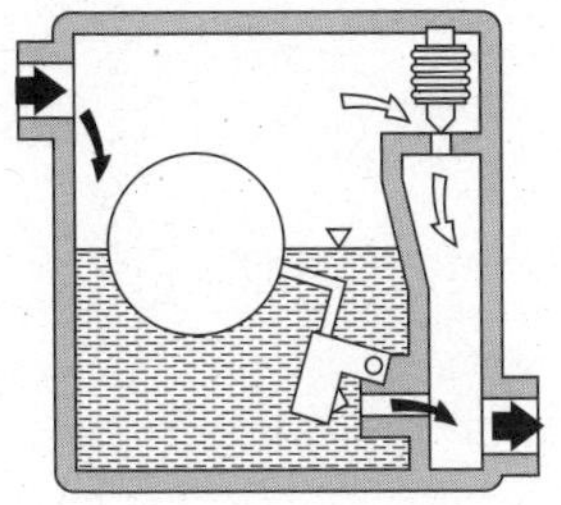	*Advantages*: suitable for widely fluctuating loads and pressures; easy to install and maintain; removes condensate continuously as it forms; types with balanced pressure air vents automatically discharge air. *Disadvantages*: can be damaged by water-hammer and corrosive condensate; normally three or four differently sized valves and seats are required to cover the normal working range.
Inverted bucket trap	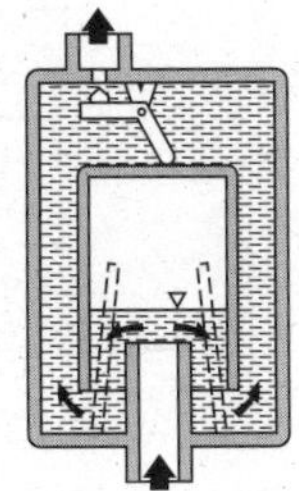	*Advantages*: can be made for high pressure and superheated steam; will withstand water-hammer; can be made of corrosion resisting materials; a check valve should be fitted at the inlet where used with superheated steam; working parts are simple. *Disadvantages*: wasteful of steam if oversized; does not respond well to severe fluctuations of pressure and discharges air slowly; a thermostatic air vent fitted in a by-pass is recommended; should be lagged when used outdoors. *Notes*: no longer manufactured but some may still be found in service; open top bucket traps have similar advantages and disadvantages.
Thermostatic steam trap	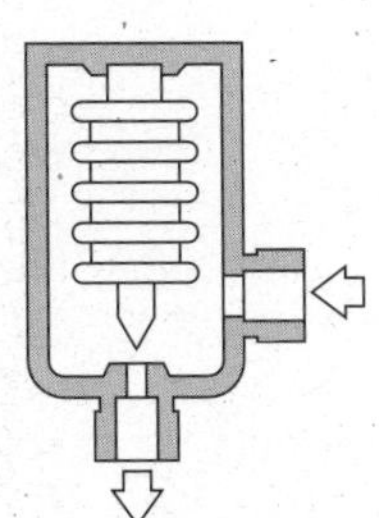	*Advantages*: compact; automatically discharges air; valve is wide open on start-up, so cool condensate and air discharge quickly; capacity is high; unlikely to freeze if condensate can run from trap outlet; maintenance is easy; traditional elements have corrugated brass or phosphor bronze bellows, newer designs have a stainless steel bellows or diaphragm-type element. *Disadvantages*: older type elements liable to damage by water hammer, corrosive condensate or superheated steam (stainless steel elements are more robust and some designs are suitable for use with superheated steam).

Table continues

Table 1.22 Characteristics of steam traps and air vents — *continued*

Type	Schematic	Notes
Liquid expansion steam trap	Unlagged cooling leg Approx 3 m	*Advantages*: can be used with superheated steam and at higher pressures than balanced pressure traps; valve is wide open on start-up, so cool condensate and air discharge quickly; capacity is high; operates by continuous discharge, so quiet in operation and unaffected by vibration, steam pulsation and water-hammer; automatically discharges air. *Disadvantages*: does not respond quickly to change in load or steam pressure; element can be damaged by corrosive condensate. *Note*: because element is on discharge side of valve orifice, trap will hold back condensate. This permits use of some sensible heat from condensate provided that water-logging of steam space is acceptable; if this is not the case, a cooling leg must be fitted before the trap.
Bi-metallic steam trap		*Advantages*: usually small and robust; when cold valve is wide open and air is freely discharged; capacity is greatest when condensate is coolest; some types are not damaged by freezing; withstands water hammer and some are unaffected by corrosive condensate; suitable for use on high pressure and superheated steam; will work over wide range of pressures without need to change size of valve orifice, although position of orifice may need to be adjusted; holds back condensate until cooling occurs thus using some of the sensible heat. *Disadvantages*: will not discharge condensate until it has cooled below saturation temperature, so unsuitable for use where condensate must be cleared as soon as it forms unless a cooling leg is provided; responds slowly to changes in steam pressure and condensate load.
Thermodynamic steam trap		*Advantages*: very compact but has large discharge capacity; will work over full range of pressures without adjustment; can be used with superheated steam and can withstand vibration or severe water-hammer; normally made of stainless steel and therefore can withstand corrosive condensate and is not damaged by being frozen. *Disadvantages*: normally requires a minimum pressure differential in order to function; on starting up, if pressure at trap builds up slowly it can discharge a lot of air, but if pressure builds up quickly the resulting high velocity air can shut the trap in the same way as steam and it will air bind; operation of trap can be noisy; due to blast, discharge operation sight glasses and check valves should be fitted about 1 metre from the trap.
Balanced pressure air vent		Similar to balanced pressure steam trap. Valve is wide open when plant is cold; as temperature surrounding the element approaches steam temperature the internal liquid expands thereby generating a pressure within the element which closes the valve seat.
Liquid expansion air vent	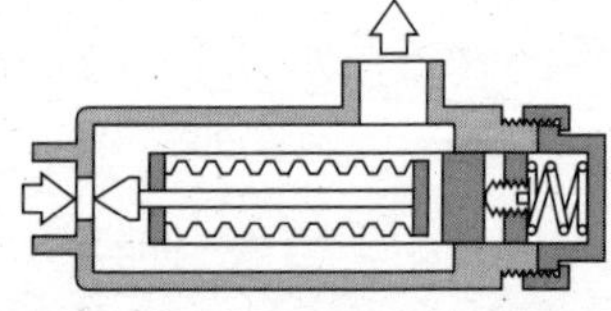	Similar to liquid expansion steam trap. Changes in temperature cause the oil filled element to expand or contract causing the valve to move towards or away from its seat.

Note: where water-hammer is present or the steam is superheated, the liquid expansion air vent is the better choice since either of these conditions may damage balanced pressure units. Both the liquid expansion and balanced pressure vents are suitable for any pressure within their range without changing the valve seat, but if conditions vary greatly liquid expansion units may require re-setting

Feed tanks are made from various materials, including cast iron, carbon steel and austenitic stainless steel.

1.5.2.5 Space heating equipment

Space heating by steam often uses a heat exchanger to transfer heat from the steam to a secondary hot water circuit, which uses standard hydronic heating equipment. Figure 1.23 shows a heat exchanger, controlled to maintain a constant secondary flow temperature. Alternatively, it is possible to use a range of emitters powered directly by steam including radiators, natural convectors, fan coil units and radiant panels. Steam radiators usually operate from steam at 0.33 bar with vacuum condensate removal. Vacuum condensate pumping can be problematical and maintenance costs high.

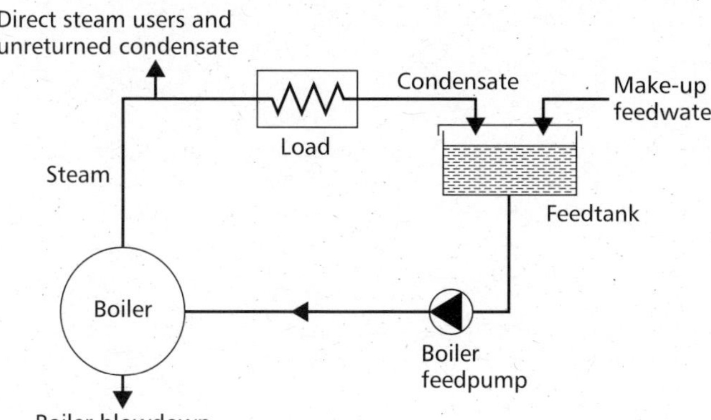

Figure 1.22 Feed-water loop in a steam circuit (courtesy of Spirax-Sarco Ltd)

1.5.3 Equipment for warm air systems

1.5.3.1 Heat sources

Suspended unit heaters

These are small independent gas-fired heaters, with outputs up to 100 kW, typically comprising a burner and heat exchanger inside a painted steel casing, see Figure 1.24. A low powered axial fan blows recirculated air horizontally across the heat exchanger and directly into the heated space. The basic form uses an atmospheric gas burner, usually of the ladder type, firing into a simple pressed steel heat exchanger, which is aluminised or similarly treated to provide corrosion protection. The degree of modulation possible is limited by the need to avoid condensation in the heat exchanger and flue; 60% of full output is the normal minimum output. Flues are usually single skin stainless steel terminating with a cowl at least 1 m above the roof. A draught diverter is usually built into the heater itself.

Variations on this basic design include:

— stainless steel heat exchangers for use in aggressive environments or with fresh air inlet

— room sealed units with induced draft fan and ducted combustion air inlet

— condensing burners

— on/off, two stage or modulating control

— centrifugal fans, for use with air distribution ducting.

Heaters are normally mounted at heights between 2.5 m and 3.5 m above floor level, but higher mounting is possible. Only limited distribution ducting is possible due to the low available fan discharge pressure.

Cabinet heaters

These are larger (up to 300–400 kW output) individual heaters, normally gas- or oil-fired, and used in industrial premises where quiet operation and close environmental control are not essential. They are usually floor mounted, but some versions are suitable for high level mounting.

A typical unit comprises an externally mounted forced-draught burner firing into a steel combustion chamber, with flue gases passing through a tubular heat exchanger before exiting through the flue, see Figure 1.25. Some low cost designs use atmospheric burners. Stainless steel or a protective coating may be used to increase longevity.

A centrifugal fan in the base of the heater blows air across the heat exchanger and the heated air is discharged horizontally through discharge louvres on the top. Alternatively, air may be discharged through distribution ductwork, although the limited fan pressure available on some heaters can mean that extensive ducting is impractical. Inlet air is usually recirculated room air but some heaters can have a ducted inlet for combustion air and/or ventilation air. Flues are usually single-skin stainless steel terminating with a cowl at least 1 m above the roof.

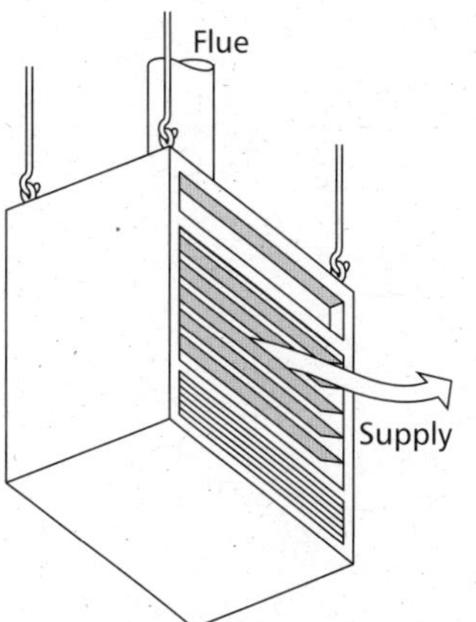

Figure 1.24 Suspended warm air heater (reproduced from EEBPP Good Practice Guide GPG303 by permission of the Energy Efficiency Best Practice Programme)

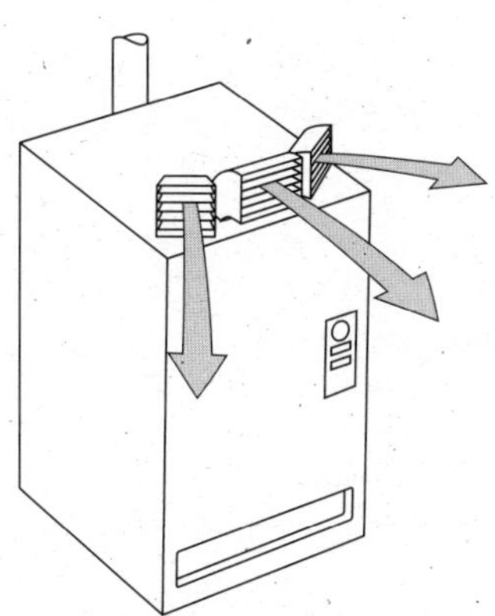

Figure 1.25 Floor-standing cabinet heater (reproduced from EEBPP Good Practice Guide GPG303 by permission of the Energy Efficiency Best Practice Programme)

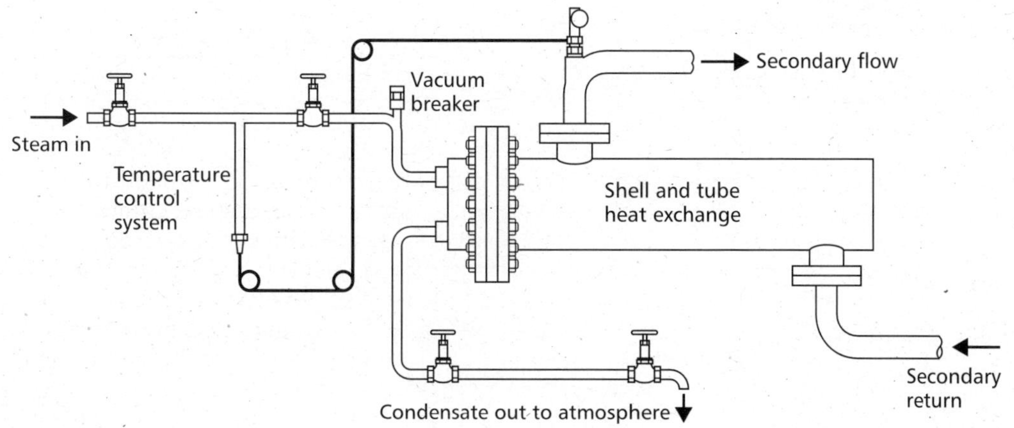

Figure 1.23 Steam-to-water heat exchanger for a hydronic space heating system (courtesy of Spirax-Sarco Ltd)

Condensing gas-fired cabinet heaters include an additional stainless steel heat exchanger to cool the flue gases to condensing point. They are relatively uncommon as the high efficiency of non-condensing heaters makes it difficult to justify the extra cost of the additional heat exchanger.

Direct fired heaters

These flue-less gas fired heaters are usually of the cabinet type. The gas is burnt directly in the main ventilation airstream (with no heat exchanger) and the products of combustion are therefore distributed into the heated space. A 'cheese grater' burner configuration is usual, with a perforated stainless steel V-shaped shroud around the burner tube. Modulating control of heat output is usually provided. Control of combustion and ventilation is critical to ensure that sufficient dilution of the combustion gases is achieved. Guidance on combustion and ventilation air is given in BS 6230[(77)]. Direct fired heaters are always used with a fresh air inlet, but some recirculation may be permissible.

Air handling units

Although air handling units can incorporate any of the above heater types, heating is more commonly provided by a hot water heater battery supplied from a boiler system or occasionally by direct electrical heating elements. In industrial premises, small individual fresh air supply units with recirculation facilities and water or steam heater batteries may be used. These are most commonly used when hot water or steam is readily available due to process usage.

Induced jet systems

Induced jet systems distribute warm air via high velocity ducts, see Figure 1.26. The heat source for these systems is generally a large central gas- or oil-fired unit, built in the style of a specialised air handling unit or cabinet heater. Direct fired heaters must always have the burner situated in the fresh air supply, but some re-circulation is permissible providing it is introduced downstream of the burner, see BS 6230[(77)].

1.5.3.2 Ductwork and diffusers

Heating systems involving comprehensive ducting are usually combined with ventilation systems and are therefore also covered in section 2.

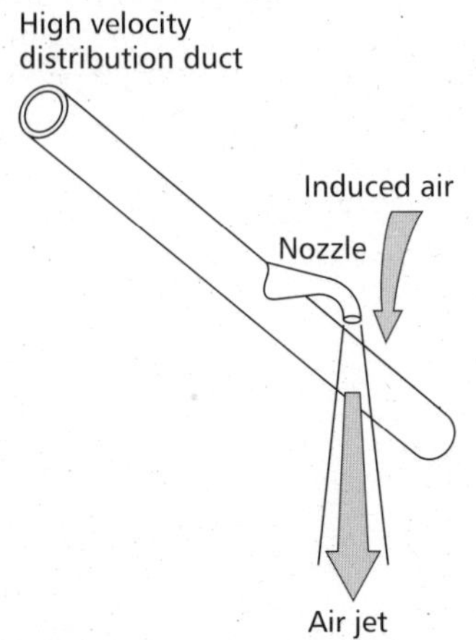

Figure 1.26 Induced jet warm air heating (reproduced from EEBPP Good Practice Guide GPG303 by permission of the Energy Efficiency Best Practice Programme)

Where individual heaters as described in section 1.5.3.1 are used, duct systems should be limited to provide air distribution through a single space. It is difficult to duct heat to a production area and its associated offices successfully from a single heater.

Duct systems for induced jet heating are usually circular in cross-section and installed at high level in the roof space. Purpose designed nozzles and induction hoods are used to provide the necessary induction and throw, normally producing high duct velocity.

Diffusers are considered in section 2.5.13. The characteristics of various types of air terminal devices are described, including information on typical face velocities and noise levels. Diffusers may be radial, part radial or linear and normally utilise the Coanda effect and/or swirl to avoid excessive room air movement.

1.5.3.3 Heat recovery

Mechanical ventilation systems, including those that incorporate heating, offer the opportunity to recover heat from air returned by the ventilation system. In energy terms alone, recirculation of air is the most efficient form of heat recovery since it involves little or no energy penalty, but must be limited by the need to maintain an adequate supply of fresh air. Various types of equipment are available for heat recovery, which can both reduce heat requirements in winter and cooling requirements in summer. Heat recovery devices are described in detail in section 2.5.6.

1.5.3.4 Heat distribution combined with fresh air provision

Systems that combine ventilation, heating and cooling are considered in section 2.

It is important to ensure that as much care is given to the successful distribution of heated air as is given to the distribution of ventilation air, since airflow characteristics and circulation patterns will differ between modes.

1.5.3.5 Heating combined with air conditioning

Buildings with central air conditioning systems normally include provisions for heating, cooling and ventilation. There are a number of different types of systems, including the following:

- *Dual duct systems*: two separate ducts are employed to circulate cooled and heated air to zonal mixing boxes. Thermostatic controls in each zone ensure that air from the hot and cold ducts are mixed in appropriate proportions to achieve the required conditions in the zone. Mixing two air streams to produce an intermediate comfort temperature wastes heating and cooling energy, particularly in constant volume systems.
- *Variable air volume (VAV) systems*: these offer significantly improved energy efficiency compared with constant volume systems, although both systems represent a significant energy cost.

— *Fan coil systems*: these systems heat or cool air in the heated space using coils fed by heated or chilled water, which is distributed by conventional hydronic circuits. A fan coil is a packaged assembly comprising coils(s), condensate tray, circulating fan and filter. The fan recirculates air from the space continuously through the coil(s) either directly or via the void in which the fan coil is located.

(*a*) *Two-pipe non-changeover systems*: a single coil is supplied with chilled water only via a water circuit. Heating is normally provided either by a separate perimeter system or by electric heaters in the fan coil units.

(*b*) *Four pipe systems*: separate heating and cooling coils are incorporated, fed by heating and chilled water circuits respectively.

These systems are covered in section 2.

1.5.3.6 Controls for warm air systems

Control strategies for warm air systems can be kept reasonably simple. Where individual heaters are used it is usually sufficient to provide time control by time-switch or optimiser with on/off temperature control using an air temperature sensor or thermostat. Manufacturers generally offer these simple controls as part of their equipment. BMS or other centralised control can be used but is often not considered necessary.

It is normal practice for each heater to have a dedicated room thermostat to provide individual control. When small output heaters are used it is sometimes possible to control more than one heater from a thermostat but four is considered to be the practical maximum. Averaging from several sensors is not normally used except for central systems since control zones are rarely large enough to justify averaging.

Most individual heaters incorporate a fan run-on circuit, so that the main fan continues to run in order to cool the heat exchanger after the burner has been switched off (for energy efficiency and to reduce heat exchanger stress) until a pre-set low-limit leaving air temperature is reached.

Two-stage burner control may be used to provide finer control of temperature. The heater fan may continue to be run at full speed or run at slow speed at the low burner output condition. For gas- or oil-fired heaters the low fire output is typically 60% of full output.

The best control of room temperature is obtained using modulating control of the heater output. This can be provided on most forms of warm air heater, but the turn-down ratio is severely limited on indirect gas- or oil-fired heaters. Modulation can be used to maintain a constant room temperature or a constant leaving air temperature. The latter is usually used when the warm air is providing a tempered make-up air supply rather than full space heating. A low-limit control is usually required to prevent the modulating control from reducing the leaving air temperature to such a level as to cause discomfort.

De-stratification systems should be controlled to prevent build up of unacceptable temperature gradients. For low velocity systems the fans should be controlled to run during the full heating period (often from the heater time control). For high velocity systems thermostatic control is preferable to avoid cool drafts.

CIBSE Guide H[63] provides more detailed information on control systems.

1.5.3.7 Other standards and guidance

There are a number of other standards relevant to warm air heating; these include:

— BS 5864[99] and BS EN 1319[100] for domestic systems

— BS 5991[101] for indirect gas-fired industrial systems

— BS 5990[102] for direct gas-fired industrial installations.

1.5.4 Radiant heaters

This section deals with equipment used to provide heating with a high proportion of radiant output and good directional properties, characteristics that make radiant heaters suitable for heating areas within larger open spaces. In practice, this restricts it mostly to gas and electric radiant heaters that operate at relatively high temperatures. Steam and high-pressure hot water tubes and radiators may also be used, as can air-heated radiant tubes. All are capable of operating temperatures up to 150 °C but their outputs are less readily directed and have a lower radiant percentage than the gas and electric types described below.

1.5.4.1 Gas-fired radiant heaters

Gas-fired radiant heaters are typically of two types: radiant overhead tube heaters and radiant plaque heaters. Radiant tube heaters may be either flued or un-flued. Radiant plaques are un-flued and offer very high efficiencies and are well-suited to spot heating. The relevant British Standard is BS 6896[103].

Radiant tube

Figure 1.27 shows a typical overhead radiant tube heater. Radiant tube heaters are available in several configurations: U-tube (as shown), linear and continuous (multi-burner). Outputs from individual units are typically in the range of 10 to 40 kW and up to 180 kW can be obtained from multi-tube or continuous tube assemblies, operating at a temperature of around 500 °C. They may be mounted at heights between 3.5 and 20 metres and are mostly used for general area heating, rather than local spot heating. Low-level mounting is avoided to ensure even distribution of heat and to minimise the effects of noise. Reflectors are usually made of polished stainless steel or

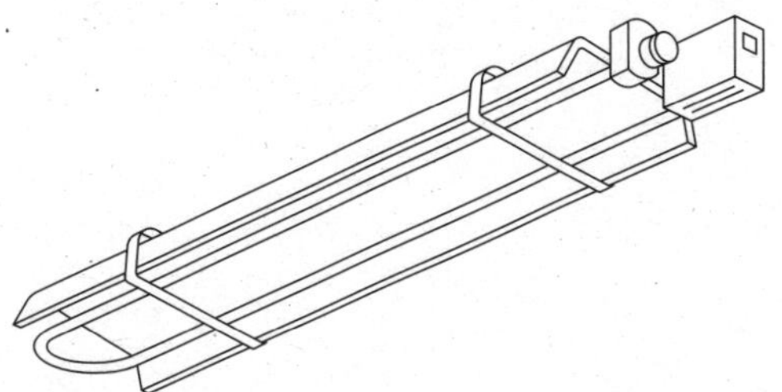

Figure 1.27 Gas-fired overhead radiant tube heater (reproduced from EEBPP Good Practice Guide GPG303 by permission of the Energy Efficiency Best Practice Programme)

rigid aluminium, shaped for optimum heat distribution. Tubes are usually steel, often blackened for maximum efficiency. Stainless steel may be used for the first section of tube from the burner, particularly with high output burners. Minimum ventilation requirements for un-flued heaters are given in BS 6896[103].

Radiant plaque

A typical radiant plaque heater is shown in Figure 1.28. Heaters of this type offer outputs typically in the range of 5–40 kW. They operate at around 900 °C and are often used for local spot heating. Due to the high operating temperatures, the ceramic burners glow red/orange in use. Like un-flued radiant tube types, they must be located where ventilation rates are high to avoid condensation and to dilute flue gases. A cone configuration is available to provide 360° coverage of a particular location; domestic patio heaters are small-scale portable versions of this type of heater.

1.5.4.2 Electric radiant heaters

Electric radiant heaters typically use quartz-enclosed radiant elements operating at up to 2000 °C and parabolic reflectors. They have good directional properties and 100% efficiency in converting from electricity to heat; however, energy costs are high and upstream carbon dioxide emissions are high when electricity is generated from fossil fuels. They are mostly used for local spot heating, mounted at levels between 2 and 4 metres. A typical unit is shown in Figure 1.29.

1.5.4.3 Controls for radiant heating

As noted in section 1.4.6.3, control of radiant heating should ideally rely on the sensing of dry resultant temperature, which requires the use of a black-bulb thermometer. Hemispherical black-bulb sensors are available for wall mounting, but suffer from the disadvantage that they are not located at the point where control is required. Also,

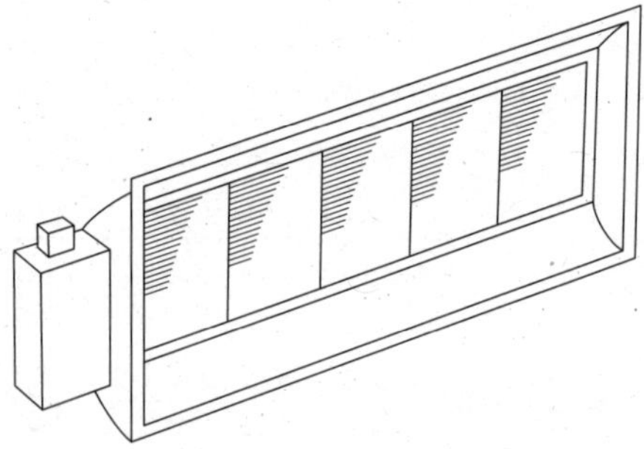

Figure 1.28 Gas-fired radiant plaque heater (reproduced from EEBPP Good Practice Guide GPG303 by permission of the Energy Efficiency Best Practice Programme)

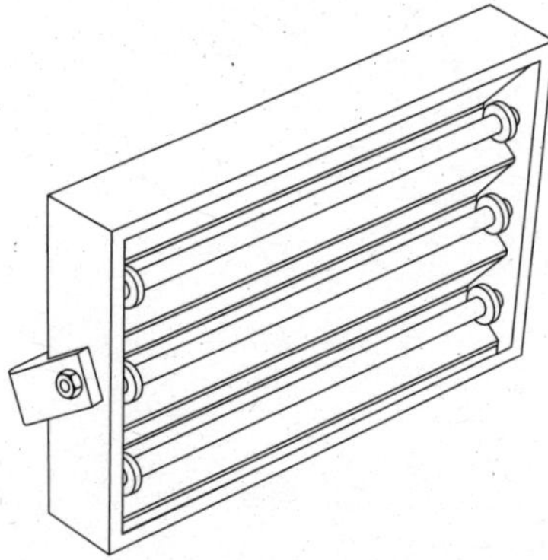

Figure 1.29 Electric radiant heater with quartz enclosed elements and parabolic reflectors (reproduced from EEBPP Good Practice Guide GPG303 by permission of the Energy Efficiency Best Practice Programme)

they tend to be slow to respond. Control based on sensing air temperature is also used, particularly when the whole space is being heated (as opposed to spot heating). Stand-alone controllers may be used or the control function may be integrated into a building management system (BMS).

1.5.5 Chimneys and flues

1.5.5.1 Environmental legislation affecting chimneys and flues

Several different strands of legislation are relevant to the design of flues and chimneys, depending on the power of the plant they serve, the fuels used and where they are located.

The Environmental Protection Act 1990[104] gives powers to local authorities to control pollution from industrial and other processes, which includes the generation of heat and power. Large scale ('Part A') processes, with an output exceeding 50 MW, are subject to control by the Environment Agency. Local authorities control smaller scale ('Part B') processes, which may include large boilers and CHP units. One of the many requirements is for the use of 'best available techniques not entailing excessive cost' ('BATNEEC') to meet limits on levels of contaminants in flue discharges.

The Environment Act 1995[105] includes provisions for 'local air quality management' and sets air quality standards for seven key urban pollutants: nitrogen dioxide, carbon monoxide, sulphur dioxide, PM10 particles, benzene, 1,3-butadene and lead. An area where any of the standards are likely to be exceeded must be designated as an 'air quality management area' and action taken to reduce levels. This can lead to additional restrictions on development in those areas.

Part 1 of the Clean Air Act 1993[106] prohibits the emission of 'dark smoke', including emission from a chimney of any building. Part 2 empowers the Secretary of State to prescribe limits on the rates of emission of grit and dust from the chimneys of furnaces, including boilers and other heating appliances. Section 14 of the Act requires that chimney heights must be approved by local authorities for furnaces burning liquid or gaseous fuel at a rate equivalent to 366.4 kW or more, solid matter at a rate of 45.4 $kg \cdot h^{-1}$ or more, or pulverised fuel.

The legislation has an important impact on the design of chimneys and flues, particularly on the height at which combustion products are discharged to the atmosphere. Chimneys contribute to the control of local pollution levels by dispersion and consequent reduction of concentrations at ground level. Dispersion is effective over a range of around 50 to 100 times the chimney height, beyond which it has little effect. For large plant or plant with special characteristics or restrictions, it is likely that individual dispersion modelling will be required. However, plant used for heating can for the most part be dealt with using published guidance. *The Clean Air Act Memorandum: Chimney Heights* (3rd edition)[107] has long been recommended as a source of this guidance and remains valid. However, some types of plant require additional considerations to meet the requirements of the Environmental Protection Act; reference should be made to HMIP Guidance Note D1: *Guidelines for Discharge Stack Heights for Polluting Emissions*[108]. CIBSE TM21[109] provides guidance on minimising pollution at air intakes, including the contribution made by chimneys and flues. For natural gas and other very low sulphur fuels, guidance may also be obtained from British Gas publication IM/11[110].

1.5.5.2 The Building Regulations

Part J of the Building Regulations[111] applies to all chimneys and flues, irrespective of the type of building, or the capacity of the appliance they serve. It includes the following requirements:

- that sufficient combustion air is supplied for proper operation of flues
- that combustion products are not hazardous to health
- that no damage is caused by heat or fire to the fabric of the building.

Similar requirements are contained in Part F of the Building Standards (Scotland) Regulations[44] and the Building Regulations (Northern Ireland)[45].

Approved Document J[8] gives guidance on how to satisfy the requirements of Part J. It also makes clear that although Part J applies to all heat producing appliances, the guidance in the Approved Document itself deals mainly with domestic installations. Accordingly, the specific guidance it contains is limited to solid fuel installations of up to 50 kW rated output, gas installations of up to 70 kW net (77.7 kW gross) rated input and oil installations of up to 45 kW rated heat output. The guidance includes:

- the positioning of flues in relation to boundaries and openings
- protection from heat for persons likely to come into contact with flues
- the diameter of flues required for different types of appliances
- materials from which flues and chimneys may be constructed
- how chimneys may be lined to serve gas fired appliances.

For installations with ratings higher than those mentioned above, the guidance referred to in section 1.5.5.1 applies. Specialist assistance is likely to be required for large installations (above 366 kW), which are also subject to the Clean Air Act. However, some larger installations may be shown to comply by adopting the relevant recommendations contained in this Guide, and codes of practice and standards produced by BSI (particularly BS 6644[112] and BS 5854[113]) and the Institution of Gas Engineers.

1.5.5.3 Principles of flue and chimney design

A chimney or flue must produce sufficient suction to enable the installed plant to operate as intended and to disperse flue gases effectively. A natural draught chimney produces suction at its base by virtue of the difference in the density between the column of hot gas within the chimney and the outside air. This can be expressed by the formula:

$$\Delta p_d / H = (\rho_a - \rho_g)\, g \qquad (1.35)$$

where Δp_d is the pressure difference between top and bottom of chimney (Pa), H is the height of the chimney (m), ρ_a is the density of ambient air (kg·m^{-3}), ρ_g is the mean density of flue gases (kg·m^{-3}) and g is the acceleration due to gravity (m·s^{-2}).

The draught produced by a chimney is proportional to its height and the temperature of the gas within it. Figure 1.30 shows the draught available for typical winter and summer ambient conditions at various chimney temperatures. This gross draught is available to provide the energy required to move the flue gases through the particular boiler, flue and chimney system.

System resistance

The chimney/flue cross-sectional areas must be selected taking account of system resistance to gas flow and the required efflux velocity from the chimney terminal. It is important that the flue layout is carefully considered and designed to limit shock losses at bends etc. In general the following aspects should be observed in flue design:

(*a*) Position the boilers as close as possible to the chimney to limit friction and heat losses in the connecting flue system.

(*b*) Avoid all short radius 90° bends in flue systems.

(*c*) Avoid abrupt section changes and use transformation sections with 15° included angles.

(*d*) Arrange the entry section to slope at 45° or more to the horizontal

(*e*) Avoid protrusion of the flues beyond the inner face of the chimney or main flue connection.

(*f*) Make flues circular or square and avoid aspect (width to depth) ratios greater than 1.5 to 1.

(*g*) Slope flues up towards the chimney where possible.

(*h*) Provide clean-out doors at each bend in the flues, at the chimney base, and adjacent to fans and dampers to aid maintenance.

(*i*) Avoid long 'dead' chimney pockets under the flue entry points, which are corrosion zones, and can cause harmonic pulsation problems.

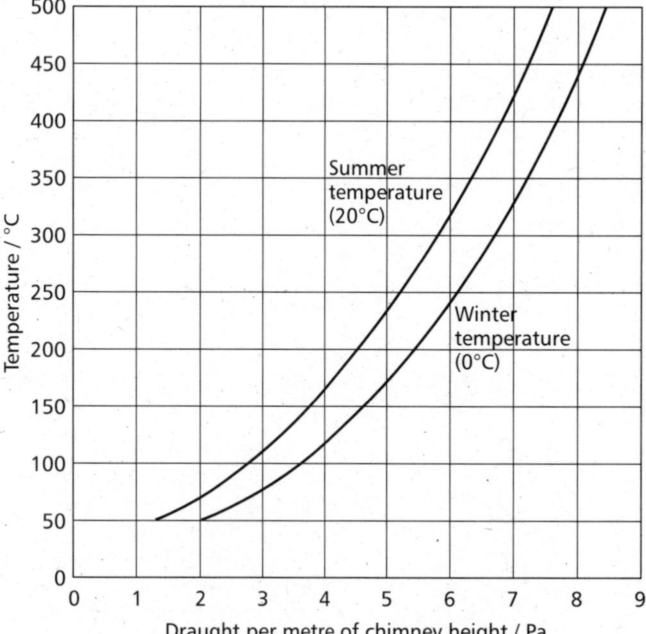

Figure 1.30 Chimney draught at summer and winter temperatures

Chimney efflux velocity

Chimney gas efflux velocities need to be high enough to avoid 'down-washing' of flue gases on the leeward side of the chimney. Guidance on chimney design is usually based on minimum full-load efflux velocities of 6 $m \cdot s^{-1}$ for natural draught and 7.5 $m \cdot s^{-1}$ for fan forced or induced draught installations. Low efflux velocities may also cause inversion, whereby cold air enters the top of the chimney and flows downward, reducing chimney internal skin temperatures below the acid dew-point and causing acid smut emission. The maintenance of an adequate efflux velocity at all loads is difficult where one chimney serves more than one boiler, particularly if each boiler has high/low or modulating firing.

It may not always be possible to achieve efflux velocities of 6 $m \cdot s^{-1}$ on natural draught plant, particularly if the whole flue and chimney system is designed on this velocity basis, due to the excessive system resistance involved. In such cases, the system can be designed for a lower velocity and a nozzle fitted at the chimney outlet to increase efflux velocity to the extent that the excess available draught allows.

Flue corrosion and acid smut formation

Flue gases have a dew-point below which water vapour condenses. With sulphur bearing fuels, a second acid dew-point occurs at a higher temperature that depends on the type of fuel, amount of excess air, sulphur content and combustion intensity. The sulphur in the fuel is oxidised to SO_2 during the combustion process and a proportion of this is oxidised further to SO_3, with subsequent formation of sulphuric acid.

The peak rate of corrosion tends to occur some 30–40 °C below the acid dew-point and a dramatic increase in corrosion rate occurs below the water dew-point. Acid dew-points generally lie in the range 115–140 °C for the type of boiler plant used for heating but depend upon excess air used, flame temperature, sulphur content etc. A significant depression in acid dew-point temperature occurs where fuels have less than 0.5% sulphur content. It can also be reduced or eliminated by stoichiometric combustion conditions that can only be approached on very large plants.

A smut is an agglomeration of carbon particles resulting from a combination of stack solids and low temperature corrosion products. If the inner surface of any flue/chimney falls below the acid dew-point temperature of the waste gases, an acidic film forms on the surface. Stack solids adhere to this film and build up into loose layers, which are dislodged and ejected from the chimney as the firing rates change.

Flue/chimney area and siting

Where chimneys are oversized, or where more than one boiler is used with one flue/chimney, the inner chimney surface temperatures may fall below acid dew-point conditions, even with insulation applied. To avoid these problems, it is strongly recommended to install one flue/chimney per boiler, correctly sized for maximum practicable full load flue gas.

Chimney outlets should not be positioned such that air inlets into the building are on the leeward side of the chimney for the prevailing wind direction. Generally internal chimneys have less heat dissipation than free-standing units but where external chimneys are used they should, where possible, be positioned on the leeward side of the building or site, considering the prevailing wind direction.

When the flue/chimney area is reduced to give high flue gas velocities and a pressurised flue system, the construction of flues and chimneys must be carefully considered. With a mild steel flue/chimney system all joints should be welded or otherwise permanently sealed. Expansion should be accommodated by means of bellows type expansion joints and all explosion relief doors, clean out doors etc. should be fitted with the requisite joints to withstand pressurised flue conditions. Where concrete or brick chimneys with lining bricks are used, they should generally be sized to be under suction conditions unless the construction is specifically designed for operation under pressurised flue conditions. By combining several flues into one insulated envelope the cooling losses are reduced and the effective chimney plume height increased. The chimney outlet should be at a minimum height of 3 m above the highest point of the adjacent building roof level in order to limit wind pressure variations on the flue outlet and present the minimum face area to the prevailing wind. Chimney heights must comply with environmental legislation and the Building Regulations, see section 1.5.5.4. The sizing and height of chimneys and flues is considered in detail in Appendix 1.A2.

Cold air admission

The admission of cold air into the flue/chimney system reduces the flue gas temperatures and hence the available natural draught. Draught stabilisers deliberately introduce cold air to regulate the draught by this means. The use of draught stabilisers is not recommended when high sulphur fuels are used, as reduced flue gas temperature also produces corrosion and acid smut emissions.

Dampers for draught regulation should be fitted with safety interlocks to prevent firing against a closed damper. With high chimneys the damper should be arranged to close when the firing equipment is off-load, to isolate the boiler and limit cold air ingress to the system. This limits the cooling effect on the internal flue and chimney system, and the corrosion mechanism within the boiler gas-side heating surfaces.

Heat loss

To enable the correct chimney construction to be selected it is necessary to predict the minimum internal surface temperature likely to be obtained at the chimney terminal under all loads. An approximate value may be obtained using the following method. It should be noted that average values are used for some parameters and that radiation from the gases to the chimney is ignored in order to simplify calculations.

The rate of heat loss from the chimney or duct is given by:

$$\phi_c = U A \, (t_g - t_{ao}) \tag{1.36}$$

where ϕ_c is the heat loss rate (W), U is the overall thermal transmittance ($W \cdot m^{-2} \cdot K^{-1}$), A is the surface area (m^2), t_g is the mean waste gas temperature (°C) and t_{ao} is the outside air temperature (°C).

The overall thermal transmittance is given by:

$$\frac{1}{U} = \frac{1}{h_o} + \frac{l_1}{\lambda_1} + \frac{l_2}{\lambda_2} + ... \frac{1}{h_1} \quad (1.37)$$

where h_o is the external film coefficient (W·m^{-2}·K^{-1}), l_1 etc. is the thickness of chimney layer 1 etc. (m), λ_1 is the thermal conductivity of chimney layer 1 and h_i is the internal film coefficient (W·m^2·K^{-1}).

Values of film coefficients h_o and h_i are given in Figures 1.31 and 1.32.

The heat loss may also be deduced from:

$$\phi_c = q_m \, c_p \, (t_{g1} - t_{g2}) \quad (1.38)$$

where q_m is the mass flow rate of gases (kg·s^{-1}), c_p is the specific heat capacity at constant pressure of waste gases (J·kg^{-1}·K^{-1}), t_{g1} is the temperature of gases entering the bottom of the chimney (°C) and t_{g2} is the temperature of gases leaving the top of the chimney (°C).

Alternatively, the volume flow rate of waste gases (m^3·s^{-1}) may be used in conjunction with the specific heat capacity (J·m^{-3}·K^{-1}). The specific heat is usually taken to be 1.22 kJ·m^{-3}·K^{-1} at 200 °C.

For thermal equilibrium, equations 1.36 and 1.38 must give the same heat loss, so they may be equated, i.e:

$$U A \, (t_g - t_{ao}) = q_m \, c_p \, (t_{g1} - t_{g2}) \quad (1.39)$$

where t_g is given by:

$$t_g = \tfrac{1}{2} \, (t_{g1} + t_{g2}) \quad (1.40)$$

If the temperature of the waste gases entering the chimney or duct is known or estimated, the temperature of the gases leaving the chimney may be determined from equation 1.39. The minimum surface temperature may then be established from:

$$h_i \, (t_{g2} - t_{si}) = U \, (t_{g2} - t_{ao}) \quad (1.41)$$

where t_{si} is the temperature of the inside surface of chimney (°C).

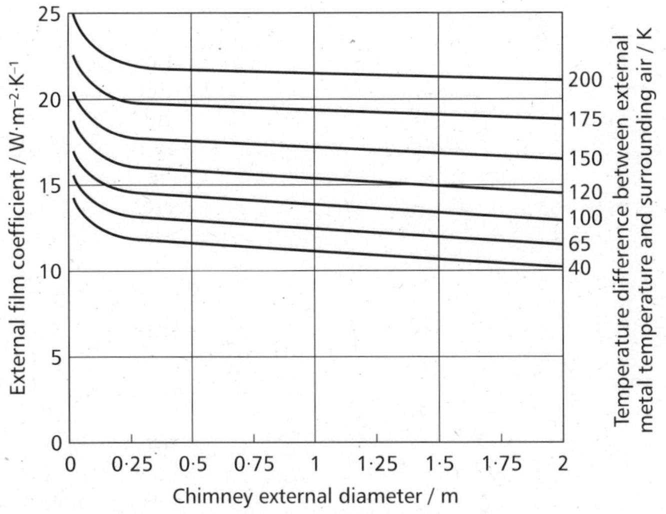

Figure 1.31 Values of external film coefficient

1.5.5.4 Compliance with Building Regulations and environmental legislation

Detailed guidance for the design of chimneys and flues for small appliances is given in Approved Document J[(8)] and BS 5440[(114)]. For higher rated outputs, the methods outlined in Appendix 1.A2 may be followed. Larger plant, which falls within the scope of the environmental legislation, should be assessed in accordance with HMIP Technical Guidance Note D1[(108)], see section 1.5.5.1. There also a general requirement to follow the manufacturer's instructions for installation and maintenance.

1.5.5.5 Draught production equipment

The draught necessary to move flue gases through the flue/chimney system and discharge them at a suitable velocity under specified firing rates can be produced in several ways, as described below.

Natural draught systems

Natural draught chimneys are generally favoured for the smaller range of open bottom cast-iron sectional boilers fitted with oil or gas burners and for suspended warm-air heaters. The natural draught in the stack has to overcome the boiler resistance to gas flow. A draught diverter is usually fitted in the flue next to the boiler outlet to maintain correct combustion conditions under all firing conditions. Flue gas velocities must be relatively low in order to reduce system resistances to a practical level, especially where chimneys are not of excessive height. As a result, chimney cross-sectional area is generally greater than for a forced draught system of similar boiler capacity.

Forced draught systems

In forced draught systems, the firing equipment is fitted with a fan to provide the necessary combustion air and to overcome the burner resistance and the boiler resistance to gas flow. The chimney draught required in these cases has to overcome less overall resistance than in the natural draught case and flue gas velocities can often be increased for a given chimney height. Forced draught is typically used with oil- or gas-fired packaged steel shell or cast iron sectional boilers or cabinet warm-air heaters.

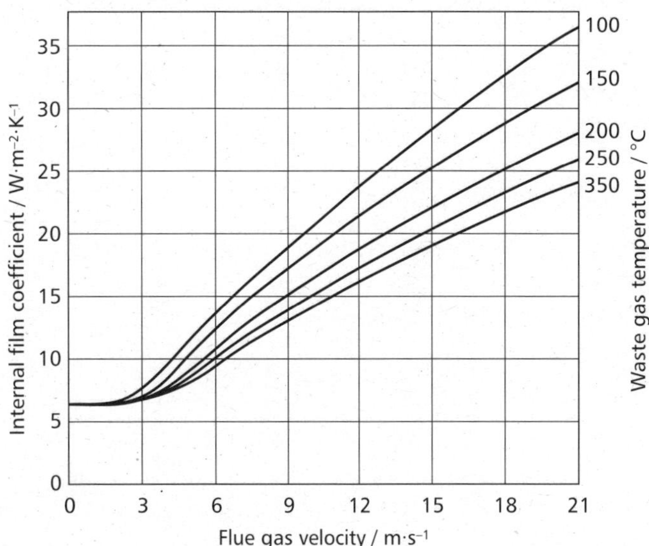

Figure 1.32 Values of internal film coefficient

Induced draught systems

A fan may be fitted at the boiler outlet to cater not only for the resistance of the firing equipment and the boiler but also, in certain instances, of the flue and chimney when burning at maximum rating. Examples of this type are found in coal-fired shell boilers and certain water tube boilers. Due to the fan power employed, draught is not dependent upon chimney buoyancy conditions and gas velocities can be increased depending upon the fan power requirement.

Balanced draught systems

A forced draught fan is fitted to provide all combustion air and overcome the resistance of air registers, or fuel bed. An induced draught fan is fitted at the boiler outlet to take the hot gases and overcome resistance of the boiler and the flues and chimney system. It is usual to fit a draught controller which, by damper control on the fans, maintains the balanced 'zero' condition in the combustion chamber. Examples of this type are found in most coal-fired boilers fitted with chain grate stokers and oil- and gas-fired water tube boilers. Due to the fan power employed high velocities can be used in the flue system, which again is not dependent upon chimney height. Generally such an arrangement is only applicable to larger installations.

Fan dilution systems

Fan dilution was developed for gas appliances in ground floor shops in mixed developments of offices, shops and flats. Fresh air is drawn in through a duct by a fan, mixed with the products of combustion, and finally discharged to the atmosphere with a carbon dioxide content of not more than 1%. In practice, fan dilution is only suitable for gas, which has very low sulphur content. A typical system is shown in Figure 1.33.

Fan dilution systems have been used extensively for launderettes, shops, restaurants, public houses etc. Many local authorities allow the discharge to be made at low level, above a shop doorway for instance, or into well ventilated areas with living or office accommodation above.

To comply with legislation:

- diluted exhaust must be discharged not less than 2 m (preferably 3 m) above ground level
- diluted exhaust must not be discharged into an enclosed courtyard
- the terminating louvre must be at least 3.54 m from the nearest building.

Fan dilution is normally used where natural draught flues are not practical. Ideally, the air inlet and discharge louvres should be positioned on the same wall or face of the building. Shielding is recommended if the louvres are likely to be subjected to strong wind forces. A damper or butterfly valve is fitted near the dilution air inlet to balance the installation. Protected metal sheet can be used for ducting as flue temperatures with this system are low, typically 65 °C.

Balanced flues

Balanced flues are used mainly for domestic gas-fired appliances and suspended warm-air heaters, but may also

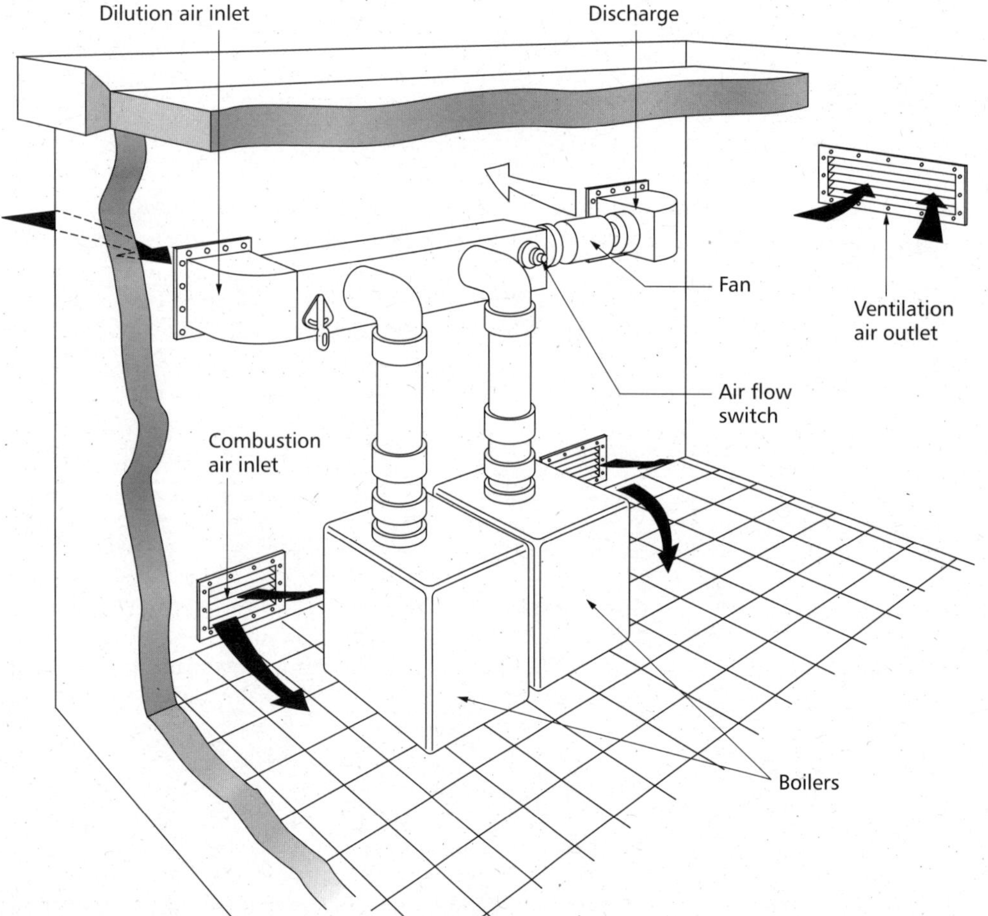

Figure 1.33 Typical fan dilution flue system

be used for low sulphur content fuels, e.g. kerosene. The appliance is of a room-sealed construction and is sited adjacent to an outside wall. The air for combustion is drawn from outside and the products of combustion are discharged using a common balanced flue terminal. The close proximity of air inlet and combustion products outlet makes the balanced flue terminal relatively insensitive to wind conditions and location.

At present, balanced flue boilers and heaters are available only in the lower output range but special designs are possible for larger outputs. Fan assistance can be used to reduce the size of the flue assembly and allow the appliance to be sited away from an external wall. Balanced flue terminals must be sited in accordance with Part J[111] of the Building Regulations.

SE-ducts and U-ducts

SE-ducts and U-ducts increase the scope for applying room-sealed gas appliances to multi-storey dwellings by making possible the connection of many appliances to a single flue system. An SE-duct is a single rising duct, with an opening at the bottom to provide fresh air for the appliance and an opening at the top to provide an outlet for combustion products. A U-duct is a pair of rising ducts joined at their base and open at the top, one to provide fresh air and the other to provide an outlet for combustion products. Only room-sealed appliances may be connected to SE-ducts and U-ducts and connection should be made in compliance with guidance obtained from the manufacturers of the appliances.

Branched flue systems

The branched flue system for gas appliances, sometimes called the shunt system, is designed for venting appliances of the conventional flue type. It represents considerable space-saving over venting each appliance with an individual flue. For further information on conditions and sizing see BS 5440[114].

1.5.5.6 Chimney linings

Chimneys should have internal surfaces that:

- have sufficient thermal insulation to maintain inner skin temperatures above the acid dew-point during normal running operations
- are chemically resistant to acids and flue gas deposits generally
- resist absorption of moisture and its re-evaporation
- can withstand fairly rapid internal gas temperature changes
- have low thermal capacity to limit heat up time
- can be installed, inspected and replaced economically.

Flexible steel liners may be used to line existing chimneys but Building Regulations do not permit their use in new masonry chimneys.

1.5.5.7 Chimney construction

Stainless steel

Stainless steel chimneys are available with either single-skin construction or with a twin wall in diameters up to 600 mm. Twin wall types may have either an air gap or insulation.

Steel

Steel chimneys are either of single or multi-flue construction, the outer windshield being designed to cater for the required wind pressures under either guyed or self-supporting design conditions. The structural requirements are covered by BS 4076[115].

With single flue construction a simple method of insulation consists of applying externally a cladding of 1.6 mm polished aluminium sheet located 6 mm from the outer mild steel chimney surface by means of heat resisting spacers at 1.2 m intervals. This provides a 6 mm stagnant air space for insulation, assisted by the reflectivity of the polished aluminium.

With high sulphur fuels and chimneys having a gas volume turndown of more than 2.5 times with modulating or two-position firing equipment, this insulation is insufficient for chimney heights above 10–12 m. A mineral wool insulation at least 50 mm thick should be substituted for the 6 mm air space. With multi-flue construction the inner flues are placed within a windshield structurally calculated for wind pressures etc. as before. The internal flues are either insulated with mineral wool, or the whole space around the flues filled with a loose insulation that can be pumped into place. Thermal expansion problems must be considered in the design and provision made for replacing any one flue at a future date.

A similar mild steel multiple flue system can be installed within a concrete structural outer shell, again providing facilities for subsequent replacement.

Brick

Brick flues/chimneys should always be lined internally. For solid or liquid fuels the lining may be gunned solid insulation refractory or diatomaceous earth type insulation. The insulation standard should not be less than the equivalent of 115 mm thickness of diatomaceous earth for flue gas temperatures up to 315 °C.

Where flue gas conditions dictate (e.g. low temperature, high sulphur and moisture) an acid resisting brick inner lining, backed by a lining of insulation material, can be used. Careful attention must be paid to the lining construction and the type of jointing mortar used to prevent flue gases leaking through behind the lining and setting up corrosive conditions.

The effect of pressurised operation on these linings is questioned and for general operation such chimneys should be operated under suction or balanced draught conditions. They must be carefully designed by a competent structural engineer who is aware of the combined physical/chemical effects involved.

Concrete construction

Similar comments to those on brick construction apply, but the insulation thickness should generally not be less than the equivalent of 150 mm diatomaceous earth in order to limit the interface concrete temperature to a maximum of 50 °C under normal boiler plant operating conditions.

Ventilated chimneys

Here a ventilated air space is situated between the inner lining and outer chimney shell. The construction should not be used in general with high sulphur fuels due to the cooling effect created and the consequent danger of acid dew-point and acid smut emission.

1.5.6 Corrosion in boilers, flues and chimneys

1.5.6.1 Mechanisms of corrosion

The most common cause of corrosion in boilers and chimneys is the presence of water vapour and oxides of sulphur following combustion of fuels containing sulphur.

When any fuel containing hydrogen and sulphur is burned, water vapour and sulphur dioxide (SO_2) are produced. A small proportion of the SO_2 is further oxidised to sulphur trioxide (SO_3), which immediately combines with water vapour to produce sulphuric acid. This will condense on any surface below the acid dew-point temperature, giving rise to corrosion. The acid dew-point is the temperature at which the combustion gases become saturated with acid vapour and, when cooled without change in pressure, condense as a mist.

The acid dew-point varies with the type of acid and its concentration. Further cooling of the gases to the water dew-point may produce corrosive effects even more serious than those produced at higher (i.e. more concentrated) acid dew-points. During normal operation it is unlikely that the water dew-point (about 38 °C) will be reached but this may occur for intermittently operated plant. When the system operation is such that the water circulating temperatures can fall to 38 °C, condensation is inevitable.

In addition to sulphur, other constituents such as chlorine and nitrogen react to give acidic gases which can combine with water vapour and thereby cause corrosion if allowed to condense on cooler metal surfaces.

In boilers that are shut-down, flue deposits become damp because of their hygroscopic nature and produce acid sulphates which are likely to cause corrosion. Acid corrosion is less likely to occur with coal rather than residual fuel oils, for the following reasons:

— the average sulphur content of coal is generally lower than that of residual fuel oils and about one tenth is retained in the ash

— the hydrogen content of coal is lower than that of other fuels, therefore the amount of water vapour produced during combustion is also lower

— the small amounts of fly ash in the flue gases tend to absorb free SO_2 and thus reduce the production of corrosive acid.

The combination of less water vapour and lower levels of SO_2 means that lower gas temperatures may be used, resulting in a corresponding gain in plant efficiency. On large, well operated and maintained plant, the production of SO_2 may be minimised by controlling the excess oxygen in the combustion zone. However, precise control is necessary and this is unlikely to be achieved on small plants.

1.5.6.2 Prevention of corrosion in boilers

During boiler shut-down in the summer months, all surfaces should be cleaned of all partially burned fuel and ash, and dampers should be left open to ensure that air is drawn through the boiler. Lime washing of all accessible surfaces may be beneficial and, where good air circulation can be obtained, trays of a moisture absorbing material, such as quicklime, should be provided.

For plant in operation, the system should be designed so that the average boiler water temperature does not fall below about 50 °C. This helps to ensure that the water dew-point is not exceeded. For details of control of boiler systems, see section 1.5.1.2 and CIBSE Guide H[(63)]. Under no circumstances should the boiler thermostat be used as a control thermostat to reduce the flow temperature in a heating system.

Low temperature hot water boiler corrosion usually occurs at the smoke box prior to the flue connection, and is often referred to as 'back-end corrosion'. Maintaining the return water temperature above 50 °C can provide protection from this type of corrosion. At start-up, a thermostatically controlled bypass between the flow and return connections can be used to blend a small proportion of hot flow water with cooler return water. Circulation is achieved either by a small shunt pump or by connecting the flow end of the bypass pipe to the primary pump discharge and controlling the flow/return blend through a three-port valve. In each case, the bypass is isolated automatically when the system return temperature reaches the pre-set minimum.

1.5.6.3 Prevention of flue corrosion

To minimise the risk of corrosion, the following points should be noted.

— Sufficient insulation should be provided to maintain inner skin temperature above the acid dew-point during normal operation.

— The flue or chimney lining should be chemically resistant to acids and flue gas deposits.

— The flue gas velocity must be sufficiently high to prevent precipitation of acids and deposits on internal flue linings.

— Avoid abrupt changes of direction in flue and stack.

The flue connection from the boiler should rise to the stack and be kept as short as possible.

1.6 Fuels

1.6.1 Classification and properties of fuels

1.6.1.1 Gaseous fuels

The main gaseous fuels are broadly classified as natural gas and liquefied petroleum gases (LPG). Natural gas consists predominantly of methane and is delivered by pipeline. LPG includes propane and butane, and is delivered as a liquid contained in a pressurised vessel. The key properties of the main gaseous fuels are shown in Table 1.23.

Wobbe number

The Wobbe number (W) is designed to indicate the heat produced at a burner when fuelled by a particular gas, and is defined as:

$$W = h_g / d^{0.5} \quad (1.42)$$

where W is the Wobbe number ($MJ \cdot m^{-3}$), h_g is the gross calorific value ($MJ \cdot m^{-3}$) and d is the relative density of the gas (relative to air at standard temperature and pressure).

Supply/working pressure

Natural gas supplies are regulated at the metering point to an outlet pressure of 2100 Pa (21 mbar). This pressure may be reduced further at the appliance to provide the required pressure at the burner. LPG is supplied via tanks or cylinders, regulated to a pressure of 3700 Pa (37 mbar) for propane and 2800 Pa (28 mbar) for butane. This pressure is not normally reduced at the appliance.

Landfill and sewage gas

Landfill gas is collected from wells inserted in land-fill sites, often complementing measures to prevent hazards arising from the escape of gas. It typically consists of between 40 and 60% methane by volume with the remainder mostly carbon dioxide and traces of many other gases. The calorific value of landfill gas is in the range 15 to 25 $MJ \cdot m^{-3}$, depending on its methane content.

Landfill gas is mostly used without processing, other than the removal of moisture and dust. Because of its low calorific value it is relatively expensive to transport and is most suitable for heat generation when it can be produced close to a heat load, which favoured its early exploitation for brick kilns adjacent to clay pits used for land fill. In other cases, it is used to generate electricity from gas turbines or reciprocating engines. The life expectancy of gas production from landfill sites is typically 15 to 30 years.

Sewage gas is produced from digestion of sewage sludge. Some of the gas produced is used to maintain optimum temperature for the digestion process. It is economic in many cases to use combined heat and power generation in this situation, and to export the surplus power to the grid.

1.6.1.2 Liquid fuels

Oil fuels

BS 2869[116] contains specifications for various classes of liquid fuels designated by the letters A to G. The fuels commonly used for heating are Class C2 (kerosene or burning oil), Class D (gas oil), Class E (light fuel oil), Class F (medium fuel oil) and Class G (heavy fuel oil). The key properties of these fuels are shown in Table 1.24. Further information can be found in CIBSE Guide C[57], section 5.5.2, including graphs showing the kinematic viscosity of fuel oils at different temperatures.

Liquid bio-fuels

Fuels may be produced from crops grown specifically for the purpose. Historically, the principal fuel crop has been coppice wood for charcoal production. In recent decades, interest has been focussed on the production of liquid and gaseous fuels suitable for use in transport. The process and the crops used determine the type of fuel produced. Thermal processing (by combustion, gasification or pyrolysis) is best suited to dry materials. Anaerobic fermentation is better suited to wet bio-mass materials, which can yield both methane rich bio-gas and liquid fuels, according to the type of fermentation used. Ethanol has been produced commercially from sugar cane, notably in Brazil. In Europe, rape seed oil is used to produce bio-diesel, which has very

Table 1.23 Properties of commercial gas supplies at standard temperature and pressure

Property	Natural gas	Commercial propane	Commercial butane
Density relative to air	0.60	1.45 to 1.55	1.9 to 2.10
Gross calorific value ($MJ \cdot m^{-3}$)	38.7	93	122
Wobbe number ($MJ \cdot m^{-3}$)	45 to 55	73.5 to 87.5	73.5 to 87.5
Supply/working pressure (Pa)	1750 to 2750	3700	2800
Stoichiometric air to gas volume ratio	9.73	24	30
Flame speed ($m \cdot s^{-1}$)	0.43	0.47	0.38
Flammability limits (% gas in air)	5–15	2–10	2–9
Boiling point (°C)	—	−45	0
Latent heat of vaporisation ($kJ \cdot kg^{-1}$)	—	357	370
Flame temperature (°C)	1930	1950	—
Ignition temperature (°C)	704	530	470

Table 1.24 Key properties of typical petroleum fuels

Property	Class C2	Class D	Class E	Class F	Class G
Density at 15 °C (kg·m^{-3})	803	850	940	970	980
Minimum closed flash point (°C)	38	60	66	66	66
Kinematic viscosity (mm^2·s^{-1}) at 40 °C	1.0 to 2.0	1.5 to 5.5	—	—	—
Kinematic viscosity (mm^2·s^{-1}) at 100 °C	—	—	≤8.2	≤20.0	≤40.0
Maximum pour point (°C)	—	—	–6	24	30
Gross calorific value (MJ·kg^{-1})	46.4	45.5	42.5	41.8	42.7
Net calorific value (MJ·kg^{-1})	43.6	42.7	40.1	39.5	40.3
Maximum sulphur content by mass (%)	0.2	0.2	3.2	3.5	3.5
Mean specific heat 0–100 °C (MJ·kg^{-1})	2.1	2.06	1.93	1.89	1.89

similar properties to petroleum-derived diesel and can be used in existing engines without significant modification.

1.6.1.3 Solid fuels

Coal is classified according to its chemical composition and graded according to size. CIBSE Guide C[57], section 5.5 gives the properties of numerous varieties of coal, including moisture, ash and sulphur content. Gross calorific value ranges from 24 to 34 MJ·kg^{-1}.

Municipal waste may be burnt unprocessed, with heat extracted or electricity generated as part of the incineration process. Alternatively it may be used to produce refuse-derived fuel pellets, which may be used to fire some types of boiler plant. It has a calorific value about two thirds of that of coal and produces around 50% more ash.

Wood fuels are of interest because their use can result in a net decrease in greenhouse gas emissions. Forestry waste results from the normal processes of forestry management, which is has the principal objective of maximising the value of the timber crop. Thinning and harvesting leave residues, consisting of branches and tree tops which have no value as timber and, if not used for fuel, would be discarded. Waste wood is also available from industrial sources, particularly from saw-milling and furniture making. Its use as a fuel has a net benefit in greenhouse gas emissions, both by avoiding the need to burn a fossil fuel and by avoiding the production of methane that would result from decomposition on the forest floor or in landfill.

Wood fuel may be produced by growing arable coppice specifically for fuel production. The carbon dioxide released on combustion will have been sequestered during growth and there is no net contribution to CO_2 emissions. Notwithstanding its environmental advantages, wood is a low quality fuel, with a calorific value of around 19 MJ·kg^{-1} when dry and only around 10 MJ·kg^{-1} at the typical moisture content (55%) when harvested.

Straw is also used as a fuel, particularly since the phasing out of straw-burning on fields in the early 1990s. It is burnt in high temperature boilers and used to supply heat and hot water, usually on a fairly small scale.

1.6.1.4 Electricity

Electricity is the most versatile form in which energy is delivered and may serve almost any end-use of energy, including those for which fuels are consumed directly. However, the high quality and versatility of electricity must be seen in the context of its high cost, which reflects the high primary energy input to electricity generation.

The *Digest of UK Energy Statistics*[117] shows that the generation mix for electricity in the UK has changed radically since 1992, when gas-fired power stations began to come on stream, displacing coal-fired plant. In 1991, 65% of all fuel used for generating electricity connected to the public electricity supply system was coal and less than 1% gas; in 2000, these proportions had changed to 33% and 35% respectively. When account is taken of the higher efficiency of gas generation, the proportion of electricity supplied from gas generation is even higher, at 39% (c.f. 31% from coal generation). Nuclear power accounted for 21% of electricity supplied in 2000, a proportion that has not changed substantially over recent years. Hydro-electricity contributed only 1.3%, although pumped-storage hydro-electricity stations perform an important role in balancing system loads.

The shift towards gas generation has several important implications for UK electricity, apart from fuel supply considerations. Gas produces negligible emissions of sulphur dioxide to the atmosphere, and reduced concentrations of other atmospheric pollutants. As a result, UK sulphur dioxide emissions from power stations have declined by around two-thirds since 1990, contributing to a greater than 50% reduction in UK emissions from all sources. The amount of carbon dioxide released per unit of heat energy obtained from gas is also lower than for coal. The current generation of gas-fired power stations using combined cycle technology are more efficient than coal-fired stations. The overall effect is that the gas generated electricity is less than half as carbon intensive as coal generated electricity. Coefficients for carbon dioxide emissions of fuels are given in section 1.6.2 below.

1.6.1.5 Renewable electricity eneration

In addition to the use of bio-fuels described above, there are many possibilities for generating electricity directly from renewable sources of energy based on solar radiation, wind, tides, waves, hydropower and geothermal heat. The UK lacks the terrain to permit further exploitation of large-scale hydroelectric power, but there are numerous opportunities for small-scale exploitation. The UK also has very limited opportunities for exploiting geothermal power but has considerable resources for wind, wave and tidal power. A wide ranging assessment of the opportunities for renewable energy in the UK was undertaken by the Energy Technology Support Unit[118] (ETSU) in the early 1990s.

The *Digest of UK Energy Statistics*[117] shows that the UK produced 2.8% of its electricity from renewable sources in 2000, of which just under half was by large-scale hydro-electricity stations. The remainder came largely from combustion of bio-fuels, led by landfill gas and refuse combustion. Wind power was the largest contributor other than large-scale hydro-electricity and bio-fuels but amounted to only 0.26% of total electricity produced.

Although the contribution to electricity generation by renewable sources is small at present, the government has ambitious targets for expanding it to reach 5% in 2003 and 10% in 2010. In this context it should be noted that renewable generating capacity doubled in the four year period between 1996 and 2000. In the short term much of this expansion will come from wind and land-fill gas.

1.6.2 Factors affecting fuel choice

1.6.2.1 Fuel prices

The price of fuel remains a very important factor affecting fuel choice and a strong determinant of life-cycle cost. Current energy prices and recent price trends may be obtained from the Department of Trade and Industry (DTI)[119]. Separate tables are given for domestic and industrial prices.

Figure 1.34 shows how industrial fuel prices changed during the decade to 2000. Most prices were relatively stable and, when allowance is made for inflation during the decade, declined in real terms. The most obvious feature of the graph is the high price of electricity compared to fuels consumed at the point of use, which serves to illustrate why electricity should be reserved for purposes in which its special advantages are needed. This normally precludes its use as a principal source of space heating, although it can be economical for localised and occasional use, particularly as radiant spot heating. Coal and gas remained broadly similar in price throughout the period shown, while heavy fuel oil increased significantly at the end of the decade as the price of crude oil rose.

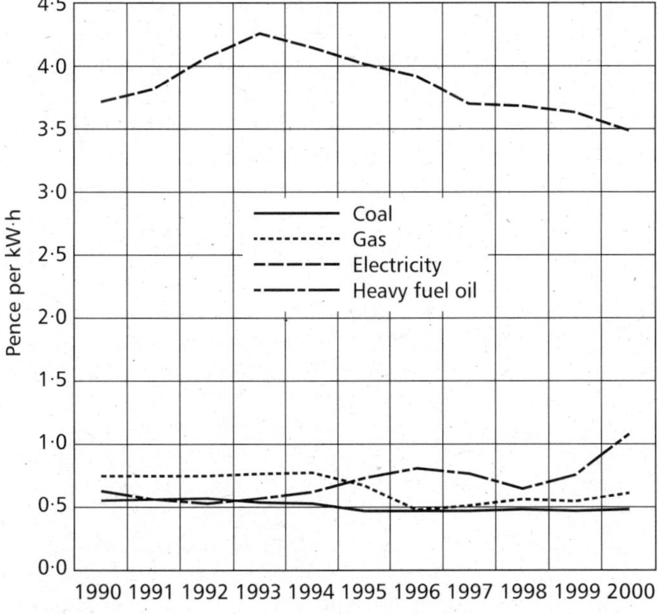

Figure 1.34 Industrial fuel prices during the 1990s in cash terms

1.6.2.2 Environmental impact

The use of energy affects the environment both at the point of use and indirectly, through the upstream activities associated with production, conversion and delivery. It can have detrimental impacts locally on air quality and acid deposition and, on a global scale, on stratospheric ozone depletion and greenhouse gas concentrations in the atmosphere, which is widely recognised as a likely cause of climate change. As heating accounts for around three-quarters of all energy used in buildings and more than a third of all final energy use in the UK, it is a very significant contributor to the total environmental impact from energy use.

The *Digest of UK Energy Statistics*[117] identifies the main sources of CO_2 emissions arising from fuel combustion: 28% from power stations; 24% from industry; 22% from transport and 15% from the domestic sector. This reveals the high CO_2 emissions associated with electricity, which should be taken into account when considering its final use. There are also some additional emissions of CO_2 during the production of gas, oil and solid fuels, which should be similarly taken account of although they are much less significant. Table 1.25 shows average CO_2 emissions, expressed in terms of carbon, attributable to each unit of energy used in the UK, taking account of upstream and overhead effects. This may be used to compare alternative options for fuel and shows the advantage of natural gas over other fuels. Electricity obtained from the public supply has an emission factor of about two and a half times that of gas.

Table 1.25 Carbon emission factors for UK in 2000–2005[117]

Fuel	Carbon emission per unit of delivered energy/ kgC·(kW·h)$^{-1}$
Natural gas	0.053
LPG	0.068
Gas oil/burning oil	0.074
Coal	0.086
Electricity (average of public supply)	0.113

1.6.2.3 Other factors affecting fuel choice

Availability of a mains supply of natural gas is a key factor in the choice of fuel, given its advantages of clean combustion and low price. In remote areas, the absence of mains gas normally leaves a choice between oil, LPG and solid fuel, all of which require significant space for storage and access for delivery. Solid fuel is often the lowest in price but has greater maintenance costs than oil or LPG. LPG may be cleanest and most convenient but is generally significantly more expensive than heating oil. Although expensive, electricity may be the best choice where heating requirements are very small, especially if it can be used with a ground source heat pump.

1.6.3 Handling and storage of fuels

1.6.3.1 Natural gas

Pressures

Natural gas is normally supplied to consumers at gauge pressures up to 5 kPa and regulated to a nominal 2.1 kPa at the gas meter before feeding to appliances. Pressure losses in pipes should not be more than 100 Pa under maximum flow conditions. Tables giving pressure losses for natural gas in steel and copper pipes are given in section 4.7 of CIBSE Guide C[(57)].

Higher operating pressures are needed for large commercial and industrial plants, where burners are fan assisted or pressurised. This may be obtained from a pressure booster, which can also allow the use of smaller pipework to appliances. The gas supplier must be consulted before fitting a pressure booster, which must include protection against disturbance to the gas supply or damage to the meter by excessive suction or pressure. This is normally achieved using a low pressure cut-off switch and a non-return valve on the gas supply side of the booster and a pressure relief by-pass around the compressor.

Pipework

Gas distribution pipework in domestic premises should comply with BS 6891[(120)] and relevant parts of the Gas Safety (Installation and Use) Regulations[(121)]. In particular, pipes must:

- (*a*) be protected from failure caused by movement when installed in walls and floors
- (*b*) not be installed within the cavity of a cavity wall
- (*c*) not be installed under the foundations of a building or a wall
- (*d*) not be installed in an unventilated shaft, duct or void
- (*e*) take the shortest practicable route through a solid structure and be enclosed in a gas-tight sleeve
- (*f*) be electrically bonded, including temporary bonding during modification.

Steel pipes should comply with BS 1387[(122)] and copper pipes with BS EN 1057[(123)].

CIBSE Guide C[(57)], section 4.7, includes tables giving pressure drop per unit length for natural gas in pipes and pressure loss factors for components such as tees, elbows and valves.

Safety

All combustion installations using gas must comply with the Gas Safety (Installation and Use) Regulations[(121)], which cover the safe installation of gas fittings, appliances and flues. They also require that installation work be undertaken by a member of a class of persons approved by the Health and Safety Executive (HSE); in practice, that means they must be registered with CORGI, the Council for Registered Gas Installers. The main requirements of the Gas Safety (Installation and Use) Regulations are outlined below but for more detailed information reference should be made to the Health and Safety Commission's Approved Code of Practice. For public, commercial and industrial buildings, workplace legislation[(124)] is also relevant.

The Gas Safety (Installation and Use) Regulations control all aspects of the installation, maintenance and use of systems burning gas (including natural gas and LPG). The text of the Regulations and guidance on how to comply with them are contained in Health and Safety Executive (HSE) Approved Code of Practice L56: *Safety in the installation and use of gas systems and appliances*[(125)]. The detailed guidance applies principally to small appliances but the similar requirements apply generally.

1.6.3.2 Liquid petroleum gas (LPG)

Storage

LPG installations are subject to legislation enforced by the Health and Safety Executive. For small storage installations, in which the tank stand in the open air, it is possible to show compliance by following the guidance given in Approved Document J[(8)] of the Building Regulations and Part 1 of LP Gas Association Code of Practice[(126)].

LPG (propane) is stored at a pressure of 690 kPa at 15 °C, and within the range 200–900 kPa as conditions vary. LPG storage tanks should be installed in the open, not enclosed by a pit or bund, and adequately separated from buildings, boundaries and fixed sources of ignition. Drains, gullies and cellar hatches close to tanks should be protected from gas entry. Reduced separation is permitted when a fire-wall is built between a tank and a building, boundary or source of ignition. Fire walls should contain no openings, have fire resistance of least 60 minutes and be at least as high as the pressure relief valve on the storage vessel.

Where LPG is stored in cylinders, provision should be made to enable cylinders to stand upright, secured by straps or chains against a wall outside the building in a well ventilated position at ground level. LPG storage vessels and LPG fired appliances fitted with automatic ignition devices or pilot lights must not be installed in cellars or basements.

An industrial LPG storage installation usually consists of one or more tanks mounted horizontally on concrete foundations. The general requirements are as for domestic storage with requirements for tanks to be sited clear of buildings to avoid the risk of overheating should a building catch fire. Table 1.26 gives installation distances for tanks of various sizes. Where supplies are to be delivered by road, consideration must be given to access for vehicles.

Pipework

Pipework for LPG is similar to that for natural gas but allowance must be made for the higher density of LPG. Section 4.3.3 of CIBSE Guide C[(57)] gives the Colbrook-White equation, from which pressure drops for LPG in flowing in pipes may be calculated.

Table 1.26 Installation distances for LPG storage tanks

Tank capacity / m³	Minimum distance / m	
	From buildings	Between vessels
<0.45	0*	0.6
0.45 to 2.25	3	0.9
2.25	7.5	0.9
>9	15	1.5

* A tank of less than 0.45 m³ capacity may be sited close to a building, allowing space for maintenance, with a minimum distance of 2.5 m from the tank filing point to any opening in the building

1.6.3.3 Oil

Storage

The storage of oil in tanks with a capacity of up to 3500 litres is covered by Part J of the Buildings Regulations[111]. Requirement J5 seeks to minimise the risk of fire from fuel igniting in the event of fire in adjacent buildings or premises by controlling their construction and separation from buildings and the boundary of the premises on which they stand. It applies to all fixed oil storage tanks with a capacity greater than 90 litres. Requirement J6 seeks to reduce the risk of pollution arising from the escape of oil and applies to tanks serving private dwellings up to a capacity of 3500 litres.

Guidance on compliance with requirements J5 and J6 for Class C2 and Class D is given in Approved Document J[8] of the Building Regulations. It cites BS 5410-1[127] as a source of guidance, supplemented by specific guidance on fire protection and prevention of fuel spillage. In particular, it recommends fire resistant fuel pipework protected by a fire valve system complying with the recommendations given in BS 5410-1, sections 8.2 and 8.3.

Larger installations must also comply with Requirement J5, for which Approved Document J states that advice should be sought from the relevant Fire Authority. Although not covered by Requirement J6, larger tanks serving buildings other than private dwellings are likely to be subject to the Control of Pollution (Oil Storage) Regulations 2001[128]. The specification of oil storage tanks is covered by BS 799-5[129].

Where supplies are to be delivered by road, consideration must be given to access for vehicles.

Temperatures for storage of liquid fuels

Fuel oils of classes E to H require heating to provide the recommended storage temperatures, which are shown in Table 1.27. Heating may be provided by steam or hot water coils, or by electric immersion heaters. It is usual to maintain tanks at the temperatures given in column 2 of Table 1.27 and raise the temperature further by a separate outflow heater to the level shown in column 3.

Class C and D fuels do not generally require heating, but some class D fuels may require heat to ensure an adequate flow of oil; both tank heating and trace heating on lagged pipes may be used to maintain temperatures in the range 0 to 5 °C in that instance.

Pipework

Single pipe delivery is suitable for class C and D fuels, normally with a positive head at the suction side of the boiler fuel pump. Class E fuel oil should be supplied from a heated storage tank via a circulating ring main, with further preheating of the fuel within the burner before feeding to the atomiser. Class F and G oils require an outflow heater to raise the oil to pumping temperature and trace heating applied to the ring main pipework and other components.

Table 1.27 Storage temperatures for fuel oils

Class	Minimum temperature / °C	
	Storage	Outflow
E	10	10
F	25	30
G	40	50
H	45	55

1.6.3.4 Solid fuels

Storage

Solid fuel is normally delivered by road vehicle and unloaded by tipping or by conveyer. Access for delivery should be designed to suit the type of delivery vehicle expected, taking account of turning circle and space for tipper operation.

Table 1.28 gives the bulk density and specific volume of various types of coal, which may be used to design storage capacity. A minimum capacity equivalent to at least 100 hours operation at full output is recommended. The usable capacity of a bunker depends upon the methods by which fuel is delivered and extracted from the bunker and may be less than the nominal volume. Rectangular bunkers with flat bases are difficult to empty completely without manual trimming. Bunkers with hopper bottoms empty completely but require vehicle access at a high level if they are to be filled by tipper. Bunker bases should be designed to suit the method of coal extraction, avoiding dead volumes that fail to leave the bunker. Low friction linings for outlet chutes may assist free flow and aid extraction.

Bunkers should be covered by grid screens, which are sized to prevent the entry of large objects that could damage the coal extraction equipment. A 100 mm grid is usual, strong enough to support the weight of operators or, if necessary, vehicles.

Table 1.28 Bulk density and specific volume of various coal types

Coal type	Size / mm	Bulk density / tonne·m^{-3}	Specific volume / m^3·tonne^{-1}
Graded	>12.5	0.80	1.25
Dry smalls	<12.5	0.83	1.20
Wet smalls	<12.5	0.88	1.14

Safety

Hazards can arise from spontaneous combustion and explosions caused by dust or methane. Monitoring of carbon monoxide levels and minimising storage volume during the summer shutdown period can help to avoid spontaneous combustion. Dust and gas explosions arise within certain concentrations, which may be monitored and controlled. Specialist advice should be sought on the prevention of explosions in solid fuel storage.

Fuel handling

Screw conveyors and elevators are used to raise coal to mechanical stoker hoppers for small boilers; overhead monorail, skip hoist and pneumatic handlers are also used. For large boiler plant, chain-and-bucket and belt-and-bucket elevators are used, as are belt, drag-link and screw conveyors.

Ash extraction and disposal

Fully automatic ash removal is available on some boilers but on others ash and clinker must be removed by hand. Various methods are available for ash handling, including screw and vibratory conveyors and vacuum systems.

For large plant, the ash may be sold directly for use as a construction material. If it is to be used for block making, it should meet the requirements described in BS 3797[130]. For smaller plant, ash is likely to removed as part of the general waste removal service, after which it may be disposed of in land fill or supplied to the construction industry.

References

1 BS EN ISO 7730: 1995: *Moderate thermal environments. Determination of PMV and PPD indices and specification of the conditions for thermal comfort* (London: British Standards Institution) (1995)

2 *Whole Life Costing: A client's guide* Construction Clients Forum 2002 (London: Confederation of Construction Clients) (2000)

3 *Conservation of fuel and power* The Building Regulations 2000 Approved Documents L1 and L2 (London: The Stationery Office) (2001)

4 *Technical standards for compliance with the Building Standards (Scotland) Regulations 1990 (as amended)* (Edinburgh: Scottish Executive) (2001)

5 *Amendments to technical booklets* The Building Regulations (Northern Ireland) 2000 Amendments booklet AMD2 (Belfast: The Stationery Office) (2000) (Republic of Ireland Building Regulation *Technical Guidance Document L* covers energy requirements in buildings in Ireland.)

6 *Ventilation* The Building Regulations 2000 Approved Document F (London: The Stationery Office) (2001) (Republic of Ireland Building Regulations *Technical Guidance Document F* covers ventilation requirements for buildings in Ireland.)

7 The Boiler (Efficiency) Regulations 1993 Statutory Instrument 1993 No. 3083 and The Boiler (Efficiency)(Amendment) Regulations 1994 Statutory Instrument 1994 No. 3083 (London: Her Majesty's Stationery Office) (1993 and 1994) (In the Republic of Ireland the EU Boiler Directive is implemented by the European Communities (Efficiency requirements for hot water boilers fired with liquid and gaseous fuels) Regulations 1994.)

8 *Combustion appliances and fuel storage systems* The Building Regulations 2000 Approved Document J (London: The Stationery Office) (2001) (Republic of Ireland Building Regulations *Technical Guidance Document J* covers combustion appliances in Ireland.)

9 Construction (Design and Management) Regulations 1994 Statutory Instrument 1994 No. 3140 (London: Her Majesty's Stationery Office) (1994)

10 *CDM Regulations — Work sector guidance for designers* CIRIA Report 166 (London: Construction Industry Research and Information Association) (1997)

11 Health and Safety at Work etc. Act 1974 (London: Her Majesty's Stationery Office) (1974)

12 *Energy demands and targets for heated and ventilated buildings* CIBSE Building Energy Code 1; *Energy demands for air conditioned buildings* CIBSE Building Energy Code 2 (London: Chartered Institution of Building Services Engineers) (1999)

13 Baldwin R, Yates A, Howard N and Rao S *BREEAM 98 for Offices* BRE Report BR350 (Garston: Building Research Establishment) (1998) (versions also available for housing, industrial units and retail premises)

14 *The Government's Standard Assessment Procedure for Energy Rating of Dwellings* (Garston: Building Research Establishment) (2001) (www.projects.bre.co.uk/sap2001/)

15 *National Home Energy Rating* (Milton Keynes: National Energy Foundation)

16 *HVAC strategies for well-insulated airtight buildings* CIBSE TM29 (London: Chartered Institution of Building Services Engineers) (2002)

17 *Energy efficiency in buildings* CIBSE Guide F (London: Chartered Institution of Building Services Engineers) (1998)

18 *The designer's guide to energy-efficient buildings for industry* Energy Efficiency Best Practice Programme Good Practice Guide GPG303 (Garston: Energy Efficiency Best Practice Programme) (2000)

19 *Environmental design* CIBSE Guide A (London: Chartered Institution of Building Services Engineers) (1999)

20 *Natural ventilation in non-domestic buildings* CIBSE Applications Manual AM10 (London: Chartered Institution of Building Services Engineers) (1997)

21 *Environmental factors affecting office worker performance: review of evidence* CIBSE TM24 (London: Chartered Institution of Building Services Engineers) (1999)

22 Barnard N, Concannon P and Jaunzens D *Modelling the performance of thermal mass* BRE Information Paper IP6/01 (Garston: Building Research Establishment) (2001)

23 Braham D, Barnard N and Jaunzens D *Thermal mass in office buildings* BRE Digest 454 Parts 1 and 2 (Garston: Building Research Establishment) (2001)

24 BS EN ISO 6946: 1997: *Building components and building elements. Thermal resistance and thermal transmittance. Calculation method* (London: British Standards Institution) (1997)

25 BS EN ISO 10211-1: 1996: *Thermal bridges in building construction. Calculation of heat flows and surface temperatures*: Part 1: *General method* (London: British Standards Institution) (1996)

26 BS EN ISO 10211-2: 2001: *Thermal bridges in building construction. Calculation of heat flows and surface temperatures*: Part 2: *Linear thermal bridges* (London: British Standards Institution) (2001)

27 BS EN ISO 13370: 1998: *Thermal performance of buildings. Heat transfer via the ground: Calculation methods* (London: British Standards Institution) (1998)

28 BS EN ISO 10077: *Thermal performance of windows, doors and shutters. Calculation of thermal transmittance*: Part 1: 2000 *Simplified methods* (London: British Standards Institution) (2000)

29 *Testing buildings for air leakage* CIBSE TM23 (London: Chartered Institution of Building Services Engineers) (2000)

30 BS EN 13829: 2001 *Thermal performance of buildings. Determination of air permeability of buildings. Fan pressurization method* (London: British Standards Institution) (2001)

31 *Guide to ownership, operation and maintenance of building services* (London: Chartered Institution of Building Services Engineers) (2000)

32 *Air distribution systems* CIBSE Commissioning Code A (London: Chartered Institution of Building Services Engineers) (1996)

33 *Boiler plant* CIBSE Commissioning Code B (London: Chartered Institution of Building Services Engineers) (2002)

34 *Automatic controls* CIBSE Commissioning Code C (London: Chartered Institution of Building Services Engineers) (2001)

35 *Refrigeration systems* CIBSE Commissioning Code R (London: Chartered Institution of Building Services Engineers) (2002)

36 *Water distribution systems* CIBSE Commissioning Code W (London: Chartered Institution of Building Services Engineers) (2003)

37 Parsloe C J *Commissioning of VAV systems in buildings* BSRIA Application Guide AG1/91 (Bracknell: Building Services Research and Information Association) (1991)

38 Parsloe C J *Commissioning of air systems in buildings* BSRIA Application Guide AG3/89.2 (Bracknell: Building Services Research and Information Association) (1998)

39 Parsloe C J *Commissioning of water systems in buildings* BSRIA Application Guide AG2/89.2 (Bracknell: Building Services Research and Information Association) (1998)

40 Parsloe C J and Spencer A W *Commissioning of pipework systems — design considerations* BSRIA Application Guide AG20/95 (Bracknell: Building Services Research and Information Association) (1995)

41 Wild L J *Commissioning HVAC systems — division of responsibility* BSRIA Technical Manual TM1/88 (Bracknell: Building Services Research and Information Association) (1988)

42 Parsloe C J *Pre-commission cleaning of water systems* BSRIA Application Guide AG8/91 (Bracknell: Building Services Research and Information Association) (1991)

43 *Standard Specification for the commissioning of mechanical engineering installations for buildings* CSA Technical Memorandum 1 (Horsham: Commissioning Specialists Association) (1999)

44 Building Standards (Scotland) Regulations 1990 (as amended 1993–2001) (London: Her Majesty's Stationery Office/Edinburgh: Scottish Executive) (1990/2001)

45 The Building Regulations (Northern Ireland) 2000 Statutory Rule 2000 No. 389 (Belfast: The Stationery Office) (2000)

46 *Energy use in offices* (ECON 19) Energy Efficiency Best Practice Programme Energy Consumption Guide ECG19 (Garston: Energy Efficiency Best Practice Programme) (2000)

47 *Energy Assessment and Reporting Methodology: Office Assessment Method* CIBSE TM22 (London: Chartered Institution of Building Services Engineers) (1999)

48 BS ISO 156861-1: 2000: *Buildings and constructed assets. Service life planning. General principles* (London: British Standards Institution) (2000)

49 *Life Cycle Costing* HM Treasury Procurement Policy and Development Division Guidance No. 35 (London: The Stationery Office) (date unknown)

50 Clift M and Bourke K *Study on whole life costing* BRE Report BR367 (Garston: Building Research Establishment) (1999)

51 *Life Cycle Costing* in *The Surveyor's Construction Handbook* (London: Royal Institution of Chartered Surveyors) (1998)

52 *Seasonal Efficiency of a Domestic Boiler in the UK* (SEDBUK) BRECSU Boiler Efficiency Database (updated regularly and available at www.sedbuk.com)

53 *Condensing boilers* CIBSE Applications Manual AM3 (London: Chartered Institution of Building Services Engineers) (1989)

54 BS 5449: 1990: *Specification for forced circulation hot water central heating systems for domestic premises* (London: British Standards Institution) (1990)

55 prEN 12828: *Heating systems in buildings. Design for water-based heating systems* (draft) (London: British Standards Institution) (2000)

56 *Domestic heating design guide* (London: Heating and Ventilating Contractors Association) (2000)

57 *Reference data* CIBSE Guide C (London: Chartered Institution of Building Services Engineers) (2001)

58 Teekaram A *Variable-flow water systems: Design, installation and commissioning guidance* BSRIA Application Guide AG16/2002 (Bracknell: Building Services Research and Information Association) (2002)

59 *Guide to community heating and CHP — commercial; public and domestic applications* Energy Efficiency Best Practice Programme Good Practice Guide GPG234 (Garston: Energy Efficiency Best Practice Programme) (1998)

60 *Small-scale combined heat and power* CIBSE Applications Manual AM12 (London: Chartered Institution of Building Services Engineers) (1999)

61 BS EN 1264: *Floor heating. Systems and components*; Part 1: 1998 *Definitions and symbols*; Part 2: 1998 *Determination of thermal output* Part 3: 1998 *Dimensioning*; Part 4: 2001: *Installation* (London: British Standards Institution) (dates as indicated)

62 *Design of mixed storage heater/direct systems* Technical Information DOM-8 (London: Electricity Council) (1980 revised 1984, 1989)

63 *Building control systems* CIBSE Guide H (London: Chartered Institution of Building Services Engineers) (1989)

64 BS 4814:1990: *Specification for expansion vessels using an internal diaphragm, for sealed hot water heating systems* (London: British Standards Institution) (1990)

65 BS 7074: *Application, selection and installation of expansion vessels and ancillary equipment for sealed water system*; Part 1: 1989 *Code of practice for domestic heating and hot water supply*; Part 2: 1989 *Code of practice for low and medium temperature hot water heating systems*; Part 3: 1989 *Code of practice for chilled and condenser systems* (London: British Standards Institution) (dates as indicated)

66 The Pressure Systems and Transportable Gas Containers Regulations 1989 Statutory Instrument 1989 No. 2169 (London: Her Majesty's Stationery Office) (1989)

67 BS 1113: 1999: *Specification for design and manufacture of water-tube steam generating plant (including superheaters, reheaters and steel tube economizers)* (London: British Standards Institution) (1999)

68 BS 2790: 1992: *Specification for design and manufacture of shell boilers of welded construction* (London: British Standards Institution) (1992)

69 BS 6759-1: 1984: *Safety valves. Specification for safety valves for steam and hot water* (London: British Standards Institution) (1984)

70 BS 759-1: 1984: *Valves, gauges and other safety fittings for application to boilers and to piping installations for and in connection with boilers. Specification for valves, mountings and fittings* (London: British Standards Institution) (1984)

71 *Steam boiler blowdown systems* HSE PM60 (London: Health and Safety Executive) (1998)

72 BS 1780: 1985: *Specification for bourdon tube pressure and vacuum gauges* (London: British Standards Institution) (1985)

73 BS 3463: 1975: *Specification for observation and gauge glasses for pressure vessels* (London: British Standards Institution) (1975)

74 BS 806: 1993: *Specification for design and construction of ferrous piping installations for and in connection with land boilers* (London: British Standards Institution) (1993)

75 *Automatically controlled steam and hot water boilers* HSE PM5 (London: Health and Safety Executive) (2000)

76 *Air curtains — commercial applications* BSRIA Application Guide AG2/97 (Bracknell: Building Services Research and Information Association) (1997)

77 BS 6230: 1991: *Specification for installation of gas-fired forced convection air heaters for commercial and industrial space heating (2nd family gases)* (London: British Standards Institution) (1991)

78 *Radiant heating* BSRIA Application Guide AG 3/96 (Bracknell: Building Services Research and Information Association) (1996)

79 *Building energy and environmental modelling* CIBSE Applications Manual AM11 (London: Chartered Institution of Building Services Engineers) (1998)

80 Day A R, Ratcliffe M S and Shepherd K J Sizing central boiler plant using an economic optimisation model *Proc. CIBSE Nat. Conf. 18 October 2001* (London: Chartered Institution of Building Services Engineers) (2001)

81 BS EN 442: *Specification for radiators and convectors*; Part 1: 1996 *Technical specifications and requirements*; Part 2: 1997 *Test methods and rating*; Part 3: 1997 *Evaluation of conformity* (London: British Standards Institution) (dates as indicated)

82 BS 4856: *Methods for testing and rating fan coil units, unit heaters and unit coolers*; Part 1: 1972: *Thermal and volumetric performance for heating duties; without additional ducting*; Part 2: 1975: *Thermal and volumetric performance for cooling duties: without additional ducting*; Part 3: 1975: *Thermal and volumetric performance for heating and cooling duties; with additional ducting*; Part 4: 1997: *Determination of sound power levels of fan coil units, unit heaters and unit coolers using reverberating rooms* (London: British Standards Institution) (dates as indicated)

83 BS 779: 1989: *Specification for cast iron boilers for central heating and indirect hot water supply (rated output 44 kW and above)* (London: British Standards Institution) (1989

84 BS 855: 1990: *Specification for welded steel boilers for central heating and indirect hot water supply (rated output 44 kW to 3 MW)* (London: British Standards Institution) (1990)

85 *Gas installation pipework, boosters and compressors in industrial and commercial premises* IGE Utilisation Procedure UP/10 (London: Institution of Gas Engineers) (1994)

86 BS EN 676: 1997: *Automatic forced draught burners for gaseous fuels* (London: British Standards Institution) (1990)

87 *Installation of gas appliances in industrial and commercial premises* IGE Utilisation Procedure UP/2 (London: Institution of Gas Engineers) (1994)

88 *Heating boilers with atomising burners.Outputs up to 70 kW. Maximum operating pressures of 3 bar* OFTEC Oil Fired Appliance Standard OFS A100 (Banstead: Oil Firing Technical Association for the Petroleum Industry) (2000)

89 *Oil fired cookers with atomising or vaporising burners with or without boilers. Heat outputs up to 45 kW* OFTEC Oil Fired Appliance Standard OFS A101 (Banstead: Oil Firing Technical Association for the Petroleum Industry) (1998)

90 *Engineering principles and concepts for active solar systems* (Golden CO: National Renewable Energy Laboratory) (1988)

91 BS 5918: 1989: *Code of practice for solar heating systems for domestic hot water* (London: British Standards Institution) (1990)

92 BS EN 12975: *Thermal solar systems and components. Solar collectors*; Part 1: 2001: *General requirements;* Part 2: 2001: *Test methods* (London: British Standards Institution) (dates as indicated)

93 BS EN 12976: *Thermal solar systems and components. Factory made systems*; Part 1: 2000 *General requirements*; Part 2: 2001 *Test methods* (London: British Standards Institution) (dates as indicated)

94 DD ENV 12977: *Thermal solar systems and components. Custom built systems*; Part 1: 2001 *General requirements*; Part 2: 2001 *Test methods*; Part 3: 2001 *Performance characterisation of stores for solar heating systems* (London: British Standards Institution) (dates as indicated)

95 BS 6785: 1986: *Code of practice for solar heating systems for swimming pools* (London: British Standards Institution) (1986)

96 *Variable speed pumping in heating and cooling circuits* BSRIA Application Guide AG 14/99 (Bracknell: Building Services Research and Information Association) (1999)

97 BS 759: *Valves, gauges and other safety fittings for application to boilers and to piping installations for and in connection with boilers*; Part 1: 1984 *Specification for valves, mountings and fittings* (London: British Standards Institution) (1984)

98 BS 6759: Part 1: 1984: *Safety valves. Specification for safety valves for seam and hot water* (London: British Standards Institution) (1984)

99 BS 5864: 1989: *Specification for installation in domestic premises of gas-fired ducted-air heaters of rated input not exceeding 60 kW* (London: British Standards Institution) (1989)

100 BS EN 1319: 1999: *Domestic gas-fired forced convection air heaters for space heating, with fan-assisted burners not exceeding a net heat input of 70 kW* (London: British Standards Institution) (1999)

101 BS 5991: 1989: *Specification for indirect gas fired forced convection air heaters with rated heat inputs up to 2 MW for industrial and commercial space heating: safety and performance requirements (excluding electrical requirements (2nd family gases)* (London: British Standards Institution) (1989)

102 BS 5990: 1990: *Specification for direct gas-fired forced convection air heaters with rated heat inputs up to 2 MW for industrial and commercial space heating: safety and performance requirements (excluding electrical requirement) (2nd family gases)* (London: British Standards Institution) (1990)

103 BS 6896: 1991: *Specification and installation of gas fired radiant overhead heaters for industrial and Commercial Heating (2nd and 3rd family gases)* (London: British Standards Institution) (1991)

104 Environmental Protection Act 1990 (c. 43) (London: Her Majesty's Stationery Office) (1990)

105 Environment Act 1995 (c. 25) (London: Her Majesty's Stationery Office) (1995)

106 Clean Air Act (1993) (c. 11) (London: Her Majesty's Stationery Office) (1993)

107 *Chimney Heights — Third edition of the 1956 Clean Air Act Memorandum* (London: Her Majesty's Stationery Office) (1981)

108 *Environmental Protection Act 1990 — Guidelines for discharge stack heights for polluting emissions* Technical Guidance Note (Dispersion) D1 (London: Her Majesty's Inspectorate of Pollution) (1993)

109 *Minimising pollution at air intakes* CIBSE TM21 (London: Chartered Institution of Building Services Engineers) (1999)

110 *Flues for commercial and industrial gas fired boilers and air heaters* British Gas publication IM/11 (London: British Gas) (date unknown)

111 The Building Regulations 2000 Statutory Instrument 2000 No. 2531 (London: The Stationery Office) (2000)

112 BS 6644: 1991 *Specification for installation of gas-fired hot water boilers of rated inputs between 60 kW and 2 MW (2nd and 3rd family gases)* (London: British Standards Institution) (1991)

113 BS 5854: 1980 *Code of practice for flues and flue structures in buildings* (London: British Standards Institution) (1980)

114 BS 5440: *Installation and maintenance of flues and ventilation for gas appliances of rated input not exceeding 70 kW net (1st, 2nd and 3rd family gases)*: Part 1: 2000: *Specification for installation and maintenance of flues*; Part 2: 2000: *Specification for installation and maintenance of ventilation for gas appliances* (London: British Standards Institution) (dates as indicated)

115 BS 4076: 1989 *Specification for steel chimneys* (London: British Standards Institution) (1989)

116 BS 2869: 1998 *Specification for fuel oils for agricultural, domestic and industrial engines and boilers* (London: British Standards Institution) (1998)

117 *Digest of UK Energy Statistics* (London: The Stationery Office) (published annually)

118 *An Assessment of Renewable Energy for the UK* (London: Her Majesty's Stationery Office) (1994)

119 *Quarterly energy prices* (London: Department of Trade and Industry) (published quarterly)

120 BS 6891: 1998 *Specification for installation of low pressure gas pipework of up to 28 mm (R1) in domestic premises (2nd family gas)* (London: British Standards Institution) (1998)

121 Gas Safety (Installation and Use) Regulations 1998 Statutory Instrument 1998 No. 2451 (London: The Stationery Office) (2001)

122 BS 1387: 1985 *Specification for screwed and socketed steel tubes and tubulars and for plain end steel tubes suitable for welding or for screwing to BS 21 pipe threads* (London: British Standards Institution) (1985)

123 BS EN 1057: 1996 *Copper and copper alloys. Seamless, round copper tubes for water and gas in sanitary and heating applications* (London: British Standards Institution) (1996)

124 *Workplace (Health, Safety and Welfare) Regulations 1992 Approved Code of Practice and Guidance* Health and Safety Executive L24 (London: HSE Books) (1992)

125 *Safety in the installation and use of gas systems and appliances — Approved Code of Practice and Guidance* Health and Safety Executive L56 (London: HSE Books) (1998)

126 *Bulk LPG storage at fixed installations — Part 1: Design, installation and operation of vessels located above ground* LPGA Code of Practice 1 (Ringwood: LP Gas Association) (1998)

127 BS 5410-1: 1997 *Code of practice for oil firing. Installations up to 45 kW output capacity for space heating and hot water supply purposes* (London: British Standards Institution) (1997)

128 Control of Pollution (Oil Storage) (England) Regulations 2001 Statutory Instrument 2001 No. 2954 (London: The Stationery Office)

129 BS 799-5: 1987 *Oil burning equipment. Specification for oil storage tanks* (London: British Standards Institution) (1987)

130 BS 3797: 1990 *Specification for lightweight aggregates for masonry units and structural concrete* (London: British Standards Institution) (1990)

Appendix 1.A1: Example calculations

1.A1.1 Sizing of water expansion vessel

It is required to determine the size of the sealed expansion vessel required if the pressure in the system is not to exceed 3.5 bar gauge (i.e. 350 kPa gauge).

Initial data:

— water volume of system = 450 litres

— design flow temperature = 60 °C

— design return temperature = 50 °C

— height of system = 7.5 m

— design pump pressure rise = 42 kPa

— temperature of plant room during plant operation = 25 °C (i.e. 298 K)

Consider first the water. It may be assumed that, at its coolest, the temperature of the water in the system will be 4 °C (i.e. 277 K). Similarly, depending on the control system, the greatest expansion could occur at part load, when the entire water system is at the design flow temperature. Table 1.9 gives the expansion between 4 °C and 60 °C as 1.71%.

$$\Delta V = 0.0171 \times 450 = 7.7 \text{ litres}$$

Ideally the pressure vessel should be connected to a position of low water pressure. This would reduce the required volume of a sealed vessel. However it is more convenient for items of plant to be located in close proximity, and in this example the expansion vessel is being connected to pipework 7.5 m below the highest position of the circuit. It must, however, be positioned on the return side of the pump, not the outlet.

The 'cold fill' pressure at the pump, due to the head of water, will partially compress the air within the expansion vessel, thus necessitating a larger expansion vessel. Thus it is advisable to pre-pressurise the air within the vessel to this pressure so that, once connected, it will still be full of air. Thus the initial air volume will be the same as the vessel volume. No further head of water should be applied as it would serve no useful purpose and would increase the operating pressure of the system, which is undesirable.

Pre-pressurisation required for a head of 7.5 m is given by:

$$p_1 = \rho g z \qquad (1.A1.1)$$

where p_1 is the initial pressure (kPa), ρ is the density (kg·m^{-3}), g is the acceleration due to gravity (m·s^{-2}) and z is the head (m).

Hence,

$$p_1 = 1000 \times 9.81 \times 7.5$$
$$= 73.58 \text{ kPa gauge} \approx 174 \text{ kPa absolute}$$

Maximum permissible pressure, p_2, at inlet to the pump:

$$p_2 = (350 - 42) \text{ kPa}$$
$$= 308 \text{ kPa gauge} \approx 408 \text{ kPa absolute}$$

Initial volume of air in vessel = V_1; final volume of air = $V_2 = (V_1 - 7.7)$ litres.

For the air, the ideal gas equation will apply, using absolute values of temperature and pressure. Note that since no hot water flows through the vessel, there should be no effect upon the temperature of the air cushion within the vessel. However, it could be affected by the plant room temperature.

The ideal gas equation is:

$$\frac{p_2 V_2}{T_2} = \frac{p_1 V_1}{T_1} \qquad (1.A1.2)$$

Therefore:

$$\frac{408\,(V_1 - 7.7)}{298} = \frac{174\, V_1}{277}$$

Hence, the minimum volume of expansion vessel required, V_1 = 14.23 litres.

As the calculation was carried out based on the maximum permissible pressure, the next size up must be selected. Since sealed pressure vessels constitute such a small portion of the equipment cost, consideration should always be given to selecting one which is larger than necessary, the advantage being a reduced operating pressure for the system.

1.A1.2 Effect of flow rate on radiator output

A radiator has a nominal output of 1.23 kW for water flow and return temperatures, t_1 and t_2, of 75 °C and 65 °C respectively in surroundings at 20 °C. It is required to determine the output when the flow rate is reduced to 40% of the design flow rate, q_n, the flow temperature remaining constant at 75 °C. The heat transfer index n has been found to be 1.25.

$$\Delta T = {}^1\!/_2\,(t_1 + t_2) - t_{ai} \qquad (1.A1.3)$$

Therefore:

$$\Delta T = {}^1\!/_2\,(75 + 65) - 20 = 50 \text{ K}$$

Using Table 1.12, for mean radiator water temperature of 70 °C, c_p = 4.191 $\text{kJ·kg}^{-1}\text{·K}^{-1}$.

Rearranging equation 1.23 to give K_m:

$$K_m = \phi \,/\, \Delta T^n \tag{1.A1.4}$$

where ϕ is the heat emission (kW).

Thus:

$$K_m = 1.23 \,/\, 501.25 = 9.251 \times 10^{-3}\ \text{kW·K}^{-1.25}$$

The design, or nominal flow rate, q_{mn}, is obtained by rearranging equation 1.22:

$$q_{mn} = \frac{\phi_n}{c_p\,(t_1 - t_2)} \tag{1.A1.5}$$

Hence:

$$q_{mn} = \frac{1.23}{4.191\,(75 - 65)} = 0.02935\ \text{kg·s}^{-1}$$

For the situation with 40% of the nominal design flow:

$$q_m = 0.4 \times 0.02935 = 0.01174\ \text{kg.s}^{-1}$$

In order to use equation 1.28, it is necessary to calculate $(K_m \,/\, q_m\, c_p)$, i.e:

$$(K_m \,/\, q_m\, c_p) = (9.251 \times 10^{-3}) \,/\, (0.01174 \times 4.191)$$

$$= 0.1880\ \text{K}^{-0.25}$$

Before using equation 1.28, a starting value for the outlet temperature, t_2, is required, for which an intelligent estimate is helpful. Clearly it is likely to be lower than the previous outlet temperature of 65 °C, but must be higher than the room temperature 20 °C. Therefore 55 °C is taken as an initial estimate for t_2 and inserted in the right hand side of the equation.

Using equation 1.28 and inserting the first estimate in the right hand side:

$$t_2 = t_1 - \frac{K_m}{q_m\, c_p}\left[\tfrac{1}{2}\left(t_1 - t_2\right) - t_{ai}\right]^n \tag{1.A1.6}$$

i.e:

$$t_2 = 75 - 0.1880\ [{}^1/_2\,(75 + 55) - 20]^{1.25} = 53.09\ °\text{C}$$

The updated value is substituted successively into the right hand side until the required accuracy is obtained, i.e:

$$t_2 = 75 - 0.1880\ [{}^1/_2\,(75 + 53.09) - 20]^{1.25} = 53.67\ °\text{C}$$

$$t_2 = 75 - 0.1880\ [{}^1/_2\,(75 + 53.67) - 20]^{1.25} = 53.49\ °\text{C}$$

$$t_2 = 75 - 0.1880\ [{}^1/_2\,(75 + 53.49) - 20]^{1.25} = 53.55\ °\text{C}$$

$$t_2 = 75 - 0.1880\ [{}^1/_2\,(75 + 53.55) - 20]^{1.25} = 53.53\ °\text{C}$$

$$t_2 = 75 - 0.1880\ [{}^1/_2\,(75 + 53.53) - 20]^{1.25} = 53.53\ °\text{C}$$

Hence:

$$t_2 = 53.5°\text{C}$$

Substituting in equation 1.22 gives:

$$\phi = q_m\, c_p\, (t_1 - t_2) \tag{1.A1.7}$$

Thus:

$$\phi = 0.01174 \times 4.191\ (75 - 53.5) = 1.058\ \text{kW}$$

Note that in this case, a reduction in the flow rate of 60% has only resulted in the heat emission reducing from the original value of 1.23 by 15%.

1.A1.3 Pipe sizing

Figure 1.A1.1 is a simplified schematic of a 2-pipe reverse-return system which, for simplicity, serves 10 emitters each required to have an output of 3.0 kW. The flow and return temperatures are to be 60 and 50 °C respectively. The design internal temperature is 20 °C, and the index of heat emission for the emitters, n, is 1.28.

Approximate distances for pipe runs:

- boiler to A = 10 m
- A to B = B to C etc. = 10 m
- E to F = 25 m
- J to boiler = 10 m

Additional components near the boiler but, for simplicity, not shown in the figure are:

- isolating valves: 4
- Y-pattern angle balancing valve: 1
- other elbows: 4
- tees, to expansion vessel and feed: 2

All elbows are assumed to be 90° with smooth radiussed inner surface.

The manual method for calculating the pressure drop around the circuit is tedious, so it is reasonable to consider the entire system to be at the mean water temperature of 55 °C. However in the following, the flow and return have been considered separately at their respective temperatures. The additional accuracy can be seen to be trivial. The pipework is all copper (BS 2871, Table X) for which pre-calculated pressure drops at 75 °C are given in Table 4.13 of Guide C [(A1.1)]. Corrections for temperature are given herein, see Table 1.21 (page 1-36).

Before commencing the pipe selection and pressure drop calculation, it is necessary to be sure of the emitter selection and design flow rates. Under the design criteria specified above, the excess temperature, ΔT, above the surrounding air temperature will be (55 – 20) = 35 K,

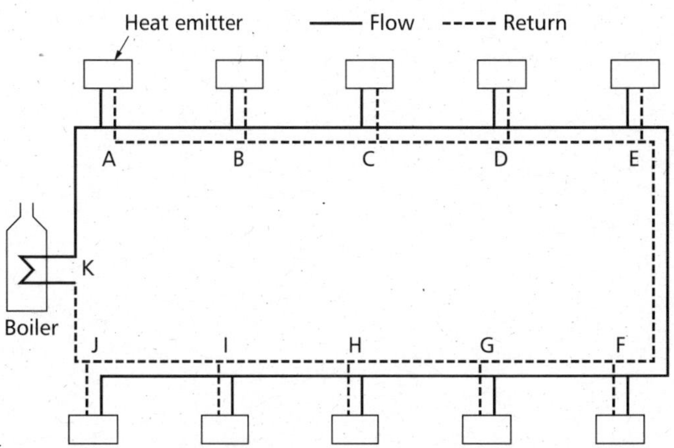

Figure 1.A1.1 Simplified layout of the pipework of a heating system, pump and other ancillaries not shown (not to scale)

rather than the nominal value of 50 K used in emitter manufacturers' catalogues. Therefore, it is necessary to calculate the nominal catalogue value required.

Re-arranging equation 1.25:

$$\phi_{50} = \phi_{35}\,(50 / 35)^{n} \quad (1.A1.8)$$

Hence:

$$\phi_{50} = 3\,(50 / 35)^{1.28} = 4.736 \text{ kW}$$

Therefore, to obtain an output of 3.0 kW at $\Delta T = 35$ K, it is necessary to select a heat emitter giving a nominal output of 4.736 kW (at $\Delta T = 50$ K).

From Guide C, Table 4.A3.1, the properties of water are as follows:

- at 60 °C: $\rho = 983.2$ kg·m^{-3}
- at 55 °C: $\rho = 985.6$ kg·m^{-3}; $c_p = 4.184$ kJ·kg^{-1}·K^{-1}
- at 50 °C: $\rho = 988.0$ kg·m^{-3}.

The mass flow for each emitter is given by re-arranging equation 5.2:

$$q_m = \phi / c_p\,(t_1 - t_2) \quad (1.A1.9)$$

Hence:

$$q_m = 3 / 4.184\,(60 - 50) = 0.0717 \text{ kg·s}^{-1}$$

For 10 emitters, the total flow will be $(10\,q_m) = 0.717$ kg·s^{-1}.

If some of the emitters are appreciably remote from one another such that heat losses from the flow pipe result in significantly different inlet water temperatures for the different emitters, the design flow rate for such emitters would need to be re-calculated.

To illustrate the sizing procedure, the following calculations show the flow along the flow pipe to the tee at D, and the return pipe from the tee at D to the boiler.

The designer has a free choice for the values of water velocity (c) and pipe diameter (d). The smaller the pipe, the greater the pressure drop, and the greater the pumping power and energy consumption. Since the pressure drop is approximately inversely proportional to d^5, an increase in diameter from one size to the next size up can greatly reduce the friction pressure drop. Section 1.5.1.3 suggests a choice of velocity of about 1.0 m·s^{-1}. Traditionally, designers have constrained themselves by further limiting the pressure drop per unit length to a 'rule-of-thumb' figure of 300 Pa·m^{-1}. In reality, the choice of water velocity should depend on the length of pipework. In the calculations which follow, the starting point has been to choose a water velocity of 1.0 m·s^{-1}. Where this results in pressure drops per unit length greater than 300 Pa·m^{-1}, the next pipe size up has been selected in order to reduce energy costs.

1.A1.3.1 Pipe sizing and pressure drops along pipes

The tables of pressure drops in Guide C (e.g. Guide C, Table 4.13) give a rough indication of velocity which aids the choice of pipe diameter. However, the tabulated velocities are not sufficiently accurate for subsequent calculations. The values of velocity (c) in Table 1.A1.1 below have been calculated, as follows.

Typically, for pipe run A–B (row 2 of Table 1.A1.1):

$$q_m = 0.717 - 0.0717 = 0.6453 \text{ kg·s}^{-1}$$

Guide C4, Table 4.13, shows that for a velocity less than 1.0 m·s^{-1}, a minimum pipe diameter of 35 mm is required.

Guide C4, Table 4.2, gives the mean internal diameter (d_i) as 32.63 mm. Therefore the cross-sectional area of the pipe (A) is:

$$A = \pi\, d_i^2 / 4 = 8.362 \times 10^{-4} \text{ m}^2$$

The water velocity is given by:

$$c = q_m / (\rho A) \quad (1.A1.10)$$

Table 1.A1.1 Calculation of pressure drops for straight pipework (flow from boiler to 'D' and return from 'D' to boiler)

Pipe run	q_m / kg·s^{-1}	l / m	d / mm	d_i / mm	c / m·s^{-1}	$(\Delta p/l)$ / Pa·m^{-1}	Δp / Pa
Flow (60 °C):							
K–A	0.7170	10	35	32.63	0.8721	224	2240
A–B	0.6453	10	35	32.63	0.7849	185	1850
B–C	0.5736	10	35	32.63	0.6978	151	1510
C–D	0.5024	10	35*	32.63	0.6111	118	1180
							Total pressure drop: 6780
Temperature correction factor (Table 5.10): $C = 1.058$							Corrected total pressure drop: 7173
Return (50 °C):							
D–E	0.2868	10	28†	26.72	0.5540	125	1250
E–F	0.3586	25	28	26.72	0.6504	185	1850
F–G	0.4303	10	28	26.72	0.7767	257	2570
G–H	0.5024	10	35*	32.63	0.6081	118	1180
H–I	0.5736	10	35	32.63	0.6948	151	1510
I–J	0.6450	10	35	32.63	0.7807	185	1850
J–K	0.7170	10	35	32.63	0.8678	224	2240
							Total pressure drop: 12450
Temperature correction factor (Table 5.10): $C = 1.104$							Corrected total pressure drop: 13745

* Initial choice of 28 mm ($c = 0.94$ m·s^{-1}) gives $(\Delta p/l) = 340$ Pa·m^{-1}
† Initial choice of 22 mm ($c = 0.90$ m·s^{-1}) gives $(\Delta p/l) = 434$ Pa·m^{-1}

Hence:

$$c = 0.6453/(983.2 \times 8.362 \times 10^{-4}) = 0.7849 \text{ m·s}^{-1}$$

From Guide C, Table 4.13, for a water temperature of 75 °C, the pressure drop per unit length ($\Delta p/l$) is 185 Pa·m^{-1}. Hence, for a length of pipe of 10 m:

$$\Delta p = 185 \times 10 = 1850 \text{ Pa}$$

However, since the flow temperature is 60 °C, rather than 75 °C, a correction factor must be applied, see Table 1.21 (page 1-36).

Table 1.A1.1 shows the pipe sizing and pressure drop for each run of straight pipe for the flow and return taken by water supplying the heat emitter at 'D'.

The flow to each branch is 0.0717 kg·s^{-1}, requiring a pipe diameter of only 15 mm.

1.A1.3.2 Pressure drops due to fittings

Guide C, section 4.9, gives extensive data on values of pressure loss factors (ζ) for pipe fittings. These should be used in conjunction with equation 4.8 from Guide C, section 4, reprinted here as equation 1.A1.11.

$$\Delta p = \zeta \, {}^1\!/_2 \, p \, c^2 \qquad (1.A1.11)$$

It should be noted that the pressure loss factors for tees, whether for the straight flow or the branch flow, are all to be used with the velocity pressure of the combined flow ($\zeta \, {}^1\!/_2 \, p \, c^2$).

Since the value of ζ for tees depends upon both the relative branch flow (i.e. branch to combined) and the relative branch diameter (i.e. branch to combined), it is convenient to determine these ratios first.

Taking the supply tee at 'D' as an example (see Figure 1.A1.2), subscript 'b' denotes flow in branch, subscript 'c' denotes combined flow upstream of branch and subscript 's' denotes 'straight' flow in pipe immediately downstream of the tee.

Hence:

$$q_{mb} / q_{mc} = 0.0717 / 0.5024 = 0.1427$$

$$d_b / d_c = 15 / 35 = 0.429$$

From Guide C, Table 4.47, for diverging flow:

$$\zeta_{c-b} = 1.66$$

$$\zeta_{c-s} = 0.67$$

From Table 1.A1.1, above, for combined flow at inlet to the tee (i.e. pipe C–D):

$$c_c = 0.6111 \text{ m·s}^{-1}$$

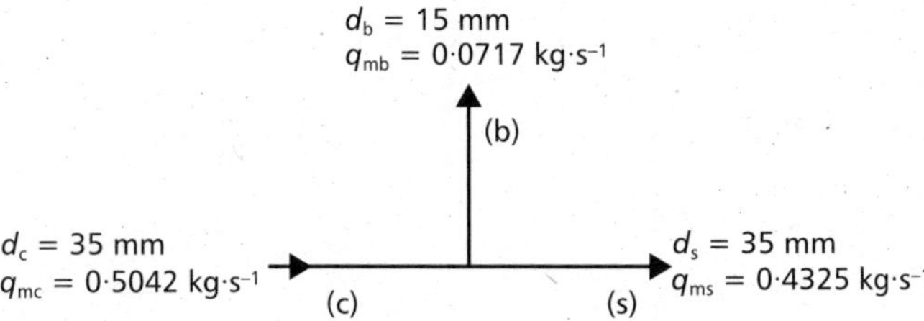

Therefore:

$$^1\!/_2 \, \rho \, c_c^2 = 0.5 \times 988.0 \times 0.61112 = 184 \text{ Pa}$$

Hence, pressure drop for the diverging tee at 'D' is given by:

$$\Delta p_{c-b} = \zeta_{c-b} \, {}^1\!/_2 \, \rho \, c_c^2$$

Hence:

$$\Delta p_{c-b} = 1.66 \times 184 = 305 \text{ Pa}$$

The calculated pressure drops for all the fittings are given in Table 1.A1.2.

Before the pressure drop for the entire circuit can be calculated, the pressure drop along each flow route would need to be determined. Some pipe sizes could then be modified to obtain a better balance.

Assuming for the moment that the flow route as used above gave the greatest pressure drop, balancing valves would be required on each of the other branches to equalise the pressure drops. Since balancing is an iterative process, the more inherently in-balance the system is, the better. Thus modifications in pipe sizes at the design stage can reduce the need for balancing.

In a two-pipe reverse return system of the type used for this example, it is not possible to foresee which flow route will produce the greatest pressure drop, i.e. which is the 'index' circuit, since this will depend on the pipe sizes chosen. The pump must be selected to provide a pressure rise equal to the pressure drop of the index circuit.

In the case above, supplying the heat emitter at 'D', the indication is that the total circuit pressure drop is the sum of the pressure drops itemised in Table 1.A1.3.

For circuits requiring variable control via control valves, reasonable control is obtained only if the control valve has a reasonable value of authority, the typical value for which is 0.5. The implication of this is that as much pressure drop occurs across this open control valve as in the rest of the circuit. It is then worthwhile considering increasing all the pipe sizes, thereby reducing both the pressure drop around the circuit and that across the control valve.

1.A1.3.3 Alternative method for calculating pressure drop due to fittings

The method for calculating the pressure drop due to the fittings given in section 1.A1.3.1 is the conventional method and is identical to that used for calculating pressure drops in ductwork due to ductwork fittings. However, the pre-calculated tables of pressure drops given in section 4 of Guide C offer an alternative method using the concept of the 'equivalent length' (l_e) of a component having $\zeta = 1$.

For example, for the pressure drop due to the diverting tee at 'D', the pressure loss factor has been determined as $\zeta = 1.66$, see Table 1.A1.2. As an alternative to calculating the velocity pressure, consider instead the combined flow at entry to the tee, $q_c = 0.5024$ kg·s^{-1}. The chosen pipe diameter is 35 mm. From Guide C, Table 4.13, the equivalent length, l_e, is either 1.5 or 1.6. (Note that this

Table 1.A1.2 Calculation of pressure drops for the pipework fittings (flow from boiler to 'D' and return from 'D' to boiler)

Item	Number	Guide C Table no.	d/mm	d_b/d_c	q_b/q_c	ζ	c/m·s^{-1}	$\frac{1}{2}\rho c_c^2$/Pa	Δp/Pa
Gate valve	4	4.52	35	—	—	4×0.3	0.8723	374	449
Y-balancing	1	4.52	35	—	—	1×3.0	0.8723	374	1122
Elbow	4	4.48(a)	35	—	—	4×0.74	0.8723	374	1107
Tee, straight	2	4.47(c)	35	—	—	2×0.82	0.8723	374	613
						Total: 8.8	0.8723	374	3291
K–D flow (60 °C):									
Elbow	2	4.48(a)	35	—	—	2×0.74	0.8723	374	326
Straight tee (A)	1	4.47(e)	35	0.417	0.1	0.7	0.8723	374	262
Straight tee (B)	1	4.47(e)	35	0.417	0.111	0.69	0.7849	303	209
Straight tee (C)	1	4.47(e)	35	0.417	0.125	0.68	0.6978	239	163
Diverging tee (D)	1	4.47(d)	28	0.429	0.143	1.66	0.6111	184	305
									Total: 4784
D–K return (50 °C):									
Converging tee (D)	1	4.47(a)	22	0.68	0.25	−0.09	0.9040	404	−36
Straight tee (E)	1	4.47(b)	28	0.519	0.20	0.64	0.6504	208	133
Elbow	2	4.48(a)	28	—	—	2×0.78	0.6504	208	324
Straight tee (F)	1	4.47(b)	28	0.519	0.20	0.64	0.7767	298	191
Straight tee (G)	1	4.47(b)	28	0.519	0.143	0.67	0.9417	438	293
Straight tee (H)	1	4.47(b)	35	0.417	0.125	0.68	0.6948	238	162
Straight tee (I)	1	4.47(b)	35	0.417	0.111	0.69	0.7807	301	208
Straight tee (J)	1	4.47(b)	35	0.417	0.10	0.70	0.8678	372	260
									Total: 1535

Note: there are no correction factors for temperature for the pressure drop due to fittings, though the density does affect the value of $\frac{1}{2}\rho c^2$

Table 1.A1.3 Pressure drops for flow serving heat emitter at 'D' for pipe sizes chosen above

Source of pressure drop	Pressure drop / Pa
Flow pipework	6780
Flow fittings	4784
Branch pipework	*
Return pipework	13 745
Flow pipework	1535
Boiler	*

* Obtained from emitter and boiler manufacturers

value is given to two significant figures only and is therefore somewhat crude.)

In terms of the equivalent length, the pressure drop is given by:

$$\Delta p = \zeta\, l_e\, (\Delta p\, /\, l) \qquad (1.A1.12)$$

From Table 1.A1.3 above, for the combined flow C–D, $(\Delta p/l) = 118$ Pa·m^{-1}. Thus, taking $l_e = 1.6$:

$$\Delta p = 1.66 \times 1.6 \times 118 = 313 \text{ Pa·m}^{-1}$$

It has been noted that the pre-calculated tables of pressure drops given in Guide C are for a water temperature of 75 °C. The pressure drop in the pipework for water at 60 °C is 6% greater than that at 75 °C and this was taken into account in Table 1.A1.3 and there is a temptation to apply a similar correction to the pressure drop for the fittings. However, the evaluation of l_e was based on a value of ζ which does not vary with temperature and therefore no further correction needs to be made. The difference between the above value of 313 Pa·m^{-1} and the value determined in Table A1.2 of 305 Pa·m^{-1} is due entirely to the tabulated values of l_e being quoted to only two significant figures.

It is likely that engineers using this method may add the hypothetical 'equivalent length' to a real length before calculating the pressure drop, and then apply a temperature correction to the combined result. Such an approach would be wrong.

Thus, the equivalent length method contains both a greater chance of error and an inherent inaccuracy. Bearing in mind the tendency to operate heating systems at temperatures lower than 75 °C, it may be wise to use the conventional 'velocity pressure' method rather than the equivalent length method. Furthermore, the equivalent length method is of no use for fluids other than water or for pipes other than those for which values of equivalent length have been determined.

Reference

1.A1.1 *Reference data* CIBSE Guide C (London: Chartered Institution of Building Services Engineers) (2001)***

Appendix 1.A2: Sizing and heights of chimneys and flues

1.A2.1 General considerations

The following information is needed for chimney and flue sizing:

(*a*) type of fuel used, its calorific value and the percentage sulphur content

(*b*) type and rated output of the boiler

(*c*) overall thermal efficiency of the boiler based on gross calorific value

(*d*) boiler flue gas outlet conditions at high and low fire, i.e. gas outlet temperatures and percentage carbon dioxide

(*e*) draught requirements at the boiler outlet at high and low fire

(*f*) height of the installation above sea level (gas volumes are increased by approximately 4% for every 300 m above sea level and allowance must be made in specifying volumes of forced and induced fans, etc., for installations at more than 600 m above sea level)

(*g*) location of plant and the character of surroundings, viz. topography, height of buildings surrounding plant, prevailing wind direction and velocities and the position of the boiler (i.e. basement or roof-top)

(*h*) winter and summer extremes of ambient temperature

(*i*) proposed general chimney construction to assess the cooling effect on gases.

Procedures for calculating chimney height are described below. For plants burning sulphur-bearing fuels where the full load SO_2 emission exceeds 0.38 $g{\cdot}s^{-1}$, the chimney height is determined by the requirements of the 1993 Clean Air Act[1.A2.1] as interpreted by the third edition of the *Clean Air Act Memorandum: Chimney Heights*[1.A2.2]. For smaller plants burning sulphur-bearing fuels, chimney heights are determined by combustion draught requirements with the proviso that such chimneys should terminate at least 3 m above the surrounding roof level or higher should the public health authority so require.

For gaseous fuels with negligible sulphur content, the method given seeks to limit the concentration of other combustion products (such as NO_2 and aldehydes) at ground level.

1.A2.2 Chimney heights for sulphur-bearing fuels

The maximum fuel burning rate at full plant loading is given by:

$$q_m = 100\ \phi \,/\, (\eta\ h_g) \qquad (1.A2.1)$$

where q_m is the maximum fuel burning rate ($kg{\cdot}s^{-1}$), ϕ is the rated boiler output (kW), η is the thermal efficiency of the boiler (%) and h_g is the calorific value of the fuel ($kJ{\cdot}kg^{-1}$).

The maximum sulphur dioxide emission for fired equipment is:

$$E_m = K_1\, q_m\, S \qquad (1.A2.2)$$

where E_m is the maximum sulphur dioxide emission ($g{\cdot}s^{-1}$), S is the sulphur content of the fuel (%), K_1 is a constant (20 for oil firing, 18 for coal firing).

Equations 1.A2.1 and 1.A2.2 may be combined to give:

$$E_m = K_2\, \phi \,/\, \eta \qquad (1.A2.3)$$

where K_2 is a factor representing the type of fuel, its calorific value and sulphur content. Values for K_2 are given in Table 1.A2.1.

Where the sulphur dioxide emission does not exceed 0.38 $g{\cdot}s^{-1}$, select the area and category from the following alternatives:

— A: undeveloped area where development is unlikely, where background pollution is low, and where there is no development within 800 m of the new chimney

— B: partially developed area with scattered houses, low background pollution and no other comparable industrial emissions within 400 m of the new chimney

— C: built-up residential area with only moderate background pollution and without other comparable industrial emissions

— D: urban area of mixed industrial and residential development, with considerable background pollution and with other comparable industrial emissions within 400 m of the new chimney

— E: large city, or an urban area of mixed heavy industrial and dense residential development, with severe background pollution.

Refer to Figure 1.A2.1 to obtain the uncorrected chimney height, using the line matching the category selected above. For fuels with more than 2% sulphur content, add 10% to this height. If the height obtained is more than 2.5 times the height of the building or any building in the immediate vicinity, no further correction is required. Where this is not so, the final chimney height is obtained by substitution in the following formula:

$$H = (0.56\, h_a + 0.375\, h_b) + 0.625\, h_c \qquad (1.A2.4)$$

where H is the final chimney height (m), h_a is the building height or greatest length whichever is the lesser (m), h_b is the building height (m) and h_c is the uncorrected chimney height (m).

Table 1.A2.2 provides solutions to the term in brackets against known values of h_a and h_b. The final chimney height may then be obtained by adding this result to the appropriate value read from the scale on the right hand side of Figure 1.A2.1. Note that 10% must be added to this latter value for fuels with more than 2% sulphur content.

Where the sulphur dioxide emission is less than 0.38 $g{\cdot}s^{-1}$, the procedure is as follows:

Table 1.A2.1 Properties of fuels and values of K_2 for equation A2.3

Type of fuel	Properties		K_2
	Calorific value / MJ·kg^{-1}	Sulphur content / %	
Liquid fuels:			
— gas oil (class D)	45.5	1.0	43.9
— light fuel oil (class E)	43.4	3.2	147.5
— medium fuel oil (class F)	42.9	3.5	163.2
— heavy fuel oil (class G)	42.5	3.8	178.8
Solid fuels:			
— anthracite 101 and 102	30.0	1.1	66.0
— dry steam coal 201	30.5	1.1	64.9
— coking steam coal 202 and 204	30.7	1.1	64.5
— medium volatile coking coal 301a and 301b	30.5	1.3	76.7
— low volatile coal 200H	30.0	1.3	78.0
— very strongly caking coal 401	29.5	1.9	115.5
— strongly caking coal 501 and 502	29.4	1.9	116.3
— medium caking coal 601 and 602	27.6	1.9	123.9
— weakly caking coal 701 and 702	26.7	1.8	121.4
— very weakly caking coal 802	25.2	1.9	135.7
— non-caking coal 902	23.8	1.8	136.1

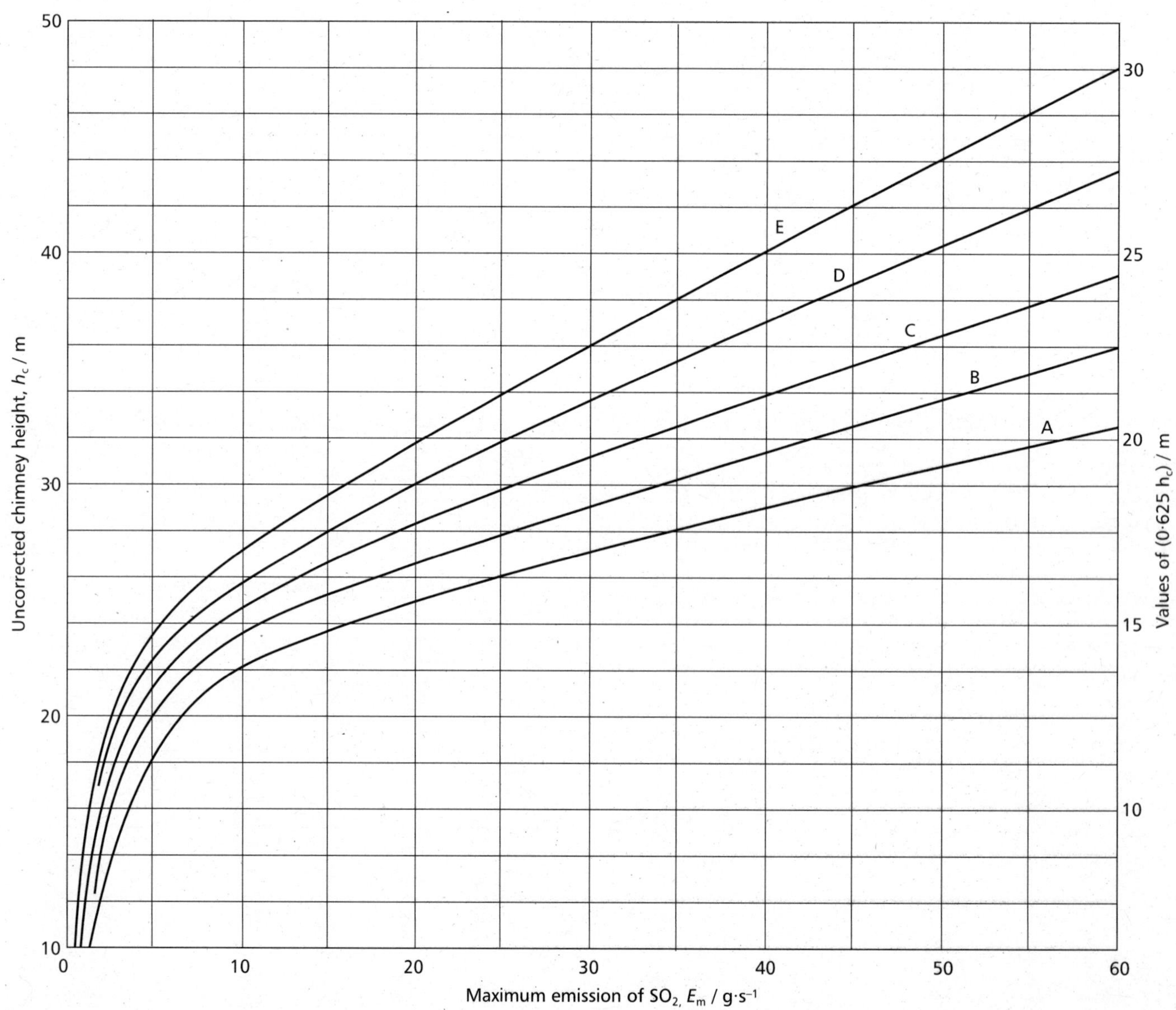

Figure 1.A2.1 Uncorrected chimney heights

Table 1.A2.2 Value of bracketed term in equation A2.4

Building height h_b / m	Value of $(0.56\,h_a + 0.375\,h_b)$ for stated building height or greatest length (h_a) / m																	
	9	12	15	18	21	24	27	30	33	36	39	42	45	48	51	54	57	60
9	8.4	10.1	11.8	13.5	15.1	16.8	18.5	20.2	21.9	23.5	25.2	26.9	28.6	30.3	31.9	33.6	35.3	37.0
12	9.5	11.2	12.9	14.6	16.3	17.9	19.6	21.3	23.0	24.7	26.3	28.0	29.7	31.4	33.1	34.7	36.4	38.1
15	10.7	12.3	14.0	15.7	17.4	19.1	20.7	22.4	24.1	25.8	27.5	29.1	30.8	32.5	34.2	35.9	37.5	39.2
18	11.8	13.5	15.2	16.8	18.5	20.2	21.9	23.6	25.2	26.9	28.6	30.3	32.0	33.6	35.3	37.0	38.7	40.4
21	12.9	14.6	16.3	18.0	19.6	21.3	23.0	24.7	26.4	28.0	29.7	31.4	33.1	34.8	36.4	38.1	39.8	41.5
24	14.0	15.7	17.4	19.1	20.8	22.4	24.1	25.8	27.5	29.2	30.8	32.5	34.2	35.9	37.6	39.2	40.9	42.6
27	15.2	16.8	18.5	20.2	21.9	23.6	25.2	26.9	28.6	30.3	32.0	33.6	35.3	37.0	38.7	40.4	42.0	43.7
30	16.3	18.0	19.7	21.3	23.0	24.7	26.4	28.1	29.7	31.4	33.1	34.8	36.5	38.1	39.8	41.5	43.2	44.9
33	17.4	19.1	20.8	22.5	24.1	25.8	27.5	29.2	30.9	32.5	34.2	35.9	37.6	39.3	40.9	42.6	44.3	46.0
36	18.5	20.2	21.9	23.6	25.3	26.9	28.6	30.3	32.0	33.7	35.3	37.0	38.7	40.4	42.1	43.7	45.4	47.1
39	19.7	21.3	23.0	24.7	26.4	28.1	29.7	31.4	33.1	34.8	36.5	38.1	39.8	41.5	43.2	44.9	46.5	48.2
42	20.8	22.5	24.2	25.8	27.5	29.2	30.9	32.6	34.2	35.9	37.6	39.3	41.0	42.6	44.3	46.0	47.7	49.4
45	21.9	23.6	25.3	27.0	28.6	30.3	32.0	33.7	35.4	37.0	38.7	40.4	42.1	43.8	45.4	47.1	48.8	50.5
48	23.0	24.7	26.4	28.1	29.8	31.4	33.1	34.8	36.5	38.2	39.8	41.5	43.2	44.9	46.6	48.2	49.9	51.6
51	24.2	25.8	27.5	29.2	30.9	32.6	34.2	35.9	37.6	39.3	41.0	42.6	44.3	46.0	47.7	49.4	51.0	52.7
54	25.3	27.0	28.7	30.3	32.0	33.7	35.4	37.1	38.7	40.4	42.1	43.8	45.5	47.1	48.8	50.5	52.2	53.9
57	26.4	28.1	29.8	31.5	33.1	34.8	36.5	38.2	39.9	41.5	43.2	44.9	46.6	48.3	49.9	51.6	53.3	55.0
60	27.5	29.2	30.9	32.6	34.3	35.9	37.6	39.3	41.0	42.7	44.3	46.0	47.7	49.4	51.1	52.7	54.4	56.1

Table 1.A2.3 Trial flue gas velocities

Chimney height / m	Trial flue gas velocity / m·s^{-1}	
	Natural draught boilers	Boilers with pressurised combustion chambers
<12	3.6	6.0
12 to 20	4.5	—
12 to 24	—	7.5
20 to 30	6.0	—
24 to 30	—	9.0
>30	7.5	12.0

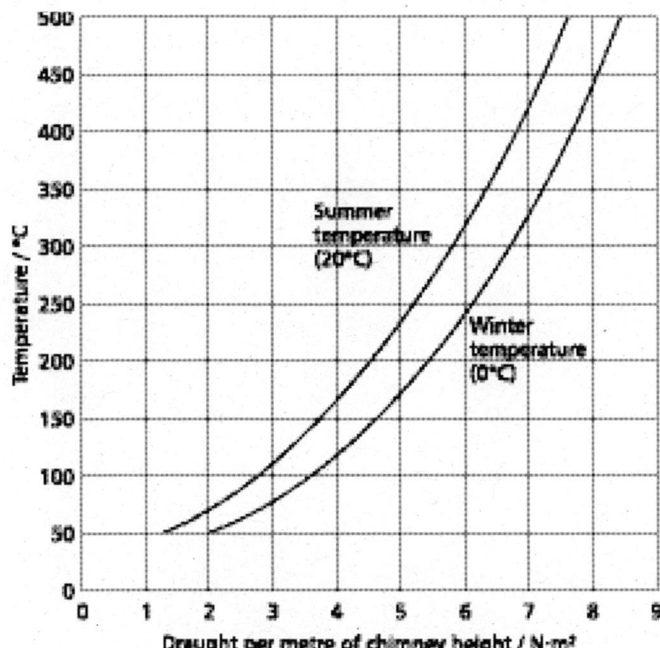

Figure 1.A2.2 Chimney draught at 0 °C and 20 °C ambient temperatures

(*a*) assess the height of buildings through which the chimney passes or to which it is attached

(*b*) add 3 m to this height to obtain the preliminary chimney height

(*c*) where the particular building is surrounded by higher buildings, the height of the latter must be taken into consideration as above

(*d*) select a trial flue gas velocity (from Table 1.A2.3) and calculate the flue and chimney resistance

(*e*) compare this with the available chimney draught (Figure 1.A2.2) and adjust the chimney height to suit, recalculating where necessary to give the highest possible efflux velocity from the chimney.

1.A2.3 Chimney heights for non-sulphur-bearing fuels

The following procedure should be followed:

(*a*) assess the boiler plant heat input rate

(*b*) for single free-standing chimneys, read the corresponding chimney height from Figure 1.A2.3

(*c*) for single chimneys passing through, or adjacent to buildings (the more usual case), the additional height may be read off from Figure 1.A2.3 and added to the building height to give the final chimney height.

Where two or more chimneys are in close proximity, the height of each should be increased slightly as follows:

(*a*) find the individual final chimney heights as before

(*b*) express the separation between a pair of chimneys as a multiple of the free-standing height of the smaller chimney

(*c*) read off the height correction factor from Figure 1.A2.4; the required increase in height is then given by:

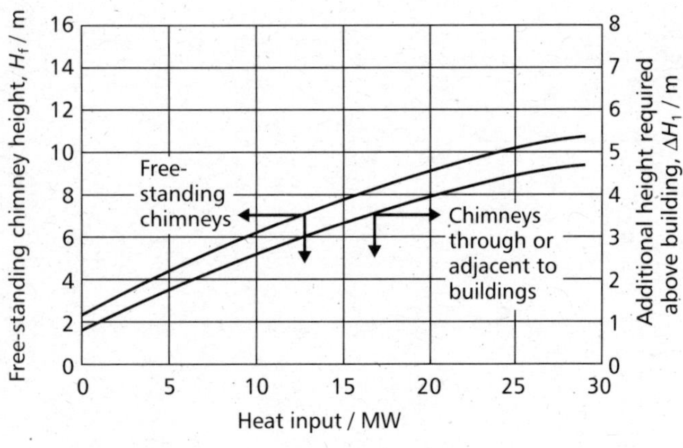

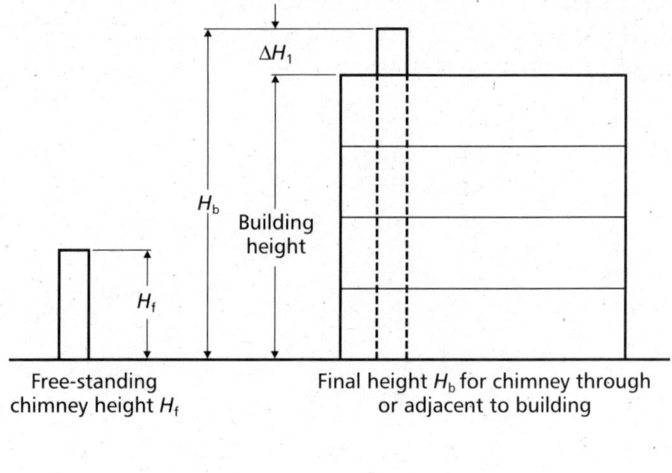

Figure 1.A2.3 Heights for single chimneys

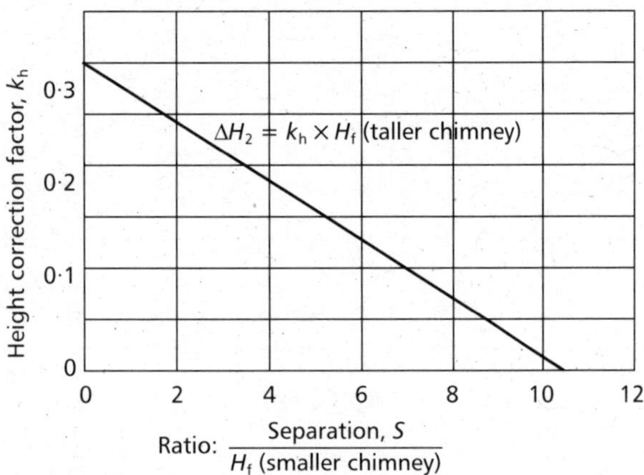

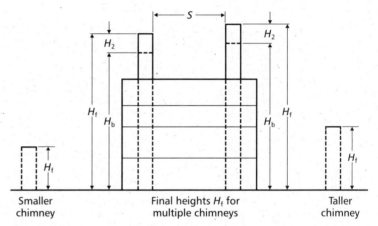

Figure 1.A2.4 Heights for adjacent chimneys

$$\Delta H_1 = k_h \times H_f \qquad (1.A2.5)$$

where ΔH_1 is the increase in height (m), k_h is the height correction factor and H_f is the free standing height of the taller chimney (m)

(*d*) repeat these steps for each pair of chimneys

(*e*) add the largest increase in height found to the final height of each chimney found as before.

Check that the height of each chimney provides the required combustion draught.

Example 1.A2.1

Figure 1.A2.5 shows a building 12 m high with three chimneys passing through it. If the heat inputs are 6 MW to A, 15 MW to B and 3 MW to C, determine the chimney heights.

From Figure 1.A2.3 (left axis), the free-standing heights are:

— chimney A: $H_f = 4.6$ m
— chimney B: $H_f = 7.8$ m
— chimney C: $H_f = 3.4$ m

From Figure 1.A2.3 (right axis), the heights to be added to that of the building are:

— chimney A: $\Delta H_1 = 1.9$ m
— chimney B: $\Delta H_1 = 3.3$ m
— chimney C: $\Delta H_1 = 1.4$ m

Using the values obtained for free-standing heights and the separations obtained from Figure 1.A2.5, the separations of pairs of chimneys expressed as a multiple of the free-standing height of the smaller chimney of each pair are AB = 2, BC = 5.4 and CA = 3.5.

From Figure 1.A2.4, the height corrections for chimney proximity are:

— chimney A: $k_h = 0.24$
— chimney B: $k_h = 0.15$
— chimney C: $k_h = 0.21$

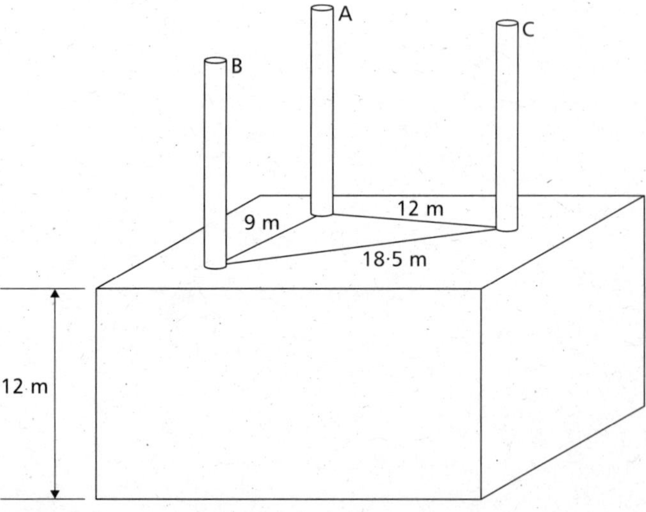

Figure 1.A2.5 Diagram for Example 1.A2.1

From equation 1.A2.5, the required increases in height are 2.1, 1.2 and 1, respectively, the largest of which must be added to the height of all three chimneys.

The final chimney heights are obtained by adding the height of the building, the additional heights above the building, ΔH_1, obtained from right-hand axis of Figure 1.A2.3 and the height corrections for chimney proximity, k_h.

Hence, final chimney heights are:

— chimney A: $H = 12 + 1.9 + 2.1 = 16$ m

— chimney B: $H = 12 + 3.3 + 2.1 = 17.4$ m

— chimney C: $H = 12 + 1.4 + 2.1 = 15.5$ m

The calculated chimney height may be then be used to check the available chimney draught at various flue gas temperatures by reference to Figure 1.A2.2.

1.A2.4 Determination of flue/chimney area

The area must be selected to provide the highest possible flue gas velocity and the smallest cooling area, bearing in mind the available draught and frictional resistance of the flue and chimney considered. In order to avoid down-wash, a chimney efflux velocity of approximately 7.5 to 9 m·s^{-1} is required, but this cannot always be achieved on natural draught plant. The procedure is as follows:

(*a*) Calculate the flue gas volume flow rates to be handled at full- and low-fire conditions at the temperatures involved at the particular boiler outlet.

(*b*) Select a flue gas velocity which appears reasonable for the plant considered (see Table 1.A2.3) and obtain the area equivalent from:

$$A = q_v / v \qquad (1.A2.6)$$

where A is the area equivalent (Table 1.A2.4) (m^2), q_v is the flue gas volume flow rate at full fire (m^3·s^{-1}) and v is the flue gas velocity (m·s^{-1}).

(*c*) Calculate the resistance to flow of a flue chimney, as follows. The pressure drop is calculated in the same manner as for ductwork. The total pressure drop is the sum of the pressure drop of the fittings and for the straight lengths of ductwork. For each fitting of the flue an additional pressure drop is given by:

$$\Delta p_1 = \zeta \, {}^1\!/_2 \, \rho \, v^2 \qquad (1.A2.7)$$

where Δp_1 is the pressure drop due to each ductwork fitting (Pa), ζ is the pressure loss factor for the fitting, ρ is the density of the flue gases (kg·m^{-1}). Velocity pressure for the flue gases at different temperatures and velocities are given in Table 1.A2.5.

For the straight lengths of ductwork there are no pre-calculated values. Thus equation 4.7 from section 4 of Guide C[(A2.3)] is used, as follows:

$$\Delta p_2 = \lambda \, (l / d_k) \, {}^1\!/_2 \, \rho \, v^2 \qquad (1.A2.8)$$

where Δp_2 is the pressure drop due to a straight length of ductwork (Pa), λ is the friction factor, l is the length of the straight ductwork (m), d_h is the hydraulic diameter (m) and v is the mean gas velocity (m·s^{-1}).

The total pressure drop is then given by:

$$\Delta p_t = \Sigma \Delta p_1 + \Sigma \Delta p_2 + \Delta p_d \qquad (1.A2.9)$$

where Δp_t is the total pressure drop (Pa) and Δp_d is the draught required at the boiler (Pa).

Some values of duct friction factors λ, are given in Table 1.A2.6 for a limited range of temperatures. Should there be a need to calculate the value of λ from first principles using Guide C[(A2.3)], knowledge of density ρ and viscosity η would be required in order to establish a value of Reynolds number, R_e. These should not differ significantly for the different flue gases resulting from combustion of different

Table 1.A2.4 Areas of various chimney sections

Circular and square sections			Rectangular and elliptical sections								
a/m	Area / m²		($a \times b$)	Area / m²		($a \times b$)	Area / m²		($a \times b$)	Area / m²	
	Circle	Square		Ellipse	Rectangle		Ellipse	Rectangle		Ellipse	Rectangle
0.3	0.07	0.09	0.3 × 0.4	0.09	0.12	0.9 × 1.0	0.71	0.90	1.5 × 1.6	1.88	2.40
0.4	0.13	0.16	0.3 × 0.5	0.12	0.15	0.9 × 1.1	0.78	0.99	1.5 × 1.7	2.00	2.55
0.5	0.20	0.25	0.3 × 0.6	0.14	0.18	0.9 × 1.2	0.85	1.08	1.5 × 1.8	2.12	2.70
0.6	0.28	0.36	0.4 × 0.5	0.16	0.20	1.0 × 1.1	0.86	1.10	1.6 × 1.7	2.13	2.72
0.7	0.39	0.49	0.4 × 0.6	0.19	0.24	1.0 × 1.2	0.94	1.20	1.6 × 1.8	2.26	2.88
0.8	0.50	0.64	0.4 × 0.7	0.22	0.28	1.0 × 1.3	1.02	1.30	1.6 × 1.9	2.39	3.04
0.9	0.64	0.81	0.5 × 0.6	0.24	0.30	1.1 × 1.2	1.04	1.32	1.7 × 1.8	2.40	3.06
1.0	0.79	1.00	0.5 × 0.7	0.27	0.35	1.1 × 1.3	1.12	1.43	1.7 × 1.9	2.53	3.23
1.1	0.95	1.21	0.5 × 0.8	0.31	0.40	1.1 × 1.4	1.21	1.54	1.7 × 2.0	2.67	3.40
1.2	1.12	1.44	0.6 × 0.7	0.33	0.42	1.2 × 1.3	1.22	1.56	1.8 × 1.9	2.68	3.42
1.3	1.33	1.69.	0.6 × 0.8	0.38	0.48	1.2 × 1.4	1.32	1.68	1.8 × 2.0	2.83	3.60
1.4	1.54	1.96	0.6 × 0.9	0.42	0.54	1.2 × 1.5	1.41	1.80	1.8 × 2.1	2.97	3.78
1.5	1.77	2.25	0.7 × 0.8	0.44	0.56	1.3 × 1.4	1.43	1.82	1.9 × 2.0	2.98	3.80
1.6	2.01	2.56	0.7 × 0.9	0.49	0.63	1.3 × 1.5	1.53	1.95	1.9 × 2.1	3.13	3.99
1.7	2.27	2.89	0.7 × 1.0	0.55	0.70	1.3 × 1.6	1.63	2.08	1.9 × 2.2	3.28	4.18
1.8	2.54	3.24	0.8 × 0.9	0.57	0.72	1.4 × 1.5	1.65	2.10	2.0 × 2.1	3.30	4.20
1.9	2.83	3.61	0.8 × 1.0	0.63	0.80	1.4 × 1.6	1.76	2.24	2.0 × 2.2	3.45	4.40
2.0	3.14	4.00	0.9 × 1.1	0.69	0.88	1.4 × 1.7	1.87	2.38	2.0 × 2.3	3.61	4.60

Table 1.A2.5 Velocity pressure ($^1/_2\,\rho v^2$) of flue gases at different temperatures

Velocity / m·s^{-1}	Velocity pressure ($^1/_2\,\rho\,v^2$) / Pa at stated temperature / °C									
	50	100	150	200	250	300	350	400	450	500
3	4.9	4.2	3.7	3.4	3.0	2.8	2.5	2.4	2.2	2.0
4	8.7	7.5	6.7	6.0	5.4	4.9	4.5	4.2	3.9	3.6
5	13.7	11.8	10.4	9.3	8.4	7.7	7.1	6.5	6.1	5.7
6	19.7	17.0	15.0	13.4	12.1	11.1	10.2	9.4	8.7	8.3
7	26.8	23.1	20.4	18.2	16.5	15.1	13.8	12.8	11.9	11.1
8	35.0	30.2	26.6	23.8	21.5	19.6	18.1	16.7	15.6	14.6
9	44.3	38.2	33.8	30.2	27.3	24.9	22.9	21.2	19.7	18.4
10	54.5	47.1	41.7	37.2	33.6	30.8	28.2	26.1	24.3	22.8
11	66.0	56.9	50.4	45.0	40.6	37.2	34.1	31.6	29.4	27.5
12	78.5	67.8	60.0	53.5	48.4	44.1	40.5	37.6	35.0	32.8
13	92.2	79.6	70.4	62.9	56.9	51.9	47.6	44.1	41.1	38.4
14	107	92.4	81.7	73.0	65.9	60.3	55.4	51.2	47.6	44.6
15	123	106	93.5	83.8	75.6	69.2	63.5	58.8	54.6	51.2
16	139	121	107	95.2	86.0	78.8	72.3	66.9	62.1	58.1
17	158	136	121	107	97.1	88.7	81.4	75.4	70.3	65.6
18	177	153	135	121	109	99.5	91.5	84.4	78.8	73.8

Table 1.A2.6 Values of duct friction factor λ for flue gases (valid for flue gas temperatures of 180–340 °C)

Flue hydraulic diameter / mm	Mean gas velocity/m·s^{-1}	Duct friction factor, λ		
		Smooth concrete or welded steel	Riveted steel or smooth cement pargeting	Brick or rough cement pargeting
150	1.5	0.0216	0.0276	0.0760
	3.0	0.0192	0.0264	0.0748
	4.5	0.0180	0.0256	0.0740
	≥ 6.0	0.0176	0.0252	0.0720
230	1.5	0.0188	0.0232	0.0720
	3.0	0.0172	0.0226	0.0704
	4.5	0.0160	0.0224	0.0684
	≥ 6.0	0.0156	0.0222	0.0672
305	1.5	0.0168	0.0216	0.0584
	3.0	0.0156	0.0204	0.0580
	4.5	0.0148	0.0200	0.0576
	≥ 6.0	0.0144	0.0196	0.0572
355	1.5	0.0160	0.0200	0.0552
	3.0	0.0146	0.0196	0.0540
	4.5	0.0140	0.0192	0.0520
	≥ 6.0	0.0136	0.0184	0.0520
460	1.5	0.0146	0.0188	0.0520
	3.0	0.0140	0.0180	0.0512
	4.5	0.0132	0.0176	0.0506
	≥ 6.0	0.0126	0.0172	0.0506
610	1.5	0.0144	0.0172	0.0500
	3.0	0.0132	0.0160	0.0492
	4.5	0.0124	0.0156	0.0480
	≥ 6.0	0.0120	0.0152	0.0476
1220	1.5	0.0120	0.0140	0.0444
	3.0	0.0108	0.0136	0.0440
	4.5	0.0104	0.0132	0.0436
	≥ 6.0	0.0100	0.0128	0.0432
1830	1.5	0.0108	0.0124	0.0404
	3.0	0.0100	0.0116	0.0392
	4.5	0.0096	0.0112	0.0388
	≥ 6.0	0.0092	0.0108	0.0380
1830	1.5	0.0108	0.0124	0.0404
	3.0	0.0100	0.0116	0.0392
	4.5	0.0096	0.0112	0.0388
	≥ 6.0	0.0092	0.0108	0.0380

fuels as the dominant constituent is nitrogen. Table 1.A2.7 gives values of flue gas density. In the absence of other information, the values of viscosity could be taken as those for nitrogen, to be found in Guide C[(A2.3)], Appendix 4.A1, Table 4.A1.5.

The total resistance obtained from equation 1.A2.9 must be compared with the available chimney draught. If the residual chimney draught is excessive, the flue areas can be recalculated using a higher flue gas velocity or a nozzle can be fitted to the chimney to take up the excessive draught by providing for increased efflux velocity. Down-wash of gases and inversion can occur at low velocities and a minimum efflux velocity of 7.5 $m{\cdot}s^{-1}$ will obviate these problems in general. Such a velocity may not be possible on small natural draught plants with non-pressurised combustion chambers as the above calculations will demonstrate. In such cases the maximum practicable efflux velocity should be sought.

Where high velocities are required, or where the flue run gives high resistance, the use of increased forced draught fan power and/or induced draught fans must be considered. The calculations are performed in a similar manner to ascertain the fan duties required to overcome the flue system resistances involved at the selected velocity.

The resistance to gas flow on low-fire should be assessed and compared with the available chimney draught. There may be excessive suction at the boiler outlet on low fire resulting in the need for control dampers/draught controllers where the values fall outside the manufacturers' stated limits.

Under high velocity flue conditions, the flues and chimneys will probably be under pressurised conditions. Extra care must be taken in flue/chimney construction where such running conditions are required and it is not good practice to pressurise flues/chimneys of brick construction.

References

A2.1 Clean Air Act (1993) (c. 11) (London: Her Majesty's Stationery Office) (1993)

A2.2 *Chimney Heights — Third edition of the 1956 Clean Air Act Memorandum* (London: Her Majesty's Stationery Office) (1981)

A2.3 *Reference data* CIBSE Guide C (London: Chartered Institution of Building Services Engineers) (2001)

2 Ventilation and air conditioning

2.1 Introduction

2.1.1 General

Ventilation and air conditioning of buildings are subjects of increasing interest because of their contribution to effective building performance and occupant satisfaction and the increasing focus on energy consumption and carbon emissions from buildings. A particular cause of interest is the revision of Part L[(1)] of the Building Regulations for England and Wales and the equivalent Part J of the Building Standards (Scotland) Regulations[(2)], which will set challenging new targets for energy efficiency of buildings. There is also a growing awareness of the connection between ventilation, building envelope and structural design issues[(3)], and there is growing interest in the whole life costs[(4)] and performance[(5)] of buildings. Since building services are required to operate throughout the life of the building, their operating costs are a very significant element of the whole life costs of the system. For all these reasons there is a need for up-to-date guidance on the design of these systems.

This guide is intended to be used by practising designers who hold a basic knowledge of the fundamentals of building physics and building services engineering.

The overall process of design development, from the initial outline design through system selection and detailed equipment specification, is summarised schematically in Figure 2.1.

2.1.2 Energy efficiency

The UK is committed to significantly reducing carbon emissions by the year 2010, with a target of a 20% cut based on 1990 levels. As well as maintaining the role of the Energy Efficiency Best Practice Programme to promote energy efficiency, the government has also introduced the Climate Change Levy, effectively a specific tax on energy use, and enhanced capital allowances for certain energy efficient measures.

It is intended that this will stimulate a greater interest in energy efficiency measures amongst building owners and operators, and that energy efficiency will be given a greater prominence in decisions about building design.

Allied to this is the introduction of the revised Part L of the Building Regulations in England and Wales[(1)]. This sets significantly more challenging targets for energy conservation aspects of buildings than has hitherto been the case. The combined effect of these regulatory measures is expected to be a significant improvement in energy performance, certainly in new buildings and those undergoing major refurbishment.

Recent studies suggest that there is likely to be a significant increase in energy consumption related to air conditioning. To meet the targets for reduced carbon emissions it is particularly important to ensure that such systems are as energy efficient as possible.

2.1.3 Whole life cost

It is now a requirement of public sector purchasers that they move to whole life cost based procurement[(8)]. The Private Finance Initiative (PFI) has already stimulated a marked increase in interest in whole life costing and there has been a growth in the availability of data to support the activity[(9)].

Proper design of ventilation and air conditioning systems can significantly reduce the whole life costs of the system. Costly modifications and alterations can be avoided by ensuring that the system requirements are properly defined and the design fully addresses the requirements.

Buildings have to adapt and change in response to business needs. Taking account of this at the design stage can also help to ensure that the system is designed to enable such adaptations to be carried out in the most cost effective manner, again reducing the whole life costs of the system.

2.1.4 Building performance

There has been growing evidence for a number of years that the effectiveness of building ventilation has a significant effect on the performance of those working in the building. Poor indoor air quality impairs the performance of employees in a workspace. Evans et al.[(10)] have estimated that design, build and operating costs are in the ratio 1:5:200. It can therefore be seen that poor standards of building ventilation can have a significant negative effect on operating costs through their adverse effect on employee performance – given that the cost of running and staffing the business is the most significant to users. Over a system life of ten to fifteen years a 1% reduction in productivity may easily equal any ‘savings’ made on the design and installation costs of the system. So it is worthwhile for building owners and operators to ensure that buildings are ventilated to provide a healthy and effective environment.

2.2 Integrated approach

2.2.1 Introduction

In selecting an appropriate ventilation strategy thought must be given primarily to meeting the requirements of the people and processes that occupy the building without being excessive and therefore wasteful. However the pursuance of

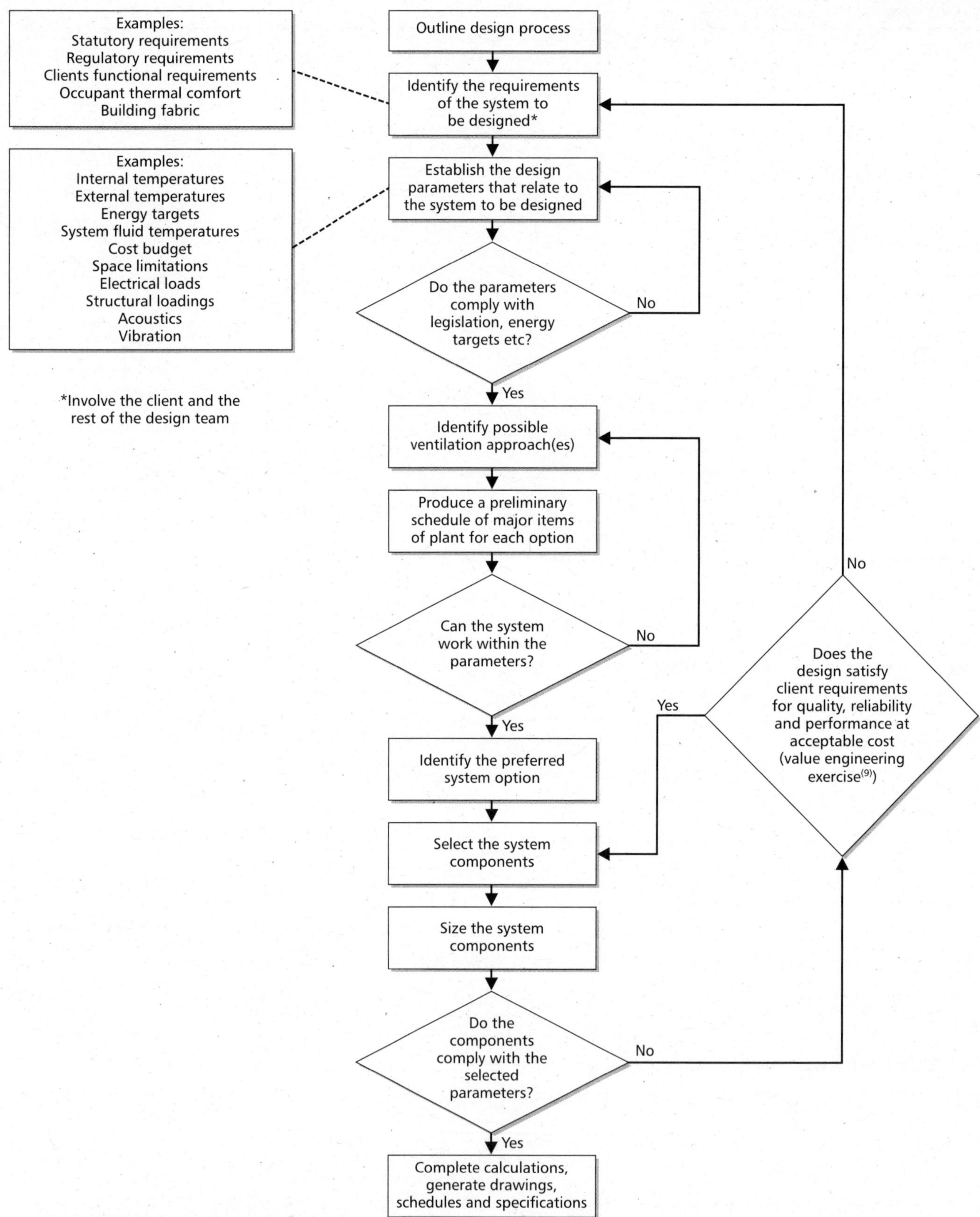

Figure 2.1 Outline design process; ventilation and air conditioning

an integrated design approach to achieve this also links the ventilation strategy with the design of the building fabric, in that as a pre-requisite all reasonable steps should be taken to maximise the potential of the fabric. This is also commonly referred to as the 'passive approach'. In particular, an appropriate degree of airtightness should be aimed at[11]. The design process must be based on a clear understanding of client and end user needs and expectations and must be followed by effective commissioning, handover and building management. Close collaboration between the architect, services and structural engineers and the client is essential from the earliest stages of the outline design process.

This section considers:

— the identification of key building performance requirements for the application of ventilation in support of these requirements

Table 2.1 Establishing performance requirements

Issue	Requirement/comments
Client brief	— To be developed in the context of the other issues
Integrated design	— Co-ordinated approach by the architect and other specialists from outline design, see section 2.2.3.1
Energy/environmental targets	— Use of existing specifications or appropriate advice from the design team required, see section 2.2.2.1 — Compatibility with indoor environment standards
Indoor environmental standards	— Use of existing standards or appropriate advice from the design team required, see section 2.3 and CIBSE Guide A[2] — Areas or objects with special requirements
Provision of controls	— Individual, local, team, zone or centralised basis — Required closeness of control (e.g. of temperature, humidity, air quality, air flow) — The required interaction of the end user with the building services, see section 2.2.2.2 — The required basis of control, e.g. temperature, CO_2, CO or other
Demands of the building occupants and activities[4]	— The business process(es) to be undertaken in the building may demand specified levels of availability of ventilation — Work patterns over space and over time (regularity, shifts, team structure) — Cellular and open plan mix with associated partitioning strategy and likelihood of change — Occupancy numbers and anticipated maximum occupancy over the building lifetime that might need to be taken into account — Average occupancy density and any areas of high or low density — Functions of space use, processes contained therein and subsequent internal loads (e.g. standard office space, meeting rooms, lecture theatres, photocopying rooms, sports hall, laboratories, manufacturing environments, retail space) — Anticipated diversity of internal loads
Investment criteria	— Constraints imposed by 'letability' requirements
Value engineering and whole life costs	— Understanding of the client's priorities towards capital cost and issues of whole life costs[5–8] — Requirements for calculations to be carried out on systems or system elements and the basis for these calculations[4,9,10] — Has the client been involved in discussions of acceptable design risk? — The importance of part load performance
Reliability	— The business process(es) to be undertaken in the building may demand specified levels of reliability of the ventilation systems
Maintenance requirements[11]	— Understanding of the client's ability to carry out, or resource, maintenance — Client willingness for maintenance to take place in the occupied space — Any requirement for 'standard' or 'familiar' components
Associated systems	— Implications of any particular requirements, e.g. fire, security, lighting, acoustic consideration.
Security	— Restrictions on size and location of any openings
Future needs	— Adaptability, i.e. the identified need to cope with future change of use — Flexibility, i.e. the identified need to cope with future changes in work practices within the current building use[2] — Acceptable design margins: it is important to distinguish, in collaboration with the client, between design that is adequate for current requirements (which may not be currently accepted best practice), design which makes sensible agreed allowances for future changes and over-design[12]
Aesthetic considerations	— The need for system concealment — Restriction on placement of grilles, diffusers etc. — Restrictions imposed by local authorities, building listing etc.
Procurement issues	— Time constraints — Programming constraints, particularly for refurbishment projects

— key factors to be considered in terms of an integrated approach to building design

— issues relevant to the selection of specific ventilation strategies, i.e. natural or mechanical ventilation, comfort cooling or air conditioning, or mixed mode; see section 2.4 for more detailed information on these issues.

Information on the determination of suitable ventilation rates is given in section 2.3. See also CIBSE Guide A: *Environmental design*[12] for information on comfort criteria.

2.2.2 Establishing key performance requirements

The key performance requirements that need to be clarified before a ventilation strategy can be selected are summarised in Table 2.1. Ideally, where the issues highlighted in the table have not been covered within the specification documents, the design team should expect to agree requirements with the client at the outset of the project to optimise the choice of strategy. If the client is unable to advise on the precise needs, they must at least be made aware of any limitations of the chosen design.

The design team should also be able to advise the client of the cost implications (on a whole life basis[4,8] if requested) of meeting their stated requirements. Requirements may subsequently be adjusted over the course of the project to meet financial constraints or changing business needs. The design team must also be able to advise on the impact of any such changes on building performance.

An appreciation of the issues shown in Table 2.1 is an essential part of the briefing process. Further guidance on briefing as it applies to building services is given in *Project Management Handbook for Building Services*[13].

2.2.2.1 Energy and environmental targets

The chosen ventilation strategy influences, or is influenced by, the setting of appropriate energy and environmental targets and the selection of suitable indoor environmental standards. For example, meeting a stringent energy target may not be compatible with the provision of close control of temperature and humidity.

Initial agreement should be reached on the standards required. Checks should be carried out continuously by the design team to ensure that the implications of any changes made during design, construction, or subsequent fit-out are understood and mutually acceptable.

Documents are available to assist in setting energy and environmental targets for a number of domestic and non-domestic building types, including:

— CIBSE TM22: *Energy Assessment and Reporting Methodology*[19], which provides energy benchmarks and target assessment methods for dealing with banks and similar agencies, hotels, offices and mixed use buildings. Table 2.2, reproduced from TM22 provides energy usage benchmarks for 'good practice' and 'typical' performance, based on four generic office classifications. TM22 also contains a breakdown by end usage for fans, lighting and desk equipment for each office type.

— The Energy Consumption Guides[20], published under the government's Energy Efficiency Best Practice Programme, which provide energy benchmarks and targets for industrial buildings, offices, public houses, hotels, hospitals, domestic properties, nursing and residential homes, and other non-domestic sectors.

— Building Maintenance Information's report *Energy benchmarking in the retail sector*[21], which provides energy benchmarks within the retail sector.

— The *Building Research Establishment Environmental Assessment Method* (BREEAM)[22], which provides an environmental assessment methodology for industrial units, offices, superstores and supermarkets and housing.

— BSRIA's *Environmental code of practice for buildings and their services*[23] provides a guide to, and case studies on, the consideration of environmental issues during the procurement process; this guidance is applicable to all types of property.

2.2.2.2 Provision of controls: end-user perspective

The provision of a suitable mechanism for the end user to control conditions within their workplace environment is fundamental to users' satisfaction with it. Any requirements of the client must be considered in the light of the designer's own experience of end user behaviour, in particular:

— ensuring fairness and consistency of control by avoiding occupants being unduly affected by controls from which they do not benefit

— providing rapid acting controls that give feedback to occupants to demonstrate response

— making sensible decisions with regards to the choice of manual versus automatic control (manual overrides should be provided where practical) any automatic change in state should happen gradually to avoid feelings of discomfort

— removing unnecessary complexity by providing controls that are simple and well labelled

Further guidance on these issues can be found in work by BRE[24] and Bordass et al[25].

Table 2.2 Office system and building energy benchmarks[13]

Fuel/application	Delivered energy for stated office classification* / $kW \cdot h \cdot m^{-2}$							
	Type 1		Type 2		Type 3		Type 4	
	Good practice	Typical	Good practice	Typical	Good practice	Typical	Good practice	Typical
Fossil fuels:								
— gas/oil heating and hot water	79	151	79	151	97	178	107	201
— catering (gas)	0	0	0	0	0	0	7	9
Electricity:								
— cooling	0	0	1	2	14	31	21	41
— fans, pumps and controls	2	6	4	8	30	60	36	67
— humidification	0	0	0	0	8	18	12	23
— lighting	14	23	22	38	27	54	29	60
— office equipment	12	18	20	27	23	31	23	32
— computer room	0	0	0	0	14	18	87	105
Total gas or oil	79	151	79	151	97	178	114	210
Total electricity	33	54	54	85	128	226	234	358

* Type 1: cellular, naturally ventilated; Type 2: open plan, naturally ventilated; Type 3: standard air conditioned; Type 4: prestige air conditioned

2.2.3 Interaction with fabric/facilities

2.2.3.1 Building fabric

The final ventilation rate is based on fresh air requirements and any additional ventilation required for comfort and cooling purposes based on estimates of:

— internal gains determined by the occupants, e.g. occupancy itself, lighting and small power loads

— internal gains determined by the fabric, e.g. insulation, glazing, thermal mass

Although the architect is associated with making many of the fabric-related decisions, the building services engineer must be able to advise on their implications for ventilation, energy use etc. and must therefore be involved in the decision making process as far as is practical, and at as early a stage as possible. The building services engineer should also be consulted prior to any changes which could affect ventilation system performance.

To engage effectively with the architect, the building services engineer must be able to enter into a dialogue on the issues introduced in Table 2.3, as a minimum. (Note that this table focuses solely on issues relating to the interaction between the building fabric and services. To these must be added, for example, consideration of the building function and broader issues, as raised in Table 2.1). Where the ventilation strategy for the building depends on its thermal mass, early consultation with the structural engineer is also needed to consider, for example, the implications for roof design. At some point it may also be necessary to involve a façade specialist, who could advise the client accordingly.

It is important to note that maximising the 'passive contribution' to be gained from the building fabric itself requires an understanding of both the advantages and disadvantages of this approach. For example, external shading reduces the need for cooling but increased insulation and airtightness may lead to the need for increased ventilation and cooling.

For a detailed explanation of the role of the building fabric in contributing to an energy efficient solution see CIBSE Guide F[26] and other publications referenced in Table 2.3. It is also important to consider the risks of air leakage through the building fabric and its subsequent impact on infiltration rates and heat loss calculations[1]. The most common air-leakage risks are:

— at junctions between the main structural elements

— at the joints between walling components

— around windows, doors and roof lights

— through gaps in membranes, linings and finishes,

— at service penetrations, e.g. gas and electricity entry points and overflow pipes

— around access and emergency openings

— through some building materials, e.g. poor quality brickwork may be permeable

2.2.3.2 Interaction with the lighting system

The design strategy for daylight provision forms part of the selection process for window and glazing types and shading devices[29]. Integration of the electric lighting system to minimise its impact on the design and operation of the ventilation system requires that internal gains from the lighting be minimised through[31,32]:

— the selection of appropriate light levels, differentiating between permanently occupied workspaces and circulation areas;

— the selection of efficient light fittings (decorative fittings may have a lower efficiency)

— the installation of an appropriate lighting control system, relative to time of day and occupancy level

— the use of ventilated light fittings

Consideration should be given to the impact of the chosen ventilation strategy on the lighting system, e.g. the use of uplighting with exposed thermal mass[33]. The integration of exposed thermal mass is discussed in section 2.4.7.

2.2.3.3 Small power loads

Small power loads arising from IT and other office-type equipment are an increasingly significant component of internal gains. Accounting for them in the design of the ventilation system requires a realistic calculation of their impact in terms of peak load and anticipated diversity. In order to reduce internal gains the designer should:

— encourage the client to select low energy equipment and introduce power cut-off mechanisms

— locate shared equipment, e.g. vending machines, photocopiers, in a space that can be readily cooled.

2.2.4 Purpose of ventilation systems

In designing any ventilation system it is necessary to understand the functions required of it, see Table 2.4. In summary these are:

— to provide adequate indoor air quality by removing and/or diluting pollutants from occupied spaces

— to provide adequate ventilation for the effective operation of processes

— to provide a heat exchange mechanism

— to prevent condensation within the building fabric.

Consideration of the requirements of each function within offices is given in section 2.3.2 and in other sectors in sections 2.3.3 to 2.3.24. In winter, any heat exchange above that needed to control air quality has a heating energy penalty. The relative importance of excess winter ventilation increases with increasing thermal insulation standards. In summer, however, ventilation rates above those required for reasons of air quality may reduce the demand for mechanical cooling, although this will only be possible if the outside air temperature is lower than the room temperature. Even if inside and outside temperatures are similar, increased air movement can create a sense of freshness and increased occupant satisfaction with the internal environment. The advantage of 'free' cooling by

Table 2.3 Issues influencing the choice of ventilation strategy

Issue	Comments
Location (see Figure 2.2)[27]	Adjacent buildings can adversely affect wind patterns. The proximity of external sources of pollution can influence the feasibility of natural ventilation. The proximity of external sources of noise can impact on the feasibility of natural ventilation.
Pollution	Local levels of air pollution may limit the opportunity for natural ventilation. It may not be possible to provide air inlets at positions suitable for natural ventilation given the inability to filter the incoming air successfully[28].
Orientation[26]	Buildings with their main facades facing north and south are much easier to protect from excessive solar gain in summer. West façade solar gain is the most difficult to control as high gains occur late in the day. Low sun angles occurring at certain times of year affect both east and west facing facades.
Form[26]	At building depths greater than 15 m the ventilation strategy becomes more complex; the limit for daylighting and single-sided natural ventilation is often taken as 6 m. An atrium can enhance the potential for natural ventilation, see section 2.2.5.1.
	Tall buildings can affect the choice of ventilation system due to wind speeds and exposure. Adequate floor to ceiling heights are required for displacement ventilation and buoyancy driven natural ventilation; a minimum floor to ceiling height of 2.7 m is recommended, see section 2.4.3.
Insulation	Insulation located on the external surface de-couples the mass of the structure from the external surface and enables it to stabilise the internal environment. In well-insulated buildings provision must be made for the removal of excess heat, for example through night cooling, see section 2.4.7.
Infiltration[11,39]	Ventilation strategies, whether natural or mechanically driven, depend on the building fabric being appropriately airtight. This implies a good practice standard of 5 $m^3 \cdot h^{-1}$ per m^2 of façade (excluding consideration of the ground floor) and requires suitable detailing. Site quality checks should be followed by air leakage pressure testing as part of the commissioning requirement.
Shading[26,27]	The appropriate use of external planting or other features can reduce solar gain. In terms of effective reduction of solar gain, shading devices can be ranked in order of effectiveness as follows: external (most effective), mid pane, internal (least effective), see Figure 2.3.
	Horizontal shading elements are most appropriate for reducing high angle solar gains, for example in summer time on south facing facades. Vertical shading devices are most appropriate for reducing low angle solar gain, e.g. on east and west facades. Control of solar shading devices should be linked with that of the ventilation system. Glare must be controlled to avoid a default to 'blinds-down' and 'lights-on' operation.
Window choice[28]	Openable areas must be controllable in both summer and winter, e.g. large openings for still summer days and trickle ventilation for the winter time. Window shape can affect ventilation performance; deep windows can provide better ventilation than shallow. High level openings provide cross ventilation, low level openings provide local ventilation, although draughts should be avoided at working level. The location of the opening areas affects the ability of the window to contribute to night cooling (see section 2.4.7). Window operation must not be affected by the choice of shading device. See section 2.5.3 for details of window characteristics.
Glazing[29,30]	Total solar heat transmission through window glazing can vary over a sixfold range, depending on the combination of glass and shading mechanisms selected. Figure 2.3 shows the relative effectiveness of eight glazing and shading systems. Figure 2.3 underlines the importance of decisions about glazing and shading to the overall ventilation strategy.
	At concept stage the percentage of glazed area (normally 20–40% of façade area) and selection of glazing type must balance thermal, ventilation and lighting needs. The choice includes single, double, triple glazing with selective coatings or gaseous fill. The type of coating may have a greater influence than the glazing type. Ideal glazing is transparent to long-wave radiation and reflective to short-wave radiation. Selective low-emissivity double-glazing is equivalent to air-filled triple-glazing.
	The use of tinted glazing may increase the use of supplementary electric lighting, increasing internal heat gains and energy use. Window frame construction and detailing must also be considered.
Thermal mass	Thermal mass is used to reduce peak cooling demands and stabilise internal radiant and air temperatures. The first 50 to 100 mm of the structure is most effective on a 24-hour basis. Thermal mass can be introduced into the ceiling/floor slab (most effective), walls or partitions, but must be 'accessible' in all cases. Heat transfer can be via the surface of the material or via cores/channels within it. The exposure of thermal mass has architectural and other servicing implications, although these effects can be reduced, e.g. by the use of perforated ceilings. See section 2.4.7 for further details of incorporating thermal mass.

natural rather than mechanical ventilation is that the fan energy, as well as the heat gained by the supply air, is eliminated.

The design requirement for an energy efficient ventilation system is to create a satisfactory internal environment given that the cooling potential of natural ventilation is limited, see sections 2.2.5 and 2.4.3. There is also less flexibility for air distribution since natural ventilation usually relies on supply air from the perimeter of the building. In contrast, mechanical ventilation can be supplied to any part of a building through the distribution ducts.

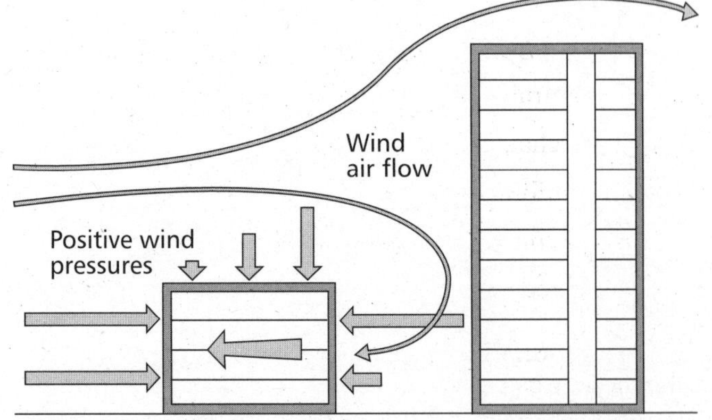

Figure 2.2 Impact of localised wind effects

Table 2.4 Purposes of ventilation

Purpose	Explanation
To provide sufficient 'background' ventilation for occupants in terms of air quality for breathing and odour control	Typical rates need to be increased where smoking is permitted or additional sources of pollution are present. Most pollutants originate from sources other than people but in such cases general ventilation has been shown to be much less effective than treating the problems at source: e.g. by specification, cleanliness and local extraction.
To provide natural cooling during the occupied period	Care must be taken to avoid excessive air change rates that may cause draughts or disturb documents. Higher rates may be practicable in spaces occupied transitionally, such as atria. The balance point above which mechanical cooling will provide a more effective solution should be considered.
To provide natural cooling outside the normal occupied period	Night cooling or 'night purging' can remove heat built-up in a structure and its contents, and provide some pre-cooling for the following day. Practical limitations will exist in terms of acceptable secure openable areas in the case of natural ventilation and on duct size and fan energy consumption for ducted mechanical systems.
To exhaust heat and/or pollutants from localised sources or areas	Examples are kitchens, toilets, vending areas and equipment rooms. This enables adjacent areas to be more comfortable with less conditioning of the air. Such systems often need to operate for longer hours than those serving the main spaces, therefore independent extract systems are preferred.
To act as a carrier mechanism for mechanical cooling and/or humidity control	This can be either via an all-air system, in which the air is treated centrally, or via air/water or unitary systems in which the air is recirculated and treated locally.
To prevent condensation within the building fabric[34]	Adequate ventilation for condensation control exceeds the minimum rate of fresh air necessary for health and comfort. There is a specific need to address the ventilation of areas where moisture generating activities occur.
To enable the efficient operation of processes	Needs are entirely dependent on the process. Ventilation may be required to ensure safe combustion or to ensure that machinery is maintained within a suitable temperature range, e.g. lift motor rooms.

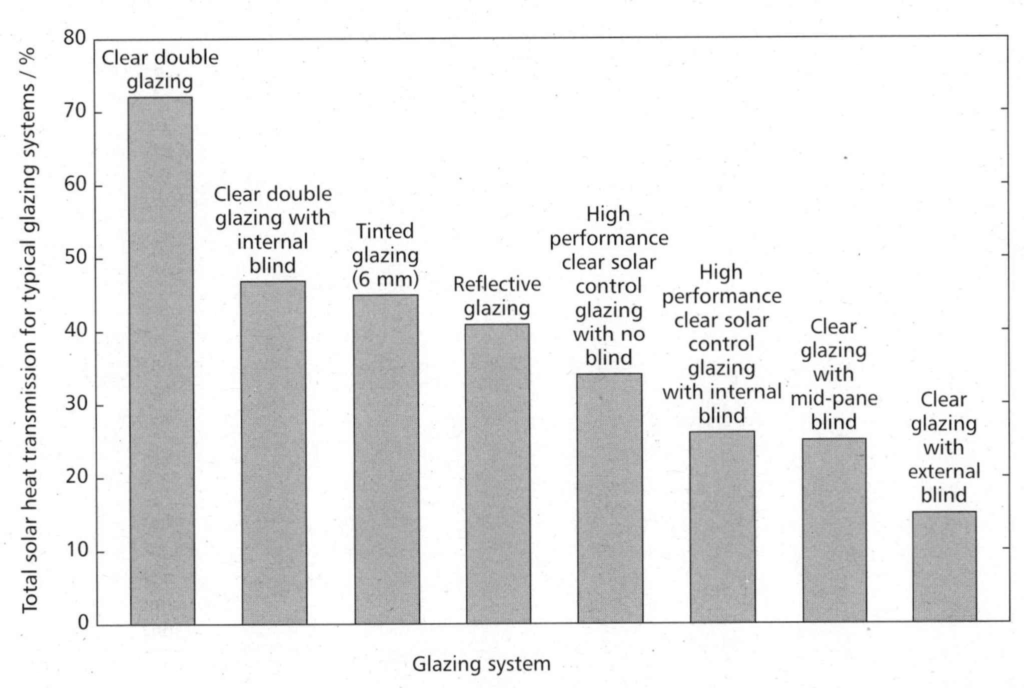

Figure 2.3 Total relative solar heat transmission for typical glazing systems (courtesy of Ove Arup & Partners)

2.2.5 Choice of ventilation strategy

This section gives an overview of the following strategies:

- natural ventilation
- mechanical ventilation
- comfort cooling
- air conditioning (which may be 'close control')
- mixed mode systems

The selection of a strategy is affected by location, plan depth, heat gains, internal and external pollutant sources, economics, energy and environmental concerns and internal layout. Ultimately it is the use and occupancy of a space that determines the ventilation needs. There is no universal economic solution, although there are some best practice indicators that are considered in subsequent sections. Each ventilation system design must be evaluated on its merits, to suit the particular circumstances.

Excessive air infiltration can destroy the performance of a ventilation strategy[11], hence good ventilation system design should be combined with optimum air tightness to achieve energy efficient ventilation. Inclusion of a requirement for air tightness in a specification does not lead to the choice of a particular design strategy. For example, mechanical ventilation is not necessarily the inevitable consequence of requiring that a building be airtight. Applying the axiom 'build tight, ventilate right', ventilation via natural openings may be suitable.

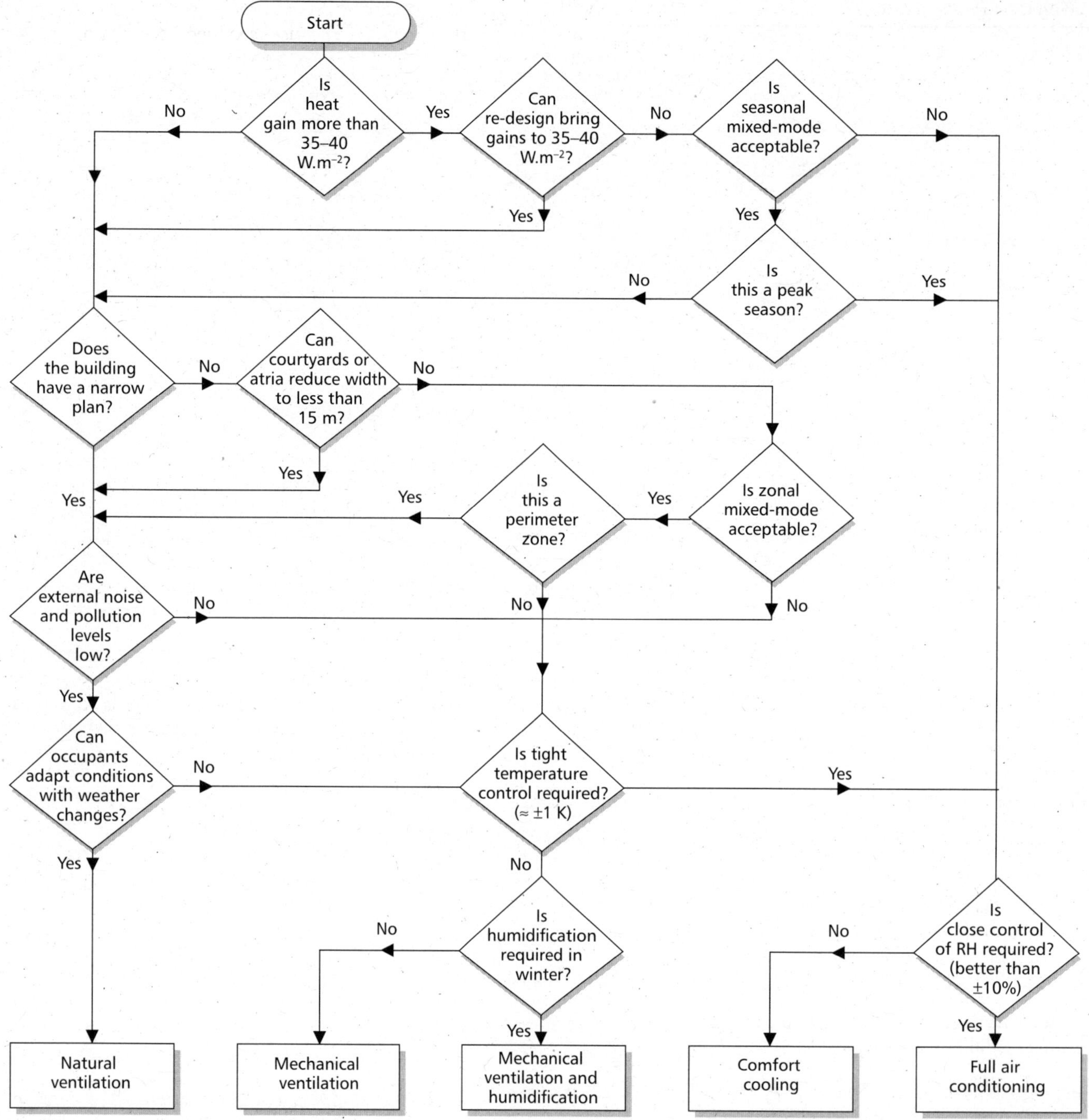

Figure 2.4 Selecting a ventilation strategy[27]

However, it cannot be assumed that a mechanically ventilated building is suitably airtight.

The client needs to understand and accept the ramifications of the selected strategy. Figure 2.4[27] illustrates a typical, broad-brush decision-making process, while Table 2.5 shows the limits of natural ventilation. However, Figure 2.4 and Table 2.5 are of particular reference to office environments and are not necessarily appropriate for other building types. See section 2.4 for details of individual strategies and further guidance on their selection.

2.2.5.1 Natural ventilation

Natural ventilation may be defined as ventilation that relies on moving air through a building under the natural forces of wind and buoyancy.

Wind driven ventilation can be single sided (through a single or double opening) or cross flow, which is more effective. Buoyancy driven ventilation can be assisted by stacks, wind towers, atria rooflights, conservatories, or by the façade itself.

Natural ventilation is generally applicable in many building types (industrial buildings being a possible exception) of up to 15 m depth, or greater if designed appropriately. The effective depth over which particular options are viable is the key limitation, see Table 2.5. However, this cannot be applied universally since few data exist for buildings with floor-to-ceiling heights greater than 3.5 m[27].

If the internal heat gains rise above 40 $W{\cdot}m^{-2}$, natural ventilation by itself may be inadequate and a strategy involving mechanical assistance will be required[27]. Table 2.6 illustrates how the design of the building fabric might be

Table 2.5 Natural ventilation options and their effective depth

Strategy	Effective depth relative to office floor-to-ceiling height
Single sided, single opening	2 × floor-to-ceiling height
Single sided, double opening	2.5 × floor-to-ceiling height
Cross flow	5 × floor-to-ceiling height
Stack ventilation	5 × floor-to-ceiling height
Atria	10 × floor-to-ceiling if centrally located

Table 2.6 Relationship between design features and heat gains

Design features	Total heat gains* / W·m^{-2} floor area			
	10	20	30	40
	Minimum room height / m			
	2.5	2.7	2.9	3.1
Controllable window opening (to 10 mm)	Essential	Essential	Essential	Essential
Trickle vents for winter	Essential	Essential	Essential	Essential
Control of indoor air quality	May be required	May be required	Essential	Essential
Design for daylight to reduce gains	May be required	Essential	Essential	Essential
Daylight control of electric lighting	May be required	May be required	Essential	Essential
100% shading from direct sun	May be required	Essential	Essential	Essential
Cooling by daytime ventilation only	Essential	Essential	Problem	Problem
Cooling by day and night ventilation	Not necessary	May be required	Essential	Essential
Exposed thermal mass	Not necessary	Not necessary	Essential	Essential

* i.e. people + lights + office equipment + solar gain

adapted to help meet this target[27]. However, this table is indicative of scale only and will vary depending on the characteristics of the particular building and on the freedom or otherwise allowed to the designer by such characteristics.

Further details of natural ventilation systems, including key components and design methods, are given in section 2.4.3.

Key characteristics of natural ventilation to be borne in mind include:

— *Risk of draught*: attention must be paid to the size and location of openings and their control.

— *User control*: users are reported to favour access to openable windows.

— *Closeness of control*: close control over temperature and humidity is not possible.

— *Capital costs*: costs are heavily influenced by the complexity of the window or ventilator design and by the building form necessary to achieve effective natural ventilation.

— *Running costs*: automated window opening will incur maintenance costs.

— *Flexibility*: this is difficult to achieve if extensive partitioning is introduced. Natural ventilation may reach its limits if heat gains increase.

— *Predictability*: performance can be modelled in theory, but in practice is subject to variation in the motivating forces of wind and weather

— *Noise*: there are no problems with plant noise but there may be an issue with external noise or transmission of internal noise.

— *Ability to deal with polluted environments*: filtration is very difficult due to the pressure drops involved.

— *Winter ventilation*: needs careful design in areas of high occupancy.

2.2.5.2 Mechanical ventilation

Mechanical ventilation may be defined as the movement of air through a building using fan power; filtration and heating of the air may also take place.

The most common strategy is 'balanced supply and extract'. Other options are mechanical supply and natural extract, natural supply and mechanical extract, natural extract and mixed supply (as used in some industrial buildings).

The ventilation delivery method may be either displacement (laminar or piston flow) ventilation, or mixing (turbulent) ventilation systems. The former introduces 'fresh' air gently, normally at low level, at a temperature close to that of the room air. Warm polluted air is extracted at ceiling height. In the latter system air entering the space is thoroughly mixed with air within the space. The distribution mechanisms can be via a floor, ceiling or wall supply.

The main roles for mechanical ventilation without the use of mechanical cooling are:

— to provide adequate background fresh air ventilation or compensate for natural means when they are inadequate for occupant well being

— to provide fresh air ventilation for fume control, when a fixed rate would normally be applied

— to cool the building when the outside air is at an appropriate temperature.

There is a considerable difference in the supply air rates for each role. Therefore if a single system is required to combine these roles it would need to be capable of variable volume flow. The typical supply air rates for background ventilation are between one and two air changes per hour (ACH) and the rate to achieve adequate cooling by ventilation is of the order 5–10 ACH, see section 2.4.2.

For further details of mechanical ventilation systems refer to section 2.4.4. Where mechanical systems are combined with openable windows, this is known as a 'mixed mode' approach, see section 2.4.5.

Key performance characteristics

Key characteristics of mechanical ventilation to be borne in mind include:

— *Risk of draught*: in theory, the draught risk is controllable provided that the system is appropriately designed and integrated.

— *User control*: control can be provided at an individual level, regardless of location; but it can be costly.

- *Closeness of control*: close control over temperature and humidity is possible (subject to air being at a suitable temperature), but with higher energy use.
- *Capital costs*: costs are heavily influenced by the amount of mechanical plant required and whether the façade is sealed; alternatively a mixed mode approach requires openings in the fabric.
- *Running costs*: maintenance costs depend on the quantity of plant. Energy costs depend on the fan pressure drop of the mechanical system and the efficiency of heat recovery (if any).
- *Flexibility*: can be achieved but with cost penalties.
- *Predictability*: performance can be predicted with appropriate commissioning and maintenance.
- *Noise*: external and fan noise can be reduced through attenuation, a space allowance will be required.
- *Ability to deal with polluted environments*: filtration is possible in harsh environments.

'Free cooling' versus mechanical cooling

Using mechanical ventilation for cooling (i.e. 'free cooling') requires careful consideration. The energy used to transport the air can be greater than the delivered cooling energy. At worst, the work involved in moving the air (both supply and recirculated) will raise its temperature, resulting in warming of the building. Therefore there is an energy balance to be struck between moving small amounts of cold air and large amounts of tempered or ambient air.

An obvious problem with using outside air ventilation without mechanical cooling as a means of cooling a building is that the temperature of the outside air is generally higher than the inside temperature at the times when cooling is most necessary. This can partly be remedied by using overnight cooling, see section 2.4.7. However, this is less energy efficient than daytime cooling, and the benefits of natural as opposed to mechanical night cooling would need to be considered.

2.2.5.3 Comfort cooling and air conditioning

Comfort cooling may be defined as the use of mechanical cooling to maintain control over the maximum air temperature achieved in the space. As a consequence there may be some incidental dehumidification of the supply air.

Air conditioning involves full control over the humidity within the conditioned space as well as temperature control. A further refinement is 'close control' air conditioning. There are many definitions of what is meant by 'close'. For example, in the context of the suitability of natural ventilation, see Figure 2.4, 'tight' temperature control is defined as ±1 K (air temperature) and 'close' control of humidity as better than ±10%. Specific circumstances may require more precise control, e.g. ±5% RH and ±1 K, or ±2% RH and ±0.5 K in critical areas. It is therefore important for the client and designer to have agreed these parameters.

Various options are available for both the generation and distribution/delivery of cooling. Traditional mechanical refrigeration and alternative means of generating cooling are considered in sections 2.4.6 to 2.4.22, which also provide design information for the full range of distribution systems. Key distribution system components are discussed in section 2.5.

A broad categorisation of heating, ventilation and air conditioning (HVAC) systems is given in Table 2.7. However, the performance characteristics of individual systems within the broad categories will vary greatly. It is also possible for systems to differ in whether, for example, they:

- operate as single or multiple zone
- employ full fresh air or recirculation
- have humidification or dehumidification potential.

The choice of the optimum system will depend on the particular circumstances and client's own priorities and, in the case of a refurbishment project, it may also be affected by the existing building services. Table 2.8 provides some assessment criteria that might be used to compare systems from the perspective of both the client and the design team. These may be supplemented to suit the context.

2.2.5.4 Mixed mode systems

Mixed mode may be defined as the combination of natural and mechanical ventilation and/or cooling systems.

Sub-classifications of mixed mode systems are[1]:

- *Contingency designs*: these are usually naturally ventilated buildings which have been planned to permit the selective addition of mechanical ventilation and cooling systems where this is needed at a subsequent date. The converse can apply.
- *Complementary systems*: natural and mechanical systems are designed for integrated operation. This is the most common variety of mixed mode. Systems can operate in a concurrent manner (simultaneously) or in a changeover manner (on a relatively frequent basis, or alternately on a less frequent basis).
- *Zoned systems*: these allow for differing servicing strategies to occur in different parts of the

Table 2.7 Broad categorisation of comfort cooling and air conditioning systems

Type	Description	Typical systems
All-air	Employing central plant and ductwork distribution to treat and move all the air supplied to the conditioned space, with fine-tuning of the supply temperature or volume occurring at the terminals	VAV and its variants, dual-duct, hot deck-cold deck
Air/water or air/refrigerant	Usually employing central plant to provide fresh air only, terminals being used to mix re-circulated air with primary air and to provide fine-tuning of the room temperature	Fan coils, VRF units, induction units, reversible heat pumps, chilled ceilings
Unitary	Small-scale versions of single zone systems within packaged units	Fan coils, reversible heat pumps, split systems, room air conditioners

Table 2.8 Possible system assessment criteria

Criterion	Comments
Control	Suitability for precise temperature control Suitability for precise humidity control
Design	Availability of guidance to assist in system design Ease of design Availability of performance data
End user acceptability	Availability of end user control
Robustness to poor design	Familiarity of client with proposed system Level of tailoring required for standard system to suit particular context
Ventilation and cooling performance	Ability to be zoned Risk of draughts Noise generation Maximum cooling load that can be handled Ability to cope with frequent variations in load Ability to cope with semi-permanent variations in load Potential for use in mixed mode systems
Indoor air quality	Ability to provide an appropriate quality of indoor air, free from contaminants and odours
Economic performance	Capital costs Life cycle costs Energy costs
Installation, commissioning and handover	Installation time Ease of installation Ease of commissioning
Flexibility	Ability to cope with changes in space layout Ability to be upgraded
Reliability	Ability of the ventilation systems to deliver required volumes and quality of air with no more than the specified levels of downtime
Ease of maintenance	Ease of cleaning Ease of replacement Requirement for maintenance in the occupied space Risks associated with transport of water or refrigerant around the building Risk of legionnaires disease
Integration	Impact on floor-to-ceiling height Minimum plant space requirements Impact on distribution Need for high levels of airtightness Encroachment into workspace Constraints imposed on other services Constraints imposed by other services
Other issues	Ease of procurement Carbon emissions Refrigerant usage Aesthetics

building. The zoned approach works best where the areas are functionally different.

The selection process is illustrated in Figure 2.5. The mixed mode approach should not be seen as a compromise solution. It needs to be chosen at a strategic level and the appropriate option selected. The ability to provide general advice on applicability is limited because the final design can range from almost fully naturally ventilated with a degree of fan assistance for still days, to almost fully air conditioned with the option to revert to natural ventilation at a later date. Some selection issues are raised below, for further details see section 2.4.5.

Selection issues to be considered include:

— *Costs*: capital and operating costs are highly variable. A balancing factor is to what extent supplementary mechanical systems have been installed.

— *Maintenance*: poor designs could result in excessively complex maintenance requirements.

— *Operability*: as above, poor designs in terms of controls complexity can result in inefficient and misunderstood system operation.

— *Window design*: a mixed mode approach might allow this to be less complicated and more robust than in buildings designed for natural ventilation alone.

— *Energy efficiency*: in relation to fully air conditioned buildings, mixed mode systems should use less energy for fans, pumps and cooling. However this is dependent upon the savings in mechanical plant that have been attained.

— *Occupant satisfaction and comfort*: mixed mode buildings offer the potential for a high level of occupant satisfaction in that they provide more options for correcting a situation.

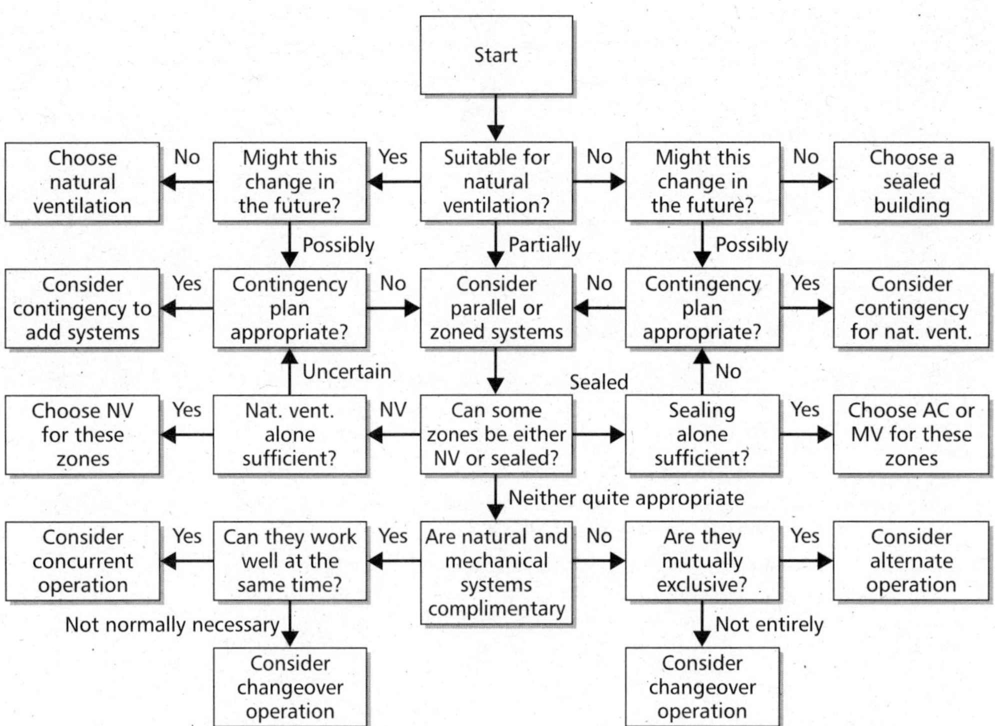

Figure 2.5 Mixed mode selection chart

2.3 Requirements

2.3.1 Introduction

A strategic consideration of requirements as part of an integrated design approach is outlined in section 2.2. Section 2.3 provides a more detailed discussion of the development of ventilation requirements for office environments. Differences to this 'standard' approach are then outlined for other building sectors. More specifically it addresses general functional requirements for the application of:

— ventilation and air conditioning in offices to provide a safe and healthy working environment

— ventilation and air conditioning in offices to provide a comfortable working environment

— ventilation and air conditioning systems in terms of protecting the building fabric (section 2.3.2.3) and energy use (section 2.3.2.4)

— specific requirements for other building sectors (sections 2.3.3 to 2.3.24), see Table 2.9.

2.3.2 Offices

The following requirements apply to offices and to a wide range of other buildings. Requirements specific to other types of buildings are given in sections 2.3.3 to 2.3.24.

2.3.2.1 Indoor air quality: basic requirements for health and safety

The issue of improving air quality in offices (and buildings in general) has previously been mainly related to sick building syndrome (SBS), but research[36] has suggested that SBS is not linked to the type of ventilation or air conditioning system used but is more likely to be a function of how well systems are installed, managed and operated. It suggested that workspaces conforming to CIBSE guidelines on temperature and air movement should not suffer from SBS, unless there are aggravating work-related factors or extreme levels of pollution.

In designing any ventilation system it is necessary to understand the functions required of it. For offices these are:

— to supply sufficient fresh air

— to provide adequate indoor air quality by removing and or diluting pollutants from occupied spaces

— to provide a heat transport mechanism.

The last has been considered on a strategic basis in section 2.2 and is considered in terms of thermal comfort in section 2.3.2.2. This section examines the function of maintaining indoor air quality in order to:

— support human respiration

— remove body odour

— remove tobacco smoke

— remove emissions from building materials and furnishings e.g. volatile organic compounds (VOCs)

— prevent radon gas entering a space via foundations and air intakes

— support safe and efficient operation of combustion appliances

— allow smoke clearance in the event of fire.

Basis of requirements

Ventilation may be used to dilute or displace and remove airborne contaminants released in a space and which would otherwise rise to unacceptable concentrations. Within the Building Regulations, guidance on achieving compliance of relevance to the designer of ventilation systems includes:

— Approved Document F: *Ventilation*[37]; Part F1: *Means of ventilation*; Part F2: *Condensation in roofs*

Table 2.9 Summary of recommendations

Building sector	Section number	Recommendation
Animal husbandry	2.3.24.1	See Table 2.28
Assembly halls	2.3.3	See Table 2.14
Atria	2.3.4	See section 2.3.4.3
Broadcasting studios	2.3.5	6–10 ACH (but heat gain should be assessed)
Call centres	2.3.24.2	4–6 ACH (but heat gain should be assessed)
Catering (inc. commercial kitchens)	2.3.6	30–40 ACH
Cleanrooms	2.3.7	See Tables 2.19 and 2.20
Communal residential buildings	2.3.8	0.5–1 ACH
Computer rooms	2.3.9	See Table 2.21
Court rooms	2.3.24.3	As for typical naturally ventilated buildings
Darkrooms (photographic)	2.3.24.4	6–8 ACH (but heat gain should be assessed)
Dealing rooms	2.3.24.5	As offices for ventilation (but heat gain should be assessed)
Dwellings (inc. high-rise dwellings)	2.3.10	0.5–1 ACH
Factories and warehouses	2.3.11	See 2.3.11.1 for regulatory requirements
High-rise (non-domestic) buildings	2.3.12	4–6 ACH for office areas; up to 10 ACH for meeting spaces
Horticulture	2.3.24.6	30–50 litre·s^{-1}·m^{-2} for greenhouses (45–60 ACH)
Hospitals and health care buildings	2.3.13	See Table 2.23
Hotels	2.3.14	10–15 ACH minimum for guest rooms with en-suite bathrooms
Industrial ventilation	2.3.15	Sufficient to minimise airborne contamination
Laboratories	2.3.16	6-15 ACH (allowance must be made for fume cupboards)
Museums, libraries and art galleries	2.3.17	Depends on nature of exhibits
Offices	2.3.2	See Tables 2.10 and 2.11
Plant rooms	2.3.18	Specific regulations apply, see section 2.3.18
Schools and educational buildings	2.3.19	See Table 2.26
Shops and retail premises	2.3.20	5–8 litre·s^{-1} per person
Sports centres (inc. swimming pools)	2.3.21	See Table 2.27
Standards rooms	2.3.24.7	45–60 ACH
Toilets	2.3.22	Building Regulations apply; opening windows of area 1/20th. of floor area or mechanical ventilation at 6 litre·s^{-1} per WC or 3 ACH minimum for non-domestic buildings; opening windows of area 1/20th. of floor area (1/30th. in Scotland) or mechanical extract at 6 litre·s^{-1} (3 ACH in Scotland) minimum for dwellings
Transportation buildings (inc. car parks)	2.3.23	6 ACH for car parks (normal operation) 10 ACH (fire conditions)

— Approved Document J: *Heat producing appliances*[38]

— Approved Document B: *Fire safety*[39]

— Approved Document L: *Conservation of fuel and power*[1]

Note that if dilution is the main basis of control then the ventilation system should be designed to produce good mixing of the incoming air with the contaminant within the space. In situations where the contaminant release is from a fixed source then it is preferable to arrange the extract location as close to the source as possible so that direct removal is achieved. Requirements will also be affected by the ventilation efficiency, i.e. whether all the fresh air supplied is used or whether some is extracted prematurely. See section 2.4.2.2 for further consideration.

Section 1 of CIBSE Guide A: *Environmental design*[12] should be consulted for the definition of, and requirements for achieving, suitable indoor air quality standards. It describes two methods for determining suitable outdoor air ventilation rates:

— a prescriptive method

— a calculation method for the control of a single known pollutant being released at a known rate.

These are summarised below. A third method has been suggested[7,8] for use where pollution sources are known but not their emission rates or limiting concentrations

(*a*) Prescribed outdoor air supply rate

The prescriptive method is based on chamber studies where tobacco smoke and body odour were considered to be the only pollutant sources. This may result in an underestimate of requirements if other pollutants are present.

(*b*) Calculation method for control of a specific pollutant

Where a single known pollutant is being release at a known rate the calculation is based on risk assessments under the Control of Substances Hazardous to Health (COSHH) Regulations.[42] The Health and Safety Executive (HSE) publishes annual guidance[43] on the limits to which exposure to hazardous airborne substances should be controlled in workplaces. This is in the form of occupational exposure limits (OELs) for long-term (8 hour) and short-term (10 minute) exposures. OELs are available for a large number of substances. While these concentration limits must not be exceeded, it is recommended that exposure should be kept as low as is reasonably practical. Compliance with these limits is a fundamental requirement of the COSHH Regulations.

For situations where exposure may be longer than 8 hours a day, or where more susceptible members of the general population, such as the elderly, the young and those prone to ill-health, are involved values lower than the OELs should be applied. It has been suggested that one fifth of the OEL might be an acceptable standard, although limited information is available. Further guidance on pollutant levels for the general population is also available from the World Health Organisation[44].

For a single contaminant under steady conditions, equation 2.1 may be applied to determine the flow of outdoor air that, with good mixing, would maintain the contaminant concentration at a specified level.

$$Q = \frac{q\,(10^6 - C_i)}{(C_i - C_o)} \qquad (2.1)$$

where Q is the outdoor air supply rate (litre·s^{-1}), q is the pollutant emission rate (litre·s^{-1}), C_o is the concentration of pollutant in the outdoor air (ppm) and C_i is the limit of concentration of pollutant in the indoor air (ppm).

This equation can be adapted for:

— pollutant thresholds quoted in mg·m^{-3} and situations where C_i is small or the incoming air is free of the pollutant in question, see CIBSE Guide A[12], section 1.7.3.1

— situations where the ventilation results in a non-uniform concentration so that a higher than average concentrations exist in the occupied zone and the outdoor air supply rate requires to be increased, see CIBSE Guide A, sections 1.7.3.1 and 1.7.4

— non-steady state conditions that might allow the outdoor air supply rate to be reduced, see CIBSE Guide A, section 1.7.3.2.

A more comprehensive analysis of the relationship between contaminant concentration and ventilation rate is given in BS 5925[45].

Note that the existing guidelines for the calculations of outside air ventilation rates are based on the assumptions that the air outside the building is 'fresh' and that the pollutant load is inside the building. For buildings in city areas or adjacent to busy roads the quality of the outside air needs to be assessed, as this can also be a source of pollutants. Where specific problems are anticipated, an air quality survey should be undertaken. This should include measurements at likely times of peak pollution.

The use of natural ventilation means that it is much more difficult to clean the air entering the building. Mechanical ventilation and air conditioning systems can filter the incoming air to remove dust and dirt, but only specialised air treatment can remove gaseous pollutants (e.g. oxides of carbon and nitrogen from traffic fumes). In all building types, gaseous pollutants can be minimised by careful siting of ventilation inlets, see section 2.4.3 and CIBSE TM 21[28].

In mechanically ventilated buildings, effective air filtration relies on good maintenance[46]. Poor filtration performance can allow dirt and dust to accumulate within a ductwork system, reducing the efficiency of heat exchange equipment and providing potential sites for microbiological activity. Spores and bacteria can then be released into the occupied space, causing potential comfort and health problems. Natural ventilation systems, on the other hand, are generally more accessible for cleaning and maintenance, and there are no components subject to high humidity, such as cooling coils, or humidifiers, which can harbour biological growth.

As well as assessing external air quality, the sources of internal pollution should also be reviewed so that their effect can be minimised or even eliminated. Ventilation should not be used in place of source control to minimise pollutant concentrations in a space.

(*c*) Calculation method for control of multiple pollutants

There is no accepted approach for the derivation of exposure limits for mixtures of contaminants, although some guidance is given in EH40[43]. In such cases it is recommended that specialist assistance be sought from occupational hygienists or toxicologists. Likewise, guidance currently only exists for a small number of substances in terms of acceptable limits to avoid sensory, as opposed to health, effects[44]. In practice, the exposure of workers in non-industrial environments to these same concentrations of contaminants would not be acceptable and a multiplying factor of 0.1 has been suggested.

A method to deal with the dilution of pollution from non-human sources has been suggested[40,41], see equation 2.2:

$$Q_c = \frac{10\,G}{E_v\,(P_i - P_o)} \qquad (2.2)$$

where Q_c is the outdoor air supply rate to account for the total contaminant load (litre·s^{-1}), G is the sensory pollution load (olf), E_v is the ventilation effectiveness, P_i is the design perceived indoor air quality (decipol) and P_o is the perceived outdoor air quality (decipol). These units are defined elsewhere[40,41].

However, this proposal is still subject to discussion and has not yet gained international acceptance.

Human respiration

Carbon dioxide is a dense odourless gas produced by combustion and respiration. The rate of ventilation required for the supply of oxygen for breathing is far outweighed by any requirement for the dilution of exhaled carbon dioxide (CO_2). A build-up of this gas in a room leads to a feeling of stuffiness and can impair concentration. Elevated levels of CO_2 in the body cause an increase in the rate of respiration. Slightly deeper breathing begins to occur when the atmospheric concentration exceeds 9 000 mg·m^{-3} or 5 000 ppm (0.5% by volume). This is the maximum allowable concentration of CO_2 for 8-hour exposures by healthy adults[43]. In the USA, one half of this limit (0.25%) has been taken as appropriate for general building environments[47].

These figures are based on sedentary occupations; minimum ventilation rates for various activity levels to prevent these limits being exceeded are given in Table 2.10.

For most applications involving human occupancy, the CO_2 limits shown in Table 2.10 are not usually taken as a design criterion as much more air needs to be provided to meet criteria such as the dilution of odours or tobacco smoke.

Within the UK, a CO_2 figure of 800–1000 ppm is often used as an indicator that the ventilation rate in a building is adequate. One thousand parts per million would appear to equate to a 'fresh air' ventilation rate of about 8 litre·s^{-1} per person. In Sweden, the equivalent indicator is 1000 ppm, with a desired level of 600–800 ppm. Note that as outside air itself contains carbon dioxide (approx. 350 ppm), a 50% reduction in internal levels from 1600 ppm to 800 ppm requires a four-fold increase in ventilation rate.

Table 2.10 Ventilation rates required to limit CO_2 concentration for differing activity levels

Activity	Minimum ventilation requirement / (litre·s^{-1} per person)	
	0.5% CO_2 limit	0.25% CO_2 limit
Seated quietly	0.8	1.8
Light work	1.3–2.6	2.8–5.6
Moderate work	2.6–3.9	N/A
Heavy work	3.9–5.3	N/A
Very heavy work	5.3–6.4	N/A

Body odour

The ventilation rate required depends on whether the criterion is (*a*) acceptability to the occupants or (*b*) acceptability to visitors entering the occupied space. In studies on auditoria[48], it was found that that the occupants themselves were insensitive to changes in ventilation over the range 5–15 litre·s^{-1} per person, although there were always nearly 10% of the occupants dissatisfied with the odour level.

Similarly, it has been shown that an outdoor flow rate of 7 to 8 litre·s^{-1} per person is required to restrict the level of body odour so that no more than 20% of the entrants to the occupied space were dissatisfied. The sensitivity was such that halving the ventilation rate increased the proportion dissatisfied to 30%, while more than three times the ventilation rate was required before the proportion decreased to 10%.

Therefore in the absence of further information, it is recommended that 8 litre·s^{-1} per person should be taken as the minimum ventilation rate to control body odour levels in rooms with sedentary occupants. There is evidently a relationship between CO_2 concentration and body odour intensity in occupied rooms. Thus for intermittent or varying occupancy, the control of ventilation rates by CO_2 concentration monitoring can be effective in matching the supply of air supply to the changing requirements.

Tobacco smoke

The suggested outdoor air supply rate of 8 litre·s^{-1} is based on sedentary occupants and the absence of any other requirements, e.g. the removal of moisture. This is consistent with the requirements for the removal of body odour but assumes the absence of any smoking. There are no definitive criteria for the required dilution of tobacco smoke. Uncertainties relate particularly to the respirable particulate component (see page 2-16). Evidence suggests that particle removal by filtration is necessary to avoid excessively high ventilation rates.

Smoking also produces undesirable odours, particularly to non-smokers. One study[49] has shown that filtration of the smoke particles did not alleviate the odour nuisance, indicating that much higher rates of ventilation are now required to avoid dissatisfaction of more than 20% of visitors to a room occupied by cigarette smokers. Ventilation rates for smokers of 4 or 5 times that required for non-smokers have been suggested although, allowing for the fact that a minority of the occupants may be smokers, the overall ventilation rate may be only twice that needed for non-smoking situations.

If smoking is prohibited, then the rate for 'no smoking' may be used, see Table 2.11. For the other situations described in the table, it has been assumed that each smoker present consumes an average of 1.3 cigarettes per hour. It should be noted that, regardless of the ventilation rate used, the health risks of cigarette smoke cannot be completely eliminated. It is recommended that designers consult current guidelines, such as those issued by the Health and Safety Executive[50], and ensure that clients are made aware of any risks involved in the chosen design strategy. Legal advice may also be advisable.

Table 2.11 Recommended outdoor air supply rates for sedentary occupants[6]

Level of smoking	Proportion of occupants that smoke / %	Outdoor air supply rate / (litre·s^{-1} per person)
No smoking	0	8
Some smoking	25	16
Heavy smoking	45	24
Very heavy smoking	75	36

Volatile organic compounds (VOCS)

VOCS cover a wide range of compounds having boiling points in the range of 50–260 °C and hence existing in vapour form at room temperature. They are particularly prevalent in new and recently refurbished buildings, coming from a variety of sources including:

- people, animals, plants
- consumer products (cleaning agents, paints, glues, solvents etc.)
- building materials and treatment (damp-proofing, furnishings etc.)
- building services and other equipment
- outdoor air.

Analysis is normally restricted to measuring the total VOC content in air. ASHRAE Standard 62[51] suggests that complaints are unlikely to arise for total VOC concentrations below 300 mg·m^{-3}, whereas above 3000 mg·m^{-3} complaints are likely. Details of the appropriate ventilation provision can be found in section 1 of CIBSE Guide A[12].

Respirable particles (PM_{10})

Respirable particles are those constituents of the air that are not in purely gaseous form. They can be ingested into the lungs while breathing and cause a wide range of health problems. The most potentially dangerous particulates are asbestos fibres but there are concerns about other 'man-made mineral fibres' (MMMF) which are widely used for insulation within buildings. Particulate matter is monitored in the UK as PM_{10}, i.e. particles generally less than 10 microns in diameter. A large number of epidemiological studies have shown that day-to-day variations in concentrations of particles are associated with adverse effects on health from heart and lung disorders, and a worsening of the condition of those with asthma. Details of the appropriate ventilation provision can be found in section 1 of CIBSE Guide A[12].

Radon

Radon is a colourless and odourless radioactive gas. It comes from the radioactive decay of radium, which in turn comes from the decay of uranium. Radon is emitted from uranium-bearing soils and emission rates therefore vary depending on the geological conditions of the location. Radon is implicated in the cause of lung cancer. Protection from exposure to radon at work is specified in the Ionising Radiation Regulations[52], made under the Health and Safety at Work etc. Act [53]. A limit for radon in non-domestic buildings has been set at 400 Bq·m^{-3}, above which action must be taken to reduce the concentration. Guidance on appropriate action can be found in BRE report BR 293[54].

Combustion appliances and products

Adequate fresh air must be supplied to meet the requirements for combustion in fuel burning appliances. Details of these requirements are laid down in BS 6798[55], BS 5410[56] and BS 5440[57]. Part J of the Building Regulations, with its associated Approved Document[58], also governs flues from gas fired combustion appliances of up to 60 kW and from solid fuel and oil burning appliances of up to 45 kW. For guidance on how to ventilate larger installations, i.e. boiler houses and plant rooms, refer to section 2.3.18.

Guideline values for concentrations of combustion products are given in CIBSE Guide A[12], section 1, Table 1.8. The most common are nitrogen dioxide (NO_2), sulphur dioxide (SO_2), and carbon monoxide (CO). These may either be created within the occupied space or may re-enter buildings, e.g. from chimney smoke or from the exhausts of cars through windows overlooking car parks.

Gas and refrigerant detection methods

Gas detection methods are dealt with in section 2.3.18. Refrigerant detection methods are also considered in that section, with further guidance in the case of split systems in section 2.4.21.

Smoke control and clearance

Ventilation for the control of smoke in the event of a fire, and its subsequent clearance, is a specialist subject. Guidance is given in CIBSE Guide E: *Fire engineering*[58]. If natural ventilation is to be achieved by means of an atrium, guidance is also available in BRE Report BR 375[59].

2.3.2.2 Ventilation for internal comfort

Temperature

CIBSE Guide A[12], Table 1.1, gives recommended summer and winter dry resultant temperatures corresponding to a mean predicted vote of ±0.25 for a range of building types. However, as noted in Guide A, control within an air conditioned building is normally based on a response to internal air temperatures. In a standard office environment this corresponds to 22–24 °C and 21–23 °C where comfort cooling or air conditioning, respectively, are available. In a naturally ventilated environment, the acceptable dry resultant temperature range is less well defined and various approaches have been suggested, see Table 2.12.

Section 1.4.3 of CIBSE Guide A[12] considers factors that influence the criteria for comfort cooled or air conditioned spaces. A summary of the factors most related to the design of the ventilation or air conditioning systems is given in Table 2.13. However, CIBSE Guide A should be consulted for detailed guidance.

Table 2.12 Alternate approaches to design criteria for naturally ventilated offices

Criterion	Source
Mean temperature during occupied periods with acceptable deviation, e.g. mean summer dry resultant temperature of 23±2 °C in an office with a formal dress code, and 25±2 °C in an office with an informal dress code	BRE *Environmental design guide*[60]
Thresholds never to be exceeded, e.g. (*a*) a maximum temperature of 27 °C; (*b*) the internal temperature is never to exceed the external temperature.	CIBSE AM10[27]
A threshold that can be exceeded for a specified period, e.g. (*a*) dry resultant temperature not to exceed 25 °C for more than 5% of the occupied period; (*b*) dry resultant temperature not to exceed 25 °C for more than 5% of the occupied period or 28 °C for more than 1% of the occupied period	CIBSE Guide A[12]; BRE *Energy Efficient Office of the Future specification*[61]

Table 2.13 Factors in office environments influencing thermal comfort relating to ventilation or air conditioning system design[6]

Factor	Issues to be considered	Guide A section number
Humidity	— Little effect on feelings of warmth for sedentary, lightly clothed people at dry resultant temperatures of 23 °C and below. — If room humidity is greater than 70% the risk of condensation and microbiological growth may be increased. Dust mite levels may also increase with high humidity.	1.4.3.1
Clothing	— The insulation value of clothing (i.e. clo value) can influence the acceptable dry resultant temperature for *sedentary* occupants, e.g. in the case of a thick pullover, a reduction of 2.1 K.	1.4.3.2
Activity	— The metabolic rate (hence heat generated) is affected by activity. For people dressed in normal casual clothing (clo = 0.5–1.0), an increase of 0.1 met corresponds to a possible reduction of 0.6 K in the recommended dry resultant temperature.	1.4.3.3
Temperature changes	— A smooth change in dry resultant temperature should be aimed at to avoid discomfort.	1.4.3.4
Adaptation and climate	— The theory of adaptive thermal comfort, i.e. that the preferred internal temperature is affected by the prevailing external conditions, is still being debated.	1.4.3.5
Age	— The requirements of older people for higher temperatures are thought to be associated with their generally lower activity levels.	1.4.3.6
Gender	— The requirements of women for slightly higher temperatures are though to be related to their generally lower clo values.	1.4.3.7
Occupants' state of health, disability, and physical condition	— Little is know about this factor, although higher temperatures are usually required for bed-ridden or immobilised people due to their lower met and clo values.	1.4.3.9
Draughts	— The influence of mean relative air speed on the thermal comfort of occupants is dependent partly upon the temperature of the moving air (see predicted mean vote (PMV), Guide A[12], section 1.4.2.2), the air flow rate, and its direction. — An excessive air flow rate can give rise to complaints of draughts, especially in winter; the back of the neck is particularly susceptible. — If the room air speed exceeds 0.15 $m \cdot s^{-1}$ the dry resultant temperature should be increased from its still value. An air speed of >0.3 $m \cdot s^{-1}$ is not recommended, unless it is in a naturally ventilated building where it is specifically for cooling. — Dissatisfaction with draughts is also affected by fluctuations in air speed. These are defined by the turbulence intensity (TI) and consequently a calculated draught rating (DR), which should not exceed 15%. — The relative air speed over a body's surface increases with activity. If activity levels exceed 1 met, 0.3 $m \cdot s^{-1}$ should be added to the air speed relative to a stationary point	1.4.3.10
Vertical air temp. differences	— The gradient in either direction (floor to ceiling and vice versa) should be no more than 3 K in the occupied zone. — If air velocities are higher at floor level than across the upper part of the body, then a maximum gradient of 2 $K \cdot m^{-1}$ is recommended.	1.4.3.11
Asymmetric thermal radiation	— This is affected by the proximity to adjacent cold surfaces e.g. single glazed windows, adjacent hot surfaces e.g. overhead radiant heaters and the intrusion of short wavelength radiation e.g. solar radiation through glazing.	1.4.3.14

Humidity

The role of humidity in maintaining comfortable conditions is discussed in section 1.5 of CIBSE Guide A[12]. An acceptable range of 40–70% RH is suggested. However, to minimise the risk of mould growth or condensation and maintain comfortable conditions, a maximum design figure of 60% RH is suggested for the design of air conditioning systems. Within naturally ventilated buildings, humidity levels as low as 30% RH (or lower) may be acceptable for short periods of time, but care is needed to restrict airborne irritants such as dust or tobacco smoke. Precautions should also be taken to avoid shocks due to static electricity through the specification of equipment and materials, e.g. carpets.

Internal gains

In the absence of information from the client, the British Council for Offices recommends the following allowances for internal gains when specifying ventilation systems[62]:

— solar gains not to exceed 60–90 $W \cdot m^{-2}$ depending upon façade orientation

— occupancy based upon 1 person per 12 m^2, but diversified wherever possible to 1 person per 14 m^2 at the central plant

— lighting gains of not more than 12 $W \cdot m^{-2}$ at the central plant

— office equipment gains of not more than 15 $W \cdot m^{-2}$ when diversified and measured over an area of 1000 m^2 or more, but with an ability to upgrade to 25 $W \cdot m^{-2}$. Local workstation levels are quoted as typically 20–25 $W \cdot m^{-2}$.

2.3.2.3 Ventilation of building fabric to avoid interstitial condensation

Many structures are vulnerable to interstitial condensation, which can cause rotting of wood-based components, corrosion of metals and reduction in the performance of thermal insulation. Condensed water can also run or drip back into the building causing staining to internal finishes or damage to fittings and equipment. The traditional view has been that these problems are caused by water vapour generated in the building diffusing into the structure.

Avoidance measures have therefore concentrated on the inclusion of a vapour control layer on the warm side of the structure, appropriate placing of insulation, or ventilating the structure to intercept the water vapour before it can condense. Ventilation is specifically required in cavities above the insulation in cold pitched and flat roofs, behind the cladding of framed walls and below timber floors.

Many problems can occur from water entrapped within materials, moving within the structure under diurnal temperature cycles. Under these circumstances it is helpful to distinguish between 'ventilated' and 'vented' air spaces. A ventilated space is designed to ensure a through flow of air, driven by wind or stack pressures whereas a vented space has openings to the outside air that allow some limited, but not necessarily through, flow of air. As the air in the space expands and contracts under diurnal temperature cycles, water vapour will be 'breathed' out of the structure. This mechanism can be very effective in large span structures where it can be very difficult to ensure effect through ventilation of small cavities.

Detailed design guidance for the provision of ventilation within structures is available in CIBSE Guide A[12], BS 5250[34] and BRE Report BR 262[63].

2.3.2.4 Energy use

Energy use in offices has risen in recent years because of the growth in IT, air conditioning (sometimes specified when not required), and intensity of use. However, this trend is offset by considerable improvements in insulation, plant, lighting and controls. The Energy Efficiency Best Practice programme has produced ECG 19: *Energy use in offices*[20]. This provides benchmarks, based on data gathered in the 1990s, which take account of increasing levels of IT provision for four types of office buildings:

- naturally ventilated cellular
- naturally ventilated open-plan
- standard air conditioned
- prestige air conditioned.

Despite perceptions to the contrary, energy-efficient offices are not expensive to build, difficult to manage or inflexible in their operation. Nor do they provide low levels of comfort or productivity. Energy-efficient techniques that work well tend to be reliable, straightforward, and compatible with the needs of the building operator and occupants. Capital costs are often similar to those for normal offices, although budgets may be spent differently; for example, on measures to reduce cooling loads rather than on air conditioning.

Further opportunities for improving energy efficiency should be sought when other changes occur, e.g. refurbishment, fit-out, alteration, and plant replacement. Building Regulations[64] and the associated Approved Document L[1] require much greater attention to energy issues during refurbishment, as the scope of the regulations in England and Wales has been widened to bring such activity within the meaning of controlled work and material change. The Scottish regulations are currently being revised and it is anticipated that they will adopt a similar approach. Best results in terms of energy efficiency are obtained when there is a good brief, good design with attention to detail, sound workmanship and commissioning, and good control and management.

Energy efficient office design can reduce energy costs by a factor of two. ECG 19[20] gives details of the characteristics of best practice energy efficient design, as well as details of the benchmarks for the four office types. Careful attention to energy efficiency should be a constant theme of the design of the ventilation and air conditioning of a building.

2.3.3 Assembly halls and auditoria

2.3.3.1 General[65,66]

Assembly halls and auditoria, e.g. theatres, concert halls, conference centres, places of worship, are generally characterised by large but variable occupancy levels, relatively high floor to ceiling heights, sedentary occupation, and stringent acoustic requirements. Places of worship tend to be serviced with a low cost, simple solutions.

Specific issues that need to be addressed for assembly halls and auditoria include the following:

- flexibility of the space being served and if the seating is fixed or removable
- acoustic control measures including plant location, vibration, noise break-out, fan noise, silencers, flexible connections, duct linings, etc.
- integration of relatively large air handling plant and distribution ductwork
- occupancy patterns and part load operation
- viability of heat recovery devices and possible variable speed operation
- zoning of the plant (for large auditoria)
- treatment and integration of builders' work plenums (including control and zoning)
- air terminal device selection, integration with seats, control of draughts and noise regeneration
- stage ventilation and cooling and assessment of lighting heat gains
- temperature control at rear of auditorium due to reduced height
- background heating, and out-of-hours heating
- cooling and ventilation to control rooms etc.

2.3.3.2 Design requirements

Normal design requirements for buildings are shown in Table 2.14. Mechanical ventilation systems for assembly halls and auditoria need to be designed to meet the sound control requirements described in section 5.

2.3.3.3 Strategies

Mechanical ventilation (low level supply, high level extract)

Low level supply is often via a plenum beneath the seating. Air is extracted at high level, returned to the

Table 2.14 Design requirements: assembly halls and auditoria

Parameter	Design requirement
Fresh air ventilation rates	To suit occupancy levels
Air change rate	3–4 air changes per hour for displacement strategy
	6–10 air changes per hour for high level mechanical strategy
Temperature and humidity:	
— heating only	20 °C; 40% RH (minimum)
— with cooling	20–24 °C; 40–70% RH

central plant for heat recovery or exhausted to atmosphere. This approach is suitable for raked fixed seating halls and auditoria. Displacement-type room air distribution strategies are often used. The advantages are that only the occupied zone is conditioned, not the entire space and the potential for 'free cooling' is maximised as supply air temperatures are usually 19–20 °C. Air volumes and energy consumption and maintenance costs are usually less when compared with high level supply, although central plant sizes are normally similar.

Mechanical ventilation (high level supply and extract)

This system is usually selected where a flexible space is required, seating is removable, or where it is not feasible or prohibitive in terms of cost to provide under-seat plenums.

Natural ventilation

Supply is by attenuated inlet builders' work ducts at low level and high level. Extract is by attenuated outlets at high level, relying on stack effect to ventilate and cool the area. This approach has potentially the lowest running costs but may require a number of provisions to ensure adequate airflow rate and to limit peak temperatures in summer. Particular considerations include providing suitable air paths, inlets and exhaust positions, solar protection, mass exposure and night cooling.

Ventilation control

Options for ventilation control strategies include:

— demand-controlled ventilation and cooling depending upon (*a*) return air carbon dioxide levels[67], (*b*) occupancy levels

— space temperature and humidity

— time control

— night-time purging of the space and possible pre-cooling of structure.

2.3.4 Atria

2.3.4.1 General

The incorporation of an atrium will not automatically lead to energy savings, especially if the atrium requires artificial lighting and air conditioning (often for the health of the planting as much as the occupants)[26]. However, if well designed, an atrium can bring the advantages of:

— enhanced opportunities for natural ventilation by stack effect and allowing air to be drawn from both sides of the building towards a central extract point

— preheating of ventilation air

— additional working space.

2.3.4.2 Requirements

Environmental conditions

Environmental conditions within an atrium are dependent upon the degree of comfort required. Saxon[68] defines four categories of atrium:

— simple unenclosed canopy or enclosure without comfort control

— basic buffer space with partial control to assist plants

— tempered buffer space with partial control to assist in achieving some degree of human comfort

— full comfort atrium.

Buoyancy driven ventilation (mixed and displacement)

Many atria are sealed and mechanically ventilated and, sometimes, mechanically cooled. However, natural ventilation can provide high rates of air change and also induce cross ventilation of the surrounding office areas. Natural ventilation is driven by wind pressure and thermal buoyancy. The limiting case is likely to be buoyancy alone, i.e. when there is no breeze.

There are two kinds of buoyancy driven ventilation, defined by the position of the openings[69]:

— mixing ventilation

— displacement ventilation.

In mixing ventilation, openings are placed at the top of the atrium only; warm air leaves the atrium reducing the pressure and allowing cool air to enter via the same opening. The cool, dense air falls to the floor mixing with the warm air as it falls. This results in the air temperature at floor level being above ambient by an amount depending on the size of the opening; the larger the opening the smaller the difference between the inside and outside temperatures. Mixing ventilation leads to a relatively uniform vertical temperature distribution.

In displacement ventilation, openings are placed at the top and bottom of the atrium; warm air leaves the upper opening and cooler air enters the lower opening. Assuming a steady input, equilibrium is reached where a stationary boundary exists between the warm air at high level and the cool air at lower level. Reducing the size of the openings lowers the position of this boundary and increases the temperature of the upper zone but the temperature of the lower zone remains at, or close to, the ambient temperature.

In many situations displacement ventilation is appropriate for summer conditions. To promote ventilation the air in the atrium should be as warm as possible over the greatest proportion of the atrium height. In most atria occupation occurs at floor level, excluding galleries and staircases. Therefore it is important to keep the temperature at floor level as low as possible. However if the atrium is open to the surrounding space, or if it provides high level walkways, the high temperatures in these occupied spaces might become unacceptable. The design strategy should therefore be based on the absorption of solar radiation by surfaces above the occupied space. The position of the stationary boundary is important; ideally the hot layer will be confined to a level above adjacent occupied spaces. This suggests that atria should have sufficient height to ensure that this will occur.

Displacement ventilation can be used to reject heat when the outside temperature is below the atrium temperature. At night, heat retained in the massive elements of the atrium will generate stack effect to provide useful night cooling. However, it is possible for the temperature in the atrium to fall below the ambient temperature and thereby cause a reversal of the stack effect.

Atrium openings

For displacement ventilation driven by the stack effect, openings will be required at the top and bottom of the atrium of between 5 and 10% of the roof glazing area[70]. For atria with large areas of vertical glazing facing between south and west, the openable areas should be a similar percentage glazing area. The more shading that can be provided, the smaller the openings need to be for a given thermal performance.

Roof vents

Roof vents must be carefully positioned within the form of the roof so that positive wind pressures do not act on the outlets causing reverse flow[27]. It is normally possible to arrange the outlets such that they are always in a negative pressure zone. This may be achieved by:

- designing the roof profile so that for all wind angles the openings are in a negative pressure zone
- using multiple vents that are automatically controlled to close on the windward side and open on the leeward side.

Ventilation enhancement and fire safety

On hot, still days natural ventilation can be supplemented by extract fans in the atrium roof. Subject to fire office approval, a combination of natural and powered ventilation can also form part of the smoke control or clearance system. It is essential that fire conditions be considered at an early stage so that the possibility and benefits of a dual-purpose system can be evaluated. Guidance on fire safety and atria is available elsewhere[39,58,70,71].

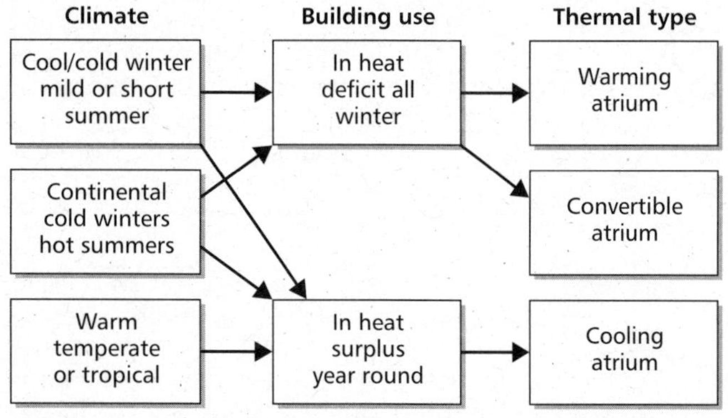

Figure 2.6 Selection of thermal type of atrium

Flexibility

The designer should be aware of any intention to use the atrium area for other purposes, e.g. concerts or the provision of catering, when selecting the ventilation strategy.

2.3.4.3 Strategies

Types of atrium

Saxon[68] defines three types of atrium with regards to their thermal properties, see Figure 2.6. These are:

- *warming atrium*: which normally collects heat
- *cooling atrium*: which normally rejects heat
- *convertible atrium*: which changes mode according to the season.

The purpose of the atrium will be affected by climate and building use as this impacts on internal heat gains within the adjacent accommodation.

(*a*) Warming atrium

(*i*) In winter

A warming buffer atrium is normally designed to admit heat freely (from solar gain or the surrounding accommodation) and will therefore tend to be at higher than ambient temperatures. Even if the atrium is unheated, its temperature in winter will be above the ambient. This may be used as a means of pre-warming ventilation air. Unless the atrium has a low protectivity[81] (i.e. the ratio of separating wall area to the atrium external envelope area), the temperature at night should be maintained above the night set-back, given the flow of heat from the building to the space and stored heat in walls and the floor. The chosen ventilation strategy will affect heating energy consumption.

Air circulation is desirable, even in winter, to avoid cold air stratifying at the ground level where people pass through. Additional heat can be gained within the atrium by coupling its ventilation system with that of the accommodation, air being discharged into the atrium after heat recovery. If full comfort is sought then coupling becomes even more advantageous. This can be achieved by using the atrium as a return air plenum. This allows solar gains to be collected and food smells to be contained.

(*ii*) In summer

The main concern in summer is to prevent overheating. The primary means of achieving this is through shading[72]. External shading is more effective than internal shading and movable devices can prevent the loss of useful daylight. The stack effect can be used to induce ventilation either of the atrium alone or of the whole building.

(*b*) Cooling atrium

The function of the atrium is to provide a source of cooling for the surrounding accommodation. This cooling can be as a result of night cooling within the atrium creating a thermal buffer zone. More commonly the atrium is used as a supply or return air plenum.

(*c*) Convertible atrium

A convertible atrium will function in a similar manner to the warming atrium in winter, but require more protection against overheating in summer to avoid the need for impractical ventilation rates. Pre-cooling of the atrium space may also be employed to reduce the temperature of any radiant surfaces.

Ventilation modes

Saxon[68] defines five possible ventilation modes:

- complete separation of ventilation for the atrium and that for the occupied space
- intake of primary air via atrium and the rest separate
- exhaust of used clean air into the atrium, the rest separate
- use of the atrium as a supply air plenum to occupied spaces
- use of the atrium as a return air plenum.

The advantages and disadvantages of these modes, with regard to degree of comfort, are shown in Figure 2.7.

	Comfort type				
	Canopy	Buffer	Temp. buffer	Full comfort	Thermal type
No vent. relationship	Normal	Normal	Possible	NA Behaves as separate room	Warming Convertible Cooling
Intake via atrium	No effect	OK summer NA OK winter	OK summer NA OK winter	NA	Warming Convertible Cooling
Exhaust to atrium	Slight effect	Useful	Useful	NA	Warming Convertible Cooling
Atrium as supply plenum	NA	NA	NA	Possible Useful	Warming Convertible Cooling
Atrium as return plenum	NA	NA	Collects solar useful	Useful	Warming Convertible Cooling

Figure 2.7 Selection of ventilation mode

2.3.4.4 Calculation of atrium performance

A suitable choice of thermal model should be made. Guidance on the prediction of winter conditions in atria at an early stage of the design is available[38]. Models for calculating ventilation flow rates such as SERI-RES, DOE-2 and BREEZE are listed in the *European Passive Solar Handbook*[72].

2.3.5 Broadcasting studios (radio and TV)

2.3.5.1 General

The general requirement is to provide a comfortable environment within the constraints imposed by the production of television programmes. Specific issues that need to be addressed include:

- high lighting loads in studios
- high occupancies for shows with audiences
- rapid changes in load
- variable operation times and periods
- sensitivity to air movement and noise
- high equipment loads in technical areas
- critical areas requiring a high degree of reliability
- 24-hour operation
- multiplicity of studio arrangements
- adaptability to respond to changing technological and business requirements.

2.3.5.2 Design requirements

Tables 2.15 and 2.16 provide some typical design requirements. The loads given apply to the working area only. The areas identified provide typical examples and not intended to be exhaustive. Arenas are often used for bigger shows. Small presentation studios may be used for linking programmes; these are subject to similar loads but of short duration and are normally occupied all day by a presenter.

Mechanical ventilation systems for broadcasting studios need to provide a high level of reliability, as the system is critical to the proper functioning of the building and the business conducted within it. Consequential losses arising from failure can be very significant in this type of building.

Table 2.15 Typical design requirements: broadcasting studios — general areas

Description	Size / m^2	Occupancy	Noise level	Heat loads / W·m^{-2}	
				Lighting	Equipment
Flexible studio (light entertainment)	Up to 2000 (typically 400)	10 crew 50–100 audience	NR20–NR25 NR30 with audience	500, 200 over seating	100
Drama studio	150–2000	4–10	NR15	500 over 2/3rds. of floor area at any one time	100
Fixed rig studio (e.g. news and current affairs)	150	4–10	NR20–NR25	200	100
Radio studio	5–30	1–10	NR15	20	70

Table 2.16 Typical design requirements: broadcasting studios — technical areas

Description	Size / m^2	Occupancy	Noise level	Equipment heat load
Control room:				
— production*	50	8–10	NR20–NR30	6–8 kW; 70 $W \cdot m^{-2}$
— vision*	50	8–10	NR20–NR30	4–8 kW; 70 $W \cdot m^{-2}$
— sound	16	2–3	As for studio	2–4 kW
Voice-over booth	2.5	1	NR15–NR20	2–4 kW
Editing room:				
— equipment outside room	—	1–4	NR20–NR30	2–6 kW
— equipment within room	—	1–4	NR35–NR40	1–8 kW
Central apparatus room	†	N/A	NR45	Typically 750–1000 $W \cdot m^{-2}$
Transmission room	†	N/A	NR30	Up to 500 $W \cdot m^{-2}$

* These areas may be combined
† Dependant on size of facility

Television studios may have 2–3 lighting rigs to suit different requirements. For programmes such as news and current affairs, which have less need to create visual interest and that run all day, fluorescent lighting may be used in addition to tungsten, thereby reducing the lighting load.

Heat loads can be highly intermittent. Game shows last for only 1/2 to 1 hour. During this time the lighting may be brought up and down on the audience. For drama studios, only one of a number of sets may be fully lit at a time. Setting up studios for shows can take several days, during which time loads will be low.

Within the occupied zone near floor level environmental conditions should be 21±1 °C, rising to 23±1 °C at times of peak load. Relative humidity should ideally be between 40% and 60%. Humidity control is not normally required in the UK. Achieving good humidity control in studios can be problematic due to the rapid load changes. Close control of conditions may be required in tape storage areas to reduce deterioration. It is preferable that tapes are stored under the same environmental conditions as the room in which the tapes are to be used; this minimises sticking and problems to do with static electricity.

Air speeds in television studios should be in the order of 0.2 $m \cdot s^{-1}$, but not higher than 0.3 $m \cdot s^{-1}$ in order to avoid visual disturbance of hair, clothing, scenery drapes and dry ice, and noise in microphones. Air movement is critical for drama studios.

Mechanical ventilation systems for broadcasting studios need to be designed to meet the sound control requirements described in section 5: *Sound control*. Typical noise level criteria are given in Tables 2.15 and 2.16. Reference should also be made to the noise criteria established in the BBC's *Guide to acoustic practice*[73]. Noise is particularly critical in drama studios and 'quality' radio studios. As in other applications, background noise from a ducted air system provides a degree of masking of extraneous noise from adjacent areas. If the background noise level is substantially lower than the criterion set, then the extraneous noise normally masked by the ventilation may become apparent.

2.3.5.3 Strategies

Systems need to be able to cope with high loads and with rapid changes in load. Air-based systems are often preferred due to concerns over water within the space. Central plant may be preferred due to restrictions on maintenance access.

Variable air volume systems may provide an energy efficient solution for television studios. Constant volume systems provide an even airflow at a constant noise level, which may be important for technical reasons, but can be wasteful of energy in large installations.

Blow-through coils with airside damper control may be preferred to waterside control to respond to rapid load changes. Overcooling can be a problem if response is too slow. Steam injection may be used for fast response to meet humidity requirements.

High reliability for critical areas is normally provided by redundancy on individual units and/or in the number of units provided. Dual power supplies and generator back-up are also generally provided. High loads can lead to rapid temperature rises (that may activate sprinklers). Systems should also be designed so that they can be readily adapted to respond to changing requirements. To separate audience and performance areas for control purposes, studios may be zoned into quartiles by multiple damper assemblies.

Attenuation should be provided to reduce ingress of noise from outside and from central plant. Noise from balancing dampers can be a particular problem and should be avoided if possible. Air speeds inside the studio are critical with regard to noise, see section 2.3.5.2. Particular problems can arise with boom microphones located close to high-level supply diffusers, both due to noise from the diffuser and wind-generated noise from excessive air movement.

False floors are normally provided in studios but are not generally used for air supply since they are normally filled with cabling, including PVC cables. Acoustic and fire-break issues also need to be addressed.

Equipment heat gains in technical areas may be treated directly by providing dedicated supply and/or extract ducts to the equipment cabinets.

Radio studios are the most critical areas with regard to noise levels. Constant volume systems are preferred while the studio is in use.

Where cooling loads are relatively low, cooling systems such as displacement ventilation and chilled ceilings may be used. Where areas are occupied 24-hours a day, consideration must be given to how the systems will be maintained without loss of cooling or ventilation during studio use.

2.3.6 Catering and food processing

2.3.6.1 Kitchens

General

Adequate ventilation in catering premises is required for the following purposes:

— To introduce sufficient clean, cool air and remove excess hot air in order for the occupants to breathe and remain healthy and comfortable. Often it is not possible to achieve normal comfort conditions in kitchens because of the difficulties of counteracting the heat released from appliances. Under these circumstances care should be taken to ensure that acceptable working conditions are not breached.

— Provide sufficient air for complete combustion in appliances to prevent carbon monoxide levels exceeding 300 ppm for 10 minutes(42) or 10 ppm as an average over 8 hours(44), and to dilute and remove combustion products.

— Dilute and remove odours, vapours and steam from the cooking process.

Local ventilation must be kept clean from fat residues to avoid loss of efficiency and minimising the risk of fire.

Research by the HSE on exposure of kitchen and factory workers to cooking fumes reinforces the importance of providing and maintaining good ventilation in catering kitchens and industrial cooking areas, particularly where meat, fish and cooking oils are directly heated. A fundamental requirement of the Control of Substances Hazardous to Health (COSHH) Regulations(42) is that employers should prevent the exposure of their employees to hazardous substances or, where that is not reasonably practicable, ensure that there is adequate control of hazardous substances. The fumes generated by directly heating foods during frying, grilling and stir-frying have been identified as containing small quantities of carcinogens. Although deemed to be adequate, available information on this issue is limited at the time of writing, making it impossible to state conclusively that no risk exists with current controls. It is therefore important that fume extraction systems are provided and maintained to current standards. Designers should ensure that they are aware of latest revisions to any related guidance.

Requirements

(*a*) Canopy extract

Air needs to be removed from cooking and subsidiary areas at a constant rate to take away combustion fumes and cooking odours as close to the source as possible. It is advisable that the bulk of extraction from the kitchen is via hoods above gas-fired and all other appliances capable of generating heat, water vapour, fumes and odours.

It is recommended that the plan dimensions of the canopy exceed the plan area of cooking appliances. An overhang of 250–300 mm all round is normally adequate for island canopies. Wall-mounted canopies normally have a overhang of 250 mm at the front and 150 mm at the sides. Greater overhangs may be required at some appliances.

Canopies and ductwork need to be constructed from non-combustible materials and fabricated so as not to encourage the accumulations of dirt or grease, nor to allow condensation to drip from the canopy. The ductwork needs suitable access for cleaning and grease filters need to be readily removable for cleaning or replacement.

The amount of air extracted via the canopies should be calculated from the information supplied with the particular appliances, and not based simply on general advice or overall air change rate. Where details of the equipment are known, HVCA specification DW 171(74) describes a method for calculating the ventilation requirement whereby each cooking appliance is allocated a thermal convection coefficient. This is the recommended volume of air to be extracted in $m^3{\cdot}s^{-1}$ per m^2 of surface area of the appliance. The area of each appliance is multiplied by the coefficient for that appliance and the values for each item of equipment under the canopy are added together to determine the total volume to be extracted. The factor will vary depending on whether the appliance is fired by gas or electricity.

Where the ventilation requirements of the individual cooking appliances are not available, an approximate air flow rate can be calculated from the total hood size, canopy area and hood face velocity, as follows:

$$Q_{hood} = 1000 \times A_{hood} \times V_{hood} \tag{2.3}$$

where Q_{hood} is the approximate hood air flow rate (litre·s^{-1}), A_{hood} is the canopy area (m^2) and V_{hood} is the hood face velocity ($m{\cdot}s^{-1}$). Table 2.17 provides typical hood face velocities.

Table 2.17 Hood face velocities

Cooking duty	Hood face velocity / $m{\cdot}s^{-1}$
Light	0.25
Medium	0.4
Heavy	0.5

(*b*) Ventilated ceiling extract

Where ventilated ceilings are used in place of canopies, the ventilation rates should be calculated taking into account room size and function. As a guide, a ventilation rate of not less than 17.5 litre·s^{-1} per m^2 of floor area and not less than 30 air changes per hour (ACH) is advisable. A lower air change rate may be needed to avoid discomfort from draughts where the kitchen is divided into separate rooms. The Heating and Ventilating Contractors' Association recommends that a general ventilation rate of 40 ACH be used in areas of larger kitchens not treated by canopies.

(*c*) Replacement air

If the kitchen is in a sealed area (i.e. not adjacent to dining areas) replacement air should comprise typically 85% supplied by mechanical ventilation and 15% by ingress of air from the surrounding areas. This ensures that the kitchen is maintained under a negative pressure to prevent the escape of cooking odours. In basement areas containing kitchens and restaurants, the supply plant to the restaurant areas should be sufficient to offset the down-draught from street level in addition to supplying air to the kitchens.

If non-air conditioned, properly ventilated restaurants adjoin the kitchens, the majority of air may be drawn from the dining area. If the restaurant is air conditioned, air may be drawn from it at a maximum of 7 litre·s^{-1} per person. The difference between the extract and replacement air should be provided by a separate kitchen supply system.

Air drawn from adjacent areas should be clean. It is not advisable to draw make-up air from rooms where smoking is allowed. Where make-up air is drawn via serving hatches or counters it is recommended that air velocities do not exceed 0.25 m·s^{-1} to avoid complaints of draughts. However, higher velocities may be tolerated or desirable at hot serving counters. The make-up air can be drawn in through permanent grilles if the serving hatches are small or likely to be closed for long periods. These should be sized on the basis of 1.0–1.5 m·s^{-1} airflow velocity.

The incoming air from the ventilation system needs to be arranged so as not to affect adversely the performance of flues associated with open-flued gas appliances(75).

In smaller kitchens sufficient replacement air may be drawn in naturally via ventilation grilles in walls, doors or windows. Provision should be made to prevent pest entry by using a fine mesh in the grille; however, it may be necessary to compensate for restrictions in the airflow by increasing the size of the grille.

(*d*) Cooling air

The effective balancing of incoming and extracted air, together with removal at source of hot vapours, should prevent the kitchen from becoming too hot. Air inlets from mechanical ventilation systems can be positioned to provide cooling air over hot work positions. Extra provision may be required, either by an overhead outlet discharging cool air or by air conditioning. Free standing fans are not recommended due to health and safety considerations and their effect on the efficiency of the designed ventilation systems.

(*e*) Discharge

High level discharge of extracted air, with discharge velocities of about 15 m·s^{-1}, are often needed to prevent nuisance to neighbouring properties. The design of the discharge stack should prevent down-draughts and re-entry of fumes into the building.

2.3.6.2 Food processing

General

Food processing covers cooking, preservation and packing. Normally, mechanical ventilation, and sometimes air conditioning, will be required.

Requirements

The designer should take into account the heat dissipation based on the energy used in the production process and should make an approximate heat balance for the calculation of air quantities. The ventilation of special food manufacturing processes will need detailed consideration in consultation with food production specialists/managers. Plant may need to be designed to meet individual requirements; for example, a fairly closely controlled temperature is necessary in sweet and chocolate manufacture and local cooling is an essential part of the manufacturing process.

In cooking areas the general guidance given in section 2.3.6.1 applies. In addition to local ventilation, general ventilation will be necessary. It is preferable to supply air over working areas and extract over cooking equipment or other high heat dissipation areas, but care must be taken to avoid local excess cooling of the processes.

Regular maintenance of kitchen ductwork is essential to reduce the risk of fire(74). Ductwork should be routed in a manner that will enable routine cleaning to be carried out. Drains may be necessary in some cooling processes, as may fire dampers and grease filters.

2.3.7 Cleanrooms

2.3.7.1 General

A cleanroom is a room in which the concentration of airborne particles is controlled to specified limits and which is constructed and used in a manner to minimise the introduction, generation and retention of particles within the room. Cleanrooms are classified according to the maximum permitted number of particles of a certain size. Commonly used classifications are given in BS EN ISO 14644-1(76) and FS209E(77), see Table 2.18. The appropriate classification must suit the work that is to be undertaken and it is often the nature of the work that will dictate the arrangement of the ventilation systems.

Table 2.18 Comparison of cleanroom classifications

USA Federal Standard 209E(77)	BS EN ISO 14644-1(76)	MCA(78) ('at rest')
—	1	—
—	2	—
1	3	—
10	4	—
100	5	A or B
1000	6	—
10 000	7	C
100 000	8	D

The Medicines Control Agency (MCA), which publishes the *Rules and Guidance for Pharmaceutical Manufacturers and Distributors*(78) (known as the 'orange book'), uses the FS209E classifications and, in addition, sets limits for microbiological contamination. Classifications may also relate to 'as built', 'at rest' and 'in operation' states.

The appropriate classification must be agreed with the client as the cleanroom suites will often require validation in terms or air change rates, particle counts and other environmental criteria.

Information on the design of cleanrooms is available within the series of *Baseline Guides* produced by the International Society for Pharmaceutical Engineering*.

*International Society for Pharmaceutical Engineering, 3816W Linebaugh Avenue, Suite 412, Tampa, Florida 33624, USA (http://www.ispe.org)

2.3.7.2 Design requirements and strategies

Generally, the design of the ventilation systems must take account of the following factors, which will need to be agreed with the client:

- classification, i.e. 'at rest' or 'in operation'
- nature of work, e.g. semiconductor/electronics or pharmaceutical
- laminar or turbulent flow requirements
- minimum air change rates
- pressure differentials
- room construction, fabric leakage rates and other air paths
- HEPA filtration standards
- room layout, including fittings and equipment
- open or closed door design
- controls and alarms
- validation requirements.

Mechanical ventilation systems for cleanrooms need to provide a high level of reliability, as the system is critical to the proper functioning of the building and the business conducted within it. Consequential losses arising from failure can be very significant in this type of building.

Filters are one of the major influences on the level of cleanliness in cleanrooms, but must not be considered in isolation. The method used to supply air to the room is a crucial factor, along with how the room is used in operation. The location of fixed furniture, equipment and workstations needs to be considered as they affect airflow patterns and create dead zones within the room. Wherever possible the product should be upstream of the operative. The cleanest zone is the area in immediately in front of the HEPA filter and the product should be in this zone if possible. There should special clothing for operatives with changing rooms etc. Variable speed fans should be used to maintain constant airflow when HEPA filters become dirty. Clean benches are frequently used to upgrade a section of the clean room or carry out work in a normal working area.

Air can be supplied by laminar- or non-laminar-flow methods. Airflow patterns may need to be controlled or located so that the cleanest air can be directed across workstations where the tasks are actually performed.

Non-laminar-flow cleanrooms can achieve up to USA Federal Standard 209E class 1000, whilst laminar-flow clean rooms can achieve class 1 in 'in operation' state. Turbulent-flow clean rooms may achieve higher classifications in 'at rest' state. Non-laminar-flow systems can achieve FS209E 'at rest' class 100 (MCA grade B). Such systems are common in pharmaceutical applications.

In non-laminar-flow clean rooms, air is supplied to the room by individually ducted HEPA filter modules or air diffusers in the ceiling. Alternatively, an in line HEPA filter housing installed in the supply duct as close to the room as possible can be used. The grade of HEPA filter specified will need to suit the room classification. Air should be exhausted through grilles in the walls near the floor as there is no requirement on uniformity of airflow patterns. Air velocities must ideally be between 0.15 and 0.45 m·s^{-1}; lower velocities allow contamination to settle out, high velocities allow contamination to agglomerate.

For non-laminar-flow cleanrooms, observation of certain design criteria is essential. Table 2.19 provides general design guidance for non-laminar-flow clean rooms.

In laminar-flow cleanrooms, air enters the room through filters covering the whole ceiling (downflow) or on one wall (crossflow), and is exhausted through the entire opposite surface, with air flowing in parallel lines and at uniform velocity. Thus, air makes only one pass through the room and any contamination created in the room is carried out. Velocities of 0.45 m·s^{-1} are necessary to prevent settling out. Such rooms are costly to construct and it may be appropriate to subdivide the room into areas having different classifications according to the processes being undertaken. Due to the quantities of air being circulated some form of recirculation should be considered to reduce energy costs. Table 2.20 provides general design guidance for laminar-flow clean rooms.

Table 2.19 Design guidance for non-laminar-flow clean rooms

Parameter	Value for achievable class (USA Federal Standard 209E)[77]		
	1000	10 000	100 000
Room pressure differential to adjacent areas	15 Pa	15 Pa	5–10 Pa
Ventilation rate (depending on type ofwork)	40–120 ACH	20–40 ACH	10–20 ACH
Clean air inlet area as a percentage of ceiling area (typically for 'in operation'status)	20–50	10–20	5–10
Terminal velocity at clean air inlet	0.15–0.45 m·s^{-1}	0.15–0.45 m·s^{-1}	0.15–0.45 m·s^{-1}
Return locations	Low level or floor	Low side wall	Side wall or ceiling
Wall return spacing	Continuous on all four walls	Intermittent on long walls	Non-uniform
Return face velocities	0.5–1 m·s^{-1}	1–2.5 m·s^{-1}	2.5 m·s^{-1}

Note: Air supply may be drawn from outside or recirculated, subject to client requirements

Table 2.20 Design guidance for laminar-flow clean rooms

Parameter	Value for achievable class (USA Federal Standard 209E)[83]	
	1 and 10	100
Room pressure	15 Pa	15 Pa
Ventilation rate	500–600 ACH	500 ACH
Clean air inlet area as a percentage of ceiling area	90–100%	90%
Terminal velocity at clean air inlet	0.15–0.45 m·s^{-1}	0.15–0.45 m·s^{-1}
Return locations	Perforated wall/floor	Low level or floor

2.3.8 Communal residential buildings

2.3.8.1 General[79]

Communal residential properties are buildings containing separate residential units with some degree of communal facilities. For the purposes of this Guide, the following have been considered:

— residential care homes

— student accommodation

— military barracks.

As with domestic properties, effective ventilation is best provided by reducing air leakage, extracting moisture and pollutants at source, and providing occupant controllable ventilation. Natural ventilation is particularly suitable for achieving this.

2.3.8.2 Requirements

Overall ventilation rates of between 0.5 and 1 air change per hour are generally appropriate.

Wherever possible, residents should be able to maintain autonomy and control over their immediate environment. In the case of student accommodation the emphasis is on dealing with intermittent occupation and appropriate integration with heating system controls. In residential care homes occupancy is less intermittent and control of the heating and ventilation is likely to be more centralised under the control of a warden.

For communally shared facilities within residential care homes and student accommodation, it will be necessary to make different arrangements for areas of higher occupancy (e.g. television rooms) or areas of excessive moisture or odour generation (e.g. laundry rooms, and cafeteria areas) requiring ventilation direct to the outside.

Within residential care homes it may be necessary to service conservatories, which should, if possible, be separated from other living spaces by doors to prevent excessive heat loss in winter. External draught lobbies or revolving doors should be specified for all major entrances/exits.

In both types of accommodation the needs of smokers may affect the chosen system design, in particular the servicing of smoking lounges. However, as stated above on page 2-15, it should be noted that the provision of ventilation cannot completely remove the health risks associated with cigarette smoke.

2.3.8.3 Strategies

The required ventilation rates can be achieved by using trickle vents with passive stack ventilation (PSV)[80] systems or extract fans in kitchens and bathrooms. Alternatively, whole-building ventilation systems with heat recovery (MVHR) can be used if the building is well sealed. CIBSE TM23: *Testing buildings for air leakage*[11] recommends an air leakage index of 8 $\text{Pa}\cdot\text{m}^3\cdot\text{h}^{-1}$ at 50 Pa as good practice for dwellings with balanced whole-house mechanical ventilation and 15 $\text{Pa}\cdot\text{m}^3\cdot\text{h}^{-1}$ at 50 Pa for dwellings with mechanical ventilation. Best practice standards for such dwellings are 4 and 8 $\text{Pa}\cdot\text{m}^3\cdot\text{h}^{-1}$ at 50 Pa, respectively.

2.3.8.4 Further considerations

The maintenance implications of MVHR systems must be considered[81], as must the consequences of system failure if there is no passive ventilation back-up. Guidance on system optimisation is available, see section 2.4.4 and elsewhere[82].

2.3.9 Computer rooms

2.3.9.1 General

Under operational conditions, computer equipment is susceptible to the temperature, humidity and the cleanliness or otherwise of the surrounding environment. Computer rooms have a number of specific characteristics that need to be taken into account when selecting and designing ventilation and air conditioning systems. These include:

— 24-hour operation

— high sensible loads (typically 500 to 1000 $\text{W}\cdot\text{m}^{-2}$)

— low occupancy and latent loads

— close control of temperatures and humidity required

— high levels of reliability required, with some redundancy to ensure 24-hour operation

— deep raised floors to deal with extensive cabling

— noise levels generally above those for offices due to the computer equipment

— capability for expansion to allow for frequent upgrading of computer equipment

— mainframe computers with tight temperature control requirements may require dedicated chilled water systems.

Mechanical ventilation systems for computer rooms need to provide a high level of reliability, as the system is critical to the proper functioning of the building and the business conducted within it. Consequential losses arising from failure can be very significant in this type of building.

It is particularly important to establish the required loading of the space, the specific requirements of any mainframe computer and the capability for expansion as these are subject to wide variations.

To minimise the effect of the external environment, computer suites are generally provided with highly insulated walls, floors and roofs, and no windows. The building structure should be airtight and vapour-sealed to facilitate close control. Air locks may also be provided at entrances. In many instances computer rooms will normally operate with the lighting off for much of the day.

Heating should be provided in critical areas to maintain a suitable minimum temperature under winter conditions during computer shutdown.

Computer rooms can be grouped into three approximate size categories:

— *small*: in offices, typically 1% of area served, often less critical than larger computer rooms; telephone equipment rooms

— *medium*: IT-intensive organisations, such as financial organisations with dealing facilities, typically 1–2% of area served on the floors plus 2–5% for a main computer room

— *large*: stand-alone data centres; switching centres.

2.3.9.2 Design requirements

Typical design requirements for computer rooms are shown in Table 2.21.

Requirements should be checked with equipment manufacturers as wider control bands and higher temperatures may be permissible.

2.3.9.3 Strategies

To provide close control of temperature and humidity, specialist computer room air conditioning units are normally provided. These units generally include:

— cooling coil (DX, glycol or chilled water)

— reheat coil (usually electric due to limited use)

— humidifier (typically steam due to straightforward maintenance and health and safety requirements)

— filtration (panel filters)

— fans (single or multiple dependent on duty)

— compressors (DX and glycol units only).

The units can be mounted within the computer room or in service corridors adjacent and come in a variety of sizes. Various degrees of sophistication are possible depending on the reliability required from the individual units. The most usual arrangement is a wardrobe-type unit with common fan drives, controls, heater battery, cooling coil and humidifiers. Reliability is then improved by incorporating redundant units. Alternatively 'modular' units can be used with common controls but individual fans, heaters, cooling coils and even humidifiers in each module, so that a module failure has little effect on the overall performance.

Table 2.21 Typical design requirements: computer rooms

Parameter	Requirements
Internal temperature	To suit computer equipment: typically 21 ± 2 °C; rate of change not to exceed 3 $K \cdot h^{-1}$
Internal relative humidity	50 ± 5% RH; rate of change not to exceed 10% in 1 hour
Filtration	To suit computer equipment: typically 60% efficiency to BS EN 779[83]
Noise criteria	NR55 (range NR45–NR65)
External temperatures	Design temperatures based on a 1% failure rate may not be acceptable; heat rejection plant in particular requires careful selection to ensure it can perform in practically all conditions
Internal heat gains	600 $W \cdot m^{-2}$ sensible (range 500–1000 $W \cdot m^{-2}$)
Ventilation	Computer rooms are generally pressurised by oversupply (1 ACH typical) to prevent infiltration gains and local variations in temperature and humidity; otherwise minimum fresh air to suit occupancy.

To a large extent, the choice of the type of cooling will be determined by the size of the computer room and the availability, or otherwise, of chilled water. DX cooling is generally used in smaller rooms where chilled water is not readily available 24 hours a day. The DX cooling coil rejects heat through external air cooled condensers. On large installations the proliferation of air-cooled condensers tends to present an unacceptable solution.

Glycol systems are based on a DX cooling coil in the room unit with heat rejection into a glycol closed water system. Dry air coolers are used to reject heat from the glycol system either centrally or on an individual unit-by-unit basis. An additional 'free cooling' coil can be added to the room unit to allow it to operate without running the compressors when the external ambient temperature is low. Glycol systems are generally used for large computer rooms where 'free cooling' can save significant amounts of energy.

Chilled water room unit cooling coils fed from a central chilled water system may be used in smaller rooms where chilled water is available 24 hours a day, and in larger rooms where simplicity of the room unit may have a benefit.

A high sensible cooling ratio is an important consideration for any selected unit to minimise the operation of the cooling coil and humidifier together. Elevated chilled water temperatures (e.g. 10–16 °C) may be used for this reason. The higher temperatures also provide the energy benefit of increased central refrigeration plant efficiency.

Common controllers can be provided but it is usual for each unit to be separately controlled to cater for variations in gains across the computer room. Common central monitoring of the alarms is usual.

To improve system redundancy, dual pipework systems may be used. Generator back-up for the cooling system is normally provided in critical applications. This may be a 'no-break' facility where high loads would give an unacceptable temperature rise between power failure and the generators coming on-line.

Air supply is normally through the ceiling or floor. Supplying air at low level and extracting over the computer equipment has the advantage that the heat released upwards from the equipment can more easily be removed without it affecting the occupied areas. High level supply may be through diffusers or a ventilated ceiling.

Consideration should be given to the operating and maintenance requirements of the installation. Temperature and humidity recording/alarm devices may be necessary together with other operational alarms. Locating equipment in an adjacent service corridor may be preferred for critical/sensitive applications as this will reduce maintenance access requirements to the space.

2.3.10 Dwellings (including high rise)

2.3.10.1 General

Fresh air supplies within dwellings are necessary for:

- the health and safety of the occupants
- the control of condensation, often the dominant pollutant arising from moisture generated by cooking, washing and clothes drying
- the removal of odours
- the removal of pollutants such as VOCs
- the removal of allergens arising from dust mites
- the safe operation of combustion appliances.

As moisture is the most significant pollutant, its control forms the basis of the ventilation strategy. The key is to avoid a situation where the relative humidity exceeds 70% for a prolonged period[84]. This can usually be achieved with a whole house ventilation rate of 0.5 air changes per hour[85]. Alternatively, more rapid extraction in response to moisture release within the dwelling, either by humidity sensors or manually, can be beneficial in removing moisture before it is absorbed by furnishings and/or the fabric of the building itself[86].

In domestic situations, it is particularly important to inform occupants of the intended operation and purpose of the selected ventilation system to ensure that it achieves its intended purpose. This will ensure that they:

- do not tamper with the system in the belief that it is costing them money to run
- do not interfere with the performance of the system through blocking air inlets or extracts, or by altering sensor settings.

2.3.10.2 Requirements

As with non-domestic buildings, the underlying concept should be to 'build tight, ventilate right'[85]. Detailed guidance on requirements and acceptable ventilation solutions can be found in Approved Document F[37]. Guidance on achieving an airtight construction can be found in CIBSE and BRE publications[11,87].

Figure 2.8[88] illustrates the impact of uncontrolled air leakage on the ventilation rate. The greater the air leakage the greater the ventilation rate and the more varied and uncontrollable it will be. Air leakage must often be reduced to bring the overall ventilation rate within the prescribed range. The airtightness of UK dwellings can range from 2 ACH to above 30 ACH at an applied pressure of 50 Pa. This equates to an air infiltration rate of 0.1–1.5 ACH, with an average of 0.7 ACH. Target air leakage rates for domestic properties are:

- 5–7 ACH at 50 Pa for dwellings having local extraction and background ventilation
- 4 ACH at 50 Pa for dwellings having whole house ventilation systems.

2.3.10.3 Strategies

The normal strategy is to extract directly at source from wet zones using mechanical extract ventilation (local or whole-house) or passive stacks. Fresh supply air is brought into the living rooms and bedrooms either by natural ventilation methods or as make-up, either induced by the negative pressure or via a mechanical whole-house ventilation system. Additional ventilation may be necessary if smoking takes place. However it should be noted the health risks of smoking cannot be completely eliminated by ventilation (see page 2-15).

In high radon areas, sealing the foundations, combined with sub-floor venting, may be required. Specialist advice should be sought. Guidance is available from BRE[89].

Balanced flue combustion appliances are preferable in dwellings fitted with mechanical ventilation incorporating extraction, as their operation is not affected by pressure differences. Guidance on safety relating to combustion products is provided in BS 5440[57] and BS 5864[90] and Building Regulations Approved Document J[38].

Passive stack ventilation[91]

A passive stack system comprises vents located in the kitchen and bathroom connected via individual near-vertical circular or rectangular ducts to ridge or tile terminals. Moist air is drawn up through the ducts by a combination of stack and wind effects. The ducts, which are normally 80–125 mm in diameter[92], should have no more than two bends at greater than 30° to the vertical to minimise the resistance to air flow, and be insulated where they pass through cold spaces to reduce the risk of condensation. Replacement air enters via trickle or similar ventilators located in the 'dry' rooms and via air leakage.

Standard passive stack ventilation (PSV) systems have a simple inlet grille to the duct. Humidity sensitive vents are available that can provide increased flows when humidity is high. Acoustic treatment may be required to reduce ingress of external noise. Fire dampers are required where ducts pass through a fire-separating floor.

PSV systems can be combined with extract fans in hybrid systems, the fan being located in the kitchen.

Advantages:

- No direct running costs.

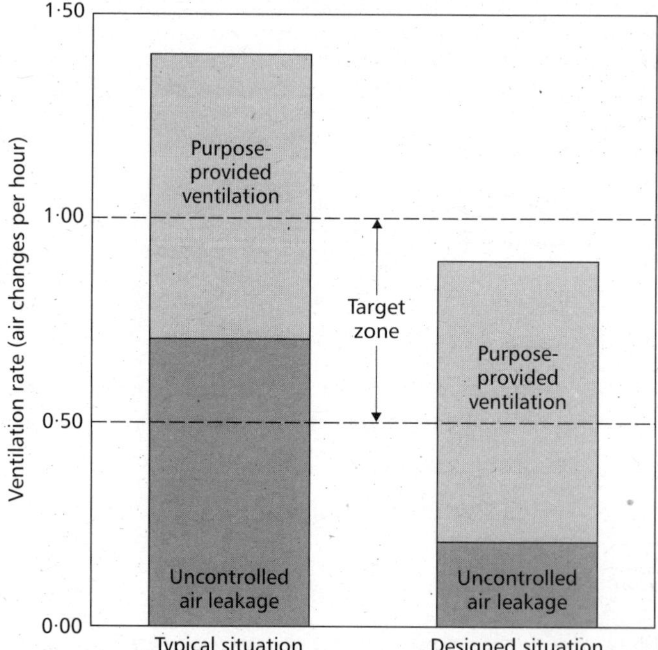

Figure 2.8 Impact of air leakage on ventilation rate

- System will last the lifetime of the building.
- System is silent in operation.
- System requires no electrical connection.

Disadvantages:

- Ventilation rate can be highly variable.
- Ventilation rate may be inadequate in poorly ventilated dwellings.
- Existing house layouts may make it difficult to accommodate duct runs.
- Site installation must be of good quality to avoid flow restrictions and excessive pressure drops.
- Uncontrolled systems waste energy due to continuous operation.

Local extract fans[86]

These are installed in kitchens and bathrooms to provide rapid extraction (typically 15–60 litre·s^{-1}) of moisture and other pollutants. They normally operate under occupant control or humidity control, or operate in association with door or light switches. Fans can be window, ceiling or wall mounted but are most effectively located at high level away from the source of fresh air, i.e. an internal door or trickle ventilator. In a kitchen they are ideally combined with a cooker hood. Ceiling mounted fans should be ducted to outside; however, it should be noted that ductwork lengths of as little as 1 m can considerably impair performance if an incorrect type of fan has been fitted[93]. Replacement air is provided by trickle ventilators or air leakage.

Fans should be located so as not to produce draughts and so as not to draw combustion products from open-flue appliances[38,90,91]. Note that cooker hoods require permanently open vents as close as possible to the hood. Control can be by manual switching or through being wired into door or light switches. Another option is humidity control with manual override, although the sensor may cause the fan to operate when moisture generation is not taking place, e.g. on warm humid summer days. The sensor needs to be positioned with consideration to where the major source of moisture is located. It may be more suitable to install cowled shutters to avoid noise problems with external gravity back-draught shutters rattling in the wind.

Advantages:

- Simple and widely applicable.
- Provides the possibility of rapid extract.
- System is easily understood.

Disadvantages:

- Perceived by occupants to have high running costs and is prone to tampering by occupants.
- Noise can be an issue.
- System requires occasional maintenance.

Heat recovery room ventilators[88]

These are a development of the extract fan and are mounted in external walls. They incorporate a heat exchanger that recovers approximately 60% of the heat from the outgoing air. This is passed across to the incoming air to preheat it. The extract fan is often dual speed, providing low speed continuous trickle ventilation or high speed extract. High-speed extract can be under manual or humidity control.

Advantages:

- Provides continuous low level ventilation.
- Provides the option of rapid extract.
- Recovers heat energy.
- Allows filtration of the supply air.
- Almost silent in operation at trickle speed.

Disadvantages:

- Occupants perceive the systems to have high running costs.
- Regular maintenance is required.
- Some recirculation is possible, due to the close proximity of supply and extract grilles.

Mechanical supply ventilation[94]

A fan unit is typically mounted in the roof space and delivers air that has been filtered and tempered by the roofspace into the dwelling. The system works on the principle of continuous dilution, displacement and replacement of air in the dwelling. Air discharge from the dwelling is via purpose provided egress vents and/or leakage paths. Fans typically run continuously at low speed, with manual or humidity controlled boost to a higher speed when required. Temperature controls can incorporate single roof space sensors or sensors in both the roof and living spaces. The latter system adjusts the flow rate of the unit to suit the temperatures in both spaces, thereby providing the optimum energy benefits for the occupants. Fan units incorporating highly efficient motor technology can provide a significant net energy gain to the dwelling.

Advantages:

- Simple and well established as a means of controlling condensation.
- Compatible with open flued appliances.
- Utilises any heat gain in the loft space.
- Allows filtration of the air before it enters the space.

Disadvantages:

- Occupants perceive the systems to have high running costs.
- Noise can be an issue.
- Systems are prone to tampering by occupants.
- Regular maintenance is required.
- Limited research has been carried out into system performance.
- Effectiveness depends on building shape/ layout.

Continuous mechanical extract[94]

Continuous mechanical extract ventilation is a simpler alternative to a supply and extract system (see below). Further information on design, installation and operation is given in BRE Digest 398[81].

Whole-house mechanical ventilation[81]

A whole-house mechanical ventilation system normally combines supply and extract ventilation in one system. A heat exchanger can be incorporated to preheat the incoming air. These systems can be effective at meeting part of the heating load in energy efficient dwellings thereby helping to distribute the heat. Typically, warm moist air is extracted from kitchens, bathrooms, utility rooms and WCs via a system of ducting, and passed across a heat exchanger before being exhausted. Fresh incoming air is preheated and ducted to the living room and other habitable rooms.

Ducts may be circular or rectangular and range in size from 100 to 150 mm in diameter. Air velocities should be kept below 4 $m{\cdot}s^{-1}$. Vertical exhaust ducts should be fitted with condensate traps, horizontal exhaust ducts should slope away from fans to prevent condensate running back. Both supply and extract grilles should be located at high level as far as practical from internal doors, but at a sufficient distance from each other to avoid 'short circuiting', i.e. a minimum of 2 m. Suitable louvres or cowls should be fitted to prevent ingress of rain, birds or insects.

Such systems can provide the ideal ventilation almost independent of weather conditions. During normal operation the total extract airflow rate will be 0.5–0.7 ACH based on the whole dwelling volume, less an allowance for background natural infiltration if desired. Individual room air change rates will be significantly higher, possibly 2–5 ACH, in rooms with an extract terminal. To be most effective a good standard of air tightness is required, typically better than 4 ACH at 50 Pa. Airflows need to be balanced at the time of installation. Extract rates from bathrooms and kitchens can be boosted during times of high moisture production although care should be taken not to cause draughts. The system can be acoustically treated to reduce noise ingress.

Transfer grilles are necessary only if the system is part of a warm air heating system but may be fitted in other cases, if desired. If the bottom edges of internal doors clear the floor surface by 5–8 mm there is likely to be sufficient opening for air movement. Transfer grilles are usually positioned not more than 450 mm above the floor. If placed higher they may allow the rapid movement of toxic combustion products or facilitate the spread of fire. Fire dampers should be inserted where the ductwork passes through separating walls and floors, and are desirable in kitchens, e.g. cooker hoods.

It is claimed that such systems are effective in reducing condensation due to the controlled ventilation and air-tight structure reducing cold air draughts. Manufacturers also claim that they improve indoor air quality and help in controlling dust mite populations.

Advantages:

— Provides controlled preheated fresh air throughout the house.

— Reduces the heating demand in very airtight dwellings.

— Reduces the risk of condensation.

Disadvantages:

— Ductwork can be difficult to accommodate.

— Initial costs are high.

— The systems has an ongoing maintenance liability: 6-monthly or annually.

— An adequate level of airtightness must be provided.

— Installation and commissioning is more complex than for other systems.

Comfort cooling and air conditioning

Systems are available which incorporate a heat pump into a whole-house mechanical ventilation system. Little information is available on their performance[95]; similarly with other proposed systems of domestic comfort cooling or air conditioning[96]. The decision to install such systems in domestic properties should not be taken lightly and designers should concentrate on enhancing the fabric performance to eliminate this need. If a comfort cooling and air conditioning system is proposed, key concerns for the occupants would be the ongoing maintenance requirements and acoustic considerations, both internal and external.

2.3.10.4 High rise dwellings

See section 2.3.12 for non-domestic high rise buildings.

High rise dwellings pose particular problems because of wind-induced pressures at the higher levels, i.e. above 6 storeys. This requires that special attention be paid to trickle ventilator selection[96–100]. Whole-house mechanical ventilation systems, see above, are an option[101].

If every dwelling unit comprises a self-contained ventilation system, care must be taken to ensure that inlets to dwellings e.g. windows, trickle ventilators, or mechanical air intakes are not contaminated by ventilation outlets or combustion flue gases from adjacent dwellings. This may encourage the use of centrally ducted ventilation and heating systems[93], particularly in gas or oil heated properties.

The balancing of common toilet and bathroom ducts in high rise buildings is considered in section 2.3.12.

2.3.11 Factories and warehouses

This section considers the ventilation of industrial buildings and warehouses; see section 2.3.15 for ventilation of industrial processes.

2.3.11.1 General

Minimum ventilation rates are determined by the fresh air requirements for occupants laid down in the Factories Act[102] and Health and Safety at Work etc. Act[103]. However these requirements are often exceeded by other criteria such as the ventilation requirements of the particular manufacturing processes.

There is no simple relationship between the building and process energy. The combination can be considered as:

— *Process incidental*: i.e. the process makes few demands on the internal environment. In many ways requirements are similar to office accommodation except that the space may be taller, the systems less sophisticated and environmental conditions often less demanding.

— *Process significant*: i.e. the servicing is dictated primarily by the comfort and performance requirements of the people in the building but affected by the needs of the process, e.g. humidification for textile weaving.

— *Process dominant*: i.e. the process demands very little of the building (e.g. it may be outside) or it may totally dominate the situation, for either quality or health and safety reasons.

Suitable systems will vary depending upon the degree of separation between accommodation types. Within a well-defined office area natural ventilation may suffice. Mechanical ventilation is required where occupancy is dense or where the opening of windows is not desirable. Within the production space, refer to section 2.3.15.

2.3.11.2 Requirements

Energy use

It is often difficult to distinguish between the energy consequences of the systems required for the industrial processes and those required for the buildings that contain them. However surveys of energy use commissioned under the Energy Efficiency Best Practice Programme (EEBPP) have shown that the worst and best performing buildings can differ by more than 100% within a particular industrial sector. EEBPP Energy Consumption Guide ECG 18[104] categorises industrial buildings as follows:

— *Storage and distribution buildings*: i.e. warehouses; these are typically 7.5 m high, contain pallet racking, and are naturally ventilated to 16 °C for single shift operation during the day, condensation protection being required at night. Refrigerated warehousing requires specialist treatment.

— *Light manufacturing buildings:* these are typically 5 m high and include areas for offices, storage and dispatch. They are largely naturally ventilated with occasional local mechanical extraction. Shift operation may be longer than for storage buildings.

— *Factory/office buildings*: these are typically 4 m high, possibly with a suspended ceiling in office areas, with little other differentiation between production, office and storage spaces. Some local mechanical ventilation or air conditioning may be present.

— *General manufacturing buildings*: these are typically 8 m high to accommodate tall equipment, gantry cranes and local storage racking. Mechanical ventilation may be provided to areas of high heat gain or for the clearance of process contaminants.

Table 2.22 provides energy targets relating to ventilation. However, these figures should be treated with caution, as the industrial building stock is extremely diverse; for example, high bay warehouses of 14 m height are not included in this classification. Further guidance is available on establishing building specific energy targets[105].

Table 2.22 Building related energy use[104]

Classification	Electricity consumption for fans, pumps and controls / $kW \cdot h \cdot m^{-2}$ per year	Total electricity consumption of building / $kW \cdot h \cdot m^{-2}$ per year
Storage and distribution	5	50
Light manufacturing	6	55
Factory-office	10	31
General manufacturing	10	20

Air infiltration control

Air infiltration typically accounts for as much as 30% of the heat loss of an industrial building[105]. To minimise air infiltration problems the following needs consideration:

— structural integrity should be checked by infra-red thermography

— external windbreaks should be considered on exposed sites

— if a false ceiling has been installed to reduce ceiling heights in office areas, ensure that gaps have been sealed to prevent the leakage of warm air into the ceiling void

— goods doors should not be installed facing the prevailing wind or opposite each other; if this is not possible the goods loading area should:

(*a*) be partitioned-off, either internally or externally, with the partitioning insulated to the same level as the external wall

(*b*) have rapid closing doors suitable for frequent use, either push-button or automatic, or

(*c*) have plastic strip curtains (although these are not a substitute for doors and there are safety considerations), or

(*d*) have an air curtain, or

(*e*) have a pneumatic seal around loading bays.

Heat recovery

See section 2.5.6 for details of heat recovery devices. Before considering heat recovery ensure that ventilation rates are minimised and can be adequately controlled. Where the extracted air is contaminated only with particles it may be possible to filter it and return it to the workplace. This eliminates heat losses but will result in more stringent maintenance requirements. If the recycled air is hot it may be discharged back into the workplace at low level during the winter; ductwork should also be provided to allow the hot air to be rejected to outside during the summer. The use of central plant will assist in the installation and economics of heat recovery but may prejudice its controllability.

Control

Plant can be controlled by time control or air flow rate control. Larger centralised systems should be zoned. Time control can be by means of:

- manual switching (should be easily accessible, with a well-labelled on/off switch)
- timeswitch
- push button or automatic presence detection allowing pre-set timed operation (useful for intermittently occupied areas)
- electrical interlock to associated production machinery (if local).

Airflow rate control can be achieved by:

- air temperature
- contaminant concentration
- number of machines in operation
- duct pressure (where zone isolation dampers are used on a centralised system).

Two-speed or variable speed motors should be considered. When contemplating reducing airflow rates, designers should be aware that limits may be in place to maintain a minimum duct velocity.

2.3.11.3 Strategies[105]

Natural ventilation

Subject to constraints imposed by industrial processes, natural ventilation can be particularly effective in industrial buildings due to the relatively high ceilings. The most effective ventilation will be obtained by using a combination of low and high level openings (e.g. windows and rooflights). With heat gains up to 20 W·m^{-2}, simple systems can be used that may be cheaper to install than those relying on mechanical plant. With heat gains of 20–40 W·m^{-2}, more sophisticated natural ventilation strategies may be required which may cost more to install. However, life cycle costing could demonstrate the potential for overall savings due to reduced operational costs.

It may be possible to extend the applicability of natural ventilation by grouping process equipment into a few mechanically ventilated areas. For optimum energy efficiency, any natural ventilation should be controllable as natural air change rates in industrial buildings can be quite high (particularly if goods doors are left open). The correct strategy is to design the building to be as airtight as possible and to provide the required amount of ventilation by controllable means. If space is to be subsequently partitioned off for the creation of office accommodation ensure that this will not affect the operation of the ventilation system.

Mechanical ventilation

For general factory ventilation consider the use of high level extract fans (either wall or roof mounted). These are effective at removing heat but are ineffective at controlling fumes, see sections 2.3.2.1 and 2.3.15. Consider providing all mechanical ventilation systems with back-draught shutters or dampers to prevent air infiltration when the fans are not in use.

Prevent excessive fan power requirements by ensuring that all ductwork is appropriately sized, i.e. pressure drops not more than 1 Pa·m^{-1}. This usually equates to an air velocity of about 10 m·s^{-1} in main ducts and 4 m·s^{-1} in branch ducts. Over-sized fans should not be used as they will operate at sub-optimal efficiency and/or may require throttling in order to provide the suction or airflow rates required. Make-up air should be introduced to minimise energy use and discomfort, and to ensure the continued safety of heating appliances.

Make-up air

Make-up systems should be specified to provide the optimum building pressure balance. The choice of pressure balance will depend upon the processes taking place within the building, see sections 2.4.3 and 2.3.15. Negative pressures may upset heating appliances with traditional flues. Positive pressure may facilitate uniform heating and help prevent the ingress of untreated external air. Direct gas firing is a particularly efficient way of tempering large volumes of fresh air if required as make-up.

2.3.11.4 Further considerations

Automatic doors

These are probably the most energy efficient solution for low traffic situations where it is inconvenient or impracticable to open doors manually. However, they become effectively permanently open doorways when traffic is dense.

Air curtains[106,107]

Air curtains condition the incoming air at the entrance in order to minimise cold draughts. They do not act as a physical barrier to prevent the entry of outside air but use heating energy to temper air that enters the doorway. They prevent the natural convection of warm air out of the top of a doorway being replaced by cold air at the bottom.

The heat input of an air curtain must be sufficient to temper the quantity of air coming in at the entrance. An air curtain will not be effective if the velocity of the incoming air is excessive. This can occur as a result of under-pressure within the building from extract systems, stack effect with leaky or tall buildings, or wind effects on an exposed site. The width of an air curtain discharge grille should be just wider than the doorway opening; an air curtain narrower than the doorway is ineffective. Opening and closing of doors can disrupt the air stream, which takes some time to re-establish. The heating capacity of an air curtain can have an effect on the space temperature within the building entrance and suitable controls need to be fitted to adjust the heat output and air stream characteristics if necessary.

2.3.12 High rise buildings (non-domestic)

This section relates to non-domestic high rise buildings. Domestic high rise buildings are covered in section 2.3.10.

2.3.12.1 General

Whilst the aims of the ventilation strategy for buildings of 20 storeys or more do not necessarily differ from those of other buildings, there are specific design issues that need to be taken into consideration when selecting and designing ventilating and air conditioning systems. In particular these include stack effects, high winds and hydraulic pressures.

2.3.12.2 Stack effect, high winds, hydraulic pressures

Stack effects created by buoyancy pressures are magnified by the height of the building. In cold climates the interior air will usually be warmer than the outside air. Buoyancy forces cause warm air to leak out of the upper part of the building and cold ambient air to leak in at the base of the building. This will have a number of effects including:

— requiring energy to heat infiltrated air

— driving moisture into the envelope assembly, allowing condensation to form and deteriorate the materials and insulation

— creating uncomfortable draughts and possibly annoying whistling noises

— pressure differences between floor space and shafts affecting opening and closing of doors.

In warm climates a negative stack effect occurs with cold air flowing out of the base of the building and infiltration of warm moist air at the top. Moisture condensing in the cool interior environment can cause serious damage to the building materials. Envelope tightness is not usually as carefully controlled in warm climates because leakage is not as apparent; however, the potential damage is greater than that occurring in cold climate.

Features that help combat infiltration due to the stack effect(108,109) and wind pressures include the following:

— revolving doors or vestibules at exterior entrances

— pressurised lobbies

— tight gaskets on stairwell doors leading to the roof

— automatic dampers on elevator shaft vents

— airtight separations in vertical shafts

— tight construction of the exterior skin

— tight closure and seals on all dampers opening to the exterior.

The large stack effect and high winds normally mean that natural ventilation is impracticable and therefore high rise buildings are invariably mechanically ventilated or air conditioned. One possible means of reducing the stack effect is to divide the building into small self-contained units.

Airflows in extract ducts connected to vertical duct shafts in buildings can be unbalanced by stack forces, causing increased flow in some ducts and reduced, or possibly reversed, flow in others(109). Flow reversal is particularly undesirable on toilet extracts and waste disposal chutes.

A further consideration for high rise buildings is hydraulic system head pressures. Cost, safety and technical limitations relating to maximum head pressure dictate that hydraulic systems are normally split into vertical blocks of 20–25 storeys. There are a number of alternative design solutions for achieving pressure isolation including pressure separating heat exchangers, cascading water upwards to storage tanks, and installing separate systems for vertical zones within the height of the building (this last solution is complex and costly). For condenser water-type systems an intermediate sump pump could be considered. This should be located as high as possible subject to economic pressure rating. Column pressure is lost above the sump, but retained below providing partial recovery of pump energy.

2.3.12.3 System considerations

Centralised, floor-by-floor and unitary systems are all potentially suitable for high rise buildings. For centralised systems, the number of floors that can be served is limited to 10 floors above or below (20 floors for an intermediate plant room serving floors both above and below). This is the maximum number of duct take-offs that can readily be balanced. (Note that the static regain method should be considered for ductwork sizing to assist with balancing).

There are a number of issues that will impact on the choice between a centralised, floor-by-floor, or unitary approach including the following:

— tenancy requirements

— floor plate size

— riser and/or plant room space requirements

— maintenance considerations: centralised systems will be subject to large scale disruption due to localised problems or retrofit; unitary systems can require hundreds of units with the attendant management and maintenance difficulties.

2.3.13 Hospitals and health care buildings

2.3.13.1 General

The heating and cooling load associated with ventilation plant form the major component of boiler and chiller plant capacity. It is therefore important to determine the ventilation strategy at an early stage of design to ensure that the systems are tailored to the requirements of each area. In practice this means that areas with specific requirements have dedicated air handling systems, and that departments occupied only during office hours are served by plant separate from that serving continuously occupied areas.

In general, separate ventilation systems should be provided for each department or group of similar departments provided that they are closely grouped together.

Each operating theatre suite should ideally be provided with its own plant but it is accepted practice to have a zoned common air handling unit serving two adjacent suites. There are many examples where common air handling plant has been provided for an entire operating department which, in the event of plant failure or maintenance shut-down, will render the whole department inoperative. Also, it means that it would be uneconomic to operate a single theatre for emergency or maternity use out of normal hours.

For health care buildings within the UK, it should not be assumed that the entire building needs to be closely temperature controlled. Ward areas (with the exception of isolation rooms and other special rooms) should be designed for natural ventilation unless situated in a noisy or heavily polluted location. Ancillary areas such as toilets, bathrooms, utility rooms, etc. should be provided with an extract system. It is a general requirement for health care buildings that the building has an overall positive or neutral pressure and the extracted air replaced by treated make-up air supplied to, for example, internal areas, staff base, etc. in ward areas.

2.3.13.2 Cleanliness and infection control

Ventilation systems should be of the all-fresh-air type to minimise risk of infection. In areas such as non-invasive imaging, equipment rooms and staff areas, local recirculatory air systems in the form of fan coil or split air conditioning units may be used, supplemented by primary air.

Air handling plant for all medical areas should be of the 'blow-through' type with only the frost coil and pre-filter upstream of the fan to ensure that there is no inward leakage of air downstream of the coils and main filter. Ventilation systems should be fully ducted. If contamination occured only the affected rooms and associated ductwork would require cleansing. With a return air ceiling plenum, access to the void above the room would be necessary for cleaning.

2.3.13.3 Ductwork and distribution

Ductwork systems should be low velocity designs to minimise fan power energy and noise. Attention should be given to eliminate cross-talk in areas where confidentiality is necessary or where patients may be noisy.

Ductwork systems should be cleaned on completion and provided with sufficient access points to ensure that adequate cleaning can be undertaken.

Air terminals should be selected with ease of cleaning as a primary consideration. Internal acoustic linings should be avoided. Room-side supply air attenuators as a minimum should be suitably lined to prevent fibre migration and to facilitate cleaning.

2.3.13.4 Ventilation system design

There are many mechanically ventilated spaces that do not require close control of temperature and where a summer upper limit of 25 °C will be acceptable. Ventilation systems should be designed with a small temperature difference between supply air temperature and room design temperature to achieve acceptable variation in room temperature for the majority of spaces, without the need for local temperature control.

As a general principle, space heating should be provided independently and not rely on adding heat to the ventilation supply air. However, in theatre suites and high dependency areas such as intensive care, heating requirements would normally be met by the ventilation system.

Most ventilation systems are constant volume type to satisfy pressure regimes or to offset fixed extraction rates. Variable air volume (VAV) systems may be appropriate for areas where cooling loads are variable. They will also be more energy efficient in these situations than constant volume systems.

Mechanical ventilation systems for hospitals and health care buildings need to be designed to meet the sound control requirements described in section 5. There is often a high proportion of rooms requiring full height partitions for fire compartmentation and acoustic separation and this requires that VAV systems have devices to balance both supply and extract to each area. This means that VAV systems are costly.

An economic case can be made for heat recovery on continuously operating ventilation systems. To avoid the risk of cross infection, air/water heat recovery systems are preferred and air/air systems would be subject to agreement with the infection control officer and would normally exclude dirty extracts.

In hospitals, the patients are dependent to varying degrees on the staff for evacuation in the event of fire. This, combined with various fire risk rooms, results in a higher than normal requirement for sub-compartments and compartmentation of risk rooms. It is therefore important to minimise the number of fire- and smoke-operated dampers by appropriate routing of ducts when compartmentation requirements are determined.

In many departments in hospitals, especially in operating departments and high dependency areas, the ventilation will need to remain operational in the event of fire when other areas would be under firefighters' control. In these circumstances, the ventilation system should shut down only in the event that smoke is detected in the supply air.

Mechanical ventilation systems for hospitals need to provide a high level of reliability, as the system is critical to the proper functioning of the building and the business conducted within it. Consequential losses arising from failure can be very significant in this type of building. It should be noted that the external design conditions for health care buildings are more onerous than for other building types and summer/winter values are based on those not exceeded for more than 10 hours per year.

For specific ventilation requirements reference should be made to appropriate NHS Health Building Notes and Health Technical Memoranda, with particular reference to HTM 2025[110].

Ventilation rates for typical spaces are given in Table 2.23.

2.3.13.5 Humidification

It should not be assumed that humidification is required in all areas. The avoidance of infection and, in particular, *Legionellae* is of paramount importance, especially as many patients will have limited resistance. The recommended method of humidifying the supply air is by steam injection from plant steam (clean steam is not required). Electrical generation of steam is low in initial cost but high in running cost and should be avoided. Alternative methods of humidification would normally be subject to agreement with the infection control officer.

Table 2.23 Hospitals and health care buildings: ventilation rates

Space	Ventilation rate / air changes per hour
Toilets:	
— general	10
— en suite	6
Bathrooms:	
— general	10
— en suite	6
Dirty utility room	10
Changing rooms	5
Isolation rooms	10 (minimum)
Delivery rooms	10 (minimum)
Recovery rooms	15
Treatment rooms	6 (minimum to offset heat gain)

Table 2.24 Hospitals and health care buildings; filtration requirements

Application	Filter class*
Pre-filters on air handling plant, protection to heat recovery source coils	G3
Final filter for general spaces	F6
Final filter for clinical spaces; protection to HEPA filters	F8
Aseptic suite; sterile services department; operating theatre ultra-clean units	H10–H14

* See Tables 2.46 and 2.47 (page 2-120) for details of filter classes

2.3.13.6 Filtration requirements

Various levels of filtration performance are required, see Table 2.24.

2.3.13.7 Specialist areas

Certain areas have ventilation requirements that cannot be achieved by normal methods. These include audiology rooms where extremely low background noise levels must be achieved and aseptic suites where low particle counts are necessary. In these instances it is recommended that specialist contractors take responsibility for both the building enclosure and the building engineering services, including ventilation, within the enclosure.

2.3.14 Hotels

2.3.14.1 General

Hotels present a number of design challenges. Running costs are usually of high importance to the operator but the control of these should not affect guest comfort levels. Obtaining energy cheaply and using it efficiently are both areas that should be reviewed. Maintenance also needs to be carefully considered as many hotels have limited on-site technical support.

Guests directly paying for a service are reluctant to accept compromises in temperature, service or the quality of the environment that would allow the hotel to reduce its energy consumption. Therefore it is important to avoid waste. To achieve this, systems need to be responsive and readily controllable. Means to turn off, or turn down, systems when they are not required should be provided, but must be straightforward and easily managed by non-technical staff.

The level of service will depending on the type of hotel. Understanding the type and the branding of the hotel is important to choosing the right system. In the UK, standard solutions range from electric heating with natural ventilation to full air conditioning. Many hotel operators will have well-developed standard solutions. Different types of hotels will also have different occupancy rates and this can have a major impact on sizing of central plant and public space systems. A business hotel will have a full occupancy at between 1.1 and 1.3 persons/room whereas a family or resort hotel will have a much higher occupancy, typically up to at least 2.0 persons/room. A rate of 2.4 persons/room may not be unreasonable for a busy budget hotel near an airport.

2.3.14.2 Design considerations and strategies

There are three principal areas within a hotel: guest bedrooms (including en-suite bathrooms), public areas and 'back of house' areas. Each of these is serviced in a different manner and requires different operating schedules. The diversities applied to central plant can therefore be quite high and the likely peak loads need to be carefully considered. A spreadsheet showing the combined load at hourly intervals is an effective way of reviewing how the different loads interact and can be used in design discussions with the client. It can also be used as the first step in analysing the potential for a combined heat and power (CHP) approach. Hotels, particularly those with swimming pools, are usually good candidates for CHP.

Guest bedrooms

For an air conditioned hotel, a common approach is to employ a four-pipe fan coil unit located above the entrance lobby but it is also possible to locate the unit against the perimeter wall or above the bathroom, provided that adequate access is available for maintenance. The unit should be sized to allow a rapid and individual response to each room. Other common solutions are water source heat pumps and variable refrigerant flow (VRF) systems. These have the advantage of using less riser space but may require more maintenance. Care must also be taken with refrigerant systems to ensure that the effects of a refrigerant gas leak can be dealt with safely[111].

Environmental control needs to be clear and responsive. Controls should be simple to understand and to operate. Acceptable noise levels can also be an issue and need to be agreed with the client. A reasonable standard is to design for an overnight condition of NR30 on low speed and allow higher noise levels to meet the design load. Luxury hotels may require an overnight level of NR25.

Care should be taken not to oversize the selected system while ensuring that the system remains responsive. The peak solar load is unlikely to coincide with the peak internal loads. Depending on occupancy, a peak room cooling load between 1.5 and 2.0 kW will normally be adequate for the UK. For a well constructed and insulated building, the heat gains to a typical bedroom when occupied will offset the heat losses. Therefore heating costs can be low and a design can be developed that will provide the most effective and controllable means of meeting this intermittent low load. Some hotels have adopted electric heating because of the ease of control and the saving on installed cost.

Some hotels choose to limit the energy consumption of the bedroom systems by the use of occupancy detectors, key fobs or central booking systems. These can be used to turn off electrical systems and turn down the air conditioning when the guests are not in the room. This has been shown to make significant energy savings but care needs to be taken to ensure that guest comfort levels are not affected and that critical loads such as the 'minibar' (if present) are not isolated.

For compliance with building regulations, the minimum extract rate for a bathroom is 15 litre·s^{-1} but many hotels use higher values such as 25 litre·s^{-1}. This will provide 10 to 15 air changes per hour in the bathroom and balance the supply of fresh air for two occupants in the room. At these higher rates, tempered air is usually supplied directly to the room or to the fan coil unit within the room to avoid large gaps under doors or external air grilles. Some hotels choose even higher values to minimise condensation in bathrooms and improve air quality generally, particularly if smoking is allowed.

The supply location needs to be positioned to reduce the likelihood of draughts over the bed and in areas that may be used by the occupants when walking to and from the bathroom. The fresh air supply should be designed to take account of the fact that many UK guests will turn off the air-conditioning before going to sleep and this should not, ideally, limit the incoming fresh air. It is common to keep the bedroom supply and bathroom extract systems running continuously to maintain room air quality and to ensure adequate extract from the bathroom at unusual hours. Therefore heat recovery should be considered for these systems

Public areas

Public areas such as reception, conference, bar and restaurant areas are generally characterised by high, but variable, occupancy levels and lighting loads. The chosen system will need to be responsive and capable of delivering high quantities of fresh air when required to do so. This will often suggest all-air systems but these need to be carefully zoned to allow individual control of spaces. Where possible, separate systems for the different areas are ideal, but multi-zone systems are also used and these are sometimes supplemented with fan coil units to provide more individual control. Constant volume systems with reheat are occasionally used but can be wasteful of energy. VAV systems are also used but should be treated with care to ensure that adequate fresh air is delivered to the space under all conditions.

The design of the systems for the public areas will need to achieve criteria imposed by licensing regulations. The level of occupancy to which the hotel wishes to be licensed should be agreed with the client at an early stage to ensure that the air systems will be capable of delivering the correct fresh air quantities to meet the requirements of the licensing authority. Typical design occupancies range from 1 person per 1.2 m^2 for 'theatre' style conference rooms, to 1 person per 2 m^2 for bars and restaurants and 1 person per 4 m^2 for reception and entrance areas. These figures should be confirmed at an early stage as the operator may wish to have the hotel licensed for higher densities. The fresh air quantities should allow for some smoking but not necessarily at the peak occupancies quoted above.

'Back of house' areas

The 'staff only' areas will require a variety of systems to suit their different uses. Typically, these areas will include managers offices, kitchens, laundries or linen handling, staff changing, staff dining, training, IT and computer rooms. Reference should be made to the guidance given for kitchens (section 2.3.6.1) and computer rooms (section 2.3.9).

The general office areas will normally be treated to the same level as the public spaces, (i.e. for an air conditioned hotel they will be air conditioned). Some hotels believe in extending this to cover further areas, such as the staff dining rooms and this needs to be clarified with the client as early as possible. It is common for the kitchens to be cooled, at least in part, so that salads, pastries and deserts can be well presented.

Many hotels contract-out their laundry, but linen handling space will still be needed. These areas require high air change rates to remove the high levels of dust and lint that will be generated during sorting. A figure of 15 air changes per hour may be considered as reasonable. Linen chutes will also generate high dust levels in the collection room.

Increasingly, hotels have sophisticated billing systems and therefore the computer room housing the central IT equipment must be properly conditioned.

2.3.15 Industrial ventilation

2.3.15.1 General requirements

In an industrial context, ventilation is usually employed to remove airborne contaminants arising from processes or machines. Satisfactory ambient conditions can be achieved by dilution where contaminant sources are weak, of low toxicity, and are either scattered or mobile. However, it is usually more appropriate to remove the contaminant at, or close to, its source by means of local exhaust, e.g. vehicle exhaust removal systems in garages.

Sources of industrial contaminants often require large extract airflow rates to ensure that the released pollutant is effectively captured and conveyed away by the extract system. In such cases, particular attention should be paid to ensuring adequate replacement or make-up air. It may be necessary to directly heat the incoming air in winter or, in order to reduce the resulting high energy consumption, to duct the outdoor air directly to the source location.

Certain processes, such as paint spraying may require filtration of the incoming air. Similarly it may be necessary to remove the contamination from the exhaust air before it is discharged to outside. Special industrial air cleaning devices are available for this purpose, see section 2.5.4.

The basic factors that affect the choice between natural and mechanical ventilation are:

— quantity of air required

— quality of air required

— consistency of control required

— isolation required from external environment.

It is almost certain that mechanical ventilation will be necessary given the likelihood of high airflow rates and the need to treat the incoming air, i.e. by heating, cooling, or filtration. Mechanical ventilation systems can be designed to provide constant or variable flow rates distributed as required throughout the building. When a building is located in a noisy environment, it is often impracticable to provide adequate natural ventilation without excessive sound transmission through the openings. In such circumstances, mechanical ventilation systems with appropriate acoustic treatment can be used. Mechanical ventilation can also be designed to control room pressures to prevent the ingress or egress of contaminants.

Ideally, industrial ventilation systems should limit the exposure of workers to airborne contaminants to zero, or as near zero as is practicable. As a minimum, limits should be maintained below the most recently published occupational health limits(43). These are updated annually and it is essential that current information be used.

If extract rates are too low, short term or long term damage to health will occur or, at the very least, serious discomfort will be experienced. If too much air is handled, fan and ductwork costs (both capital and running) are excessive, incoming air treatment costs are high, draughts may be difficult and expensive to prevent, and the industrial processes may be affected by overcooling or costly increases in chemical evaporation rates.

The most effective method of preventing a contaminant from entering the breathing zone of a worker is to isolate the process by total enclosure. This solution is essential where highly toxic substances are involved and may be appropriate for automated processes. Normally some degree of access to the process will be required. It is desirable to limit this access to the minimum necessary for a particular process e.g. access to a low emission chemical process within a fume cupboard via a sliding door, to components to be welded together, or to surfaces to be spray painted. In all cases the contaminant must be drawn away from the breathing zone of the worker.

Guidance on achieving energy efficient ventilation design within industrial buildings is available from BRECSU* and, for industrial processes, by ETSU† under the government's Energy Efficiency Best Practice programme.

2.3.15.2 Exhaust hood suction dynamics

The velocity of the air induced by suction at an exhaust hood decreases rapidly with distance from the opening. In theory, the velocity at a given distance from an opening can be predicted from an equation of the form:

$$V_x = \frac{Q}{B\,x^n + A} \qquad (2.4)$$

*Building Research Energy Conservation Support Unit (BRECSU), Garston, Watford WD2 7JR, UK (www.bre.co.uk/brecsu/index.html)

†Energy Technology Support Unit (ETSU), Building 156, AEA Technology plc, Harwell, Didcot, Oxfordshire, OX11 0RA, UK (www.etsu.com/eebpp/home.htm)

where V_x is the air velocity at distance x from the opening (m·s^{-1}), Q is the volume flow rate of air (m^3·s^{-1}), x is the distance from the opening (m) and A, B and n are constants depending on the geometry of the opening and the flow characteristics. Values for these constants are usually obtained experimentally.

Figure 2.9 shows solutions of this equation for circular openings having unflanged and flanged edges. Note the improvement in performance when the suction is focussed by the flange. The efficiency of capture can be further improved by side screens which also reduce the influence of cross draughts. The ultimate extension of this principle is to enclose the process completely. Velocities are given as percentages of velocity at the opening V_0. Distances from opening are given as percentages of the diameter, d.

Solutions to equation 2.4 for various types of openings are given section 2.5.4.

The momentum of the air induced by suction at an opening must be sufficient at the part of the process most remote from the opening to overcome a combination of the following forces:

— *gravitation*: due to the density of the air/contaminant mixture in relation to the surrounding air

— *friction*: to overcome drag on the mixture due to the neighbouring bulk of room air

— *dynamic*: due to the initial momentum of the contaminant on release from source and/or disturbing forces due to movement of room air, e.g. cross draughts.

Gravitational and dynamic forces may be used to assist capture. Heavy dust particles having some momentum should be directed into an opening close to the source and, ideally, should be collected and removed from the exhaust without further transport. Transporting large particles through a duct requires very high velocities.

If emitted into a workspace with low momentum, the concentration of contaminant immediately adjacent to its source will be high but normally complete mixing with workspace air will occur within a short distance from the source. An obstructed bayonet plume from a hot source will entrain and mix with room air thus expanding the plume, but if an opening can be used to contain the

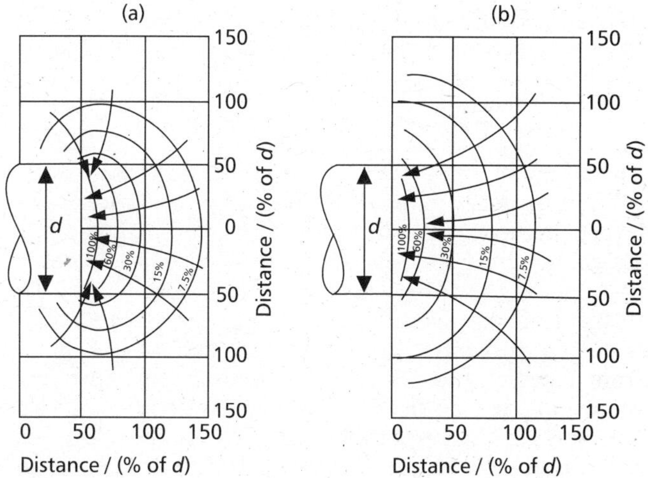

Figure 2.9 Isovels for circular openings; (a) sharp edged opening, (b) flanged opening

plume, induction may prove sufficient to avoid the need for additional fan-induced forces.

2.3.15.3 System design

Individual exhaust hoods can be either discharged separately to outside via individual fans, or connected via a multi-branch system to central fan(s) depending upon:

- compatibility of substances evolved by different processes; if in doubt, use separate exhausts
- access to the outside wall: multiple roof penetration might not be acceptable
- aesthetics of multiple discharges
- potential for air cleaning and recirculation of heat recovery from exhausts (see section 2.5.4)
- balancing: multi-branch dust handling systems must be self-balancing, obstructions within duct work could create blockages
- process usage pattern: ventilation may need to be isolated when a process is not in use and operation of an isolating damper may upset system balance unless a variable volume fan is used; (the VAV fan would be controlled from a system pressure sensor, which could become blocked if dust is transported within the duct).

If make-up air requirements are small they can be drawn from outside or surrounding areas via cracks or openings in the fabric. However, negative pressure must not be allowed to develop at a level at which swing doors are held open or cold draughts are produced in occupied spaces near doors or windows etc. Careful positioning of perimeter heating will minimise discomfort by warming the incoming air. If make-up is too low, the performance of one hood may be affected by the operation of other hoods.

It is preferable to supply the make-up air via a handling system, which cleans, heats (in winter) and, exceptionally, cools and dehumidifies the air, as appropriate. Large volumes of make-up air may be required. This has considerable implications for energy consumption, therefore consideration must be given to:

- supply of tempered make-up air direct to the process (e.g. by push-pull system)
- partial recirculation of exhaust air after removal of contaminant using high efficiency air cleaning(112), see section 2.5.7
- recovery of heat from exhaust to incoming make-up air but avoiding transfer of contaminants, see section 2.5.6.

Make-up air must be supplied into the space in such a way as to avoid causing draughts across the process, which would affect the efficiency of capture.

2.3.16 Laboratories

2.3.16.1 General(113)

The design of laboratory projects will generally be biased towards the design of the ventilation systems for (*a*) fume control, (*b*) containment, or (*c*) providing specific close environmental conditions for either animal welfare or research processes.

The choice of protection to be provided will need to be identified by the client or end user as part of their safety assessment of the work undertaken. Operator protection may be provided by fume cupboards, microbiological safety cabinets or other local exhaust ventilation systems.

The design of laboratories will need to take many factors account, including the following:

- number of fume cupboards, their performance criteria and diversity of use
- number of microbiological safety cabinets
- local exhaust ventilation systems
- minimum ventilation rates to dilute odours and contaminants
- pressure differentials or air flow direction with respect to adjacent spaces
- temperature criteria and heat gains
- filtration standards
- standby capacity
- plant space
- fume discharges to atmosphere
- ductwork materials
- running costs.

Mechanical ventilation systems for laboratories need to provide a high level of reliability, as the system is critical to the proper functioning of the building and the business conducted within it. Consequential losses arising from failure can be very significant in this type of building.

Information on the design of laboratories is available within the series of *Baseline Guides* produced by the International Society for Pharmaceutical Engineering*.

2.3.16.2 Design requirements and strategies

Fume cupboard installations

The performance criteria for the fume cupboard will need to be established by the end user and will be a function of face velocity and containment factors. Generally good containment can be achieved at face velocities of 0.5 $m \cdot s^{-1}$ and may still be achieved at lower face velocities depending on the design of the fume cupboard. The face velocity and containment factor are normally specified in accordance with a sash working height of 500 mm. The specification of lower face velocities should be in conjunction with suitable type testing conditions and agreement to containment levels necessary to suit the end user's activities. Higher face velocities may be required for radioactive work but velocities exceeding 0.7 $m \cdot s^{-1}$ can create turbulence around the operator that may affect the containment performance of the fume cupboard.

*International Society for Pharmaceutical Engineering, 3816W Linebaugh Avenue, Suite 412, Tampa, Florida 33624, USA (www.ispe.org)

A minimum air change rate in a mechanically ventilated laboratory may be set between 6 and 15 air changes per hour, depending on the type of work that is being undertaken and the need to remove or dilute odours. Where fume cupboards are installed the face velocity may dictate the amount of air to be extracted and supplied, and this may exceed minimum ventilation requirements.

Where single or a small number of fume cupboards are installed, then constant volume 'face and bypass' fume cupboards may be considered with the fume cupboard acting as the return air path for the room.

Where large numbers of fume cupboards are to be installed then variable volume ventilation systems should be considered. Such systems enable a diversity in use to be applied and hence the size and cost of central plant can be reduced compared with that required for constant volume systems. In addition to the energy savings realised, the increased capital cost of the controls can be offset by the reduced costs of central plant and reduced plant room space requirements. The primary energy saving is achieved by the ability to deliver and extract reduced quantities of air. Central plant diversities of 50–70% can be applied to large installations. The diversity should take into account the number of fume cupboards in the laboratory, the number of users, and the type of work being undertaken. It may be appropriate to undertake studies to this effect, which may lead to lower diversities being applied.

Central extract systems will need to take account of the requirements for discharge of fumes via flue stacks. To achieve suitable dispersal of fumes the discharge velocity should generally not be less than 15 $m \cdot s^{-1}$. With variable volume systems consideration should be given to providing automatic make-up air controls to collector ducts, in order to maintain discharge velocities. Flue stack heights may be in accordance with BS 7258[113] or can be determined by wind tunnel testing or dilution and dispersal calculations.

The use of individual extract fans may be appropriate if the fume cupboards are dispersed around the building in a way that would preclude the installation of a common collector duct.

Microbiological laboratories[114]

The design of laboratories for work on biological agents requires attention to the following particular factors:

- containment category
- number, size and class of safety cabinets
- operational requirements of the laboratory
- standby plant
- pressure differentials
- location/safe change requirement for HEPA filtration
- fumigation and sterilisation procedures
- safe access for maintenance of filters and other areas of potential contaminant concentration.

Guidance from the Advisory Committee on Dangerous Pathogens[115] defines hazard groups and provides recommendations for containment levels for laboratories and animal rooms along with appendices providing useful information and recommendations. Table 2.25 summarises the requirements and recommendations for laboratory containment.

The containment levels are as follows:

- *Containment Level 1*: suitable for work with agents in hazard group 1, which are unlikely to cause disease by infection, some agents in this group are nevertheless hazardous in other ways, i.e. allergenic, toxigenic etc. It is preferable to maintain an inward air flow by extracting room air to atmosphere.

Table 2.25 Summary of laboratory containment requirements and recommendations

Measure	Requirement for stated hazard level			
	None	Low	Medium	High
ACDP containment level	1	2	3	4
Isolate from other areas	No	No	Yes/partial	Yes
Air lock	No	No	Optional (self closing) shower	Yes, via air lock and interlocking outer and inner doors; provide
Sealable for decontamination	No	No	Yes	Yes
Inward airflow/negative pressure	Optional	No, unless mechanically ventilated	Yes; –30 Pa in laboratory	Yes; –70 Pa in laboratory; –30 Pa in air lock; alarm system required
Supply filtered	—	Yes	Yes	HEPA filtered
Monitor air pressures	—	No	Yes, on supply	Yes
Effluent treatment	No	No	HEPA filtration of extract air	Double HEPA filtration of extract air, treatment of liquid waste and solid waste
Microbiological safety cabinet/enclosure	No	Yes, where airborne hazard	Yes	Yes
Safety cabinet class (user defined)	—	Class I	Class I, II or III	Class III
Autoclave site	—	In suite	In suite	In laboratory, double ended
Emergency shower	Agree with users	Preferred; agree with users	Yes	Yes

— *Containment Level 2*: suitable for work with biological agents in hazard group 2. Restricted access required. Maintain at a negative air pressure and keep doors closed while work is in progress.

— *Containment Level 3*: suitable for work with biological agents in hazard group 3. The laboratory to be separated from other activities in the same building with access restricted to authorised persons. The laboratory is to be maintained at a negative air pressure generally only when work with biological agents is in progress, although some clients may require pressure differentials to be maintained continuously. Extract must be HEPA filtered. The laboratory is to be sealed for disinfection, which may require gas-tight shut-off dampers on ductwork systems and sealed fittings and services penetrations. Ventilation systems should also incorporate a means of preventing reverse air flows. Design of systems to achieve the required inward airflow should aim for simplicity.

— *Containment Level 4*: suitable for work with biological agents in hazard group 4. Maintain at a negative air pressure. Input air to be HEPA filtered, extract air to be double HEPA filtered.

Hazardous work within the laboratory will generally be undertaken in microbiological safety cabinets. Safety cabinets provide protection against dangerous pathogens. There are three classes of safety cabinets:

— *Class 1 safety cabinets*: provide user protection. The cabinet has a through flow of air and incorporates an integral HEPA filter. A variable speed fan is provided in the extract ductwork to overcome the changing resistance of the filter. Suitable for use with hazard groups 1, 2 and 3.

— *Class 2 safety cabinets*: protect the operator and the work by recirculating some of the air through a HEPA filter to provide a down-flow over the working area. An integral variable speed fan is provided to overcome the changing resistance of the filters. The main extract fan in the exhaust duct may require to be either variable or constant volume, depending on the manufacturer. Class 2 safety cabinets are divided into two types: high protection, for use with groups 1, 2, and 3; low protection for use with hazard groups 1 and 2.

— *Class 3 safety cabinets*: totally enclosed units designed to provide a high degree of user protection. Air is drawn in and exhausted via HEPA filters. The operator uses gloves to manipulate experiments. Suitable for hazard groups 1 to 4.

2.3.17 Museums, libraries and art galleries

2.3.17.1 General

Most buildings control their environment for human health and comfort reasons during periods of occupation. However, buildings used for the display or storage of objects, books and documents requiring long-term preservation must be kept within appropriate relative humidity and temperature ranges 24 hours a day so as to minimise damage to the collections they contain.

Historic materials are vulnerable to:

— physical damage, due to expansion and shrinking

— chemical deterioration, due to corrosion in damp conditions or by pollutants

— bio-deterioration (destruction by moulds or insects)

Damage is caused by atmospheric moisture, heat, direct sunlight, ultraviolet radiation, and external and internal atmospheric contaminants. It is most often a combination of these factors that causes significant damage.

2.3.17.2 Design considerations

Different materials may have their own distinct requirements. This means that conditions within a building may need to vary in different locations to suit their specific requirements. Since objects, books and archives may be added to, changed or re-organised, it is important that allowance be made in the design for varying the conditions within the space in order to match changing needs. This must be commensurate with sound energy-efficient practice.

The particular physical condition of objects or groups of objects may necessitate different environmental conditions. Therefore specific ranges of relative humidity for the conservation of historic materials can be decided only in discussion with whoever is responsible for their physical well-being, usually a conservator. When this does not take place, the design is often based on idealised ranges that may be inappropriate.

Seasonal differences in the moisture content of fresh air need to be considered when determining the appropriate level of ventilation air; for instance, in winter external air often has a lower moisture content than in summer. While fresh air ventilation is necessary for human respiration, historic materials may also require air to be replenished in order to reduce the concentration of contaminants from off-gassing materials. This needs to be balanced against the potential for transporting harmful external pollutants into the building by ventilation. If mechanical ventilation is fitted, the use of particle and gaseous filtration is recommended for historic materials vulnerable to external pollutants that are likely to be of high concentration in urban locations. It is advisable for mechanical ventilation to be controlled by carbon dioxide sensors in order reduce the fresh air supply to the minimum requirement.

Materials such as paper, parchment, textiles, leather and wood may be kept within the broad range of 40% to 65%. However, the rate of change must be controlled because maintaining a stable relative humidity is more important than an actual set point within the range.

Metals and minerals benefit from an RH level below 50%, while bronze and glass should be kept below 40% RH. In areas where large numbers of people may congregate, it is important to consider that while the human comfort RH range of 40% to 60% may be suitable for most materials, those that require drier conditions may need to be displayed or stored within microclimates.

For room temperature, the range 18–24 °C, which is acceptable for human comfort, is also acceptable for historic materials. However, where materials have become acclimatised to a more elevated temperature, active cooling should only be considered after discussion with the conservator and, if appropriate, the conservation architect. Temperatures lower than 16 °C may be desirable for some materials such as photographs and film or where the temperature may be designed to vary in order to maintain a stable relative humidity.

2.3.17.3 Environmental control

Typical means of achieving controlled conditions in other building types can also be used in museums, libraries and archives. These are close control air conditioning, the use of dessicant or refrigerant rehumidifiers and, where conditions become too dry, humidifiers. Conservation heating is specific to environmental control in historic buildings. However this strategy is more appropriate to spaces where human comfort conditions are not required throughout the year. Conservation heating consists of control of heating systems with humidity and temperature sensors to provide environmental conditions for long-term conservation of objects, books and documents. Indoor relative humidity may need to be reduced at any time of the year, so the control systems should be set up to operate continuously.

Typically, a conservation heating system will maintain room temperatures 3–5 °C above their 'unheated' level in winter. This is in contrast with domestic winter heat input, which is designed to provide an average temperature increase of 8–10 °C. In good summer weather, there may be no call for corrective action for weeks on end, but weather changes can quickly produce damaging humidity conditions. Monitoring shows that the total heat input during the summer is small but important. This low level of heat input means that energy consumption is significantly lower than that for domestic heating systems. Depending on the size of the space to be controlled, solutions may vary from a single humidistat-controlled electric radiator to full multi-zoned schemes with computer building management systems.

Human beings do not generally notice changes in relative humidity, therefore locations with historic materials should be provided with instrumentation for the monitoring relative humidity and temperature.

Mechanical ventilation systems for libraries need to be designed to meet the sound control requirements in section 5 of this guide.

2.3.18 Plant rooms

Plant areas should be ventilated as necessary to ensure the correct operation of equipment and the safety, health and comfort of personnel.

2.3.18.1 Boiler rooms

Boiler rooms and other spaces containing fuel-burning appliances must be supplied with adequate fresh air to meet the requirements for combustion and to prevent overheating of the space. Compliance with the regulations governing the ventilation of such appliances must be maintained. Details are given in relevant Building Regulations Part J[38], British Standards e.g. BS 6798[55], BS 5410[56] and BS 5440[57]. Reference should also be made to section 1 of this Guide.

Rooms containing a gas installation should be ventilated to prevent the accumulation of gas as could occur from minor leaks. Ducts containing gas pipework should be ventilated to a safe position, preferably direct to outside air. Measures for routing pipework may include enclosing the pipework in a ventilated gas-tight sleeve ('pipe-in-pipe'). It should be ensured that ventilation arrangements do not impair any provisions for fire/smoke separation. Refer to Gas Safety Regulations[116], Council for Registered Gas Installers (CORGI) and Institution of Gas Engineers[117] for guidance.

Oil tank chambers should be ventilated to the open air to prevent stagnation, independently of any other portion of the premises and preferably by natural means.

2.3.18.2 Refrigeration plant rooms

Refrigeration plant rooms should be provided with ventilation as required for the safety, health and comfort of personnel and for emergency purposes in the event of a major leak. Reference should be made to BS 4434[116].

2.3.18.3 Battery rooms

Depending on type of batteries present, ventilation should be provided so that any potentially explosive gaseous mixtures are dispersed safely below non-hazardous levels. Battery life can also be reduced by high continuous space temperatures, e.g. temperatures greater than 25 °C[116].

2.3.18.4 Electrical plant rooms

Particular care should be taken to ensure adequate ventilation for rooms containing electrical plant to prevent build-up of heat generated by the equipment.

These include the following:

- IT, communications rooms and incoming frame rooms that have active heat generating equipment
- transformer rooms
- electrical switchrooms
- uninterruptable power supply (UPS) rooms.

2.3.18.5 Water storage areas

Storage temperatures should comply with the requirements of the Water Regulations[119,120] and CIBSE and HSE recommendations concerning the growth of *Legionella*[121,122].

2.3.18.6 Lift motor rooms

Reference should be made to CIBSE Guide D[123].

2.3.19 Schools and educational buildings

2.3.19.1 Schools

General

The Department for Education and Skills's *Guidelines for Environmental Design in Schools*[124] recommend that, as far as possible, school buildings should be naturally ventilated. Exceptions are WCs, changing rooms, craft design and technology areas, kitchens, laboratories and other special activity areas where contamination or high heat gains might occur that may require local or other mechanical ventilation.

Requirements

Table 2.26 lists some required ventilation rates drawn from the Schools Premises Regulations[125].

(*a*) Airtightness

A level of airtightness for schools is not specified although a maximum of 0.3 ACH has been suggested[126]. This is required to minimise heat losses when unoccupied.

(*b*) Air movement

Air movement at the level of the occupant must be at a temperature and velocity to ensure comfort. Natural ventilation should therefore be controllable to allow users to adjust the ventilation rate as required. Adjustments should be achieved by the appropriate use of window types and opening sizes, including trickle ventilators. Ideally openings should be provided in more than one face of each room to maximise cross ventilation. Guidance is available on the passive solar design of schools to facilitate solar-induced stack effect to encourage ventilation on days with little wind[127]. Passive stack enhancement may also be considered. Particular care should be taken to ensure that any odours arising from the use of volatile organic compounds (VOCs) during construction work, or arising from school activities, can be dealt with.

(*c*) Make-up air

Make-up air may be taken from surrounding spaces if this will not increase ventilation rates in teaching spaces beyond that required, in which case a secondary supply of fresh air may be provided.

(*d*) Window selection

Sash windows are often used in schools because they provide high and low level openings, thereby giving occupants a considerable amount of control. However, only 50% of their area is available for ventilation. Side-hung casement windows give a greater openable area but care must be taken to ensure that they do not present a safety hazard when fully open[126]. In upper stories, the opening of windows is often restricted to minimise the risk of children falling out.

(*e*) Atria

Care should be taken with the design of atria within schools premises, which may be provided as low cost teaching space and buffer zones to classrooms. Ventilation provision must be sufficient to prevent overheating without compromising acoustic separation[126].

(*f*) Draught lobbies

Effective draught lobbies should be specified where possible to minimise the amount of disadvantageous ventilation caused by occupants moving in and out of the building[126].

Further considerations

The Department for Education and Skills (DfES) has embraced the concepts of environmental assessment of its premises. It places emphasis not just on energy use but also on ease of maintenance. Guidance can be found in DfES publications[124,131]. Designers can gain credits by:

— demonstrating due consideration to the provision of ventilation (including the client and user in the development of the design with regards to risk assessment)

— the timely provision of completed record drawings and operation and maintenance (O&M) manuals

— the provision of training on the operation of any controls to the caretaker.

Table 2.26 Required ventilation rates in schools premises

Area	Ventilation rate	Notes
General teaching areas	3 litre·s^{-1} per person as minimum	
	8 litre·s^{-1} per person for rapid ventilation by opening windows or vents	Ventilation systems, whether natural or mechanical, should be capable of providing approximately 8 litre·s^{-1} per person of fresh air in all teaching areas medical examination or treatment rooms, sleeping and living accommodation
		Adequate measures should be taken to prevent condensation and remove noxious fumes from every kitchen and other room in which there may be steam or fumes.
		Guidance specific to the education sector with regards to health and safety issues as described in the Workplace Regulations[103] has been produced by the HSE[128]
Laboratories	—	To satisfy COSHH requirements[42] and DfES guidance on fume cupboards[129]
Wash rooms	6 ACH minimum	
Swimming pools	—	Refer to specialist guidance[130] and section 3.21.7

2.3.19.2 Higher education premises

Residential accommodation

Developments in the UK have demonstrated the potential for low energy residential accommodation, both through high levels of insulation and mechanical ventilation with heat recovery[139] or through passive ventilation via trickle ventilators and local mechanical extract where required[84].

Lecture theatres, study areas and design studios

Occupancy patterns can be dense but intermittent, or extended but sparse. Environmental control tends to be remote from the individual occupants. Teaching spaces designed to serve more than 100 people usually require some form of mechanical ventilation, although this may be as part of a mixed mode approach e.g. punkah fans within ventilation stacks. High levels of thermal mass and night cooling can also be effective in reducing energy demand. Control of airflow rates can be achieved through CO_2 sensors to establish a minimum rate. Care must be taken in the case of naturally ventilated solutions to avoid noise problems from external sources.

The breadth of design options for innovative low energy designs is illustrated in case studies by BRECSU[133–135] and the Higher Education Estates Department*.

Specialist areas

Guidance on suitable treatments for other types of space found within higher and further education premises such as laboratories, learning resource centres, swimming pools, catering facilities can be found elsewhere in section 2.3.

2.3.20 Shops and retail premises

2.3.20.1 General

The general aim of the ventilation and air conditioning strategy is to provide a comfortable environment within the occupied zone. This is achieved by providing fresh air for the customers and staff and the removal of the heat from the space which arises from lighting, equipment, solar and occupancy gains.

2.3.20.2 Design requirements

The temperature within the space will vary according to season but is typically 18–22 °C depending on the requirements of the retailer. The upper limit may be permitted to rise in summer to prevent an unacceptable temperature differential between the retail space and the circulation space outside (i.e. outside or covered mall).

Minimum fresh air should be provided to satisfy occupancy loads based on the client's requirements or Building Regulations Approved Document F[37], whichever is the greater. Fresh air is typically introduced at a minimum rate of 5 litre·s^{-1} per person. This rate is lower than the minimum stated in Building Regulations of 8 litre·s^{-1} per person, which is for an occupiable room that is defined as not including a shop or circulation space. These require a minimum of 1 litre·s^{-1}·m^{-2}. The typical minimum fresh air rate is based on a typical occupancy of 1 person per 5 m^2. This fresh air rate is for a retail area in which smoking is not permitted. Minimum fresh air for occupation is supplied to the space via a supply AHU or via an extract fan in conjunction with openings on an external wall.

Heat gains will be a function of the building and the specific application but will often be characterised by one or more of the following:

- transient occupancy with high peak value
- high solar gains local to large areas of glazed shop front
- high lighting gains for display purposes
- localised equipment loads, e.g. hot food counters.

Infiltration of air from the outside due to door opening can be a particular concern. The problem may be exacerbated if there are openings on opposite facades of a store encouraging cross-ventilation driven by wind or stack forces (e.g. if opening onto a shopping mall). Locating openings on a single façade will help to balance these forces. Draughts within stores caused by infiltration can be minimised by the sealing of the building structure or the use of lobbies on entrances to deflect/direct airflow.

2.3.20.3 Strategies

Ventilation and air conditioning of the space can be achieved by various methods using centralised or unitary equipment. The choice of plant is governed by the retailer's particular requirements, the availability of external plant space, the size of the retail space and the availability of services supplied by the lessor.

Systems served by centralised plant can take the form of displacement or constant volume systems, both using recirculation or free cooling to provide the volume necessary to enable distribution of conditioned air at an acceptable temperature. Examples of minimum fresh air systems include unitary cooling split DX air conditioning or 2- or 4-pipe fan coil units.

Consideration should be given to recovery of heating/cooling energy that would normal be rejected. The ventilation system design may allow for the integration of air-to-air heat recovery devices, which transfer heat from the exhaust air stream to allow fresh air inlet. Waste heat from air-cooled condensers used in the refrigeration process may be recycled and utilised to reduce the load on space-heating plant. Cooling recovery at low level using spilled air from display cabinets may be recycled and introduced to cold stores etc, reducing the loads on cooling plant.

It is now common for major outlets to be provided with a water loop for the air conditioning system. This provides users with the flexibility to provide their own heat pumps as necessary to meet their individual requirements. This type of system may also balance well with the diversity of activities undertaken by the occupier, often requiring simultaneous heating and cooling. Water source heat pump systems are well to meet such requirements.

---
*Estates Team, HEFCE, Northavon House, Coldharbour Lane, Frenchay, Bristol BS16 1QD (www.heestates.ac.uk)

Leakage and build-up of refrigerant in a public space can be a danger to health due to decomposition products from smoking or naked flames in the presence of certain refrigerants. The occupier should prepare an emergency procedure to be followed in the event of leakage. BS EN 378[111] should be consulted for guidance on procedures.

Ventilation rates within constant volume systems can be controlled using CO_2 or air quality sensors. Temperature control of central systems should be averaged where possible either using space sensors or a duct-mounted sensor in the extract system. Temperature control of unitary systems should be by individual or group controller, depending on the number of systems.

The building should be maintained under positive pressure by ensuring that the rate of supply exceeds the rate of extract. Extracts should be positioned in the areas of high heat gain, e.g. lighting displays or hot food counters.

For food stores, the type and performance of refrigerated display cases will influence the design of the ventilation and conditioning system in a number of ways:

- Display cases may require temperature and humidity levels within the space to be maintained below maximum limits.
- Losses from display case will locally cool the space.
- Display cases with integral heat rejection will provide a net heat input to the space.
- The performance of display cases is susceptible to draughts from doors and ventilation systems.

Losses from display cases can vary quite significantly, depending on case design. Refrigerated areas commonly require heating throughout the year. The losses can lead to a 'cold aisle' effect in refrigerated areas of a store. One means of reducing this effect is by recovering some of the cold air spilt from the display cases, which may then by used to cool other areas of the store via the ventilation system.

Some display cases reject heat to the space, rather than to external heat rejection plant via a refrigeration system. Such display cases will impose a net heat gain on the ventilation system.

Internal draughts into cases from the ventilation system are avoided by the careful positioning of supply points from the ventilation and air conditioning equipment.

Smoke extract from retail units may be installed as separate stand-alone systems, which act as additional safety ventilation systems, or be incorporated into the general ventilation systems which serve the retail unit (known as 'dual purpose'). There are three possibilities in smoke extraction design each with a different purpose:

(*a*) *Life safety*: systems designed to maintain tenable conditions on escape routes and other occupied areas.

(*b*) *Firefighting access/property protection*: systems designed to increase visibility for, and reduce heat exposure to, trained firefighters. This allows earlier and less hazardous attack on the fire. Such systems will help to reduce property damage by increasing fire brigade effectiveness.

(*c*) *Smoke purging*: systems designed to enable smoke to be cleared from a building after a fire has been brought under control.

It is necessary to decide which, or which combination, of these three objectives is to be achieved before commencing a design. BRE Report BR 368[70] should be consulted, in conjunction with BS 5588: Parts 9, 10 and 11[136].

2.3.21 Sports centres

2.3.21.1 Ventilation requirements

The recommended environmental conditions and ventilation rates for sports centres vary according to the activities being undertaken, see Table 2.27.

2.3.21.2 Multi-purpose halls/facilities[138]

Ventilation is required to remove players' body heat and odours, supply fresh air, keep spectators cool, maintain comfortable summertime conditions and prevent condensation. If the facility is also to be used for public entertainment, the relative importance of these functions depends on the activities taking place in the hall and the number of people present.

The ventilation system should be designed for controlled ventilation rates that can vary according to the occupants' needs at any given time, without introducing large volumes of cold air into the space that may cause discomfort and high heating loads.

For badminton, a draught-free playing area should be provided with air velocities less than 0.1 $m \cdot s^{-1}$ to prevent deflection of the shuttlecock. The location of inlet and extract grilles and openings must also be considered with regards to the flight paths of the shuttlecocks[139].

Table 2.27 Environmental conditions for sports centres[137]

Facility	Temperature / °C	Ventilation
Multi-purpose centre:		
— sports activities	12–18	8–12 $litre \cdot s^{-1} \cdot person^{-1}$
— sedentary activities	18–21	8–12 $litre \cdot s^{-1} \cdot person^{-1}$
Fitness centres	16–18	10–12 ACH
Weight training	12–14	10–12 ACH
Squash courts:		
— courts	16–18	4 ACH
— spectators	18	4 ACH
Ancillary halls:		
— sports	15	1.5 ACH
— non-sports	21	3 ACH
Changing rooms	20–25	10 ACH
Reception, administration and circulation spaces	16–20	Up to 3 ACH
Crèche	21	Up to 3 ACH
Refreshment and bar areas	18	Not less than 8 $litre \cdot s^{-1} \cdot person^{-1}$*
Swimming pool	27–31†	4–6 ACH 8–10 ACH if extensive water features

* Consult local licensing authority

† At least 1 K above water temperature

2.3.21.3 Fitness suites and weight training facilities

Effective ventilation is usually the most critical factor because of the metabolic heat gains, body odour and humidity that can rapidly occur in such spaces. Air conditioning is sometimes used but alternative, less energy-intensive approaches should be considered.

Special considerations may need to be made for spas, saunas, and solaria.

2.3.21.4 Squash courts

Squash courts should be well ventilated to keep walls free from condensation and remove the players' body heat, which can be considerable. Incoming air must not be drawn from changing rooms, bar areas, showers or any other parts of the building with high humidity levels.

In general, each court should have an extract fan centrally placed at high level. Fresh air can be drawn in through airbricks behind the playboard. This should be perforated to provide 10% free area.

Extract fans should over-run for 15 minutes after the courts have been vacated to ensure that all stale air has been removed. Fans should be linked to the court lighting circuit where practicable. The rate of ventilation in the spectator gallery may have to be based on maximum occupancy.

2.3.21.5 Ancillary halls

Ancillary halls may be used for a variety of both sporting and social activities, including public entertainment. Therefore the range of potential activities should be confirmed with the client prior to finalising the design of the ventilation system. A wide range of air change rates may be required, e.g. to remove smoke and ventilate the space for discos and dances. Consultation with the local licensing authority may also be necessary if the hall is to be used for public entertainment.

2.3.21.6 Changing rooms

These normally require a mechanical supply and extract system in larger facilities. In small facilities, satisfactory conditions may be achieved with conventional radiators and convectors combined with natural ventilation or local extract fans. The high fresh air requirement offers the opportunity for heat recovery to be cost effective.

2.3.21.7 Swimming pools

The recommended pool water temperature varies depending upon the activity. For competition swimming the pool is held at 26 °C. For leisure use a temperature range of 28–30 °C is more appropriate; for spas, remedial and other hot pools a pool temperature of 36 °C may be maintained. The air temperature in the pool hall should be at a minimum of 1 K above the pool water temperature. Such environmental conditions tend to create high humidity, therefore ventilation should be provided in order to:

- control humidity
- prevent condensation on inner surfaces
- maintain a satisfactory indoor environment including the prevention of down-draughts
- remove airborne pollutants
- dilute disinfectant fumes.

Humidity levels within the pool hall should be maintained between 50–70% RH. For design purposes, airflow rates of 10 litre·s^{-1} per m^2 of total pool hall area and a minimum of 12 litre·s^{-1} per person of outside air should be provided[140]. Overall air change rates of 4–6 ACH are recommended for standard use or 8–10 ACH where there are extensive water features.

Supply and extract rates should be balanced, or preferably set to maintain a marginally lower pressure in the pool hall than outside or in the adjoining accommodation. This will inhibit the migration of moisture and odour. Although bathers out of the water will be susceptible to draughts, air movement at the pool surface must be sufficient to prevent the accumulation of gases released from the chemically treated water.

Warmed air should be provided to maintain changing rooms at 24 °C, and preferably supplied at low level to assist in floor drying if no provision is made for under floor-heating. Permanent extraction from the clothes storage area should be balanced by an air supply at a rate of 6–10 ACH. A separate extract system should be provided for the WCs.

Ventilation systems for swimming pool halls are either 100% fresh air systems or partial recirculation systems. The latter allow the fresh air supply to be adjusted while maintaining the overall supply volumes to the pool hall, hence maintaining air distribution patterns. However, it is essential that damper positions and control regimes are arranged to ensure adequate introduction of fresh air (30% minimum) and expulsion of contaminated air. Internal accumulations of chlorinous by-products are damaging to the building fabric and potentially dangerous to people. Therefore it is necessary to ensure a minimum ventilation rate at all times when the pool is occupied.

Savings can be made by minimising the intake of outside air for the 100% fresh air system using two-speed or variable speed fans. The impact of any savings is increased if a pool cover is used during periods when the pool is not in use. Both 100% fresh air and recirculation based systems are suitable for installing heat recovery and heat pumps or dehumidification systems.

Extract air from pool halls can be corrosive to the internal surfaces of ventilation systems. Adequate protection should be provided for exposed internal surfaces if maintenance and replacement costs are to be kept to a minimum.

2.3.21.8 Ancillary areas

Suitable ventilation systems must also be provided for ancillary areas as shown in Table 2.27. Office areas, rest rooms and circulation spaces may be serviced by natural ventilation. Mechanical extract will be required in kitchen areas to ensure that odours do not reach public spaces. There must be adequate ventilation and segregation for smoking.

2.3.21.9 Operational issues

Ventilation systems can consume nearly half of the energy used in sports centres. Within areas other than swimming pools, more efficient ventilation can be obtained by using the following[141]:

— *variable speed fans*: to cope with varying occupancies or activities, linked to modulating dampers using automatic humidity control

— *ventilation heat recovery and recirculation*: which can reduce running costs for sports centres by 10%.

Maintenance costs represent a high proportion of the total expenditure on a sports building over its lifetime. Routine tasks will be made much easier if appropriate space is allocated for plant rooms, voids and distribution routes. Inspection of many mechanical items will need to take place every three months so there should be easy access to dampers, fans, filters, flexible connections and heat exchangers (plate heat or run-around coils).

2.3.22 Toilets

The Building Regulations[2,37] make specific provision for the ventilation of toilets. In England and Wales, for dwellings, one or more ventilation openings must be provided of area $^1/_{20}$th. of the floor area (some part of which must be at high level, i.e. at least 1.75 m above floor level), or mechanical extract must be provided at a minimum rate of 6 litre·s^{-1}. In non-domestic buildings, sanitary accommodation (which includes washing facilities) again requires either one or more ventilation openings of area $^1/_{20}$th. of the floor area (some part of which must be at high level) or mechanical ventilation at a minimum rate of 6 litre·s^{-1} per WC or 3 air changes per hour.

In Scotland, for dwellings, a ventilator must be provided of area $^1/_{30}$th. of the floor area (some part of which must be at least 1.75 m above floor level), or mechanical extract must be provided at a minimum rate of 3 air changes per hour.

Toilets are very often provided with the absolute minimum ventilation to comply with the regulations, in order to achieve very minor cost savings. The result of such economy can be a unpleasant toilet atmosphere. This unpleasantness is easily avoided at very marginal extra cost by ensuring that the ventilation system exceeds the statutory requirements.

2.3.23 Transportation buildings and facilities

2.3.23.1 General

The exhaust gases produced by combustion engines contain toxic components and smoke. Wherever vehicular access is provided it is necessary to consider how ventilation can be provided that will limit the concentrations of dangerous contaminants to permitted and/or acceptable limits.

2.3.23.2 Tunnels

Road tunnels require ventilation to remove the contaminants produced by vehicle engines in normal use. Ventilation may be provided by natural or mechanical means, or may be traffic induced. Detailed requirements for the ventilation of road tunnels are published by the Highways Agency[142]. Railway tunnels are subject to the requirements of both owners/clients and the Health and Safety Executive's Railways Inspectorate, who should be consulted for detailed design requirements.

2.3.23.3 Car parks

The general requirement is for engineering systems that will remove the hazards of carbon monoxide from vehicle exhaust emissions and prevent the build up of vapours from fuel leaks etc. The increasing use of diesel engined vehicles also requires control of airborne particles.

Above-ground car parks should be provided with natural ventilation openings in the outside walls of at least 5% of the floor area. Openings on opposite sides should be provided to promote ventilation without being adversely effected by wind direction.

Mechanical ventilation is required for car parks that are enclosed or located in basements. The system should be independent of any other systems and provide 6 ACH for normal operation and 10 ACH in a fire condition. Extract points should be placed so as to eliminate pockets of stale air, and be distributed so that 50% of the extract is a high level and 50% at low level, with particular attention at low points and drains. The system should be divided into two parts, each connected to an independent power supply that will continue to operate in the event of mains failure.

Where many vehicle engines are likely to be running simultaneously, e.g. at exit and entrances, consideration should be given increasing the ventilation rates to maintain the acceptable contamination levels based on vehicle emissions. Limiting concentrations of exhaust pollutants are included in the HSE's annual guidance publication EH40: *Occupational Exposure Limits*[43]. If separate from the general car park ventilation system, the ventilation can be controlled using carbon dioxide detectors at appropriate locations.

Manned pay stations may need positive supply air, with the air intake located away from the contaminated roadways.

For further information see ASHRAE Handbook: *HVAC Applications*[143].

2.3.23.4 Bus terminals

Bus terminals vary considerably in physical configuration. Ideally, buses should be able to drive through a loading platform and not have to manoeuvre within the area.

Naturally ventilated terminals with large open ends may expose passengers to inclement weather and strong winds. Therefore, enclosed platforms with appropriate mechanical ventilation should be considered. Alternatively, enclosed passenger waiting areas can be considered for large terminals with heavy bus traffic. The waiting areas can be pressurised and heated, with normal air volumes depending on the layout and number of boarding gates.

The exhaust gases from diesel engines that affect the ventilation design are carbon monoxide, hydrocarbons, oxides of nitrogen and formaldehydes. Exposure limits are given in HSE EH40[43].

The ventilation rate also needs to provide odour control and visibility, which would generally require a 75:1 dilution rate of outside air to bus exhaust gases. The overall rate of fume emission can be determined from considering the bus operation, terminal configuration and traffic movements. The overall ventilation required can be reduced by removing exhaust gases at the point of discharge.

The guidance given above relates to diesel engined vehicles. However, the use of alternative fuels is increasing and these also need to be considered. For buses fuelled by natural gases, the normal emission rate of unburnt fuel is low. However, if the high pressure gas fuel line were to break, then a large quantity of gas would be released causing a potentially explosive atmosphere. Such a situation would require the prompt use of purging ventilation. Initially, the gas, while cold, will collect at ground level and therefore purging needs to be at this level. However, when warmed, methane tends to rise, as will unburnt methane in the exhaust gases. Therefore, potentially stagnant air zones at high level need to be eliminated. For further information see ASHRAE Handbook: *HVAC Applications*[143].

2.3.23.5 Enclosed loading bays

The requirement in ventilating enclosed loading bays is for the dilution of exhaust gases in normal operation and provision for smoke extract under fire conditions.

Consideration should be given to the nature of the loading bay and vehicle movement in order to develop a system that will meet the required standards. Generally, the large entrance door will provide the necessary inlet air and the fume extract can be combined with the smoke extract for general ventilation. As with car parks and enclosed bus terminals, extract should be provided at high and low levels.

2.3.23.6 Garages (vehicle repair)

In view of the dangerous nature of the accessories to the repair and storage of motor vehicles and the risk of pollution from waste gases and products, the heating, ventilation, fire protection and safety of functional structures is regulated.

Ventilation systems should be designed to limit the contamination levels to acceptable limits[42,128]. Where vehicles are stationary at fixed repair stations, direct exhaust for the emissions should be provided by means of a flexible hose and coupling attached to the tailpipe. The use of such systems will reduce the overall ventilation requirement.

Particular care needs to be taken where inspection and repair pits are present as vehicle and fuel fumes, being heavier than air, will tend to flow into these areas. Therefore a separate extract system is required.

Where garages contain spray booths the relevant codes must be complied with.

For further information see ASHRAE Handbook: *HVAC Applications*[143].

2.3.23.7 Railway stations/terminals, underground railway stations

Where the railway tracks are enclosed under a canopy or buildings above, it will be necessary to consider how the fumes produced by the locomotives are to be exhausted/diluted. The design requirements will be similar to those for bus stations, i.e. reduce the level of contaminants and odours to acceptable limits and provide sufficient air circulation to maintain visibility.

For further information see ASHRAE Handbook: *HVAC Applications*[143].

2.3.23.8 Airport terminals

Airports generally consist of one or more terminal buildings, connected by passageways to departure gates. Many terminals have telescoping loading bridges connecting the departure lounges to the aircraft. These eliminate heating and cooling problems associated with open doorways.

The aim of any ventilation system should be to create a positive internal pressure that will prevent the odour and pollutants from entering the buildings.

Terminal buildings have large open circulation areas, check-in facilities, retail outlets, offices and ancillary areas. As occupancy can vary considerably through the day, it is important that the ventilation/air conditioning system is able to respond these changes. However, due to the large volume of the circulation spaces it is possible to use the building volume to absorb the sudden changes and peak flows. Ventilation systems can be designed with recirculation (to provide heat reclaim), controlled by air quality detectors, thereby automatically reacting to passenger flows.

The system design should also incorporate sufficient zone control to accommodate the widely varying occupancy levels in different parts of the building, or even between adjacent departure gates. If available, histograms on passenger movement for departure and arrival are useful in estimating the design occupancy.

Filtering of the outdoor air with activated carbon filters should be considered to reduce the presence of noxious fumes. However, the siting of air intakes away from the aircraft jet exhausts may obviate the need for filtration and will reduce operating costs. However, since it may be difficult to predict if fumes will affect the air intake location, supply systems should incorporate facilities to enable carbon filters to be added at a later stage, if necessary.

2.3.24 Miscellaneous sectors

The following information on other sectors has been included mainly to identify specialist sources of information that are available. Material from the 1986 edition of CIBSE Guide B has been included but not necessarily updated and designers are advised to obtain specialist advice for current guidance.

2.3.24.1 Animal husbandry[144,145]

Farm buildings

Guidance on the housing of animals on farms may be obtained from the Animal Welfare Division of the Department for Environment, Food and Rural Affairs (DEFRA). Reference should also be made to the Welfare of Farm Animals (England) Regulations[146].

Buildings for farm animals fall into two main groups:

- buildings for housing 'hardy stock', such as milking-cows, breeding-pigs and sheep, that do not require any great control of environmental conditions
- buildings such as pig farrowing houses, fattening houses, veal calf houses, laying and broiler poultry houses etc., which require the environmental conditions to be controlled such that the highest possible productivity is obtained at the lowest food and management costs.

Hardy stock require housing only to protect them from extremes of weather, ventilation being provided by low level and ridge ventilators with protection against direct and through draughts. However, care must be taken to ensure adequate ventilation in high density enclosed houses where forced ventilation will be necessary. Humidity is not usually a problem.

Table 2.28 Temperatures and ventilation rates suitable for housed livestock

Animal species	Optimum temperature range / °C	Ventilation rate	
		Winter / (litre·s^{-1} per kg of body weight)	Summer / (litre·s^{-1} per kg of body weight)
Adult cattle	0–20	0.5	0.20–0.38
Calves	10–15	0.10	0.26–0.53
Pigs	5–25	0.10	0.26–0.53
Piglets:			
— at birth	35	0.08	0.08
— after 2 days	28–33	0.06	up to 0.06
Fattening pigs	11–22	0.10	0.26–0.53
Laying poultry	20–25	0.4	1.5–2.6
Broiler chickens	15–25	0.2	0.8–1.3

For animals requiring close control of conditions, mechanical ventilation is essential, provided by supply and/or extract fans depending on the requirement for positive or negative pressures within the houses. Winter recirculation can be used to conserve heat. Safeguards must be provided against fan failure or livestock will be seriously affected during hot weather. Adequate ventilation will also minimise the occurrence of high humidity. Table 2.28 gives optimum air temperatures and ventilation rates.

Animal rooms[147–149]

The specification of the design for animal rooms would be undertaken by the holder of the premises certificate, with the approval of the Home Office local inspector. Designers must ensure that all necessary procedures are followed. The environmental conditions and degree of control required for animal rooms depend on the species and the intended use of the facilities. Tables 2.28 and 2.29 show the conditions required for various animals and for different applications.

For precise experimental work, close control of temperature (±1 K) and relative humidity (±10%) may be required at different conditions within the overall operational stage. Uniformity of the environment throughout the space is also important and in some cases the direction of air movement needs to be controlled to minimise, for example, the pollution in the spaces through which the laboratory operatives move.

Requirements may also include standby equipment and/or safety features that are automatically initiated in the event of a failure of the main system.

2.3.24.2 Call centres

Concern has been expressed regarding employee motivation and stress in telephone call centres. Little guidance has been produced on the ventilation aspects of call centre design, precedence being given to acoustic and lighting issues. This is partly due to the disparate nature of call centres.

The ideal call centre is characterised by space 15–18 m in depth on a single level, operator teams of up to 12–15 people, large floor-to-ceiling heights, good ventilation, and lighting, and raised floors[150]. However, in reality, call

Table 2.29 Animal room environmental design conditions

Animal	Surface area / m^2	Average metabolic rate at 21 °C* / W	Number of animals per 10 m^2 of floor area	Typical animal room gain / W·m^{-2}	Recommended temperature range / °C	Relative humidity / %
Mice	0.01	0.5	2000	100	21–23	40–70
Rats (at 60 days)	0.031	1.5	485	73	21–23	40–60
Guinea pigs (at 60 days)	0.07	3.0	400	120	17–20	40–70
Chicken:						
— at 4 weeks	0.04	2.4	230	55	21–23	40–60
— at 24 weeks	0.21	12.0	100	120	16–19	40–60
Rabbits (adult)	0.20	11.0	32	35	16–19	40–60
Cats	0.20	8.0	16	13	18–21	40–60
Dogs:						
— male	0.65	26.0	5	13	12–18	40–70
— female	0.58	22.0	5	11	12–18	40–70

*Based on resting metabolism *Notes*: (1) Assume 35–40% as latent gain. (2) Figures should be used as a guide only and will vary depending on conditions. (3) Animal numbers per m^2 based on figures for an average experimental holding room.

centres are housed in a large variety of building types from converted warehouses to highly specified office buildings.

Space occupancy densities also vary. There may be as little as 6–7 m^2 per person in a centre dealing with simple enquiries or as much as 10–14 m^2 per person in newer, full service centres or where confidentiality is important[151]. The latter figure allows for support areas such as lounges, catering, training facilities and team meeting areas. The subsequent amount and concentration of heat gains will therefore vary and may result in the selection of, for example, VAV, chilled ceilings/beams or fan coils.

The ventilation system designer should be aware of:

- the intended staffing levels and how these might change in the future (e.g. additional staff) as this will affect cooling loads and the potential requirement for upgrading the system
- the pattern of changing staff levels over the day, week or seasonal basis (e.g. as a consequence of shift patterns); this could affect system zoning and the ability to use night cooling as a pre-cooling strategy, or as a free cooling strategy
- the degree to which staff operate IT equipment, e.g. single or multiple screen systems
- the anticipated importance of 'churn' (e.g. will temporary areas be screened-off for periods within open plan areas, thereby interrupting airflow and causing pockets of stale air?)
- the maintenance constraints imposed by the system selection and shift arrangements (will it be necessary to isolate as much plant as possible away from the working space to facilitate ongoing maintenance?)
- the potential need to separated off areas within the space (either by full height partitions or screens) to protect the open plan workstations from noise and distraction and to separate support functions and office equipment
- the support features that will be provided and whether or not they will require separate servicing (e.g. is there a need to isolate hot snack areas to prevent odours from drifting?)
- the interaction between the ventilation system and individual staff; it is important to ensure a good quality environment across the entire space as staff will be unable to change the position of their work stations or alter the ventilation
- the possibility that the ventilation system will add to background noise levels and thereby affect the ability of staff to deal with incoming calls.

2.3.24.3 Court rooms

The Lord Chancellor's Department (LCD) should be consulted for guidance on environmental policy and court room design[152,153].

The LCD's policy is to maximise the use of natural ventilation principles to maintain satisfactory environmental conditions as part of their commitment to provide environmentally friendly buildings.

Mechanical ventilation systems for court rooms need to be designed to meet the sound control requirements as set out in section 5 of this guide.

2.3.24.4 Darkrooms (photographic)

Small darkrooms for occasional use or for purely developing processes may often be ventilated naturally with a suitable light trap, although consideration should be given to providing mechanical extract using an air change rate of 6 to 8 air changes per hour. For general purpose darkrooms, however, the air change rate should be ascertained from consideration of the heat gain from the enlarger, lights etc. plus the occupants, on the basis of a temperature rise of 5–6 K. In industrial and commercial darkrooms that have machine processing, the machines will very often have their own extract ducting, the air supply being drawn from the room itself. It will usually be necessary to provide a warmed and filtered mechanical inlet in such cases. In special cases, involving extensive washing processes, the humidity gain may be significant and require consideration.

2.3.24.5 Dealing rooms

Dealing rooms are characterised by much higher heat gains from IT equipment than those for general office areas. Small power requirements are typically in the order of 500 W per trading desk, but can vary between 200 and 1000 W[154]. Occupation densities can be as high as one trading desk per 7 m^2.

Loads are a function of the IT equipment and are subject to technological developments. Developments may have spatial as well as power implications. These may affect load intensity. For example, flat panel displays (FPD) have lower cooling requirements than cathode ray tubes (SRT) displays, but occupy less space thereby permitting a greater density of occupation[155].

The selection of suitable air conditioning is primarily determined by the high cooling load. The need to minimise disruption, reliability and maintenance requirements are is a key consideration. Systems normally incorporate a high degree of redundancy. Risks associated with pipework and condensate leakage should be minimised.

Ceiling mounted system options include fan coils and variable air volume (VAV) systems. However, supplying cooling from above to deal with the heat from the equipment will create a large amount of air movement, thereby increasing the risk of draughts. An alternative approach is to supply cool air directly to desktop computers through the floor void to remove the heat directly, reducing air movement in the occupied space and the risk of draughts. This approach may be used in conjunction with the fan coil units, VAV system or chilled beams/ceilings that deal with the balance of the load.

Mechanical ventilation systems for dealing rooms need to provide a high level of reliability, as the system is critical to the proper functioning of the building and the business conducted within it. Consequential losses arising from failure can be very significant in this type of building.

2.3.24.6 Horticulture[156]

Guidance on sources of information on the design of horticultural buildings may be obtained from the Commercial Horticultural Association, a trade association based at the National Agricultural Centre*.

Environmental conditions in greenhouses must be favourable to plant growth. This involves heating during cold weather and the limitation of high temperatures due to solar gains in the hot weather. In some cases, carbon dioxide enrichment and humidity restriction will also be required. The internal design temperature should be in the order of 16 °C when the external temperature is –7 to –10 °C.

Greenhouse crops require ventilation to limit the rise in air temperature, provide carbon dioxide for photosynthesis, and restrict the rise in humidity due to transpiration. Automatic ventilators, controlled by an air thermostat, can be opened at a pre-determined temperature (approximately 24 °C). Rates of ventilation of the order of 30 to 50 litre·s^{-1} per m^2 of greenhouse floor area are desirable, which is equal to 45 to 60 air changes per hour for conventional houses. Low level ventilators may be required in addition to the ridge ventilators to increase the stack effect during still conditions.

Propeller extract fans (side wall mounted) with ventilation duties to the rates given have the advantage of positive air movement through crops, thus promoting growth. Inlet air should have a velocity not exceeding 1 m·s^{-1} and be diverted with an upward component, thus preventing cooler air being drawn directly on to the crops. A combination of automatic ventilators and fans will allow for failures of either system.

A complete mechanical ventilation system, using PVC ductwork with air supply discharge holes, can be used for winter heating with heated re-circulated air, and summer cooling with 100% fresh outdoor air. Fans giving a constant 10 to 20 ACH can be supplemented by automatic ventilators or extract fans during hot weather. This type of system has the advantage of even, closely controlled temperatures, with positive air movement throughout the year. However, the initial outlay is likely to be high.

Other aspects worth consideration are:

— automatic solar shading equipment
— automatic day and night temperature and lighting sequencing
— evaporative cooling pad air inlet and exhaust fan system
— air purification
— plant cooling by evaporation using overhead spraying
— earth heating plant propagation beds.

2.3.24.7 Standards rooms

It is usual for standards rooms to be designed to meet the same conditions as those maintained for the manufacturing processes, and reference should be made to the appropriate section. In practice, the environmental conditions within standards rooms may well be more exacting, in order to (*a*) sample and test equipment over varying environmental conditions for set time periods, or (*b*) sample and test equipment manufactured in various areas of the factory maintained at different environmental conditions.

Mechanical ventilation systems for standards rooms need to provide a high level of reliability, as the system is critical to the proper functioning of the building and the business conducted within it. Consequential losses arising from failure can be very significant in this type of building.

*National Agricultural Centre, Stonleigh Park, Kenilworth, Warwickshire, CV8 2LG, UK (www.ukexnet.co.uk/hort/cha/)

2.4 Systems

2.4.1 Introduction

This section is not intended to provide step-by-step design guidance, but to summarise the key issues and performance targets that need to be addressed during design. The guidance contained in this section should be read in conjunction with CIBSE Guides A[12] and F[26]. For details of refrigeration methods, see section 5 .

2.4.2 Room air distribution strategies

2.4.2.1 Room air diffusion: criteria for design

Air diffusion is the main interface between the system and the occupants. If the air diffusion is not well designed the system will fail, no matter how accurately building loads have been modelled and how carefully the plant and equipment have been selected.

The effectiveness of all ventilation and air conditioning systems depends on the method by which supply air is introduced to, and vitiated air removed from, the space. The parameters that influence the quality of the air at any point in the room are the following:

— air supply velocity
— temperature differential between the room and supply air
— purity of the supply air
— position of the air supply terminals
— room shape and geometry, including projections
— position, size, and shape of all sources and sinks for heat and contaminants
— temperature of any heat sources and sinks
— rates of evolution and sorption of contaminants
— other factors influencing air movement, such as movement of the occupants and machinery, and air infiltration.

As discussed later, if terminal devices are poorly selected or positioned this can result in draughts, stagnation, poor air quality, inappropriate mixing, large temperature gradients and unwanted noise. The terminal type and layout may be affected by architectural or structural considerations, but conversely particular room air diffusion requirements should form part of the integrated/co-ordinated building design and/or structure (e.g. floor supply).

The occupants' perception of the effectiveness of the system will normally be determined by:

- the velocity of air adjacent to any uncovered or lightly covered skin (e.g. neck and ankles)
- temperature of air stream in relation to the that of still air adjacent to other parts of the body
- the level of activity taking place
- the occupants' clothing
- the purity of air in the breathing zone
- the individual's susceptibility and acclimatisation
- the appearance and positioning of any ventilation devices or openings
- the noise emitted.

The above are discussed in detail in section 1.4 of CIBSE Guide A[(12)].

ISO 7730[(157)] recommends that, during cooling, the mean air velocity should be less than 0.25 $m \cdot s^{-1}$ for moderate thermal environments with light, mainly sedentary, activity and that, in winter, it should be less than 0.15 $m \cdot s^{-1}$. No minimum velocity is suggested, although stagnant zones could result in temperature gradients between the ankle and the neck greater than the 3 K recommended. It is likely that sufficient air movement will be generated by other means.

The occupied zone can be defined as a region, the outer limits of which are described by an envelope 1.8 m from the floor and 0.15 m from the walls. However, in the case of low level supply terminals, the occupied zone is any region where the occupants are likely to linger for significant periods. In the case of desk terminals, this definition does not apply. For desk terminals, mixing occurs over the desk surface and, for seatback terminals, mixing occurs in the regions above and between the seats.

An assessment of predicted percentage dissatisfied (PPD)[(157)] for a wide range of activity levels, clothing, body temperatures and velocities shows that, even at low activity levels, velocities as high as 1.0 $m \cdot s^{-1}$ can be acceptable in offsetting high temperatures. This technique has been applied to the concept of spot cooling in some industrial applications[(158)] whereby heat stress in the workers is avoided by keeping the local conditions below an agreed value of wet bulb globe temperature.

2.4.2.2 Ventilation efficiency[(159–161)]

Uneven temperature distribution and contaminant concentrations can occur within occupied zones due to local convection currents and the uneven distribution and mixing of contaminants within a space. If heat transfer and fresh air provision can occur, the condition of the space above this zone is usually unimportant. Displacement ventilation systems exploit this concept (see section 2.4.2.5). Conventional air conditioning systems, however, use dilution ventilation whereby mixing occurs outside the occupied zone and, under ideal conditions, all the air in the space is at the same temperature and of the same quality. The efficiency of the ventilation therefore depends on effective local removal of heat and contaminants from the space and the total energy requirements of the supply and extract systems required to achieve this. Careful account needs to be taken of potential contaminant sources within the occupied space, which will reduce the efficiency of the ventilation system.

2.4.2.3 Air distribution[(162)]

Air can be supplied to a space in a number of ways, the principal division being between diffusers and perpendicular jets. Airflow patterns for both types of terminal are strongly dependent upon the presence or absence of the Coanda effect (see below).

Diffusers may be radial, part-radial or linear and normally utilise the Coanda effect and or/swirl to reduce the risk of excessive room air movement. A perpendicular jet is formed by discharging air through grilles, louvres, nozzles or any opening that allows perpendicular flow. Direction and spread adjustment can be provided using blades and/or swivel adjustment.

Supply air terminal devices can be incorporated into any room surface, e.g. ceiling (flat or sculptured), floor, wall (high or low level), desk top, seat back or under seats. Air terminal devices other types of equipment are considered in section 2.5.13. Further guidance can be obtained from HEVAC's *Guide to air distribution technology for the internal environment*[(162)].

Air terminal phenomena[(163–172)]

Many studies of jets and their effect on room air movement have been undertaken. Figure 2.10 shows the predicted airflow patterns for various types and positions of air terminal device[(173)].

It should be noted that these patterns are based on stylised terminals. For predictions of air movement appropriate to specific air terminals the manufacturers' data must be consulted. For non-standard situations it may be necessary to model room air movement using a mock-up. In many cases it will be necessary to allow for on-site adjustment of airflow pattern, either during commissioning or during operation by the occupant (e.g. desk mounted terminals).

Air diffusion terminology

ISO 3258[(174)] gives definitions and standard terminology used in connection with air movement. Some of the more important parameters are listed below.

(*a*) Throw

A free jet having a given momentum on discharge will establish velocity profiles known as isovels, the shape of which depends on the geometry of the terminal, the temperature of the jet and any other disturbing influences. The velocity decays with increasing distance from the terminal. Throw is defined as the distance from the terminal (measured perpendicular or parallel to the face of the air terminal device depending on the predominant direction of flow) to the 0.5 $m \cdot s^{-1}$ isovel.

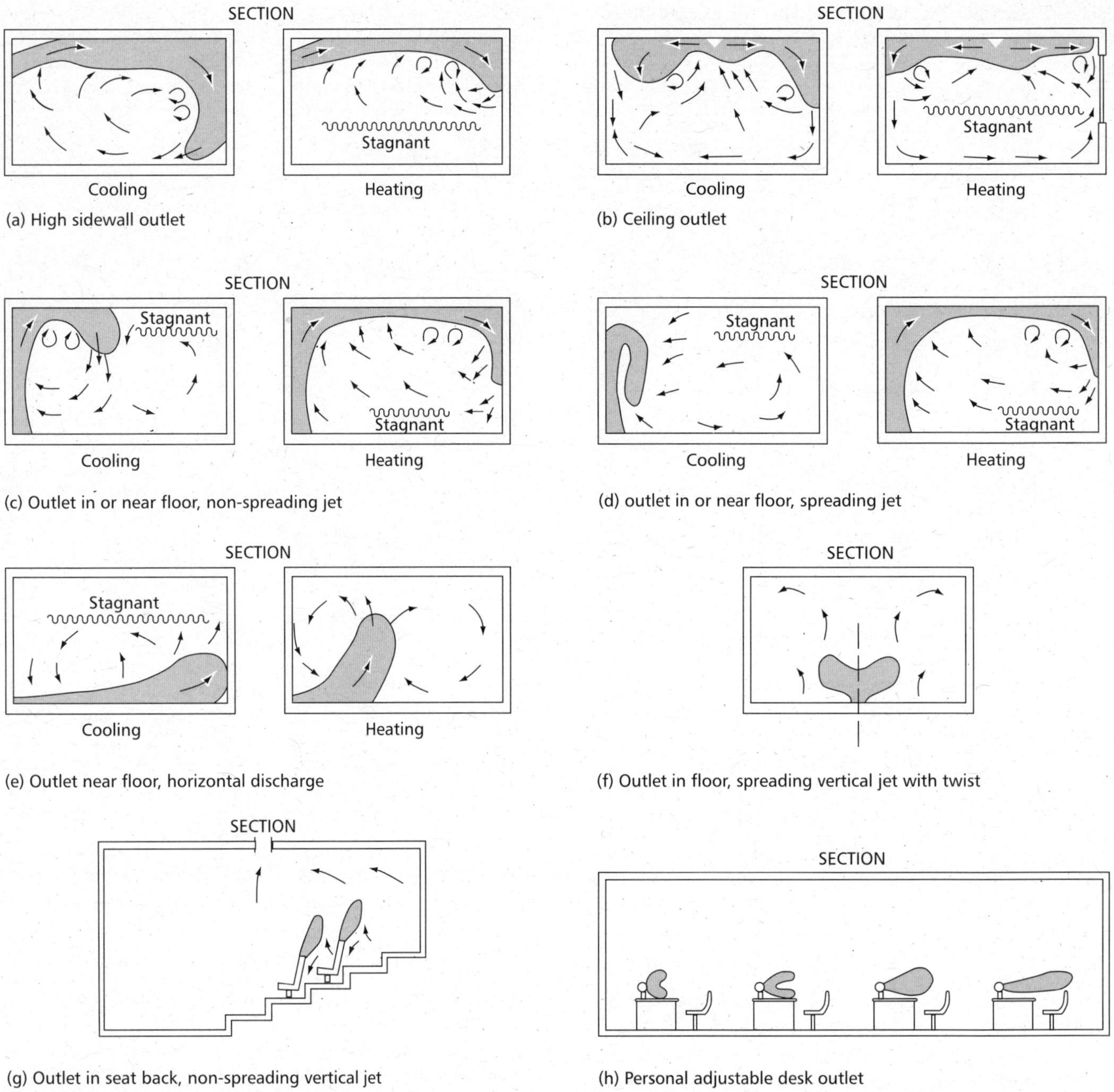

SECTION

Cooling

Heating

(a) High sidewall outlet

SECTION

Cooling

Heating

Stagnant

(b) Ceiling outlet

SECTION

Stagnant

Stagnant

Cooling

Heating

(c) Outlet in or near floor, non-spreading jet

SECTION

Stagnant

Stagnant

Cooling

Heating

(d) outlet in or near floor, spreading jet

SECTION

Stagnant

Cooling

Heating

(e) Outlet near floor, horizontal discharge

SECTION

(f) Outlet in floor, spreading vertical jet with twist

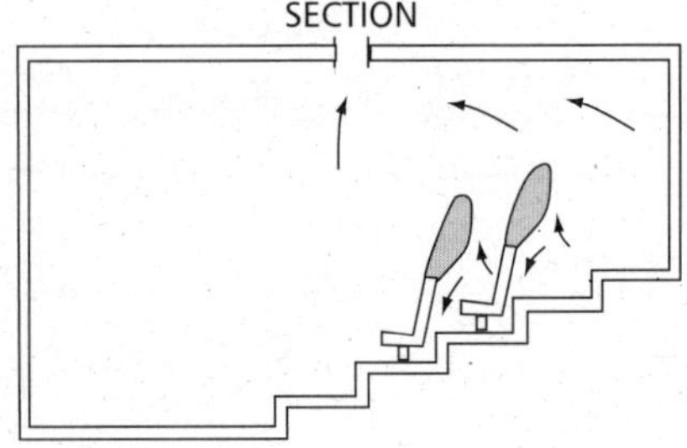

(g) Outlet in seat back, non-spreading vertical jet

SECTION

(h) Personal adjustable desk outlet

Figure 2.10 Predicted airflow patterns (reproduced from ASHRAE Handbook: *Fundamentals*, by permission of the American Society of Heating, Refrigerating and Air-Conditioning Engineers)

Normally lower velocities are required for air entering the occupied zone, typically 0.25 m·s^{-1} for cooling, 0.15 m·s^{-1} for heating. Reference should be made to manufacturers' literature for throw data and recommended mounting distances from solid surfaces and neighbouring terminals.

The maximum throw for an air terminal device depends upon the characteristics of the device, the mounting height and the influence of neighbouring devices.

(*b*) Spread

The spread of a horizontal jet is defined as the width of the 0.5 m·s^{-1} isovel. Note that most manufacturers give the width of the 0.25 m·s^{-1} isovel, which is generally of more use to the designer.

(*c*) Drop

The drop is defined as the vertical distance from the centre-line of the terminal to the bottom edge of the 0.25 m·s^{-1} isovel.

Entrainment, mixing and boundaries

Frictional forces cause a momentum transfer to take place between the jet and adjacent room air, which draws the room air in the same direction as the jet. The jet expands with distance from the terminal as it entrains adjacent room air. Hence kinetic energy is expended in creating turbulence, which transfers thermal energy and assists the dilution of contaminants. This process of diffusion may be enhanced by the introduction of a rapidly expanding jet and still further by imparting a swirling motion to the jet.

A jet that is constrained by the walls of a room, such as a full width slot, will entrain less room air and expand more slowly than a free conical jet[162,173].

Effect of temperature differential

Figure 2.10 shows that a jet which is not influenced by the proximity of a solid surface follows a path which is a function both of velocity and temperature. A warm jet tends to rise until it attaches itself to a horizontal surface, whilst a cold jet falls. Care must be taken to ensure that this does not lead to unacceptable temperature gradients in the occupied zone during heating, and excessive air velocities during cooling. The terminal must be mounted such that the 0.25 m·s^{-1} isovel does not enter the occupied zone.

The difference in temperature between the supply and return air may be greater than that between the supply air and the occupied zone, particularly with a low-level supply designed to encourage high-level stratification. This temperature difference is related to sensible heat gain and supply air mass flow, as follows:

$$q_s = m\, C_{ph}\, \Delta T \qquad (2.5)$$

where q_s is the total sensible heat gain (kW), m is the mass flow rate of supply air (kg·s^{-1}), C_{ph} is the specific heat of the air and water vapour mixture (kJ·kg^{-1}·K^{-1}) and ΔT is the room air to supply air temperature differential (K).

Therefore the mass flow rate, and hence the cost of air handling, will depend upon the temperature difference chosen by the designer. This decision will also be influenced by the evaporator temperature and the level of control of humidity. For example, a displacement system with low-level input can supply air at 18 °C with a temperature difference of about 10 K. This can be achieved with high evaporator temperatures and correspondingly low compressor power. However, high-level humidity control will suffer unless the supply air is over-cooled and reheated, normally an undesirable combination at peak load. Alternatively, a permanent bypass around the cooling coil can be provided and, if motorised dampers are incorporated at the coil face and in the bypass, part load control supply temperature can be achieved by damper modulation.

For comfort applications, air change rates are unlikely to exceed 10 ACH, corresponding to a cooling temperature differential of 8–12 K. A free horizontal jet from a rectangular grille is likely to create down draughts if providing more than 8 ACH with a cooling temperature differential greater than 8 K.

A maximum cooling differential of 10 K can be applied when either:

— the presence of the Coanda effect (see below) is assured

— for a free jet, mixing of supply air with room air outside the occupied zone can be assured without promoting discomfort.

Table 2.30 gives general guidance on the maximum air change rates that can be achieved using various air terminal devices supplying air with a cooling temperature differential of 10 K.

If sufficient mixing between terminal and occupants cannot be guaranteed (e.g. with low level supply) then the minimum supply temperature of 18 °C applies, with a temperature differential in the occupied zone of 4–5 K. However, the cooling temperature differential is ultimately determined by the maximum exhaust air temperature[175], see Table 2.31.

Table 2.30 Typical maximum air change rates for air terminal devices

Device	Air change rate / h^{-1}
Sidewall grilles	8
Linear grilles	10
Slot and linear diffusers	15
Rectangular diffusers	15
Perforated diffusers	15
Circular diffusers	20

Table 2.31 Typical cooling temperature differentials for various applications

Application	Maximum temp. differential / K
High ceiling (large heat gains/low level input)	12
Low ceiling (air handling luminaires/low level input)	10
Low ceiling (downward discharge)	5

The larger temperature differential indicated for high ceilings is possible due to the smaller influence of ceiling temperature on the mean radiant temperature experienced by the occupants.

Downward discharge is generally only satisfactory for very high air change rates, and hence small temperature differentials, or where room convection is not significant (see below). An exception is the specific case of split systems, where temperature differences can be as high as 20 K. Particular care is therefore needed in their specification, see section 2.4.21.

High-level supply jets must overcome the buoyancy forces in the room air generated by heat emitters, solar gain, occupants etc., whereas low level input cultivates these forces to assist the supply jet. For this reason, low level supply is most satisfactory for applications with high room gains and high ceilings. For low ceilings the radiant heating effect of the ceiling itself may be significant. This may also be a problem where the ceiling void is used as an exhaust air plenum, carrying air heated by air-handling luminaires.

Free descending jets are not recommended for normal use, since the low velocity approaching the occupied zone would cause instability. This could result in localised high velocities due to deflection by convective forces elsewhere in the room, see Figure 2.11. An exception is the case of laminar downflow cleanrooms[176,177] where an even velocity

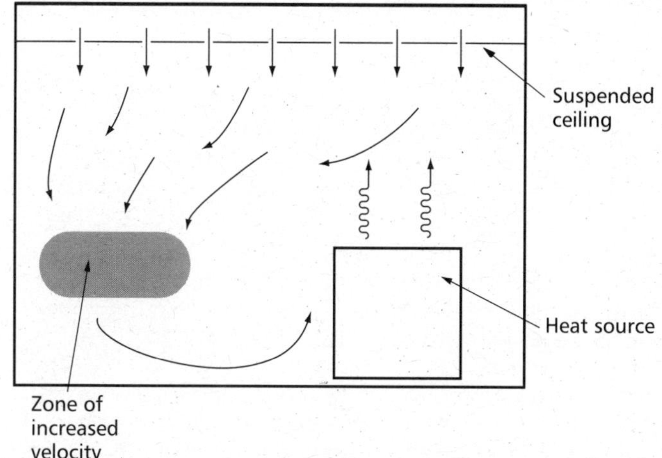

Figure 2.11 Effect of room convection currents

across the full area of 0.4 m·s^{-1} should be maintained from ceiling to floor. However, even in these circumstances, sources of extremely buoyant upflow should be avoided.

Coanda effect

When a jet is discharged from a terminal device adjacent and parallel to an unobstructed flat surface, the jet entrains air from one side only resulting in deflection of the axis of the jet towards the surface. This phenomenon, known as the Coanda effect, is due to frictional losses between the jet and the surface.

The effect diminishes with distance from the terminals as increasing volumes of air are entrained from the room-side of the jet, resulting in a reduction of jet velocity. However, the Coanda effect is maintained despite temperature differences between the jet and the room air. It is a critical factor influencing the selection and positioning of supply air terminals, particularly for rooms with low ceilings which have little space above the occupied zone in which mixing can occur.

If the Coanda effect is not present the maximum throw for any terminal is reduced by approximately 33%. The main factors that influence whether or not the Coanda effect will occur are:

— the distance between terminal and surface

— the width of jet exposed to surface

— the velocity of the jet

— the presence of projections and other disturbing influences.

The importance of these influences for side-wall terminals with various aspect ratios, velocities and temperatures differences is discussed elsewhere(170). The most important factor is temperature difference, i.e. buoyancy effects. For the usual range of temperature differences for cooling of 8–12 K, the opening should be within 300 mm of the surface to guarantee attraction. For systems designed to make use of the Coanda effect, provision should be made for on-site adjustment of the jet.

When a jet adheres to a surface, dust particles will be deposited on the surface leading to staining, hence supply air cleanliness is of paramount importance (see section 2.5.7). Cleanliness of the exhaust air is difficult to control and some staining of surfaces near to exhaust openings is inevitable.

Techniques exist(168) for predicting the influence of projections, such as downstand beams and surface mounted luminaires, on a jet flowing across an otherwise smooth surface. An obstruction may cause the jet to separate completely from the surface, hence destroying the Coanda effect, or it may separate and join some distance downstream of the obstruction.

The critical distances at which these phenomena are likely to occur depend on the depth and shape of the obstruction and size of the supply opening. The influence of supply air to room air temperature differential is small but depends upon the extent to which mixing has occurred before the jet meets the obstruction.

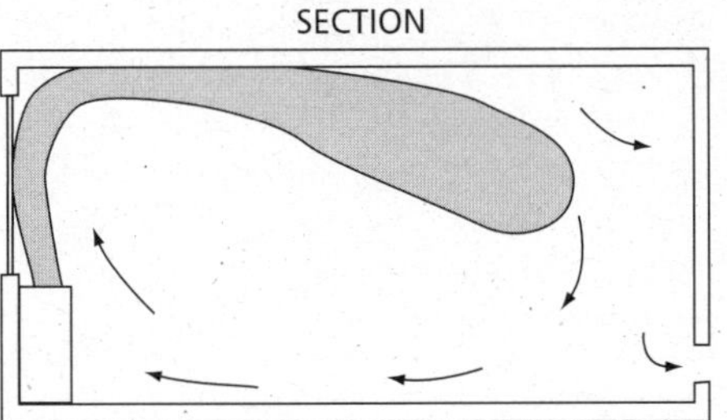

Figure 2.12 Effect of a horizontal surface on a jet

Figure 2.12 shows the effect of a horizontal surface on a jet rising close to the vertical surface. The Coanda effect is maintained after the change in direction provided that the velocity is adequate, particularly in the case of cooling jets, and that the temperature differential between supply and room air is not too large. Guidance for selecting optimum supply velocities and temperature is given elsewhere(171).

Interaction between jets

Figure 2.13(a) shows possible room air velocity patterns for two jets directed towards each other along a 3 m high ceiling. The individual velocities of the two air streams must not be greater than the 0.25 m·s^{-1} at the boundary otherwise discomfort may occur due to excessive downdraughts.

The envelopes of two converging jets may also interfere with each other, combining to form a single, wide jet with a maximum velocity at the new axis between the two jets, see Figure 2.13(b). A similar phenomenon occurs with two jets moving in tandem, see Figure 2.13(c). The downstream jet entrains and accelerates the decaying upstream jet and forms a wider jet with an axis further from the neighbouring surface. The cumulative effect of a series of single-way jets can result in a deep jet that intrudes into the occupied zone resulting in unacceptably high room velocities.

Figure 2.14 shows examples of possible layouts for ceiling diffusers. The main problems likely to be encountered are those described above. Down-draughts may been encountered in areas marked 'X' and this problem may be eliminated by avoiding terminals with excessive throw, particularly in large spaces where stagnation between terminals is unlikely to occur. The layout shown in Figure 2.14(c) may cause convergence problems with long rooms.

For side-wall applications, the spacing of diffusers should be in accordance with manufacturers' recommendations. However, in the absence of such recommendations, Table 2.32 may be used in conjunction with throw and deflection data to determine the diffuser spacing. For a terminal mounted close to a wall, spacing should be halved to give the minimum distance from the centreline to the wall. Table 2.33(175) indicates typical turndown limits for various types of fixed air terminal device.

Table 2.32 Data for determining spacing of ceiling diffusers

Deflection / deg.	Spacing / m	
0	0.20 L_x	0.33 L_y
22.5	0.25 L_x	0.50 L_y
45	0.30 L_x	1.0 L_y

Note: L_x = throw (m) where axial velocity has decayed to 0.25 m·s^{-1}; L_y = throw (m) where axial velocity has decayed to 0.5 m·s^{-1}

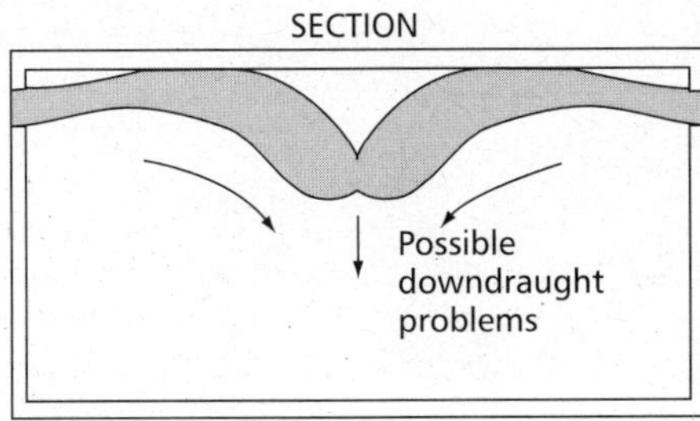

(a) Opposing jets

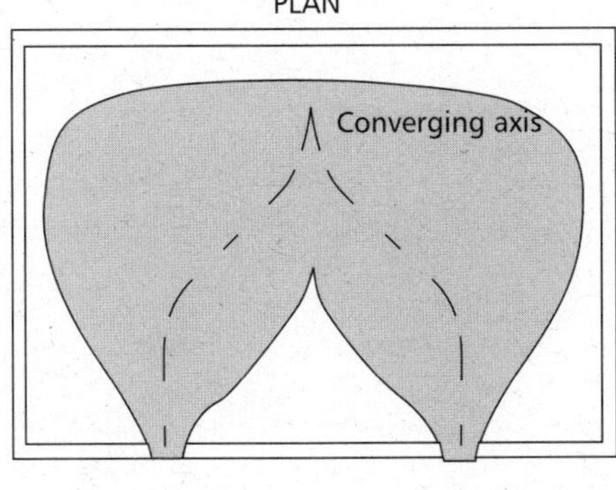

(b) Converging jets

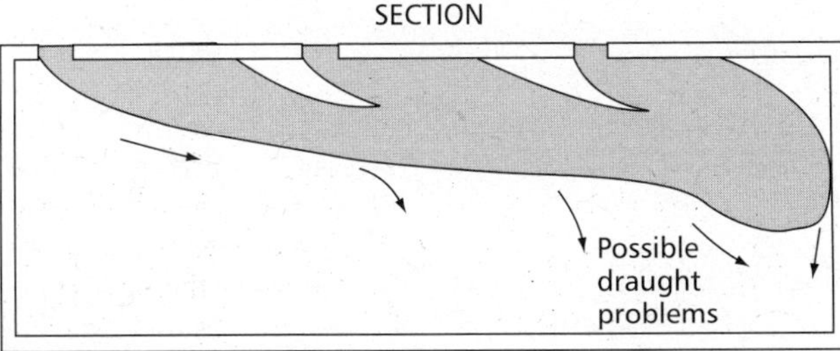

(c) Three jets in series

Figure 2.13 Room air velocity patterns; interactions between jets

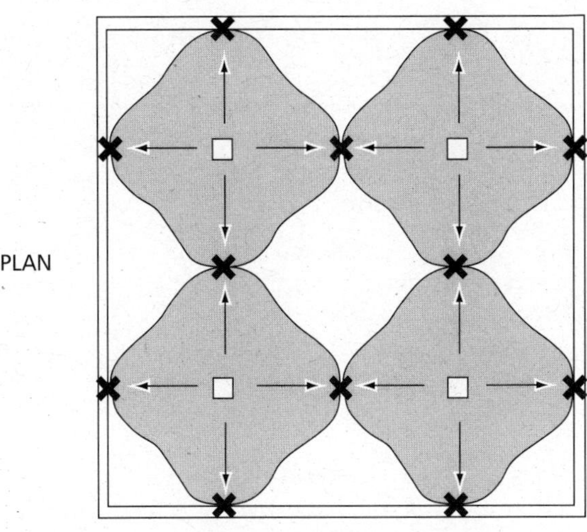

(a) Four-way ceiling diffusers, symmetrical layout

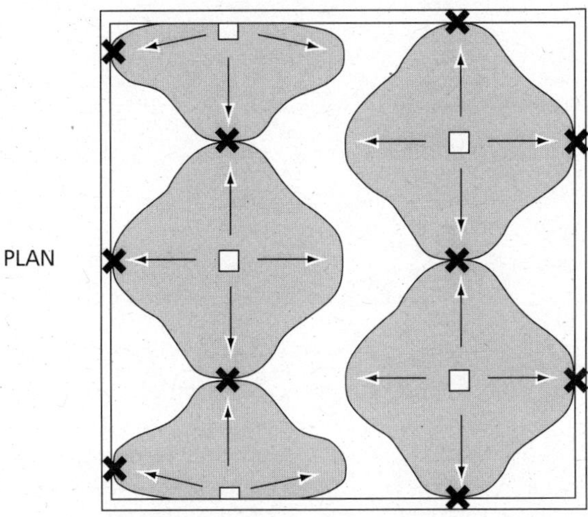

(b) Four-way ceiling diffusers, off-set layout

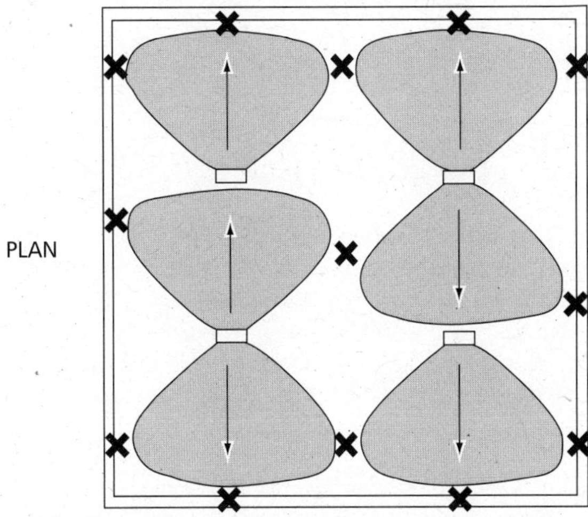

(c) One-and two-way ceiling diffusers, contra-flow layout

Figure 2.14 Supply terminal layouts for open plan spaces

Table 2.33 Turndown limits for types of fixed air terminal device[175]

Type of outlet	Maximum turndown / %
Ceiling mounted:	
— not using Coanda effect	50
— using Coanda effect	40
Floor mounted outlets:	
— perforated plate and fixed bar grille	60
— free jet outlets	50
— outlets with swirl	40
Desk outlets:	
— linear type	50
— ball type	50
— outlets with swirl	40

Exhaust terminals

The positioning of the opening has little influence on the airflow pattern in the space because the zone of localised high velocities associated with exhaust openings is very close to the opening, see section 2.3.15.

Exhaust terminals may be sited to advantage as follows:

— in a stagnant zone where supply jet influence is limited

— close to a source of unwanted heat and/or contamination, e.g. above a luminaire

— close to an excessively cold surface to increase its surface temperature and thereby reduce radiant losses and cold draughts

— at a point of local low pressure, e.g. the centre of a ceiling diffuser.

The following positions should be avoided:

- within the zone of influence of a supply air terminal since this allows conditioned air to pass directly to exhaust without first having exchanged heat with its surroundings; this results in very low ventilation efficiency
- close to a door or aperture which is frequently opened since this leads to the exhaust handling air from outside the conditioned space
- in a position which causes contaminated room air to be drawn through the occupants' breathing zone.

2.4.2.4 Duct and plenum design

Air terminal devices will only perform as intended if the approach velocity is even. If the duct connections and/or volume flow regulators created eddies at the terminal, the following problems may arise:

- unpredictable throw, spread and drop
- breakdown of Coanda effect
- high noise levels
- balancing is difficult or impossible.

Design procedures for duct and plenum connections to various types of air terminal are given elsewhere(162); also see section 2.4.4.

If the ceiling is to be used as an exhaust plenum, it is important to create a uniform negative pressure throughout the whole ceiling void to ensure even exhaust throughout all terminals. This is particularly important where exhaust is by means of air handling luminaires, the performance of which varies with airflow rate.

Ceiling voids should be made as large as possible and, if obstructed by luminaires, ductwork etc., exhaust stub ducts should be provided to ensure even exhaust over the full ceiling area.

2.4.2.5 Displacement ventilation(178,179)

In buoyancy-driven displacement-flow ventilation systems, air is supplied at a low velocity from low-level wall-mounted or floor-mounted supply air terminal devices directly into the occupied zone, at a temperature slightly cooler than the design room air temperature. The air from a wall-mounted terminal flows downward to the floor due to gravity and moves around the room close to the floor, creating a thin layer of cool air. Natural convection from internal heat sources, such as occupants and equipment, causes upward air movement in the room. The warm, contaminated air forms a stratified region above the occupied zone, which is then exhausted at high level. The height of this layer depends upon the relationship between the incoming airflow and the rate of flow in the plumes. The boundary will stabilise at a level at which these two flow rates are equal.

The airflow in displacement ventilation has both horizontal and vertical air movement characteristics. Horizontal air movement occurs within the thermally stratified layers that are formed between the upper (warm) and lower (cool) air layers in the room. Vertical air movement is caused by the presence of cold and warm objects in the space. Warm objects, such as people, create upward convection currents; cold objects, such as cold windows and walls, cause downward currents.

For given rates of ventilation and pollutant discharge, the air quality in the occupied zone of a room with displacement ventilation can be higher than that using a mixed-flow ventilation method. In displacement ventilation, air movement above the occupied zone is often mixed and it is when this mixed region extends down into the occupied zone that the air quality becomes similar to that in a mixed-flow system.

With displacement ventilation, a vertical temperature gradient is unavoidable. ISO 7730(157) recommends a vertical temperature gradient for sedentary occupants of less than 3 K. This equates to approximately 3 $K \cdot m^{-1}$ if workers are assumed to be seated, although a limit of 1.8 or 2 $K \cdot m^{-1}$ is often proposed for offices (i.e. 5 K limit for a typical floor-to-ceiling height of 2.5 m). However, as 30–50% of the overall supply-to-extract temperature difference occurs between the supply air and that at ankle level in the main space, a limiting difference between floor and ceiling height for typical office applications can be taken as 7–10 K. The supply air temperature should not be lower than 18 °C for sedentary occupancy and 16 °C for more active occupancy. It is also recommended that the limits of variation of temperature across the room should be within a temperature range of 3 K, i.e. ± 1.5 K about the mean room air temperature.

A combination of near-floor temperatures below 22 °C and airflows in excess of 0.15 $m \cdot s^{-1}$ may cause discomfort due to cold feet, so occupants should be located a sufficient distance from diffusers. Equipment manufacturers should be consulted for detailed performance characteristics.

The zone around a supply air diffuser within which the supply air conditions have the greatest effect is labelled the near-zone. The permitted near-zone extent together with the maximum allowable comfort temperature at the near-zone perimeter for a given supply air temperature dictates the air volume per diffuser and its size. In an office the near-zone may be 1 m, in a commercial application or in a foyer it may be 3 m. The maximum cooling load that can be delivered by displacement ventilation is therefore limited to 25 $W \cdot m^{-2}$ due to discomfort considerations(180).

Displacement ventilation can be employed for many applications and building types. It is often used in conjunction with chilled ceiling or chilled beam systems. However there are conditions under which the system is less effective than traditional mixed flow ventilation strategies. These include(181):

- where the supply air is warmer than the room air (except under particular circumstances where cold downdraughts exists over the supply position)
- where contaminants are cold and/or more dense than the surrounding air
- where surface temperatures of heat sources are low, e.g. <35 °C
- where ceiling heights are low, i.e. <2.3 m (the preferred height is not less than 3 m)
- where disturbance to room airflows is unusually strong.

Displacement ventilation devices[179,181]

(*a*) Pure displacement terminals

Pure displacement terminals aim to get air into the room with a minimum of eddies, room air mixing and temperature pick-up before it reaches the occupants. Hence there is a very small temperature difference between the supply air and that of the occupied zone. It is possible to maximise the use of outdoor air for free cooling and this may eliminate the need for mechanical cooling (e.g. through groundwater).

(*b*) Induction-type diffusers

Induction-type diffusers are intended to promote various levels of eddy mixing of the room air at the diffuser face. This allows lower supply air temperatures and hence marginally greater displacement cooling capacity. They have a larger approach temperature, generally require some mechanical cooling and impart a higher turbulent intensity with potential discomfort. A substantial diffuser open area is needed to obtain low velocities.

(*c*) Swirl-type diffusers

Swirl-type diffusers introduce air at far higher velocities, promote full mixing in the occupied zone, and disrupt buoyancy plumes. Thus they lose many of the displacement benefits. Horizontal diffusers appear to be less disruptive but need to be considered carefully in the light of their impact in terms of high velocities and sub-room temperatures near to occupants.

(*d*) Effect of extract grilles

Extract grilles have a relatively minor impact on the system operation. The main consideration is their frequency with varying ceiling heights. The higher the ceiling the greater the possible depth of the polluted air layer and so the air can travel further in order to reach a grille without gaining sufficient depth to encroach into the occupied zone.

Control of displacement ventilation systems[181]

The main forms of control are:

— *Constant supply air temperature, constant airflow rate*: in which the supply air temperature is maintained constant at a design value selected to be at least 1 K below the required zone mean air temperature. Variations in heat gain will affect the temperature gradient within the space so that provided the maximum heat gain does not create a temperature gradient in excess of comfort limits, acceptable conditions will be maintained.

— *Constant supply air temperature, variable airflow rate*: the supply airflow rate may be adjusted to accommodate higher variations in heat load and maintain a substantially constant temperature gradient within the occupied zone. This adjustment can be automatically controlled to maintain a constant difference between the room air temperature and supply air temperature.

— *Variable supply air temperature*: this form of control is not as effective in displacement ventilation systems as it is in mixed flow systems because the supply air temperature required to maintain an acceptable mean room air temperature is not so directly related to internal heat gains.

Using a control system to maintain substantially constant thermal conditions within a room requires a temperature sensor located in a position that provides a reading that is representative of the occupied zone. In view of the vertical temperature gradients associated with displacement flow, the room air temperature sensor is best placed at about head height in a location free from significant draughts.

2.4.3 Natural ventilation systems design

2.4.3.1 General

Natural ventilation is the airflow through a building resulting from the provision of specified routes such as openable windows, ventilators, ducts, shafts, etc, driven by wind and density differences. It may be used to provide:

— outside air for ventilation purposes

— cooling for thermal comfort.

Natural ventilation is considered in detail in CIBSE AM10: *Natural ventilation in non-domestic buildings*[182].

2.4.3.2 Strategy

There are a number of strategies that can be adopted. The basic forms are outlined in this section and illustrated in Figure 2.15. The pattern of airflow through the whole building should be considered for all operational regimes — winter and summer, as well as night ventilation, if required. Ventilation strategy should be considered on the basis of the whole building rather than just room-by-room. Circulation areas such as stairwells or corridors can be used as plenums or supply ducts, although care must be taken to avoid these routes acting as 'short circuits'. Consideration should be given to where the fresh air will be brought from, e.g. it may be beneficial to draw the air from one side of the building to:

— avoid noise and traffic fumes from a busy road

— draw cooler air from a shaded side of the building to maximise the cooling.

The magnitude and pattern of natural air movement through a building depends on the strength and direction of the natural driving forces and the resistance of the flow path. The driving forces for natural ventilation are wind and density difference.

(*a*) Wind

Wind driven ventilation, see Figure 2.16, is caused by varying surface pressures acting across the external building envelope. The distribution of pressure depends on:

— the terrain

— local obstructions

— the wind speed and its direction relative to the building

— the shape of the building.

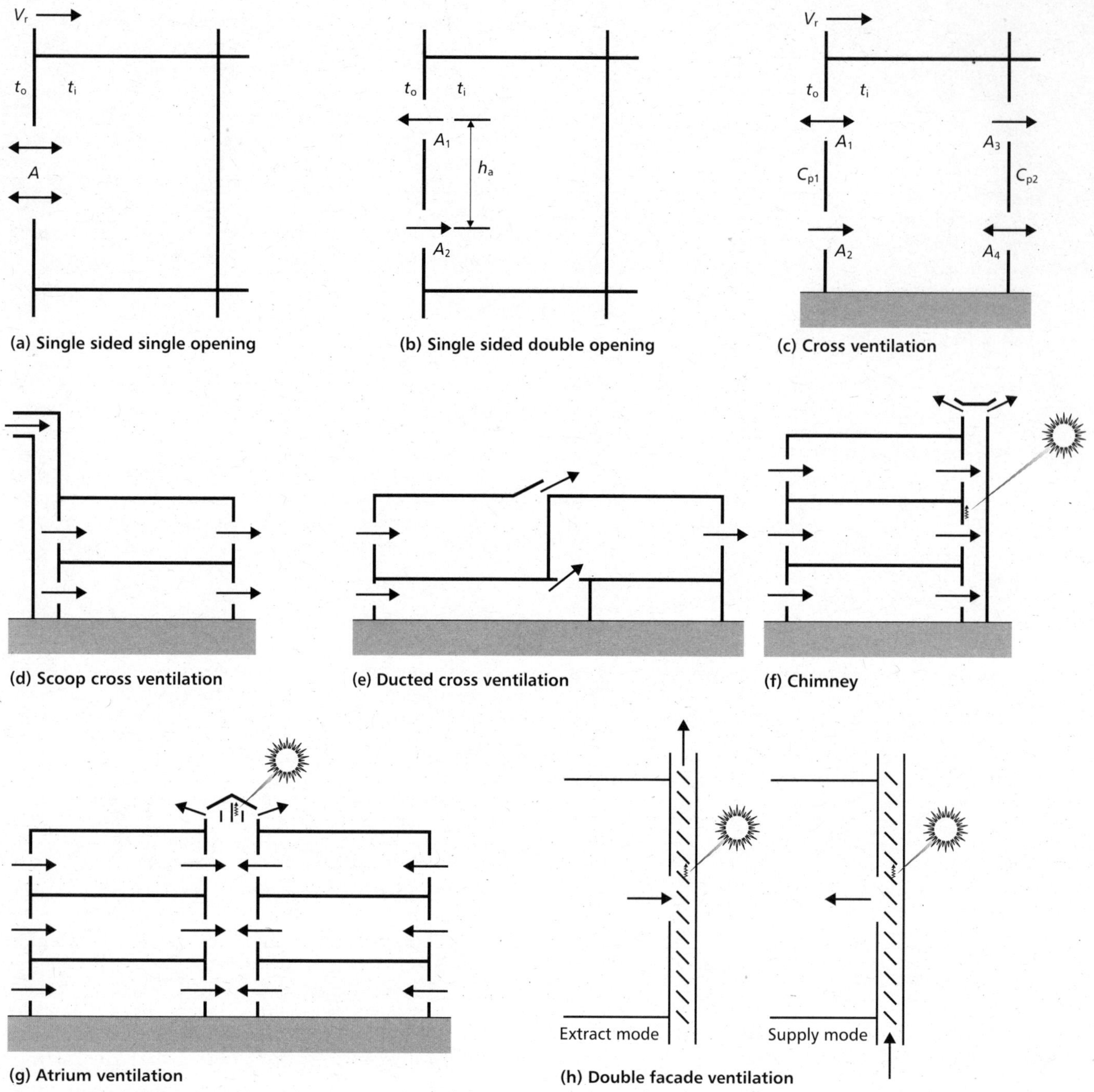

Vr
to
ti
A
A1
ha
A2
Cp1
A3
Cp2
A4
(a) Single sided single opening
(b) Single sided double opening
(c) Cross ventilation
(d) Scoop cross ventilation
(e) Ducted cross ventilation
(f) Chimney
(g) Atrium ventilation
Extract mode
Supply mode
(h) Double facade ventilation

Figure 2.15 Ventilation strategy options

Wind velocity
Wind pressure field

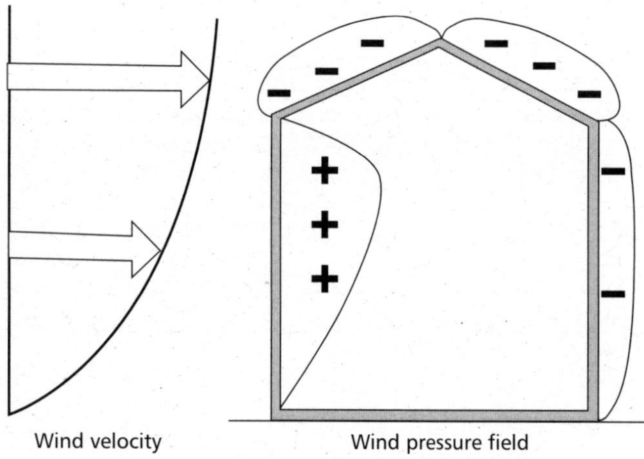

Figure 2.16 Wind driven ventilation

Air will flow through the building from areas of high surface pressure to areas of low pressure. In very general terms, building surfaces facing into the wind will experience positive pressures; leeward surfaces and those at right angles to the wind direction will experience negative pressure (suction). As wind velocity increases with height and the wind pressure increases as the square of wind speed, high rise buildings can experience very large wind pressures.

(*b*) Density differences (buoyancy)

Warm air is lighter than cold air. If two columns of air at different temperatures are separated by a dividing boundary, a difference in pressure will exist across that boundary due to the different pressure gradients on either side. In the normal situation, where the inside of the building is warmer than outside, the pressure difference acts inwards at the lower levels of the building and outwards at high level.

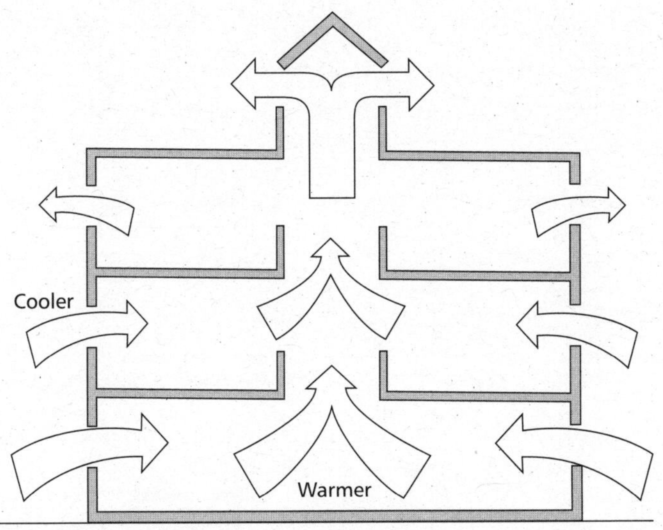

Figure 2.17 Buoyancy driven ventilation

When openings are placed in the boundary separating the two air columns, an upward airflow will be created through the building, exhausting warm air at high level and replacing it by cooler air at the lower levels, see Figure 2.17. This is known as the stack effect.

Stack effects do not occur just over the whole height of the building. Stack pressures will be exerted over any vertically spaced openings that are inter-connected. For example, in a large window opening, air will tend to flow in at the bottom and out at the top.

For more detailed information on the wind and stack driving forces, refer to section 4 of Guide A[(12)]. The basic forms of natural ventilation strategy are outlined below. The rules of thumb for estimating the effectiveness of natural ventilation given in the following paragraphs are based on section 3 of CIBSE AM10[(182)] and on BRE Digest 399[(183)]. In certain situations, (primarily if heat gains are low) the limits given in these rules of thumb may be increased. The strategies described are essentially natural, but can use mechanical ventilation to supplement the ventilation during hot, still weather.

Single-sided ventilation

Single-sided ventilation relies on opening(s) on one side only of the ventilated enclosure. It is closely approximated in many cellular buildings with opening windows on one side and closed internal doors on the other side. Single-sided ventilation can be applied in offices approaching 12 m in depth, if the windows have sufficiently large openable areas. A limiting depth of 10 m is suggested as a reasonable criterion[(184,185)].

(*a*) Single opening

For a single ventilation opening in a room, see Figure 2.15(*a*), the main driving force for natural ventilation in summer is normally wind turbulence. Relative to the other strategies, lower ventilation rates are generated and the ventilating air penetrates a smaller distance into the space. Single-sided single opening ventilation is effective to a depth of about 2 times the floor-to-ceiling height. The formulae for estimating the airflow rates due to the driving forces of wind and temperature difference are as follows:

Wind only:

$$Q_w = 0.05\, A\, V_r \qquad (2.6)$$

Temperature difference only:

$$Q_s = 0.2\, A \left(\Delta t\, h\, g \,/\, (\bar{t} + 273)\right)^{0.5} \qquad (2.7)$$

Wind and temperature:

$$Q_t = \left(Q_w^2 + Q_s^2\right)^{0.5} \qquad (2.8)$$

where Q_w is the airflow rate due to wind alone ($m^3 \cdot s^{-1}$), Q_s is the airflow rate due to temperature difference alone ($m^3 \cdot s^{-1}$), Q_t is the total airflow rate due to temperature difference and wind ($m^3 \cdot s^{-1}$), A is the area of the opening (m^2), V_r is the wind speed at building height ($m \cdot s^{-1}$), Δt is the inside–outside temperature difference (K), h is the height of the opening (m), g is the acceleration due to gravity ($m \cdot s^{-2}$) and $\bar{t}$ is the average of inside and outside temperatures (°C).

(*b*) Double opening

Where multiple ventilation openings are provided at different heights within the facade, then the ventilation rate can be enhanced due to the stack effect, see Figure 2.15(b). The ventilation rate will be further enhanced by any wind pressures that may be acting on the ventilation opening. Single-sided double opening ventilation is effective to a depth of about 2.5 times the floor-to-ceiling height.

The stack-induced flows increase with the vertical separation of the openings and with the inside to outside temperature difference. To maximise the height over which the stack pressures act, it may be necessary to separate the ventilation openings from the window itself. As well as enhancing the ventilation rate, the double opening increases the depth of penetration of the fresh air into the space. Low level inlets should be positioned to minimise the risk of ankle level draughts in cold weather. The formulae for estimating the airflow rate due to the temperature difference are as follows:

$$Q_s = C_d\, A_w \left(2\, \Delta t\, h_a\, g \,/\, (\bar{t} + 273)\right)^{0.5} \qquad (2.9)$$

$$\frac{1}{A_w^2} = \frac{1}{A_1^2} + \frac{1}{A_2^2} \qquad (2.10)$$

where Q_s is the airflow rate due to temperature difference alone ($m^3 \cdot s^{-1}$), C_d is the discharge coefficient (0.61 for large openings), A_w is the effective area of the combined openings (m^2), A_1 and A_2 are the areas of the upper and lower openings respectively (m^2), Δt is the inside–outside temperature difference (K), h_a is the vertical distance between centres of the openings (m), g is the acceleration due to gravity ($m \cdot s^{-2}$) and $\bar{t}$ is the average of inside and outside temperatures (°C).

Cross ventilation

Cross ventilation occurs where there are ventilation openings on both sides of the space concerned, see Figure 2.15(c), and is usually wind driven. As the air moves across the zone, there will be an increase in temperature and a reduction in air quality as the air picks up heat and pollutants from the occupied space. Consequently there is a limit on the depth of space that can be effectively cross-ventilated. This implies a narrow plan depth for the building, which has the added benefit of enhancing the potential for natural lighting. Cross ventilation is effective up to 5 times the floor-to-ceiling height.

The formulae for estimating the airflow rate are as follows:

Wind only:

$$Q_w = C_d \, A_w \, V_r \, \Delta C_p^{0.5} \tag{2.11}$$

where:

$$\frac{1}{A_w^2} = \frac{1}{(A_1 + A_2)^2} + \frac{1}{(A_3 + A_4)^2} \tag{2.12}$$

Temperature only:

$$Q_s = C_d \, A_b \, \left(2 \, \Delta t \, h_a \, g \,/\, (\bar{t} + 273)\right)^{0.5} \tag{2.13}$$

where:

$$\frac{1}{A_b^2} = \frac{1}{(A_1 + A_3)^2} + \frac{1}{(A_2 + A_4)^2} \tag{2.14}$$

Wind and temperature:

— for $Q_w > Q_s$:

$$Q_t = Q_w \tag{2.15}$$

— for $Q_w < Q_s$:

$$Q_t = Q_s \tag{2.16}$$

where Q_w is the airflow rate due to wind alone ($m^3 \cdot s^{-1}$), Q_s is the airflow rate due to temperature difference alone ($m^3 \cdot s^{-1}$), Q_t is the total airflow rate due to temperature difference and wind ($m^3 \cdot s^{-1}$), C_d is the discharge coefficient (0.61 for large openings), V_r is the wind speed at building height ($m \cdot s^{-1}$), ΔC_p is the difference in pressure coefficient between inlet and outlet, A_w and A_b are the effective areas of the combined openings (m^2), A_1 and A_2 are the areas of the upper and lower openings respectively on the windward side of the building (m^2), A_3 and A_4 are the areas of the upper and lower openings respectively on the leeward side of the building (m^2).

Ideally the form of the building should be such that there is a significant difference in wind pressure coefficient between the inlet and outlet openings. Consideration should also be given to the resistance to airflow. Insufficient flow may be generated, particularly in summer conditions, if openings on one side of the building are closed, or if internal partitions (particularly full height ones) restrict the flow of air across the space. In such situations, the ventilation mechanism will revert to single sided.

In order to improve air distribution into deeper spaces, it is possible to use ducted or underfloor ventilation pathways. This can provide ventilation to internal spaces or a perimeter zone local to a pollution source (e.g. a busy road). Because of the low driving pressures with natural ventilation (<10 Pa), it is important to design the supply duct for very low pressure drops.

The normal approach to cross ventilation is via opening windows, but other approaches have been used with success, particularly in hot desert countries. One example of this approach is the wind scoop.

Wind scoops, see Figure 2.15(d), capture the wind at high level and divert it into the occupied spaces to exhaust on the leeward side. The performance of a wind scoop strategy is enhanced when there is a dominant prevailing wind direction, (e.g. at a coastal site). Where wind direction varies frequently, multiple inlets would be necessary, with automatic control to close the leeward and to open the windward ventilation openings. Since wind speed increases with height, the pressure will be greatest at the top of the structure, thereby generating a positive pressure gradient through the whole building.

When designing a wind scoop, the effect of stack pressures must be considered, since these may act in opposition to the intended direction of flow.

Stack ventilation

This term is used to describe those ventilation strategies that utilise driving forces to promote an outflow from the building, thereby drawing fresh cool air in via ventilation openings at a lower level. The approach utilises the density difference between a column of warm air and surrounding cooler air. Stack ventilation can be effective across a width of 5 times the floor-to-ceiling height from air inlet to the stack inlet.

Stack pressures are a function of the temperature difference and the height between inlet and outlet. Therefore the driving force reduces at the higher stories and this needs to be counteracted by providing increased opening areas.

The height up the building where the inflow changes to an outflow is called the 'neutral pressure level'. The position of the neutral pressure level is a function of the density difference of the two air columns and the vertical distribution of the openings. Typically the neutral pressure level is designed to be located above the top floor to avoid recirculation of stale air from the lower floors back through the upper floors. The neutral pressure level can be raised by either increasing the size of the roof vent, or by reducing the size of the openings on the lower floors.

The driving forces for stack ventilation can be enhanced by designing the stack outlet to be in a wind-induced negative pressure region.

At night, as outside temperatures drop, the temperature difference driving the stack ventilation will increase. This enhances the ventilation rates that can be achieved for night cooling using stack ventilation.

If a building makes extensive use of passive cooling by thermal mass, then on the hottest days room temperatures may be below the outside temperature, potentially producing a negative buoyancy effect in the stack. This will reduce ventilation rates, a beneficial effect for thermal comfort if the outside temperature is above the room temperature.

By its nature, the ventilation strategy is essentially cross ventilation, as far as the individual occupied zones are concerned, in that air enters one side of the space and exits via the opposite side. The air may flow across the whole width of the building and exhaust via a chimney, or it may flow from the edges to the middle to be exhausted via a central chimney or atrium.

(*a*) Chimney ventilation

Chimneys provide a means of generating stack driven ventilation, see Figure 2.15(f). The essential requirement is for the air in the chimney to be warmer than the ambient air. If the chimney has a large surface area exposed to the prevailing weather, this should be well insulated.

Where chimneys provide no functional purpose other than ventilation, they may be sized just to satisfy the pressure drop requirements. Chimneys can also act as light wells, solar collectors, architectural features, locations for weather stations, and (historically) as security aids/watch towers. They can be in the form of a single linear chimney or several smaller chimneys distributed around the building. If the building faces onto a busy road, it would be possible to place the inlets on the facade away from the noise and pollution source with the chimneys on the road side.

It is possible to enhance the stack pressures by means of absorbing solar gain (the so-called 'solar chimney') introduced via glazed elements. Location of the solar chimney on the sunny side of the building in order to capture the solar radiation will generally result in cooler air being drawn in from the opposite shaded side.

Care should be taken to ensure that there is a net heat gain into the chimney during cooler weather i.e. the solar gain must be greater than the conduction loss. In cold weather, the conduction heat loss will result in low surface temperature for the glass that may be sufficient to generate down draughts inhibiting the general upward flow through the chimney. The outlet should be located in a negative wind pressure zone. The wind driving pressures can be enhanced by careful design of the roof profile and/or the chimney outlet configuration.

As a means of providing adequate ventilation on very hot and still days, consideration should be given to installing extract fans in the tower to pull air through the building. The fan should not provide a significant resistance to flow when the chimney is operating in natural draught mode.

(*b*) Atrium ventilation

An atrium is a variation on the chimney ventilation principle, see Figures 2.16(g) and 2.18. The essential difference is that the atrium serves more functions than the chimney; e.g. it provides space for circulation and social interaction. These can restrict the flexibility to locate the atrium to maximum advantage for ventilation purposes. The design of atria is discussed in detail by Saxon(193); see also section 2.3.4.

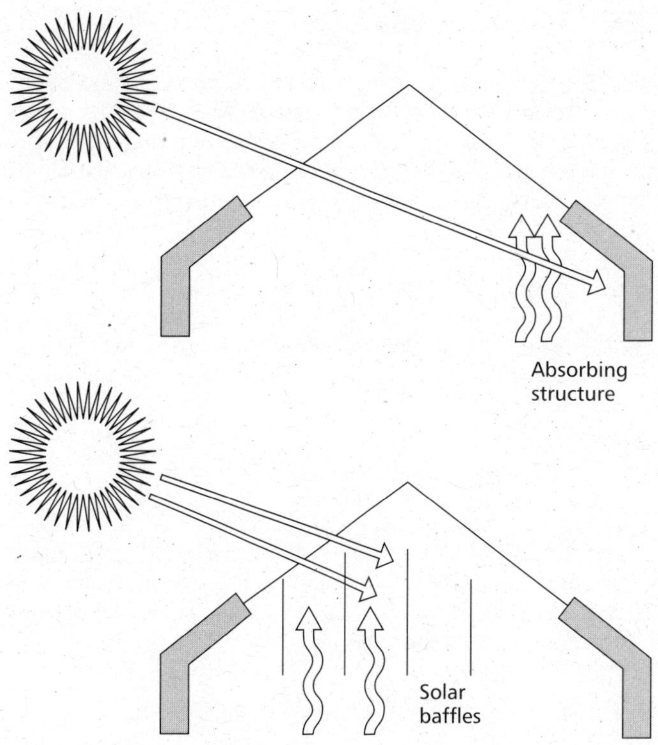

Figure 2.18 Atrium ventilation

The maximum distance from building perimeter to atrium must conform to the cross ventilation limits given earlier (i.e. 5 times the floor-to-ceiling height). With a centrally located atrium, the air can be drawn from both sides of the building, thereby doubling the plan width of the building that can be ventilated by natural means. (Note that the same effect could be achieved by a central spine of chimneys.)

The atrium also provides an opportunity for introducing daylight into the centre of a deep plan building. Because atria are designed to capture natural light, they are by definition solar assisted. To promote natural ventilation, the air temperature in the atrium should be as high as possible over as great a proportion of the atrium height as possible. If the atrium is open to the surrounding space, or if it provides high level walkways between floors, then excess temperatures at occupied levels may be unacceptable. The design should therefore seek to allow solar gain to be absorbed by surfaces such as:

— elements of the structure,

— solar baffles or blinds which act as shading devices.

As with the chimney ventilation strategy, roof vents must be carefully positioned within the form of the roof so that positive wind pressures do not act on the outlets thereby causing reverse flow. This is achieved by:

— designing the roof profile so that the opening is in a negative pressure zone for all wind angles

— using multiple vents which are automatically controlled to close on the windward side and open on the leeward side.

Natural ventilation can be supplemented on hot still days by the use of extract fans in the atrium roof. Subject to approval by the fire officer, these can also form part of the smoke control system.

(*c*) Facade ventilation

The double facade is a special form of solar chimney, where the whole facade acts as an air duct, see Figure 2.15(h). It can act as an extract plenum similar to a solar chimney. In order to provide absorbing surfaces to promote convective flow in the facade, cavity blinds are used. These also prevent direct gain passing through the facade to the occupied space.

Alternatively, the cavity could be used as a supply plenum. Outside air is introduced into the cavity at low level and the cavity acts as a solar collector, pre-heating the outside air. The warmed air is then supplied into the occupied zones via ventilation openings between the cavity and the space. If the air in the cavity is too hot, then it can be exhausted to outside or to a heat recovery device.

The efficiency of the solar collector mode can be significantly reduced if the conduction losses are too high. The possibility of condensation should also be checked based on the conditions of the air entering the cavity and the temperature of the glass.

2.4.3.3 General system issues

If external pollution levels or heat gains are high, it is unlikely that natural ventilation on its own will be able to maintain air quality and thermal comfort within acceptable limits. A prerequisite for the use of natural ventilation to provide cooling for thermal comfort is control of heat gains into the occupied space.

This section outlines general issues that should be considered when designing a natural ventilation system and the strategies available. More detailed guidance and information is contained in CIBSE AM10[182]. Section 2.4.7 provides guidance on the use of night cooling to minimise summer overheating. Details of equipment for natural ventilation are given in section 2.5.3.

It should be recognised that not all parts of a building need to be treated in exactly the same way. Different natural ventilation strategies may be applied to different parts of a building as appropriate. Natural ventilation can also be combined with mechanical ventilation (and/or air conditioning) to those parts of a building with particular environmental requirements in a 'mixed mode' system. Reference should be made to section 2.4.5 for guidance on mixed mode systems. The following sections outline general issues that should be taken into account during the selection and development of a natural ventilation strategy or strategies.

Building form and fabric

The interaction between building form and ventilation strategy is outlined in section 2.2.3. Natural ventilation relies on the building envelope (rather than any mechanical system) to provide the primary environmental control. The building form will need to facilitate the airflow strategy. Particular consideration should be given to the following:

- building spacing and orientation and their impact on building shading and wind effects
- plan width/floor-to-ceiling height ratio to achieve effective ventilation; as airflows across the zone sufficient height is required for stratification to lift heat and contaminants above the downstream occupied space
- good solar control by sensible choice of glazing ratios and by shading provision (although a balance must be achieved in allowing appropriate natural lighting levels); buildings with their main facades facing north and south are much easier to protect from excessive solar gain in summer
- openings in the external facades to provide airflow paths
- thermal capacity (exposed soffits etc.) to absorb heat gains; refer to section 2.4.7 for design details
- airtightness to minimise energy losses and cold draughts in winter and to assist the controllability of natural ventilation; refer to CIBSE TM 23[11] for airtightness targets.

Thermal comfort

Section 1 of CIBSE Guide A[12] should be referred to for detailed guidance on thermal comfort. Natural ventilation should for most of the year be able to maintain temperatures within the control bands given in section 1 of Guide A for air conditioned buildings. However, temperatures will inevitably rise during peak summer conditions. Natural ventilation is therefore suited to buildings where an increase in peak summer temperatures is permissible (see section 2.3.2.2 for temperature requirements).

To reduce any overheating, it is essential that the level of both internal and climate induced gains are minimised. Night cooling (ventilation of the building at night when ambient temperatures are lower) is often used to limit temperature rise. The air cools the fabric of the building and the stored cooling is then available the next day to offset heat gains. The thermal capacity of buildings may be increased (commonly by exposing soffits) to increase the amount of cooling that may be stored. Refer to section 2.4.7 for further guidance and design details.

Although natural ventilation cannot offer control of space humidity, the relative humidity in non-air conditioned buildings will not exceed 70% unless there is a very high level of internal moisture generation. Low internal humidity can be caused by excessive infiltration/ventilation in very cold weather.

The ability to open windows to provide increased air movement can provide a beneficial cooling effect in summer (see CIBSE Guide A[12], section 1). However, the high ventilation flow rates associated with summer conditions can cause nuisance draughts that may disturb papers etc. This can be reduced by specifying that the openable part of the window to be above desk height.

The minimisation of draughts is a particular issue for natural ventilation systems in winter. The potential problem can be reduced in a number of ways:

- provide multiple trickle ventilators (or similar)
- use specially provided ventilation openings positioned so that the air is warmed before reaching the occupied space (e.g. behind a radiator, or in a floor void with a suitable convector heater)

— use a separate mechanical ventilation system which can pre-heat the air.

Air quality

Mechanical ventilation and air conditioning systems can filter the incoming air to remove dust and dirt. Gaseous pollutants can be minimised by careful siting of ventilation inlets. However, in a naturally ventilated building, there is usually one inlet per room outlet and the inlets are more evenly distributed over the building facade (both horizontally and vertically). It is therefore more difficult to locate all the inlets away from sources of pollution.

Consideration should be given to source control measures to minimise the internal pollutant load, including elimination of sources of pollution (e.g. by choosing alternative materials) or, if this is impractical, locating the pollution source (e.g. a photocopier) near to a ventilation extract.

Where air is passed from one zone to another the flow of fresh air should be sufficient to provide acceptable air quality in the downstream zone.

The fresh air rate is normally specified in terms of a constant flow rate. Natural ventilation cannot provide a constant flow rate but the important parameter is the time-averaged flow, rather than the instantaneous, flow rate. This means that, within reason, the fresh air rate can vary and there will not be any significant variation in indoor air quality because of the reservoir provided by the volume of the space.

Refer to CIBSE TM21[28] for guidance on the nature and characteristics of pollutants in the outdoor air and their impact on indoor air quality.

Heating

In winter, any fresh air over and above that required for controlling indoor air quality represents an energy penalty. If the ventilation is to be provided by opening windows, then the windows should be capable of being well sealed when closed to minimise energy loss due to infiltration.

There is usually a significant difference in the required airflows in summer and winter and precise control of ventilation flows is difficult to achieve with an opening window. Separate ventilation openings, such as trickle ventilators, may be installed to provide the winter ventilation requirement.

The interaction between the ventilation and heating system should also be considered. If an area of the building gets too warm (e.g. due to solar gain through a window), the instinctive reaction of the occupant is likely to be to open the window rather than to turn down the heating. Measures to reduce conflict include:

— localised controls such as thermostatic regulating valves

— interlocks between the heating system and opening windows

— compensated variable temperature heating circuits.

Acoustics

External noise should not normally present a significant problem unless opening windows face onto busy main roads or are within 100 m of a railway line. A partially open window typically has a weighted sound reduction index of 10–15 dB compared to 35–40 dB for thermally insulating double glazing[186]. Measures to improve acoustic performance include:

— the use of acoustic baffles

— siting the opening windows on a quiet side of a building

— use of acoustic ventilators (as opposed to windows)

— placing buffer zones (e.g. a circulation space) adjacent to the noise source.

Discomfort can be caused by too little background noise as well as by high noise levels. Background noise levels should generally achieve a reasonable compromise between audibility and privacy. External noise can provide a beneficial masking effect for indoor acoustic privacy.

As well as thc ingress of external noise, consideration also needs to be given to internal acoustic design issues including:

— conflict between partitioning for acoustic privacy and provision of air paths

— exposed thermal mass increases the number of hard surfaces, see section 2.4.7.

Acoustics is dealt with in detail in section 5.

Flexibility

Flexibility should be provided to cope with changing occupant requirements over the life of the building. Systems can be designed to be capable of relatively simple upgrading (and downgrading) so that extra cooling systems can be added when and where required. Contingency planning is required at the design stage to provide:

— sufficient space for the subsequent installation of additional equipment

— an adequate floor-to-soffit height to enable additional servicing to be routed through floor or ceiling voids

— breakout floor zones that could form future service risers.

Control

The control strategy should consider all normal operational modes (e.g. winter, summer, night cooling) as well as emergency modes such as smoke control. It should also consider how the controls should 'fail-safe' in the event of power failure. Modulation of airflow is normally achieved by regulating the size of the ventilation openings in response to changing demand, either automatically or manually.

Typical features for automatic control may include:

— CO_2 or occupancy sensors to control ventilation rates in heating mode

- internal temperature control of ventilation in cooling mode
- night cooling if the inside or slab temperature is high (refer to section 2.4.7)
- wind speed sensors to throttle back vent openings at high wind speeds, possibly in combination with rain sensors to indicate potential driving rain problems
- wind direction sensors to open vent on leeward side
- solar gain sensors for feed forward control to increase ventilation when gains are high.

The positioning of sensors to obtain representative readings is very important. In particular, internal temperature sensors should not be too close to windows as incoming fresh air may not have mixed with the room air and the sensed condition may not therefore be representative. External temperature sensors should not be placed on sunny walls that can absorb solar radiation and elevate the sensor reading throughout the 24-hour cycle.

Automatically controlled openings could be modulated, open/shut, have intermediate fixed positions, or open in sequence where a number of vents serve a common zone. Operation should be a function of prevailing weather conditions as well as the required ventilation rate since these will influence the driving forces. Wind speed override may be required to prevent excessive ventilation under windy conditions.

Manual control is the most common form of control. It provides increased personal control over the environment in their workspace by the occupants, a factor often associated with increased occupant satisfaction. Control should be[187]:

- territorial, positioned locally and, ideally, affect a single person
- intuitive
- accessible.

Problems may arise if a single opening is required to provide ventilation for a group of occupants. This can be minimised if the window unit has high and low level openings for independent control by occupants internally and at the perimeter respectively. This may require actuators on the high level openings operated by a remote controller (that could also be used as part of an automatically controlled night cooling regime).

Intuitive manual control will not necessarily lead to windows being opened at the optimum time of day. The instinctive reaction is to open windows to increase ventilation as indoor temperatures increase later in the day, whereas higher ventilation rates may be more beneficial earlier in the day, when ambient temperatures are lower.

Refer to section 2.4.7 for night cooling control strategies. If night cooling is under manual control, windows will either be closed or left open for all the unoccupied hours resulting in either:

- inadequate pre-cooling, with overheating the following afternoon or
- overcooling, with cold discomfort problems the next day (or a need for heating).

These problems can be avoided by some form of automatic control of window opening or by provision of a separate mechanical night ventilation system.

Energy efficient naturally ventilated buildings

An energy efficient naturally ventilated building will provide the required levels of thermal comfort and acceptable indoor air quality under all seasonal conditions and will also meet acoustic requirements for the internal conditions with a minimum use of energy. For further guidance on the energy efficient application of natural ventilation refer to section 6 of CIBSE Guide F[26].

Heat recovery

With improving insulation standards, ventilation heat loss is becoming an increasingly important element of the energy balance, particularly given the trend to greater fresh air rates to improve indoor air quality. A high efficiency of heat recovery is difficult to achieve in a naturally ventilated building, except in very special circumstances such as a double façade, see Figure 2.15(h). The use of high levels of thermal capacity is a way of achieving some energy recovery, since it allows heating in winter (and cooling in summer) to be stored for use at different times of the day (refer to section 2.4.7). The efficiency of this process is lower than air-to-air heat recovery devices in mechanical ventilation systems but the parasitic energy losses can also be much lower.

Security

If a ventilation strategy relies on opening windows (especially if they are left open overnight for night ventilation), particular thought needs to be given to the security implications. Movement of ventilation openings at night and entry of birds through openings can also cause problems with movement detection security systems.

Rain

The large ventilation openings that may be needed to deliver the required airflow should be designed to avoid rain entering the building, taking account of the effects of driving wind, splashing etc. Particular thought needs to be given to ventilators left unattended during night ventilation.

Fire safety

The ventilation strategy may interact with the requirements for fire and smoke control, particularly if the building needs to be subdivided into separate compartments. Ventilation routes that penetrate a fire separation are not allowed to compromise its rating. Fire rated ductwork or fire dampers may be used to maintain the separation[143]. Any ventilation openings penetrating a separation would need to be closed in the event of a fire incident using measures including:

- fire doors held open by magnetic catches that release on a fire or smoke alarm

— fire (or fire/smoke) dampers in ducted ventilation paths or transfer grilles.

Although penetrations may be accepted on partitions along a horizontal means of escape, greater concerns would be expressed for partitions surrounding vertical means of escape such as stairwells. The requirements for atrium buildings with phased evacuation are more restrictive than buildings with single stage evacuation.

The relationship between the escape routes and the normal ventilation flow path should always be considered as part of the overall strategy. For example, in a building with a central atrium, the escape routes should be toward the perimeter, always moving people in the direction of reducing smoke concentration.

Guidance on fire smoke control issues can be found elsewhere including CIBSE Guide E[(58)], BRE Report BR 368[(70)], BS 5588[(143)] and Approved Document B[(39)].

Testing and commissioning

The commissioning (setting to work) of a natural ventilation system is relatively straightforward. However, fine-tuning of the system should be carried out for at least one year after handover. Guidance on initial set-points and fine-tuning is provided in BSRIA Technical Note TN11/95[(188)].

Commissioning of building management systems (BMS) should be in accordance with CIBSE Commissioning Code C: *Automatic controls*[(189)].

Maintenance

Provision should be made to ensure that equipment associated with natural ventilation systems is accessible for maintenance. This is a particular issue for automatic vents located at high level in atria.

2.4.3.4 Performance assessment

Analyses will normally first need to determine the airflow rates required to meet the ventilation and/or cooling requirements and then, secondly, to size the components of the natural ventilation system to provide the airflow rates. This section outlines the basic tools available for these steps and describes a number of specific tools for more detailed analysis of issues such as air movement.

Assessment of ventilation requirements

See section 2.3.2.1 for required airflow rates for ventilation purposes. Airflow rates for cooling will normally be based on a summertime temperature prediction using some form of thermal analysis. An overview of some of the assessment techniques available to determine airflow requirements is given in Appendix 2.A1. These include simple (dynamic) modelling and simulation.

Sizing components

Both explicit and implicit calculation methods are available for sizing components. Explicit equations and methods have been developed for calculation in one step. Equations relating to simple strategies and geometries have been given in section 2.4.3.2. For analysis of more complex cases, reference should be made to CIBSE AM10[(182)]. Implicit methods use an iterative process, adjusting the component sizes until the required airflows are achieved. These range from single zone models to more complex multi-zone models (see Appendix 2.A1).

All of the calculation methods require data on component airflow characteristics and the wind and stack pressures driving the ventilation. There is a vast the range of data available on flow characteristics of components[(190)]. Data provided by the manufacturers is preferred for specific flow components. If these data are not available then, for large openings, the orifice flow equation given in section 4 of CIBSE Guide A[(12)] should be used, where the area is the openable area of the device. When considering the openable area of a window, this must be the orifice area normal to the airflow, not the facade area of the window unit that is openable. For large openings there can be two-way flow when buoyancy predominates[(182)].

The wind driving pressures are proportional to the velocity pressure of the wind, which, in turn, is proportional to the square of the wind speed. The factor that relates the surface pressures to the wind velocity pressure is the pressure coefficient. Reference should be made to section 4 of CIBSE Guide A[(12)] and other sources[(190)] for pressure coefficient data.

The calculation of stack driving pressures relies on the prediction of the temperature distribution through the building. The external temperature will be defined by the weather data used as the basis of design. The internal temperature for design purposes is normally taken as the air temperature specified to pertain in each of the internal spaces at the design condition.

Detailed analysis

Computational fluid dynamics (CFD) and physical models are often used for more detailed analyses of air movement and to provide visualisations of airflow behaviour (refer to Appendix 2.A1).

2.4.4 Mechanical ventilation systems design

2.4.4.1 General

This section outlines general issues that should be taken into account during the selection and development of a mechanical ventilation strategy.

2.4.4.2 Mechanical ventilation strategies

There are several possible arrangements for the supply and extraction of air in mechanical ventilation systems[(93)]. These are described in the following sections.

Balanced supply and extract

Extract and supply systems are installed as two separately ducted networks. This offers the maximum flexibility by permitting contaminants to be removed at source and allowing for heat recovery. It is also weather independent. However, effective building sealing is required as the system is designed to be pressure neutral. Capital costs are high due to the expense of two separate ductwork systems and increased fan energy requirements. Regular cleaning and maintenance are also necessary.

Sometimes systems may be set up to be slightly unbalanced to maintain the building under a small negative pressure (e.g. for dwellings) or small positive pressure (e.g. for commercial buildings).

Mechanical supply and natural extract

Supply air is mechanically introduced into the building, displacing indoor air through purpose provided openings and/or infiltration. A proportion of the air can be recirculated. This is used in situations where positive pressure is required to prevent the inward leakage of air, e.g. clean rooms. It can be used to provide uniform ventilation, or can be set to provide individual airflow rates. The supply air can be treated as required, e.g. heated or filtered, the latter facility making it suitable for allergy control.

Noise may also be an issue. Air intakes must be carefully located to avoid drawing in external pollutants and must not be obstructed or blocked. The removal of pollutants at source is not possible.

Mechanical extract and natural supply

A fan is used to extract air from the space and create a negative pressure that draws in an equal mass of fresh air from outside. If the under-pressure is greater than that developed by the wind and temperature differences then the system is weather independent, if not it is dominated by infiltration.

Mechanical extract can be provided on a local basis, either from industrial processes or sources of moisture e.g. bathrooms. It can also be provided by a centralised system on a whole house, or non-domestic environment where a suction pressure is desirable to prevent the egress of contaminants, e.g. chemical laboratories.

Excessive under-pressure must be avoided as it may give rise to back-draughting of combustion products, the ingress of radon or other soil gases, and noise problems. The system cannot easily be adapted to provide individual control.

In terms of delivering the air to the space this can be achieved by either displacement or mixing ventilation.

(*a*) Displacement ventilation

This is based on the provision of a low-level, low-velocity air supply that is at a temperature just below that of the room. The air then rises due to buoyancy, created by heat sources within the space, to form a concentrated layer of pollutants at the ceiling from whence it is extracted. This system is considered to provide 'less polluted' air within the occupied zone and is 100% fresh air based. It is also thought to be energy efficient in that both fan power and cooling requirements are reduced. There is limited cooling capacity unless it is combined with active cooling systems such as chilled beams. Ideally, a minimum floor-to-ceiling height of 2.7 m is required. Appropriate diffusers must be selected. For further details of displacement ventilation system design refer to section 2.2.5.

(*b*) Mixing ventilation

This is based on the air being supplied into the room in a manner that creates sufficient turbulence for the contaminants within the space to be equally distributed. The extraction of air then dilutes the concentration of pollutants within the space. Mixing systems allow for recirculation, although the mixing within the space must be uniform. The system performance is not dependent upon room height or room layout. Air can enter the space either via the floor or via the ceiling.

(*c*) Floor-based supply

A floor-based supply is usually selected if raised floors are already in place for IT systems. Floor-based systems allow the ceiling mass to be exposed. They may however restrict the furniture layout unless any underfloor units or distribution grilles are designed for easy relocation. Access for maintenance is, in theory, easy.

(*d*) Ceiling-based supply

Ceiling-based systems allow greater flexibility of furniture layout and also allow heat to be more efficiently extracted from light fittings.

2.4.4.3 System considerations[93]

Air handling units

The air handling unit should be located as close as possible to the ventilated space, in order to minimise the length of the ductwork run. Guidance on the sizing of plant rooms to allow the safe maintenance of mechanical ventilation plant is available elsewhere[191].

Ductwork and system velocities[192]

Ductwork should have as large a cross-sectional area as possible to produce low velocity systems and reduce system pressure drops. Figure 2.19[181] illustrates the running and capital costs for systems having different design air velocities. These figures show how the running costs are reduced for low velocity systems, and how some components become more expensive while others become cheaper. The benefits of the energy efficient (i.e. low velocity) system include a reduction in electricity costs of approximately 70%, while the additional capital cost is recovered in less than five years.

The basis of the comparison is as follows:

— all systems supplying 2 $m^3 \cdot s^{-1}$ of air

— all systems supplied by a centrifugal fan operating at an efficiency of 70%

— pulley and motor efficiencies of 90% and 80%, respectively

— electricity cost: 5 pence per kW·h

— annual run time: 3000 hours

— noise levels less than 40 dBA.

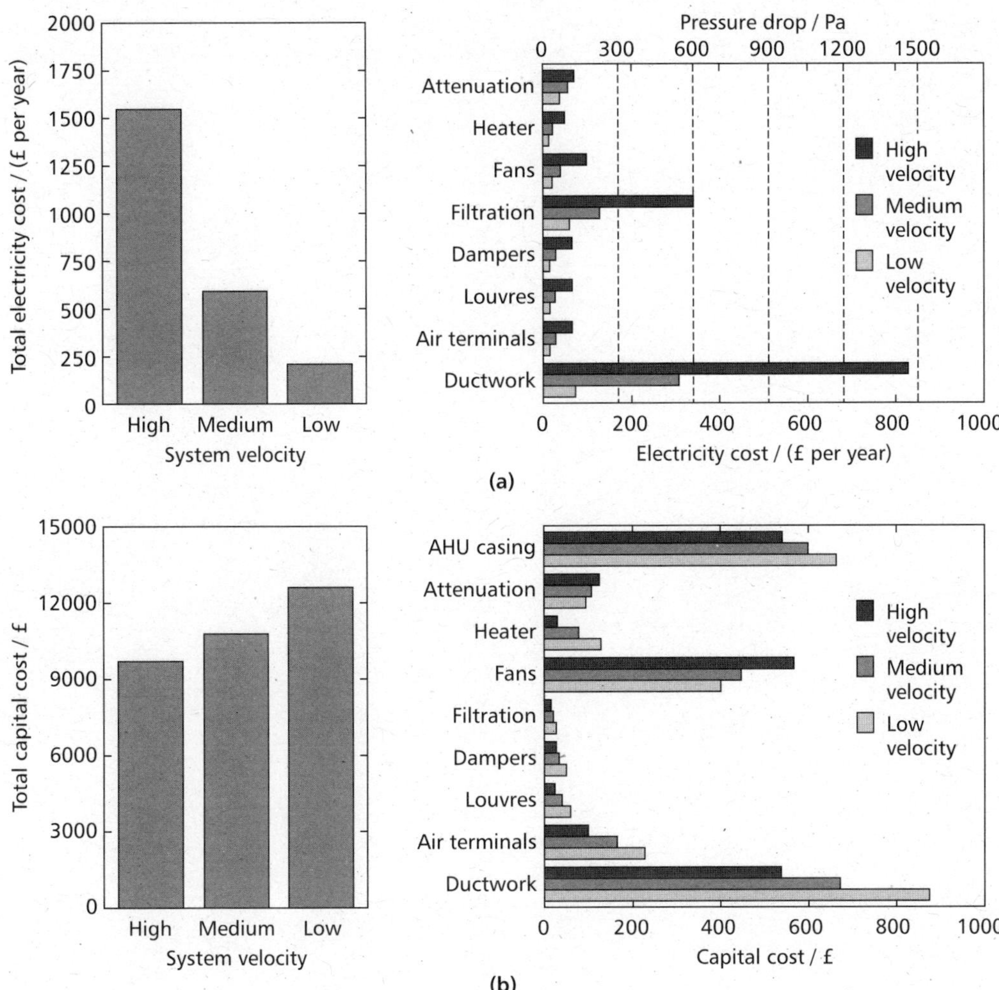

Figure 2.19 Comparison of high, medium and low velocity systems[82]; (a) electricity costs, (b) capital costs

In a low velocity system, the air handling unit face velocity would typically be less than 2 $m \cdot s^{-1}$ with the main duct velocity less than 3 $m \cdot s^{-1}$. In a medium velocity system these figures would become 2–3 $m \cdot s^{-1}$ and 5 $m \cdot s^{-1}$ respectively. In a high velocity system the air handling unit velocity would typically be greater than 3 $m \cdot s^{-1}$ with the main duct velocity at 8 $m \cdot s^{-1}$.

Air leakage from ductwork should be minimised to prevent the wastage of fan power. Ductwork should be insulated accordingly and runs through unoccupied spaces should be minimised. Testing of ductwork air tightness should be undertaken[193].

Good duct design should achieve airflow that is as laminar as possible throughout the ductwork run to reduce the pressure drop. To achieve this:

— changes to the direction of the flow should be minimised

— where possible 2–3 diameters of ductwork should be allowed either side of components before changing direction

— radius bends should be used in preference to right-angled bends

— Y-junctions should be used in preference to T-junctions

— turning vanes should be used wherever appropriate

— for rectangular ductwork, the aspect ratio should be as close to unity as possible.

Ductwork noise is considered in detail in section 5.

Noise

Noise should be prevented from getting through to the occupied spaces. Design features in support of this objective, which largely correspond to those required for energy efficiency, include the following:

— a low air velocity in the ductwork

— the use of round ducts

— the use of bends with large internal radii

— smooth transitions and changes in flow direction

— the use of low-noise control vanes

— low air leakage.

Ductwork hygiene and filtration

In order to maintain ductwork hygiene, both the supply and recirculated air streams should be clean[194]. Access must be available for cleaning to minimise the build up of microbial growth on ductwork, fan blades or coils[46]. The latter can result in loss of performance. There is also a need for regular inspections. To minimise pressure drops caused by filtration, the airflow entering a filter should be laminar, requiring the filter surface to be as large as possible. A manometer should be installed across each filter bank to ascertain when filters need changing and access doors should be provided for ease of filter replacement.

Heat recovery

Heat recovery within mechanical ventilation systems becomes economic when the value of the recovered heat or cooling outweighs the increase in fan capital and running costs, as well as those of the heat recovery equipment. The viability of heat recovery increases:

— as the number of air changes per hour increases and the heating/cooling season lengthens

— as the temperature difference between supply and extract air streams increases

— with increased proximity of the supply and extract air streams, although it can still be considered when they are not adjacent through the use of a run-around coil.

Heat recovery can increase the overall pressure drop and subsequent fan power used by 50%, although options such as double accumulators offer high heat recovery efficiencies and lower pressure drops. See section 2.5.6 for guidance on heat recovery equipment

When heat recovery devices are used in full fresh air systems, parasitic losses should be avoided in summertime operation by the use of a by-pass. Effective damper control for minimum fresh air and free cooling on recirculation systems should be provided through enthalpy control, see section 2.4.3.2

Fire protection

Ductwork must not contribute to the spread of fire, smoke or gases. Therefore in passing through a fire partition the ductwork must not decrease the fire protection properties of the structure. See CIBSE Guide E[(58)] for guidance on fire protection.

Energy efficient control of mechanical ventilation systems

Increased system efficiency, i.e. reduced specific fan power, can be achieved by the following measures:

— Select efficient fans (see section 2.5.11).

— Select appropriate attenuation, filtration and heat recovery devices to reduce system pressure drops.

— Choose appropriate ductwork and system velocities to reduce system pressure drops.

— Vary the volume of air through the system, e.g. through the use of two-speed or variable speed fans. This can be achieved through variable speed drives or inlet guide vanes. (The latter technique is not recommended due to its relative inefficiency.) Further information on variable speed fans is available in EEBPP General Information Report GIR 41[(195)].

— Ensure local extraction by the appropriate location of plant in order to minimise duct runs, and hence fan power.

— Use intelligent zoning to avoid the system operating to suit the needs of one small area.

— Switch off systems when they are not in use or not required. Systems may run for longer than intended for a various reasons, e.g. controls may have been overridden and not reset afterwards; automatic controls (e.g. frost thermostats or hidden hardware or software interlocks) may have switched on systems unnecessarily as a consequence of poor setting, calibration or programming. Suitable fault detection should be incorporated, e.g. by reporting the running hours of devices and systems during periods when they are programmed to be off.

— Appropriate coverage of a building by mechanical ventilation, i.e. using natural systems where applicable (mixed mode approach), see section 2.4.5.

— Control fan operation according to occupancy in both variable or constant volume systems.

— Log hours of operation of systems to identify if systems are operating unintentionally, particularly outside the occupied period. Anticipatory systems (e.g. for optimum start or night cooling) are prone to such behaviour.

— Take care to avoid parasitic loads that may increase energy consumption. Examples include heat recovery systems which break down unnoticed (or continue to operate when cooling is required); 'free cooling' control systems which introduce the wrong proportions of outside air; and unnecessary heating of air intended for night cooling. Ideally the performance of such systems should be automatically monitored against the design intentions. Alternatively, systems can be designed deliberately to allow such technical problems to become noticed.

The supply of air to a space can be controlled by a number of manual or automatic means. The general principles of these were considered in section 2.4.3.3 under *Control*. The most popular options are:

— *CO_2 sensing*: useful in buildings where there are wide variations in the ventilation requirement, e.g. bingo halls, cinemas, theatres and meeting rooms.

— *Temperature sensing*: useful where it may be advantageous to increase the flow of air when conditions are favourable to take advantage of free cooling

— *Humidity sensing*: fresh air rates can be increased when internal humidity levels are too high, an option used for example in areas where moisture is produced, e.g. kitchens and bathrooms

— *Occupancy sensing*: this enables systems to be switched off when rooms are not occupied.

2.4.4.4 Performance assessment

Mechanical ventilation and air conditioning systems are controlled services for the purposes of the Building Regulations for England and Wales and the provisions of Part L apply. Within these provisions it is possible to make an assessment of specific fan power (SFP) defined by the Approved Document[(1)] as:

the sum of the design total circuit watts including all losses through switchgear and controls such as inverters, of all fans that supply air and exhaust it back to outdoors (i.e. the sum of supply and extract fans) divided by the design ventilation rate through the building

Minimum standards are given within the Building Regulations of a maximum limit of 2.0 W per litre·s^{-1} in new buildings and 3.0 W per litre·s^{-1} for a new system in a refurbished building or where an existing system is being substantially altered. ECG 19[20] currently suggests a single good practice figure of 2 W per litre·s^{-1} based on its benchmark data set. However, it has been suggested within the industry that in new premises it may be possible to attain SFPs of 1.0 W per litre·s^{-1}.

Appendix 2.A1 considers a fuller range of assessment techniques available to calculate ventilation and cooling requirements and to look in more detail at air movement.

2.4.5 Mixed mode systems design

2.4.5.1 Introduction[1,196]

Mixed mode ventilation solutions can take a variety of forms and it is essential to be clear about the chosen strategy, i.e:

- contingency
- complementary (either operated concurrently or in a changeover manner)
- zoned.

These strategies are outlined below.

2.4.5.2 Strategy

Contingency designs

Contingency designs are usually naturally ventilated buildings that have been designed to permit the selective addition of mechanical ventilation and cooling systems where these may be needed at a later date. Occasionally the passive measures may themselves be the contingency plan, with an initially fully air conditioned building designed to be amenable to subsequent naturally ventilated operation, either in part or in whole. Some 1970s offices have been refurbished in this way. Guidance on refurbishment for natural ventilation has been published by BSRIA[197].

Complementary designs

Natural and mechanical systems are both present and are designed for integrated operation. This is the most common variety of mixed mode system. Complementary designs can operate in two modes:

- *Concurrent operation*: the most widely used mode, in which background mechanical ventilation, with or without cooling, operates in parallel with natural systems. Often the mechanical system suffices, controlling draughts and air quality and removing heat, but occupants can open the windows if they so choose.
- *Changeover operation*: natural and mechanical systems are available and used as alternatives according to need, but they do not necessarily operate at the same time. Changeover may be on the basis of a variety of conditions as suggested below under *Control*.

The chosen control strategy must guard against the risk that changeover systems may default to concurrent operation. Problems of this kind tend to increase with the complexity of the proposed operating strategies.

Zoned designs

Zoned designs allow for differing servicing strategies to be implemented in different parts of the building. Many buildings operate in this manner, e.g. a naturally ventilated office with an air conditioned computer room and a mechanically ventilated restaurant and kitchen. Mixed-mode increases the range of options available, e.g. offices with openable windows at the perimeter and mechanical ventilation in core areas. The zoned approach works best where the areas are functionally different, or where the systems are seamlessly blended.

2.4.5.3 General system issues

This section outlines general issues that should be taken into account during the selection and development of a mixed mode strategy. The range of circumstances encompassed by the term 'mixed mode' system is extremely broad. It encompasses, for example, a building that is almost entirely naturally ventilated except for areas of high heat or moisture production served by mechanical systems, to one that is entirely served by air conditioning with the intention that this might in the future be converted to natural ventilation. Hence the guidance provided here must be considered in the light of the specific strategy, or its derivative, as determined in section 2.4.5.2. Furthermore, this section cannot be treated in isolation but read in conjunction with sections 2.4.3, 2.4.4 and 2.4.6, which consider the principles of the individual operating modes.

Building fabric

Mixed-mode is a term describing servicing systems that combine natural ventilation with any combination of mechanical ventilation, cooling or humidification in a strategic manner. In common with buildings that are solely naturally ventilated, this approach requires that suitable benefit be obtained from the building fabric.

The presence of mechanical systems means that a suitable balance needs to be drawn, using value engineering principles, between investment in the relatively long lived fabric and expenditure on the shorter lived (and easier to modify/replace) building services, components of which can subsequently be added when and where necessary.

Although the building services in a mixed mode system should usually cost less than in a fully mechanically serviced building, some additional investment may be needed to improve their efficiency, responsiveness, control and adaptability. The initial cost of the mechanical services and the openable windows combined can be greater than that for a sealed building.

Obviously, the greatest economies are made if the improvements to the fabric allow the building services system to be completely eliminated from part or all of the building. For example, reducing fabric and internal heat gains may allow mechanical cooling to be avoided. A highly insulated and airtight fabric with low-powered mechanical ventilation (and heat recovery) may allow both mechanical refrigeration and perimeter heating to be avoided. The effective use of external night-time temperature differentials can permit any excess heat built-up during the day to be removed at night, using natural and/or mechanical ventilation, thereby reducing or eliminating the need for mechanical cooling during the daytime.

In the particular case of zoned systems, a consideration may be to introduce 'localised' fabric enhancements to reduce heat gain, e.g. additional treatment of the roof fabric to ameliorate solar heat gains or additional solar shading of selected windows. A further option might be to introduce 'assisted passive' measures before employing full mechanical systems. This might take the form of a fan in selected natural ventilation 'stacks' for use under peak conditions or on days when inadequate external forces are available, or possibly simple desk fans.

Combining natural and mechanical systems effectively

Within complementary systems the balance between the operation of the natural and mechanical system elements needs to be optimised. This requires a 'trade-off' between the extent of passive and active features, e.g. the number and location of the openable windows will depend upon the extent of mechanical ventilation. The processes by which this balance can be achieved are given in CIBSE AM13[196].

In the case of zoned systems it requires an understanding of the problem areas that will require mechanical assistance. These might include:

— zones facing inferior environmental conditions, such as top floors, corner rooms, internal areas, areas local to non-openable façades, or areas where partitioning inhibits bulk air movements

— toilet areas

— areas where heat or odour producing equipment is located such as areas containing photocopiers or drinks machines, tea rooms, or cleaners' cupboards

— restaurants or kitchens

— areas with dense occupation or high equipment heat loads which may require comfort cooling or close control air conditioning such as meeting rooms, electronic data processing rooms, dealer rooms etc.

— atria.

Flexibility

Flexibility is of particular concern with contingency systems where future change is taken into account. This requires the provision of a building fabric with a stated indoor environment control performance and a defined strategy for subsequent adaptation through the addition and omission of either centralised or localised supplementary mechanical systems. The extent to which systems are initially installed, or allowance made for them, will depend upon the context but the decision must be taken in the light of the ease and speed of subsequent installation and the likely extent of upgrades, sub-tenancies, or critical areas.

(*a*) Plant rooms

It may be possible to include space for plant rooms that can be put to alternate use until it is required for ventilation or cooling purposes, e.g. as storage or car parking. External flat roof and undercroft locations may also be suitable. Plant room locations should preferably allow mechanical plant containers to be installed. A further option is prefabricated plant rooms that can be obtained on hire and 'plugged-in' with minimum site disruption. These can subsequently be disconnected for reuse elsewhere when a tenancy terminates.

(*b*) Distribution routes

The availability of space for routing services to and around individual rooms often determines the overall level of flexibility. The recommended heights of exposed ceiling soffit slabs to facilitate natural ventilation can often provide adequate space for a future suspended ceiling void or bulkhead, capable of accommodating a wide range of HVAC systems. A suspended floor may also allow direct expansion, chilled water and condensate pipes to be routed to any potential 'hot-spot'. With appropriate initial sizing the floor void also has the potential to become a floor supply plenum, from which rooms or larger areas can be supplied with air.

It is important to ensure continuity of the routes between the various parts of the system. A clear route without constrictions is needed from the spaces designated for main plant, via the risers, to the tertiary run-outs. Care should be taken to avoid inadequate space for connection between risers and the floors they are to serve.

(*c*) Water-based systems

Water-based distribution systems might need to include strategically located provisions for future connections, complete with isolating valves or proprietary, self-sealing couplings. Where appropriate, these basic systems need to be tested at initial completion to confirm their integrity.

Choice of HVAC system

The choice of HVAC system will depend upon the clients' functional requirements, see section 2.2.5. In the case of zoned or contingency systems the choice between free-standing or centralised systems is dependent upon:

— the size and distribution of the zones to be treated

— planning restrictions on the use of the façade

— the availability of space for logical horizontal and vertical distribution routes.

Energy efficient operation of mixed mode systems

The principles for achieving energy efficient operation in mixed mode systems are a combination of those applied to buildings operating in either natural or mechanical ventilation modes, see pages 2-65, 2-68 and 2-73. Prioritisation of these principles depends upon the extent to which mechanical systems for ventilation, cooling or humidification have been installed.

Additionally, consideration needs to be given to the following:

- Mechanical systems should be used only when and where required. The specific fan power increases with air change rate. Furthermore, as the air change rate increases, the occupants are more likely to notice the difference between when the system is operating and when it is not. This may reinforce the tendency for it to be left running unnecessarily. The use of zoned mixed mode systems helps to overcome the need for whole systems having to operate in order to service small demands.
- Natural and mechanical systems should not conflict in their operation. For example, mechanical systems competing with air coming in through the windows, or simultaneous humidification and dehumidification. Such situations can be reduced through making users aware of the rationale behind the operation of the system and having suitable trigger points for changeover operation. The state and performance of the system should be monitored and system conflicts reported.
- Systems should not default to a non-optimal state, e.g. switched on when they could be switched off or, at least, operating at reduced output. This risk can be minimised by avoiding over-complex design.

Control

The control strategy for mixed mode systems is context dependent, but aims overall for energy efficient operation, maximum staff satisfaction and ease of building management. This is achieved through:

- maximisation of the natural operating mode
- integration of natural and mechanical systems to avoid system conflicts, wasteful operation, and discomfort
- simple and effective control for occupants that is non-presumptive
- simple and effective controls for the building management that are easy to commission and operate on occupation of the building.

The general principles of a good control strategy are given in section 2.4.3.3 under *Control*. In the case of a mixed mode system it is also important to remember that the control characteristics of windows differ from the 'designed' characteristic of HVAC dampers and coils. The control authority of a window is low and non-linear or proportional, hence the use of sophisticated control algorithms will not bring greater accuracy. Given the pulsing effect of the wind or natural ventilation, continuously correcting automatic controls should be avoided and the controls response slowed.

The reactions of the occupants to the control systems must also be allowed for in terms of:

- the provision of intuitive user interfaces and control strategies
- adverse reactions to systems which appear to operate in a capricious manner noticeable by changing noise levels or creating a draught
- giving occupants the ability to manually override automatic controls and the impact on system performance
- providing a rapid response to a requested control action.

Elements of the following control sub-strategies may be included:

- *Normal working day control*: where mechanical cooling is switched on when a pre-determined temperature is exceeded.
- *Seasonal control*: where for example the building is sealed in peak winter and summer conditions under mechanical operation, but runs freely during spring and autumn.
- *Top-up/peak lopping control*: where mechanical cooling is switched on only at times of peak load.
- *Pre/post-occupancy space conditioning*: where selected areas prone to overheating may be cooled outside of working hours to ensure that the space temperature is the minimum acceptable at the start of the working day.
- *Overnight cooling*: where the building thermal mass is utilised either through natural or mechanical means, see section 2.4.7.
- *Moisture control*: where exposed direct cooling such as chilled ceilings or chilled beams are used.
- *Ventilation control*: where carbon dioxide (CO_2) sensors are used as a surrogate indicator of occupancy levels to switch on mechanical ventilation when the level exceeds a pre-set value and occupants have not elected to open windows.

Post-handover

Training of occupants in the use of the building control facilities is very beneficial in terms of ensuring energy efficient operation and user satisfaction. This may be achieved through the provision of written statements and demonstrations as part of the handover procedures.

Occupiers and designers should meet regularly for at least one year after initial occupation to review the performance of the building and to identify any alterations and improvements necessary.

2.4.5.4 Performance assessment

Some aspects of mixed mode design may be difficult to resolve or to optimise using normal calculation methods and rules-of-thumb. More detailed simulation may be desirable:

- in appraising options
- in developing new concepts and testing their robustness under all foreseeable conditions
- in demonstrating the capabilities of an option to clients
- in refining a chosen approach.

Appendix 2.A1 considers the techniques of dynamic thermal simulation and air movement analysis. In applying them specifically to mixed mode systems the designer must consider the following:

— the full variety of potential (often overlapping) operational modes and control variables

— the trigger points for each control strategy element

— the potential actions of occupants

— uncertainty concerning the actual operation of the building compared to the intent and the consequent robustness of the solution

— possible differences between parts of the building and areas of particularly demanding localised conditions, which place particular demands on the ventilation system

— possible adverse interactions between adjacent zones in different operating modes

— possible adverse effects of facilities designed for one mode and operating in another, e.g. facilities designed for summertime ventilation and cooling may not work well in cold weather, possibly leading to draughts or excessive heat losses.

The selection of appropriate weather data and treatment of heavyweight buildings within thermal models is discussed in Appendix 2.A1.

2.4.6 Comfort cooling and air conditioning

2.4.6.1 Introduction

There is a wide range of comfort cooling and air conditioning plant available. Guidance on the key potential advantages and disadvantages of specific systems is provided in sections 2.4.8 to 2.4.22.

2.4.6.2 Strategy

General guidance on the relative merits of the most common systems is available from EEBPP Good Practice Guide GPG 71[198] and on more innovative systems from an IEA Annex 28 publication[199]. CIBSE Guide F[26] adopts the classification system for HVAC systems given in GPG 71[198], see Figure 2.20, and discusses issues relating to the energy efficient design of system families.

Centralised all-air systems

These consist of (*a*) constant volume (single or multi-zone), (*b*) dual duct, or (*c*) variable air volume systems. Central plant and duct distribution are employed to treat and move all of the air supplied to the conditioned space. In constant volume systems the heating and cooling loads of the building are met by changing the temperature of the supply air. In dual duct systems the heated and cooled air are circulated separately and the two air streams are combined to produce an intermediate comfort temperature. In a variable air volume system, it is the airflow that is altered to meet the requirements of the space.

Partially centralised air/water systems

These usually employ central plant to provide fresh air only. Terminals are used to mix recirculated air with primary air and to provide fine-tuning of room temperature. Examples include VAV with terminal reheat, fan coils, unitary heat pumps and induction units. Both heating and cooling pumped water circuits are normally needed to satisfy varying requirements. Three-pipe systems with a common return are to be avoided as cooling and heating energy are wasted when the return air is mixed.

Tempered fresh air systems limit the humidification and de-humidification capacity. However, this is normally adequate for most applications and discourages attempts at unnecessarily close control of humidity, which is very

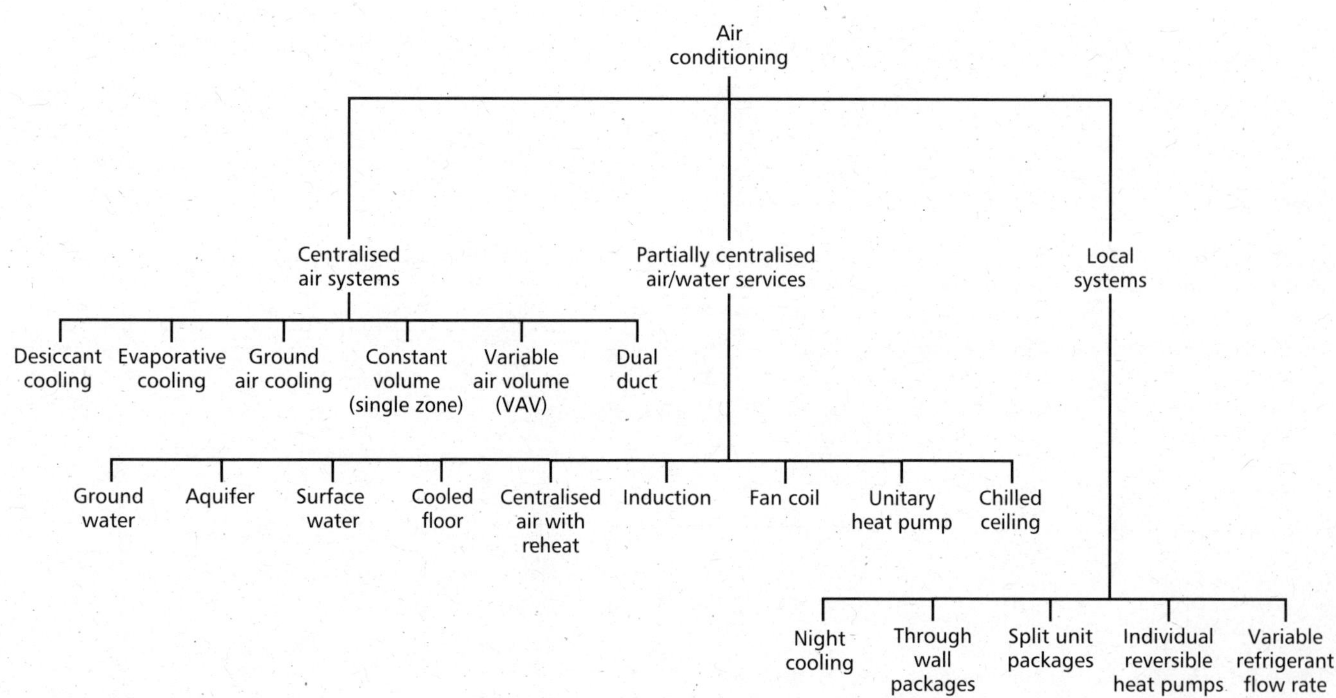

Figure 2.20 Classification of HVAC systems

wasteful of energy. The air handling unit should be sized for minimum fresh air duty only to reduce energy consumption and heat recovery should be considered. Heat recovery from the chiller units can be employed to serve the terminal reheaters. All partially centralised systems should have local inter-connected controls to produce a demand-based response at the main plant.

Savings achievable due to reduced airflows must be balanced against the restricted free cooling from fresh air, the additional energy used due to higher pressures and local fan energy, and the energy required for heating and chilled water distribution pumps.

Local air conditioning systems

These include 'through the wall' units, split systems, variable refrigerant flow units and individual reversible heat pumps. Local systems can provide filtration, comfort cooling and heating, but not humidification. They are often used as a refurbishment option. Local units may have lower coefficients of performance than centralised plant but can provide energy savings through reduced distribution losses, simpler heat rejection equipment, greater control over operating periods, and their ability to be more readily confined to the areas of greatest need.

2.4.6.3 General system considerations

This section outlines general issues that should be taken into account in the selection and development of a comfort cooling or air conditioning strategy. It should be read in conjunction with section 2.4.4 on mechanical ventilation and section 2.4.5 on mixed mode systems. Design guidance for individual HVAC systems is given in sections 2.4.8 to 2.4.22.

Energy efficient operation of comfort cooling or air conditioning systems[26]

The energy efficient design of comfort cooling and air conditioning systems starts by considering the issues raised under *Energy efficient control* in section 2.4.4.3 and *Energy efficient operation* in section 2.4.5.3. Emphasis is then placed on the cooling and humidification processes, e.g:

- Ensure plant is not oversized, see BSRIA Guidance Note GN11/97[200].
- Consider switching off humidifiers when humidity control is not critical. Allow the humidity to drift between 40 and 65%, if possible.
- Electric steam humidification can have severe implications for electricity consumption, CO_2 emissions and electricity costs. The peak use of humidifiers tends to coincide with the coolest weather when electricity is also at its most expensive. Gas-fired humidifiers should be considered as an alternative.
- Avoid simultaneous heating and cooling unless providing close control of humidification.
- Check control settings to ensure that set points are suitably high in summer and low in winter.
- Ensure that cooling is shut down in winter when it is not required.
- Turn off reheat systems in all areas during the summer unless close control of humidity is being provided.
- Ensure maximum use if made of recirculated air and fresh air for free cooling as appropriate, see *'Free cooling'* below and section 2.5.6.

These issues are considered in more detail below.

System control

Figure 2.21 summarises the various control options for comfort cooling or air conditioning systems in single zone applications. Control options for full fresh air systems are similar to those for recirculation systems but must include provision for frost protection upstream of the filters. The following notes discuss some aspects of control peculiar to air conditioning and mechanical ventilation systems.

(*a*) 'Free cooling'

Before considering a system that depends upon mechanical cooling, every opportunity should be taken to use 'free cooling', of which fresh air is the most obvious source. Cooling systems with low level input and high level extract (see section 2.4.2) may use higher supply temperatures for summer cooling and can occasionally take away the need for mechanical refrigeration by a combination of the following:

- drawing outside air from a north facing aspect
- drawing outside air from a point clear of the 'heat island' at ground level
- drawing outside air through a buried earth-cooled duct
- supplying the cooling coil with indirectly or evaporatively cooled water from a suitable source.

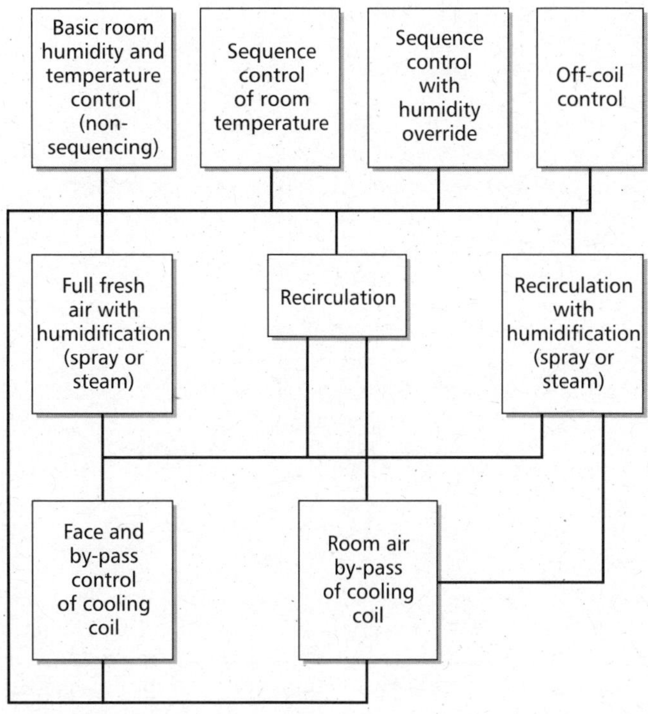

Figure 2.21 System control

In the latter case, the potential hazards of microbiological contamination must be considered.

If mechanical refrigeration is not provided, humidity control will be difficult to achieve since little dehumidification is available from the above, largely passive, sources of cooling. However, with low level input, moisture from the occupants will not mix thoroughly but will be carried to a high level with the upward momentum of the air.

If heat gains are moderate, it may be possible to use all-air systems without cooling to limit the rise in internal summertime temperatures, in which case larger air change rates would be required than for air conditioning. Again, it may be possible to limit the rise in inside temperature by drawing air into the central plant at a lower temperature than the outside dry-bulb temperature.

In most recirculation applications it will be worthwhile incorporating motorised dampers (sequenced with the coils) so that outside air, when available at an appropriate condition, may be used to achieve the desired room conditions with minimal load on the central plant. It may also be worth incorporating a means of holding the mixing dampers on full fresh air, cycling to minimum fresh air when outside air enthalpy (h_o) is greater than room enthalpy[201] (h_r), see Appendix 2.A2, Table 2.55.

'Free cooling' is also available via cooling towers providing cooling water without the need to operate the chillers. Guidance on control strategies can be found in BSRIA publication RR16/96[202].

(*b*) Frost protection

Frost protection is required upstream of the filters in both full fresh air and recirculation systems. Systems may suffer during damper sequencing from a room sensor with inherent time lags under high gain conditions in winter. Stratification through the mixing box may also be a problem (see section 2.5.5). In these cases, electric or water-fed serpentined coils should be provided, switched at 4–5 °C from a downstream thermostat.

(*c*) Simultaneous heating and cooling

Simultaneous heating and cooling can be avoided by bypassing the cooling coil with either outside, mixed, or room air. This relies on accurate damper positioning for control over room conditions and may produce elevated room humidity.

Other controls, not indicated on the system schematics in sections 2.4.8 to 2.4.22, may be required to deal with early morning boost, heat recovery and variable occupancies[202]. It should be borne in mind that the more complex the control scheme, the greater the capital cost and the greater the chances of control malfunction. In particular, humidity sensing is prone to inaccuracy and drift.

(*d*) Humidity control

An air conditioning system need not provide continuous humidification of the supply air since there will be many occasions when this facility is unnecessary in meeting the comfort needs of the occupants, see section 1 of CIBSE Guide A[12] and section 6 of CIBSE Guide F[26]. Guide A suggests that at design temperatures normally appropriate to sedentary occupancy, the room humidity should, if possible, be above 40%. Lower humidity is often acceptable for short periods. Humidity of 35% or below may be acceptable but precautions must be taken to limit the generation of dust and airborne irritants. An upper limit for humidity of 60% is proposed to minimise the risk of mould growth or condensation in areas where moisture is being generated. This can be extended to 70% in terms of maintaining comfortable conditions.

For comfort air conditioning it is usually satisfactory to supply air with sufficiently low moisture content to cater for maximum latent gain, and limit the room percentage saturation by overriding either the humidity sensor or the temperature sensor in the air leaving the cooling coil, as appropriate. Close control air conditioning is difficult to achieve with multiple zone systems, since each zone requires a dehumidifying cooling coil, reheater and humidifier to give total control of humidity.

Humidity sensors can be used to limit humidity rise by:

— controlling the output of a cooling coil by proportional control (with integral action if required)

— overriding the action of a temperature sensor controlling some combination of heating coil, cooling coil, mixing dampers and/or extract air heat recovery device

— overriding control over the reheater so that the sequencing room temperature sensor calls for further cooling and hence dryer air is supplied

— overriding control over the reheater in a variable air volume zonal reheat terminal or the mixing dampers in a dual duct terminal so that the zonal temperature sensor calls for a larger volume of dry air to be supplied to that zone

— resetting the set point of an off-coil sensor.

In the last case, the supply air moisture content is controlled by the dry-bulb temperature sensor. This gives accurate humidity control providing that the cooling coil is efficient and the variation in room humidity is predictable. A humidity sensor can be incorporated to override the cooling coil operation if the occupancy increases above the usual level. Also, simultaneous cooling/dehumidification and reheating will occur for much of the cooling season. With a system serving externally influenced spaces, the off-coil sensor set point may be reset when the moisture content of the incoming air falls below that required to deal with latent gains. Dew-point control is dealt with CIBSE Guide H[201].

If control of high humidity is not required, the limits of the proportional band of a sequence controller can be the winter and summer design room conditions. Otherwise, different conditions for summer and winter can only be achieved by using integral action to remove any offset and by resetting the set point of the room temperature sensor in response to an outside temperature sensor. Sequential control will normally require a wide proportional band, particularly if mixing dampers are included.

Humidity sensors can be used to control low humidity by:

— providing step or on/off control of a steam humidifier (see section 2.4.19, Figure 2.55)

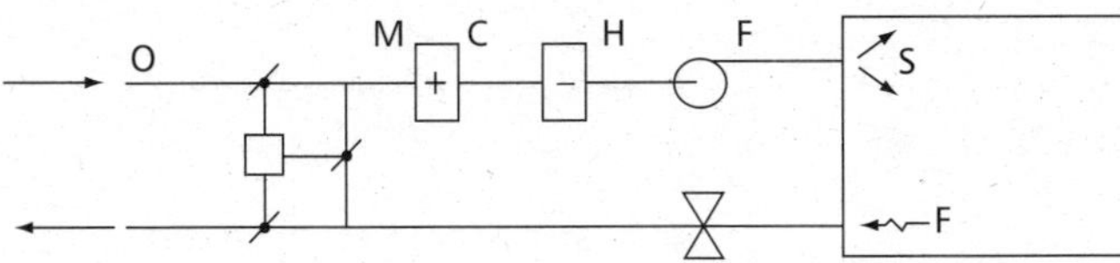

(a) "Draw-through" arrangement

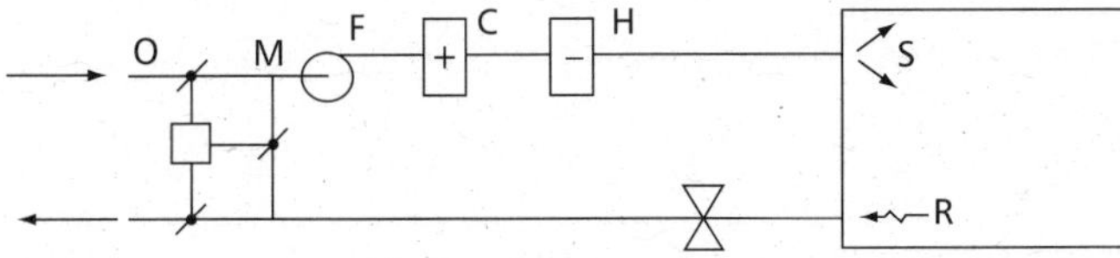

(b) "Blow-through" arrangement

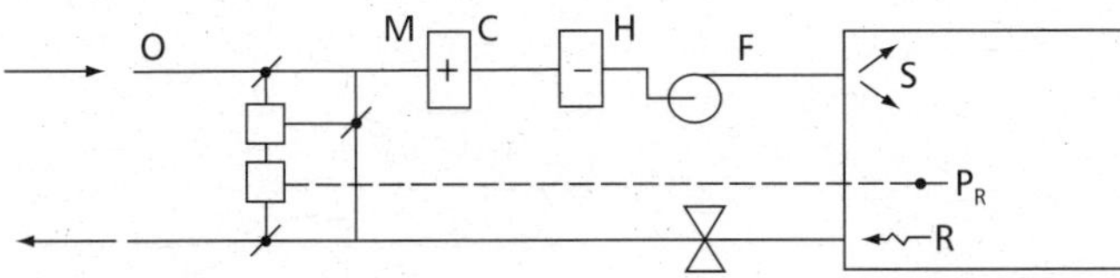

(c) Combined supply/extract fan

Figure 2.22 Supply air handling plant; alternative arrangements for position of fans

— providing proportional control of a pre-heater and/or mixing dampers to provide appropriate on conditions to a water spray-coil humidifier with the spray pump running continuously (see Figure 2.58, page 2-101)

— switching on a spray washer pump or spinning disc humidifier and providing appropriate on conditions by proportional control over the pre-heater and/or mixing dampers.

If off-coil sensors are not employed, a low limit sensor may be required to bring-in the heating coil if the supply air temperature falls below the minimum design value. This is necessary where room or return air temperature sensors are likely to be slow to respond to low supply conditions.

Fan position

The systems schematics that follow mainly indicate a 'draw-through' arrangement for the supply air handling plant, with separate extract fan, see Figure 2.22(a). Alternative arrangements include 'blow-through' and combined supply/extract fan. The former is the normal configuration for dual duct systems.

(*a*) 'Blow-through' central plant

The main advantages of positioning the fan upstream the cooling coil are that:

— a lower supply air moisture content can be achieved at a particular apparatus dew-point and chilled water temperature, see Figure 2.22(b)

— the cooling coil condensate drain will be under positive pressure, which reduces the chances of drawing airborne contaminants from the drainage system or plant room into the system.

The main disadvantages are that:

— since the cooling coil is under positive pressure there is a greater risk of condensate leakage through the casing

— an additional plenum or transition piece is required at the fan discharge to reduce the air velocity to an appropriate value at the coil face and ensure an even distribution of air over the face area.

Soiling of the fan may be reduced by locating the filter upstream of the fan, see Figure 2.22(a).

(*b*) Combined supply/extract fan

A single fan can both draw air through the extract system and blow air through the supply distribution system, providing that a balance can be achieved between extract and intake pressure losses using an appropriate combination of fixed resistance and damper in the intake.

In most cases free cooling from full fresh air will be required. Therefore, means must be provided for varying the proportion of return air to outside air at the mixing box by damper modulation. Some means of pressure relief will be required in the building or system and Figure 2.22(c) shows a relief damper controlled from a room pressure sensor, P_R. For extract systems having low resistance this damper could be replaced with simple, weighted pressure relief flaps, also see section 2.5.5.

Zoning

The loads on an air conditioning plant are rarely constant due to changes in solar gain, occupancy, or the use of lights etc. If the loads throughout the building vary together (i.e. in phase), or the variations are not large enough to drift outside of the acceptable limits, single zone control can be adopted. However, if different areas experience load changes that are out of phase, the supply air must be provided at a rate or condition appropriate to each zone.

Most deep plan buildings require division into perimeter and internal zones. The depth of perimeter zones mainly depends on the penetration of sunlight and daylight which is determined by orientation, external shading, shape and size of windows, characteristics of the glass and the type and pattern of use of blinds.

For a typical multiple zone application the following should be noted:

— For a constant volume flow rate to be maintained to each zone the system must be capable of supplying air at various temperatures at any one time. This may involve simultaneous heating and cooling of the supply air.

— All rooms with similar solar gain patterns can be zoned together provided that other variables are in phase. However, the number and position of the zonal sensors will be important. Corner rooms pose further problems.

— North facing rooms experience less variation and can be grouped with internal zones for cooling provided that heating is dealt with by other means.

— Gains through poorly insulated roofs are quite similar to gains on south facing surfaces, but if adequately insulated they may be treated as intermediate floors.

The success of an air conditioning system depends largely on wise zoning and careful positioning of sensors in relation to the sources of heat gains.

2.4.6.4 Performance assessment

Appendix 2.A1 considers the techniques of dynamic thermal simulation and air movement analysis. For England and Wales, Building Regulations Approved Document L[1] includes specific performance requirements for air conditioning systems, see section 2.4.4.4. A number of other guidance documents or techniques exist that can be used to provide target energy benchmarks, or for comparative purposes, at early stages of the design process. These include:

— CIBSE Building Energy Code 2[203]

— ASHRAE BIN method[204]

— Energy Efficiency Best Practice Programme (EEBPP) Energy Consumption Guides[205].

2.4.7 Night cooling and thermal mass

2.4.7.1 Description

Night cooling in combination with a thermally heavyweight building can be used as a means of avoiding or minimising the need for mechanical refrigeration in buildings. During the summer ambient air is circulated through the building at night, cooling the building fabric. This stored cooling is then available the next day to offset heat gains.

Interaction between the mass and the air, see Figure 2.23, can be (*a*) direct via exposed surfaces in the space or (*b*) indirect where the air is passed through floor voids, cores or air paths.

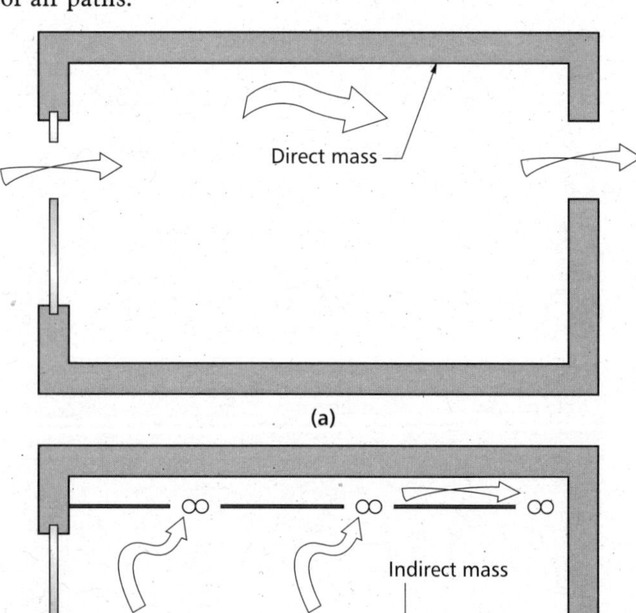

Figure 2.23 Direct and indirect heat transfer

For direct systems with exposed mass, heat transfer is both by radiation and convection. Indirect systems rely solely on convective heat transfer.

For natural ventilation, because of the low pressure drops available to drive the airflow, interaction between the thermal mass and the air is normally direct via exposed surfaces in the space. Most solutions use exposed soffits. External walls and partitions can be used to add thermal mass. Carpeting and/or a false floor will normally limit floor exposure.

Where mechanical ventilation is provided, direct and/or indirect interaction may be used. Additional fan energy will be expended to introduce cooling at night. For large systems (i.e. with pressure drops greater than 1000 Pa) this may exceed the mechanical cooling and pump energy saved[206]. System pressure drops should be minimised to maximise energy efficiency.

As the cooling provided is a function of the temperature difference between the thermal mass and the space, night cooling is most suited to buildings where the temperatures are permitted to rise during peak summer conditions. In the UK, night-cooled solutions can provide up to 50–60 $W \cdot m^{-2}$.

Where mechanical cooling is provided, night cooling of the building mass can either be by introducing outside air or by using the mechanical cooling system when outside temperatures are high. Scope exists in many mechanically cooled buildings for the controlled use of the building mass as an energy store.

It can provide the following benefits:

— reduction in mechanical cooling requirements during the occupied period

— take advantage of cheaper night-time electricity tariffs

— improved comfort in low capacity systems.

However, it is often the case that there is a requirement for space temperatures to be maintained below a maximum in the summer and not be permitted to rise. This will limit the benefit of night cooling in reducing mechanical cooling requirements.

2.4.7.2 Design

Figures 2.24 and 2.25 illustrate a number of design approaches that may be used for direct and indirect solutions. Specific design issues are addressed in the following sections and include:

— thermal storage performance

— conflict with air heating/cooling

— aesthetics

— acoustics

— integration

— control strategy.

Two common problem areas for design are top floors and corner/perimeter offices. Economic or structural constraints may mean that the roof cannot be designed to

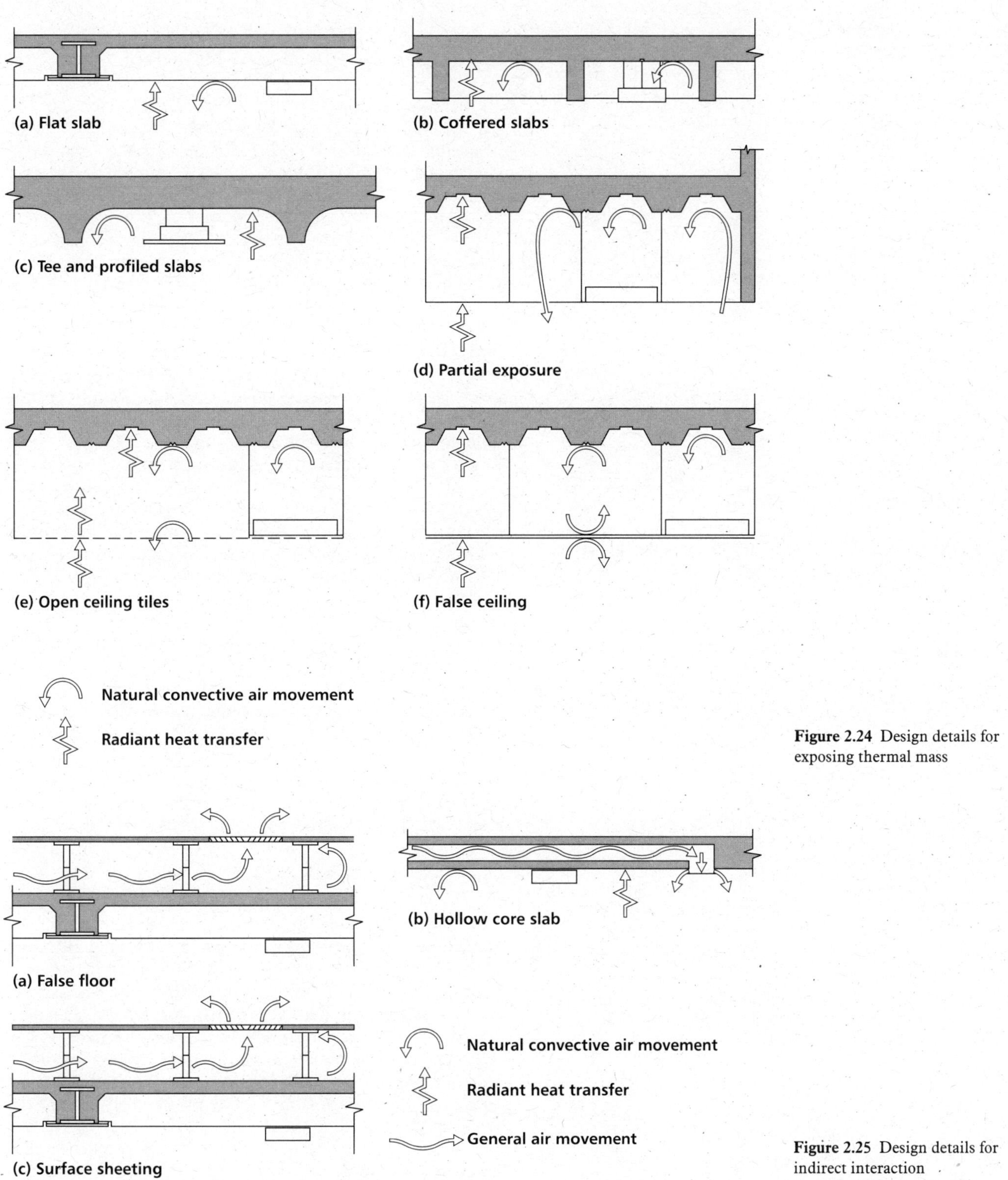

Figure 2.24 Design details for exposing thermal mass

Figure 2.25 Design details for indirect interaction

incorporate the same level of thermal mass as the other floors. In these cases it may be possible to add mass via other elements or an alternative design strategy may need to be considered. For corner/perimeter offices high heat gains and losses may mean that supplementary cooling or alternative design strategies may be required.

It should also be recognised that exposing thermal mass may lead to a significant increase in the heating demand during the winter months due to the thermal mass acting as a store for unwanted infiltration and conduction heat losses at night[(33)]. In contrast there can be a reduction in heating demand during the summer as excess heat from internal gains can be stored for later use more effectively by the heavier constructions; a form of heat recovery. For lighter constructions the excess heat will tend to be rejected to the outside rather than stored.

Thermal storage performance

The thermal storage performance of a building element is dependent on two key factors:

— the ability of the element to conduct and store the thermal energy

— rate of heat transfer between the element and the air.

For most floor construction types the ability of the concrete slab to conduct and store the thermal energy is superior to the rate of surface heat transfer. Therefore the surface heat transfer characteristics generally determine the thermal storage performance of a concrete floor slab.

(*a*) Direct systems

For direct systems with elements exposed to the occupied space (e.g. the underside of a slab), surface heat transfer is by a combination of radiation and natural convection. Basic equations for these situations are given in section 3 of CIBSE Guide C[192]. For exposed plane surfaces typical values are 5 $W \cdot m^{-2} \cdot K^{-1}$ for radiation and 2–3 $W \cdot m^{-2} \cdot K^{-1}$ for natural convection. High surface emissivity is needed to achieve good radiant heat transfer. The degree of geometric exposure of the surface of an element to the space should also be taken into account for radiant heat transfer and is normally calculated using form (or shape) factors[192,207]. The high level of radiant cooling provided by an exposed element allows the same level of thermal comfort to be achieved at a higher air temperature.

The airflow within the space for night cooling should ideally be such that the contact between the cool air and the thermal mass is encouraged. Measures such as high-level vents may enhance interaction with exposed soffits.

Improvements in surface heat transfer can be achieved by increasing the surface area by forming coffers or profiling the surface. This can significantly increase the exposed surface area and hence convective heat transfer. Radiant heat transfer benefits will normally be limited if the profiling has a similar overall exposed area to that of a plane surface when viewed from the occupied space. Partial thermal exposure of a slab surface can be achieved by using open cell or perforated ceiling tiles. This permits air to circulate between the ceiling void and space below for convective surface heat transfer. In addition, open cell ceilings with a high reflectance may permit a significant amount of radiant heat exchange between the slab above and the space below.

Solid false ceilings will prevent any direct heat exchange between the slab and the space. However, a significant amount of heat exchange may still be possible if the ceiling itself is made of a conductive rather than insulative material.

Surface finishes will insulate the slab from the space below (or above), although thin layers of relatively conductive materials such as plaster shouldn't have a significant effect.

(*b*) Indirect systems

For indirect systems with air passing through floor voids, cores or air paths the main surface heat transfer mechanism is convective heat transfer between the air and the store. If convective heat transfer is poor, as is normally the case for airflow in floor voids (typically 2–3 $W \cdot m^{-2} \cdot K^{-1}$)[206], performance will be limited.

Convective heat transfer coefficients may be increased by using mechanical means to create forced convective heat transfer rather than relying on natural buoyancy forces. High rates of forced convective heat transfer (i.e. 10–15 $W \cdot m^{-2} \cdot K^{-1}$ and upwards) can readily be affected by creating highly turbulent airflow at the surface. This can be achieved by blowing air through hollow cores in slabs or creating air paths through which air can be blown across the surface of a slab[208]. The improvement will ultimately be limited by the thermal characteristics of the concrete.

Forced convection heat transfer coefficients for cores or other air paths may be calculated by using equations given in section 3 of CIBSE Guide C[192]. (It should be noted that these equations are for smooth tubes and therefore represent a worst case, as surface roughness will act to increase turbulence and heat transfer). Values for the pressure drop for passing the air through the cores or other air paths can be calculated using equations in section 4 of CIBSE Guide C[192] (which take into account surface roughness).

Thermal admittance (Y-values) can be used to provide a simple measure of thermal performance for different construction types[12]. Thermal admittance takes account of both the surface resistance and thermal properties of the element and provides a measure of the dynamic thermal storage performance of an element. This is useful for direct comparison of alternative building element constructions.

Analysis of the performance of thermal mass storage systems should take reasonable account of parameters relating to the storage process, including heat flows in the thermal store and surface heat transfer. Modelling of heat flow in two and three dimensions may also be desirable when analysing geometrically complex building components such as coffered and profiled floor slabs (see BRE Information Paper IP6/2000[209]).

Night ventilation rates and thermal mass are linked in terms of the cooling provided and should be considered in tandem for design analysis. Increasing night ventilation rates without sufficient thermal mass to store the cooling will be of limited benefit, as will increasing the thermal mass above that required to effectively store the cooling introduced.

Conflict with air heating/cooling

For mechanical ventilation systems, there is a potential for conflict between heat exchange with the thermal mass and heating/cooling of the air. If air is heated/cooled by a central supply unit and then brought into contact with the thermal mass, heat exchange with the thermal mass may (depending on the relative temperatures) absorb this heating/cooling. Thus the thermal mass will be in conflict with the central supply unit. This could be overcome by providing a bypass to control the thermal link between the supply air and the thermal mass. The bypass could also be used to control when the thermal mass is accessed for storage and discharge. Modulation of the airflow could also be used to vary the rate of storage and discharge.

Where the supply air is cooled, another option is to bring the return air into thermal contact with the thermal mass, e.g. in the ceiling void. The cooled return air provides cooling in the space either by recirculation or by cooling the supply air via a heat recovery device. This avoids any conflict between supply air cooling and the thermal mass. Return temperatures in the ceiling void may be elevated by heat pick-up from lights increasing the cooling effect of the thermal mass.

Aesthetics

Exposed soffits should be acceptable aesthetically both in terms of general form and quality of surface finish.

Sculpted/profiled/vaulted soffit constructions have been developed to improve the appearance of exposed soffits. Fire protection requirements may also have an impact on the visual appearance. Where there is a desire to conceal parts but not all of the slab construction, a partial solution could be adopted. Open ceiling tile solutions could be considered where full concealment is desirable. Although these solutions may not achieve the same level of thermal performance they may be beneficial in terms of acoustics performance and co-ordination.

Acoustics

Exposing a concrete soffit to take advantage of its thermal mass means the absence of a suspended ceiling, and hence the loss of acoustic absorbency provided by the ceiling material. This can give rise to increased reverberation time and increased reflected sound across an open plan space. Counter measures include acoustically absorbent partitions, absorbent banners hung from the ceiling, acoustic plaster, integration of acoustic elements at high level with lighting and profiled slabs to reduce propagation. Sculpted coffers can be designed to focus sound onto acoustic absorbers located in suspended light fittings or back on its source, or below carpet level(25). The effect of acoustic plaster or other finishes on the heat transfer can be significant and should be considered.

For solutions that use partial false ceilings, it may be necessary to adopt measures to avoid flanking transmission between zones. See section 5 for detailed guidance on acoustics and surface finishes.

Integration

The absence of a suspended ceiling (and with it the ease of integration of services) can have significant design implications. Where suspended ceilings are provided modular lighting fittings can easily be integrated. More careful consideration is required where the soffit is exposed to achieve a high level of thermal mass, although it may be possible to integrate the lighting within the coffers. Other options identified in the Steel Construction Institute report *Environmental floor systems*(208) include pendant systems, floor or furniture-mounted uplighters, cornice and slab recessed(182). With uplighting, the soffit form is highlighted as an important consideration together with a high surface reflectance of at least 70–80% and a gloss factor of no more than 10% (otherwise lamp images will be visible). Perforations in the light fitting can be used with downlighters to avoid the effect of cavernous coffers.

Routing of conduit and other services should also be considered as surface mounting may not be acceptable. Solutions include dropping through from the floor above, embedding a conduit network in the slab with access points, or routing in hollow cores in slabs.

Partial false ceilings or open ceilings can provide some access to the thermal mass whilst also providing a means of integrating services.

Maximising the use of natural light is important with regard to minimising light energy consumption. Light shelves have been used in a number of buildings to improve the distribution of natural light penetration into a space. The effectiveness of this approach is reliant on reflection from the soffit. As well as a high surface reflectance, the form of the soffit is also important. Plane surfaces are suitable, but 'waffled' surfaces or surfaces with ribs running perpendicular to the flow of natural light will compromise the use of light shelves. Profiling parallel to the flow of natural light can be used to optimise daylight penetration. The design of the soffit should be suitable for integration with possible partitioning layouts.

Control strategy

The control of night cooling is important not only in avoiding overheating, but also in avoiding an unreasonable increase in heating demand by cooling unnecessarily (i.e. overcooling). Inappropriate control strategies can result in significant increases in heating demand (+20%) without appreciable reductions in peak temperatures(33).

Strategies are based on a number of criteria including:

— establishing a requirement for cooling (based on zone or slab temperatures)

— cooling availability (i.e. external temperature plus pick-up must be less than the internal temperature)

— avoiding conflict with the heating system (minimum internal set-point)

— scheduled operating periods (to suit occupancy patterns, tariffs).

— disabling heater and heat recovery devices during night cooling

— disabling/enabling mechanical cooling

— avoiding conflict between thermal mass and air heating/cooling

— bypassing/modulation of airflow to control charging and discharging

— damper settings.

Refer to BSRIA Technical Note TN14/96(210) for detailed guidance on suitable strategies. Where the mechanical cooling is provided, refer to BSRIA Technical Note TN16/95(211) for detailed guidance on pre-cooling strategies.

2.4.7.3 Construction

The quality of finish required for exposed soffits and the geometrical form will have an influence on whether precast or in-situ construction is to be used for the floor system. One particular issue for pre-cast construction is sealing between units with differential deflection.

The quality of construction of the thermal storage element and surface finishes will have an impact on the thermal storage performance; air gaps under surface finishes can seriously reduce heat transfer. Thermal imaging could be considered as a technique for identifying problem areas with poor heat transfer(212).

For systems where indirect solutions are used the following should also be considered:

— access to voids, cores and air paths for maintenance purposes

— dust sealing of concrete surfaces within voids cores and air paths.

Slab temperature sensors should be installed at a depth that is representative of the storage capacity of the slab, typically 25–50 mm. Sensors located too close to the surface may be influenced by local effects (e.g. air blowing across the slab, hot plumes rising from equipment). Sensors located too deep into the slab will experience little diurnal swing.

As noted previously, airtightness and conduction losses are particular issues for heating demand in thermally heavyweight buildings. Losses can be stored by the thermal mass resulting in a significant increase in heating demand to overcome this stored cooling. Particular attention should therefore be paid to the sealing and insulation of the building envelope during construction.

2.4.8 Chilled ceilings/chilled beams

2.4.8.1 General[178]

Conventional cooling methods such as fan coils and VAV systems provide cooling almost entirely by convective heat transfer. An alternative strategy is to provide cooling by a combination of radiation and convection using, for example, chilled ceilings. Such systems cool objects within the space, as well as the space itself. Although they are commonly known as radiant cooling systems, only 50–60% (maximum) of the heat is transferred by radiation.

Chilled ceilings use chilled or cooled water as the cooling medium, normally between 13 °C and 18 °C. There are many different types of chilled ceiling devices, but essentially they fall into three main categories, see Figure 2.26. These are:

- *Radiant ceiling panels*: in which the cooling capacity is distributed across the ceiling using serpentine chilled water pipework.
- *Passive chilled beams*: which have a more open structure and a heavier reliance on natural convective air movement; cooling is concentrated in finned coils similar to conventional heat exchangers.
- *Active chilled beams*: which are similar to the above but with the air movement through the beam being mechanically assisted.

With active chilled beams ventilation is an integral part of the beam, being induced by the central air handling plant. However with passive chilled beams and panels, ventilation has to be introduced separately, either by mixed flow or more normally by displacement ventilation. Chilled beams can either be capped or uncapped, i.e. unconnected to the ceiling void or connected to the ceiling void. They can also be flush mounted to the ceiling or hung, exposed, from the ceiling although care is needed to ensure that the required performance is achieved at the selected distance between the beam and the ceiling.

Chilled ceilings can be applied to both new-build and refurbishment projects. However, they are not suitable for situations where a close-controlled environment (i.e. temperature and humidity) is required. They may also be used in conjunction in mixed-mode applications[213]. However, in this context, it is very important to consider condensation control, see page 2-82.

2.4.8.2 Design

Chilled ceilings and beams are often used in conjunction with displacement ventilation. Depending on the configuration, cooling loads up to 120 W·m^{-2} may be achieved.

Cooling performance

Cooling performance is highly dependent on the size and layout of chilled panels or beams. It is also a function of the room temperature. For cooling loads up to about 80 W·m^{-2}, displacement ventilation may be combined with chilled panels with the chilled panels providing 50 W·m^{-2} and displacement ventilation providing 30 W·m^{-2}. To provide this level of cooling from panels will require about two-thirds of the ceiling area to be covered. Passive chilled beams in combination with displacement ventilation can provide 70–120 W·m^{-2} of cooling.

For loads greater than 120 W·m^{-2}, active chilled beams are essential as they have a higher cooling capacity. Performance will be adversely affected by high heat loads directly below beams. It will also decrease with room temperature. For example, a system able to deliver 100 W·m^{-2} at a room temperature of 24 °C will provide no cooling at a room temperature of 14 °C. Care must also be taken to consider the possible effect of downdraughts from chilled ceilings delivering high cooling outputs. At these loads physical testing or CFD modelling of the design may be required. Further information on these systems is available elsewhere[214].

The ratio of convective to radiative heat output for various systems is shown in Table 2.34.

Systems can be used in conjunction with a low quality source of cooling due to the relatively high cooling water temperatures required. Examples of this might be

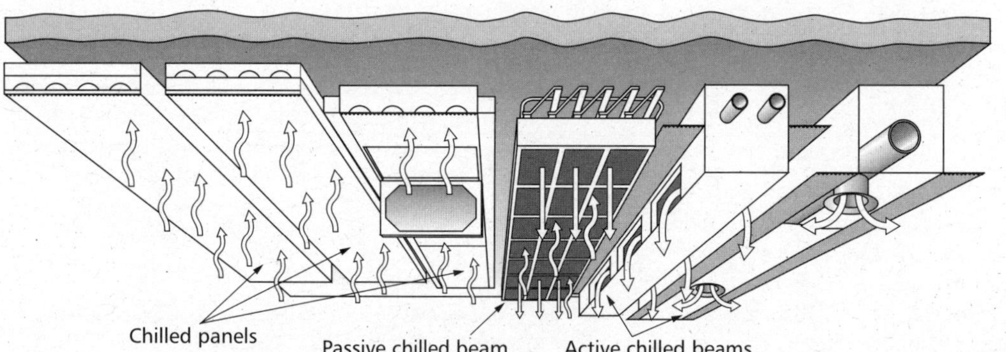

Figure 2.26 Chilled ceiling categories

Table 2.34 Convective and radiative proportions of heat output for chilled beams/panels

System type	Proportion of heat output (%)	
	Convective	Radiative
Active chilled beams	90–95	10–5
Passive chilled beams:		
— capped	80–90	20–10
— uncapped	85–90	15–10
Chilled panels	40–50	60–50

groundwater (see section 2.4.15) or cooling towers. This will increase their coefficient of performance(215). As cooling is supplied within the space this limits the requirements for the ventilation system to provide fresh air, thus also saving fan energy.

Combination with displacement ventilation

Tests have shown that when chilled ceilings are combined with displacement ventilation there is more downward convection than is the case with displacement ventilation alone, although upward convection should still be dominant in the vicinity of the occupants. The flow field resulting from chilled beams may give a more mixed condition in the occupied zone than chilled panels. Similarly, uncapped passive beams may result in stronger downward convection currents than capped passive beams.

A physical testing and CFD modelling study(216) shows that when displacement ventilation without chilled ceilings is employed, the airflow patterns are chiefly upward when the internal thermal loads are equivalent to the cooling capacity of the displacement ventilation system. On condition that the supply air temperature and air velocity are maintained within recommended values, a high order of thermal comfort and air quality are usually obtained. The addition of chilled beam devices to offset higher internal thermal gains progressively erodes the predominant upward airflow region as thermal loads are increased. When the cooling load of the chilled ceiling devices is about three times that of the displacement ventilation system, the flow field is similar to a conventional mixed airflow system, except in the vicinity of heat sources where upward convective plumes entrain air from the displacement cool air layer at floor level. When displacement ventilation is employed with chilled ceilings the radiant cold panels slightly increase the depth of the mixed warm and contaminated upper region but do not affect the displacement airflow characteristics of the lower part of the room. The environmental thermal comfort conditions, however, are generally of a very high order.

Control strategies

Many of the advantages offered by chilled beam and ceiling systems are due to the simplicity of these systems, since they are inherently self-compensating in their thermal cooling. It is important that this level of simplicity is also maintained within the control system used, which is in many ways akin to a simple radiator heating system.

Ideally, beams should be controlled in groups using 2-port, 2-position control valves. These can be pulse controlled to vary the length of time open depending upon the variance between measured room temperature and set point.

Most systems now have speed control (static inverter) on the pumps in order to maintain a constant system pressure as the system volume flow rate requirement varies. Where speed control is not being used a simple pressure by-pass valve on the end of the circuit should be used.

System controls are normally set up to mimic those of a fan coil system, i.e. 2-, 3- or 4-port valves on the outlet, either on/off or infinitely variable controller and a room sensor. The control strategy should ensure that condensation risk is eliminated, see the following paragraph. For central control a 3-port valve is needed to regulate the inlet water temperature. If 2-port valves are used in rooms, then a header tank between the chiller and pipework will ensure a constant flow rate to the chiller. A by-pass valve at the end of each branch decreases the pressure in the pipework and is particularly important with a 2-port valve system. This also ensures that a constant chilled water supply is available.

Condensation risk(217)

The avoidance of condensation on the surface of chilled panels and beams has been a major design issue in the UK, with fears over the relatively wet climate of the UK. It has been assumed that without dehumidification of the outside air, 'office rain' could occur.

Condensation detection should always be incorporated into the chilled beam control system. This should be considered as being ideal for active beam systems but essential for passive beams and chilled ceilings. In most buildings, it is unlikely that condensation will occur within an active beam system but it can occur as a symptom of a fault within the system. Occasions when coil condensation can occur include during commissioning when chilled water is being balanced before the chilled control/mixing system has been commissioned, if windows are left open or even broken, AHU dehumidifier pump failure or human error resulting in chilled water temperatures being reduced.

Condensation detection should be by direct dew point sensing using a device clamped to the pipework. It is not practical to measure independently the room temperature and humidity in order to calculate the dew point. The inherent lack of accuracy found in most humidistats is acceptable when measuring in order to maintain the humidity within a wide band for comfort. However, they should not be used for dew-point calculation.

When condensation is detected either the chilled water supply temperature should be ramped up one degree at a time to ride above the dew point. Alternatively the chilled water should be shut off completely and alarms raised on the building energy management system (BEMS), since the condensation may be a symptom of a fault in the system.

Condensation will start to form if the ceiling surface temperature falls below the room air dew point temperature. Various condensation avoidance strategies have been developed to minimise or eliminate the risk of this condition occurring. In principle the selection of an appropriate control strategy and set point should not allow the development and formation of condensation. Equally it should not unduly limit the cooling output from the ceiling, nor its ability to be used within a mixed mode application.

To minimise the condensation risk, it is important to lag the chilled water pipework between the panels or beams as these surfaces will be cooler. This also increases the ceiling output, as the difference between the panel/beam temperature and the room temperature is larger. Alternatively if the chilled water temperature is maintained at the same level, the room dew point can be allowed to increase to reduce the requirement for dehumidification of the ventilation supply air.

Control of the chilled water temperature provides an effective means of avoiding condensation. Although it is more energy efficient than using supply air dehumidification control, it may result in a loss of comfort conditions if the room dew point becomes too high.

These techniques can be used in combination, e.g. dehumidification with supply air temperature control. Note that measurement of the room dew point temperature through a combination of the dry bulb temperature and relative room humidity measurements requires accurate sensors that are regularly re-calibrated.

Condensation can also be avoided by reducing the room dew point temperature by reducing the supply air temperature. This may increase the risk of draught, particularly when using displacement ventilation.

Maintenance

Chilled water pipework is present throughout the building. Care must be taken with zoning and provision of sufficient drainage points. Providing that the system remains problem free, maintenance costs should be lower than those for conventional systems.

Noise

Compared to fan coils and VAV systems, chilled ceiling systems do not generate sufficient background noise to provide sound privacy. It may be necessary to increase the sound insulation in the partitioning system or increase the height of any partitions. Consideration should also be given to the use of electronic sound conditioning (broadband and characterless).

Performance monitoring

Guidance on modelling the performance of chilled ceilings in conjunction with displacement ventilation is available at both early stage design[216] and detailed design[178].

2.4.8.3 Construction

Ceiling layout

In practice the high heat gains in modern office spaces are served by chilled beams and chilled panels, or chilled beams alone. It is important to consider the ceiling layout in terms of its effect on the overall performance, e.g. the positioning of beams at the perimeter areas, with panels being used in the inner zones, see Figure 2.27. It is also important to consider integration with the light fittings.

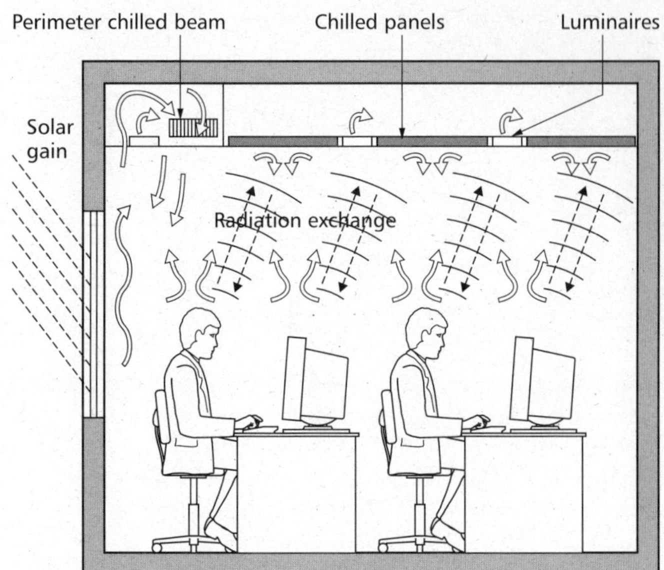

Figure 2.27 Typical ceiling layout incorporating chilled panels and chilled beams

Space allowances

The requirement for ductwork space and associated ventilation plant can be reduced in comparison with conventional systems. However, space is required for the central cooling and distribution systems. For active chilled beams, an air supply must be allowed for. Passive chilled beams require space for overhead air recirculation, and beam stack height below.

A floor-to-slab height of at least 2.4 m is required for passive and active chilled beams to ensure a high degree of thermal comfort. The height limitation must be determined from case to case depending on expected heat loads and the features of the beams such as their width and depth.

2.4.9 Cooled surfaces (floors and slabs)

2.4.9.1 Description

Cooling to the space is provided via radiation and convection heat exchange with cool exposed surfaces, usually floors and ceilings. A pipe network is used to cool the surface. This may be attached to a panel-type construction or imbedded in a slab if the slab surface is exposed. The panel-type systems are generally thermally lightweight systems that have a rapid response to load changes. The slab systems are heavyweight with the thermal capacity to store cooling but a slow response to load changes.

Cooled surfaces are most suited to buildings with low to medium heat gains and summer temperatures are permitted to rise. Sensible cooling only is provided. The cooling capacity of the system is a function of the space/surface temperature differential. Relatively high (e.g. 18 °C) water temperatures are typically used for cooling, permitting the use of low grade cooling direct from sources such as cooling towers, air blast coolers (see Figure 2.28) or aquifers. This helps to avoid or reduce the requirement for mechanical refrigeration. The system may also be used for heating during winter. Indeed, most floor systems are selected for heating rather than cooling.

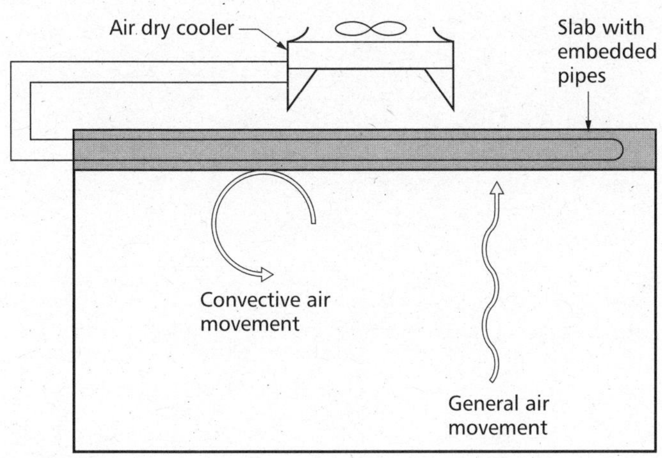

Figure 2.28 Air blast cooler

2.4.9.2 Design

The cooling effect of the surface is a function of the surface–space temperature differential and the surface area. It can be estimated using equations for surface heat transfer given in CIBSE Guide A[12], section 5 (equation 5.133). Manufacturers' data should be referred to for accurate performance data.

Permissible surface temperatures can be constrained by comfort requirements, minimising condensation risk and control practicalities. For comfort, radiant temperature asymmetry should be less than 5 K for cooled floors, 10 K for cooled walls, and 14 K for cooled ceilings[12]. Minimum surface temperatures should be such that they do not cause a significant condensation risk. This risk can be reduced if the system is being used in conjunction with a mechanical ventilation plant providing humidity control.

Increases in output for cooled ceilings may be achieved by profiling the surface. This provides a larger area for heat transfer. Convective heat exchange with the air in the space will increase approximately in proportion to the area. Radiant heat transfer will normally be limited if the profiling has a similar overall exposed surface area to that of a plane surface when viewed from the occupied space. The geometric exposure can be calculated using form (or shape) factors[192,207].

Exposure of soffits raises a number of issues that should be considered including aesthetics, acoustics and integration. Refer to section 2.4.7 for further guidance.

Design issues for the pipework system include the location and spacing of pipes. For panel-type systems, pipes are generally spaced 100–300 mm apart[218]. Wide spacing under tile or bare floors can cause uneven surface temperatures. For slab systems, pipework may typically be located 40–100 mm below the surface at 150–450 mm spacing[218] to achieve effective storage and heat conduction to the surface, see Figure 2.29. Optimum values can be evaluated using conduction models.

Surface finishes should not be insulative and should have high emissivity. Insulation to prevent perimeter and back heat losses should be considered.

Flexibility in operation (e.g. heating in perimeter zones with cooling internally) and future adaptability should be provided by suitable zoning of the pipework layout and the configuration of the pipework distribution system.

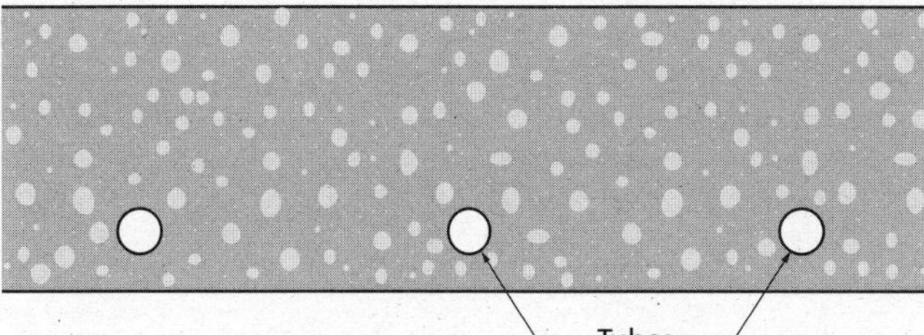

Figure 2.29 Cooling pipework in structural concrete slab

The length of pipework runs should be determined to suit zoning and to avoid excessive pressure drop.

For lightweight systems, response to load changes will be fairly rapid. For slab systems having high thermal inertia, reaction to load changes will be slow. This should be reflected in the control strategy adopted. The slab temperature may be controlled to within the normal space comfort band to minimise the risk of overcooling, e.g. 20–22 °C. This can be achieved with cooling water temperatures in the region of 18 °C. Cooling water may be circulated during the day and/or night. This will be determined by a number of factors including:

- *output required*: high outputs may require top-up cooling during day as well as cooling at night
- *cooling source*: the cooling source may be more energy efficient at night or only able to produce sufficiently low temperatures at night
- *energy tariffs*: cheaper tariffs may be available at night favouring night-time operation.

2.4.9.3 Construction

Because of the inherent problem of access to repair leaks, considerable care should be taken during the construction process to minimise the likelihood of their occurrence. Plastic or plastic-coated pipework is normally used to avoid corrosion problems and silting. Longer lengths may also be used reducing the number of joints and associated risk of leakage.

Distribution to the pipes is often via supply and return manifold headers. Single continuous lengths of pipes between the supply and return headers are preferred to avoid joints and increasing the risk of leakage. The pipes are normally arranged in a serpentine configuration.

For panel-type systems, there are a variety of construction methods available, see Figures 2.30 and 2.31, including:

- support via joists or battens
- attachment to the underside of the floor
- support in a floating floor panel with suitable grooves for laying the pipework.

For floor systems, insulation should be considered to minimise downward heat flow. Providing a reflective finish below the pipework will help to promote upward heat flow. Heat diffusion and surface temperature uniformity can be improved by the addition of metal heat transfer plates, which spread the cooling beneath the floor.

For slab systems, construction can either be in-situ or in pre-cast units. Pre-casting in factory conditions may be preferred from the point of view minimising the risk of

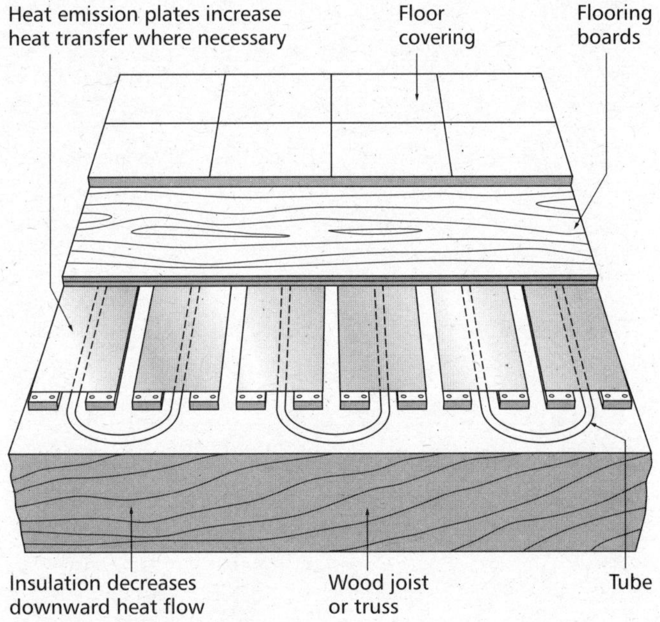

Figure 2.30 Cooling pipework in sub-floor

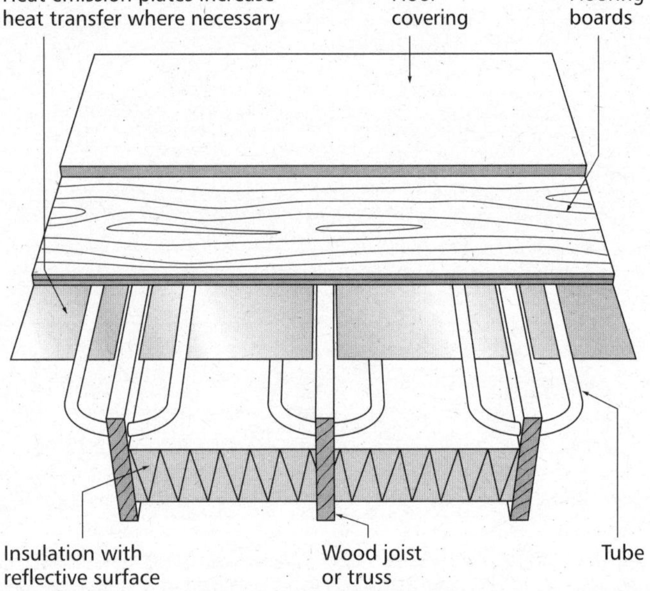

Figure 2.31 Cooling pipework below sub-floor

leaks. The pipework may be supported by the steel reinforcement cage or on the bearing slab for floating slab applications, see Figure 2.32. The pipe ends may be located in a connecting box fixed to the shuttering with its opening facing upwards or downwards as required for connection to the distribution system, see Figure 2.33. It may be necessary to pressurise pipes to stiffen them until the concrete has set. During construction, pipework terminals should be capped to prevent debris getting into the pipes. Slab temperature sensors should be installed at a depth that is representative of the storage capacity of the slab. Temperatures close to the surface may be influenced by local effects (e.g. air blowing across the slab, hot plumes rising from equipment).

2.4.10 Desiccant cooling systems

2.4.10.1 Description[219]

Desiccants are hygroscopic materials that readily absorb or give off moisture to the surrounding air. They can be

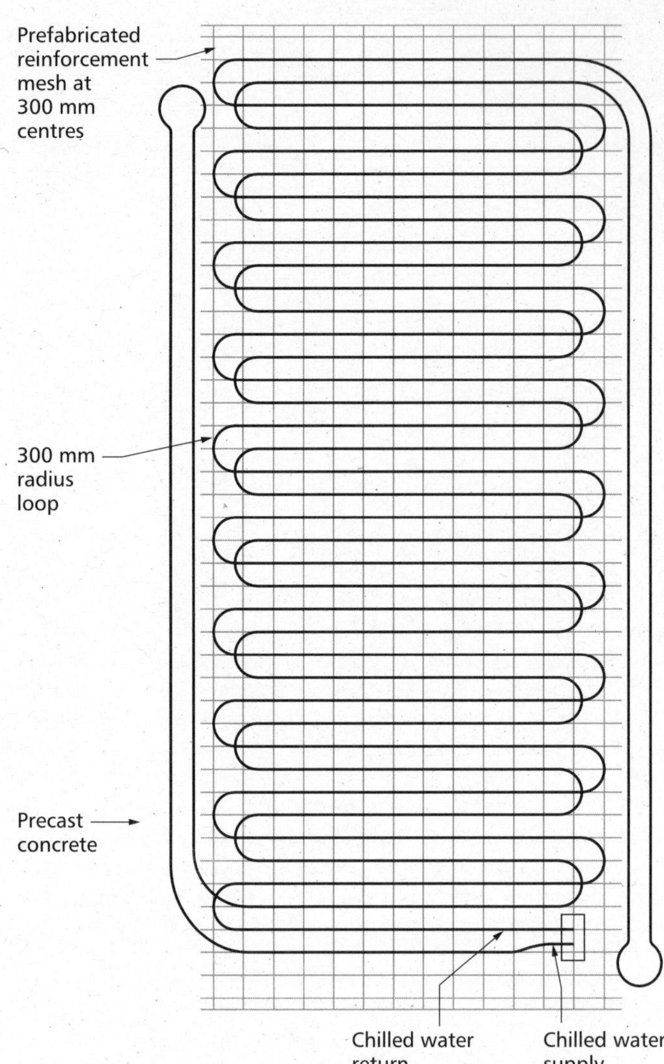

Figure 2.32 Cooling pipework supported by reinforcement cage

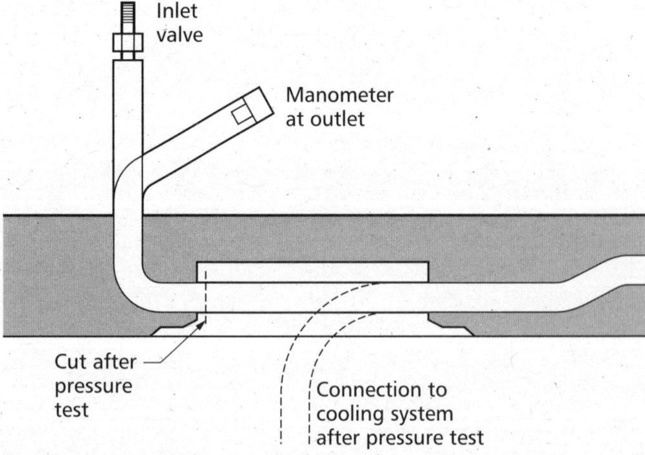

Figure 2.33 Pre-mounted connection box for cooling pipework

solids or liquids, although application of dessicant technology in the UK is currently based on the use of solid material. They may be natural or synthetic substances.

The moisture containment of a hygroscopic material in equilibrium depends upon the moisture content of the surrounding air and varies widely for different desiccants. The moisture content also varies for different temperatures at the same relative humidity.

If the desiccant material contains moisture in excess of the surrounding air stream then it will release moisture to the air with the absorption of heat and there will be a cooling effect equal to that of evaporation. If the desiccant material contains moisture below that of the surrounding air it will absorb moisture from the air. Heat will be released corresponding to the latent heat given off if a corresponding quality of water vapour were condensed.

Desiccants transfer moisture because of a difference between the water vapour pressure at their surface and that of the surrounding air. As the water content of a desiccant rises so does the water vapour pressure at its surface.

Both higher temperatures and increased moisture content boost the vapour pressure at the surface. When the surface vapour pressure exceeds that of the surrounding air, moisture leaves the desiccant. After the heat dries the desiccant, its vapour pressure remains high so that it has little ability to absorb moisture. Cooling the desiccant reduces its vapour pressure so that it can absorb moisture once again. This is referred to as 'regeneration'.

Dessicant systems can be applied where:

— high latent loads are present that would otherwise require very low chilled water temperatures, e.g. supermarkets
— contaminant control is required
— a source of low-grade energy such as waste heat or solar energy can be used to regenerate the dessicant.

2.4.10.2 Design

Operation

Figure 2.34 shows a typical air conditioning plant using solid desiccant technology

Outside air (A) passes through the filter before entering the desiccant wheel where moisture is removed from the air (B). During this absorption process the temperature of the air rises and is then cooled by the thermal wheel (C). The air is now drier and cooler and may be further cooled by either evaporative cooling (D) or mechanical cooling (D1), dependent upon the required final condition.

The cooler, dehumidified air is then introduced to the space where it provides all the latent cooling requirement and some sensible cooling, depending on the type of system chosen, either all-air or air/water.

The return air leaves the space via a filter (E) before entering an evaporative cooler (F). This cool humid air enters the thermal wheel (which acts as the cooling for the supply air) and is heated by the supply air (F). It is then further increased in temperature by the heater (G) where it regenerates the desiccant wheel. In order to save energy, some of the air bypasses the heater and the desiccant wheel (J). The psychrometric process is shown in Figure 2.35.

Performance

Like any other system, performance is dependent on the external and internal conditions. The difference between desiccant systems and those based on HCFC/HFC-use is the impact of the ambient moisture content. Increased moisture content reduces the performance of the desiccant system to a greater degree than increased temperature, which can more easily be handled.

Performance is also dependent on the efficiency of the energy recovery system and humidifiers. By using a desiccant in conjunction with an energy recovery system and evaporative coolers a supply air condition of between 12 °C and 19 °C at a chosen moisture content (g·kg^{-1}) can be achieved. The system can be used in all types of air conditioning systems, but is particularly effective with radiant cooling either by chilled ceilings or fabric thermal storage.

The cooling and dehumidification capacity of a dessicant system is controlled by changing the temperature of the heater for the reactivation air. During the winter when ambient conditions are low the system operates in a heat recovery mode. Efficiencies in excess of 85% can be achieved by using the desiccant wheel as a sensible and latent heat recovery unit in conjunction with the heat recovery wheel. This reduces energy consumption during the heating season.

A desiccant system may handle up to 50% of the internal heat gain without any energy input by using only exhaust air evaporative cooling and the thermal wheel. At approximately 75% of required capacity the desiccant system provides 1 kW of cooling for each kW of regeneration heat input. However, at peak design load, the output

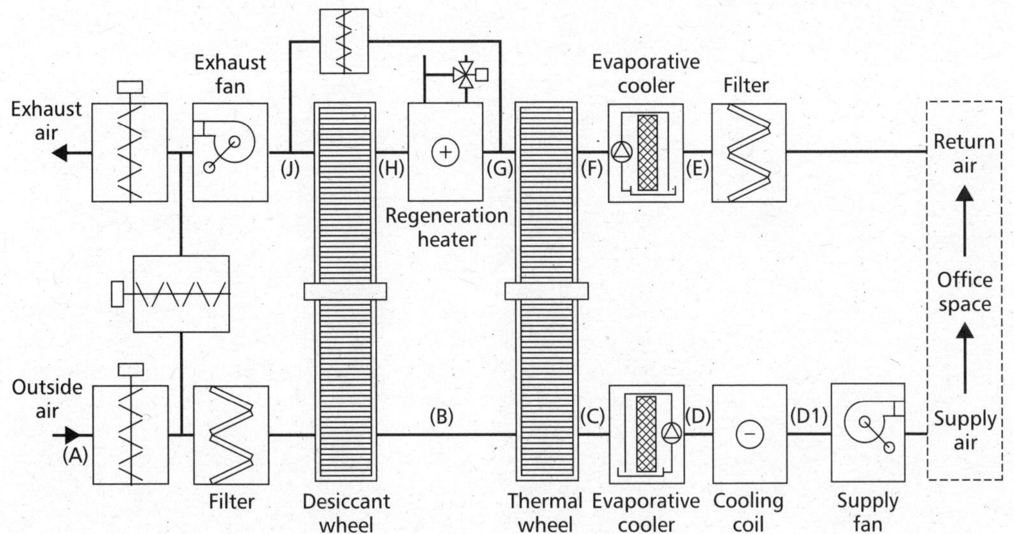

Figure 2.34 Typical air conditioning plant using solid desiccant technology

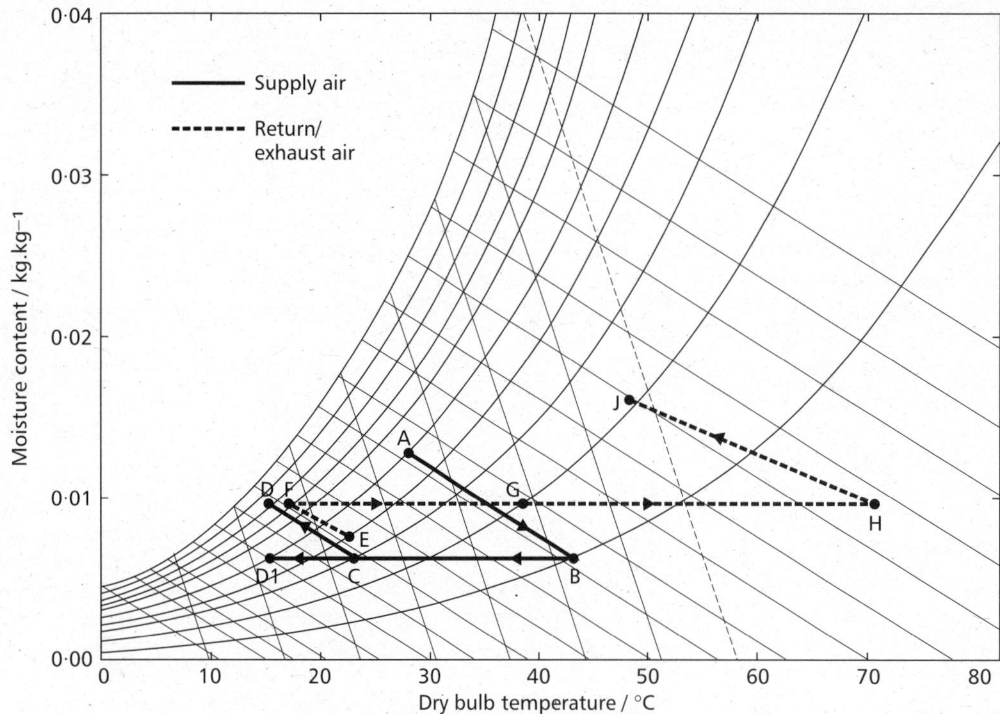

Figure 2.35 Psychrometric process for desiccant cooling

of the desiccant system can drop to as low as 0.5 kW of cooling per kW of regeneration heat. As this is for a very small proportion of its operating period, detailed analysis may still reveal savings over more conventional systems. It is critical that the system control philosophy is understood both by the designer and the operator of the system to ensure that the maximum potential savings are made.

The regeneration heater energy requirement is at its greatest during the summer months. However, in the case of a commercial office building, this is generally less than the winter heating load. The same equipment may therefore be used for both summer regeneration and winter heating.

System enhancements

The system performance can be enhanced in terms of energy usage by:

— solar or gas regeneration of the desiccant

— when the desiccant is inactive bypassing the wheel, so reducing system resistance and hence fan energy.

Maintenance

The useful life of a desiccant material largely depends on the type of contamination in the air-streams they dry and the operational practice. A properly maintained system may last for 20 years.

Capital and running costs

The capital cost of a desiccant plant is higher than that of a conventional plant, particularly for smaller systems (i.e. below 5 $m^3 \cdot s^{-1}$). This should be balanced against running cost and CO_2 production savings. A cost and environmental benefit analysis will be required for individual projects.

2.4.10.3 Space requirements

The physical space requirement for the air handling plant is in the order of 20% more than that for a conventional system, but savings can be made on reduced refrigeration plant depending upon the final air condition required.

2.4.11 Dual duct and hot deck/cold deck systems

2.4.11.1 Description

Dual duct systems employ two ducts to circulate separately cooled and heated air to zonal mixing boxes. Zonal temperature sensors ensure that air in the hot and cold ducts are mixed in appropriate proportions to deal with the prevailing load. Mixing two air streams to produce an intermediate comfort temperature wastes heating and cooling energy, particularly in constant volume systems. This may restrict their use to those applications where reclaimed energy can be used. Variable volume systems offer significantly improved energy efficiency compared with constant volume systems, although both systems represent a significant energy cost.

Dual duct systems have the ability to deal with heating and cooling loads simultaneously. Room air movement is constant and wet services above ceilings are avoided. However, central plant and distribution systems tend to be larger and more costly than other systems, despite the practice of sizing ductwork for high velocities.

Hot deck/cold deck systems are similar in principle to dual duct systems, the major difference being that zonal mixing occurs at the discharge from the central air handling plant. Hence each zone requires a separate supply from the central plant. This arrangement is best suited to applications involving a small number of zones and where plant can be located centrally. It may also be appropriate for noise sensitive spaces.

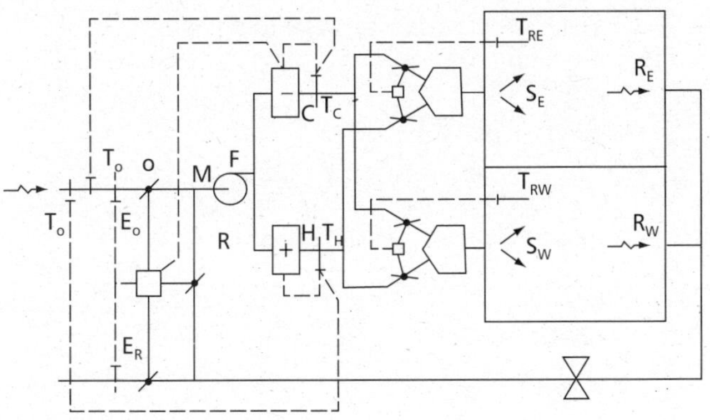

Figure 2.36 Dual duct system

2.4.11.2 Design

Dual duct constant volume

A typical system configuration is shown in Figure 2.36, with the associated psychrometrics in Figures 2.37 and 2.38. Supply temperatures from the air handling unit should be controlled to provide minimum heating and cooling to satisfy the hottest/coolest zone. Allowance should be made for the reduction in latent cooling due to mixing at part load.

Although the total volume flow handled by the fan remains constant, each duct handles a variable volume. Consequently the same problems of static pressure fluctuations occur as in VAV systems and require similar remedies at the terminals. Furthermore, with mixing devices operating under part load there is a risk of cross-flow between the two ducts if significant imbalance exists between inlet pressures.

The following methods can be used to maintain system balance:

- change in duct static pressure resets the set points of the sensors controlling the hot and cold duct temperatures, hence maintaining constant flow rate in each duct (an unusual solution)
- static pressure sensors in each duct cause the operation of dampers at the inlet to both hot and cold ducts (suitable for small systems only)
- employ mixing devices with integral factory-set constant volume regulators (the common solution).

Alternative arrangements and additional features can be employed to deal with specific requirements, see below.

(*a*) Fresh air preheat

A preheater can be incorporated into the fresh air intake to deal with minimum fresh air quantities in winter. This avoids the possibility of freezing of the cooling coil due to stratification of fresh and return air through the mixing box and fan.

(*b*) Fresh air dehumidification

If the outside air is likely to be very humid at part load, a separate dehumidifying coil can be located in the fresh air inlet to avoid using very low temperatures at the main cooling coil.

(*c*) Dual duct reheat

The cooling coil is located within the central plant so that all the air is cooled and dehumidified, some being reheated in the hot duct, thus providing better humidity control.

(*d*) Dual duct/dual fan

The provision of separate fans for the hot and cold ducts enables the hot duct to handle air recirculated through air handling luminaires. This assists with winter heating and increases cold duct volume and hence the availability of dry air in summer. Sufficient fresh air must be assured for zones drawing minimum quantity from the cold duct. A bypass between hot and cold ducts will ensure that fans handle constant volumes.

Dual duct VAV

Alternative arrangements incorporate single or dual supply fans, either with all fans being variable volume or with variable volume cold duct and constant volume hot duct. A cooling coil may also be incorporated into the constant volume system and hence provide the facility to serve some zones with constant volume variable temperature air, some with variable volume cooling, and others with a mixture.

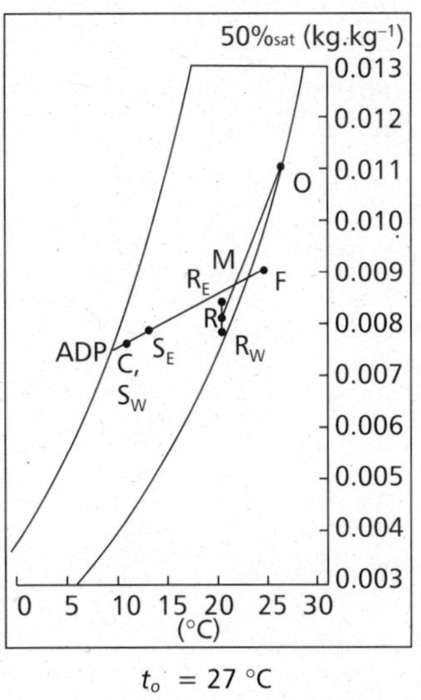

Figure 2.37 Psychrometric chart: dual duct, hot deck/cold deck

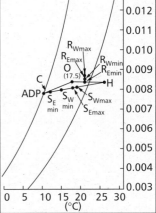

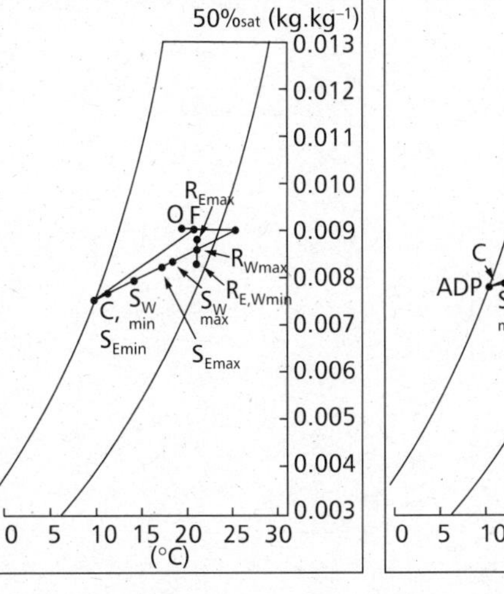

Figure 2.38 Psychrometric chart: dual duct, hot deck/cold deck

The cold duct functions in the same manner as a basic VAV system providing the facility, at full volume, to deal with maximum cooling load for each zone. The hot duct connection on the mixing box is kept closed until the cooling VAV damper reaches its minimum setting. Any further reduction in cooling loads is dealt with by opening the hot duct damper. Hot duct temperature may be programmed against outside air temperature as appropriate.

The cold duct fan should be regulated under the dictates of a static pressure sensor, in a similar manner to that of a conventional air conditioning system.

Hot deck/cold deck systems

As each zone has a separate supply from the central plant, problems of plant imbalance on damper turndown are reduced. Hence low velocity distribution is possible, giving reduced fan running costs. However, problems can occur with interaction between separately controlled zones having very different volume flow requirements.

Packaged 'multizone' air handling units capable of serving a limited number of zones are available (Figures 2.39 and 2.40) while site constructed coil/damper arrangements may have as many zonal branches as can be physically incorporated.

Damper quality is an important factor in ensuring satisfactory part load control and economy of operation. A maximum leakage of 5% when closed should be specified. Precise control action is required in the transmission of the signal from room sensor through control system, actuators and damper linkages.

2.4.11.3 Construction

There are many types of mixing box using various methods of operation. Devices are available both in constant volume form and with sequenced cold duct VAV and mixing. See section 2.5 for equipment descriptions.

Basic functions usually performed include:

- mixing air from hot and cold ducts in appropriate proportions to match room load under the dictates of a room air temperature sensor
- mixing air thoroughly to avoid stratification
- attenuating noise generated at mixing dampers
- maintaining constant supply volume against variations in duct pressure.

Figure 2.41 shows one type of mixing device. Such devices may be individually controlled or several may be slaved from one master device, as with VAV systems. Leakage will always occur through 'closed' dampers. Leakage rates vary from 3–7% of full flow rate for small, well-made devices up to 10–20% for large and site-assembled units. This leakage represents an additional load on the system under peak conditions.

Where mixing devices are provided with integral constant volume regulators, most types are capable of maintaining a preset volume to within ±5% despite fluctuations of duct static pressure between 250 and 2000 Pa, if necessary. Factory-set volumes need to be checked after installation. The two main types of static pressure regulator are:

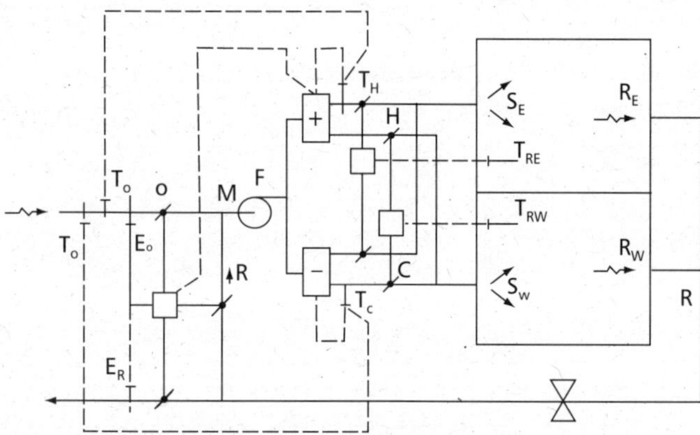

Figure 2.39 Multizone hot deck/cold deck system

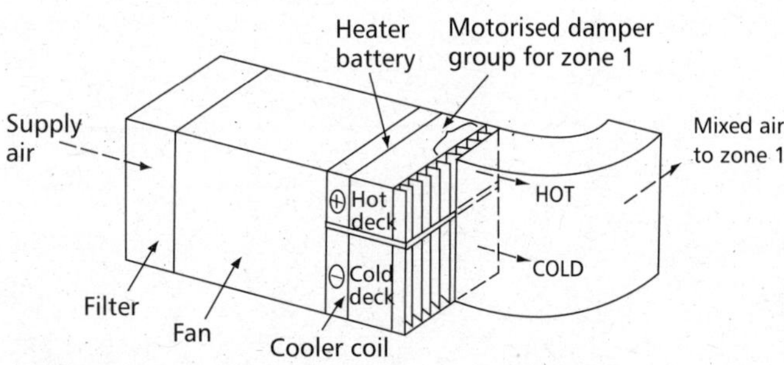

Figure 2.40 Typical packaged multizone arrangement

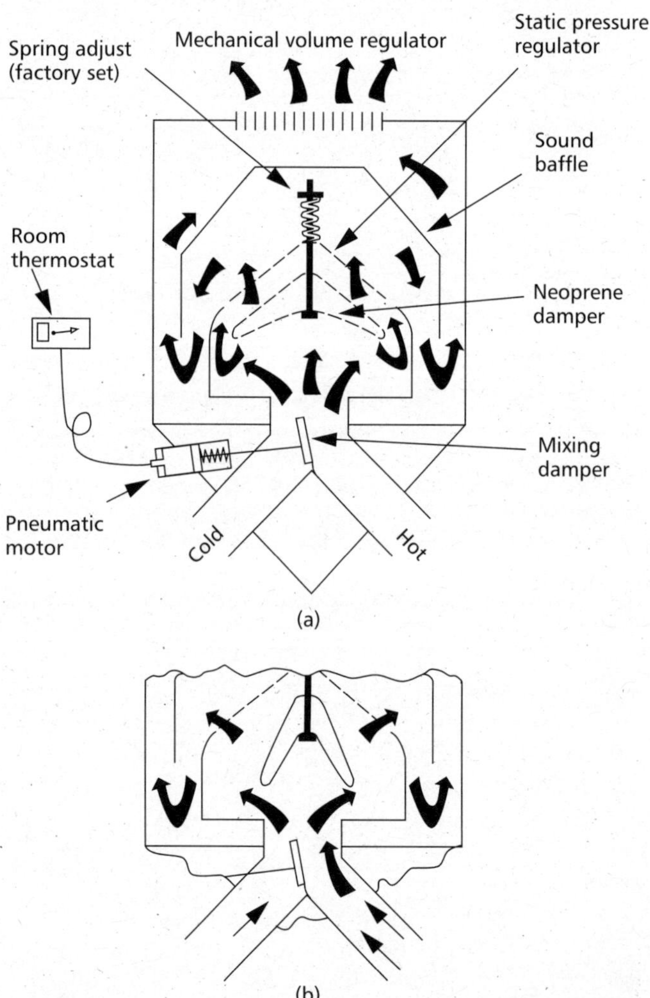

Figure 2.41 Constant volume dual duct unit with integral static pressure regulator and air terminal device; (a) high inlet duct pressure, (b) low inlet pressure

— *mechanical*: a spring loaded regulator in the mixed air stream closes as the pressure increases, the mixing dampers operating as a single unit direct from a room sensor

— *pressure actuated*: a room sensor operates the hot duct damper whilst the cold duct damper responds to resultant changes in flow sensed by a static pressure differential sensor across an integral resistance.

Stratification can occur if there is inadequate mixing after the terminal, and is a particular problem if a multiple outlet mixing device is installed with its outlets stacked vertically.

Noise regeneration at the unit is normally reduced by suitable lining materials and internal baffles. Larger terminals may require separate attenuation.

2.4.12 Evaporative cooling (direct and indirect)

2.4.12.1 Description

In evaporative cooling systems the evaporation of water is used to decrease the dry-bulb temperature of air. There are two main categories of evaporative cooling:

— *Direct evaporation*: water is evaporated directly into the supply air stream, adiabatically reducing the air stream's dry bulb temperature but increasing its absolute humidity. Direct coolers may operate using spray air washers or wetted media.

— *Indirect evaporation*: two air streams are used. A secondary air stream is cooled directly using evaporation and then exhausted. This secondary stream may be outdoor or exhaust air. The cooler moist secondary air cools the primary supply air indirectly through an air-to-air heat exchanger. (When the secondary stream is exhaust air, the heat exchanger can also be used to pre-heat outdoor air in the winter.) Hence indirect evaporative cooling provides sensible cooling without increasing the latent capacity of the supply air.

When designed as a standalone system, an evaporative cooling system requires three to four times the air flow rate of a conventional air conditioning systems. Because of the higher airflow rates, larger ducts are required. However, the higher airflow rates and the absence of recirculated air may improve indoor air quality. In practice, because of the limited cooling capacity of an indirect evaporative cycle, the primary air is often cooled again by direct evaporation or by a mechanical cooling system. This is called a two-stage or indirect-direct system. In practice, within the UK, the technology is used as a supplementary cooling measure only, or in combination with desiccant cooling.

2.4.12.2 Performance details

The lowest temperature that can theoretically be achieved is the dewpoint temperature of the treated air. The resulting cooling depends on the wet-bulb depression and the cooler effectiveness. In Arizona, where evaporative cooling is used successfully to provide comfort conditions, this is 18 °C whereas in the UK it is 9 °C. As a result, evaporative cooling can meet moderate sensible cooling loads under dry conditions with no latent cooling loads. It cannot address latent cooling loads. With high wet bulb temperatures, evaporative cooling systems will not deliver the required cooling. These systems are ineffectual in humid climates.

The saturation effectiveness depends on the equipment design (e.g. contact time, area and air stream velocity, condition and adjustment). For direct spray types, effectiveness is put at 50–90% with the higher values being associated with double spray arrangements. Direct wetted media coolers could have an effectiveness of between 85–95%. Typically indirect pre-cooling stages achieve 60–80% effectiveness. System effectiveness should be considered where more than one stage takes place.

2.4.12.3 System enhancements

Evaporative cooling may be enhanced by:

— combining it with other technologies to provide supplementary cooling, e.g. hollow core systems

— using it in systems that have low cooling loads, e.g. displacement ventilation

— using it to pre-cool condenser air

— using an indirect evaporative pre-cooler to recover heat energy in winter.

2.4.12.4 Control strategies

The control strategy depends on the number of stages (up to three) in place. Control is related to the set point temperatures of the operating modes of the different system components. The operation of that component can be on/off or modulated within its operating range.

2.4.12.5 Critical design factors

The following factors must be considered:

— evaporative coolers need to be shaded

— the effect of design conditions: close control is difficult

— higher air velocities are required for a standalone system although the temperature depression is less and its humidity exceeds the room air, hence comfort conditions should not be adversely affected.

2.4.12.6 Maintenance

Extra maintenance is required in comparison with a conventional system in terms of the preventative care needed to drain the system and flush the wetted media to prevent the accumulation of mineral deposits. This is particularly important when the system is turned off after summer.

Current guidance on the treatment of water used within direct evaporators[(220)] would suggest that water treatment should not be undertaken, i.e. the water will need to discharge to waste. Also see CIBSE TM13[(121)] for guidance on measures to reduce the risk of Legionnaires' disease. No distinct guidance is given for indirect evaporative systems.

2.4.12.7 Applications

Evaporative cooling is most often used in buildings with relatively small cooling loads, or buildings that do not require tight humidity and temperature control, such as warehouses. It can be used with retrofit applications provided that ducting requirements can be met.

2.4.12.8 Space allowances

Evaporative coolers are somewhat larger than conventional HVAC units for a smaller cooling capacity. Moreover space may also be required for larger air ducts, typically 15–30% for a direct system. Hence their use tends to be restricted to providing supplementary cooling or in combination with desiccant cooling in the UK.

2.4.12.9 Maintenance and health

In the UK, designs have used indirect evaporative cooling systems. Corrosion and scaling of the indirect evaporative cooling coil tubes can occur. These should be rust-resistant, copper bearing, galvanised iron. Scaling in and around the spray area may need to be controlled with chemicals.

2.4.13 Fan coil units

2.4.13.1 Description

A fan coil is a packaged assembly comprising coils(s), condensate tray collection, circulating fan and filter, all contained in a single housing. The fan recirculates air from the space continuously through the coil(s) either directly or via the void in which the fan coil is located. The units can provide heating as well as cooling of the space through the addition of a heating coil. Ventilation is usually provided by a separate central air handling unit (AHU) or it can be drawn through an outside wall by the room unit itself.

Benefits provided by fan coil units include:

— significantly smaller ventilation plant and distribution ductwork than all-air systems

— individual zone control of temperature, if suitable controls fitted

— high cooling capacity

— flexibility to accept future changes in load and layout.

The fan energy requirement for central AHUs supplying fresh air only is normally considerably less than for an all-air system AHU. However, additional power is required by the fan coil units to circulate the room air. The centrifugal and tangential fans used in fan coil units typically have efficiencies far less that of the most efficient AHU fans. Fan coil systems generally have relatively high maintenance costs and short operating lives. The designer should be aware that there is potential for water leaks above the occupied space with fan coils installed in the ceiling void.

Fan coils are best suited to applications with intermittent medium to high sensible loads and where close humidity control is not required, e.g. offices, hotels, restaurants etc.

Fan coils are available in many configurations including:

— *chassis units*: normally horizontal units for mounting in ceiling void

— *cased units*: normally vertical configuration for floor mounting against a wall.

Vertical units require floor and wall space. Vertical units located under windows or on exterior walls are suitable for buildings with high heating requirements. Horizontal models conserve floor space but require adequate floor-to-ceiling heights to ensure that the void in which they are to be located is of sufficient depth.

Fan coil units with free cooling are suitable for some applications (on outside walls of low-rise buildings) and can provide additional economy of operation.

2.4.13.2 Design

The types of fan coil system can be categorised as follows:

— *Two-pipe changeover*: a single coil is supplied with either chilled or heated water via a common water circuit connected to central heating and cooling plant via three-port changeover valves. This method is appropriate only where the summer/winter transition is easily distinguishable, which is not normally the case in the UK.

— *Two-pipe non-changeover*: a single coil is supplied with chilled water only via a water circuit. Heating is normally provided either by a separate perimeter system or by electric heaters in the fan coil units. The use of electric reheaters is not generally recommended for energy efficiency but may be appropriate where heat energy requirements are low, possibly due to high internal gains. Heating the ventilation air can also be used when heat energy requirements are low, although significant energy wastage through fan coil cooling of heated ventilation air can result if zone loads are not similar. Supply air temperatures are usually limited to a maximum of 45 °C.

— Four-pipe: four-pipe fan coils incorporate separate heating and cooling coils, fed by heating and chilled water circuits respectively. Ventilation air can be introduced in the following ways:

  — distributed from a central AHU to stub ducts fitted with dampers located near to the fan coil inlets

  — distributed from a central AHU to fan coil inlet plenums, although care must be taken to avoid the central unit fan pressure adversely affecting the fan coil fans

  — distributed from a central AHU and introduced into the space separately via conventional air terminal devices

  — drawn through an outside wall by the fan coil room unit itself, see Figure 2.42.

The central AHU and distribution ductwork are normally sized to meet only the fresh air requirements of the occupants and so are much smaller than those for an all-air system. Separate introduction of the ventilation air may have energy advantages in some applications by enabling

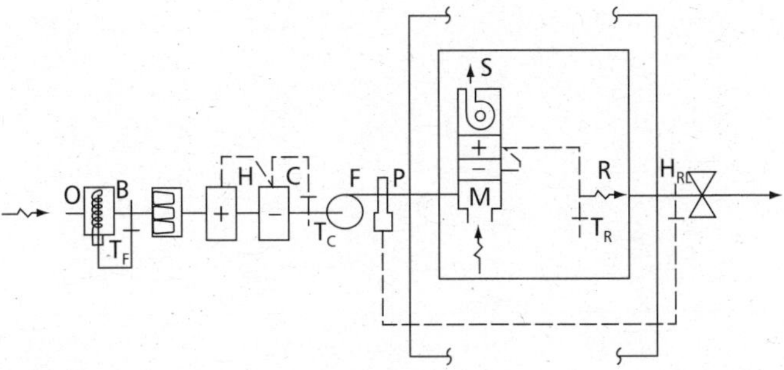

Figure 2.42 Four-pipe fan coil system

the fan coils to be switched-off during mid-season when there is no requirement for heating or cooling.

The central AHU is typically a full fresh air system with off-coil control of heating and cooling coils, including humidification if required, see section 2.5.10. The ventilation air will normally be supplied at a neutral temperature to minimise loads on the fan coils[187]. This temperature may be scheduled down against outside air to provide an element of 'free' cooling in warmer weather. Where required, the unit may provide central control of humidity levels at the dictates of the supply of return air condition or a combination of the two. Refer to section 5 of CIBSE Guide H[201] for detailed guidance on control.

The fan coils provide temperature control on a zone-by-zone basis. Depending on the chilled water temperatures and space conditions, they are also likely to provide some local dehumidification. Fan coil unit capacity can be controlled by coil water flow (waterside), air bypass (airside), or occasionally fan speed. Waterside control can be via four-, three- or two-port coil control valves. Airside control can be via air dampers with actuators supplied with the fan coil. It is potentially simpler to install and commission, and can avoid maintenance problems caused by valves blocking, but may require slightly larger units and can suffer from problems such as carryover. It should be understood that airside control is generally less energy efficient than waterside control as there is always a hot or cold coil operating simultaneously at full duty within the fan coil, and air leakage occurs at the coil dampers.

Water flow and air bypass can be controlled at the dictates of either return air or room temperature sensors. Fan coil units can be supplied complete with integral return air sensors. Control of room conditions can be coarse under certain conditions, as there may be a significant temperature difference between the ceiling void return air temperature and the room temperature, resulting in a reduction of control accuracy. However this arrangement is regarded as an acceptable compromise for most applications because it is cheaper and easier to install than separately wired room sensors. Fan speed control may be automatic (BMS or power-enabled) or manual. Automatic control is usually on/off. Manual speed selection is normally restricted to vertical rooms units where there is access to the controls. Units are available with variable speed motors for either step or modulated speed control. Room temperature sensing is preferred where fan speed control is used, as return air sensors will not give a reliable measure of room temperature when the fan is off. Room temperature sensing may also enable the fans to be turned off if the room temperature is near to the set point, thereby saving fan energy.

The size of the fan coil will normally be determined by the airflow required to cool the space and the water flow temperature. Where cooled ventilation air is introduced separately fan coil sizes will be smaller. The fan coil cooling load should include dehumidification that may take place at the unit. This dehumidification is uncontrolled. Selection purely on sensible loads may lead to significant undersizing. In winter, humidified ventilation air may be dehumidified by the fan coils. Fan coil dehumidification can be reduced by running the chilled water system at elevated temperatures. 'Wet' systems are based on flow/return chilled water temperatures in the region of 6–12 °C. 'Dry' systems operate at higher temperatures in the region of 10–16 °C. This requires larger units to provide the same cooling but can improve the efficiency of the central cooling plant and provide increased opportunity for 'free' cooling.

Where air is returned via the ceiling void, heat pick-up from light fittings may result in temperatures onto the coils being significantly higher than room temperature[221]. This should be taken into account in unit sizing.

Consideration should be given to avoiding conflict between heating and cooling to avoid unnecessary energy waste, particularly where a separate perimeter heating system is provided. One possible approach is to control the heating and cooling in sequence from a common temperature sensor, also to ensure that there is an adequate dead band between heating and cooling. Care should be taken to avoid conflict between fan coil units with separate control systems but located in the same space. This can be overcome by operating several fan coils under a master/slave system from a master controller with sensor.

Where the ventilation air is used for heating, the supply air temperature may be scheduled against outside air temperature or to meet zone requirements. Increasing the supply air temperature may also be used in two-pipe changeover systems as the outside temperature drops to provide heating to zones with small cooling loads. Changeover to heating can then be delayed until all zones require heating. Fan coils provide the opportunity for early morning pre-heat with the primary AHU held off.

2.4.13.3 Construction

Gravity condensate drain systems are preferred for 'wet' systems. Sufficient space should be provided in the ceiling void to achieve an adequate fall. Pumped condensate systems are available but will require maintenance and are inherently less reliable. It is considered good practice to provide condensate overflow systems on 'dry' fan coil systems to cope with accidental local moisture gains and as actual air psychrometrics can differ from the dry design

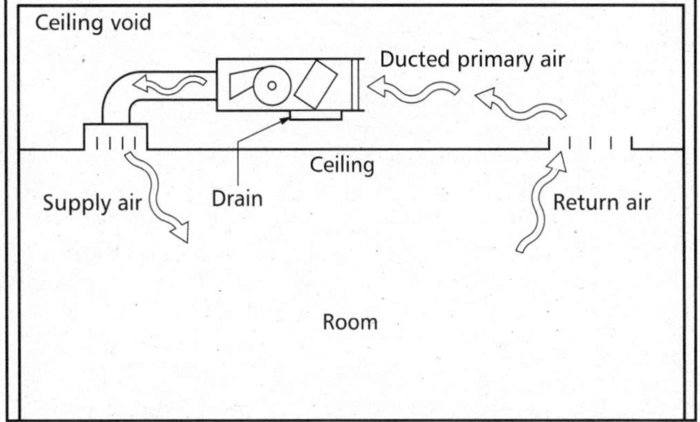

Figure 2.43 Ceiling void fan coil unit with separate primary air

situation. Condensate systems should be provided with suitable traps and air gaps. Drain pans should be fitted under each cooling coil (extending below the cooling valves) with a fall to a drain connection in the bottom of the pan. Drain pans should be removable for cleaning.

Attention should be paid to the combined inlet and casing noise levels and the discharge noise levels to ensure acoustic requirements are met. The information should be available from the fan coil manufacturer. For units installed in ceiling voids, return air grilles in the ceiling can be a particular source of noise. Return air grilles should not be grouped in such a manner that they accentuate noise levels.

Discharge ducting should be designed to avoid noise problems in the room. Generally, noise levels of fan coils will increase as external static resistance is applied across the unit and therefore external static resistance should be designed to be as low as possible. Allowance should be made for the use of flexible corrugated ducting and additional bends caused by site obstructions. There should be adequate return air grilles in the space being served as modern partitioning systems can be comparatively airtight.

Filters are typically a pad type to G2/G3 (see section 2.5.7.3) or a cleanable wire mesh type or cardboard cartridge type that may offer maintenance advantages. Filters are primarily for protecting the coil fins from blocking and fans from build-up of dirt and debris.

Sufficient access should be provided for maintenance, particularly for the fan and motor, cleaning or changing of filters as appropriate, and cleaning and inspection of the condensate drain pan and system. See section 2.5 for equipment requirements.

2.4.14 Ground cooling (air)

2.4.14.1 Description

Ground air cooling systems are primarily used for precooling outdoor air in summer. The outdoor air is supplied to the ventilation system via an underground ducting system where the air exchanges heat with the ground, see Figure 2.44. The thermal mass of the ground helps to compensate for seasonal and diurnal temperature variations. The cooling effect in summer is accompanied by an air preheating effect in winter.

The use of ground air cooling is best suited to climates having a large seasonal and diurnal temperature variations. Sensible cooling only of the supply air is provided. The cooling capacity of the system is limited by ground temperatures and by the ratio of the ground coupling area to building area. The system may be used on its own for applications with low levels of gains and where a rise in peak summertime temperatures is permissible. To meet higher cooling loads it may be used in combination with other technologies, in particular those that provide cooling in the space (e.g. cooled ceilings, slab cooling).

In areas of moving ground water, performance may be significantly improved by replenishment of the cooling. However, the presence of ground water involves extensive sealing precautions. The use of ground air cooling is not suited to rocky ground, nor in areas with radon gas.

2.4.14.2 Design

There are a number of key factors that need to be taken into considered during design including:

- size of system
- vertical depth of pipework
- pipework system including header ducts
- location of intake.

The size of the system will be a function of the cooling required and the area available. Smaller systems, e.g. for improving comfort in dwellings, can be built at relatively low cost. In particular, the header ducts can be of a simple design. Systems requiring large header ducts and those immersed in groundwater are considerably more expensive.

Ground temperatures vary as a function of depth and time of year, see Figure 2.45. Pipework should be positioned vertically as deep as possible in the ground without incurring prohibitive excavation costs (i.e. 2–4 m)[209]. The system may be located beneath buildings with unheated basements. However, if the basement (or lowest floor) is heated, a significant amount of heat is lost, even if well insulated, causing the ground to heat up and performance to drop.

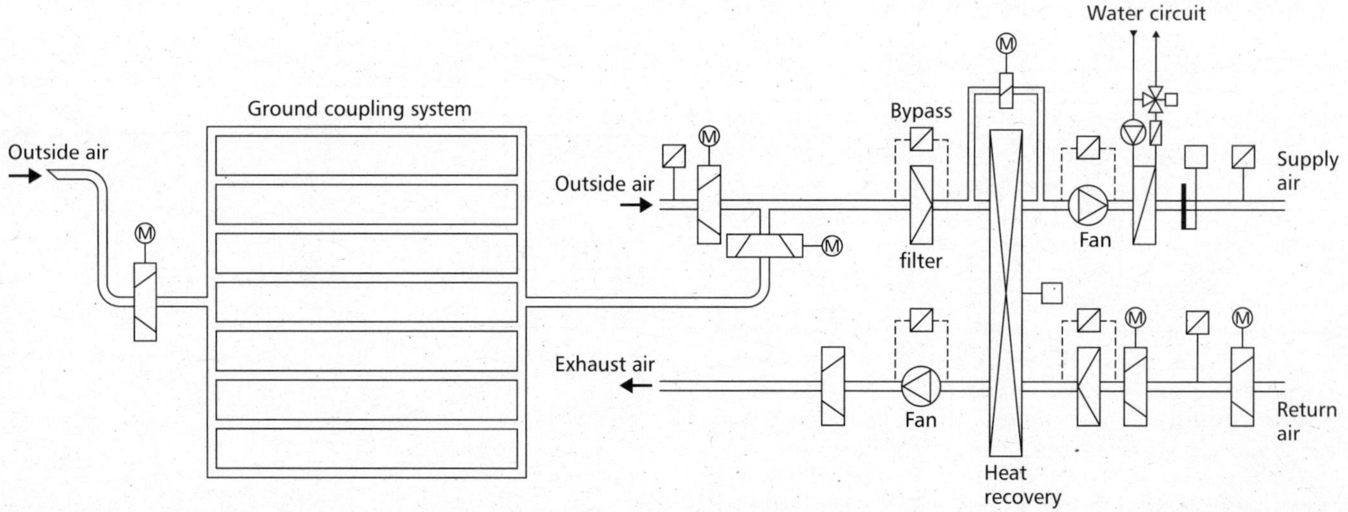

Figure 2.44 Ground air cooling system

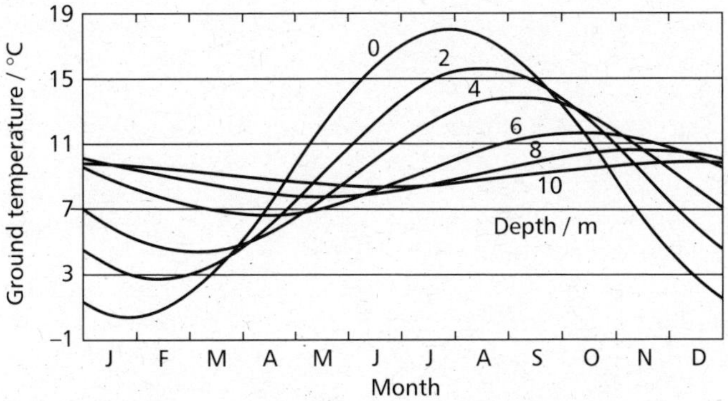

Figure 2.45 Ground temperatures as a function of depth below ground

Parameters that need to be considered when designing the pipework system include the following:

— *Horizontal spacing of the pipes*: this should be such that the mutual interference between adjacent pipes is not too great (e.g. 1 m)[209].

— *Design air velocity*: this should be selected to achieve good heat transfer performance without incurring high pressure drops (e.g. 2 $m \cdot s^{-1}$)[209].

— *Pipe diameter and length*: these should be selected to achieve effective heat exchange[207], typically 80% of the maximum possible (e.g. 200 mm diameter pipes of 20–25 m length, with larger pipes at increased lengths)[209].

— *Soil type*: this has a limited influence on thermal performance (e.g. ±10%)[209], with wet and heavy soils performing better than dry, light soils.

In larger plant, distribution and collection header ducts should be provided. The headers should be adequately sized to ensure that the pressure loss for all flow paths is similar to balance flow rates and for maintenance purposes. For inspection and cleaning, the ducts should be sized to provide crawling access, as a minimum.

The location of the air intake will have an impact on air quality and fouling. Raising the intake above the ground can prevent ingestion of radon gas (which may seep through the ground at any point), reduce the concentration of exhaust fumes from road vehicles, and reduce the air intake temperature. To further assist in ensuring low intake temperatures, intake of air should be avoided above parts of the building exposed to strong sunshine or over macadamised surfaces. Fouling can be avoided both by restricting access and by mounting a tight-fitting grille.

Selection of a suitable operating strategy will depend on the level of load to be met and whether the ground cooling is operating in conjunction with an auxiliary cooling system. Three possible strategies are identified below:

— For low cooling loads the supply air is passed continuously through the system during occupied periods. Ground regeneration takes place when outdoor temperatures are low.

— For medium cooling loads, the supply air is passed through the system only during occupied periods when cooling is needed to maintain required space conditions, e.g. when the ambient temperature exceeds a pre-set maximum. Otherwise, the supply air bypasses the system. This will preserve the stored cooling for use during peak conditions. At night, when ambient temperatures are lower, air is passed through the system for ground regeneration.

— When used in conjunction with an auxiliary cooling system to meet higher loads, air is passed though the ground air cooling system continuously. Direct control of the space conditions is achieved by the auxiliary system. The ground air system acts to pre-cool the supply air. Ground regeneration takes place when outdoor temperatures are low.

More detailed design guidance, charts and analysis tools are available for the early design assessment and simulation of ground air cooling systems[209]. Thermal design simulation packages that have the facility to model three dimensional conduction can also be used for assessment purposes.

2.4.14.3 Construction

Ground air cooling system pipes may be plastic, cement or cement fibre. As the location of ground air cooling system pipes makes them very difficult to repair, particular consideration should be given to durability. Thin-walled ribbed pipes or hoses are not recommended. The latter are also more subject to fouling and are very difficult to clean.

Straight pipes are easier to inspect and maintain than curved pipes. Curved pipes should be fitted with a non-corrosive wire with which to draw through cleaning materials. To ensure that condensate and any cleaning water can drain off, ground air cooling system pipes should be inclined at approximately 1% towards the intake (i.e. against the direction of the airflow).

Due to temperature changes, pipes are subject to considerable thermal expansion. The header ducts must be designed to accept thermal expansion. For this, rubber seals may be provided that not only permit axial movement but also protect against groundwater. To prevent long-term lateral movement, the pipes may be cemented-in at the centre.

Both distribution and collection header ducts should, as far as possible, be airtight and fitted with drainage and siphon, see Figure 2.46. Drainage will enable condensate, ground water or water remaining from cleaning to escape. This is

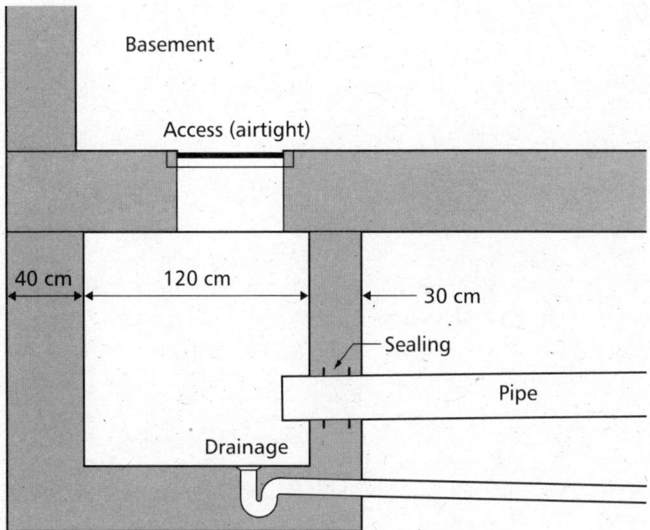

Figure 2.46 Distribution/collection header duct arrangement

particularly important for the distribution header duct as it is at a lower level than the collection header duct.

Constructing the header ducts of concrete will add thermal mass to the system. The preheating effect of the distribution header duct in winter will help to protect against icing.

2.4.15 Ground cooling (water)

2.4.15.1 Description[222,223]

In the UK, the annual swing in mean air temperature is around 20 K. The temperature of the ground, however, even at modest depths, is far more stable. At just two metres below ground level the swing in temperature can reduce to about 8 K, while at a depth of 50 m the swing is reduced to 0 K. In addition, at this depth the ground temperature is approximately equal to the air temperature at that level, that is about 11–13 °C. This stability and ambient temperature makes groundwater a useful source of renewable energy for heating or cooling systems in buildings.

This energy source is usually accessed using a water-to-water heat pump, which provides a means of controlling the temperature of the water delivered to the building and facilitates the most economic sizing of the groundwater collection system. Heating from groundwater almost always requires a heat pump to achieve the necessary delivery temperature. However, useful cooling can be provided by direct connection to the groundwater source. This is known as passive cooling, and is the subject of this section. Section 2.4.16 deals with the use of ground coupled heating and cooling using heat pumps.

Ground water systems are suitable for both retrofit and new-build applications in almost any type of building, including residential. The only proviso is that the geological conditions are suitable and there is sufficient land available on which to install the selected ground water coupling system.

Systems are defined as either open or closed loop. An open loop system relies on the direct extraction and use of groundwater. A closed loop system relies on the conductive heat transfer from the surrounding earth or rock into a continuous loop of pipe through which water is circulated.

Open loop systems

These are relatively common and have been incorporated in building designs for many years where there is a readily available supply of accessible natural water. They include not just well systems, but also systems using adjacent lakes, rivers and ponds. The use of sea water has also been recorded. An Environment Agency licence must be obtained for both the abstraction and use of groundwater. The Agency must be assured that no pollutant (other than heat, and even that may be limited as a condition of the licence) will enter the groundwater source. The licence will be for a specific extraction rate.

Although thermally very efficient, open loop systems tend to suffer from physical blockage from silt and from corrosion due to dissolved salts unless great care is taken in screening, filtering and chemically treating the water. The licence conditions, maintenance and durability issues can significantly increase the overall whole life operating costs, which has reduced the popularity of open loop systems.

Typical open loop systems require, following assessment of the geological suitability of the location, two vertical boreholes be drilled to a suitable depth to access the aquifer. The system must then be tested to ensure that the water quality is acceptable and that the required and licenced extraction and re-injection rates can be met. Decisions about filtration and materials specification can then be made.

A hydraulic system is then installed which extracts water, passes it through the primary coils of a heat exchanger and re-injects the water into the aquifer through the re-injection well. Typical groundwater supply temperatures are in the range 6–10 °C and typical re-injection temperatures are 12–18 °C (although this may be controlled under the extraction licence).

A schematic showing the basic functions of a passive ground water cooling system is shown in Figure 2.47.

Open loop systems fed by groundwater at 8 °C can typically cool water to 12 °C on the secondary side of the heat exchanger. With a water extraction rate of 25 litre·s^{-1} and a maximum re-injection temperature of 18 °C this could provide a peak cooling capacity of 900 kW·h. The cooled water on the secondary side of the heat exchanger may be used for a variety purposes as in conventional cooling design, including, for example:

— circulation through an underfloor cooling or chilled ceiling or beam system

— to supply fan coil units.

Underfloor cooling systems may require a higher circulation temperature to minimise the risk of condensation.

The groundwater cooling system in the BRE Environmental Building (see Figure 2.48) provides 35 kW of cooling with the borehole temperature picking up 5 K across the primary coils of the heat exchanger. The secondary coils deliver cooled water to underfloor coils which reduce internal temperatures by 2 K at peak loads.

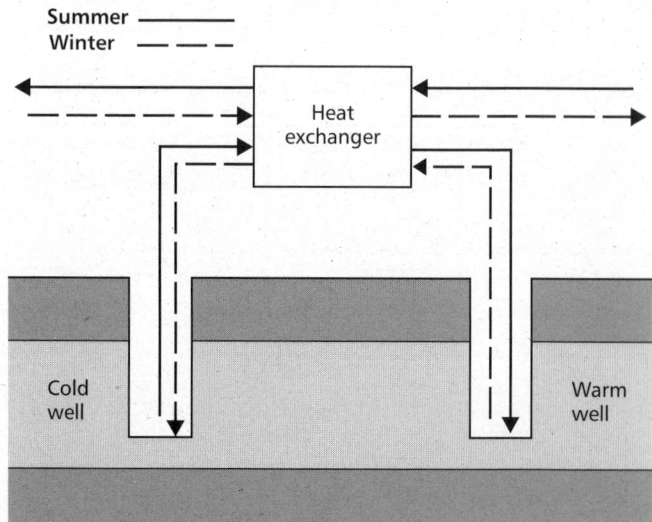

Figure 2.47 Ground water cooling system

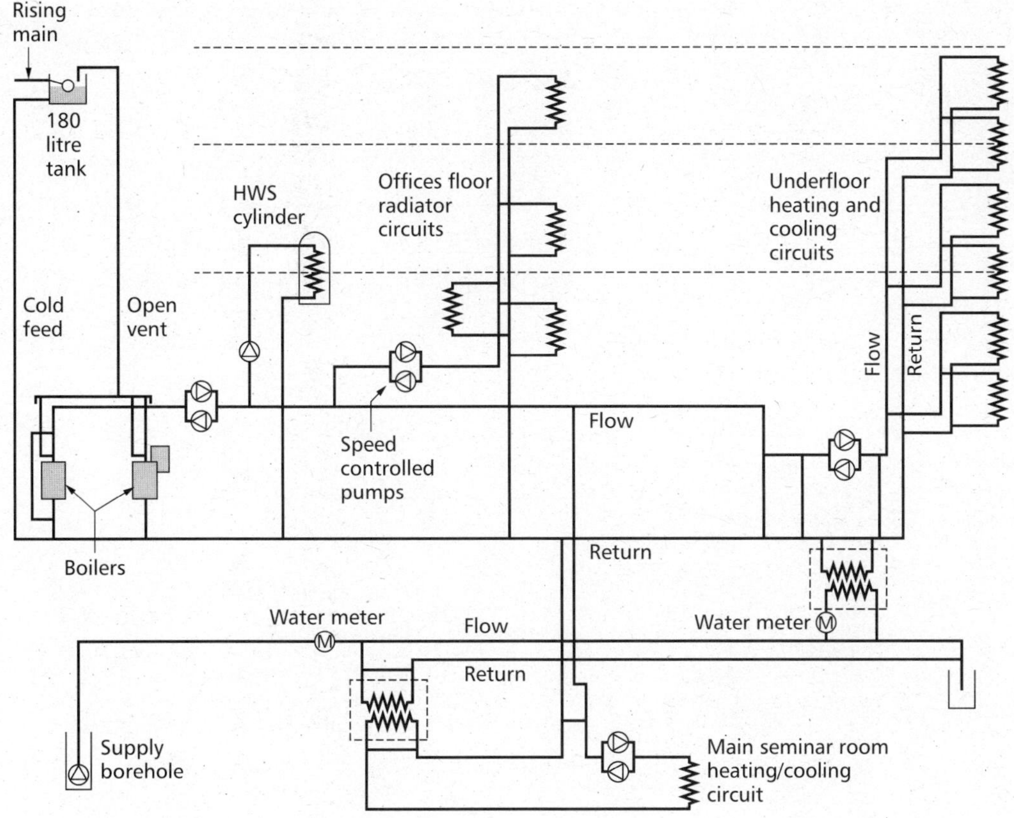

Figure 4.38 Schematic of BRE groundwater cooling system

Closed loop systems

These systems are extremely simple, comprising a continuous loop of high-density polyethylene pipe, through which water is circulated, buried in the ground. The water is recirculated by a conventional pump and can be used directly by the cooling distribution system in the building. There are a number of types of closed loop:

— *Vertical boreholes*: these are inserted as U-tubes into small diameter (130 mm) pre-drilled boreholes up to 100 m deep. These are backfilled with high-density grout both to seal the bore and prevent cross-contamination of any aquifers the borehole may pass through and to ensure good thermal contact between the pipe wall and the surrounding ground. Vertical boreholes have the highest performance and means of heat rejection, particularly if there is a movement of groundwater across the loop.

— *Horizontal loops*: these are laid singly or in pairs in trenches approximately 2 m deep, which are back-filled with fine aggregate. They require a greater plot area than vertical loops but are cheaper to install. However, since the ground temperature is more stable at greater depths, their performance is affected by how close they are to the surface.

— '*Slinkies*': these are a variation of horizontal loops, so-called because they are supplied as a tightly coiled spring similar to but larger than the children's toy of that name. The spring is released and the resulting looped pipework is either spread horizontally at the bottom of a trench one metre in width and depth or installed vertically in a two metre deep narrow (0.25 m) trench. Performance is similar to that of a horizontal loop but may be reduced if the pipe overlaps itself. It is a useful technique for situations where excavation is easy and a large amount of land is available, and is a cost effective way of maximising the length of pipe installed and hence the overall system capacity.

2.4.15.2 Performance

Heat transfer rates are likely to be low because of the small temperature differences between the loop circulating water and the ground. Extrapolating from closed loop ground source heat pump design suggests that vertical boreholes may deliver 25 $W \cdot m^{-1}$ bore depth, but this has not yet been widely achieved. Horizontal systems are likely to yield less cooling since the ground temperature will be higher in summer when the main demand for cooling occurs.

2.4.15.3 Critical design factors

Peak cooling loads and the related monthly energy demand profiles will be required before any system sizing can be started. Drilling may present problems if a water-bearing sand layer is encountered and the borehole continually fills with sand. In these circumstances a cased borehole drilling method will be required, adding to both drilling time and cost. Homogenous rocks such as middle and upper chalk are easy to drill, as are sandstone and limestone. Pebble beds, gravel and clay can be problematic. Site specific advice may be sought from specialist groundwater cooling consultants. Advice may also be sought from the British Geological Survey*. About 50% of the UK landmass is suitable for aquifer based open loop technology, and virtually 100% is suitable for closed loop installations.

2.4.15.4 Space requirements

For both open and closed loop systems the main space implications are external to the building and it must be

*British Geological Survey, Keyworth, Nottingham NG12 5GG, UK

recognised that the ground loop installation operation itself can occupy a significant part of the total site area. This is often at a time in the normal construction programme when other groundworks are being carried out and site huts etc. are being located.

As far as possible the horizontal distance between open loop system pits should be at least 100–150 m.

2.4.15.5 Economics

The economic analysis should relate to the area of space served within the building and the relative costs of useful cooling delivered. Passive cooling system installation costs are dominated by the cost of excavation of the boreholes or loop arrays. Operating costs of the circulating costs must be carefully assessed. Sewerage costs will be incurred if it is not possible to discharge water back to the ground.

2.4.15.6 Maintenance

With open loop systems it can be difficult to pressurise the ground to return the water, hence there may be problems with boreholes silting-up due to the growth of algae and the settling of suspended solids. No defrost cycle is required for the water-source heat pumps as they operate over a more moderate range of temperatures.

2.4.16 Heat pumps

(*Note*: dehumidifers are considered in section 2.5.10.)

2.4.16.1 Description

A heat pump is a machine that transports low-grade energy and converts it into useful heating energy. Heat pumps are available as both heating only or reverse cycle heating/cooling systems and are classified classified according to the type of heat source and the heat distribution medium used, e.g. air-to-water, air-to-air etc. Table 2.35 lists examples of heat source and distribution systems.

Under certain circumstances the heat from a source is transferred to the heat pump by a secondary medium and an intermediate circuit. The secondary medium is used to prevent cross contamination and to protect the overall system in case of breakdown (e.g. pipe breakage) or freezing. The secondary medium can be brine or glycol, or a similar low temperature medium, e.g. fluorocarbon refrigerant.

Table 2.35 Examples of heat source and distribution systems

Heat source	Heat distribution medium	Typical distribution system
Air (ambient, heat recovery)	Air	Air diffusers Individual units: — dehumidifiers
Water (surface, ground, industrial waste, process cooling water)	Water	Radiators: — underfloor coils — fan coils — induction units
Ground (closed loop)	Water	Radiators: — underfloor coils — fan coils — induction units

Each of these systems can be applied as heating only or reverse cycle heating/cooling in the following situations:

— *commercial*: offices, shops, hotels

— *domestic*: institutional residential buildings, dwellings, conservatories

— *recreational*: leisure centres, pubs and clubs

— *industrial*: factories, warehouses and processing

— *educational*: schools and further education.

2.4.16.2 Design

Enhancement of operational efficiency of systems

Systems can be enhanced by employing:

— heat recovery from air, steam or water (Figure 2.49)

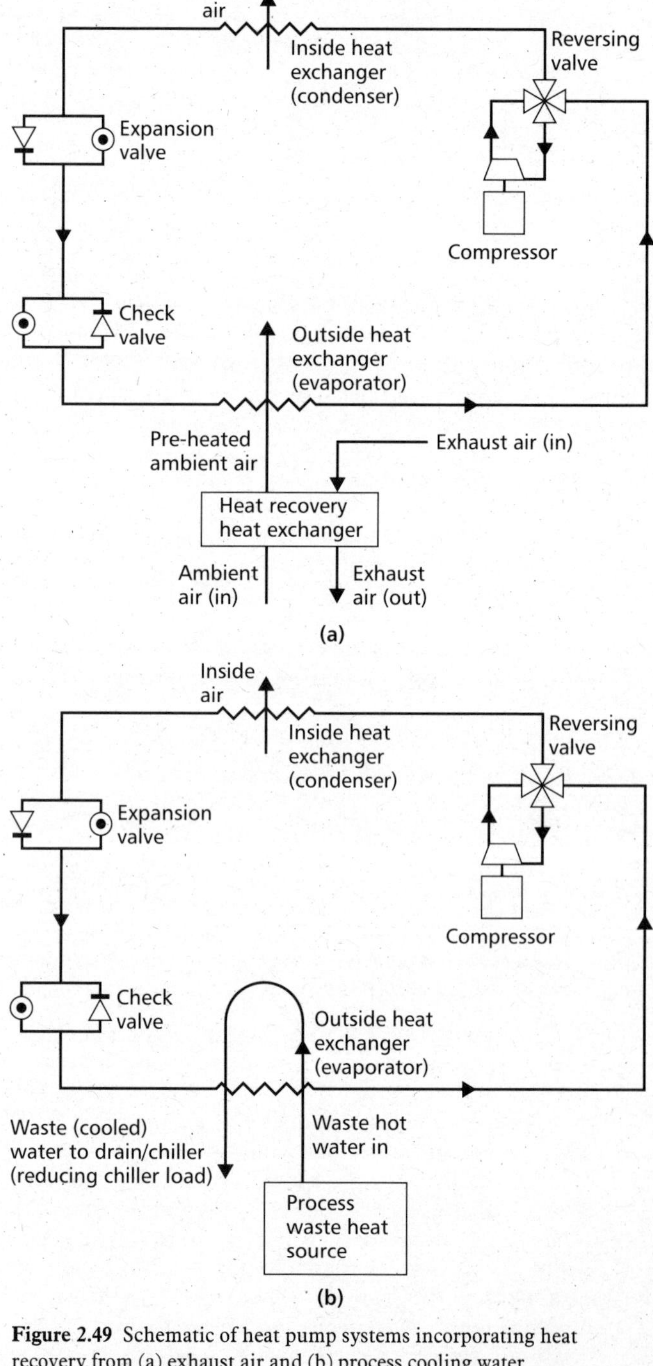

Figure 2.49 Schematic of heat pump systems incorporating heat recovery from (a) exhaust air and (b) process cooling water

— renewable primary energy sources, e.g. solar, wind, water, ground, geothermal etc.

System performance evaluation

Like other refrigeration systems, the performance efficiency of heat pumps is expressed as a coefficient of performance (COP). All coefficients of performance relate to the ratio of energy or heat output to the energy input.

(*a*) Theoretical COP

For the vapour compression cycle where a cooling output is considered, the COP is the ratio of refrigeration effect to the work done by the compressor and is known as the COP_R.

For the vapour compression cycle where a heating output is considered, the COP is the ratio of heat from the condenser to the work done and is know as COP_H, i.e:

$$\text{COP}_H = \frac{\text{Enthalpy change due to condensation of vapour}}{\text{Enthalpy change due to compression of vapour}} \quad (2.17)$$

Hence, from Figure 2.50, the theoretical coefficient of performance is given by:

$$\text{COP}_H = \frac{H_3 - H_4}{H_3 - H_2} \quad (2.18)$$

The theoretical COP gives an indication of the viability of a particular heat pump option and a full economic assessment is always necessary in final selection of equipment. Seasonal performance factors (SPFs) may be used to account of variations in energy source conditions and any additional energy usage within the systems, pumps, defrost, distribution and running hours.

(*b*) Practical COP

The coefficient of performance for the heat pump itself is termed the appliance COP. This is useful when comparing one heat pump with another. When considering heat pumps for heating, it has become accepted industry practice for the input energy to include energy used by the following, in addition to the energy used by the compressor:

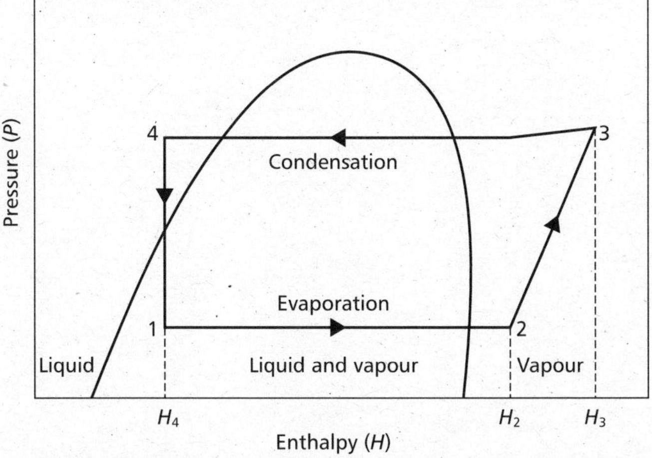

Figure 2.50 Pressure enthalpy diagram for the vapour compression cycle

— outdoor fans or pumps required by the low temperature source

— crankcase heater.

The appliance COP should not be used to determine the running costs of an installation but only as one of the criteria considered when selecting a particular heat pump.

(*c*) Overall system efficiency and seasonal COP

Overall system efficiency can be established and expressed as a COP by including the energy input to supplementary heating and distribution fans or pumps as part of the total energy input. It is not a true COP because items that are not part of the heat pump operation are also considered. But it does give an indication of the total energy used by the system compared to the heat output, enabling an estimation of consumption and running costs to be established.

The seasonal coefficient of performance of a heat pump is defined as the appliance COP averaged over the heating season. The values of coefficients of performance are dependent on compression ratios, temperatures, cycle arrangements, source and distribution temperatures and will also vary depending on which of the coefficients of performance is being considered. Table 2.36 shows the variation of COP values for a typical vapour compression air-to-air heat pump using ambient air as a source.

Table 2.36 Variation of COP for a typical vapour compression air-to-air heat pump

Theoretical COP		Actual COP		
COP_R	COP_H	Appliance	System	Seasonal
4	5	3.0	2.3	2.5 to 3.0

Control strategy

Correct control of the heat pump system is vital to maintain performance. Particular care must be taken with the heat pump system to avoid rapid cycling as this is both harmful to the equipment and inefficient in energy usage. Controls can be divided into two groups: those installed for unit protection by the manufacturers and those for the correct operation of the unit and system.

Critical design factors

To provide correct selection and application of the heat pump systems to ensure the operation is at maximum efficiency, consider the following:

— designing for heating only or heating/cooling

— designing to suit energy source

— high overall operational efficiency

— selecting a suitable primary power source

— environmental considerations

— controls for stand-alone systems, multiple systems or building management systems

— simplicity of the design (avoid over-complication).

2.4.17 Induction units

2.4.17.1 Description

Induction units use the energy in a high velocity primary air jet to induce room air to flow over a coil and hence promote air circulation within the conditioned space. The benefits provided by induction units include:

— significantly smaller ventilation plant and distribution ductwork than all-air systems

— individual zone control of temperature.

In order to produce the air jet velocity needed to induce airflow, induction systems need to operate at higher pressures than those of low velocity systems, resulting in fan power and energy penalties. Induction units are best suited to applications with intermittent medium to high sensible loads but where close humidity control is not required, e.g. offices, hotels, shops and restaurants.

Induction units are normally cased in a vertical configuration for wall mounting although units designed for overhead installation are available. The vertical units require floor and wall space. Vertical units located under windows or on exterior walls are suitable for buildings with high heating requirements.

2.4.17.2 Design

The various types of induction system are as follows:

— *Two-pipe changeover*: coils are supplied with either chilled or heated water by a common water circuit connected to central heating and cooling plant via three-port changeover valves. This method is appropriate only where the summer/winter transition is easily distinguishable.

— *Two-pipe non-changeover*: coils are supplied with chilled water only via a water circuit, see Figure 2.51. Heating is normally provided either by a separate perimeter system or by electric heaters in the induction units. The use of electric reheaters is not generally recommended for energy efficiency, but may be appropriate where heat energy requirements are low (possibly due to high internal gains). Heating the primary air can also be used when heat energy requirements are low, although significant energy wastage can result if zone loads are not similar through induction cooling of heated ventilation air. Primary air temperatures are usually limited to a maximum of 45 °C.

— *Four-pipe*: induction units incorporate separate heating and cooling coils, fed by heating and chilled water circuits respectively[201]. The primary air volume supplied by the central ventilation unit must be adequate to:

— meet fresh air requirements of the occupants

— provide adequate induction of room air to generate satisfactory air movement

— provide sufficient sensible cooling with induced air without generating unacceptable levels of noise

— deal with the dehumidification load at achievable chilled water temperature

— provide winter humidification, if necessary.

Induction units are rarely used to dehumidify room air due to the inconvenience of condensate disposal. Therefore, all latent loads must be dealt with by the primary air. Secondary water temperatures must therefore be elevated above the maximum likely dew point temperature of the room air, see Figure 2.52. The elevated temperatures can improve the efficiency of the central cooling plant and provide more opportunity for 'free cooling', see Figure 2.53.

The central ventilation unit is typically a full fresh air system with off-coil control of heating and cooling coils, including humidification if required. The ventilation supply air temperature will normally be scheduled against outside air temperature to provide cooling in the summer. Dehumidification should be controlled to minimise the

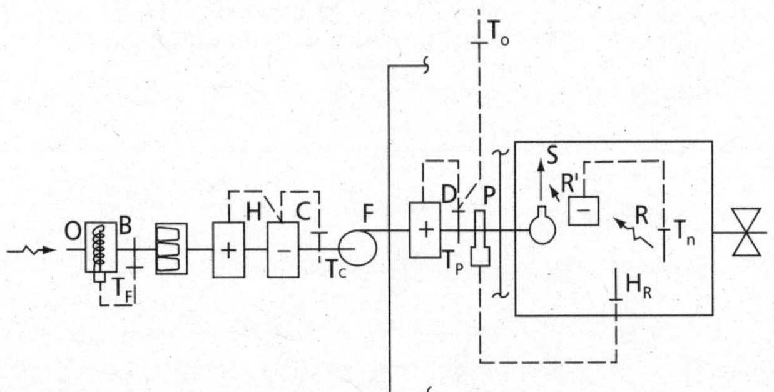

Figure 2.51 Two-pipe non-changeover induction system

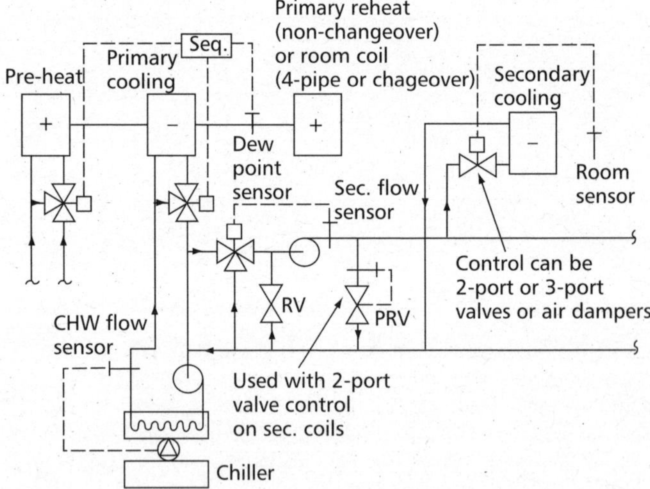

Figure 2.52 Induction system: water control (dry room coils)

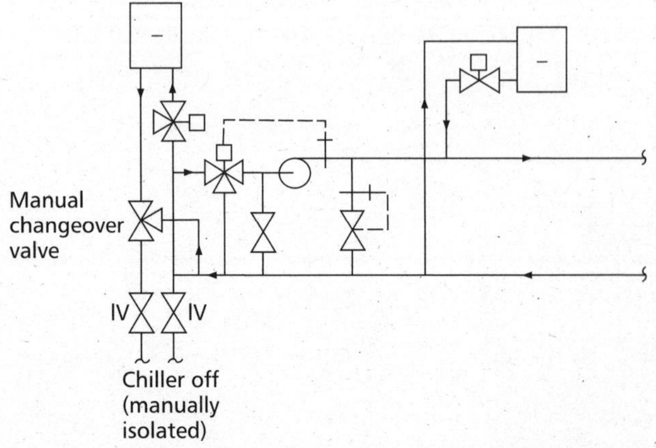

Figure 2.53 Induction system: utilisation of 'free cooling' in primary chilled water

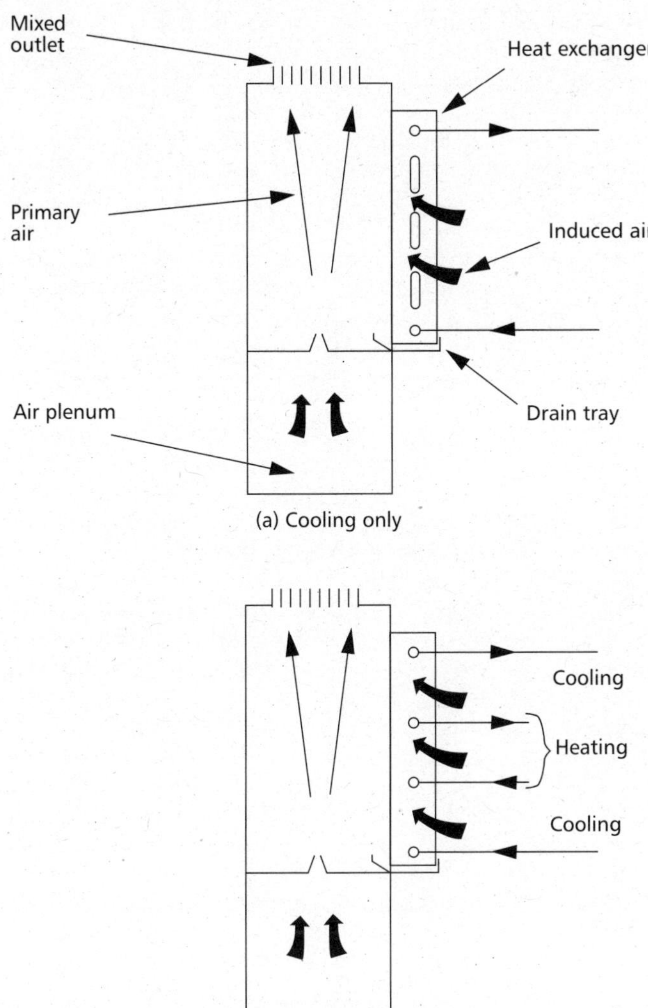

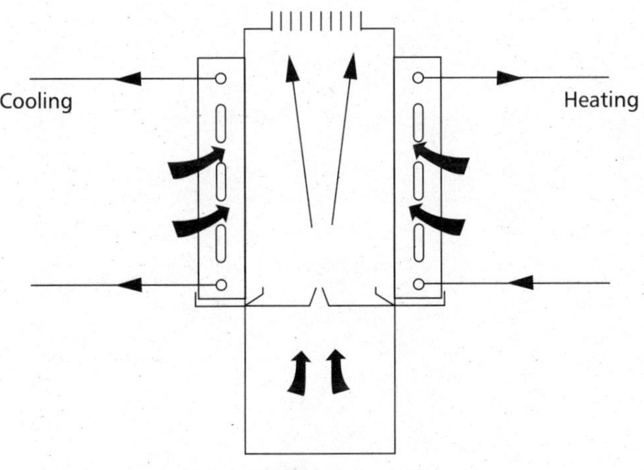

Figure 2.54 Induction units: alternative coil arrangements

risk of condensation. This may be by limiting the supply air moisture content, or at the dictates of a return air humidity sensor, or a combination of the two. Ductwork distribution systems are often medium or high pressure.

In winter the air may be supplied at a neutral temperature or scheduled to provide heating, normally either against outside air temperature or to meet zone requirements. With two-pipe changeover systems, heating may be provided to zones with small cooling loads by increasing the supply air temperature as the outside temperature falls. Changeover to heating can then be delayed until all zones require heating. Humidification may be controlled at the dictates of the supply or return air condition, or a combination of the two.

The induction units provide temperature control on a zone-by-zone basis. Induction unit capacity can normally be controlled by coil water flow (waterside) or air bypass (airside). Waterside control can be via four-, three- or two-port coil control valves. Airside control is potentially simpler (one actuator) and will avoid maintenance problems caused by valves blocking but, depending on the configuration, may require slightly larger units and can suffer from problems such as carryover.

Consideration should be given to avoiding conflict between heating and cooling to avoid unnecessary energy waste, particularly where a separate perimeter heating system is provided. One possible approach is to control the heating and cooling in sequence from a common temperature sensor.

Induction units may be used for natural convective heating with the primary plant off. This may assist with early morning pre-heating, which will be costly in terms of energy consumption unless provision is made for recirculation. Access should be provided for maintenance, particularly for cleaning and inspection of the condensate drain pan.

2.4.17.3 Construction

Drain pans should be fitted under each cooling coil to collect moisture from temporary latent loads. Drain pans should be removable for cleaning.

2.4.18 Room air conditioners

2.4.18.1 General

Also known as window units and through-wall air conditioners, these are packaged units incorporating a room air-side evaporator (direct expansion cooling coil), an outside air-cooled conditioner, a compressor and an expansion device. Winter heating is often by electric coil, although some manufacturers offer a low-pressure hot water coil as an option. Where appropriate, moisture penetration may be minimised by the use of high efficiency louvres. Dust penetration may be minimised by the use of sand trap louvres. The main advantage of room air conditioners is that they are self-contained, requiring only an appropriate electricity supply and an outside wall in which to be mounted, normally at low level. No plant space is required. It is also possible to install heat pump versions for increased energy efficiency. Manufacturers' literature needs careful interpretation and corrections to ratings will normally be required to account for UK conditions.

2.4.18.2 Control

In their basic form, these units offer the crudest form of air conditioning. Room occupants normally have control over the units through switching of the compressors. However, this gives consequent swings in room temperature, humidity and noise level.

2.4.19 Single duct constant air volume systems

2.4.19.1 Description

While maintaining a constant air volume, single duct constant volume systems vary the supply air temperature in response to space conditions. The simplest system is a supply unit serving a single-temperature control zone; a single-zone system. Applications include large rooms such as lecture theatres. They should not be used for multiple zones with different heating/cooling loads because control of conditions will be very poor and they will be very inefficient in operation.

Single-zone systems with room control maintain temperature closely and efficiently. The same systems with off-coil control are also used where air is to be supplied to a number of zones at the same conditions. Examples of this are displacement systems, see section 2.4.1, and systems that provide fresh air in conjunction with space conditioning systems, such as fan coil units.

The multi-zone reheat system is a development of the single-zone system. Conditioned air is supplied by the central unit, generally at a fixed cold temperature. This air is then reheated as required by heaters in the supply ductwork to each zone. This provides space temperature control for zones of unequal loading. However, energy wastage can occur when air cooled by the central unit is subsequently reheated. Where the total air supply is greater than the outside air requirement, recirculation is normally used to minimise energy requirements. For full fresh air systems, heat recovery devices should be considered, see section 2.5.6.

2.4.19.2 Design

Single-zone room control

The typical arrangement for a simple single zone system is shown in Figure 2.55. The temperature sensor T_R controls the cooling coil and reheater in sequence within its proportional band, see Figure 2.56. The humidity sensor H_{RH} will bring in the cooling coil out of sequence and T_R will call for simultaneous reheat to deal with overcooling.

Energy wastage by reheating after dehumidification can be reduced by using face-and-bypass dampers. In the scheme shown in Figure 2.57, T_R positions the dampers in sequence with the heating coil to provide an appropriate supply condition rather than controlling cooling directly via the cooling coil. When combined with appropriate cooling media temperatures, see Figure 2.58, this method provides adequate humidity control without wasteful reheat. Room humidity will rise, particularly at low sensible heat loads. However protection against high humidity can be provided by using a humidity sensor (H_{RH}) to override damper control, the reheater being brought in to deal with resultant overcooling. The cooling coil can be installed without a control device, provided that chilled water temperatures are maintained at an appropriate level.

Figure 2.59 shows a typical arrangement with recirculation. The temperature sensor T_R controls the cooling coil, mixing dampers and reheater in sequence within its proportional band (see Figure 2.60).

In the scheme shown in Figure 2.61, instead of directly controlling flow of the cooling medium through the cooling coil, an appropriate supply condition is provided by positioning the bypass and recirculation dampers in sequence with the heating coil in response to an appropriate signal from T_R. This gives closer control of room humidity than face-and-bypass dampers because air extracted from the conditioned room air only is bypassed around the cooling coil.

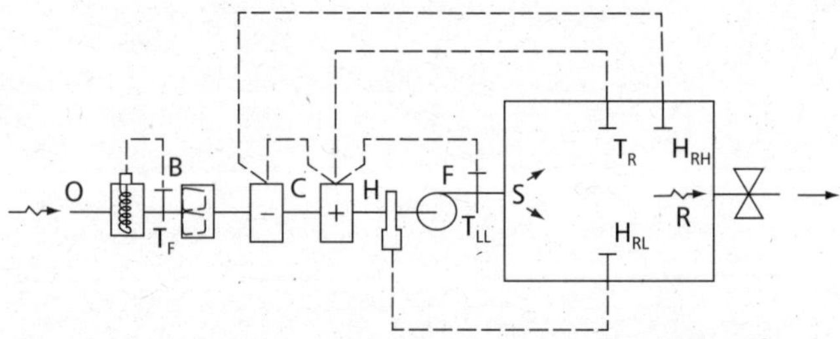

Figure 2.55 Full fresh air system with steam humidification; sequence control with humidity override

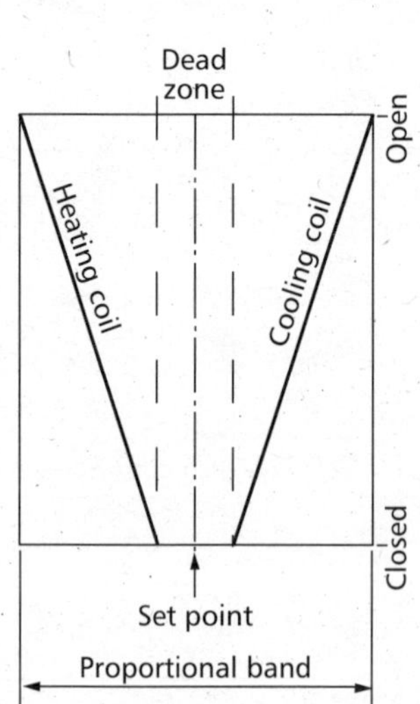

Figure 2.56 Sequential control of heating and cooling coils

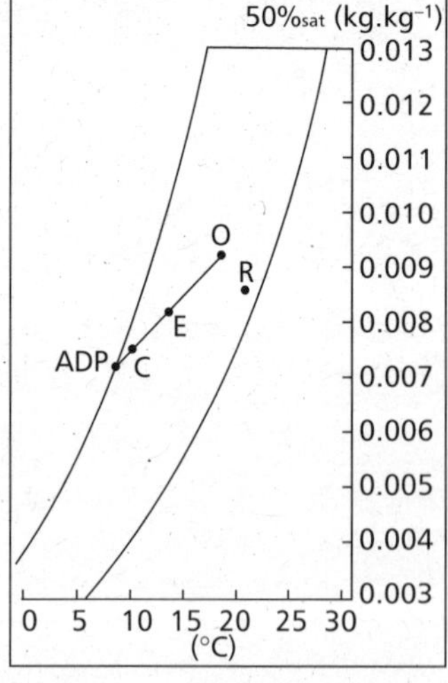

Figure 2.58 Full fresh air with steam humidification; sequence control with face-and-bypass dampers; psychrometric process

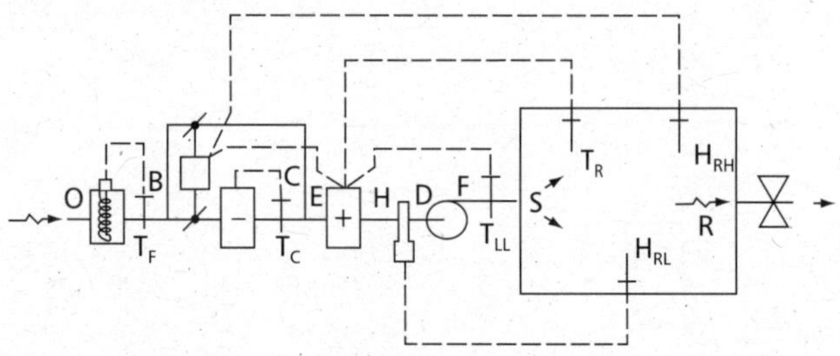

Figure 2.57 Full fresh air system with steam humidification; sequence control with face-and-bypass dampers

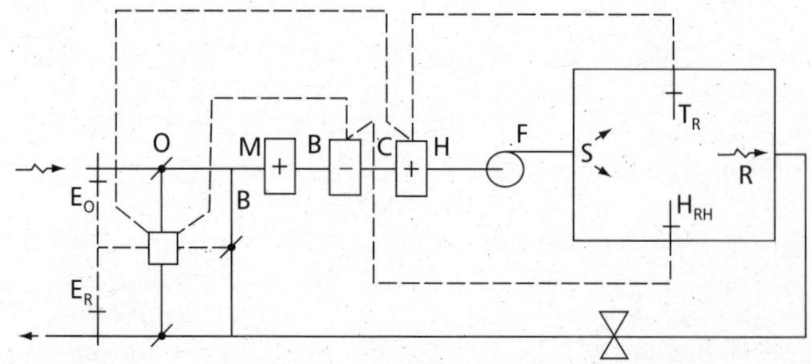

Figure 2.59 Recirculation: sequence control with humidity override

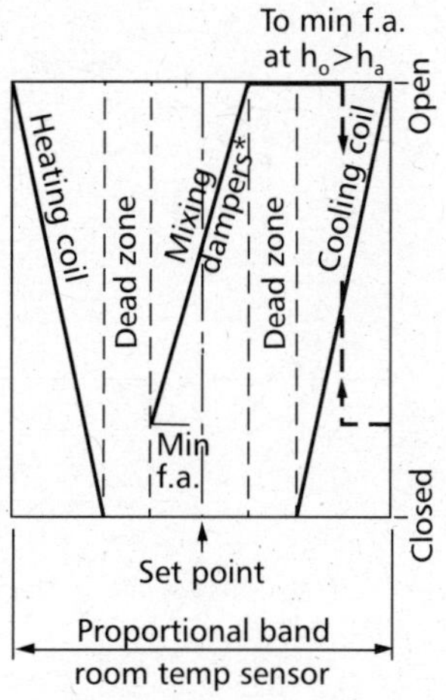

* For a full fresh air system with heat recovery, the mixing dampers are replaced by the heat recovery device in the above sequence.

Figure 2.60 Sequential control for recirculation systems

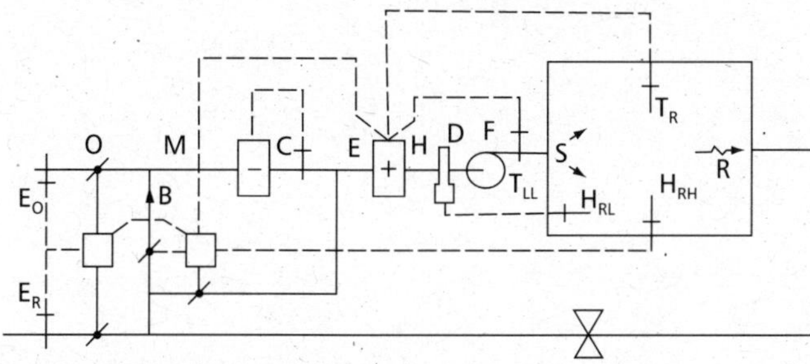

Figure 2.61 Recirculation with steam humidification: sequence control with room air bypass

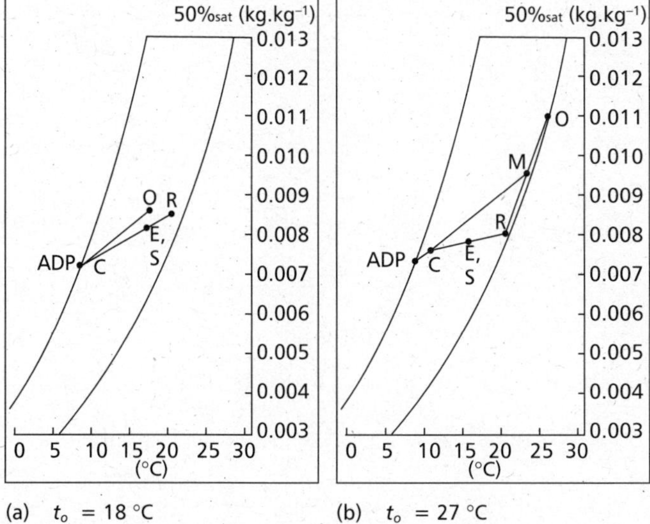

Figure 2.62 Recirculation with steam humidification: sequence control with room air bypass; psychrometric chart

A part-load analysis of mass flow and temperature balance can be used to determine the on- and off-coil conditions for the cooling coil and hence the resultant room percentage saturation (see Figure 2.62). Control is otherwise similar to face-and-bypass control.

Single-zone off-coil control

Figure 2.63 shows an arrangement in which the off-coil dry bulb temperature sensor T_C controls the cooling coil, pre-heater and reheater in sequence to achieve its set point, adjusted against the outside temperature sensor T_O, if appropriate. Alternatively, the room temperature sensor

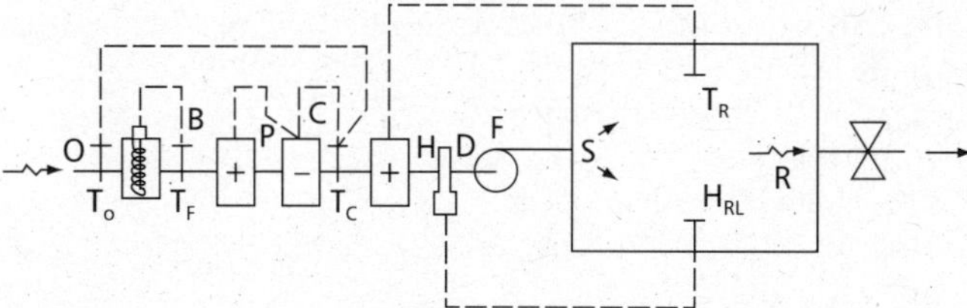

Figure 2.63 Full fresh air with steam humidification; off-coil control

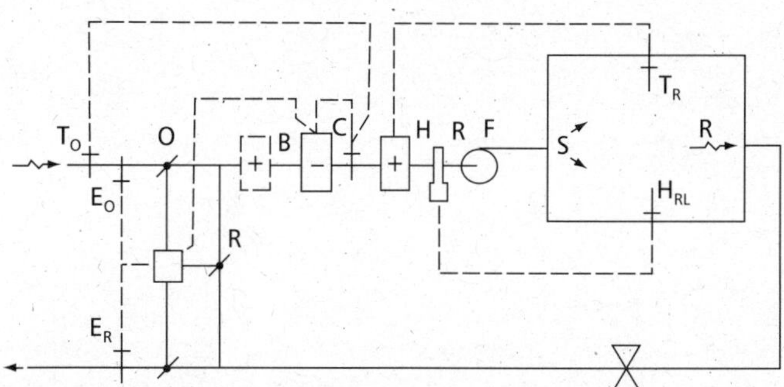

Figure 2.64 Recirculation; off-coil control

T_R can be used to control the output of the reheater to achieve the desired room temperature.

Figure 2.64 shows the typical arrangement with recirculation. The off-coil dry-bulb temperature sensor T_C controls the cooling coil, mixing dampers and heating coil in sequence within its proportional band (see Figure 2.60). The pre-heater (shown dotted) is incorporated into the sequence only if large fresh air rates promote high mixing ratios, hence low winter temperatures, through the air handling plant. Alternatively, a low limit sensor could be used to bring in the heating coil as necessary, see section 2.4.4. If adiabatic humidification is employed to deal with the associated low winter moisture contents, a pre-heater may be necessary to heat mixed air. The pre-heater is optional, but if not present a low limit sensor should be provided to bring in the reheater to prevent cold draughts on start-up during wide load variations.

Multi-zone reheat system

Figure 2.65 shows a typical arrangement for a terminal reheat system. Air is treated centrally and distributed at a common temperature and moisture content such that:

— the temperature is sufficiently low to deal with the greatest sensible heat gain (or lowest net loss)

— the moisture content is at a level which will satisfy the zone having the lowest sensible heat ratio

— adequate fresh air is provided to the zone having the highest mixing ratio of local fresh air to supply air.

For any zone that experiences overcooling by the centrally treated air, the room temperature sensor T_R brings in the respective zonal reheater.

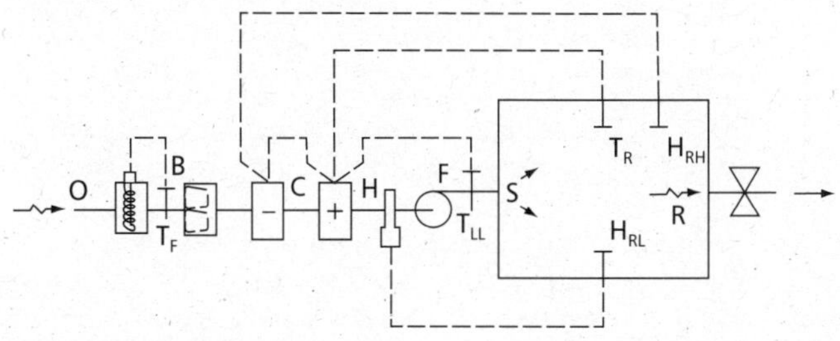

Figure 2.65 Terminal reheat

The condition of the distribution air can be varied with outside temperature when the system is serving perimeter zones only. Internal zones are likely to experience high cooling loads even at low external temperatures, hence the air leaving the central plant must be kept at the minimum design condition. Serving perimeter and internal zones from one plant can prove wasteful of energy unless humidity control necessitates low supply temperatures or it is possible to achieve low supply temperatures by utilising sources of 'free cooling'.

In order to reduce unnecessary reheat, control signals from the reheater control actuators can be analysed centrally, the resetting schedule for the off-coil sensor being based on the zone requiring the lowest supply air temperature, i.e. minimum reheat requirement.

Dew-point systems provide saturated air at the cooling coil at all times to provide very stable humidity conditions when air is reheated to the desired space temperature. However, these systems are only necessary for special applications such as laboratories, and should normally be avoided as they can be very inefficient.

2.4.19.3 Construction

See section 2.5 for equipment requirements.

2.4.20 Single duct variable air volume (VAV) systems

2.4.20.1 Description

VAV systems control the temperature in a space by varying the quantity of air supplied rather than the supply air temperature. Terminal devices at the zones modulate the quantity of supply air to the space. The supply air temperature is held relatively constant, depending on the season. VAV systems can provide reduced fan energy consumption in comparison with constant volume systems. They are primarily suited to applications with a year round cooling load such as deep plan offices. Potential problem areas include: humidity control, provision of sufficient outside air, and air movement. Where close humidity control is critical, e.g. laboratories or process work, constant volume airflow may be required.

2.4.20.2 Design

The control of VAV systems is considered in detail in CIBSE Guide H[201]. Varying the volume of air supplied to a space has the following consequences:

- its ability to offset sensible heat gains is reduced
- its ability to offset latent heat gains is reduced
- if the mixing ratio remains constant, its ability to dilute odours, carbon dioxide etc. is reduced
- unless special air terminal devices are utilised, its ability to create room air movement is reduced.

The volume of supply air is normally varied in relation to room air temperature (sensors T_{RE} and T_{RW} in Figure 2.66) and will respond only to changes in sensible gain. Hence, unless the main load variations are caused by occupancy changes, unacceptable humidity rise and depletion of fresh air can result. The effect on room air movement will depend largely on the turndown efficiency of the terminal device, see section 2.4.2.1. Generally, humidity rise on turndown can be kept within acceptable limits provided that a cooling differential of about 8–12 K is used, see Figure 2.67. Limiting turndown and incorporating reheat may be used in zones with particularly high latent gains such as conference rooms.

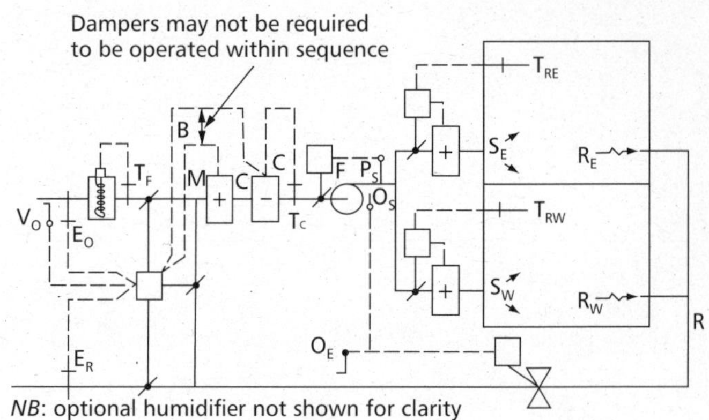

Figure 2.66 VAV with terminal reheat

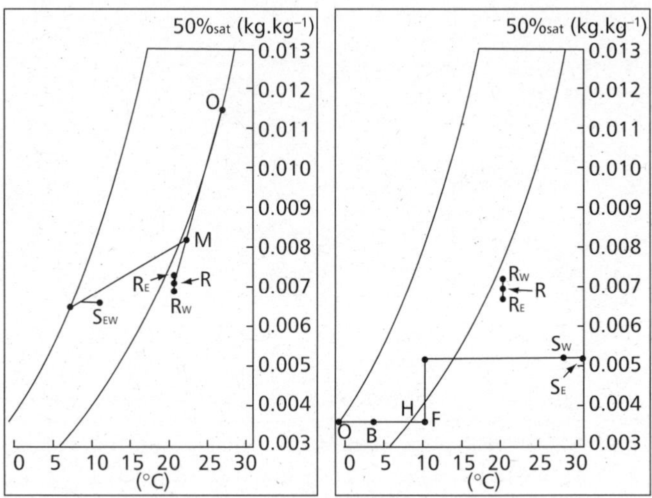

Figure 2.67 VAV with terminal reheat; psychrometric process

Fresh air rates on turndown can be maintained at the central plant by means of an inlet velocity sensor to control the position of the mixing dampers.

The efficiency with turndown depends on:

- the position selected for sensing flow changes
- the mechanism employed for reducing total flow rate (see section 2.5.11)
- the mechanism by which flow dependent signals are converted to movement at the actuator.

If the supply fan duty is to be modulated from a static pressure sensor in the supply ductwork, the sensor must be in a position that gives a reasonable indication of total flow requirements. Medium to high duct velocities are needed to improve sensor sensitivity to flow changes[201,224,225].

The extract system must respond to changes in the supply flow rates to avoid over/under-pressurisation of the building. This may be dealt with at two levels:

(*a*) *Individual control zones*: if zones are separated by solid partitions any imbalance in supply flow rates between zones must produce corresponding changes in extract flow rates. Thus the extract duct for each zone will contain a damper controlled to follow changes in supply volume. In the case of a multi-storey open plan building, this may be necessary on a floor by floor basis.

(*b*) *Choice of fan characteristics*: the supply and extract fans will usually be of different types to cope with dissimilar system pressure requirements. Hence, their characteristics will differ accordingly.

Air handling unit (AHU) fans normally achieve variable volume by variable speed drive, variable pitch or inlet guide vane control, see section 2.5.11.

For perimeter zones where minimum loads fall below the potential cooling at full turndown, some means of heating will be necessary to avoid overcooling. (*Note*: this may also be a consideration for internal zones with intermittent loads, e.g. meeting rooms.)

If a step change in load from net cooling to net heating occurs in all zones simultaneously, a changeover coil in the central plant may be used to supply either constant temperature heated or cooled air. Where there is no step change, the system can be controlled to cycle between heating or cooling depending on the requirement of the majority of the zones using the thermal inertia of the building to limit hunting. Alternatively, it may be possible to reset the set point of the off-coil sensor in the manner of a variable temperature system, typically by scheduling against outside air temperature. This has the advantage of expanding the range of loads that the system can accommodate and eliminating some of the disadvantages of turndown. However, fan running costs increase because of the reduced turndown over the whole year.

Terminal reheat

To meet heating requirements reheater batteries are provided in the terminal devices. These are normally controlled in sequence with airflow from a room temperature sensor. As the requirement for cooling reduces (and heating increases), airflow is reduced to a minimum and the reheaters are brought on. Compared to constant volume reheat, this reduces energy consumption as the amount of air being cooled and then reheated is reduced.

Perimeter heating

If significant perimeter down-draught is likely, under-window heating may be desirable, see Figure 2.68. The output of the heating system must be controlled in such a way as to prevent the heat appearing as a cooling load. One solution is to control the heating and cooling in sequence from a common temperature sensor. Water temperature should also be scheduled against outside air temperature and compensated for different orientations if appropriate. The resetting schedule is shown in Figure 2.69 and is based on providing sufficient heating to deal with the greatest potential cooling at maximum turndown. An extension of this principle is to utilise a VAV system for internal zones and a variable temperature air conditioning system to deal with perimeter loads.

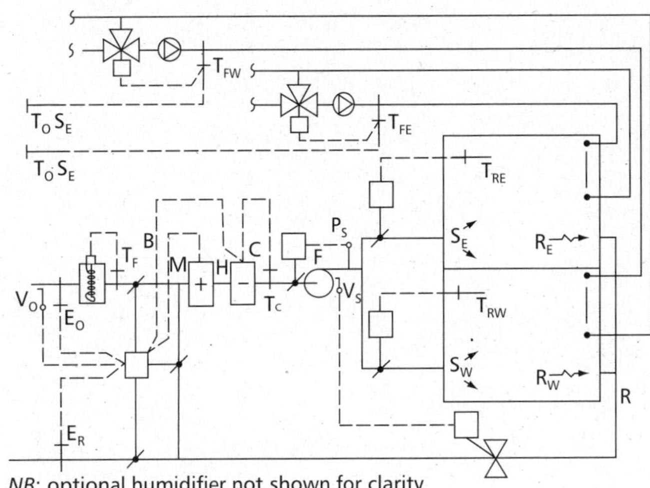

Figure 2.68 VAV with perimeter heating

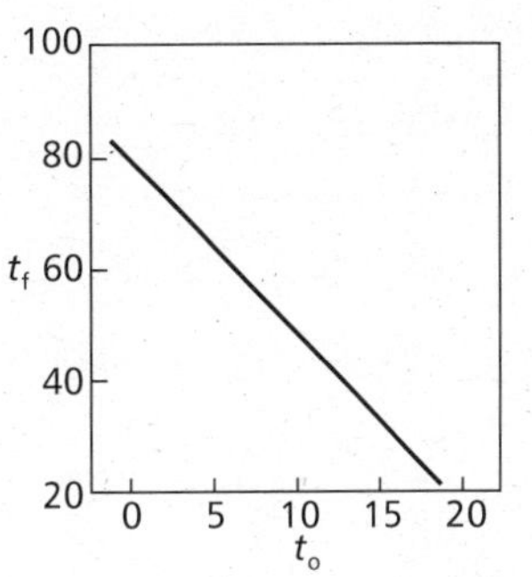

Figure 2.69 VAV with perimeter heating; resetting schedule for flow temperature sensors against outside air temperature

Induction VAV — air terminal

A separate constant volume primary air duct or system is used to encourage constant throw from supply air terminals. A separate source of primary air can be used to provide a constant fresh air supply, scheduled against outside air temperature as appropriate. Primary air is discharged at a constant volume through induction nozzles or slots at the variable volume supply outlet, which may be in the form of a side-wall grille, ceiling diffuser or induction nozzle.

Induction VAV — ceiling plenum

Air from the central unit is mixed with air from the ceiling void, which has been heated through exhaust luminaires. Primary air reduces with cooling load whilst total air supply volume is kept relatively constant. This results in good fan economy whilst room air movement is greater than that obtained from conventional throttling devices.

Fan-assisted VAV

In principle, this system is similar to the ceiling plenum induction system but uses a fan within each terminal unit to enhance room air movement on turndown and blend warm air from the ceiling void with that from the central unit.

There are two arrangements in common use, whereby the fan and VAV damper are connected either in parallel or in series (see Figure 2.70(e) and 2.70(f) respectively). The parallel arrangement requires the fan and damper to be controlled in sequence, the fan being brought in only on full turndown. With the series configuration the fan runs continuously, thus maintaining constant room air movement (and noise generation) with varying proportions of

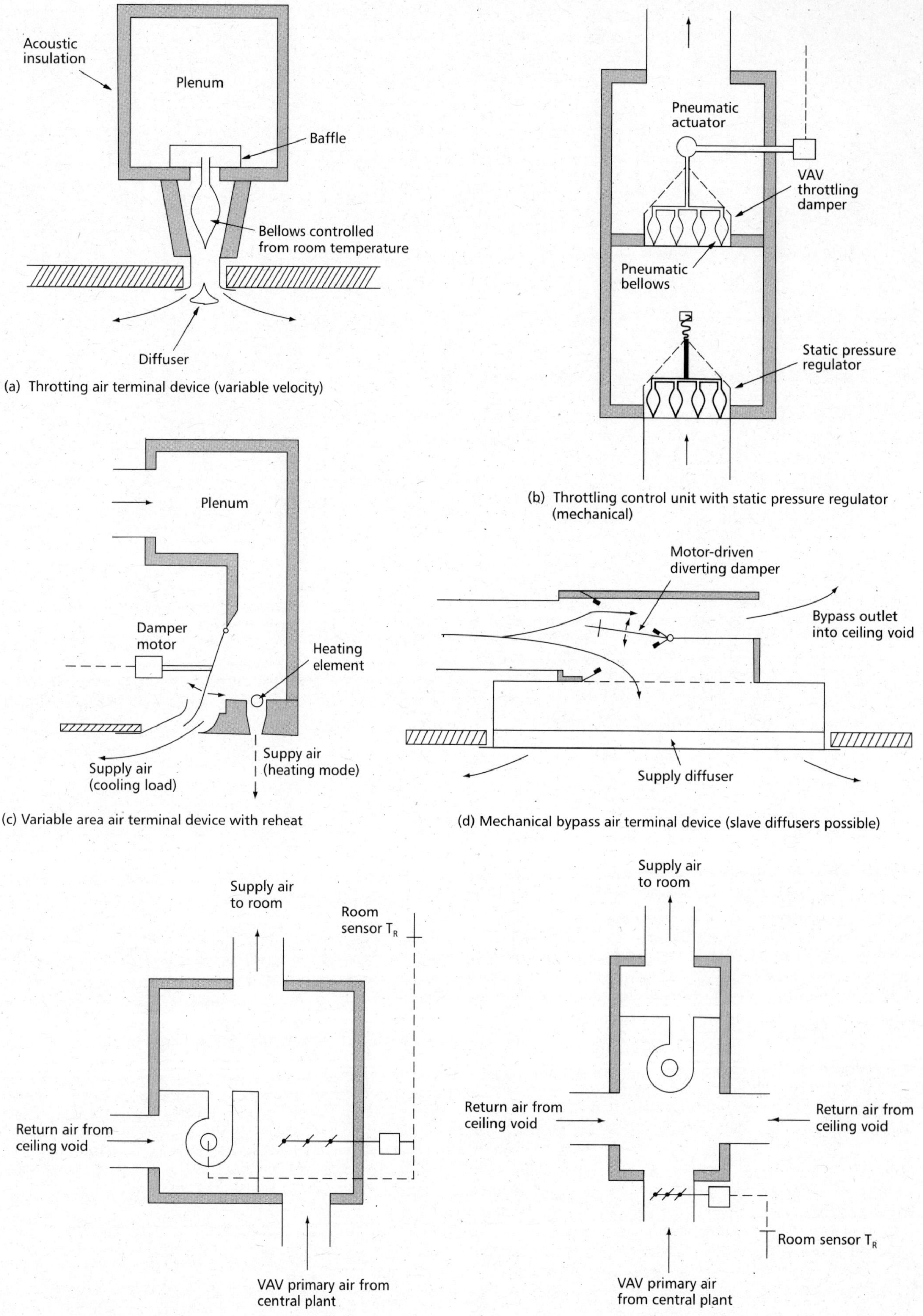

Acoustic insulation

Plenum

Baffle

Bellows controlled from room temperature

Diffuser

(a) Throtting air terminal device (variable velocity)

Pneumatic actuator

VAV throttling damper

Pneumatic bellows

Static pressure regulator

(b) Throttling control unit with static pressure regulator (mechanical)

Plenum

Damper motor

Heating element

Supply air (cooling load)

Suppy air (heating mode)

(c) Variable area air terminal device with reheat

Motor-driven diverting damper

Bypass outlet into ceiling void

Supply diffuser

(d) Mechanical bypass air terminal device (slave diffusers possible)

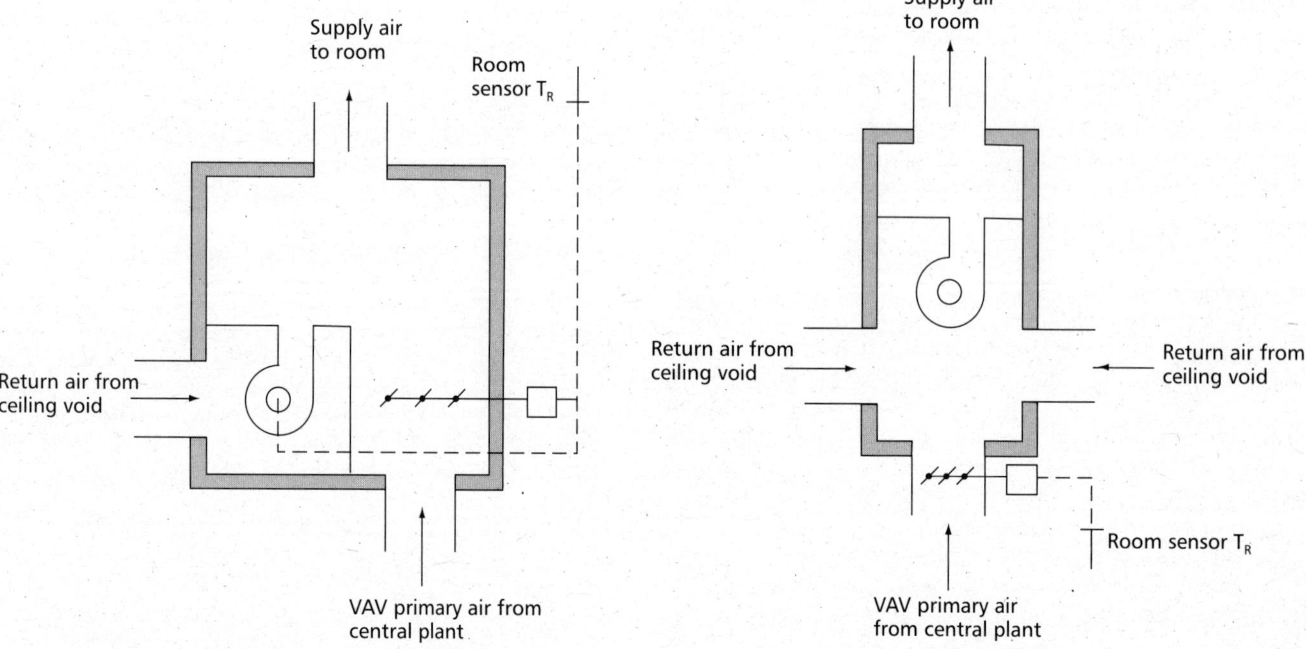

(e) Fan assisted control unit — parallel arrangement

(f) Fan assisted control unit — series arrangement

Figure 2.70 VAV devices

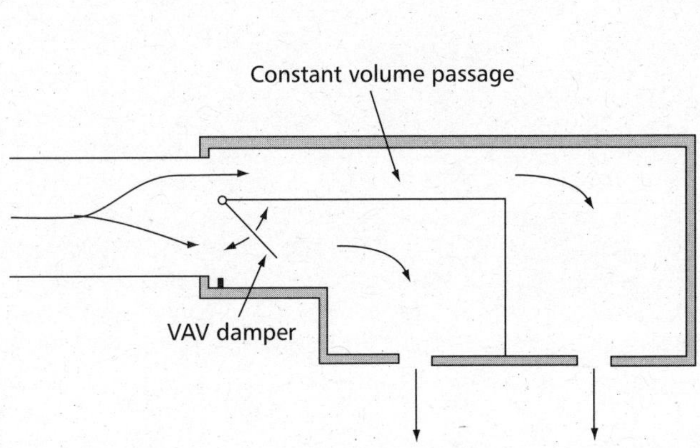

(g) Induction air terminal device using slots

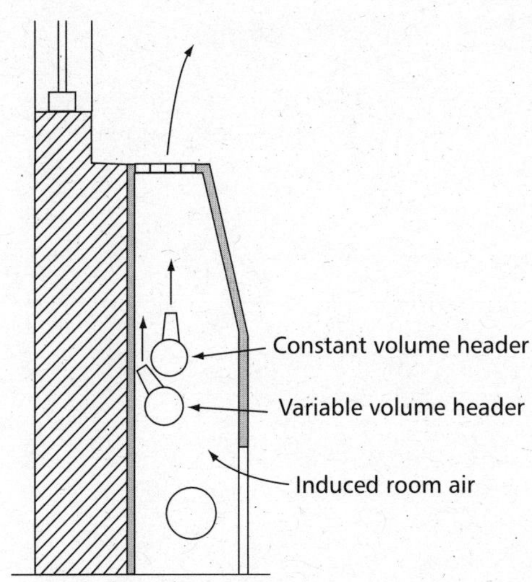

(h) Induction air terminal device using nozzles — located under window

Figure 2.70 VAV devices — *continued*

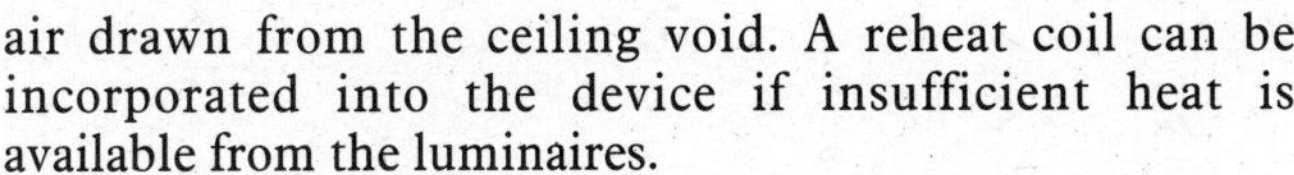

air drawn from the ceiling void. A reheat coil can be incorporated into the device if insufficient heat is available from the luminaires.

Fan-assisted terminals with reheat can be used for early morning preheat with the central plant held off.

2.4.20.3 Construction

See section 2.5 for equipment requirements.

The VAV device for varying airflow to a control zone may either form part of the air distribution system and serve a number of conventional air terminal devices, or it may be the air terminal device itself. In the latter case it may incorporate some means of maintaining reasonably constant throw. Figure 2.70 shows examples of these devices.

Flow rate may be modulated by:

— throttling by dampers

— throttling by variable area

— mechanical bypass by diverting supply air back to the air handler (constant volume fan).

Control of the device can be achieved by the system being operated, utilising the pressure available in the supply duct, or by the use of an external power source, either electric or pneumatic.

The device may also incorporate some means of system balance under varying flow conditions, normally by automatic damper adjustment from a static pressure sensor. Alternatively, this function may be fulfilled by a separate damper box.

Most modern VAV systems use velocity reset VAV boxes. Primary air volume is set between minimum and maximum settings in relation to space temperature. These are pressure dependent and the system is essentially self-balancing.

VAV devices may be actuated mechanically, by means of a spring loaded regulator which closes as pressure increases, or pressure-actuated using the changes in branch pressure to position a throttling damper. Both types increase fan pressure requirement by 100 to 200 Pa.

2.4.21 Split systems

2.4.21.1 General notes

Split systems[224,226] are room air conditioner units, or small air handling units, incorporating a direct-expansion cooling coil, a filter and a fan to recirculate room air. They can be connected to a remote air, or water-cooled, condensing unit via low-pressure vapour and high-pressure liquid refrigerant lines. The external units are normally roof mounted and contain twin compressors, heat exchangers and air circulation fans. In cooling mode the external unit heat exchangers function as a refrigerant condenser producing liquid which is circulated to the remote room units. This passes through the coils, absorbs heat, evaporates and the gas is returned to the compressors. When operating in a heating mode the functions are reversed.

A three-pipe system can be installed to offer simultaneous heating and cooling within a building. Applications include small commercial and retail premises.

2.4.21.2 Performance

The maximum capacity of an external unit is of the order of 30 kW. Up to eight room terminals, having outputs typically in the range 2.5–15 kW, may be served by one external unit. There is normally a 100 m limitation in the length of pipework between the external unit and the most remote room unit, with a maximum height difference of about 50 m.

2.4.21.3 Control

With smaller units, control can be achieved by switching the compressor. Larger direct expansion coils may incorporate refrigerant flow control or hot-gas bypass, possibly with multi-stage loading and unloading of reciprocating compressors.

2.4.21.4 Maintenance

Care must be taken in their design to ensure oil entrainment in the refrigerant lines. Appropriate refrigerant leakage detection measures must be put in place.

2.4.22 Sea/river/lake water cooling

2.4.22.1 Description

Water is pumped from the depths by an open loop system and cooling extracted via a heat exchanger, see Figure 2.71. This cooling can either be used directly or indirectly. Direct applications include cooling the space (e.g. via chilled beams/ceiling, water-cooled slabs) or the supply air. Examples of indirect use are as condenser water or with heat pumps to provide heating and cooling. In winter, warm water returning to the heat exchanger can be used to pre-heat incoming fresh air. The primary benefits are 'free cooling' and low operating costs. Such systems are restricted to buildings that are located near a water source with suitable temperatures and thermal capacity. (*Note*: small lakes can warm up significantly during the summer.)

2.4.22.2 Design

Key design parameters include:

— the depth from which water is drawn

— water temperature

— water flow rate.

Generally, the greater the depth, the lower the water temperature. However, pump head will also increase with depth, and so the cooling benefits will need to be balanced against pump energy requirements.The water temperature will also determine the function for which the water can be used, i.e. direct cooling or condenser water cooling. Equations for surface water heat transfer are provided in CIBSE Guide C, section 3[(192)].

The water flow rate required will be determined by the water temperature and the cooling loads or heat rejection requirements. Operation of the system will generally be at the dictates of the cooling system. Temperature limits may be used to determine the operating mode, e.g. free cooling below, condenser water cooling above.

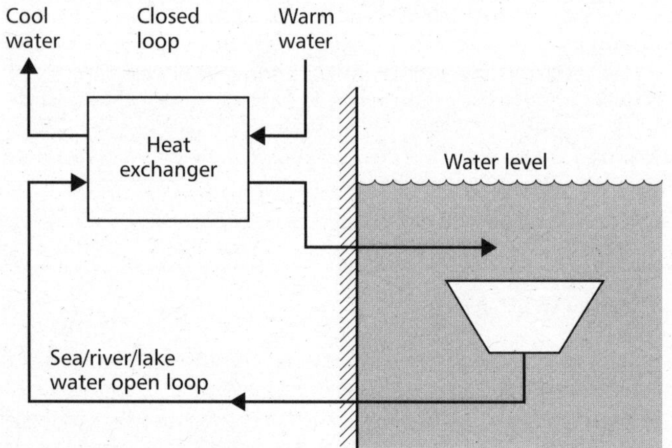

Figure 2.71 Schematic of sea/river/lake water cooling system

2.4.22.3 Construction

Suitable materials should be selected and measures undertaken to minimise fouling, biological growth and corrosion, particularly in marine environments. Possible corrosion resistant materials include titanium and treated aluminium. Screens and filters should be provided to protect against fouling of the heat exchangers. Cathodic protection can be used to impede marine growth and corrosion. (*Note*: chlorine has been used to minimise biological growth but is harmful to the environment and marine life.)

2.5 Equipment

2.5.1 Introduction

This section sets out critical design issues relating to the specific items of equipment and the key points to be considered in the selection of equipment.

2.5.2 Ventilation air intake and discharge points

Each intake and discharge point should be protected from the weather by louvres, cowls or similar devices. Any space behind or under louvres or cowls should be 'tanked' and drained if there is a possibility of penetration by, and accumulation of, rain or snow that could stagnate and give rise to unpleasant odours within the building. Bird screens and insert mesh should be used to prevent entry by birds or other large objects. Intake points should be situated to minimise pollution from potential sources (existing and planned) including:

— traffic

— boiler flues and exhausts from standby generators (or combined heat and power engines)

— cooling towers and other heat rejection plant

— vents from plumbing, oil storage tanks etc.

— ventilation exhausts from fume cupboards, kitchens, toilets, car parks, print rooms

— stagnant water (e.g. on flat roofs)

— roosting ledges for birds (droppings can be a source of biological contamination)

— gardens or areas of vegetation (sources of fungal spores or pollen)

— areas where leaves or other litter might accumulate

— radon gas.

Because traffic is generally a ground level pollutant, there is normally a reduction in pollutant concentration with height, so that concentrations are lower at roof level. Vehicle loading bays can be subject to traffic pollution.

Whilst wet cooling towers give rise to the greatest health concern because of the potential risk of *Legionnella*, other heat rejection equipment can also affect system performance by elevating the temperature of the intake air and increasing the cooling demand on the system.

Locating system discharge and intake points close together facilitates the use of some heat recovery strategies. However, it will also increase the risk of 'short-circuiting'. Even extract systems from 'normal' occupied areas will contain pollutants generated by internal sources. These may not represent a health hazard but may still result in an odour nuisance if recirculated. The more remote the intake from the discharge point the less the risk of short-circuiting. Locating the intake and discharge on different facades can also help to reduce the risk. However, wind forces on the two fan systems (which will be balanced for openings on the same façade) may affect fan performance and cause flow instabilities, particularly where fan pressures are low. The influence of wind pressures can be reduced by:

- positioning openings within a zone of minimal pressure fluctuation
- providing balanced openings which face in two or more opposite directions or an omni-directional roof-mounted cowl.

Measures that should be considered to minimise re-entry from contaminated sources include[227]:

- group exhaust to increase plume rise due to the greater momentum of the combined exhaust
- place inlets on roof where wind pressures will not vary greatly with direction to ensure greater stability
- avoid locating exhaust outlets within enclosures or architectural screens that may hold contaminants within areas of flow recirculation
- discharge exhausts vertically
- locate wall exhausts on the upper third of a façade and intakes on the lower third to take advantage of normal wind separation on a building façade (although consideration should be given to flow recirculation that can occur on a leeward façade)
- avoiding locating inlets and exhausts near edges of walls or roofs due to pressure fluctuations.

Toxic and hazardous exhaust must not be discharged in a manner that will result in environmental pollution. The local authority Environmental Health Officer should be consulted to ensure that the proposed discharges will be acceptable. A European Directive[228] gives mandatory air quality standards for smoke and sulphur dioxide, see also section 2.3.2.1. A vertical discharge stack, capable of imparting a high efflux velocity to the exhaust, may be required. If so, provision must be made for handling rainwater and avoiding corrosion. Industrial processes resulting in polluting emissions to air, water or land come under the requirements of the Environmental Protection Act[229]. Sections 1.6.4 and 1.6.5 of CIBSE Guide A[12] provide guideline values for pollutants and guidance on filtration strategy, respectively. Reference should also be made to CIBSE TM21[32] for more detailed guidance on pollution sources and assessment methods.

2.5.3 Natural ventilation devices

2.5.3.1 Openable window design

Window performance testing

BS EN 12207[98], which partially replaces BS 6375: Part 1[230], classifies window and door performance according to their permeability, see Table 2.37. Reference air permeabilities are recorded for each class of window related to the permeability of both the overall area and of the opening joint. These are defined at a test pressure of 100 Pa. BS EN 12207 describes how limits can be defined for other test pressures and how windows are subsequently classified according to the relationship between the two permeability assessments.

Figure 2.72 shows the upper limits of each class, which are derived from the reference air permeabilities at 100 Pa related to the area and length of opening joint, see Table 2.37.

Table 2.37 Reference air permeabilities at 100 Pa and maximum test pressures related to overall area and length of opening joint[98]

Class	Reference air permeability at 100 Pa and maximum test pressure			
	Related to overall area		Related to length of opening joint	
	Permeability / $(m^3 \cdot h^{-1}) \cdot m^{-2}$	Max. test pressure / Pa	Permeability / $(m^3 \cdot h^{-1}) \cdot m^{-1}$	Max. test pressure / Pa
0*	—	—	—	—
1	50	150	12.50	150
2	27	300	6.75	300
3	9	600	2.25	600
4	3	600	0.75	600

* Not tested

Required window functionality

General information on window design and selection is available from other CIBSE publications[29,182]. There are a number of important criteria, which are outlined in the following sections.

(*a*) Ventilation capacity

The ventilation capacity is the amount of air that will flow through a given window area of different designs. It depends on the ratio of the effective open area to the facade area of the window unit. Ventilation capacity will be maximised by increasing the vertical separation and magnitude of those open areas. This will in turn depend on the way the window opens (i.e. side, top/bottom, centre pivot, sliding etc.), and the distribution of the open area over the vertical height of the window. Figure 2.73 shows the open areas for a horizontal centre pivot window compared to a side hung window. A typical pressure gradient caused by inside–outside temperature differences is also shown. The centre pivot window has a much higher ventilation capacity because the open area is concentrated at regions of high-pressure difference. In contrast, much of the open area of side hung windows is in a region of small pressure difference.

(*b*) Controllability

Good control at small openings is particularly important for winter comfort. The flow characteristic is influenced by the mode of opening the window and factors such as the

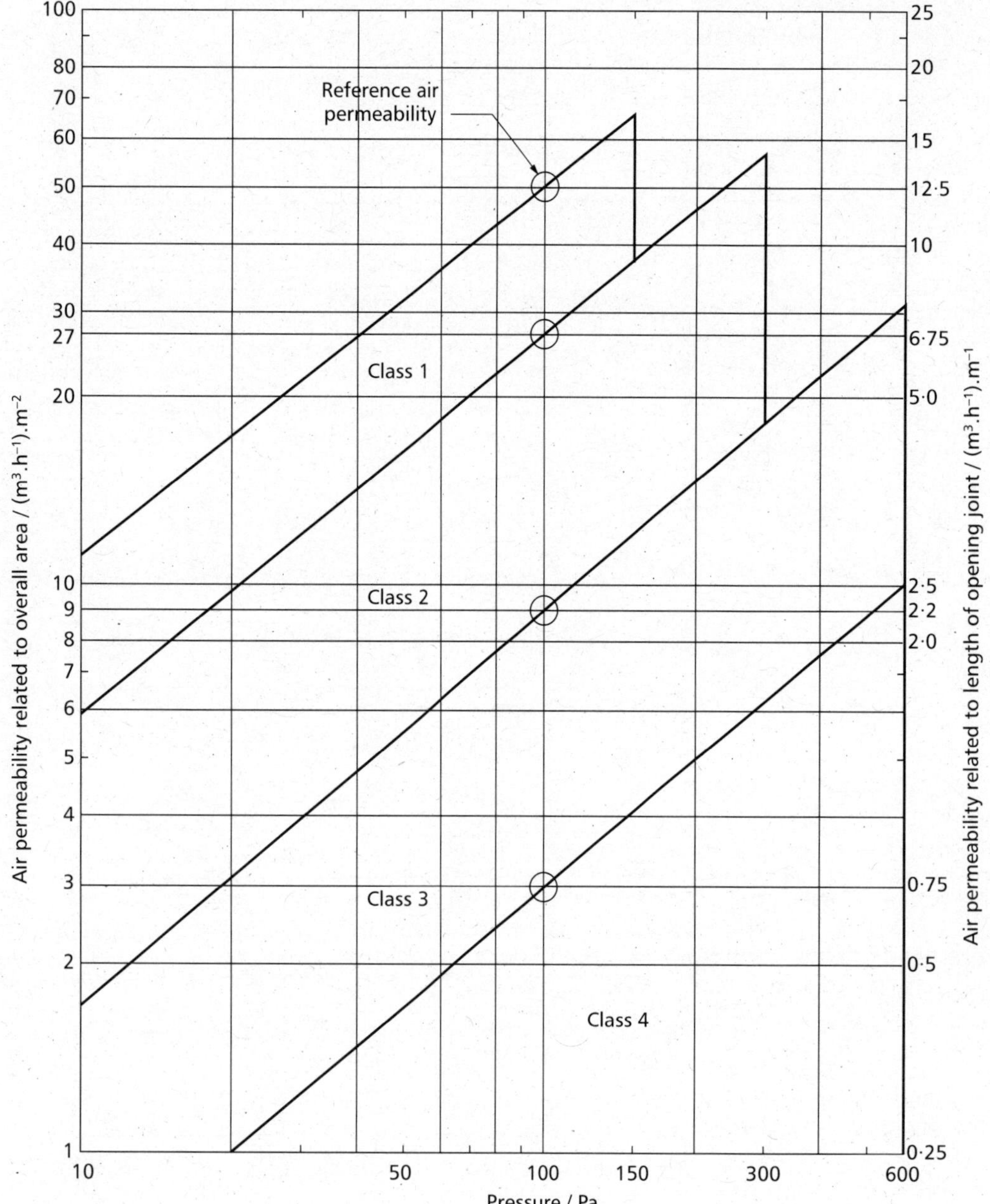

Figure 2.72 Classification of doors and windows by air permeability (reproduced from BS EN 12207 by permission of the British Standards Institution)

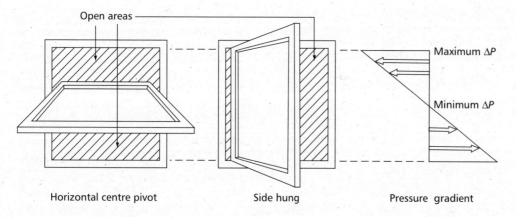

Figure 2.73 Ventilation capacity of different window configurations

shape and thickness of the window frame. Figure 2.74 illustrates that the effective open area of a window may not increase very rapidly until the opening angle is quite large.

(*c*) Impact on comfort

The position of the room air inlet will have an effect on comfort factors such as draughts. Air entering the space at the occupied level can improve comfort in summer, when the air movement will provide a cooling benefit. In winter when the entering air is much colder, the same opening may result in discomfort from draughts. Consequently, separate winter openings may be preferred (either separate high-level windows or trickle ventilators). To avoid high summer ventilation rates (causing papers to be disturbed), the height of that part of the window where air enters the space should be above desk level, by say 150 mm.

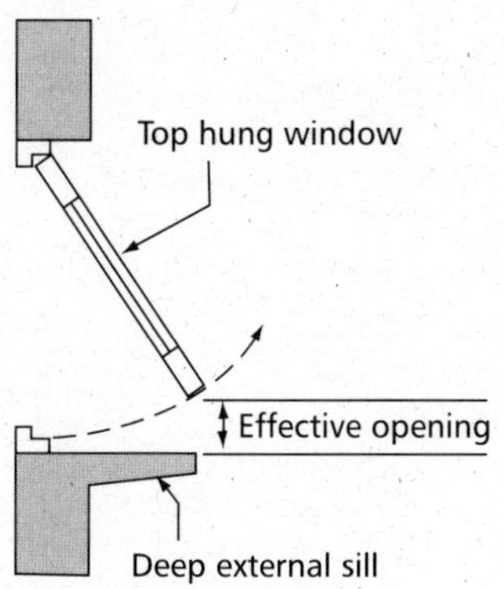

Figure 2.74 Effect of a sill on the effective open area of a window

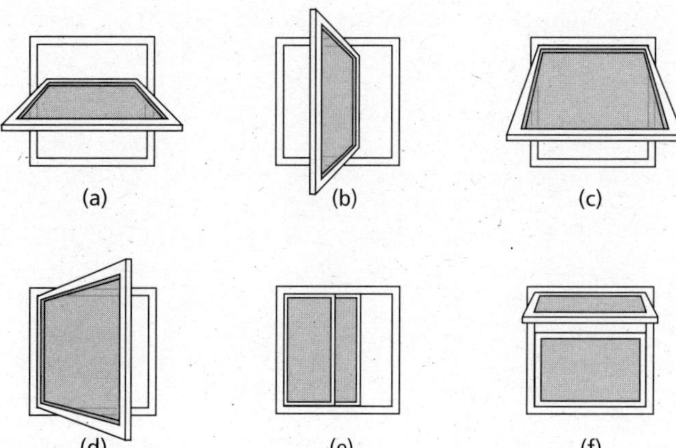

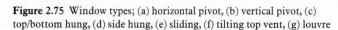

Figure 2.75 Window types; (a) horizontal pivot, (b) vertical pivot, (c) top/bottom hung, (d) side hung, (e) sliding, (f) tilting top vent, (g) louvre

(*d*) Thermal contact

In strategies utilising night cooling and thermal capacity, the ventilation air needs to be able to make good thermal contact with the fabric in order to effect good heat transfer.

(*e*) Security

The implications of open windows, particularly in night ventilation mode, need to be considered. Some window designs can be lockable in a part-open position which allows adequate night ventilation rates but which minimises the risk of intruders gaining access to the building.

(*f*) Integration with solar control strategies (particularly blinds)

There are a number of ways in which the blind and window opening may interact. These include:

— the movement of the window may be restricted by an independent internal (or external) blind; this is mainly a problem for pivoting windows

— with pivoting windows and mid-pane blinds, there is the impact on shading performance when the angle of the blind louvres to the incident radiation changes as the window is opened

— the effect of the blind in providing a resistance to airflow; the blind elements (unless they are mid-pane) will provide an obstruction to the free area of the opening (this is independent of window type, see Pitts and Georgiadis[(243)]).

(*g*) Maintenance and cleaning of windows

Maintenance is an important feature; can the window be cleaned from the inside?

Window specification

Information on the performance characteristics of various window types, see Figure 2.75, is given below. The effect of these different characteristics should be assessed with reference to the criteria listed above.

(*a*) *Horizontal pivot windows*: have a high ventilation capacity because large open areas are created at a separation equivalent to the window height. With single-sided ventilation, air will enter at the lower level and exit via the top of the window. An opening of 22° is usually considered the norm for 'fully open', and for a typical 1200 mm wide by 1600 mm high window this results in an effective open area of 0.66 m^2. They are easily adjustable to provide control of the ventilation rate. Maximising the height of the top of the window in the room will help exhaust warmer air at ceiling level when operating in single-sided ventilation mode. Glazing at high level will also promote good levels of natural light deep into the space.

When operating in wind-driven cross-ventilation mode, air will enter at the top and bottom of the window. The air entering through the top gap will be directed upward and this can improve thermal contact with exposed ceilings for effective night ventilation. Solar radiation striking the opaque surfaces of the wall or the ground adjacent to the facade can generate rising convection currents. These can be deflected into the room if the outward projection of the window extends beyond the window reveal.

(*b*) *Vertical pivot windows*: because the opening is distributed uniformly over their height, these windows have a lower ventilation capacity. For the same 22 degree opening, the effective open area is reduced by 40% relative to the horizontal pivot.

Vertical pivot windows can act as a form of 'wind scoop' for wind directions parallel to the face of the building. Because they have a large vertical opening, they are more likely to allow rain into the building. Carefully designed weather-stripping is required for both horizontal and vertical centre pivot windows to achieve a good performance in winter.

(*c*) *Top/bottom hung windows*: as ventilators, these are less effective still, since all the opening area is concentrated at one end of the window height. The effective open area is about 35% of the horizontal pivot type. Depending on where the opening is, the summer ventilation will either provide cooling to the occupant and poor thermal contact with the ceiling, or vice versa. Top hung windows can act as scoops for warm air rising up the outside of the building (e.g. from convection currents generated by solar gain on building surfaces).

(*d*) *Side hung windows*: these are similar in performance terms to vertical pivot windows. Because of the greater distance from window edge to pivot (and hence greater turning moment), they are more susceptible to being blown by gusts of wind. Inward opening windows can cause clashes with furniture positions. The combination of top hung winter ventilators and side hung summer windows (with effective weather-stripping) provides good all-round performance. The top hung winter ventilator can also provide a secure opening for summer ventilation that, in combination with the side hung opening, will enhance stack effect.

(*e*) *Sliding windows (including sash)*: depending on whether they are vertical sliding (sash) or horizontal sliding windows, these will have similar ventilation characteristics to the horizontal and vertical pivot window respectively. Sliding windows can provide good control over summer ventilation. Sash windows allow the stack effect to be controlled through adjustment of the opening size at both the top and bottom of the window. However, ensuring a good seal in the closed position requires particular attention. This is important in terms of reducing draughts and energy losses in winter. Recent designs have significantly improved the performance of sliding windows in this respect. The design of sash windows needs to be such as to facilitate easy opening of the upper sash.

(*f*) *Tilting top vents*: these provide smaller opening areas than the other systems, because the opening portion occupies only a proportion of the window height. However they can provide good draught-free ventilation, especially in cross-ventilation mode. If the vent is bottom hung, opening inwards, (the 'hopper' window), the natural flow pattern may encourage good thermal contact with the ceiling. However care must be taken to protect the opening from driving rain.

(*g*) *Tilt and turn windows*: these are a combination unit offering bottom and side hung options (although the side hung mode is mainly intended for cleaning purposes). A study of several buildings by Willis et al.[187] suggests that the tilt setting provides too much ventilation in winter and insufficient in summer. The turn mode can cause clashes with furniture.

Whereas windows perform many functions, sections 2.5.3.3 to 2.5.3.7 describe openings in the facade whose sole purpose is to provide ventilation. Note that any such devices should offer a very low resistance to airflow as the driving forces for natural ventilation may only be in the region of 10 Pa. Further guidance on product development and natural ventilation design tools is available from BRE[232].

2.5.3.2 Air bricks and trickle ventilators

Air bricks incorporate no provision for control of infiltration rate. Automatic ventilators, which provide nominally constant infiltration under variable wind velocities, should be considered as an alternative. The concept of 'build tight, ventilate right' is increasingly recognised as the basis of good design for ventilation. This relies upon an airtight fabric and the provision of a means of controlled background ventilation. In a naturally ventilated building this is often provided by trickle ventilators with higher rates of ventilation provided by other means such as the window.

Trickle ventilators are designed to provide the required minimum fresh air rate, particularly in winter. For England and Wales, Building Regulations Approved Document F[37] should be consulted for further details of the requirements.

Draughts, especially those occurring at ankle height, can be avoided by directing the incoming air upwards, or positioning the ventilators at high level, e.g. > 1.75 m above the floor. This allows incoming air to mix with the warmer room air before reaching floor level. Alternatively, air can enter through wall ventilators positioned behind heaters. The form of the ventilator should promote rapid mixing with the room air to minimise cold draughts. General guidance on the use of trickle ventilators has been published by BRE[232].

Added to this is the daily 'reservoir' effect of the trickle vents that purge the room overnight and provide a room full of fresh air ready for the following day's occupants. The larger the room volume, as with the higher ceilings in naturally ventilated rooms, the longer this reservoir effect will last during the occupied period. As trickle vents are intended to promote background ventilation only (about 5 litre·s^{-1} per person), their main application is for fresh air supply in the winter months. Twenty-four hour use of trickle ventilation can provide a reservoir of fresh air that may be sufficient to maintain air quality throughout the day. With higher pollutant loads, rapid ventilation by opening windows for short periods or by mechanical ventilation might be required. For this reason, trickle ventilators are usually used in conjunction with other types of ventilation opening.

Trickle vents can be in the window frame, part of the glazed unit or independent of the window (usually above it). Various refinements on the basic trickle ventilator are available. Acoustic trickle ventilators are available, which reduce noise level by about 38 dB, but bring a penalty of increased pressure drop.

Control options available include:

— *Basic (uncontrolled)*: consisting of a series of holes or slots covered with a formed plastic cover to give protection from the weather; no control is possible, hence positioning and appropriate selection are very important.

— *Standard controllable (including 'hit and miss')*: closure may be possible through the use of a manually operated slide that covers the openings; occupants need to understand the operation of such devices.

— *Humidity controlled*: mostly used in kitchens and bathrooms within dwellings, as the scope for use in offices is limited with moisture not being the dominant pollutant.

— *Pressure controlled*: generally used in offices; inside/outside pressure difference is one possible control strategy.

— *Pollutant (e.g. CO_2, CO, smoke controlled)*: used in schools, theatres, shopping malls etc. and sometimes in dwellings; practical use for offices is limited as, except for CO_2 (where considerable drift has been reported), these are not normally the dominant pollutants.

The ventilation performance of trickle ventilators is traditionally specified in terms of 'free air space' or 'open area'. However, in reality, the airflow performance of two ventilators having the same free area (i.e. the physical size of the smallest aperture totalled over the ventilator) can be different due to the differing complexities of the airflow paths. In order to minimise resistance to airflow, the main air passage (excluding insect screens etc.) should have a minimum dimension of 5 mm for slots, or 8 mm for square or circular holes. Acoustic effectiveness is considered in the light of the 'effective area' or 'equivalent area'. This is considered in detail in section 5 and BRE guidance(234).

Effective area is also considered to be a more realistic measure of airflow performance, although it is not yet used as the basis of a test method. It is defined as the area of a single sharp-edged hole (in a thin plate) that passes the same volume airflow rate and at the same applied pressure difference as the vent being tested. It requires to be measured on an airflow test rig. Most trickle ventilators with the same equivalent area will have similar airflow performance, even though their free areas might differ. A European standard to improve air flow performance testing methods is in preparation(235), although it is not known whether this will be adopted in the UK.

2.5.3.3 Louvres

These are usually constructed of either glass or aluminium blades. Security bars can be fitted inside the louvres and this enhances their potential application in the night ventilation mode. Versions incorporating acoustic attenuation are also available. Whilst providing good control over summer ventilation, adjustable louvres usually present the greatest crack length for a given opening. However, conventional hinged louvres are usually difficult to seal when closed, making it difficult to limit infiltration losses.

2.5.3.4 Roof ventilators

In combination with low-level openings in the fabric, roof ventilators can be used to take advantage of summer stack effect, particularly for tall spaces. However, they must be specified to have low crack leakage or wind-induced draughts will cause discomfort in winter.

Rooftop ventilators generally fall into two categories: ridge and circular. The ridge type is less obtrusive but their efficiency is impaired by variations in wind direction, whereas circular stack outlets, if positioned correctly, are not affected. For maximum effect the outlet should be on the ridge of a pitched roof and the cap should project sufficiently above the ridge to minimise the influence of turbulence arising from wind blowing up the slope of the roof. Natural ventilation openings should never be installed on the slope of a roof nor should they be located in high-pressure areas of the building environment, where down-draughts are likely to occur.

2.5.3.5 Fixed lights

Fixed lights may give crack leakage rates between zero and 1 $m^3 \cdot h^{-1}$ per metre length of visible perimeter of glass, depending on the gasket material. Therefore crack leakage from roof lights should not be relied upon to provide winter ventilation.

2.5.3.6 Dampers

Dampers are usually used for applications where automatic control is required. In the context of natural ventilation, this is usually for air inlets below false floor level, and at main exhaust points (e.g. roof vents). Again, the key performance criterion is the ability of the damper to provide an airtight seal when closed to minimise energy losses in winter. If effective control is required, then a significant proportion of the available pressure differential must occur across the damper in order to provide control authority. This goes against the design requirement to minimise pressure drops because of the relatively low driving forces available with natural ventilation. This is partly compensated for by the fact that higher pressure differentials are available in the winter, when minimum damper openings are required.

2.5.3.7 Shafts and ducts

Many ventilation strategies rely on shafts to take air vertically through a building. Similarly, ducts (including floor voids) are used to provide horizontal distribution. The criteria for sizing these airways are very different to those used in sizing conventional mechanical ventilation systems in order to keep pressure drops within the range available from natural driving forces. This means that adequate space must be allowed to incorporate these larger ducts or shafts. A second crucial issue is the requirement to keep the inlet ducts clean to minimise air quality problems. This will require inlet screens and access for cleaning.

By definition, shaft outlets are at high level and therefore are in a region of higher wind speed. This means that the magnitude of the wind pressure acting on the shaft is likely to be large. Wind effects will probably dominate the pressure distribution through the system except at very low wind speeds. It is therefore vital that outlets are designed to create wind pressures that reinforce the intended flow direction. Usually this means creating a negative pressure coefficient at the top of the shaft, the exception being the wind scoop.

Orme et al.(190) provides information on the above roof pressure coefficients. For isolated buildings with no local flow interference, the minimum height of the stack above roof level to avoid back-draughts is given by:

$$h = a\,[0.5 + 0.16\,(\theta - 23)] \qquad (2.19)$$

where h is the height above roof level (m), a is the horizontal distance between the outlet and the highest point of the roof (m) and θ is the pitch of the roof (degree).

For roof pitches of less than 23°, the height of the outlet must be at least 0.5 m above the roof level. These simplified relationships represent a minimum stack height; greater heights may well provide higher suction pressures. This can be beneficial since it is possible to generate a suction greater than that generated on an opening on the leeward vertical face of the building.

More information on pressure coefficients over roofs is given in BS 6399-2[236]. For complex roof profiles or where surrounding buildings or other obstructions disturb the wind, model testing would be advisable.

As well as the position of the roof outlet, the geometry of the cowl will also effect the pressure coefficient. The cowl should prevent rain entering the stack and can provide flow acceleration local to the outlet to further reduce static pressures.

2.5.3.8 Combined openings

When designing the ventilation inlets, it is usual to use combinations of opening types in an overall design. These openings may be combined in a single window unit (e.g. opening window with a trickle vent in the frame), or may be independent. Combinations of window types in a single window unit should be considered. For example, a hopper over a centre pivot window has many advantages. The hopper can provide night ventilation, and also helps provide air to occupants deeper into the room. The centre pivot allows high summer ventilation rates and is especially beneficial to those nearer the perimeter. The different sizes of opening also allow finer control over ventilation rate by progressively opening the hopper, then closing the hopper and opening the main window and then opening both together.

As the design of the window unit is developed, the other functional requirements of the window need to be considered (e.g. lighting, shading, security, transmission losses etc.). Considerable development effort is underway to produce such 'multi-function' windows, see Figure 2.76[182].

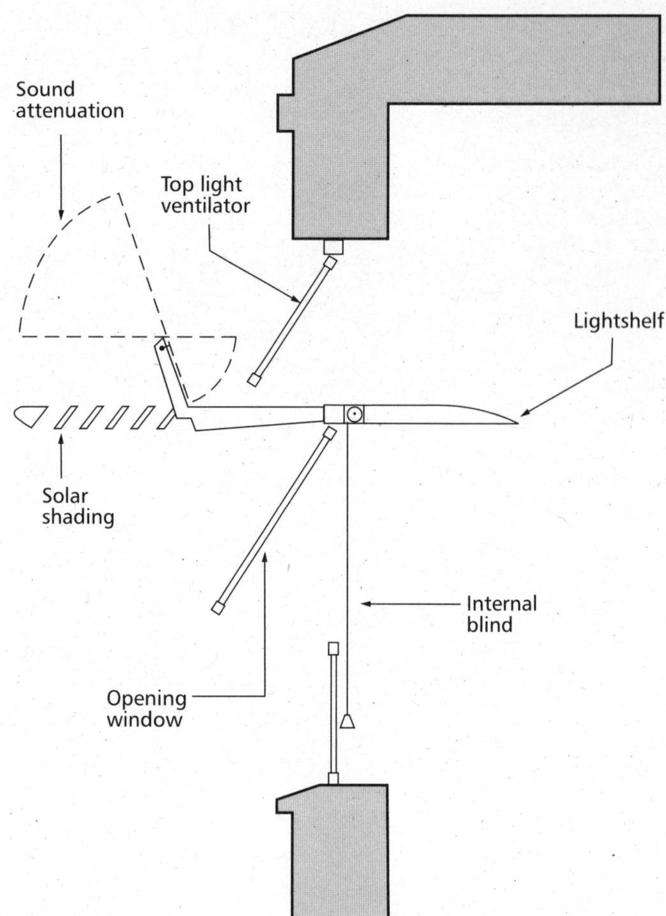

Figure 2.76 'Multi-function' window unit

2.5.3.9 Internal obstructions

Transfer grilles may be required as a minimum to allow air movement across a building if cellular accommodation has been provided. The resistance of these transfer grilles must be included in the design calculation when sizing the facade openings.

2.5.3.10 Control options for natural ventilation openings

Control options for natural ventilation openings should be specified with the needs of the occupants in mind, see section 2.4.3. Control mechanisms for natural ventilation opening include the following

Window/damper actuators

A number of different actuator types are available for window control. These are electrically driven and include chain, helical cable, piston, and rack and pinion type actuators. Because of their linear action, the last two types suffer some disadvantage because they protrude into the space. The actuator will have to cope with the weight of the window and with any wind forces. The use of vertically pivoted windows minimises the effect of the weight of the window but they are less efficient as ventilators. If dampers are used, then conventional control mechanisms (pneumatic or electric actuators) can be considered.

Sensors

Any automatic control system must be regulated in response to signals from appropriate sensors. Equipment to be specified includes the following:

— *Temperature sensors*: room temperature sensors may be sufficient to indicate excessive ventilation rates because of the influence of ventilation on room temperature. However this approach will need to be integrated with heating system controls to avoid the two systems fighting each other. Other control parameters may be required as well as temperature.

— *Wind sensors*: wind speed sensors (anemometers) can be used to reduce window opening as wind speeds increase in order to maintain a nominally constant ventilation rate. They may also be used in conjunction with rain sensors to give an indication of potential ingress of driving rain. Wind direction sensors can be used to shut exhaust vents on the windward side of a building and simultaneously open leeward vents in order to avoid back-draughts.

— *Solar sensors*: solar sensors (pyranometers) can be used to indicate periods of high solar gain. The sensor must integrate the gain over a certain period to avoid hunting during periods of patchy cloud.

— *Rain sensors*: windows and vents may need to be closed during periods of rainfall to prevent ingress of water. Typical sensors include the 'tipping bucket', which collects rainfall and tips over at a certain level. Each tipping action generates a pulse, the frequency of which can be used to determine the intensity of the rainfall. An alternative approach is to use a device whereby the capacitance changes as the area of moisture on its surface increases. The sensor is heated to dry off the surface when the rain stops.

— *Air quality sensors*: several approaches to measuring air quality have been used. These usually rely on taking a particular pollutant as indicator for the overall air quality. CO_2 and humidity sensors have been most commonly used, the former in commercial buildings, the latter in residential buildings where condensation is a bigger problem.

— *Occupancy sensors*: infra-red sensors which detect movement have been used to identify the presence of occupants and adjust ventilation rates (and lighting etc.) accordingly.Further details on the application of these sensors can be found elsewhere[188].

2.5.4 Exhaust systems

2.5.4.1 General

Table 2.38 gives solutions to the equation for calculating air velocity at a set distance from an exhaust hood for

Table 2.38 Air volume flow equations for hoods and canopies

Type of opening	Equation	Notes
Canopy	Cold source: $Q = 1.4\, P D v$	If $D > 0.3\, B$, use equation for hot source Canopy should overhang tank by 0.4 D on each side
	Hot source, exposed horizontal surface: $Q = 0.038\, A_s \sqrt[3]{h D} + 0.5\,(A - A_s)$	Q is progressively under-estimated as D increases above 1 m Canopy should overhang tank by 0.4 D on each side
	Hot source, exposed sides and top: $Q = 0.038\, A_s \sqrt[3]{(h A_t D)/A_s} + 0.5\,(A - A_s)$	Q is progressively under-estimated as D increases above 1 m Canopy should overhang tank by 0.4 D on each side
Plain slot	$Q = L v \left(4 X \sqrt{X/W} + W\right)$	Aspect ratio R should be not less than 10
Flanged slot	$Q = 0.75\, L v \left(4 X \sqrt{X/W} + W\right)$	Aspect ratio R should be not less than 10 If $X > 0.75\, W$, use equation for plain slot
Plain opening	$Q = v \left(10 \sqrt{R}\, X^2 + A\right)$	Aspect ratio R should not exceed 5; equation may be used for $R > 5$ but with loss of accuracy
Flanged opening	$Q = 0.75\, v \left(10 \sqrt{R}\, X^2 + A\right)$	Aspect ratio R should not exceed 5; equation may be used for $R > 5$ but with loss of accuracy If $X > 0.75\, W$, use equation for plain opening

Symbols:

A = area of hood/opening (m^2)
A_s = horizontal surface area of source (m^2)
A_t = total exposed heated surface area of source (m^2)
B = breadth of source (m)
D = height above source (m)
L = length of hood/opening (m)
P = perimeter of source (m)
Q = volume flow rate ($m^3 \cdot s^{-1}$)
R = aspect ratio (L/W)
W = width of hood/opening (m)
X = distance from source (m)
h = rate of convective heat transfer ($W \cdot m^{-2}$)
v = control velocity ($m \cdot s^{-1}$)

Table 2.39 Control velocities for hoods

Condition	Example	Control velocity / m·s^{-1}
Released with practically no velocity into quiet air	Evaporation from tanks, degreasing etc.	0.25–0.5
Released at low velocity into moderately still air	Spray booths, intermittent container filling, low speed conveyor transfers, welding, plating	0.5–1.0
Active generation into zone of rapid air motion	Spray painting in shallow booths, conveyor loading	1.0–2.5
Released at high initial velocity into zone of very rapid air motion	Grinding, abrasive blasting	2.5–10

Note: the higher values apply if (*a*) small hoods handling low volumes are used, (*b*) hoods are subject to draughts, (*c*) the airborne contaminant is hazardous, or (*d*) hoods are in frequent use.

Table 2.40 Convective heat transfer rates for horizontal surfaces

Surface temp. / °C	Rate of heat transfer / W·m^{-2}
100	580
200	1700
300	3060
400	4600
500	6600

various types of opening and the appropriate equations for air volume flow rates through overhead canopies for both cold and hot processes[237]. Appropriate control velocities and convective heat transfer rates are given in Tables 2.39 and 2.40 respectively.

Table 2.41 shows the effects of adjacent surfaces on the basic form of hoods and canopies. However, specific processes may require other hood arrangements not shown in either Table 2.38 or 2.41. The American Conference of Government Industrial Hygienists' (ACGIH) publication, *Industrial ventilation*[112], which gives a wide range of empirically based design data sheets for many common industrial processes, should always be consulted before proceeding with the design of a local exhaust system.

The size, aspect ratio, position and number of openings used depends upon:

- the size and nature of the source (opening must overhang source if possible)
- the dynamics and rate of evolution of contaminant
- the access needs and position of the operator
- the prevailing room air currents (side baffles should be provided if possible).

2.5.4.2 Overhead canopies

Overhead canopies are only appropriate for hot processes which cannot be kept covered, and must not be used if the operator is likely to lean over the process or if strong cross draughts are likely to occur. Baffle plates can be incorporated into larger hoods to ensure an even velocity across the opening, whilst very large hoods should be sectioned, each section having its own off-take.

2.5.4.3 Lateral exhaust

For processes in which the emission momentum is small or tends to carry the pollutant horizontally away from the source, horizontal slots or hoods at the edge of a work surface or tank may be used. Slots may be arranged one above the other, see Figure 2.77, or facing each other along opposite long edges, depending upon the vertical distance of the source above the rim of the tank. If the most remote part of the source is less than 0.5 m from the slot, a single exhaust slot along the longer edge is adequate otherwise two slots, on opposite sides of the source, are required.

Table 2.41 Effect of side walls and adjacent surfaces

Type of opening	Baffle	Effect
Canopy, cold source	Side walls	Reduces effective perimeter, hence flow rate Q is reduced
Canopy, hot source	Side walls	Reduces cross draughts but minimal effect on flow rate Q
Plain slot	Long side on flat surface	$Q = L\,v\left(X\sqrt{2X/W} + W\right)$
Plain opening	Long surface on flat surface	For $R \leq 2$: $Q = v\left(5\sqrt{(2/R)}\;X^2 + A\right)$ For $2 < R \leq 5$: $Q = v\left(5\sqrt{(R/2)}\;X^2 + A\right)$
Flanged slot or opening	Long side (not flanged) on flat surface	For $X > 0.75$, calculate flow rate Q for plain arrangement and multiply by 0.75 W

Symbols:
A = area of hood/opening (m^2)
L = length of hood/opening (m)
Q = volume flow rate (m^3·s^{-1})
R = aspect ratio (= L / W)
v = control velocity (m·s^{-1})
W = width of hood/opening (m)
X = distance form source (m)

2.5.4.4 Jet-assisted hoods

Jet-assisted hoods are non-enclosing hoods combined with compact, linear or radial jets. They are used to separate contaminated zones from relatively clean zones in working spaces. They prevent contaminated air from moving into clean zones by creating positive static pressures, typically in the form of an air curtain.

2.5.4.5 Push-pull hoods

For sources larger than 1 m across, a push-pull hood arrangement should be used, see Figure 2.78, whereby a slot or row of nozzles is used to blow air across the source. Design data for the hood illustrated in Figure 2.78 are given below.

Exhaust air quantity:

$$Q_e = (0.5 \text{ to } 0.75) \times A \tag{2.20}$$

where Q_e is the exhaust air flow rate (m^3·s^{-1}) and A is the area of open surface (m^2).

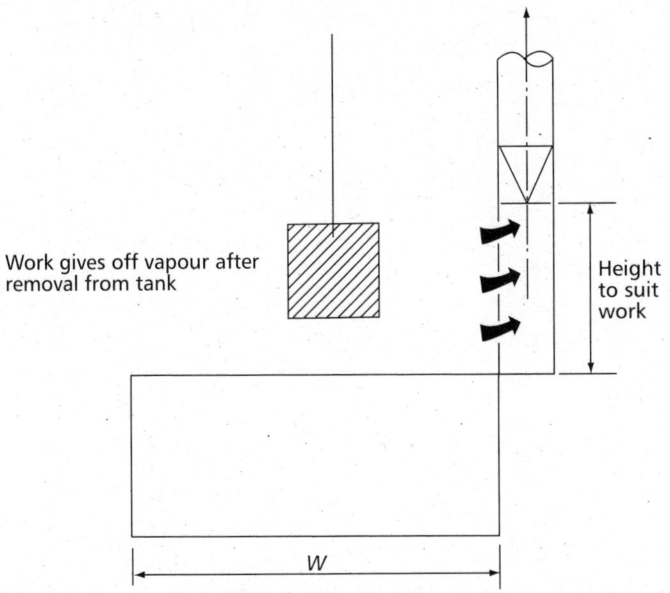

Figure 2.77 Open surface tank with drying facility, single side exhaust

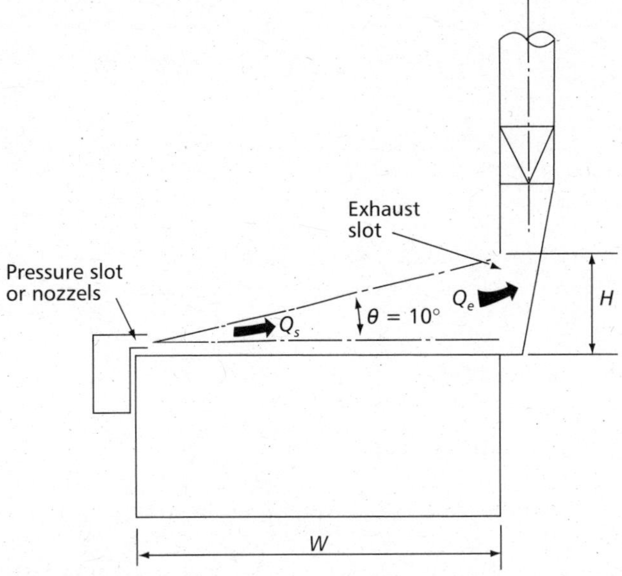

Figure 2.78 Push-pull hood

The value of the numerical factor depends on the temperature of the liquid, presence of cross-draughts, agitation of liquid etc.

Supply air quantity:

$$Q_s = \frac{Q_e}{w \times E} \tag{2.21}$$

where Q_s is the supply air flow rate ($m^3 \cdot s^{-1}$), w is the throw length (m) and E is the entrainment factor (see Table 2.42).

Height of exhaust opening:

$$H = 0.18\, w \tag{2.22}$$

where H is the height of the exhaust opening (m).

Width of supply opening:

— size for a supply velocity of 5–10 $m \cdot s^{-1}$.

The input air volume is usually about 10% of the exhaust volume and the input air should be tempered to avoid frost damage. The source must not be placed in the input air path since this could result in deflection of the contaminant into the workspace. If necessary, baffles or screens should be used to deflect cross draughts.

2.5.4.6 Equipment selection principles and integration

Air cleaning equipment may be selected to:

- conform with emissions standards; industrial processes resulting in polluting emissions to air, water or land come under the requirements of the Environmental Protection Act(229)
- prevent re-entrainment where they may become a health or safety hazard in the workplace
- reclaim usable materials
- permit cleaned air to be recirculated

Table 2.42 Entrainment factors for push-pull hoods

Throw length / m	Entrainment factor
0–2.5	6.6
2.5–5.0	4.6
5.0–7.5	3.3
>7.5	2.3

- prevent physical damage to adjacent properties
- protect neighbours from contaminants.

Circular ductwork is normally preferred as it offers a more uniform air velocity to resist the settling of material and can withstand the higher pressures normally found in exhaust systems. Design velocities can be higher than the minimum transport velocity but should never be significantly lower. Fans (or other air-moving devices) and duct materials and construction should be suitable for the temperatures, abrasion and corrosion likely to be encountered. Fans should normally be located downstream of the air cleaner to reduce possible abrasions and create a negative pressure in the air cleaner so leakage will be inward. However, in some instances the fan may be located upstream from the cleaner to help remove dust.

Exhaust stacks must be designed and located to prevent the re-entrainment of discharged air into supply system inlets, see section 2.5.2. Toxic and hazardous exhaust must not be discharged in a manner that will result in environmental pollution and the local authority Environmental Health Officer should be consulted to ensure that the proposed discharges will be acceptable.

2.5.5 Mixing boxes

A mixing box is a plenum in which recirculated and fresh air are mixed before entering an air handling unit. It may be part of the ductwork installation, a builder's work chamber or a standard module attached to packaged plant.

Mixing boxes must be designed to provide sufficient mixing so that freezing outside air does not stratify below warm recirculation air on entering the filters. If in doubt, a frost coil at the air intake should be provided. Dampers should be located and set to promote mixing of the airstreams. Parallel blade dampers may assist mixing. Air blenders/baffles can also be used.

To improve the rangeability of a motorised control damper, the face velocity should be increased to 5–6 $m \cdot s^{-1}$ by adjusting the duct size or by blanking-off an appropriate area of the duct at the damper. Damper quality is critical; play in linkages and pivots should be minimal and leakage on shut-off should be less than 0.02.

2.5.6 Heat recovery devices

2.5.6.1 General

This section provides guidance on devices used to recover heat between two separate airstreams. In energy terms alone, recirculation of air is the most efficient form of heat recovery since it involves little or no energy penalty. However, recirculation is only possible if the ventilation rate is fixed by cooling rather than ventilation needs, and is therefore only applicable to all-air systems. The air quality implications of recirculation can also limit its use.

Heat recovery devices used in ventilation systems generally provide heat recovery from exhaust to supply air in winter and can also recover cooling in peak summer conditions. They are also used in specific system configurations such as indirect evaporative cooling, see section 2.4.12. Devices used to recover heat from process applications (e.g. dryers, flues) may transfer the heat to the process or to another application. Selection of equipment should be suitable for process exhaust temperatures. Where the recovered heat is fed to a ventilation system, modulation control is normally required to prevent overheating in warm weather.

Buildings should be airtight as infiltration has a significant impact on the viability of heat recovery(238).

Technical considerations for design and selection of heat recovery devices include:

- heat recovery efficiency (sensible and total)
- airflow arrangement
- fouling (filters should be placed in both supply and exhaust airstreams)
- corrosion (particularly in process applications)
- cross-leakage
- condensation and freeze-up
- pressure drop
- face velocity
- construction materials (suitability for temperatures, pressures, contaminants)
- maintenance (in particular cleaning of surfaces)
- controls.

The heat recovery efficiency (or effectiveness) of a device is normally defined as follows:

$$\text{Efficiency} = \frac{\text{Actual heat transfer}}{\text{Maximum possible heat transfer}} \qquad (2.23)$$

The maximum theoretical efficiency is a function of the exchanger flow configuration; counterflow exchangers have a higher theoretical efficiency than parallel flow exchangers. Practical consideration often favour crossflow arrangements that lie between the two(239).

Sensible heat recovery devices do not transfer moisture. Latent heat is only transferred when the warmer airstream is cooled below its dew point and condenses. Total heat recovery devices transfer both sensible heat and moisture between the airstreams. Moisture transfer is desirable in hot, humid climates to reduce the moisture in the supply air and in cold, dry climates to raise the moisture in the supply air.

Drains should be included to collect and dispose of the condensate. In extreme conditions, where the temperature also drops below 0 °C, frosting or icing can occur. This can be prevented by pre-heating the supply air or reducing the effectiveness of the heat exchanger. Alternatively the heat exchanger may be periodically defrosted.

Pressure drops depend on a number of factors including exchanger design, airflow rates, temperatures, and connec-

Table 2.43 Comparison of heat recovery devices(242)

Device	Typical heat recovery efficiency / %	Typical face velocity / $m \cdot s^{-1}$	Cross-leakage / %	Typical pressure drop / Pa	Modulation control	Features
Recuperator	50 to 80 (sensible)	1 to 5	0 to 5	25 to 370	Bypass	No moving parts Easily cleaned
Run-around coil	50 (sensible)	1.5 to 3	0	100 to 500	Pump or bypass valves	Flexibility; exhaust air stream can be separated from supply
Thermal wheel	65 to 90 (total)	2.5 to 5	1 to 10	100 to 170	Wheel speed or bypass	Latent transfer Compact large sizes Cross air contamination possible
Heat pipe	50 to 65 (sensible)	2 to 4	0	100 to 500	Tilt angle down to 10% of maximum	No moving parts except tilt High cost, few suppliers
Regenerator	85 to 95 (sensible)	1.5 to 3	<1 to 5	70 to 300	Regulating changeover period	Relatively high capital cost but high efficiency Self-cleaning action from flow reversal

tions. These pressure drops should be minimised as they impose a fan energy penalty that will need to be balanced against the recovered energy. Face velocities are normally limited by the need to avoid excessive pressure drops. Larger devices will have lower pressure drops and higher efficiency but will cost more and require more space. The selection and evaluation of heat recovery devices should include the following parameters:

— cost expenditure on device, filters etc. and savings on other plant (e.g. boilers) due to heat recovery

— energy, both recovered and required to operate the system (e.g. fan, pump, wheel)

— maintenance requirements

— space requirements of device, filters etc.

Energy analysis may be undertaken using simulation modelling or spreadsheets calculations based on hourly conditions(240), or using graphical approaches such as load duration curves(241). Table 2.43, which is based on information from ASHRAE(242), compares a number of heat recovery devices. These devices are described below. See BSRIA Technical Note TN11/86(243) and CIBSE Research Report RR2(244) for further information on selection and evaluation of heat recovery devices.

2.5.6.2 Recuperators

Recuperators usually take the form of simple and robust air-to-air plate heat exchangers, see Figure 2.79. Their efficiencies depend on the number of air passages and hence the heat transfer area between the two airstreams. If the passages are large the heat exchanger may be easily cleaned and will be suitable for heat transfer from particulate-laden exhaust air.

Modulation control is normally achieved by means of a bypass. This can be used to reduce fan pressure drops when heat recovery is not required. Little or no air leakage occurs between the airstreams. In applications with high differential pressures (> 1000 Pa) exchangers should be selected to avoid plate deformation.

Recuperators normally conduct sensible heat only, but water permeable materials can be used to transfer moisture.

2.5.6.3 Run-around coil

Finned air-to-water heat exchangers are installed in the ducts between which the heat is to be transferred. A water or water/glycol (for freeze protection) circuit is used to transfer heat from the warm extract air to the cooler supply air (or vice versa in summer), see Figure 2.80. An expansion tank is required to allow fluid expansion and contraction. Overall heat transfer efficiencies are relatively low, as it is a two-stage heat transfer process, and pump

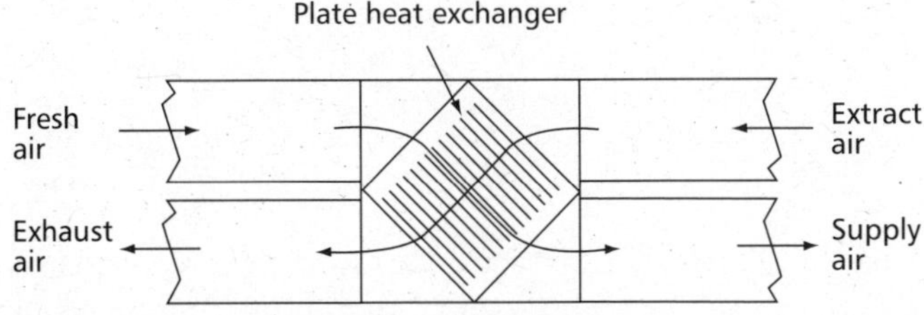

Figure 2.79 Recuperator using a plate heat exchanger

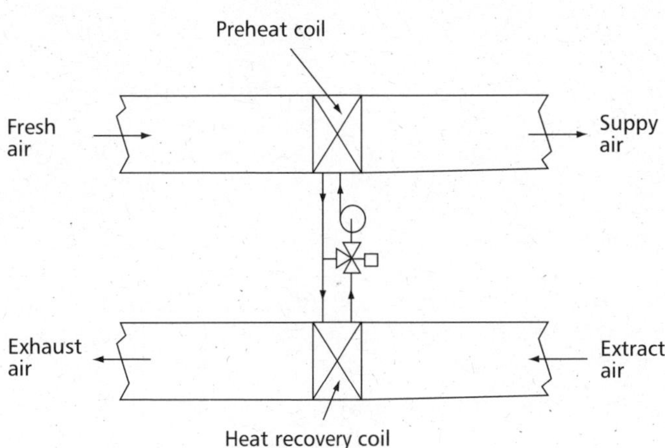

Figure 2.80 Run-around coil arrangement

energy (in addition to the fan energy penalty) and maintenance costs need to be taken into account. However, the system is flexible in application, as it places no constraints on the relative location of the two airstreams and can be extended to include multiple sources and uses. They are suitable for applications where contaminants in the exhaust airstream prohibit recirculation.

Modulation control can be achieved by pump operation and/or valve bypass arrangements on the coils.

2.5.6.4 Thermal wheels

A thermal wheel comprises a cylinder, packed with a suitable heat transfer medium, that rotates slowly within an airtight casing which bridges the ducts between which heat is to be transferred, see Figure 2.81. Thermal wheels are generally quite compact and achieve high efficiencies due to a counterflow configuration. The heat transfer properties are determined by the material contained in the wheel, i.e:

— corrugated, inorganic, fibrous, hygroscopic material which transfers both sensible and latent heat; air flows through the channels formed by the corrugations

— corrugated metal (aluminium, stainless steel or monel): latent heat transfer is restricted to that resulting from condensation when the temperature of the heat transfer medium falls below the dew-point temperature of the warm airstream.

Maintenance requirements for the thermal wheel need to be taken into account, since they can be difficult to clean(243), as do the additional energy penalties due to the drive (although these are usually low).

Cross-contamination occurs by carryover and leakage. Carryover occurs as air entrained within the wheel is transferred to the other airstream. A purge section can be installed where recirculation is undesirable. Leakage

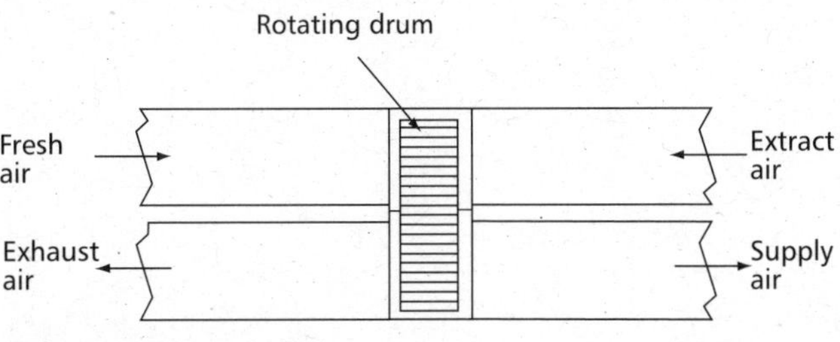

Figure 2.81 Thermal wheel

occurs due to the pressure difference between the two airstreams. This can be minimised by avoiding large pressure differences, providing an effective seal, and placing the fans to promote leakage into the exhaust airstream. Hygroscopic media may transfer toxic gases or vapours from a contaminated exhaust to a clean air supply.

Modulation control is commonly achieved either by the rotational speed of the wheel or by bypassing the supply air. Heat recovery efficiency increases with wheel speed but is ultimately limited by carryover.

2.5.6.5 Heat-pipes

The heat-pipe is a passive heat exchanger of which there are two main types:

— *horizontal*: in which a wick within the tubes transfer liquid by capillary action

— *vertical*: in which heat from the warmer lower duct is transferred to the cold upper duct by means of a phase change in the refrigerant, see Figure 2.82.

Finned tubes are mounted in banks in a similar manner to a cooling coil. Face velocities tend to be low (e.g. 1.5 to 3.0 $m \cdot s^{-1}$) in order to improve efficiency.

Modulation control is normally achieved by changing the slope, or tilt, of the heat pipe.

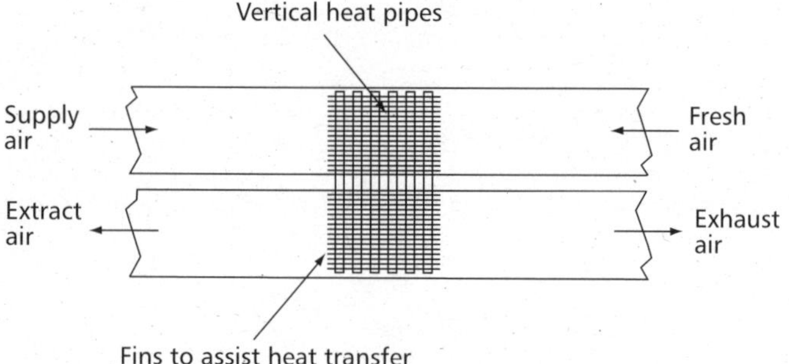

Figure 2.82 Vertical heat-pipe arrangement

2.5.6.6 Regenerator

A regenerator, see Figure 2.83, consists of two accumulators (or a single unit split into two halves) with a damper arrangement to cycle the supply and exhaust air flows between the two. In the first part of the cycle, the exhaust air flows through, and heats, one of the accumulators. The dampers then changeover so that supply air flows through and absorbs the heat from that accumulator. The second accumulator acts in reverse to match, heating the supply air in the first part of the cycle and absorbing heat from the exhaust air in the second. The changeover period is normally of the order of one minute.

Claimed sensible efficiencies for these systems can be quite high at 85%. Latent efficiencies are normally significantly lower and vary with flow velocity and accumulator material. Modulation of the heat recovery efficiency can be achieved by regulating the changeover period.

On damper changeover the exhaust air contained within the damper, accumulator and exhaust ductwork reverses and becomes supply air. The length of exhaust ductwork should be minimised to limit this cross-leakage. Also, the

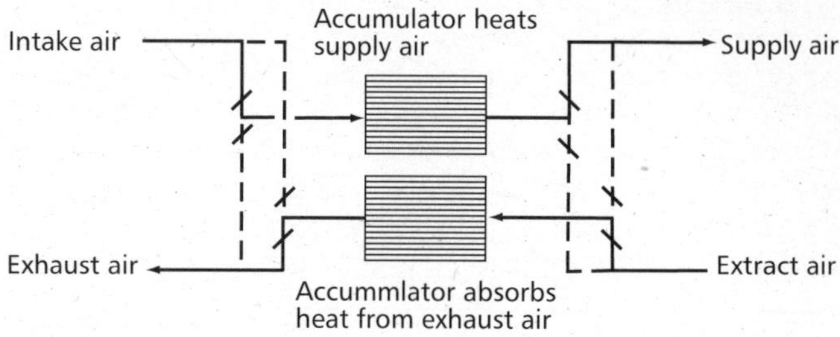

Second part of cycle

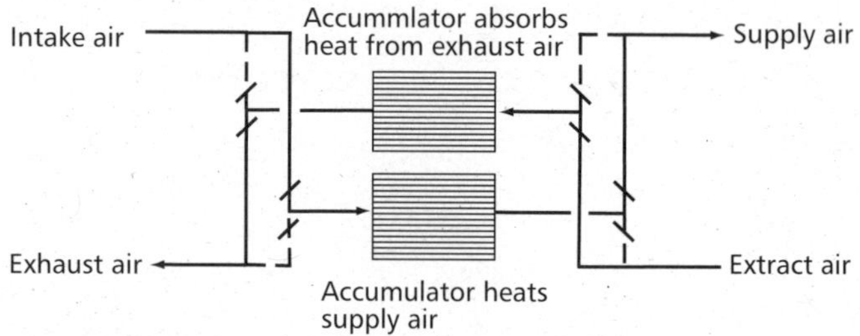

Figure 2.83 Regenerator

time required for damper changeover should be kept to a minimum using high torque dampers. Cross-leakage can range from below 1% on well designed systems up to 5% and above. Typical face velocities are 1.5 to 3.0 $m \cdot s^{-1}$. Reducing the velocity will reduce the pressure drop, but will have only a limited heat transfer benefit as efficiencies are normally high anyway.

2.5.6.7 Heat pump

Heat pumps use the conventional vapour compression cycle to transfer heat from one fluid to another. They may be used in applications where there is a high heat recovery potential but it is not possible to recirculate exhaust air back to the supply, e.g. swimming pools. See section 2.4.16 for further information on heat pumps.

2.5.7 Air cleaners and filtration

2.5.7.1 Nature of airborne contaminants

Atmospheric dust is a complex mixture of solid particulate matter, comprising dusts, smokes, and fumes and non-particulate vapours and gases. A sample of atmospheric dust may contain minute quantities of soot and smoke, minerals such as rock, metal or sand, organic material such as grain, flour, wool, hair, lint and plant fibres and, perhaps, mould spores, bacteria and pollen. Particles are not generally called dust unless they are smaller than 80 μm.

Smokes are suspensions of fine particles produced by the incomplete combustion of organic substances such as coal or wood, or by the release into the atmosphere of a wide variety of chemical compounds in a finely divided state. Smoke particles vary considerably in size from about 0.3 μm downwards. Fumes are solid particles, predominantly smaller than 1.0 μm, formed by the condensation of vapours.

Non-particulate contaminants consist of vapours condensable at normal pressures and temperatures, and gases, of which the most damaging to plants and buildings is

Table 2.44 Typical amounts of solids in the atmosphere for various localities

Locality	Total mass of solids / mg·m^{-3}
Rural and suburban	0.05–0.5
Metropolitan	0.1–1.0
Industrial	0.2–5.0
Factories or work rooms	0.5–10.0

Table 2.45 Analysis of typical atmospheric dust in relation to particle size

Range of particle size (diameter) / mm	Amount of solid as percentage of number of particles and total mass of particles / %	
	Number of particles	Total mass of particles
30 to 10	0.005	28
10 to 5	0.175	52
5 to 3	0.250	11
3 to 1	1.100	6
1 to 0.5	6.970	2
Less than 0.5	91.500	1

sulphur dioxide. Carbon monoxide and various oxides of nitrogen are also present in minute quantities. There is a wide variation in atmospheric solids between rural, suburban and industrial areas, as shown in Table 2.44.

Table 2.45 shows an analysis of a sample of atmospheric dust, in terms of the total numbers of particles for the size range. The figures may be considered typical for average urban and suburban conditions, but wide variations may be encountered in particular cases. Current emphasis in office and other 'standard' accommodation is on the removal of particles smaller than 10 µm. These, along with chemicals outgassed from carpets and furnishings in modern workspaces, have been linked with reports of sick building syndrome and are able to penetrate into the lungs, causing respiratory problems. Considerable work has been carried out on the performance of filters and air cleaning units in relation to cigarette smoke, see section 2.5.7.3.

2.5.7.2 Definitions

The following definitions, drawn from BS EN 779(83) are commonly used in describing the properties of air filters.

— *Rated air flow rate*: the quantity of air the filter is designed to handle as specified by the manufacturer. Expressed in m^3·s^{-1} (for a reference air density of 1.20 kg·m^{-3}).

— *Face velocity*: the airflow rate divided by the face area (m·s^{-1}).

— *Initial pressure drop*: the pressure drop (Pa) of the clean filter operating at its rated airflow rate.

— *Final pressure drop*: the pressure drop (Pa) up to which the filtration performance is measured for classification purposes.

— *Atmospheric dust spot efficiency* (E): a measure of the ability of the filter to remove atmospheric dust from the test air. This efficiency is measured on a light transmission basis (%).

— *Average atmospheric dust spot efficiency* (E_m): the average of the dust spot efficiency values (%).

— *Synthetic dust weight arrestance* (A): a measure of the ability of the filter to remove injected synthetic dust from the air (%). This arrestance is calculated on a weight basis.

— *Initial synthetic dust weight arrestance* (A_1): the first dust weigh arrestance (%) obtained from a dust feed increment of 30 g.

— *Average synthetic dust weight arrestance* (A_m): the average of the values of synthetic dust weight arrestance (%).

2.5.7.3 Filter testing

Tests for filters for general purposes

The comparative method of testing of air filters for general purposes, BS 6540: Part 1(245), has now been superseded by BS EN 779(83).

These tests are intended for filters for use in air systems handling between 0.24 m^3·s^{-1} and 1.4 m^3·s^{-1} and with initial atmospheric dust spot efficiencies no greater than 98%. For higher efficiencies, the sodium flame test given in BS 3928(246) is appropriate.

Based on their average synthetic dust weight arrestance or average dust spot efficiency, see Table 2.46, filters are classified into two groups, as follows:

— *Group G*: coarse dust filters, classes G1–G4

— *Group F*: fine dust filters, classes F5–F9.

If the initial average dust spot efficiency is less than 20%, the filter is automatically classified as group G and no further tests, other than arrestance, are carried out.

If the filter is classified as a fine dust filter it is subsequently tested for:

— air flow

— initial pressure drop

— atmospheric dust spot efficiency.

— synthetic dust weight arrestance

— dust holding capacity

— average efficiency

— average arrestance

— pressure drop.

Table 2.46 Classification according to filtration performance(83)

Characteristics	Filter group	Filter class	Old EU rating	Class limits / %	
				Average arrestance, A_m	Average efficiency, E_m
Coarse*	G	G1	EU1	$A_m < 65$	—
		G2	EU2	$65 \leq A_m \leq 80$	—
		G3	EU3	$80 \leq A_m \leq 90$	—
		G4	EU4	$90 \leq A_m$	—
Fine	F	F5	EU5	—	$40 \leq E_m < 60$
		F6	EU6	—	$60 \leq E_m < 80$
		F7	EU7	—	$80 \leq E_m < 90$
		F8	EU8	—	$90 \leq E_m < 95$
		F9	EU9	—	$95 \leq E_m$

* Initial dust spot efficiency < 20%

(*a*) Atmospheric dust spot efficiency

Otherwise known as the blackness test, this test involves sampling upstream and downstream air quality by drawing sample air quantities over target filters and comparing changes in opacity with time.

(*b*) Synthetic dust weight arrestance

This gravimetric test uses a synthetic dust comprised of carbon, sand and lint in controlled proportions similar to those found in a typical atmosphere. A known mass of dust is injected into test apparatus upstream of the filter and the dust passing the filter is collected in a more efficient final filter. The increase in mass of the final filter is used to calculate arrestance.

(*c*) Dust holding capacity

The synthetic dust weight arrestance test can be continued in cycles to achieve a picture of changes in efficiency and arrestance with increasing dust loading until the rated maximum pressure loss or minimum arrestance has been reached. The dust holding capacity can be determined from the total mass of synthetic dust held by the filter.

Test for high efficiency filters

The preferred pan-European test method for testing high efficiency HEPA and ULPA (ultra-low particle arrestor) filters is BS EN 1822[247]. This test method is based on scanning by a particle counter at the most penetrating particle size (MPPS) of the filter. MPPS is variable and is determined by testing samples of the filter medium used in the manufacture of the filter being tested. The challenge aerosol is DEHS mineral oil or equivalent, but other oils are permitted. Condensation nucleus counters (CNC) are used for monodispersed aerosols and laser particle counters (LPC) for polydispersed aerosols.

Based on their performance in the aerosol challenge test HEPA and ULPA filters are classified into two groups, as follows, see Table 2.47:

- *Group H*: HEPA filters, classes H10–H14
- *Group F*: ULPA filters, classes U15–U17.

BS 3928[246], which is still valid in the UK, describes a test method for high efficiency filters not covered by BS EN 779[83], i.e. filters having a penetration less than 2%. It is not considered to be as vigorous as a DOP or CNC test. Testing involves generation of an aerosol of sodium chloride containing particles ranging in size from 0.02 to 2 μm. The amount of particulate matter passing through the filter is determined by sampling both upstream and downstream of the filter and passing each sample through a flame photometer to determine the concentration of sodium chloride particles captured. BS 3928[246] is based on Eurovent 4/4[248] and results achieved under both standards should be comparable.

On-site testing

The efficiency of a filter installation depends not only on the filter efficiency but also on the security of the seal between the filter and the air system. This is particularly vital in high efficiency particulate air filters (HEPA) installations; hence penetration must be established immediately prior to use and at regular intervals throughout the working life of the system.

Tests that have been used to determine on-site penetration include:

- *Di-octyl-phthlate (DOP) test*: DOP is an oily liquid with a high boiling point. Normally, DOP vapour is generated at a concentration of 80 $mg{\cdot}m^{-3}$ and the downstream concentration is determined using a light scattering photometer via a probe which scans the entire downstream face of the filter installation.
- *Sodium flame*: a portable version of BS 3928[246] test apparatus that utilises a salt-stick thermal generator to produce an aerosol and an oxy-propane flame and portable photometer for penetration assessment.

Gas and vapour removal

Most manufacturers quote efficiencies for removal of a wide range of gases and vapours based on upstream and downstream concentrations. Adsorption filters are also rated in terms of the mass of gas/vapour that can be adsorbed before saturation of the adsorbent.

Specification and testing methods have been developed for gas and vapour removal by filters and re-circulating air cleaning units[249]. This work has looked at the performance of a wide range of systems including active bonded carbon units and electrostatic filters. Specialist advice should be sought on any requirements.

Dry testing

In applications such as cleanrooms used for the production of semi-conductors, testing for local leaks with an aerosol such as DOP would result in filter contamination and

Table 2.47 Classification of HEPA and ULPA filters[247]

Type	Filter group	Filter class	Old EU rating	Overall value / %		Local value* / %	
				Efficiency	Penetration	Efficiency	Penetration
HEPA	H	H10	EU10	85	15	—	—
		H11	EU11	95	5	—	—
		H12	EU12	99.5	0.5	—	—
		H13	EU13	99.95	0.05	99.75	0.25
		H14	EU14	99.995	0.005	99.975	0.025
Fine	U	U15	EU15	99.999 5	0.000 5	99.997 5	0.002 5
		U16	—	99.999 95	0.000 05	99.999 75	0.000 25
		U17	—	99.999 995	0.000 005	99.999 9	0.000 1

* Local values lower than those given in the table may be agreed between supplier and purchaser

subsequent production problems. In these circumstances filters are tested using atmospheric air or polystyrene latex spheres (PSL).

2.5.7.4 Filter application and selection

Table 2.48 (page 2-122) presents a broad classification of air cleaners and Figure 2.84, illustrates the various characteristics of dusts, mists etc., together with other relevant data. Table 2.49 (page 2-123) provides recommended filter specification data drawn from the National Engineering Specification[250] and promoted within BSRIA guidance[251,252]. CIBSE Technical Memoranda TM26[46] considers other means of reducing the admittance of micro-organisms other than just the installation of a HEPA filter. Under certain conditions, air filters can support the growth of micro-organisms and act as a source of contaminants. Standard air filters can be obtained with an anti-microbial coating that is reported to kill or inhibit the growth of micro-organisms on the filter material and any trapped dust and debris. However, due to the potential for the active biocide to outgas from the surface, the user of such systems should take steps to ensure that they are safe for building occupants. Anti-microbial ductwork coatings are also available. However they also have a potential for the active biocide to outgas from the surface.

Ultraviolet germicidal irradiation (UVGI) is provided by ultraviolet lamps mounted in the supply ductwork. The UV light causes inactivation of micro-organisms by disrupting their DNA. This system is claimed to be effective against all types of bacteria and fungi, as well as spores and viruses, which are normally found in the air. The user of such systems should ensure that staff are protected from exposure to the UV radiation. Photo-catalytic oxidation technology involves the action of low energy ultraviolet on a catalyst in the presence of water vapour that generates hydroxyl radicals that destroy micro-organisms. As this is an

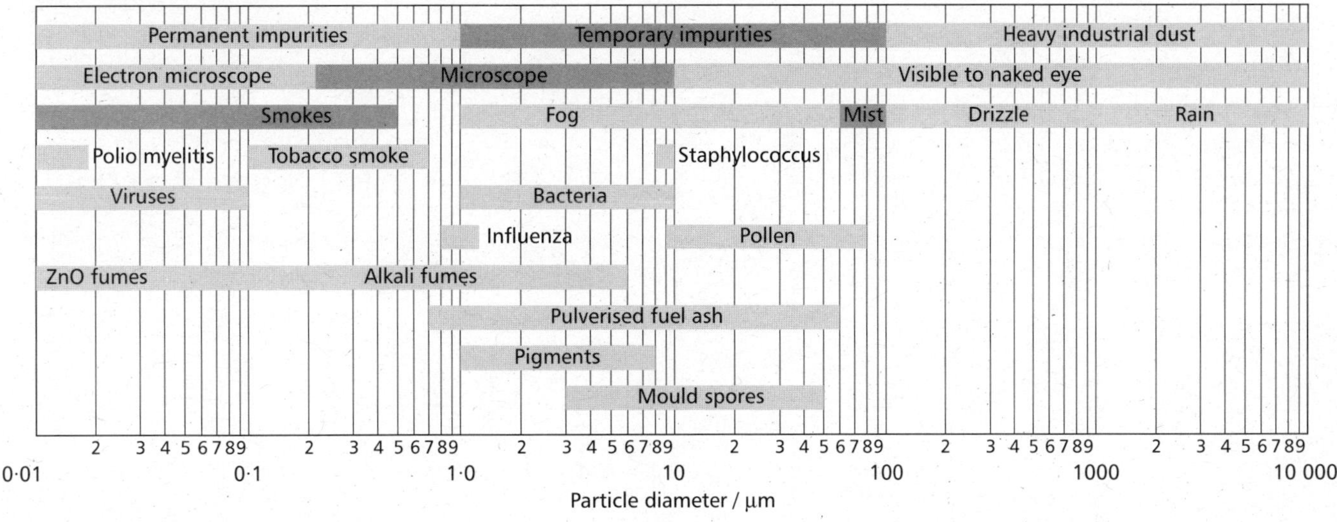

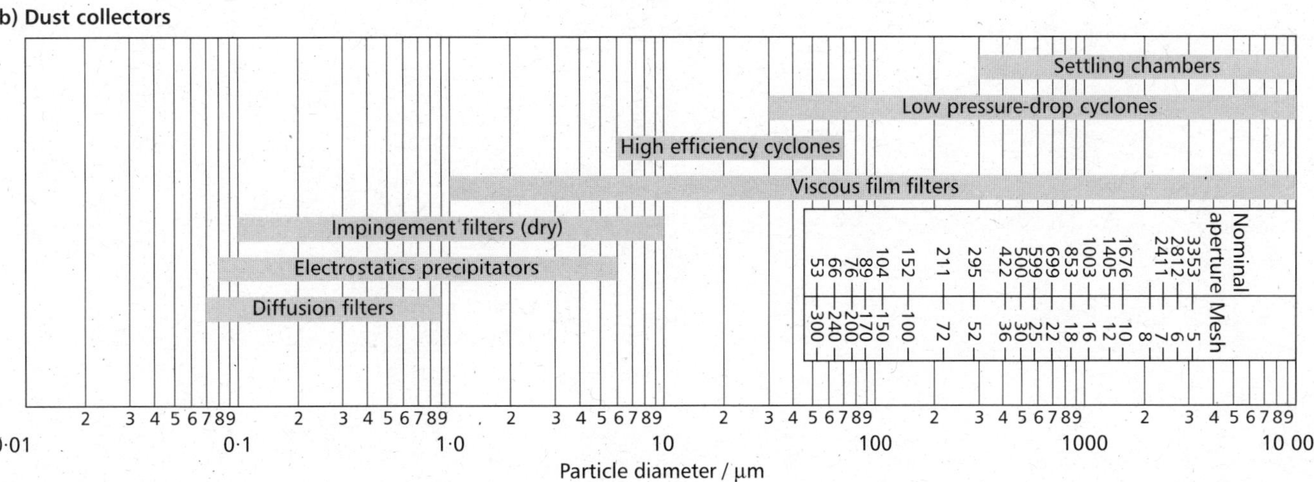

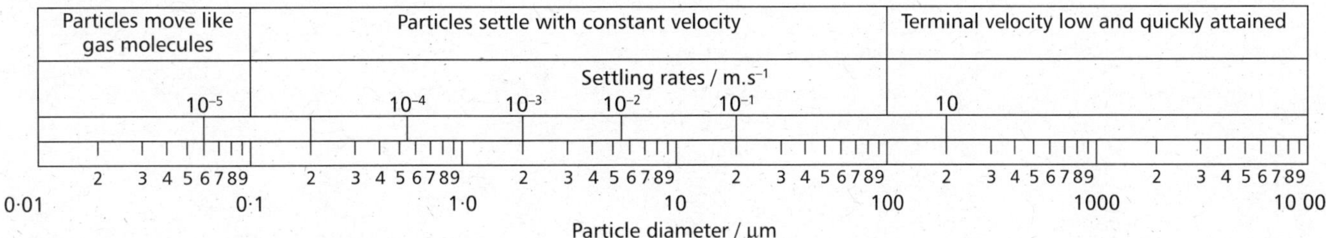

Figure 2.84 Characteristics of dusts and mists

Table 2.48 Classification of air cleaners

Type	Remarks	Method of cleaning	Face velocity / m·s^{-1}	Resistance at face velocity / Pa: Initial	Resistance at face velocity / Pa: Final	Dust holding capacity	Relative efficiency / %: Sodium flame	Relative efficiency / %: Synthetic dust	Relative cost
Viscous impingment:									
— panel or unit	Thickness ranges 12–100 mm; small or intermediate air volumes; good for particles > 10 μm diameter; efficiency decreases with dust loadings; used as after-cleaners	Permanent (washable) or disposable	1.5–2.5	20–60 (depending on thickness)	100–150	High; can be critical	10	> 85	Low
— moving curtain	Will handle heavy dust loads; intermediate or large air loads; used as precleaners etc.	Continuous or intermittent; can be automatic	2–2.5	30–60	100–125 (operating)	Self-cleaning by immersion	10	> 85	Medium
Dry:									
— panel, bag, cartridge or unit with fabric or fibrous medium	Small or intermediate air volumes	Usually disposable	1.25–2.5	25–185 (depending on efficiency)	125–250	Generally not as high as viscous impingement; can be critical	30–80 (depending on filter type, medium and face velocity)	96–100	Low to high
— moving curtain	Intermediate or large air volumes	Continuous or intermittent; can be automatic or disposable	2.5	30–60	100–175 (operating)	Self-cleaning	Can be selected over a wide range		Medium to high depending on efficiency
— absolute or diffusion (HEPA)	Pre-filter necessary; small air volumes; particles down to 0.01 μm diam.	Disposable	Up to 2.5	Up to 250	Up to 625	Low	> 99.9	100	High
Electrostatic:									
— charged plate	Pre-filter desirable; after-filter used to collect agglomerates; power-pack and safety precautions necessary (up to 12 kV); particles down to 0.01 μm diam; intermediate to large air volumes	Washable or wipable; can be automatic	1.5–2.5	Negligible; resistance added (40–60 Pa) to improve uniformity of air distribution		Can be critical	—	Not suitable over 5 μm diam.	High; low maintenance costs
— charged medium	As for charged plate	Disposable	1.25	25	125	High	55–65	Not suitable over 5 μm diam.	High; low maintenance costs
Adsorption units	Should be protected from dust, oil and grease; used for odour removal*	Can be reactivated	Low	Low; can be selected; constant		Medium adsorbs up to half its own weight of many organic substances	95 (dependent on gas to be removed)		High
Mechanical collectors	Not suitable for particles less than 0.01 μm diam.	To be emptied	Varies with design	50–100 (some act as air movers)	Constant	High	—	—	High; low maintenance costs

* Odours can also be removed by combustion, masking or liquid absorption devices

Note: air washers used for humidification or dehumidification purposes sometimes also act as air cleaning devices. These include capillary air washers, wet filters, adsorption spray chambers etc., for which manufacturers' data should be consulted.

Table 2.49 Recommended filter specification data

Filter data to be specified	Essential	Desirable
Air flow rate ($m^3 \cdot s^{-1}$)	•	
Air velocity ($m \cdot s^{-1}$)		•
Initial filter pressure drop (Pa)	•	
Final filter pressure drop (Pa)	•	
Average arrestance (%)	•	
Initial dust spot efficiency (%)	•	
Average dust spot efficiency (%)	•	
Minimum dust holding capacity (g)	•	
Class of filter (EU number)		•
Size of filter (height, width, limiting depth (mm))	•	
Casing		•
Test standards	•	
Access		•
Filter medium		•

oxidation process the microbial hydrocarbons are reduced to carbon dioxide and water. This technique can be used against bacteria, fungi/spores, viruses and allergens.

2.5.7.5 Filter maintenance

The life of a filter depends upon the:

— concentration and nature of contaminants

— filter efficiency

— dust holding capacity corresponding to rise in pressure loss between clean and dirty conditions

— face velocity at the filter.

A maintenance regime can be based on time intervals or on condition. Details of external conditions that may affect filter life, such as the entering pollution concentration, may be determined in consultation with the local Environmental Health Officer. Alternatively, a local survey may be undertaken. Some filter manufacturers provide prediction data for hours of use for different localities. Tables 2.44 and 2.45 give typical data on the amount and nature of solids in the atmosphere. Issues of external air quality, including sulphur dioxide and particulate matter (PM_{10}), are discussed in the *Air quality strategy for England, Scotland, Wales and Northern Ireland*[253], which is subject to periodic review.

If condition-based maintenance is being used the filter pressure differential is monitored. Replacement filters are installed when a specific differential is attained. If the filter represents a significant proportion of the total pressure loss of the system, and there is no provision for automatic fan duty adjustment (e.g. a VAV system), then the rise in pressure loss due to filter soiling should not exceed 20% of the total system loss with a clean filter. This differential can be reported via a building energy management system (BEMS). Note that a method of alerting maintenance staff of filter failure or blockage is also required for the time-based replacement method.

Further details on filter maintenance can be found in guidance produced by BSRIA[251] and HVCA[254]. Designers are also referred to CIBSE TM26[46].

2.5.7.6 Filter installation

BSRIA has analysed the whole life performance of filter systems[251,252] (i.e. the balance between space and capital costs and the operating costs such as inspection, change, energy and costs of associated equipment e.g. duct cleaning and redecoration). The conclusion is that filter performance depends not only on the filter specification but also on the design and installation of the filter system.

Poor filter installation will neutralise the benefits of specifying good filters[93]. The overall efficiency for the filter installation must be not less than that specified for the filter. It is suggested that:

— air intakes are located at high level away from the direction of the prevailing wind to prolong filter life and improve the quality of the intake air

— air filters should be protected from direct rain by using weather louvres to prevent water logging

— filters should be installed upstream of mechanical equipment to provide protection for that equipment; a final filter should be located downstream of the fan under positive pressure to reduce the risk of dust entering the system downstream of the filter

— adequate access for cleaning should be provided

— filter frames should be of good quality to prevent leakage and distortion; side withdrawal will make this difficult to achieve.

2.5.8 Air heater batteries

2.5.8.1 General

A heater battery comprises one or more rows of finned tubes, connected to headers and mounted within a steel sheet casing having flanged ends. Tubes in an individual row are usually connected in parallel but sometimes, for water only, may be series-connected as a serpentine coil in a single row. Tubes may be horizontal or vertical except for serpentine coils, which always have horizontal tubes, or steam batteries that always have vertical tubes. Tube rows are usually connected in parallel.

2.5.8.2 Materials

Tubes should be of solid drawn copper, expanded into collars formed on the copper or aluminium fins. Tube wall thickness should not be less than 0.7 mm for LTHW or 0.9 mm for HTHW or steam. Aluminium fins are usually acceptable, except in corrosive atmospheres, and should not be less than 0.4 mm thick. If copper fins are used they should not be less than 0.3 mm thick. Fins should not be spaced more closely than 330 fins per metre.

Provision should be made in the tube arrangement, by bowing or otherwise, to take up movement due to thermal expansion. Casings and flanges should be of adequate gauge in mild steel, painted with a rust resisting primer. Alternatively, the casings may be in galvanised mild steel with flanges painted in rust resistant primer. Occasionally both casings and flanges may be galvanised after manufacture.

2.5.8.3 Test pressure

Batteries should be tested with water at 2.1 MPa or 1.5 times the working pressure, whichever is the greater.

2.5.8.4 Heating medium

This is usually LTHW, MTHW, HTHW or dry steam. Where steam is used for preheat coils handling 100% outdoor air, so-called 'non-freeze' heater batteries should be selected. These coils have co-axial steam and condensate tubes that prevent build-up of condensate, and consequent risk of freezing, in the lower part of the battery.

2.5.9 Air cooler batteries

2.5.9.1 General

A cooler coil consists of one or more rows of horizontal finned tubes connected to headers and mounted within a steel sheet casing having flanged ends. Tubes in individual rows are connected in parallel and rows are usually connected in series, although sometimes they may be interlaced. Piping connections must be made such that the coldest air flows over the coldest row, thus approximating contra-flow heat exchange. Condensate drain trays through the depth of the coil are essential. These must be fitted at vertical intervals of not more than 1 m to facilitate proper drainage from the fins. Each such condensate collection tray must be drained using not less than a 22 mm connection. Eliminator plates are necessary if face velocities exceed 2.25 $m \cdot s^{-1}$. Cooler coils should normally be located on the low pressure side of the supply fan to avoid condensate leakage through the casing.

2.5.9.2 Materials

Tubes should be of solid drawn copper, electro-tinned and expanded into collars formed in aluminium. Alternatively, for more aggressive environments, solid copper tubes should be expanded into collars formed in copper fins, the whole assembly then being electro-tinned. Tube wall thickness should be to suit the test pressure, but not less than 0.7 mm. Aluminium fins should not be less than 0.4 mm thick and copper fins not less than 0.3 mm thick. Fins should not be more closely spaced than 330 per metre. Facings should be of an adequate gauge of steel, welded or with black mild steel angle flanges, the whole assembly being hot-dipped galvanised after manufacture. A suitable alternative corrosion-resistant construction may be used. Condensate collection trays should be of not less than 2 mm black mild steel, galvanised after manufacture, and then coated on the inside with bitumenised paint. Suitable alternative corrosion-resistant materials may be used.

Return bends should be housed within removable covers, allowing sufficient space for the bends to be lagged and vapour-sealed. Alternatively, particularly where a cooler coil is mounted on the high pressure side of a supply fan, return bends should be provided with airtight galvanised steel covers, with adequate provision for condensate drainage back to the main sump.

2.5.9.3 Sprayed cooler coils

These are generally similar to unsprayed coils, except that eliminator plates must always be fitted; also, the main sump tank is deeper and provides a reservoir of water for the spray pump. An array of standpipes and spray nozzles is fitted on the upstream side of the coil, the main sump is made of 3.2 mm black mild steel, galvanised after manufacture and coated internally with bitumenised paint. Aluminium fins must not be used.

2.5.9.4 Test pressure

Cooler coils should be tested with water at 2.1 MPa or 1.5 times the working pressure, whichever is the greater.

2.5.9.5 Cooling medium

The cooling medium is usually chilled water or, occasionally, chilled brine. Where the latter is used the reaction of the brine with the piping and pumping materials must be considered and suitable steps taken to prevent corrosion.

2.5.9.6 Refrigerant cooling coils

When the coil is a refrigerant evaporator, additional care must be taken with its design, material selection, and control because of interaction with the refrigeration system. The normal vapour-compression refrigeration system using an oil-miscible refrigerant and thermostatic expansion valve has limited rangeability.

For a wide control range it is usually necessary to divide the coil into two or more sections, each with its own thermostatic expansion valve, isolating inlet solenoid valve and, sometimes, its own suction line. By this means, as each section is isolated, the rangeability of the whole is increased as far as the limit of the operation of the sections remaining. For sectional control, the psychrometric effect of coil section arrangement must be appreciated, as shown in Table 2.50. It is also common practice to connect a separate compressor or condensing unit to each section or to pairs of sections on a multi-section coil in order to increase the total control range. When this is done it is advisable to connect the compressor and coil sections such that each section performs an equal share of the duty. This avoids a tendency towards frosting due to unequal evaporating temperatures.

2.5.10 Humidifiers

2.5.10.1 Requirements for humidity control

The need to provide humidity control is considered in CIBSE Guides A(12) and H(201) and in section 2.4.4.

2.5.10.2 System classifications

The variety of equipment types likely to be encountered is shown in Tables 2.51 and 2.52 (page 2-126). However, the trend is now towards steam and ultrasonic systems due to the fear of risks to health. Some older system types are included in the tables because they may be found in existing buildings. The tables distinguish between direct and indirect humidifiers:

— *Direct humidifiers*: have a particular application in industrial fields. They discharge water particles or vapour directly into the space to be treated. The air in the space absorbs the moisture to a degree

Table 2.50 Psychrometric effect of coil selection arrangement

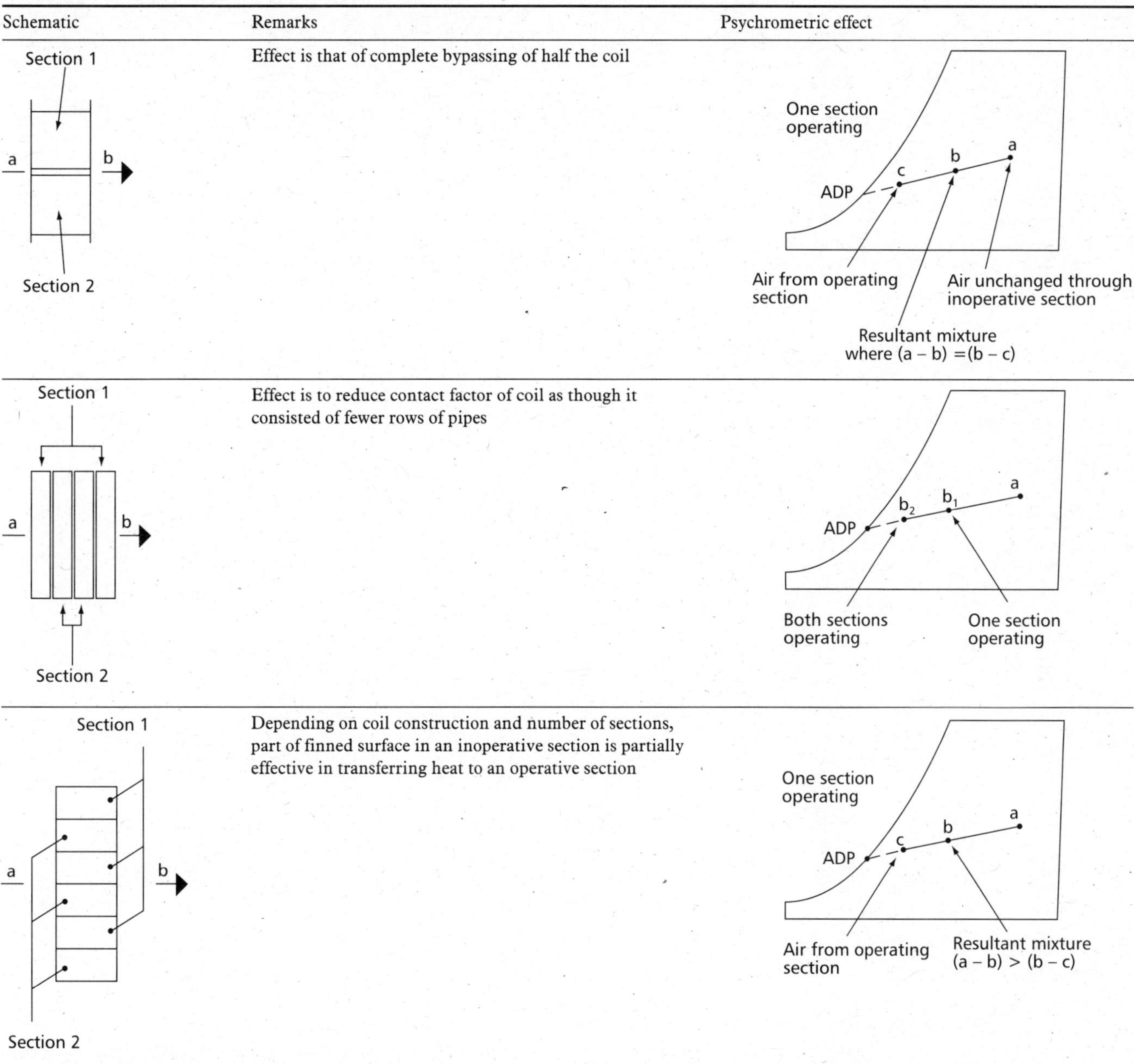

Schematic	Remarks	Psychrometric effect
Section 1; a; b; Section 2	Effect is that of complete bypassing of half the coil	One section operating; ADP; c; b; a; Air from operating section; Air unchanged through inoperative section; Resultant mixture where (a – b) =(b – c)
Section 1; a; b; Section 2	Effect is to reduce contact factor of coil as though it consisted of fewer rows of pipes	ADP; b_2; b_1; a; Both sections operating; One section operating
Section 1; a; b; Section 2	Depending on coil construction and number of sections, part of finned surface in an inoperative section is partially effective in transferring heat to an operative section	One section operating; ADP; c; b; a; Air from operating section; Resultant mixture (a – b) > (b – c)

consistent with the air movement or turbulence and the fineness of the particles created by the apparatus.

— *Indirect humidifiers*: the addition of moisture to the air takes place within the apparatus itself, the air leaving in a near saturated state. Moisture is presented to the air as a mist or surface film, depending upon the type of apparatus.

If humidification takes place without the addition or removal of heat (i.e. adiabatic), the process relies on evaporation. Sensible heat is taken from the air to provide the latent heat of evaporation necessary to convert water into a vapour of the same temperature. In doing so the temperature of the air is reduced although the total heat of the system remains constant. There are three basic types of adiabatic humidifier[255]:

— *Air washers* (and *evaporative coolers*, see below): found usually in large central air conditioning systems.

— *Wetted media*: used in residential and small commercial buildings (not in UK).

— *Water atomising*: having a wide range of applications as a result of their large capacity range.

Through an efficient humidifier the air can be cooled almost to its entering wet-bulb temperature and can then effectively remove sensible heat gains from the building. In practice, internal temperatures may be maintained at or near the external dry-bulb temperature. These evaporative cooling systems are discussed further in section 2.4.12.

Isothermal humidification means that the process occurs at a constant temperature. As such there is no cooling or heating applied to the ventilation process. Strictly, there is a very slight heat input and temperature rise as the water vapour introduced is often at, or near, steam temperature. Isothermal humidifiers can be divided into two categories[255]:

— *steam humidifiers*: including those where the steam is produced remotely

— *vapour generators*: where heat energy is converted to water vapour within the apparatus itself.

Table 2.51 Non-storage humidifiers; direct and indirect

Aspect	Direct or indirect			Indirect	
	Mechanical disc	Mechanical pressure	Vapour injection	Compressed air	Hydraulic separators
Application	Commercial/industrial	Commercial/industrial	Commercial/industrial	Industrial	Industrial
Separation efficiency	90%	90%	Up to 80%	Variable	Variable
Thermal efficiency	Low	Low	Restricted (humidifying only)	Low	Low
Filtration	Nil	Nil	Nil	Nil	Nil
Basis of operation	Revolving disk	Fan/pump	Steam	Air jet	Water jet
Saturating method	Fine spray	Fine spray	Vapour	Fine spray	Fine spray
Use	Humidifying	Humidifying	Humidifying	Humidifying	Humidifying
Advantages	Fineness of mist	Fineness of mist	Low maintenance cost	Low initial cost	Low initial cost

Table 2.52 Storage humidifiers; indirect

Aspect	Spray washers	Capillary washers	Sprayed coils	Pan
Application	Commercial/industrial	Commercial/industrial	Commercial/industrial	Commercial/industrial
Separation efficiency	70–90%	97%	Up to 95%	Low
Thermal efficiency	Up to 80%	Up to 80%	Up to 95%	Low
Filtration	Low under 20 μm particle size	90% by weight down to 3 μm particle size	Low	Low
Basis of operation	Pump	Pump	Pump	Static water
Saturating method	Fine spray	Surface film	Surface film	Surface film
Use	Humidifying /dehumidifying	Humidifying /dehumidifying	Humidifying /dehumidifying	Humidifying
Advantages	Variable saturation by water control	High efficiency, high filtration, minimum space	High efficiency	Low initial cost requirement

See BSRIA AG10/94[255] and manufacturers' information for a more detailed evaluation of the advantages and disadvantages of the various approaches.

2.5.10.3 Direct humidifiers

Hydraulic separation

Water separators operate direct from the high-pressure mains supply, the water jet impinging on a cylindrical or volute casing, suitable ports liberating the water as spray.

Compressed air separation

Where compressed air is available, high-pressure jets can be utilised to produce a fine water spray. Air atomising systems have larger water openings in the nozzles than water separators and hence are less susceptible to fouling from water impurities.

Mechanical separation

Mechanical separators operate at constant water pressure. They are often of the spinning disc type in which water flows as a film over the surface of a rapidly revolving disc until thrown off by centrifugal force onto a toothed ring where it is divided into fine particles. Alternatively, water is injected into a scroll-shaped housing and separated by the action of either a fan or a pump. Some mechanical separators produce fine droplets that are lighter than air, termed aerosols, which are non-wetting.

Vapour injection

For pre-heating in drying rooms and other applications direct injection of steam can provide a simple and effective method of increasing the moisture content of air provided that the rise in wet-bulb temperature from the heat in the steam does not cause control problems.

2.5.10.4 Indirect humidifiers

Spray washers

The efficiency of spray washers is governed by:

— the fineness of atomisation achieved by the spray

— the quantity of water sprayed into the chamber in relation to the air capacity

— the length of the unit and, consequently, the time for which the air is in contact with the water mist.

To obtain maximum efficiency the face velocity is limited to 2.5 $m \cdot s^{-1}$. Efficiencies to be expected are 70% for a single-bank spray washer, 85% for a double-bank spray washer, and 95% for a triple-bank spray washer, with a distance between each bank of about 1 m.

Suggested rates of water flow are approximately 5 litre·s^{-1} of water per 3 m^2 of face area of the spray chamber per bank of sprays, which is equivalent to approximately 7 litre·s^{-1} of water per 10 m^3 of air per second. To provide the fine degree of atomisation required, gauge pressures in the region of 200 kPa are required at the spray nozzles.

This type of humidifier is particularly prone to bacteriological growth and other forms of contamination since water storage ponds may remain still for long periods during warm weather.

Capillary type washers

In principle capillary type washers are built up from unit cells, each cell packed with filaments of glass specially orientated to give the minimum resistance to air flow with the highest efficiency.

The cells are sprayed from nozzles at a gauge pressure of 40 kPa, producing coarse droplets of water which, by capillary action, produce a constant film of moisture over each glass filament. The air passing through the cell is broken up into finely divided air streams providing maximum contact between water and air, resulting in high efficiency of saturation. Most dust particles down to 3 μm in size are also eliminated from the air stream, and it is therefore necessary to provide a constant flush of water through the cells to eliminate the danger of blockage.

Alternatively, an intermittent supply, controlled by time clock, may be used to flush the cells with water at predetermined intervals. The face velocity through the washer chamber is similar to the spray type, i.e. 2.5 m·s^{-1} with a maximum of 2 m·s^{-1} through the cells.

Saturation efficiency of 97% can be achieved with as little as 0.8 litres of water per 10 m^3 of air per second, although a minimum of 4.5 litres per 10 m^3 of air per second is required for flushing purposes. The cells have a maximum water capacity of 11 litres per 10 m^3 of air per second.

Capillary cells are arranged in parallel flow formation, where the air and water pass through the cell in the same direction, or in a contra-flow arrangement with water and air passing through the cell in opposite directions. Selection is governed by the humidifying or dehumidifying duty required from each cell and also the degree of cleanliness of the air handled.

Prevention of bacteriological and other contamination must also be considered.

Sprayed coils

Coils fitted into casings and sprayed from low-pressure nozzles provide an efficient means of humidification. The efficiencies obtained are in direct relation to the contact factor of the coil and thus depend on the number of rows provided, the spacing of the fins etc.

The recommended rate of spray is about 0.8 litre·s^{-1} per m^2 of face area with a gauge pressure at the spray nozzles of 50 kPa.

Precautions must be taken to prevent bacteriological and other contamination. Ideally, water circulation should be continuous.

Pan humidifiers

The simplest form of indirect humidifier is the pan type that consists of a shallow tank in which the water is kept at a constant level by a ball float valve.

The air passing over the surface of the water picks up moisture and the water may be warmed to increase effectiveness. Efficiencies are low and depend upon the area of water surface presented to a given volume of air. Disadvantages arise from the odours that can result from the static water surface.

Use of this type of humidifier is discouraged because of the high risk of bacteriological contamination.

Mechanical separators

Mechanical separators of the revolving disc type can, in addition to their usefulness as direct humidifiers, be mounted into a chamber similar to a spray washer, taking the place of the spray system and pumping set. Water treatment should be considered in hard water localities as any free aerosols not absorbed in the plant may be carried through into the conditioned space, evaporating and precipitating salts on surfaces in the form of a white dust.

Steam humidifiers

Steam provides a relatively simple and hygienic method of humidification providing that the heat in the system can be absorbed. Generally the use of main boiler steam is limited in application to industry due to the characteristic odour and traces of oil which may be present.

For application to ventilation systems, secondary steam can be generated at low or atmospheric pressure from mains steam, an electrode boiler or electrical resistance boiler.

Ultrasonic humidifiers

Ultrasonic humidifiers rely on the principle of ultrasonic nebulisation brought about by a rapidly oscillating crystal submerged in water. The crystal, a piezo-electric transducer, converts an electrical signal into a mechanical oscillation. This forms a cavity between the crystal and the water creating a partial vacuum. At this precise instant the water is able to boil, creating a low temperature gas. This is then followed by a positive oscillation creating a high-pressure wave that is able to expel the pocket of gas through to the surface of the water. Condensation occurs, but the net result is the release of finely atomised water that is readily able to evaporate.

Rotating drum humidifiers

Rotating drum humidifiers consist of a cylinder or belt that is partially submerged in a water trough. The drum or belt rotates to continuously wet the surfaces. The rate of evaporation is usually controlled by stopping or starting the rotation of the drum. Some humidifiers incorporate a fan.

Infrared evaporators

Infrared lamps evaporate water contained in reservoirs or pans. Parabolic reflectors are used to reflect and focus the infrared radiation downward onto the water. Units can be duct mounted or, if equipped with an integral fan, can be positioned in the room to be humidified.

2.5.10.5 Excess moisture elimination

Indirect water-type humidifiers normally induce more moisture than that required to saturate the air. To prevent excess moisture entering the ducting system an eliminator section is generally incorporated in the humidifier. This comprises either a series of vertical plates profiled to cause directional changes of the air or, alternatively, mats of interlaced plastic or metal fibres retained in suitable frames. Depending upon the depth of the coil an eliminator section is not required with sprayed coil coolers if the face velocity is below 2.25 $m \cdot s^{-1}$.

2.5.10.6 Humidifier positioning

Research[255] shows that humidifiers are often placed where space permits, and hence are not necessarily in the location that best suits control or humidification requirements. The preferred position for the humidifier is downstream of the supply fan and clear (i.e. downstream) of any turning vanes or dampers but sufficiently upstream of the space for complete absorption to have occurred. A rapid absorption design (i.e. one that creates greater dispersal across the cross-sectional area of the duct) may be required to avoid the formation of condensation or water droplet impingement if there are nearby obstructions within the duct. An alternative location should be sought if this is not possible. The next best choice is just upstream of the fan, provided that the water has been suitably absorbed by the air. This is to avoid fan failure due to the fan being wetted.

2.5.10.7 Materials

Pollution in the air handled, and the nature of water used for humidification purposes, can create chemical conditions that may require the use of protective coatings, plastic materials or other metals in preference to steel. However some materials provide suitable conditions for growth of bacteria and these should be avoided. A list of such materials is given elsewhere[255].

2.5.10.8 Water supply

Scale formation

Treatment of water may be necessary where, for example, available water supplies contain a high degree of temporary hardness or calcium salts in free suspension. The local area water authority should be contacted to identify the water quality and the manufacturer's or supplier's advice subsequently sought on water treatment requirements. Any precipitation that does take place can be dealt with by the use of special inhibitors or dispersant treatments.

Health hazards arising from humidification

Expert advice must be sought to ensure that all humidification systems are safe in their design, operation, and subsequent upkeep. Designers are advised to be aware of the latest guidance, in particular that produced by the Water Regulations Advisory Scheme[256], Health and Safety Executive[257] and CIBSE[121,258]. The HSE's Approved Code of Practice (ACOP) L8[257] applies to any humidifier or air washer where a spray of water droplets is produced and the water temperature is likely to exceed 20 °C, as infection is caused by inhaling airborne droplets and the formation of *Legionella* is promoted within water temperatures in the range of 20–45 °C. Additional guidelines are available for humidifiers used for medical purposes[259].

To avoid risks, it is suggested that designers specify equipment that does not create a spray, i.e. steam or evaporative humidifiers[122]. Where humidifiers that create a spray are used, the risk should be controlled by ensuring that the equipment, and the water supplied to it, is kept clean. This involves regular cleaning and disinfection, continuous water circulation and the drainage of tanks and headers when not in use. Note that water treatment chemicals are not recommended for use in humidifiers and air washers when buildings are occupied. Using water direct from the mains supply, rather than recirculated or stored water, will reduce microbiological contamination. However local authority approval will be needed under the Water Regulations[119].

2.5.10.9 Energy use

Steam injection systems, whether drawn from a steam distribution system or from local electric boilers give rise to very significant energy consumption, increasing with the closeness of control required, see Figure 2.85[26]. Where steam is available on site it is sensible to make use of it and directly inject steam to provide humidification. Local electrically powered humidification units generally have independent controls and can cause significant increases in electricity consumption. Ultrasonic systems are becoming more popular and use up to 90% less energy than electrode boiler systems. However electricity is required for the water purification plant and reheating may be needed if the air temperature is reduced by the evaporative cooling effect.

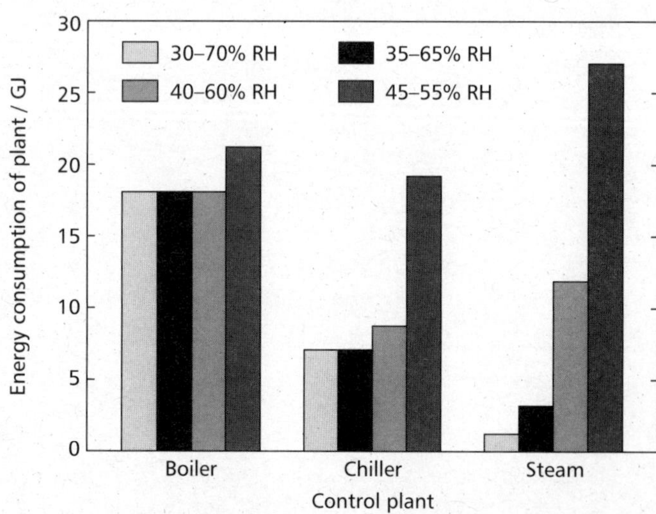

Figure 2.85 Energy use and effect of humidity control

2.5.11 Fans

2.5.11.1 General

Fans consume a large proportion of the total energy in mechanically ventilated buildings. A high priority should therefore be given to achieving energy efficient fan operation. Fan volumes and pressure drops should be minimised by good design. Benchmarks for fan volumes and pressure drops are provided in CIBSE Guide F(26). The specific fan power should be 2 watts per litre·s^{-1} or less to achieve good practice in offices; very energy efficient systems can sometimes achieve around 1 watt per litre·s^{-1}. Consideration could be given to over-sizing parts of the system to reduce pressure drops, e.g. the air handling unit, as this is normally responsible for the majority of the losses. Selection should favour the more efficient fan types and try to ensure that the fans will be operating at peak efficiency.

Volume control should be incorporated to meet varying levels of demand. This may be at the dictates of temperature, pressure or air quality sensors. Flow control may be achieved by a number of means including:

— on/off, multi-speed or variable speed operation

— varying the blade pitch for axial fans

— inlet guide vanes.

Dampers can also be used but are less energy efficient. See EEBPP General Information Report GIR 41(195) for further information on volume control.

2.5.11.2 Fan types and components

Table 2.53 provides a summary of fan types. The following definitions should be used in relation to fans:

— *Casing*: those stationary parts of the fan which guide air to and from the impeller.

— *Guide vanes*: a set of stationary vanes, usually radial, on the inlet or discharge side of the impeller, covering the swept annulus of the impeller blades (or wings); their purpose is to correct the helical whirl of the airstream and thus raise the performance and efficiency of the fan.

— *Impeller*: that part of a fan which, by its rotation, imparts movement to the air.

— *Axial-flow fan*: a fan having a cylindrical casing in which the air enters and leaves the impeller in a direction substantially parallel to its axis.

— *Centrifugal or radial-flow fan*: a fan in which the air leaves the impeller in a direction substantially at right angles to its axis.

— *Cross-flow or tangential fan*: a fan in which the air is caused to flow through the impeller in a direction substantially at right angles to its axis both entering and leaving the impeller through the blade passages.

— *Mixed-flow fan*: a fan having a cylindrical casing and a rotor followed by a stator in which the air flowing through the rotor has both axial and radial velocity components.

— *Propeller fan*: a fan having an impeller other than of the centrifugal type rotating in an orifice; the air flow into and out of the impeller not being confined by any casing.

2.5.11.3 Fan performance

Definition of terms

Fan performance is expressed in terms of fan size, air delivery, pressure, speed and power input at a given air density. Efficiency will be implied or specifically expressed. The size of a fan depends on the individual manufacturer's coding but is directly expressed as, or is a function of, either the inlet diameter or the impeller diameter. Other terms are defined in BS 4856(260) and BS 848: Part 1(261) as follows:

— *Reference air*: for the purposes of rating fan performance, reference air is taken as having a density of 1.200 kg·m^{-3}; this value corresponds to atmospheric air at a temperature of 20 °C, a pressure of 101.325 kPa and a relative humidity of 43%.

— *Fan total pressure*: the algebraic difference between the mean total pressure at the fan outlet and the mean total pressure at the fan inlet.

— *Fan velocity pressure*: the velocity pressure corresponding to the average velocity of the fan outlet based on the total outlet area without any deduction for motors, fairings or other bodies.

— *Fan static pressure*: the difference between the fan total pressure and the fan velocity pressure.

— *Fan duty (total)*: the inlet volume dealt with by a fan at a stated fan total pressure.

— *Fan duty (static)*: the inlet volume dealt with by a fan at a stated fan static pressure.

— *Air power (total)*: the product of the fan total pressure and the fan duty (total).

— *Air power (static)*: the product of the fan static pressure and the fan duty (static).

— *Shaft power*: the energy input, per unit time, to the fan shaft including the power absorbed by such parts of the transmission system as constitute an integral part of the fan, e.g. fan shaft bearings.

— *Fan total efficiency*: the ratio of the air power (total) to the shaft power

— *Fan static efficiency*: the ratio of the air power (static) to the shaft power.

The fan laws

For a given system in which the total pressure loss is proportional to the square of the volume flow, the performance of a given fan at any changed speed is obtained by applying the first three rules (the air density is considered unchanged throughout):

— *Rule 1*: The inlet volume varies directly as the fan speed.

— *Rule 2*: The fan total pressure and the fan static pressure vary as the square of the fan speed.

— *Rule 3*: The air power (total or static) and impeller power vary as the cube of the fan speed.

Table 2.53 Summary of fan types

Fan type	Efficiency / %		Advantages	Disadvantages	Applications
	Static	Total			
1 Axial-flow (without guide vanes	50–65	50–75	Very compact, straight-through flow. Suitable for installing in any position in run of ducting.	High tip speed. Relatively high noise level comparable with type 5. Low pressure development.	All low pressure atmospheric air applications.
2 Axial-flow (with guide vanes)	65–75	65–85	Straight-through flow. Suitable for vertical axis.	Same as type 1 but to lesser extent.	As for type 1, and large ventilation schemes such as tunnel ventilation.
3 Forward-curved or multivane centrifugal	45–60	45–70	Operates with low peripheral speed. Quiet and compact.	Severely rising power characteristic requires large motor margin.	All low and medium pressure atmospheric air and ventilation plants.
4 Straight or paddle-bladed centrifugal	45–55	45–70 60 (non-shrouded)	Strong, simple impeller. Least likely to clog. Easily cleaned and repaired.	Low efficiency. Rising power characteristic.	Material transport systems and any application where dust burden is high.
5 Backwards-curved or backwards-inclined blade centrifugal	65–75	65–85	Good efficiency. Non-overloading power characteristic.	High tip speed. Relatively high noise level compared with type 3.	Medium and high pressure applications such as high velocity ventilation schemes.
6 Aerofoil-bladed centrifugal	80–85	80–90	Highest efficiency of all fan types. Non-overloading fan characteristic	Same as type 5.	Same as type 5 but higher efficiency justifies use for higher power applications.
7 Propeller	< 40	< 40	Low first cost and ease of installation.	Low efficiency and very low pressure development.	Mainly non-ducted low pressure atmospheric air applications. Pressure development can be increased by diaphragm mounting.
8 Mixed-flow	45–70	45–70	Straight-through flow. Suitable for installing in any position in run of ducting. Can be used for higher pressure duties than type 2. Lower blade speeds than types 1 or 2, hence lower noise.	Stator vanes are generally highly loaded due to higher pressure ratios. Maximum casing diameter is greater than either inlet or outlet diameters.	Large ventilation schemes where the higher pressures developed and lower noise levels give an advantage over type 2.
9 Cross-flow or tangential-flow	—	40–50	Straight across flow. Long, narrow discharge.	Low efficiency. Very low pressure development.	Fan coil units. Room conditioners. Domestic heaters.

For changes in density:

— *Rule 4*: The fan total pressure, the fan static pressure and the fan power all vary directly as the mass per unit volume of the air which in turn varies directly as the barometric pressure and inversely as the absolute temperature.

For geometrically similar airways and fans operating at constant speed and efficiency the performance is obtained by applying the following three rules (the air density is considered unchanged throughout):

— *Rule 5*: The inlet flowrate varies as the cube of the fan size.

— *Rule 6*: The fan total pressure and the fan static pressure vary as the square of the fan size.

— *Rule 7*: The air power (total or static) and impeller power vary as the fifth power of the fan size.

2.5.11.4 Types of fan

Axial-flow fans

Axial-flow fans comprise an impeller with a number of blades, usually of aerofoil cross section, operating in a cylindrical casing. The fineness of the tip clearance between impeller blades and casing has a marked effect on the pressure development of the fan and, in turn, its output and efficiency. The blades may also have 'twist', i.e. the pitch angle increases from tip to root. The pitch cannot be increased beyond the stall point of the aerofoil and the centre of the impeller has to be blanked-off by a hub to avoid recirculation. The hub acts as a fairing for the motor. Large hubs and short blades characterise a high pressure to volume ratio, and vice versa. Refinements include guide vanes to correct whirl at inlet or discharge and fairings and expanders to recover a greater proportion of the velocity head in the blade swept annulus.

Axial-flow fans are of high efficiency and have limiting power characteristics, but as the highest pressure single-stage axial-flow fans develop only about one-fifth of the pressure produced by a forward curved (multi-vane) fan, they are best suited for high volume/pressure ratios. However, axial-flow fans may be staged or placed in series and when fitted with guide vanes the aggregate pressure developed is proportional to the number of stages for a given volume. A two-stage fan can be contra-rotating, and without the use of guide vanes the pressure developed may be up to 2.75 times greater than that of a single stage.

Centrifugal fans

Centrifugal fans comprise an impeller that rotates usually in an involute casing. The air flows into the impeller axially, turns through a right angle within it and is discharged radially by centrifugal force. The scroll acts as a collector that permits vortex flow to the casing outlet and converts some of the high velocity pressure at the blade tips into static pressure. There are several variations of the basic form, see below.

— *Forward-curved or multi-vane*: the impeller has a relatively large number of short forward-curved blades. The air is impelled forward in the direction of rotation at a speed greater than the impeller tip speed. For a given duty this type of fan is the smallest of the centrifugal types. It operates with the lowest tip speed and is often referred to as a low-speed fan. As the velocity of the air does not decrease within the blade passages, the efficiency is not high and the motor can easily be overloaded if the system resistance is overestimated.

— *Straight-radial or paddle-blade*: the impeller has a few (typically six) straight blades which may be fixed by the roots to a spider, or may have a back-plate and shroud-plate. This is the simplest, and least efficient, of fan types but is well suited to applications where airborne material is present as the blades are unlikely to clog. The impeller is of high mechanical strength and is cheap to refurbish. Renewable blades or wear plates are often fitted.

— *Backwards-curved blade*: the air leaves the impeller at a speed less than the impeller tip speed and the rotational speed for a given duty is relatively high. The impeller has from ten to sixteen blades of curved or straight form, inclined away from the direction of rotation. Because the blades are deep, good expansion within the blade passages takes place and this, coupled with a relatively low air speed leaving the impeller, ensures high efficiency and a non-limiting power characteristic.

— *Aerofoil blade*: a refinement of the backwards-curved fan in which the impeller blades are of aerofoil contour with a venturi throat inlet and fine running clearance between inlet and impeller. The casing is compact and the volumetric output is high. It has the highest static efficiency, but is a relatively high-speed fan due to the low pressure development.

Propeller fans

Propeller fans comprise an impeller of two or more blades of constant thickness, usually of sheet steel, fixed to a centre boss and are designed for orifice or diaphragm mounting. They have high volumetric capacity at free delivery, but very low pressure development. However, this may be increased by fitting the fan in a diaphragm, which in turn may be installed in a circular or rectangular duct of area greater than the blade-swept area. The efficiency of propellor fans is low.

Cross-flow or tangential fans

These comprise a forward-curved centrifugal type impeller but with greatly increased blade length and the conventional inlets blocked off. The impeller runs in a half casing with conventional discharge but no inlet. Air is scooped inwards through the blade passages on the free side, but at the opposite side of the impeller, due to the influence of the casing, the air obeys the normal centrifugal force and flows out of the impeller and through the fan discharge.

The principle of operation relies on the setting up of a long cylindrical vortex stabilised within the impeller which, being much smaller in diameter than the impeller, rotates at high angular velocity. This in turn drives the main airstream past the blades of the fan with higher velocity than the peripheral speed of the blades themselves. In effect the air flows 'across' the impeller, almost at right angles to the axis. Because this fan is so different from other types direct comparisons are not valid. A serious disadvantage of this type is that it cannot be operated at shaft speeds widely different from that for which it has been designed. Consequently it obeys the fan laws only within narrow limits of speed change. It operates with a high discharge velocity and an expander is desirable when connected to ductwork, especially as the efficiency (which is rather less than that for the multi-vane fan) peaks at near-free delivery conditions. The discharge opening is characteristically narrow so the fan is not easily applicable to ducting but is well suited to fan coil units and electric space heaters.

Mixed-flow in-line fans

Mixed-flow fans comprise an impeller with a number of blades, often of aerofoil section, similar to the axial flow fan. The hub is of conical shape such that the passage of air through the impeller has both axial and radial components, hence the term mixed-flow. Mixed-flow fans are of high efficiency and can be designed for higher pressure duties than axial flow fans. To remove the swirl generated by the passage of air through the impeller, stator guide vanes are fitted downstream. These vanes are generally highly loaded due to the high pressure ratios. If the inlet and outlet flanges are to be of the same diameter a change in casing profile is necessary in the region of the guide vanes. Separation of airflow can occur if the conditions for which the fan was designed are not maintained in practice.

Bifurcated fans

Bifurcated fans handle atmospheres normally detrimental to the life of the fan motor, including saturated and dust-laden atmospheres, heated air, hot gases and corrosive fumes. They are normally direct drive with the motor isolated from the system air stream.

2.5.12 Air control units

2.5.12.1 General

When various areas to be air conditioned have differing heat gain patterns with respect to time, these can be met from a central plant in which either the temperature or volume (or both) of the air supplied to each area is varied to meet the particular requirements of the area. Such temperature or volume control may be carried out in ductwork serving a number of rooms or zones, or may be carried out in the terminal units feeding individual rooms.

2.5.12.2 Control of volume

Volume control may be achieved by:

— *Damper*: normally of the butterfly or multileaf type and capable of controlling the volume, providing the pressure drop across the damper does not exceed about 40 Pa. If the pressure drop is higher, there will be a tendency to generate excessive noise. Normally the damper is supplied as a separate component for direct installation in the ductwork and not as part of a terminal unit. Final adjustment is carried out manually on site.

— *Pressure regulating valve*: an assembly consisting of one or two rows of shaped blades, the size of which changes when volume adjustment is required. Because of the particular blade shape, the device gives volume adjustment up to pressure drops of about 630 Pa without generating excessive noise. The majority of dampers are set on site, but they can be controlled from a static pressure sensing element. Such units are generally supplied as a separate component for direct installation in the ductwork and not as part of a terminal unit.

— *Mechanical volume controller*: a device which is self-actuating and capable of automatically maintaining a constant pre-set volume through it, provided that the pressure drop across it is above a minimum of about 120 Pa and below a maximum of about 250 Pa. As the supply air pressure increases, most devices of this type tend to close progressively by means of a flexible curtain or solid damper; a multi-orifice plate fixed across the complete airway of the unit. As such a unit achieves volume reduction by reducing the airway, there is a tendency to generate noise, particularly when working at high air pressures. For this reason, the volume controller is generally supplied in an acoustically treated terminal unit. It is factory pre-set to pass a specific volume and, when installed, will automatically give a pre-balanced air distribution system up to and including the terminal unit. It can be adjusted on-site, if desired.

2.5.12.3 Control of temperature

This may be achieved by:

— *Blending*: two separate airstreams, one warm, one cool, are supplied to a zone and mixed in a terminal unit to produce a supply air temperature which offsets the zone cooling or heating loads.

— *Reheat*: controlled reheat of a pre-conditioned, low temperature air supply by means of hot water, steam or electric coils, may be used to give a resultant supply air temperature which will satisfy the zone requirement.

2.5.13 Air terminal devices

Air can be supplied to the space in a number of ways[162], the principal division being between diffusers and perpendicular jets. Airflow patterns for both types are strongly dependent upon the presence or absence of the Coanda effect (see page 2-54). Table 2.54 summarises the types of air terminal devices, and provides information on typical face velocities (based on any local control devices being fully open) and noise levels.

Diffusers may be radial, part radial or linear and normally utilise the Coanda effect and/or swirl to reduce the excessive room air movement.

A perpendicular jet may be formed by discharging air through grilles, louvres, nozzles or any opening which allows perpendicular air flow; direction and spread adjustment can be provided using blades and or swivel adjustment. Supply air terminals can be incorporated into any room surface, e.g. ceiling (flat or sculptured), floor, wall (high or low level), desk top, seat back or under seats.

Table 2.54 Types of air terminal device

Type	Application	Location	Core velocity / m·s^{-1}		Description and remarks
			Quiet	Commercially quiet	
1 Perforated or stamped lattice	Supply, extract, transfer	Ceiling, sidewall, floor	Up to 4	Up to 6	Simple form of grille with small free area. Alternatively can be used as supply diffuser with high air entrainment allowing large quantities to be diffused. For low-level 'laminar flow' panels to give displacement ventilation, a velocity of 0.25 m·s^{-1} is used.
2 Aerofoil blades (one row adjustable)	Supply, extract	Ceiling, sidewall, desk top	7	10	Frequently used grille with large free area. Directional control in one plane only for supply applications.
3 Aerofoil blades (two rows adjustable)	Supply	Sidewall	7	10	As type 2 but with directional control in two planes.
4 Fixed blade	Supply, extract		6	9	Robust grille with limited free area. Some directional control possible using profiled blades.
5 Non-vision	Extract, transfer	Side wall	7	10	Low free area. Designed to prevent through vision.
6 'Egg crate'	Extract	Ceiling, side wall	7	10	Generally largest free area grille available.
7 Fixed geometry diffusers	Supply, extract	Ceiling, floor, desk top	7	10	Radial discharge diffusers offer good air entrainment allowing diffusion of large air quantities. Square or rectangular diffusers can provide 1-, 2- or 3-way diffusion. Angled blades can be used to apply twisting motion to supply air.
8 Adjustable diffusers	Supply	Ceiling	4	6	As type 7 but offers horizontal or vertical discharge. Can be thermostatically controlled.
9 Slot and discharge, linear diffusers	Supply, extract	Ceiling, side wall, desk top, under window	6	9	Offers vertical or horizontal single or multiple slots. Care must be taken with design of plenum box. Desk top units may incorporate induction of room air.
10 Air handling luminaires	Supply, extract	Ceiling	7	10	As type 9 but single slot only. Normally used in conjunction with extract through luminaire.
11 Ventilated ceiling nozzel	Supply, extract		—	—	Void above ceiling is pressurised to introduce air at low velocity through many single holes or through porous panels. Air entrainment is restricted and natural air currents may affect room air distribution.
12 Nozzels, drum and punkah louvres	Supply	Ceiling, side wall, under window, seat back			Adjustable type can be rotating drum or swivelling ball, with or without jet for long throws and personal air supply or 'spot' cooling. Fixed multiple nozzels are used for high-induction applications. Velocities depend on throw, noise and induction requirements.

References

1 *Conservation of fuel and power* The Building Regulations 2000 Approved Document L (London: The Stationery Office) (2001)

2 *Technical standards for compliance with the Building Standards (Scotland) Regulations 1990* (London: The Stationery Office) (1999)

3 Thomas R (ed.) *Environmental Design: An Introduction for Architects and Engineers* (2nd edition) (London: E & F N Spon) (1999)

4 *Whole Life Costing: A client's guide* Construction Clients Forum 2000 (London: Confederation of Construction Clients) (2000)

5 Allard R Get a whole-life *Building* **266** (18) 69 (May 2001)

6 *Ventilation and air conditioning (requirements)* and *Ventilation and air conditioning (systems and equipment)* in CIBSE Guide B: *Installation and equipment data* (London: Chartered Institution of Building Services Engineers) (1986) (out of print)

7 Hayden G W and Parsloe C J *Value engineering of building services* BSRIA Applications Guide AG 15/96 (Bracknell: Building Services Research and Information Association) (1996)

8 *Whole life costs* Construction Procurement Guidance No. 7 (London: Office of Government Commerce) (2000) (www.ogc.gov.uk)

9 *Building Services Component Manual Life Manual* (Oxford: Blackwell Science) (2001)

10 Evans R, Haste N, Jones A and Haryott R *The long term costs of owning and using buildings* (London: Royal Academy of Engineering) (1998)

11 *Testing buildings for air leakage* CIBSE TM23 (London: Chartered Institution of Building Services Engineers) (2000)

12 *Environmental design* CIBSE Guide A (London: Chartered Institution of Building Services Engineers) (1999)

13 *Project management handbook for building services* BSRIA Applications Guide 11/98 (Bracknell: Building services Research and Information Association) (1998)

14 *Flexible building services for office based environments — Principles for designers* CIBSE TM27 (London: Chartered Institution of Building Services Engineers) (2001) (available to CIBSE members only via CIBSE website)

15 BS ISO 15686-1: *Buildings and constructed assets. Service life planning*: Part 1: 2000: *General principles* (London: British Standards Institution) (2000)

16 Nanayakkara R and Fitzsimmons J *Cost benchmarks for the installation of building services* BSRIA Applications Guide 20-1/99CD (Bracknell: Building Services Research and Information Association) (1999)

17 Parsloe C *Design for maintainability* BSRIA Applications Guide AG 11/92 (Bracknell: Building services Research and Information Association) (1992)

18 Crozier B *Enhancing the performance on oversized plant* BSRIA Applications Guide AG1/2000 (Bracknell: Building services Research and Information Association) (2000)

19 *Energy Assessment and Reporting Methodology* CIBSE TM22 (London: Chartered Institution of Building Services Engineers) (1999)

20 *Energy use in offices* (ECG 19); *Energy efficiency in hotels* (ECG 36); *Energy consumption in hospitals* (ECG 72); *Energy consumption guide for nursing and residential homes* (ECG 57) Energy Consumption Guides (Action Energy) (various dates) (www.actionenergy.org.uk)

21 *Energy benchmarking in the retail sector* BMI Index Special Report 281 (London: Building Maintenance Information) (July 1999)

22 *BREEAM 98 for offices — an environmental assessment method for offices* BREEAM 98 (1998); *New industrial units — an environmental assessment for new industrial, warehousing and non-food retail units series* BREEAM 5/93 (1993); *An environmental assessment for new superstores and new supermarkets* BREEAM 2/91 (1991) (Garston: Building Research Establishment) (dates as indicated)

23 *Environmental code of practice for buildings and their services* BSRIA COP 6/99 (Bracknell: Building services Research and Information Association) (1999)

24 Bordass W T, Bromley A K R and Leaman A J *Comfort, control and energy efficiency in offices* BRE Information Paper IP3/95 (Garston: Building Research Establishment) (1995)

25 Bordass W T, Bunn R, Cohen R and Leaman A J The Probe Project: technical lessons from PROBE 2 *Proc. CIBSE Nat. Conf., Harrogate, October 1999* (London: Chartered Institution of Building Services Engineers) (1999)

26 *Energy efficiency in buildings* CIBSE Guide F (London: Chartered Institution of Building Services Engineers) (1999)

27 *Natural ventilation in non-domestic buildings* CIBSE AM10 (London: Chartered Institution of Building Services Engineers) (1997)

28 *Minimising pollution at air intakes* CIBSE TM21 (London: Chartered Institution of Building Services Engineers) (1999)

29 *Daylighting and window design* CIBSE Lighting Guide LG10 (London: Chartered Institution of Building Services Engineers) (1999)

30 Baker N V and Steemers K *The LT Method 2.0: an energy design tool for non-domestic buildings* (Cambridge: Cambridge Architectural Research) (1994)

31 *Code for interior lighting* (London: Chartered Institution of Building Services Engineers) (1994)

32 Slater A I, Bordass W T and Heesman T A *People and lighting controls* BRE Information Paper 6/96 (Garston: Building Research Establishment) (1996)

33 Braham D, Barnard N and Jaunzens D *Thermal mass in office buildings* BRE Digest 454 (Garston: Building Research Establishment) (2001)

34 BS 5250: 1989: *Code of practice for the control of condensation in buildings* (London: British Standards Institution) (1989) (under revision)

35 *Mixed mode ventilation* CIBSE Applications Manual AM13 (London: Chartered Institution of Building Services Engineers) (2000)

36 Jones P J, O'Sullivan P E et al. *Internal conditions and the response of office workers* Workplace Comfort Forum (London: Royal Institute of British Architects) (1995)

37 *Ventilation* The Building Regulations 1991 Approved Document F (London: The Stationery Office) (1995)

38 *Heat producing appliances* The Building Regulations 1991 Approved Document J (London: The Stationery Office) (1992)

39 *Fire safety* The Building Regulations 1991 Approved Document B (London: The Stationery Office) (2000)

40 Fanger P O The new comfort equation for indoor air quality *Proc. ASHRAE Conf. IAQ '89: The Human Equation — Health and Comfort, San Diego CA, USA, April 1989* (Atlanta GA: American Society of Heating, Refrigerating and Air Conditioning Engineers) (1989)

41 *Guidelines and Ventilation Requirements in Buildings European Concerted Action: Indoor Air Quality and its Impact on Man* Report No. 11 (Luxembourg: CEC Directorate General Information Market and Innovation) (1992)

42 Control of Substances Hazardous to Health Regulations (COSHH) Statutory Instrument 1999 No. 437 (London: The Stationery Office) (1999)

43 *Occupational exposure limits* EH40 (Bootle: Health and Safety Executive) (published annually)

44 *Air quality guidelines for Europe* (Copenhagen: World Health Organisation) (1998)

45 BS 5925: 1991: *Code of practice for ventilation principles and designing for natural ventilation* (London: British Standards Institution) (1991)

46 *Hygienic maintenance of office ventilation ductwork* CIBSE TM26 (London: Chartered Institution of Building Services Engineers) (2000)

47 Jansenn J E Ventilation and acceptable indoor air quality ASHRAE Standard 62-1981 *Proc. Annual American Conference of Government Industrial Hygienists* **10** 59–64 (1984)

48 Fanger P O *Body odour and carbon dioxide, Minimum ventilation rates* IEA Energy Conservation in Buildings and Community Systems Programme: Annex IX (final report) (Paris: International Energy Agency) (1986)

49 Leaderer B P and Cain W S Air quality in buildings during smoking and non-smoking occupancy *ASHRAE Trans.* **89** (Part 2B) (1983)

50 *Proposal for an Approved Code of Practice on passive smoking at work* HSE CD151 (London: Her Majesty's Stationery Office) (1999)

51 *Ventilation for acceptable indoor air quality* ASHRAE Standard 62-1999 (Atlanta GA: American Society of Heating, Refrigerating and Air Conditioning Engineers) (1999)

52 Ionising Radiations Regulations 1999 Statutory Instrument 1999 No. 3232 (London: The Stationery Office) (1999)

53 Health and Safety at Work etc. Act (London: Her Majesty's Stationery Office) (1974)

54 Scivyer C R and Gregory T J *Radon in the workplace* BRE Report BR 293 (Garston: Building Research Establishment) (1995)

55 BS 6798: 2000: *Specification for installation of gas-fired boilers of rated input not exceeding 70 kW net* (London: British Standards Institution) (2000)

56 BS 5410: *Code of practice for oil firing*: Part 1: 1998: *Installations up to 45 kW output capacity for space heating and hot water supply purposes*; Part 2: 1978: *Installations of 45 kW and above capacity for space heating, hot water and steam supply purposes*; Part 3: 1976: *Installations for furnaces, kilns, ovens and other industrial purposes* (London: British Standards Institution) (dates as indicated)

57 BS 5440: *Installation and maintenance of flues and ventilation for gas appliances of rated input not exceeding 70 kW net (1st, 2nd and 3rd family gases)*: BS 5440-1: 2000: *Specification for installation and maintenance of flues*; BS 5440-2: 2000: *Specification for installation and maintenance of ventilation* (London: British Standards Institution) (2000)

58 *Fire engineering* CIBSE Guide E (London: Chartered Institution of Building Services Engineers) (1997)

59 *Natural ventilation in atria for environment and smoke control: an introductory guide* BRE Report BR 375 (Garston: Building Research Establishment) (1999)

60 Rennie D and Parand F *Environmental design guide for naturally ventilated and daylit offices* BRE Report BR 345 (Garston: Building Research Establishment) (1998)

61 *A performance specification for the Energy Efficient Office of the Future* General Information Report GIR 30 (Action Energy) (1995) (www.actionenergy.org.uk)

62 *Best practice in the specification for offices* BCO Guide 2000 (London: British Council for Offices) (2000)

63 *Thermal insulation: avoiding risks* BRE Report BR 262 (Garston: Building Research Establishment) (1994)

64 The Building Regulations 2000 Statutory Instrument 2000 No. 2531 and The Building (Amendment) Regulations 2001 Statutory Instrument 2001 No 3335 (London: Her Majesty's Stationery Office) (2000)

65 *Conference centres and lecture theatres* BSRIA Library Bulletin LB4/90 (Bracknell: Building Services Research and Information Association) (1990)

66 *Concert halls and theatres* BSRIA Library Bulletin LB18/93 (Bracknell: Building Services Research and Information Association) (1993)

67 Potter I N, Booth W B *CO2 controlled mechanical ventilation systems* (Bracknell: Building Services Research and Information Association) (1994)

68 Saxon R *Atrium buildings: Development and Design* (London: Longmans) (1986)

69 Baker N V *Energy and environment in non-domestic buildings: a technical design guide* (Cambridge: Architectural Research) (1994)

70 *Design methodologies for smoke and heat exhaust ventilation within atria* BRE Report BR 368 (Garston: Building Research Establishment) (1999)

71 BS 5588: *Fire precautions in the design, construction and use of buildings*: Part 7: 1997: *Code of practice for atrium buildings* (London: British Standards Institution) (1997)

72 Goulding J R, Owen Lewis J and Steemers T C (eds.) *Energy in architecture — the European passive solar handbook* (London: Batsford/Commission for the European Communities) (1992)

73 *Guide to acoustic practice* (2nd edn.) (London: BBC Engineering Information Department) (1990) ISBN 0 563 36079 8

74 *Standard for kitchen ventilation systems* HVCA DW 171 (London: Heating and Ventilating Contractors' Association) (2000)

75 *Ventilation of kitchens in catering establishments* HSE Catering Sheet No. 10 (Bootle: Health and Safety Executive) (1997)

76 BS EN ISO 14644-1: 1999: *Cleanrooms and associated controlled environments. Classification of air cleanliness* (London: British Standards Institution) (1999)

77 *Airborne particulate cleanliness classes in clean rooms and clean zones* US Federal Standard 209E (Washington DC: Superintendent of Documents) (1992)

78 *Rules and Guidance for Pharmaceutical Manufacturers and Distributors 1997* (London: Medicines Control Agency/The Stationery Office) (1997)

79 *Designing energy efficient multi-residential buildings* Good Practice Guide GPG 192 (Action Energy) (1997) (www.actionenergy.org.uk)

80 *Energy efficient multi-residential accommodation, Panns Bank, University of Sunderland* BRE New Practice Initial Profile IP91 (Garston: Building Research Establishment) (1995)

81 *Continuous mechanical ventilation in dwellings: design, installation and operation* BRE Digest 398 (Garston: Building Research Establishment) (1994)

82 *Energy-efficient mechanical ventilation systems* Good Practice Guide GPG 257 (Action Energy) (1997) (www.actionenergy.org.uk) (1997)

83 BS EN 779: 1993: *Particulate air filters for general ventilation — Requirements, testing, marking* (London: British Standards Institution) (1993)

84 *Surface condensation and mould growth in traditionally-built dwellings* BRE Digest 297 (Garston: Building Research Establishment) (1985)

85 Perera M D A E S and Parkins L M Build tight — ventilate right *Building Servs. J.* **14** (6) 37 (June 1992)

86 Stephen R K *Humidistat-controlled extract fans: performance in dwellings* BRE Information Paper IP5/99 (Garston: Building Research Establishment) (1999)

87 Stephen R K *Airtightness in UK dwellings* BRE Information Paper IP1/00 (Garston: Building Research Establishment) (2000)

88 *Energy efficient ventilation in housing* Good Practice Guide GPG 268 (Action Energy) (1999) (www.actionenergy.org.uk)

89 *Radon: guidance on protective measures for new dwellings* BRE Report BR 211 (Garston: Building Research Establishment) (1991)

90 BS 5864: 1989: *Installation in domestic premises of gas-fired ducted-air heaters of rated input not exceeding 60 kW* (London: British Standards Institution) (1989)

91 *Passive stack ventilation in dwellings* BRE Information Paper IP13/94 (Garston: Building Research Establishment) (1994)

92 *Energy efficiency primer* Good Practice Guide GPG 171 (Action Energy) (1997) (www.actionenergy.org.uk)

93 *A guide to energy efficient ventilation* (Coventry: Air Infiltration and Ventilation Centre) (1996)

94 Stephen R K *Positive input ventilation in dwellings* BRE Information Paper IP12/00 (Garston: Building Research Establishment) (2000)

95 *Heat pumps in the UK – a monitoring report* General Information Report GIR 72 (Action Energy) (2000) (www.actionenergy.org.uk)

96 Meyer-Holley A et al. *The future market potential for small scale air conditioning in the UK* BSRIA Report 79570/1 (Bracknell: Building Services Research and Information Association) (November 1998)

97 BS 6375: *Performance of windows*: Part 1: 1989: *Classification for weathertightness (including guidance on selection and specification)*; Part 2: 1987: *Specification for operation and strength characteristics* (London: British Standards Institution) (dates as indicated)

98 BS EN 12207: 2000: *Windows and doors. Air permeability. Classification* (London: British Standards Institution) (2000)

99 BS EN 12207: 2000: *Windows and doors. Watertightness. Classification* (London: British Standards Institution) (2000)

100 BS EN 12207: 2000: *Windows and doors. Resistance to wind load. Classification* (London: British Standards Institution) (2000)

101 *Energy efficient refurbishment of high rise housing* NPFR 84 (Action Energy) (1995) (www.actionenergy.org.uk)

102 The Factories Act 1961 (London: Her Majesty's Stationery Office) (1961)

103 The Workplace (Health, Safety and Welfare) Regulations 1992 Statutory Instrument 1992 No. 3004 (London: Her Majesty's Stationery Office) (1992)

104 *Energy efficiency in industrial buildings and sites* Energy Consumption Guide ECG 18 (Action Energy) (1999) (www.actionenergy.org.uk)

105 *The designer's guide to energy-efficient buildings for industry* Good Practice Guide GPG 303 (Action Energy) (2000) (www.actionenergy.org.uk)

106 Alamdari F *Air curtains — commercial applications* BSRIA Applications Guide AG2/97 (Bracknell: Building Services Research and Information Association) (1997)

107 Bos J *Numerical simulation of a three-dimensional comfort air curtain* Master's Thesis (Groningen: University of Groningen) (date unknown)

108 *Commercial and Public Buildings* Chapter 3 in ASHRAE Handbook 1999: *HVAC Applications* (Atlanta GA: American Society of Heating, Refrigerating and Air Conditioning Engineers) (1999)

109 Lovatt J E, Wilson A G Stack effect in tall buildings *ASHRAE Trans.* **3825** (RP-661) 1994 Part 2 420–431 (Atlanta GA: American Society of Heating, Refrigerating and Air Conditioning Engineers) (1994)

110 *Ventilation in healthcare premises: design considerations* Health Technical Memorandum NHS Estates 2025 (London: The Stationery Office) (1994)

111 BS EN 378: *Specification for refrigerating systems and heat pumps. Safety and environmental requirements*: BS EN 378-1: 2000: *Basic requirements, definitions, classification and selection criteria*; BS EN 378-2: 2000: *Design, construction, testing, marking and documentation*; BS EN 378-3: 2000: *Installation site and personal protection*; BS EN 378-4: 2000: *Operation, maintenance, repair and recovery* (London: British Standards Institution) (2000)

112 *Industrial ventilation — a manual of recommended practice* (Lansing, MI: American Conference of Governmental Industrial Hygienists) (2001)

113 BS 7258: *Laboratory fume cupboards*: Part 1: 1994: *Specification for safety and performance*; Part 2: 1994: *Recommendations for exchange of information and recommendations for installation*; Part 3: 1994: *Recommendations for selection, use and maintenance*; Part 4: 1994: *Method for the determination of the containment value of a laboratory fume cupboard* (London: British Standards Institution) (dates as indicated)

114 BS 5726: *Microbiological safety cabinets*: Part 2: 1992: *Recommendations for information to be exchanged between purchaser, vendor and installer and recommendations for installation*; Part 4: 1992: *Recommendations for selection, use and maintenance* (London: British Standards Institution) (dates as indicated)

115 *Categorisation of biological agents according to hazard and categories of containment* (4th edn.) (London: HSE Books/The Stationery Office) (1995)

116 The Gas Safety (Installation and Use) Regulations 1998 Statutory Instrument 1998 No. 2451 (London: The Stationery Office) (1998)

117 *IGasE Utilization Procedures* (various titles) (London: Institution of Gas Engineers) (various dates)

118 BS EN 50091: *Specification for uninterruptible power supplies (UPS)*: Part 1: 1993: *General and safety requirements* (London: British Standards Institution) (1993)

119 The Water Supply (Water Fittings) Regulations 1999 Statutory Instrument 1999 No 1148 (London: The Stationery Office) (1999)

120 The Water Supply (Water Fittings) (Amendment) Regulations 1999 Statutory Instrument 1999 No 1504 (London: The Stationery Office) (1999)

121 *Minimising the risk of Legionnaires' disease* CIBSE TM13 (London: Chartered Institution of Building Services Engineers) (2000)

122 *The control of legionellosis including Legionnaires' disease* HS(G)70 (The Stationery Office) (1993)

123 *Transportation systems in buildings* CIBSE Guide D (London: Chartered Institution of Building Services Engineers) (2000)

124 *Guidelines for environmental design in schools* Building Bulletin 87 (London: The Stationery Office) (1997)

125 The Education (School Premises) Regulations 1996 Statutory Instrument 1996 No. 360 (London: The Stationery Office) (1996)

126 *Energy efficient design of new buildings and extensions for schools and colleges* Good Practice Guide GPG 173 (Action Energy) (1997) (www.actionenergy.org.uk)

127 *Passive solar schools — a design guide* Building Bulletin 79 (London: The Stationery Office) (1994)

128 *Workplace (Health, Safety and Welfare) Regulations 1992: Guidance for the education sector* (Bootle: Health and Safety Executive) (1995)

129 *Fume cupboards in schools* Building Bulletin 88 (London: The Stationery Office) (1998)

130 *Saving energy in schools swimming pools — a guide to refurbishment and new pool design for head teachers, governors and local authorities* Good Practice Guide GPG 56 (Action Energy) (2000) (www.actionenergy.org.uk)

131 *Schools' Environmental Assessment Method (SEAM)* Building Bulletin 83 (London: The Stationery Office) (1996)

132 *Cost effective low energy buildings in further and higher education* Good Practice Guide GPG 207 (Action Energy) (1997) (www.actionenergy.org.uk)

133 *The Queens Building, De Montfort University Anglia — feedback for designers and clients* Probe NPFR 102 (London: Department of Transport, Local Government and the Regions) (1997)

134 *The Elizabeth Fry Building, University of East Anglia — feedback for designers and clients* Probe NPFR 106 (London: Department of Transport, Local Government and the Regions) (1998)

135 *Passive refurbishment at the Open University — Achieving staff comfort through improved natural ventilation* GIR 48 (Action Energy) (1999) (www.actionenergy.org.uk)

136 BS 5588: *Fire precautions in design, construction and use of buildings* (10 parts) (London: British Standards Institution) (various dates)

137 *Drawing a winner — Energy efficient design of sports centres* Good Practice Guide GPG 211 (Action Energy) (1998) (www.actionenergy.org.uk)

138 *Handbook of sports and recreational building design Vol. 2: Indoor sports* (London: Sport England) (1995)

139 *Badminton* Sports Council Guidance Note 357 (London: Sport England) (1995)

140 *Energy efficiency in swimming pools for centre managers and operators* Good Practice Guide GPG 219 (Action Energy) (2000) (www.actionenergy.org.uk)

141 *Energy efficiency in sports and recreation buildings — technology overview* Good Practice Guide GPG 144 (Action Energy) (1996) (www.actionenergy.org.uk)

142 *Design manual for roads and bridges — Design of road tunnels* BD78 (London: The Stationery Office) (1999)

143 *Enclosed vehicular facilities* Chapter 12 in ASHRAE Handbook: *HVAC Applications* (Atlanta GA: American Society of Heating, Refrigerating and Air Conditioning Engineers) (1999)

144 Noton N H *Farm buildings* (Reading: College of Estate Management) (1982)

145 Sainsbury D and Sainsbury P *Livestock health and housing* (Reading: Balliere Tindall) (1979)

146 Welfare of Farm Animals (England) Regulations Statutory Instrument 2000 No. 1870 (London: The Stationery Office) (2000)

147 Clough G and Gamble M *Laboratory animal houses — a guide to the design and planning of animal facilities* (Manual Series No. 4) (London: Medical Research Council) (1979)

148 Firman J E Heating and ventilation of laboratory animal accommodation *J. of the Inst. of Animal Technicians* (1966)

149 McSheeny T (ed.) *Control of animal house environment* Laboratory Animal Handbook 7 (London: Laboratory Animals) (1976)

150 Brookes J *The demand for United Kingdom call centres continues* (London: G V A Grimley) (2000) (available from http://www.gvagrimley-callcentres.co.uk)

151 *Chase E Call centres — long term customer solution or late 90s flash in the pan?* (London: Information Facilities Management) (1999) (available from www.i-fm.net)

152 *Court standards and design guide* LCD internal document (London: Lord Chancellor's Department) (2000)

153 *A design guide for naturally ventilated courtrooms* (London: Lord Chancellor's Department) (1997)

154 *Net effect — a report on the impact of network computers on trading room design* (London: Pringle Brandon) (1998)

155 *20/20 vision — a report on the impact of flat panel displays on trading room design* (London: Pringle Brandon) (1996)

156 Livingstone F C Heating and ventilation in the service of horticulture *H & V Engineer* **43** (515) 638–644 (June 1970)

157 BS EN ISO 7730: 1995: *Moderate thermal environments — Determination of the PMV and PPD indices and specification of the conditions for thermal comfort* (London: British Standards Institution) (1995)

158 Hwang C L et al. Optimal design of an air jet for spot cooling *ASHRAE Trans.* **90** (1B) 476 (Atlanta GA: American Society of Heating, Refrigerating and Air-conditioning Engineers) (1984)

159 Skaret E and Mathisen H M Ventilation efficiency — a guide to efficient ventilation *ASHRAE Trans.* **89** (2B) 480 (Atlanta GA: American Society of Heating, Refrigerating and Air-conditioning Engineers) (1983)

160 Flateheim G Air conditioning without draft and noise *Indoor Air* 5 1761 (1984)

161 Skistad H Diffused air *Building Services J.* **6** (9) 61 (September 1984)

162 *Guide to air distribution technology for the internal environment* (Marlow: HEVAC Association) (2000)

163 Straub H E, Gilman S F and Konzo S *Distribution of air within a room for year-round air conditioning – Parts 1 and 2* Engineering Station Bulletin Nos. 435 and 442 (Urbana IL: University of Illinois) (July 1956 and March 1957 respectively)

164 Koestel H E and Tuve G L ASHRAE Research Reports 1553 and 1687 (Atlanta GA: American Society of Heating, Refrigerating and Air-conditioning Engineers) (dates unknown)

165 Miller P L and Nevins R G Room air distribution performance of ventilating ceilings and cone type circular ceiling diffusers *ASHRAE Trans.* **76** (1) 186 (Atlanta GA: American Society of Heating, Refrigerating and Air-conditioning Engineers) (1970)

166 Holmes M J *Designing variable volume systems for room air movement* Applications Guide AG1/74 (Bracknell: Building Services Research and Information Association) (1973)

167 Holmes M J and Sachariewicz E *The effect of ceiling beams and light fittings on ventilating jets* HVRA Laboratory Report 79 (Bracknell: Building Services Research and Information Association) (1973)

168 Holmes M J *Throw of vertically discharged warm air jets* Technical Note 3/76 (Bracknell: Building Services Research and Information Association) (1976)

169 Holmes M J and Caygill C *Air movement in rooms with low supply airflow rates* HVRA Laboratory Report 83 (Bracknell: Building Services Research and Information Association) (1983)

170 Jackman P J *Air movement in rooms with sidewall-mounted grilles — a design procedure* HVRA Laboratory Report 65 (Bracknell: Building Services Research and Information Association) (1970)

171 Jackman P J *Air movement in rooms with sill-mounted diffusers* HVRA Laboratory Report 71 (Bracknell: Building Services Research and Information Association) (1971)

172 Jackman P J *Air movement in rooms with ceiling mounted diffusers* HVRA Laboratory Report 81 (Bracknell: Building Services Research and Information Association) (1973)

173 *Space air diffusion* Chapter 31 in ASHRAE Handbook: *Fundamentals* (Atlanta GA: American Society of Heating, Refrigerating and Air-conditioning Engineers) (1997)

174 ISO 3258: 1976: *Air distribution and air diffusion — vocabulary* (Geneva: International Standards Organisation) (1976)

175 Sodec F *Air distribution systems* Report 3554E (Aachen: Krantz GmbH) (1984)

176 BS 5295: *Environmental cleanliness in enclosed spaces*: Part 0: 1989: *General introduction, terms and definitions for clean rooms and clean air devices*; Part 2: 1989: *Method for specifying the design, construction and commissioning of clean rooms and clean air devices*; Part 3: 1989: *Guide to operational procedures and disciplines applicable to clean rooms and clean air devices* (London: British Standards Institution) (dates as indicated)

177 *Clean work and work station requirements — controlled equipment* US Federal Standard 209B (Washington DC: Superintendent of Documents) (1966)

178 Alamdari F and Eagles N *Displacement ventilation and chilled ceilings* BSRIA Technical Note TN2/96 (Bracknell: Building Services Research and Information Association) (1996)

179 *REHVA Guide to displacement ventilation in non-industrial premises* (Brussels: Federation of European Heating and Ventilating Associations (REHVA)) (www.rehva.com)

180 Sanberg M and Blomqvist C Displacement ventilation systems in office rooms *ASHRAE Trans.* **95** (2) 1041–1049 (Atlanta GA: American Society of Heating, Refrigerating and Air-conditioning Engineers) (1989)

181 Jackman P J *Displacement ventilation* BSRIA TM2/90 (Bracknell: Building Services Research and Information Association) (1990)

182 *Natural ventilation in non-domestic buildings* CIBSE Applications Manual AM10 (London: Chartered Institution of Building Services Engineers) (1997)

183 *Natural ventilation in non-domestic buildings* BRE Digest 399 (Garston: Building Research Establishment) (1994)

184 Jackman P J *Air distribution in naturally ventilated offices* BSRIA Technical Note TN 4/99 (Bracknell: Building Services Research and Information Association) (1990)

185 Walker B R and White M K Single-sided natural ventilation — how deep an office? *Building Serv. Eng. Res. Technol.* **13** (4) 231–236 (1992)

186 BS 8233: 1999: *Sound insulation and noise reduction for buildings — Code of practice* (London: British Standards Institution) (1999)

187 Willis S, Fordham M and Bordass W *Avoiding or minimising the use of air conditioning* General Information Report GIR 31 (Action Energy) (1995) (www.actionenergy.org.uk)

188 Martin A J *Control of natural ventilation* BSRIA Technical Note TN11/95 (Bracknell: Building Services Research and Information Association) (1995)

189 *Automatic controls* CIBSE Commissioning Code C (London: Chartered Institution of Building Services Engineers) (2001)

190 Orme M, Liddament M W and Wilson A *An analysis and summary of the AIVC's numerical database* AIVC Technical Note 44 (Coventry: Air Infiltration and Ventilation Centre) (1994)

191 *Space requirements for plant access, operation and maintenance* Defence Estate Organisation (Works) Design and Maintenance Guide 08 (London: Ministry of Defence/The Stationery Office) (1996)

192 *Reference data* CIBSE Guide C (London: Butterworth-Heinemann/Chartered Institution of Building Services Engineers) (2001)

193 *A practical guide to air leakage testing* HVCA DW143 (London: Heating and Ventilating Contractors' Association) (2000)

194 *Guide to good practice — Cleanliness of ventilation systems* HVCA TR17 (London: Heating and Ventilating Contractors' Association) (2000)

195 *Variable flow control* General Information Report GIR 41 (Action Energy) (1996) (www.actionenergy.org.uk)

196 *Mixed mode ventilation* CIBSE AM13 (London: Chartered Institution of Building Services Engineers) (2000)

197 Kendrick C, Martin A et al. *Refurbishment of air conditioned buildings for natural ventilation* BSRIA Technical Note TN8/98 (Bracknell: Building Services Research and Information Association) (1995)

198 *Selecting air conditioning systems — a guide for building clients and their advisers* Good Practice Guide GPG 71 (Action Energy) (1999) (www.actionenergy.org.uk)

199 Barnard N and Jauntzens D (eds.) *Low energy cooling — Technologies selection and early design guidance* (London: Construction Research Communications) (2001)

200 Brittain J R J *Oversized air handling plant* BSRIA Guidance Note GN11/97 (Bracknell: Building Services Research and Information Association) (1997)

201 *Building control systems* CIBSE Guide H (London: Chartered Institution of Building Services Engineers) (2000)

202 de Saulles T *Free cooling systems design and application guide* BSRIA RR16/96 (Bracknell: Building Services Research and Information Association) (1996)

203 *Air conditioned buildings* CIBSE Building Energy Code 2 (London: Chartered Institution of Building Services Engineers) (1999)

204 *Energy estimating and modeling methods* Chapter 30 in ASHRAE Handbook: *Fundamentals* (Atlanta GA: American Society of Heating, Refrigerating and Air-conditioning Engineers) (1997)

205 (various titles) Energy Efficiency Best Practice Programme Energy Consumption Guides (Action Energy) (various dates) (www.actionenergy.org.uk)

206 Barnard N *Dynamic energy storage in the building* BSRIA Technical Report TR9/94 (Bracknell: Building Services Research and Information Association) (1994)

207 Holman J P *Heat transfer* (New York NY: McGraw-Hill) (1986) ISBN 0 07 Y66459-5

208 *Environmental floor systems* (Ascot: Steel Construction Institute) (1997)

209 *Modelling the performance of thermal mass* BRE Information Paper IP 6/2000 (Garston: Building Research Establishment) (2000)

210 Fletcher J and Martin A J *Night cooling control strategies* BSRIA Technical Appraisal TN14/96 (Bracknell: Building Services Research and Information Association) (1996)

211 Fletcher J *Pre-cooling in mechanically cooled buildings* BSRIA TN 16/95 (Bracknell: Building Services Research and Information Association) (1995)

212 Peason C C and Barnard N *Guidance and the standard specification for thermal imaging of non-electrical installations* BSRIA Facilities Management Specification FMS6/00 (Bracknell: Building Services Research and Information Association) (2000)

213 Arnold D Chilled beams in naturally ventilated buildings *Proc. CIBSE/ASHRAE Joint Nat. Conf., Harrogate, September 1996* (1) 333–338 (London: Chartered Institution of Building Services Engineers) (1996)

214 Abbas T *Displacement ventilation and static cooling devices* BSRIA COP 17/99 (Bracknell: Building Services Research and Information Association) (1994)

215 Butler D J G Chilled ceilings — free cooling opportunity *Proc. CIBSE Nat. Conf., Bournemouth, October 1998* 273–279 (London: Chartered Institution of Building Services Engineers) (1998)

216 Davies G A model performance *Building Serv. J.* **16** (6) 29–30 (June 1994)

217 Martin A and Alamdari A Condensation control for chilled ceilings and beams *Proc. CIBSE Nat. Conf., Alexaandra Palace, October 1997* **1** 45–52 (London: Chartered Institution of Building Services Engineers) (1997)

218 *Panel heating and cooling* Chapter 6 in ASHRAE Handbook: *HVAC Systems and Equipment* (Atlanta GA: American Society of Heating, Refrigerating and Air-conditioning Engineers) (2000)

219 Warwicker B Low humidity air and air conditioning *Building Serv. J.* **17** (11) 47–49 (November 1995)

220 *The control of legionellosis including Legionnaires' disease* Technical Guidance Note HS(G)70 (London: Health and Safety Executive) (1991)

221 *Non-residential cooling and heating load calculations* Chapter 28 in ASHRAE Handbook: *Fundamentals* (Atlanta GA: American Society of Heating, Refrigerating and Air-conditioning Engineers) (1997)

222 Bunn R Ground coupling explained *Building Serv. J.* **20** 22–24 (December 1998)

223 Zimmermann M and Andersson J (eds.) *Low energy cooling – case study buildings* IEA Energy Conservation in Buildings and Community Systems Programme (St Albans: Oscar Faber Group) (1999)

224 Jones W P *Air Conditioning Engineering* (4th ed.) (London: Edward Arnold) (1994)

225 Hittle D C et al. Theory meets practice in a full-scale HVAC laboratory *ASHRAE J.* **24** (11) 36 (November 1982)

226 Martin P L and Oughton D L *Faber and Kell's Heating and Air Conditioning of Buildings* (London: Butterworth-Heinemann) (1995)

227 *Fundamentals* ASHRAE Handbook (Atlanta, GA: American Society of Heating, Refrigerating and Air-conditioning Engineers) (1997)

228 *Air quality limits and guide values for sulphur dioxide and suspended particulates* EEC Directive 80/779/EEC Official Journal L229 30 (August 1980)

229 Environmental Protection Act 1990 (London: Her Majesty's Stationery Office) (1990)

230 BS 6375: *Performance of windows*: Part 1: 1989: *Classification for weathertightness (including guidance on selection and specification)* (London: British Standards Institution) (1989)

231 Pitts A C and Georgiadis S Ventilation air flow through window openings in combination with shading devices *Proc. 15th. AIVC Conference, Buxton* (Coventry: Air Infiltration and Ventilation Centre) (1994)

232 *Natural ventilation for offices* (Garston: Building Research Establishment) (1999)

233 White M K *Trickle ventilators in offices* BRE Information Paper IP12/98 (Garston: Building Research Establishment) (1998)

234 White M K and Stephen R *Ventilators: ventilation and acoustic effectiveness* BRE Information Paper IP4/99 (Garston: Building Research Establishment) (1999)

235 prEN 13141-1: *Ventilation for buildings — Performance testing of components/products of residential ventilation: Part 1: externally and internally mounted air transfer devices* (Brussels: Comité Européen de Normalisation) (1998) (available in UK through BSI)

236 BS 6399-2: 1997: *Loading for buildings. Code of practice for wind loads* (London: British Standards Institution) (1977)

237 Stewart L J *Design guidelines for exhaust hoods* BSRIA Technical Note TN3/85 (Bracknell: Building Services Research and Information Association) (1985)

238 *Air-to-air recovery in ventilation* AIVC Technical Note 45 (Coventry: Air Infiltration and Ventilation Centre) (1994)

239 *Air-to-air energy recovery* Chapter 42 in ASHRAE Handbook: *HVAC Systems and Equipment* (Atlanta, GA: American Society of Heating, Refrigerating and Air-conditioning Engineers) (2000)

240 *Building energy and environmental modelling* CIBSE Applications Manual AM11 (London: Chartered Institution of Building Services Engineers) (1999)

241 *New technologies for heating and cooling supply in offices* CADDET Analyses Series No.3 (Harwell: Centre for the Analysis and Dissemination of Demonstrated Energy Technologies) (1990) (http://www.caddet.co.uk)

242 *Applied heat pump and heat recovery systems* Chapter 8 in ASHRAE Handbook: *HVAC Systems and Equipment* (Atlanta, GA: American Society of Heating, Refrigerating and Air-conditioning Engineers) (2000)

243 Hamilton G *Selection of air-to-air heat recovery systems* BSRIA Technical Note TN11/86 (Bracknell: Building Services Research and Information Association) (1986)

244 *Air-to-air heat recovery* CIBSE Research Report RR2 (London: Chartered Institution of Building Services Engineers) (1995)

245 BS 6540: *Air filters used in air conditioning and general ventilation*: Part 1: 1985: *Methods of test for atmospheric dust spot efficiency and synthetic dust weight arrestance* (London: British Standards Institution) (1985) (withdrawn; replaced by BS EN 779(30)

246 BS 3928: 1969: *Method for sodium flame test for air filters (other than for air supply to I.C. engines and compressors)* (London: British Standards Institution) (1969)

247 BS EN 1822-1:1998: *High efficiency air filters (HEPA and ULPA). Classification, performance testing, marking*; BS EN 1822-2:1998: *High efficiency air filters (HEPA and ULPA). Aerosol production, measuring equipment, particle counting statistics*; BS EN 1822-3:1998: *High efficiency air filters (HEPA and ULPA). Testing flat sheet filter media*; BS EN 1822-4:2000: *High efficiency air filters (HEPA and ULPA). Determining leakage of filter element (scan method)*; BS EN 1822-5:2000: *High efficiency air filters (HEPA and ULPA). Determining the efficiency of filter element* (London: British Standards Institution) (dates as indicated)

248 *Sodium chloride aerosol tests for filters using flame photometric technique* Eurovent 4/4 (Paris: Eurovent/Cecomaf) (1984)

249 Gilbert A *Laboratory testing of air cleaners* BSRIA Specification SS 22/99 (Bracknell: Building Services Research and Information Association) (1999)

250 *Y 42: Air filtration* in National Engineering Specification (Windsor: National Engineering Specification) (1996)

251 Pike P G *Air filters* BSRIA Application Guide AG8/97 (Bracknell: Building Services Research and Information Association) (1996)

252 Bennett K M *Air filters* BSRIA Selection Guide SG7/91 (Bracknell: Building Services Research and Information Association) (1991)

253 *Air quality strategy for England, Scotland, Wales and Northern Ireland — Working together for clean air* CM 4548 (London: The Stationery Office) (2000)

254 *Standard maintenance specification for mechanical services in buildings: Vol. II: Ventilating and air conditioning* (London: Heating and Ventilating Contractor's Association) (1991)

255 Bennett K M *Humidification in buildings* BSRIA Applications Guide AG10/94 (Bracknell: Building Services Research and Information Association) (1991)

256 *Water fittings and materials directory* (Slough: Water Research Centre) (updated half-yearly)

257 *Prevention and control of legionellosis (including Legionnaires' disease)* Approved Code of Practice L8 (London: Health and Safety Executive) (1995)

258 *Public health engineering* CIBSE Guide G (London: Chartered Institution of Building Services Engineers) (1999)

259 BS EN ISO 8185: 1998: *Humidifiers for medical use. General requirements for humidification systems* (London: British Standards Institution) (1998)

260 BS 4856: *Methods for testing and rating fan coil units, unit heaters and unit coolers*: Part 1: 1972: *Thermal and volumetric performance for heating duties; without additional ducting*; Part 2: 1975: *Thermal and volumetric performance for cooling duties; without additional ducting*; Part 3: 1975: *Thermal and volumetric performance for heating and cooling duties; with additional ducting*; Part 4: 1997: *Determination of sound power levels of fan coil units, unit heaters and unit coolers using reverberating rooms* (London: British Standards Institution) (dates as indicated)

261 BS 848: *Fans for general purposes*: Part 1: 1997: *Performance testing using standardized airways* (London: British Standards Institution) (1997)

Appendix 2.A1: Techniques for assessment of ventilation

2.A1.1 General

There are a number of assessment techniques available to calculate ventilation and cooling requirements and to look in detail at air movement. This appendix provides an overview of some of these techniques. CIBSE AM11(2.A1.1) and AM10(2.A1.2) provide more detail on dynamic thermal simulation and assessment techniques for natural ventilation respectively.

2.A1.2 Ventilation and cooling

Section 2.3.2.1 includes airflow rate requirements for ventilation purposes. Airflow rate requirements for cooling purposes are normally based either on restricting peak summer temperatures in passive buildings or to meet the peak cooling load. Analyses may start by looking at peak temperatures to evaluate of the building's potential without mechanical cooling. These would assess the ventilation rates (natural and/or mechanical) and passive measures needed to meet summer temperature limits. Where cooling is to be provided, the cooling needed to maintain the temperature limits would be assessed. Airflow rates may then be calculated to deliver this cooling to the space.

There is a range of analysis methods available to suit different applications and stages in the design process. Design charts based on parametric analysis may be used (e.g. the BRE's *Environmental Design Guide*(2.A1.3)), although the user can work only within the range of variables covered by the charts. Section 5 of CIBSE Guide A(2.A1.4) provides design information on the use of thermal dynamic models for calculating peak summertime temperatures and peak space cooling loads. Simple (dynamic) models (e.g. the admittance procedure) may be used to assess cooling loads and the probability of overheating. These approaches are based on a 24-hour design cycle and are suitable for mechanically cooled buildings with a repetitive diurnal operating cycle. However, where this is not an accurate reflection of building operation due to thermal mass or passive operation, dynamic thermal simulation may be used.

Appropriate consideration should be given to issues of weather data, control and thermal mass depending on the application. Selection of appropriate weather data is discussed in CIBSE AM10(2.A1.2). Different data will be required for different purposes. For example, to estimate energy consumption, average weather data for the region will usually be the most appropriate. Data, including more extreme conditions, will be appropriate to test the ability of the building to accommodate various levels of internal heat gain and predict peak temperatures. Site-specific weather data can be of interest, but may have been collected over a relatively short period and may not necessarily be representative. It is frequently impossible to use such data to construct meaningful statistics to identify the percentage of time a specified internal temperature would be likely to be exceeded. There is also a danger that the design may lack robustness, being tailored to a unique weather sequence and reacting in a different and unpredicted way to more normal weather peaks. A more robust choice will often be to analyse the building in relation to appropriate national UK data and to make simple corrections to suit the differences between this and the site data; e.g. August average temperature and diurnal swing and August 2.5% exceeded peak temperature and the associated diurnal swing.

Loads and system performance often depend on more than one weather variable. Cooling and humidity conditions will be a function of wet bulb as well as dry bulb temperature. The performance of natural ventilation systems in particular can be affected by solar and wind conditions as well as temperatures, as these are often used to drive the ventilation. Design conditions for the individual weather variables will rarely coincide.

Controls used in the thermal model should reflect what can be expected to occur in practice. This is a particular issue in natural ventilation systems with manual control. Account should be taken of the way occupants use windows. Data are available on occupancy effects on natural ventilation, primarily based on the domestic sector. This work is summarised in AIVC Technical Note 23(2.A1.5).

Thermal mass should be modelled with appropriate surface heat transfer values and representation of heat flow within the mass, see *Thermal storage performance* (page 2-77). High thermal mass buildings must be allowed to come to their natural thermal equilibrium by having a lengthy period of simulation prior to the period over which the modelling results are reported and compared; 15 days is usually enough for this 'pre-conditioning' period, although a few buildings require longer. This can be tried first with 10 and 20 days and the results compared to check for significant differences. If a hot spell is being simulated, peak weather data should not be used throughout, as this will under-value the heat-absorbing benefits of the thermal mass. Instead, pre-conditioning with average weather for the season concerned can be undertaken, followed by a step change to the peak weather sequence — which in the UK seldom lasts more than 5 days. The design day is typically the third in the peak weather sequence.

2.A1.3 Air movement

Analyses of air movement may be needed, particularly for natural ventilation applications and air movement in large spaces such as atria. These provide information on air velocity, movement and temperature; volume flow rate; and optimal opening sizes, shapes and positions. Techniques available include computational fluid dynamics (CFD), physical models and air flow models. For room air distribution, performance is sometimes critically dependent on details of equipment design, and full-scale mock-ups may be required.

2.A1.3.1 Computational fluid dynamics (cfd)

CFD is a technique for predicting air movement that can address questions such as stratification and local air movement. It therefore has particular application to consideration of large spaces such as atria. CFD methods can predict temperature and velocity distributions in a space and can be applied to assessments of comfort involving more of the influencing parameters than is possible in zonal models. Because of the extensive nature of the computations and the time varying nature of the natural driving forces, CFD is normally only used to generate 'snapshots' of how the design would work at a given point in time.

Another potential application for CFD is external flows around the building. The purpose is to generate the wind pressure coefficients needed by all models to predict natural airflow rates.

2.A1.3.2 Physical models

Physical models are especially useful for giving the non-technical members of the client and design team a good visualisation of airflow behaviour. By their nature, physical models are implicit design tools; assumptions need to be made then tested. The two main techniques relating to natural ventilation design are the salt bath technique and wind tunnel testing.

Salt bath

The salt bath technique is used to test stack driven ventilation strategies. Stack-driven flows are analysed at small scale in the laboratory using a model of the building immersed in a perspex bath containing saline solutions of different concentrations. The method models fluid flow, not surface heat transfer, and therefore cannot predict local effects such as solar patching on the floor of an atrium. Like the CFD technique it provides only a snapshot of performance.

Wind tunnel

Wind tunnel testing is the main source of information on wind pressure coefficients. It is not a method for proving the design of a natural ventilation system, since it only deals with external flows around a building.

Air flow models

Air flow models may be used to analyse natural ventilation air flow rates based on driving pressure differences and openings. These range from single zone models to more complex multi-zone models. Single zone models[2.A1.6] are appropriate where the building is open plan and there is no temperature stratification in the space. Building types that approximate to these requirements are dwellings, many industrial buildings and small open plan office buildings. Multi-zone models subdivide the building into a number of individual spaces, substantially increasing the complexity of the analysis[2.A1.7].

Software combining multi-zone flow models with thermal simulation analysis is also available. This software can provide an integrated analysis the internal temperature distribution and the stack induced natural ventilation flow rates[2.A1.8].

References

2.A1.1 *Building energy and environmental modelling* CIBSE Applications Manual AM11 (London: Chartered Institution of Building Services Engineers) (1998)

2.A1.2 *Natural ventilation in non-domestic buildings* CIBSE Applications Manual AM10 (London: Chartered Institution of Building Services Engineers) (1997)

2.A1.3 Rennie D and Parand F *Environmental design guide for naturally ventilated and daylit offices* BRE Report BR 345 (Garston: Building Research Establishment) (1998)

2.A1.4 *Environmental design* CIBSE Guide A (London: Chartered Institution of Building Services Engineers) (1999)

2.A1.5 Dubrul C *Inhabitant's behaviour with regard to ventilation* AIVC Technical Note 23 (Coventry: Air Infiltration and Ventilation Centre) (1988)

2.A1.6 Liddament M W *Air Infiltration Development Algorithm (AIDA)* Appendix 3 in *A guide to energy efficient ventilation* (Coventry: Air Infiltration and Ventilation Centre) (1996)

2.A1.7 Feustel H E and Dieris A *Survey of air flow models for multi-zone structures* (Berkeley, CA: Earnest Orlando Lawrence Berkeley National Laboratory) (1991)

2.A1.8 Kendrick J *An overview of combined modelling of heat transport and air movement* AIVC Technical Note 40 (Coventry: Air Infiltration and Ventilation Centre) (1993)

Appendix 2.A2: Psychrometric processes

Table 2.A2.1 illustrates the basic psychrometric processes and lists the equipment concerned. See section 2.5 for details of the various items of equipment.

Table 2.A2.1 Basic psychrometric processes

Process	Method	Remarks	Psychrometric process
Heating	Electric	No additional plant required. High energy costs. Wiring and switch gear costs high for large duties. Usually only step control available.	
	Steam	Small heat transfer surface. Plant cost high unless steam required for other services. Condensate return can present difficulties. Modulating control available (2-way valve).	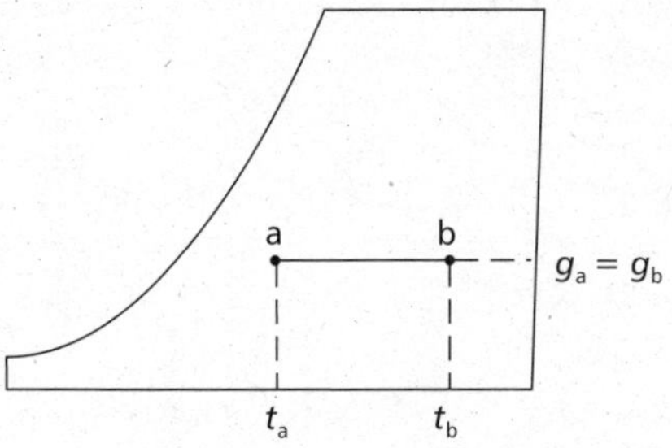 a, b, $g_a = g_b$, t_a, t_b
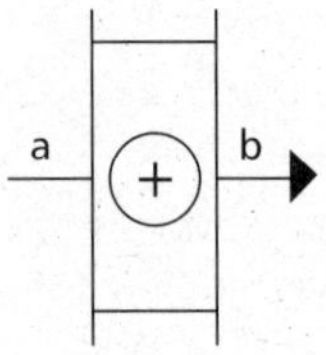	Hot water	Simple and reasonably cheap plant and distribution system. Integrates well with other heating systems. Some simplicity sacrificed to decrease heat surface with HTHW. Modulating control available (2- or 3-way valve).	
	Direct firing	Least expensive in specific cases. Can involve problems of combustion air and flue requirements. On/off control is common for smaller units while high/low flame is usually available for larger units.	
Humidification	Steam injection	Electrically heated, self-contained unit or unit supplied by mains steam. Water treatment advisable. Small space occupied. Mains units have modulating control (2-way valve), electric units are normally on/off. Mains units may require condensate drain.	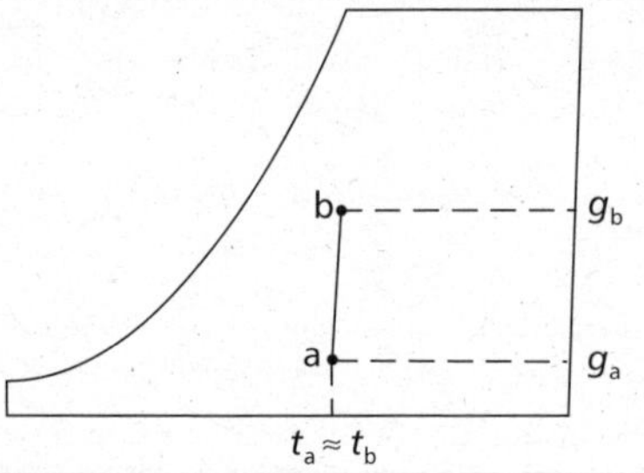 b, a, g_b, g_a, $t_a \approx t_b$
	Water injection	Involves atomising process (spinning disc, compressed air etc.). Some types are non-reciculatory and require drainage. Air is sensibly cooled as water evaporates. Contaminants from untreated water will enter airstream. Water treatment including biocidal control is essential. Space occupied depends on type. Some units mount on duct wall, other in duct line. Control is usually on/off by stopping atomiser or water supply; larger units in multiple form may be stepped. Normally modulation is not recommended unless water flow is large.	
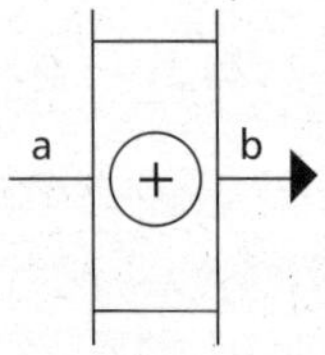	Spray washer	Bulky equipment requiring good access to tray and sprays. Also dehumidifies if supplied with chilled water (see Cooling — Air washer). Air sensibly cooled as water evaporates unless water is heated (not normal). Requires water treatment (including biocidal control) and bleed and recirculating pump. Removes both gaseous and particulate air contaminants but with low efficiency. Control indirect by modulation of inlet air condition (pre-heater or mixing dampers) or by by-pass and mixing. Saturation efficiencies range from approximately 70% for one bank facing upstream, to 85–90% for two banks opposed. Water quantity per bank is of the order of 0.4 litre·s^{-1} per m^{3}·s^{-1} of air flow. Air velocity is of the order of 2.5 m·s^{-1}.	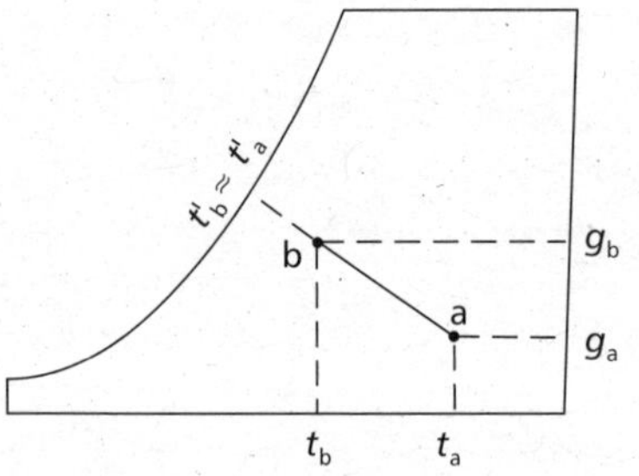 $t'_b \approx t'_a$, b, a, g_b, g_a, t_b, t_a
	Capillary washer	Similar to spray washer but less bulky and provides better air filtering. Has smaller cooling capacity than spray washer when used with chilled water. May require addition of cooling coil. Filtration efficiency is good.	

Table continues

Table 2.A2.1 Basic psychrometric processes — *continued*

<table>
<tr><th>Process</th><th>Method</th><th>Remarks</th><th>Psychrometric process</th></tr>
<tr><td>Humidification
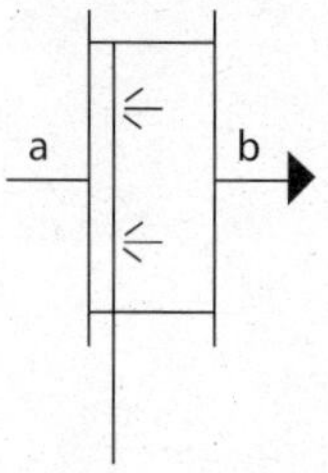</td><td>Sprayed cooling coil (not subject to refrigeration)</td><td>Utilises cooling coil as wetted pack for humidifying. Action as washer but sprays less prone to blocking. Eliminators not required unless air velocity to high.

Requires more space than non-sprayed coil but less space than washer. Water treatment advisable, bleed essential (see cooling coil). Control as for spray. Can be used to cool coil water circuit with low air on temperature, thus making t'_b greater than t'_a. This is sometimes usedin an induction system primary plant. Saturation efficiency is of the order of 0.5–1.0 litre·s^{-1} per m^3·s^{-1} of air flow. Air velocity is of the order of 2.5 m·s^{-1}.</td><td>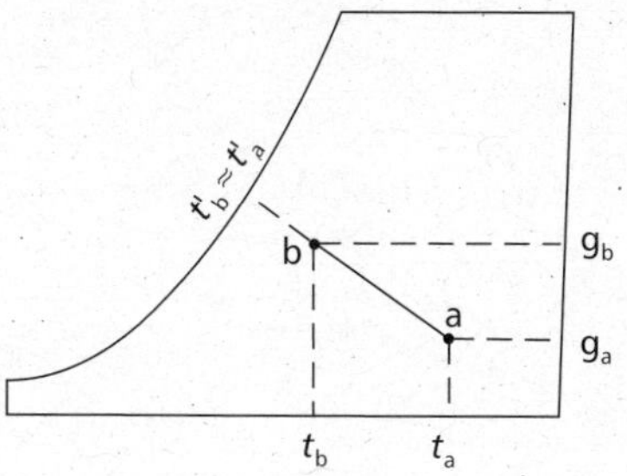</td></tr>
<tr><td>Cooling
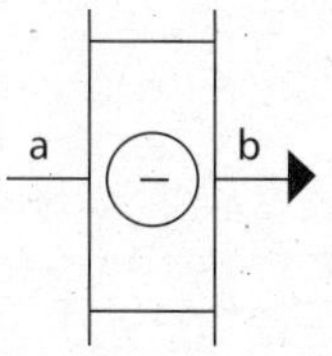</td><td>Indirect cooling coil</td><td>Supplied with chilled water or brine (usually 2 or 3 °C below apparatus dew-point required). As water is in closed circuit (except for head tank) there is no water contamination from air or evaporation. Contact factor depends on number of rows of pipes deep. Chilled water enters at air off-side. Drain is required. Control by modulating water temperature or flow rate (3-way valve). Normal to keep constant flow rate through chiller.</td><td rowspan="2">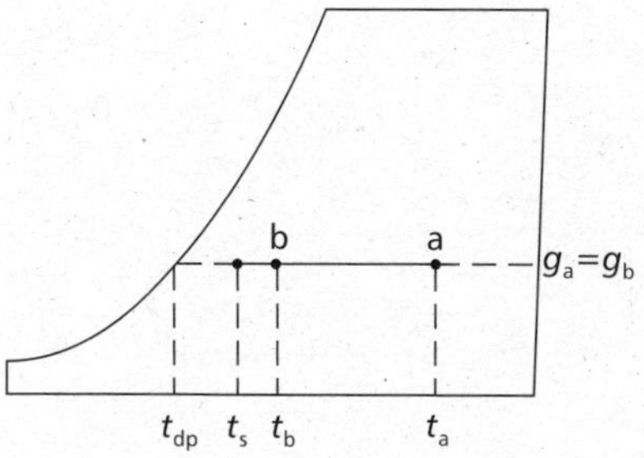
(*a*) Sensible cooling</td></tr>
<tr><td></td><td>Direct cooling coil (direct expansion coil)</td><td>Coil is evaporator of refrigeration circuit. May be cheaper overall than indirect system, but usually involves refrigerant circuit site work. Control by steps, or modulated, depending on refrigeration system. May need special circuitry. Drain is required. Complex and costly for larger installations. May be excluded by local legislation for some applications.</td></tr>
<tr><td>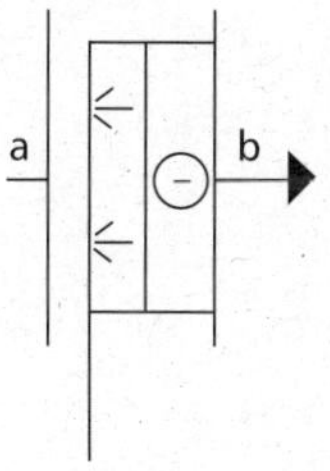</td><td>Sprayed cooling coil (subject to refrigeration)</td><td>With spray off, coil operates exactly as cooling coil. Spray sometimes used to increase surface in contact with air, results in larger contact factor. Saturation efficiency of the order of 80–90%. Water quantity of the order of 0.5–1.0 litre·s^{-1} per m^3·s^{-1} of airflow. Air velocity of the order of 2.5 m·s^{-1}.</td><td rowspan="2">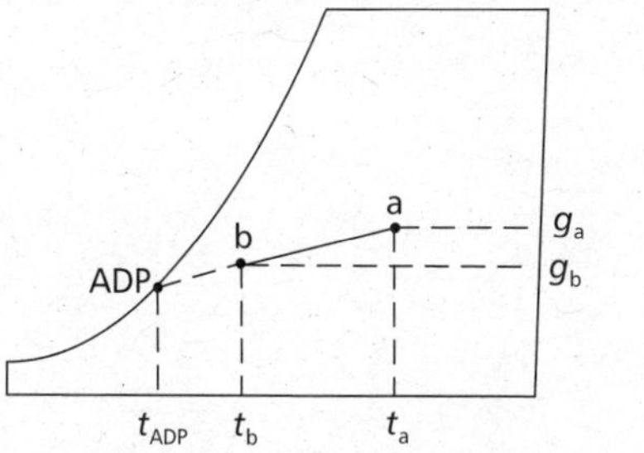
(*b*) Cooling and dehumidifying</td></tr>
<tr><td>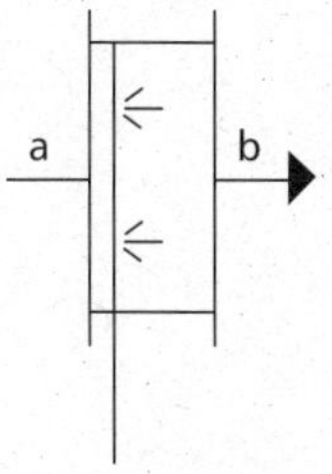</td><td>Air washer (spray washer)</td><td>See general remarks on Humidification — Spray washer. Sprays supplied with chilled water, which is liable to contamination through air washing and evaporation if also humidifying. Use with normal, non-cleanable direct expansion chiller not recommended. Overflow required. Contact factor determined by spray design and number of banks. Control by change of spray water temperature (diverting chilled water back to chiller). Saturation efficiencies range from approximately 70% for one bank facing upstream to 85–90% for two banks opposed. Water quantity per bank is of the order of 0.4 litre·s^{-1} per m^3·s^{-1} of air. Air velocity is of the order of 2.5 m·s^{-1}.</td></tr>
</table>

3 Ductwork

3.1 Introduction

3.1.1 General

This section provides basic methods and procedures needed to design air distribution systems for air conditioning and mechanical ventilation (AC/MV) systems. Design and selection of the air pressurisation device, such as a fan or integrated AHU, is an important part of the design process. Designers will need to ensure that the design criteria chosen for ductwork systems, associated air pressurisation devices and other in-line equipment can meet the requirements of Approved Document L of the Building Regulations(1). Reducing the size of an AHU can increase the pressure drop across the unit, which will require larger ducts to limit the pressure loss and thereby keep within the specified limits.

This section is intended to be used by practicing designers who hold a basic knowledge of the fundamentals of building physics. As such, rigorous mathematical derivations of formulae are not given. Section 4 of CIBSE Guide C: *Reference data*(2), provides detailed information on pressure drops in ducts and duct fittings. The quantitative data apply to the flow of clean air in ducts, but these may also be used for vitiated air where the concentration of contaminant gas is low. The airflow data should not be applied to the conveyance of particulates in ducts.

Constructional aspects of ductwork are not covered in detail. For the UK, reference should be made to the ductwork specifications published by the Heating and Ventilating Contractors' Association.

When using these design notes, the designer must firstly fully map the design process that is being undertaken. The process for each application will be unique, but will follow the general format, as follows:

— problem definition

— ideas generation

— analysis

— selection of design solution.

A suggested first pass flowchart is shown in Figure 3.1.

3.1.2 Symbols, definitions and abbreviations

3.1.2.1 Symbols

A Cross sectional area of duct (m^2)

A_s Surface area of a duct (m^2)

(A_s/l) Perimeter (m)

A_{min} Minimum choice of duct cross sectional area (m^2)

c Mean air velocity in duct (m·s^{-1})

c_p Specific thermal capacity (kJ·kg^{-1}·K^{-1})

C_1 Constant (—)

d_e Equivalent diameter (m)

d_h Hydraulic mean diameter of duct (m)

E Energy (J or kJ)

h Breadth of rectangular duct (perpendicular to the turning plane for bends) (mm)

K Capacity (sometimes called 'flow capacity') (m^3·s^{-1}·Pa$^{-1/2}$)

l Length (m)

l_n Thickness of insulation (m)

p Air pressure (static pressure) (Pa)

P_{ef} Fan electrical power consumption (W)

P_{sf} Specific fan power (W·s·litre^{-1})

p_t Air total pressure (Pa)

Δp_f Fan total pressure (increase in total pressure) (Pa)

Δp_t Drop in total pressure around the air circuit (Pa)

q_L Leakage volume flow (m^3·s^{-1})

q_m Mass flow (kg·s^{-1})

q_v Volume flow (m^3·s^{-1})

Q Quantity of heat (J or kJ)

r Mean radius of a bend (mm)

Re Reynolds number

T Thermodynamic temperature, absolute (K)

t Temperature (°C)

t_{ad} Temperature of air in duct (°C)

t_{as} Temperature of air surrounding duct (°C)

t_{ds} Dew point temperature of air surrounding duct (°C)

Δt Temperature difference (K)

U Overall thermal transmittance (W·m^{-2}·K^{-1})

w Width of rectangular duct (in the turning plane for bends) (mm)

α Turning angle of bend or elbow (°)

λ Thermal conductivity (W·m^{-1}·K^{-1})

ρ Density (kg·m^{-1})

ϕ_p Relative humidity (%)

Φ Heat flux (W or kW)

φ Heat flux density (W·m^{-2})

θ Total included angle of a taper (°)

η Dynamic viscosity (kg·m^{-1}·s^{-1})

η_f Fan efficiency (%)

η_m Fan motor efficiency (%)

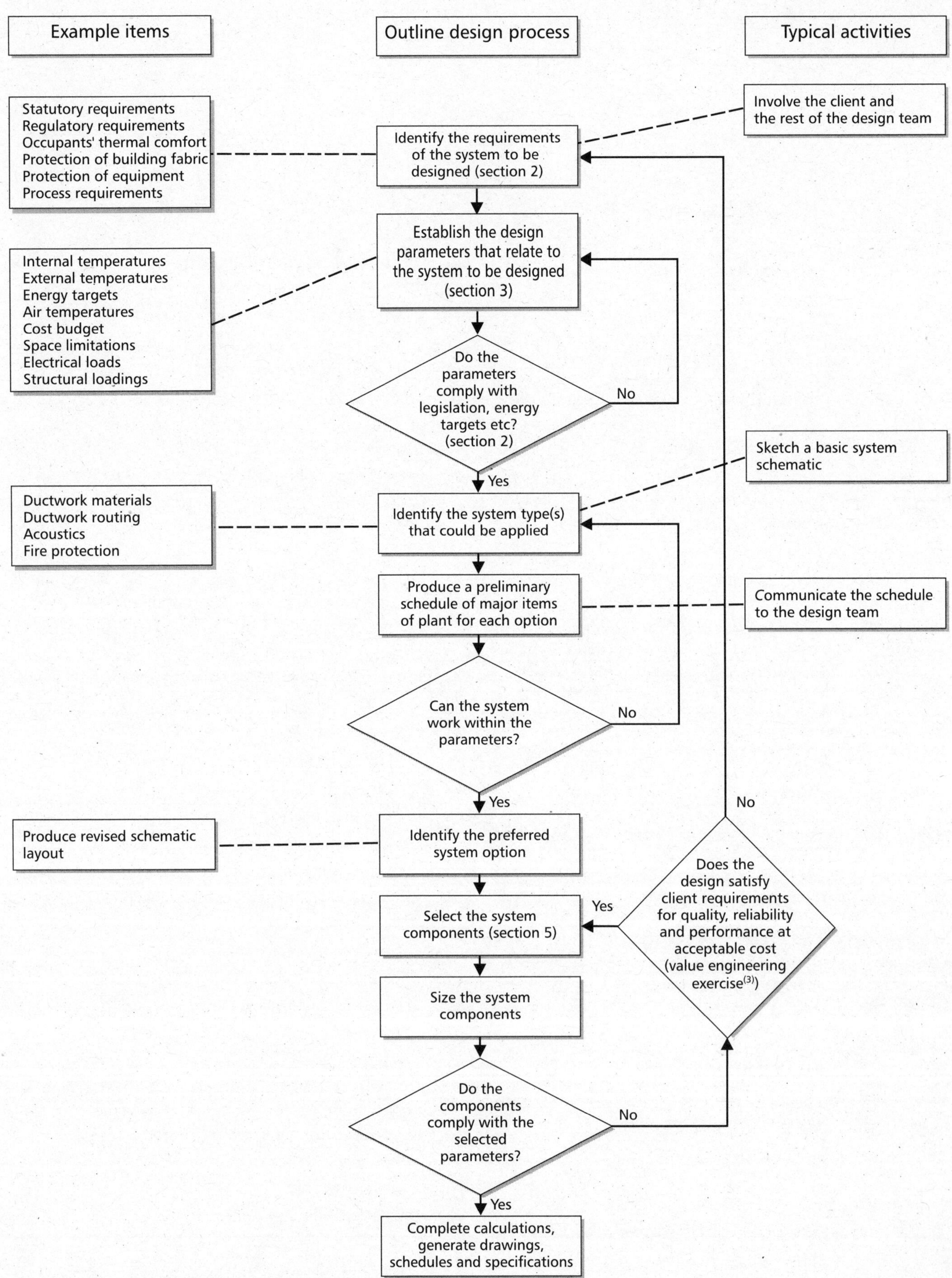

Figure 3.1 Outline design process; ductwork

η_o Overall efficiency (%)

ζ Pressure loss factor for fittings

3.1.2.2 Definitions and abbreviations

AC/MV — Air conditioned/mechanically ventilated buildings

ACH — Air changes per hour

AHU — Air handling unit

Airflow generated noise — Noise produced by turbulence in the air flow, primarily where eddies are formed as the air flow separates from the surface

Aspect ratio — Ratio of width (w) to breadth (b) for a rectangular duct

Bend 'hard' — Rotation in the plane of the longer side of the cross section (see Figure 3.2)

Bend 'soft' — Rotation in the plane of the shorter side of the cross section (see Figure 3.2)

Fan gains — Increases in duct air temperature due to heat gains from fan/motor power dissipation

FCU — Fan coil unit

Hydraulic diameter (d_h) — Term used to calculate duct dimensions for non-circular shape:

$$d_h = \frac{4 \times (\text{cross-sectional area of duct})}{\text{length round periphery of cross section}}$$

Installation effects — Unsatisfactory or reduced fan performance due to poor inlet and outlet conditions at the fan–system interface or other badly installed components

PSV — Passive stack ventilation

SFP — Specific fan power: the sum of the design total circuit watts including all losses through switchgear and controls such as inverters, of all fans that supply air and exhaust it back to outdoors (i.e. the sum of supply and extract fans) divided by the design ventilation rate through the building (see Appendix 3.A5.2.2 for example calculation)

Static pressure (p) — The pressure exerted against the sides of a duct measured at right angles to the direction of flow

Total pressure (p_t) — The sum of the static and velocity pressures

VAV — Variable air volume

Velocity pressure (p_t) — The pressure created by the speed of the airflow along the duct

VOCS — Volatile organic compounds

3.2 Strategic design issues

3.2.1 Introduction

The aim of this section is to provide a source of information on current practice in the design of ductwork for ventilation and air conditioning systems. The information is intended to provide an overview of design criteria and application requirements.

The purpose of AC/MV duct systems is to convey air to and from spaces within buildings, and provide building occupants with:

- ventilation air
- thermal comfort
- humidity control
- air filtration
- removal of contaminants.

The designer must balance the need to minimise energy use and noise generation against space availability and the costs of materials and installation, whilst providing adequate means of access for installation, cleaning and maintenance. Materials, equipment and construction methods should be chosen with respect to the whole life cycle cost of the installation. This is particularly important for new installations for which Building Regulations Approved Document L[1] sets down strict requirements for maximum fan power. The developing sustainability agenda is imposing new constraints on system performance and therefore designers need to look especially carefully at energy efficiency issues (see section 3.2.11).

Users of the environmental space serviced by the ductwork will have the following requirements:

- sufficient air volume for ventilation
- sufficient air volume delivered and removed to provide either comfort conditions or conditions that satisfy the requirements of the process being served
- satisfactory temperature of delivered air
- satisfactory noise levels within the occupied space due to the ductwork installation
- visual impact of the ductwork in keeping with the internal environment and décor
- on entry to the space, the air is well diffused and does not cause draughts
- satisfactory air quality.

3.2.2 Classification of ductwork systems

Ductwork systems for ventilating and air conditioning applications can be divided into low, medium and high pressure systems.

High pressure systems permit smaller ductwork but result in greater friction pressure drop, requiring the fan to generate higher pressures and noise generation. They are more expensive to install and, because of their greater input power requirements, are more expensive to run. This has led to a trend towards lower design pressures in systems.

Table 3.1 sets out the classification of ductwork systems adopted in this section, using the design static pressure of the system, or part of the system. It is assumed that air is being transported. The classification follows that used in

Table 3.1 Maximum positive and negative pressures and velocities for low, medium and high pressure ductwork

System classification	Design static pressure / Pa		Maximum air velocity/ $m{\cdot}s^{-1}$	Air leakage limit (per m^2 of duct surface area)* / $litre{\cdot}m^2$
	Maximum positive	Maximum negative		
Low pressure (Class A)	500	500	10	$0.027 \times p^{0.65}$
Medium pressure (Class B)	1000	750	20	$0.009 \times p^{0.65}$
High pressure (Class C)	2000	750	40	$0.003 \times p^{0.65}$

* where p is the static gauge pressure in the duct (Pa)

HVCA DW/144: *Specification for sheet metal ductwork*[(4)]. The table also gives air leakage limits, see section 3.2.10.

The duct air velocity is not a major factor in the constructional specification of ductwork. Recommended velocities for particular applications using these three system classifications are given in Tables 3.2 and 3.3.

It is permissible to operate these systems at velocities higher than the recommended values. HVCA DW/144[(4)] limits are up to 10 $m{\cdot}s^{-1}$, 20 $m{\cdot}s^{-1}$ and 40 $m{\cdot}s^{-1}$ in the cases of conventional low, medium and high pressure systems respectively. For normal applications the use of higher velocities than those recommended is not likely to be economic, and the trend is towards lower air velocities.

Two factors influence velocity selection. First, for a given volume flow, velocities should fall as the size of the duct is reduced, to avoid increasing pressure gradients. Secondly, noise generation increases rapidly with increases in velocity at grilles, bends and other fittings where the flow separates from the walls, leaving turbulent eddies in its wake. The noise generated at grilles and terminals is of particular importance. High velocity systems require noise control by using sound absorbent units between the duct system and the room outlets and inlets.

Systems with design pressures outside the values given in Table 3.1 or where the mean duct velocity exceeds 40 $m{\cdot}s^{-1}$ should be treated as special cases. Whilst some of the design information provided here may be appropriate to these special cases, the data should not be extrapolated beyond those which are given, and the designer may need to refer to the original references or other source material to confirm the appropriate design parameters.

3.2.3 Ductwork sections

3.2.3.1 General

Ducting is generally available in rectangular, circular and flat oval sections, although other sections may be made for special situations. The majority of rectangular ductwork is made to order and available in any reasonable dimensions. Ductwork less than 0.0225 m^2 cross sectional area (e.g. 150 mm × 150 mm) will generally be more economic if made from circular section.

The designer should consider the full range of sections available and combine them to suit the specific location. Recommended sizes for rectangular, circular and flat oval ductwork are given in Appendix 3.A1.

3.2.3.2 Rectangular ducting

Rectangular ducting is most common for low pressure systems because:

— it is readily adapted to fit into the space available

— it can be readily joined to such component items as heating and cooling coils and filters

— branch connections are made more easily.

For overall economy and performance, the aspect ratio should be close to 1:1 since high aspect ratios increase the pressure loss, the heat gains/losses and the overall costs. However, ducts with a 1:1 aspect ratio require a deep service area and are therefore rarely used in ceiling zones due to space limitations.

Rectangular ducting should not be the first choice for high pressure systems as it requires strengthening of the flat sides and needs to be sealed to make it suitable for this application.

3.2.3.3 Circular ducting

Machine formed, spirally wound ducting and a standard range of pressed and fabricated fittings makes circular ducting more economical, particularly in low pressure systems having a relatively small proportion of fittings. It is likely to be easier to install, particularly for the main runs of ductwork.

Circular ducting is preferable for high pressure systems and for systems operating at high negative pressures, due to its high inherent stiffness. Additional stiffening rings may be necessary at high negative pressure.

3.2.3.4 Flat oval ducting

Flat oval ducting provides an alternative to circular ducting principally where there is a limitation on one of the dimensions in the space available for the duct run (e.g. depth of ceiling space). It combines the advantages of circular and rectangular ductwork because it can fit in spaces where there is insufficient room for circular ducting and can be joined using the techniques for circular duct assembly. Flat oval ducting has considerably less flat surface that is susceptible to vibration and requires less reinforcement than the corresponding size of rectangular duct. Flat oval duct is suitable for both positive and negative pressure applications within the limits defined in DW/144[(4)].

3.2.3.5 Other sections

Other sections may be used, such as triangular to pass through roof trusses. Such sections present difficulties in the provision of fittings and connections to standard plant items, and are likely to be more expensive than traditional sections.

3.2.4 Layout

In most installations, the constraints imposed by the building or other structures (e.g. single or multiple plant rooms, split systems based on tenancy arrangements etc.), and the siting of fans, plant items and terminals, can lead to the adoption of an overall duct layout which is not ideal. The performance of a system can also be adversely affected by a lack of care and thought in the arrangement and detailing of the ductwork. The designer and installer should be aware of the characteristics of airflow in ducts and fittings so that the objectives of the design are compromised as little as possible by the constraints imposed and by space restrictions. In general, good design should ensure that the air velocities are relatively uniform across the duct section and that the generation of eddies in ducts is minimised.

The site will often dictate the main routing of ductwork systems but in general the design should seek to make the layout as symmetrical as possible; that is, the pressure loss in each branch should be as nearly equal as possible. This will aid regulation and may reduce the number and variety of duct fittings that are needed.

The number of duct fittings should be kept to a minimum and there should be a conscious attempt to achieve some standardisation of types and sizes. Increasing the numbers and variety of fittings in a system can markedly raise its overall cost.

The shorter the ductwork length, the lower is the pressure drop. Distribution lengths are influenced by:

— the shape of the building

— the number and location of plant rooms

— the provision of space for distribution.

In large buildings or industrial plants a choice between a single distribution system and multiple smaller systems may arise. Large distribution systems and their plant can have the advantage of lower operating costs but require more floor space for vertical shafts. In general, very long runs of ducting should be avoided to prevent undue heat losses or gains, excessive leakage and difficulties in balancing during commissioning. Also, the pressure losses in long runs are likely to be higher, and a more expensive class of ductwork may be needed. Multiple smaller distribution systems may be more expensive in capital and operating costs but they avoid long runs, large ducts and vertical shafts, and this may reduce overall building costs.

3.2.5 Spatial requirements

Provision of sufficient space for ductwork is essential and must be addressed at an early stage in the design process of the building.

Laying out the space required for ductwork is, to an extent, an amalgam of experience, skill and three-dimensional visualisation. Adequate space must be provided for installation and maintenance of the ductwork and associated equipment. The designer should ensure that ductwork is co-ordinated with the other engineering services to be accommodated in the same space, particularly in false ceiling voids and riser spaces where there may be several distribution systems vying for restricted space.

Branches from vertical risers to serve horizontal distribution routes should be considered with care, as this is likely to be the most congested area of the service core. If the service core is enclosed on three sides (e.g. by a lift shaft and an external wall) the horizontal distribution from the core will be extremely difficult, with little space for installation and maintenance.

The area served by a single riser will dictate the size of the horizontal branch duct. The depth selected for a branch duct will have a significant influence on the false ceiling or raised floor depth. It will also affect the overall floor-to-floor heights and hence have significant influence on building costs.

The depth of the horizontal element is a function of the number of vertical risers, generally:

— maximum number of vertical risers equates to minimum horizontal element depth

— minimum number of vertical risers equates to maximum horizontal element depth.

Adequate space must be allowed around ducts for fitting of insulation, hangers and supports during installation and for access during subsequent maintenance. Access will also be dependent on the clearance from adjacent objects such as structural items and the type of jointing method. Suitable allowances are given in Appendix 3.A2, which also shows examples of common problems associated with ductwork access.

Ductwork clearances can be reduced with care, providing jointing, insulation and maintenance of any vapour barrier is achieved. Consideration should also be given to how the ductwork will be tested and how it will eventually be replaced.

Further information is available in Defence Estates Organisation Design and Maintenance Guide 08: *Space requirements for plant access, operation and maintenance*[5], BSRIA Technical Note TN10/92: *Spatial allowances for building services distribution systems*[6] and BS 8313: *Code of practice for accommodation of building services in ducts*[7].

3.2.6 Aesthetics

Where ductwork is hidden in risers, ceiling voids and below the floor it will not have an effect on the visual environment. In some situations, ducts can be large (e.g. 1–2 m in diameter) and difficult to locate within the overall building design. In such circumstances the ductwork may be exposed and possibly made an architectural feature. The design, including the shape, location and visual appearance will need to be addressed to ensure sympathy with the visual environment.

Shopping centres, airports, auditoria, display galleries and large office complexes are possible examples where exposed ductwork may be used. Installation standards and sealing systems for such ducts may require more attention to the final appearance of the duct system than with ducts in concealed spaces.

3.2.7 Approximate sizing

Because ductwork can be large, it will often be necessary to assess the size of individual ductwork in critical locations, particularly where horizontal branches leave the main vertical risers. It is often possible to adjust the size of the vertical space well into the detailed design. Horizontal branches, however, cannot encroach on the necessary headroom.

To make a preliminary estimate of a branch size, calculate the air flow rate required in the area served by multiplying the zone volume by the number of air changes per hour and divide by 3600 to obtain the zone flow rate in $m^3 \cdot s^{-1}$. Two air changes an hour may be appropriate for offices with a separate heating system for fabric losses. Where the air is used for heating, four air changes an hour may be required or six air changes or more for an air-conditioned space. Dividing this flow rate by the velocity given in Tables 3.2 and 3.3 gives the duct cross sectional area required. For conventional systems, the aspect ratio (long side to short side) of rectangular ducting should not exceed 3:1.

3.2.8 Interaction with structure/building form

Because ductwork is likely to be the most space intensive service provided, it is important that the ductwork design is fully co-ordinated with the design of the building structure to minimise the number of bends and other fittings, each of which will increase the resistance to air flow. This is particularly important for new installations for which the Building Regulations Approved Document L[(1)] sets down strict requirements for maximum specific fan power. The structural design may have reached beyond an outline design and shape by the time that ductwork design commences.

Provided they are allowed for early in the design, it is usually possible to accommodate vertical ducts of any desired size without great difficulty from both structural and planning viewpoints. Horizontal ducts present more problems. If they are located between floors, headroom will be restricted and there will be limits on the floor area which a horizontal duct can serve. Early checks should be carried out to ensure that the vertical main ducts enable horizontal distribution without compromising the performance of the installation or the available headroom and that structural members allow branch ducts to leave the main ducts.

Distribution of the engineering services within a building are likely to follow a pattern associated with the main building circulation route which represents the main functional pattern of the building. This may not be the most efficient route for the ductwork. The large space requirements for ductwork mean that it can be desirable to locate plant close to the areas they serve.

Sufficient space needs to be provided for ease of fitting the ductwork. Providing access for maintenance is also important since it will be expensive to install retrospectively, whether ducts are horizontal or vertical. Space should also be allowed for additions and alterations.

Co-ordination of the engineering services should ensure that the area for removal of access panels and covers and entry into the ductwork is free of services and readily accessible without obstructions.

3.2.9 Zoning

Loads due to mechanical ventilation of a space are likely to be constant and zoning, if appropriate, should be based on siting plant as centrally as possible to minimise the distance that the air has to travel. As noted in section 3.2.4, strategic issues such as availability of space for multiple plant rooms or the need for separate systems to service different tenants in the building may determine the zoning arrangements.

The ductwork system may be providing heating, cooling or air conditioning, in which case the load will change due to factors such as solar gain, occupancy and the use of lights.

If the loads throughout a building vary together (i.e. are in phase), or the variations are not large enough to cause the internal conditions to drift outside the acceptable limits, a single zone can be adopted. However, if different areas experience load changes which are out of phase, supply air must be provided at a rate or condition appropriate to each zone.

Most deep plan buildings require division into perimeter and internal zones. The depth of perimeter zones mainly depends on the penetration of sunlight and daylight which is determined by orientation, external shading, shape and size of windows, characteristics of the glass and the type and pattern of use of blinds. The depth of a typical perimeter zone is 3–6 m.

For a typical multiple zone system with heating and cooling application, the following should be noted:

— For a constant volume flow rate to be maintained to each zone, the system must be capable of supplying air at various temperatures at any one time; this may involve simultaneous heating and cooling of supply air.

— All rooms with similar solar gain patterns can be zoned together provided that other variables are in phase. However, the number and position of the zonal sensors will be important. Corner rooms pose further problems.

— North facing rooms experience less variation and can be grouped with internal zones for cooling provided that heating is dealt with by other means.

— Gains through poorly insulated roofs are similar to gains on south facing surfaces but, if adequately insulated, they may be treated as intermediate floors.

The success of an air conditioning system depends largely on appropriate zoning and careful positioning of sensors in relation to the sources of heat gains.

3.2.10 Ductwork testing and air leakage limits

It is recommended as good practice that all significant installations (e.g. those with a fan capacity greater than 1 $m^3 \cdot s^{-1}$) should be tested in accordance with HVCA specification DW/143: *A practical guide to ductwork leakage testing*[(8)]. It should be noted that air leakage testing of low and medium pressure ductwork is not mandatory under HVCA specification DW/144[(4)]. Air leakage testing of high pressure ductwork is mandatory. Refer to HVCA DW/143 for details of the testing procedure. Air leakage limits for the three classes of ductwork are given in Table 3.1. The leakage factors given for classes A, B and C are those for the classes similarly designated in draft European Standards prEN 12237[9] and BS prEN 1507[10].

Further information on air leakage, including permitted air leakage at various pressures, is given in section 3.3.8.

3.2.11 Fan power energy requirements

Building Regulations Approved Document L[1] states maximum specific fan powers for buildings other than offices. Specific fan power (SFP) is defined as 'the sum of the design total circuit watts including all losses through switchgear and controls such as inverters, of all fans that supply air and exhaust it back to outdoors (i.e. the sum of supply and extract fans) divided by the design ventilation rate through the building'[1].

In new buildings, the SFP should be no greater than 2.0 W·s·litre^{-1} (e.g. 1.0 W·s·litre^{-1} supply; 0.8 W·s·litre^{-1} exhaust). In new AC/MV systems in refurbished buildings, or where an existing AC/MV system in an existing building is being substantially altered, the SFP should be no greater than 3.0 W·s·litre^{-1}. Very energy efficient systems can achieve specific fan powers of 1 W·s·litre^{-1}. The figures quoted apply to the Building Regulations for England and Wales; for Scotland the SFP is lower.

SFP is a useful benchmark for all types of buildings. However the performance criteria for use with offices is the Carbon Performance Rating which is a composite term that allows trade-off between solar control, fan, pump and chiller performance and the controls specification. Full details are provided in Approved Document L[1].

The formula for calculating fan power is:

$$P_{ef} = \frac{\Delta p_t \, q_v}{\eta_o} \tag{3.1}$$

where P_{ef} is the fan power (W), Δp_t is the difference in total pressure around the air circuit (Pa), q_v is the volume flow (m^3·s^{-1}) and η_o is the overall efficiency (%).

The selection of a fan type is primarily determined by the application and, where a choice is available, the most efficient should be chosen. Fans should be sized as close to the actual demand as possible in order to keep capital and running costs to a minimum. Motors should not be significantly oversized as efficiency and power factor will reduce. Dependant on the fan type selected, the motor may be located within or external to the duct. Motors within the duct can increase the air temperature.

In general, centrifugal fans are more efficient, more controllable and quieter. Backward-curved centrifugal fans have high efficiency (up to 80%) with aerofoil backward curved fans providing even higher efficiency. Maximum efficiency for axial flow fans is about 75%. With all fans the efficiency varies with flow rate, so the chosen fan needs to have an operating point close to the point of peak efficiency. Table 2.53 (page 2-129) gives a summary of different fan types showing their relative efficiencies. Detailed information on fan applications is provided in section 2.5.11.

Fan characteristics should be matched to the chosen method of control of volume. This can be achieved by various means, such as variable speed motors to optimise fan performance at part load. Inlet guide vanes, disc throttles and dampers are not generally recommended for energy efficiency due to the 'throttling' effect.

In theory, fans can operate at better than 80% efficiency but in practice less efficient units tend to be specified to save money or provide a safety margin. The loss of efficiency (termed 'fan gains') is dissipated as heat. This can result in an air temperature rise of up to 2 K, which can make the difference between a comfortable building and one that is too warm. Heat will also be dissipated into the ductwork from fan motors located in the duct.

Significant energy savings can be achieved by reducing unnecessary pressure drops in the system by careful sizing, routing and detailing of ductwork. In particular, pinch points in index runs require higher pressure drops than much of the rest of the system.

Variable flow control of air systems, which can be used on most distribution systems, can give considerable savings in fan energy. Variable flow control VAV systems have potentially greater air distribution savings over other central plant systems, provided that pressures are well controlled and air handling plant and drives are intrinsically efficient.

Variable speed drives also allow rapid matching of fan duties during commissioning and will provide significant savings compared with manual regulation dampers. Typical energy savings are 20% at 90% flow and 40% at 80% flow, dependent upon characteristics. Damper control increases system resistance and therefore energy savings are reduced.

Energy can be reduced in ventilation systems by:

— avoiding unnecessary bends

— using bends instead of mitred elbows

— having a 'shoe' on the branch fittings for tees

— avoiding reduced duct size (i.e. maintain cross sectional area)

— minimising duct length

— minimising the length of flexible ducting

— good inlet and outlet conditions either side of fan (see fan inlet and outlet below)

— using equipment with low pressure drops (i.e. filters, attenuators, heat exchangers).

Poor inlet and outlet conditions can cause poor fan performance, and hence inefficient operation, often referred to as 'installation effects'. These can alter the aerodynamic characteristics of the fan so that its full potential is not realised. This can be the result of practical difficulties installing the ductwork and associated equipment, which may not be in exact accordance with the original design routing. Measures to reduce installation effects at the fan inlet and outlet include the following.

(*a*) Fan inlet:

— Ensure that air enters axial fans without spin by improved inlet design or a by installing a splitter.

— Include turning vanes where there is a duct bend close to a fan inlet.

— Include a transition piece where the duct size reduces.

— Ensure flexible connections are correctly fitted without offset or slack.

— Where fans are installed in plenum chambers, ensure the fan inlet is a minimum of one diameter from the plenum wall with no obstructions.

(*b*) Fan outlet:

— Ensure a minimum of two diameters of straight duct.

— Where bends are close to the outlet, ensure that radius bends with splitters are used.

— Axial and propeller fans should preferably be fitted with guide vanes to provide energy recovery. (Where guide vanes are not fitted, air swirl will significantly increase system resistance, i.e. pressure drop. This can be corrected by a carefully designed cross-piece.)

Fan connections are considered in detail in section 3.4.6.

3.2.12 Environmental issues

For a typical AC/MV building, fan energy can consume up to 8% of the electrical consumption and therefore every effort must be made to ensure that the ductwork installation is energy-efficient.

Cleaning of ductwork must be taken into account in the design and installation stages by ensuring adequate and safe provision is made for access.

Filter removal and replacement must be considered by ensuring sufficient space and means of access is provided.

Noise in ductwork can be contentious, particularly where the system or components (e.g. intake, exhaust, air handling unit etc.) produce a noise nuisance to the building occupants, neighbours or passers by. Noise is generated where eddies are formed as flow separates from a surface. The generated noise level is particularly sensitive to the velocity. See section 3.3.11 for further details.

The visual effect of ductwork can be an environmental issue because of its physical size and location. Whilst ductwork may be hidden in risers, ceiling voids and below the floor, there will be occasions where it is exposed and possibly made an architectural feature. The design, including the shape, location and visual appearance will need to be addressed to ensure sympathy with the visual environment. Where ducting is exposed, the installation standards may require additional attention, particularly to jointing and sealing.

3.2.13 Fire issues

Fire and smoke containment/hazards are factors which influence the design and installation of ductwork systems.

Guidance on fire protection systems is given in BS 5588: *Fire precautions*[11] and in the ASFP publication *Fire rated and smoke outlet ductwork*[12]. Systems are required to be tested in accordance with BS 476: Part 20[13] and BS 476: Part 22[14] for fire and smoke dampers and BS 476: Part 24[15] for fire rated ductwork.

Building Regulations in the UK require that buildings be divided into fire compartments to inhibit the spread of smoke and fire in the building. This stops the spread of smoke and fire from one compartment to another for given periods of time, as specified by Building Regulations Approved Document B[16].

The potential for ducting to spread fire or smoke through a building must be considered at an early stage of the design. Ducts carrying contaminants with high fire potential (e.g. lint or other inflammable material) can become fire hazards unless subject to a regular inspection and cleaning regime.

Local Authorities may require that ductwork is used for smoke extract purposes, either as an additional function or by the installation of a stand alone system. These considerations will influence the planning and layout of the ducting and some guidance is given in section 3.3.12. However it is recommended that the design be discussed with the Local Authority at the earliest opportunity.

3.2.14 Weight of ductwork

The weight of ductwork, including insulation where applied, is normally insignificant in relation to the structural support capability of the structure. In some types of buildings the weight of the ductwork may be important (e.g. lightweight retail, storage and factory structures). Examples of the types of problems are insufficient support centres from which to hang the ductwork and lightweight purlins which are unable to support the weight of the installed ductwork. Sufficient structural support for fans must be provided. Information on the weight of ductwork materials is given in section 3.5.2.

3.2.15 Testing and commissioning

As noted in section 3.2.10, all ductwork installations of significant size should be tested. The needs of on-site regulation should be planned and provided for in the design stage, otherwise balancing the system within acceptable limits may not be possible. Money apparently saved by measures such as cutting down on the number of dampers or access panels in the system can be lost many times over in the extra time needed for commissioning. Procedures for commissioning air handling systems are given in CIBSE Commissioning Code A: *Air distribution systems*[17] and BSRIA Application Guide AG3/89.3: *Commissioning air systems*[18]. Further information on testing and commissioning is provided in section 3.6.

3.2.16 Cleaning

Dust will generally be deposited in operational ductwork over the lower surfaces of air distribution ducts, with the deposition increasing with distance from the fan. There may be additional deposition where the local flow of air is slowed. This will happen at points where there is a resistance to the flow of air; these include:

— filters

— heating and cooling coils
— corner vanes and changes in the direction of ducting
— changes in cross sectional area
— surface imperfections and jointing cracks between duct sections.

Once it has been deposited, a physical disturbance or a change in the flow speed would be required to re-entrain significant amounts of the dust into the air.

During the design process, in addition to ensuring adequate and safe access for cleaning, designers should take specialist advice and then stipulate their requirements for the periodic internal cleaning and maintenance of ductwork. Designers should also state any need for access for specialist cleaning equipment including size, type and location of the access openings required, with an indication of frequency of cleaning.

Further information on cleaning of ductwork is provided in section 3.7.

3.2.17 Controlling costs

Lower first costs can be achieved by:

— using the minimum number of fittings possible; fittings can be expensive and the resulting pressure loss is far greater than for straight duct sections
— ensuring ductwork is sealed to minimise air leakage; this allows reduction in both equipment and ductwork size
— using round ductwork where space and initial costs allow because it offers the lowest duct friction loss for a given perimeter, or given velocity
— when using rectangular ductwork, maintain the aspect ratio as close as possible to 1:1 to minimise duct friction losses and initial cost; this can also avoid problems with 'difficult' elbows.

3.3 Design criteria

3.3.1 Introduction

The primary function of a ductwork system is to convey air between specific points. In fulfilling this function, the duct assembly must perform satisfactorily within fundamental performance characteristics. One of the most important performance characteristics is energy efficiency, as discussed in section 3.2.11. This aspect is particularly relevant because changes to Part L of the Building Regulations[1], introduced in 2002, imposed new performance constraints on air-moving systems and equipment. Early in the process, designers need to ensure that their design can meet the overall performance requirements of Part L. The energy efficiency standards of Part L should not be regarded as an absolute target. In many situations, an improved level of performance may be beneficial in terms of whole life cost, and/or as a means of providing a trade-off opportunity to offset against another aspect of the design where achieving the required standard of energy efficiency is more difficult or more costly.

Elements of the assembly include an envelope (e.g. sheet metal or other material), reinforcement, seams, joints, support hangers and, possibly, insulation. Performance limits must be established for:

— dimensional stability
— containment of air
— vibration
— noise generation and containment
— exposure to damage, weather, temperature extremes
— support
— emergency conditions, e.g. fire
— heat gain or loss to the air stream
— adherence to duct walls of dirt and contaminants.

Due consideration must be given to the effects of differential pressure across the duct wall, airflow friction pressure losses, dynamic losses and air velocity leakage, as well as the inherent strength characteristics of the duct components. Ductwork installations can account for a significant proportion of the cost of mechanical services. Ducts should be sized and constructed in accordance with recognised sources of data and standards of construction.

3.3.2 Duct air velocities

The velocity of air flowing through a duct can be critical, particularly where it is necessary to limit noise levels. The duct air velocity is not a major factor in the constructional specification of ductwork.

Recommended velocities for particular applications, using the HVCA system classifications, are given in Tables 3.2 and 3.3. These figures are a general guide and assume reasonable distances between the fittings (e.g. four times the duct hydraulic diameter). Higher velocities may be used if additional attenuation is employed. Maximum velocities, as stated in HVCA DW/144[4] are given in Table 3.1.

Table 3.4 gives recommended maximum air velocities for rectangular and circular ducts in risers and ceiling spaces. Table 3.5 gives recommended velocities for supply and return air openings.

3.3.3 Legislation

No legislation has been produced which relates specifically to ductwork. The general requirements of the Health and Safety at Work etc. Act[21] and the Construction (Design and Management) Regulations[22] will apply during all the stages of design, installation, commissioning, operation, maintenance and finally demolition and disposal. Approved Document L of the Building Regulations[1] includes limitations on specific fan power. These are described in section 3.2.11.

Table 3.2 Recommended maximum duct velocities for low pressure ductwork systems where noise generation is the controlling factor

Typical applications	Typical noise rating (NR)*	Velocity / m·s^{-1}		
		Main ducts	Branch	Runouts
Domestic buildings (bedrooms)	25	3.0	2.5	<2.0
Theatres, concert halls	20–25	4.0	2.5	<2.0
Auditoria, lecture halls, cinemas	25–30	4.0	3.5	<2.0
Bedrooms (non-domestic buildings)	20–30	5.0	4.5	2.5
Private offices, libraries	30–35	6.0	5.5	3.0
General offices, restaurants, banks	35–40	7.5	6.0	3.5
Department stores, supermarkets, shops, cafeterias	40–45	9.0	7.0	4.5
Industrial buildings	45–55	10.0	8.0	5.0

* See CIBSE Guide A[20], Table 1.1, and Table 1.17

Table 3.3 Recommended maximum duct velocities for medium and high pressure systems

Volume flow in duct / m^3·s^{-1}	Velocity / m·s^{-1}	
	Medium pressure systems	High pressure systems
<0.1	8	9
0.1–0.5	9	11
0.5–1.5	11	15
>1.5	15	20

Table 3.4 Guide to maximum duct velocities in risers and ceilings[4]

Duct location	Duct type	Maximum air velocity / m·s^{-1} for stated room type		
		Critical	Normal	Non-critical
Riser or above plasterboard ceiling	Rectangular	5	7.5	10
	Circular	7	10	15
Above suspended ceiling	Rectangular	3	5	6
	Circular	5	7	10

Table 3.5 Maximum velocity for supply and return air openings (grilles and terminals)[4]

Supply or return air	Permitted air velocity / m·s^{-1}		
	Critical	Normal	Uncritical
Supply	1.5	2.5	3
Return	2	3	4

3.3.4 Health and safety

Health considerations will be addressed if a good inspection, maintenance and cleaning regime is applied. Further information on cleaning is provided in section 3.7.

Two aspects of safety concerning ductwork need to be addressed:

— *during design*: that there are safe and secure means of access to the ductwork and associated plant and equipment (e.g. filter housings) for inspection, maintenance and cleaning

— *during installation*: by ensuring that the ductwork can be installed safely and securely.

Fibrous materials were often used as duct linings to provide sound absorption. However, they are not now generally used because:

— they can contribute to mould growth

— fibrous materials degrade with time

— fibres can erode from the surface and be carried in the air

— fibrous materials are difficult to clean.

Suitable alternative sound absorbing proprietary materials such as acoustic foam are now used and have the advantage of not requiring facings or edge treatment.

3.3.5 Airflow in ducts

3.3.5.1 General

Air in ducts follows natural laws of motion. While the detailed prediction of flow behaviour is very difficult, good design should ensure that the air follows the line of the duct with uniform velocities and that excessive turbulence is avoided. Ductwork fittings cause major pressure losses and good design is essential, particularly where higher velocities are used. Bad design in relation to airflow can lead to vibration of flat duct surfaces, increases in duct pressure losses, unpredictable behaviour in branch fittings and terminals, and adverse effects on the performance of installed plant items such as fans and dehumidifying coils. It is much cheaper to get the design right than to try and correct abnormal flow situations on site.

3.3.5.2 Behaviour of air flowing through a duct

In normal circumstances the flow of air in ducts is turbulent with the flow generally in the direction of the duct axis. Eddies and secondary motions will result in energy dissipation due to internal fluid friction. Streamlines will not be parallel to the duct centre-line. In unobstructed straight ducts, eddies give rise to only relatively small transverse components of the duct velocity and the flow velocities are symmetrical about the duct axis.

Disturbance to the flow arising from obstructions, duct fittings or other components has two major effects:

— the eddies can be significantly larger in size and their velocities much higher

— the flow velocities across the duct become asymmetrical, i.e. much higher velocities can occur in part of the duct section, whilst in other parts even reverse flow may occur.

From the point of view of duct design the important aspects of the effects of disturbance to airflow are:

— increased pressure loss due to creation of eddies

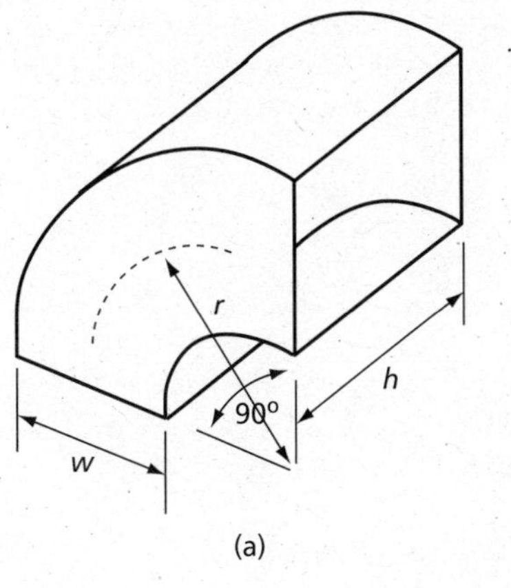

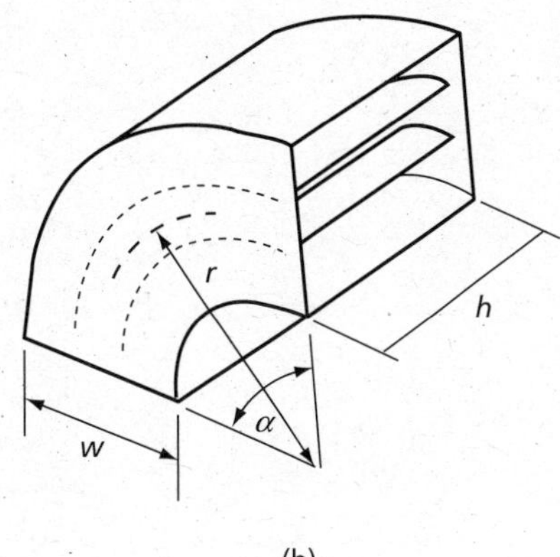

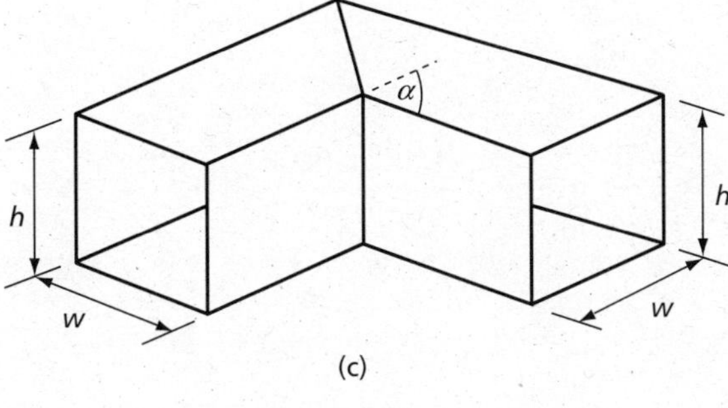

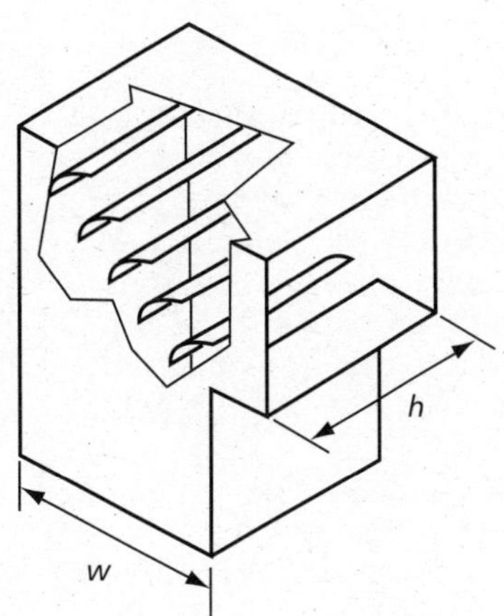

Figure 3.2 Common types of bends; *(a)* 90° radius bend without vanes, rectangular, *(b)* short radius bend with vanes (any angle), rectangular, *(c)* mitred elbow without vanes (any angle), *(d)* 90° mitred elbow with vanes

— increased pressure loss as high velocity air mixes with low velocity air

— noise generated by the interaction on eddies with the inner surfaces of the ducts.

3.3.5.3 Bends

Figure 3.2 illustrates common bend types; their influence on the airflow is described below. Bends may be characterised as 'hard' or 'soft' according to whether the change of direction is in the plane of the longer or shorter side of the cross section, respectively (see Figure 3.3).

Radiused bends

The air will flow to the outer surface causing high velocities at discharge on the outside with much lower velocities on the inside. In addition, the centrifugal effect will cause a higher static pressure at the outer surface, leading to some transverse flow towards the inner surface, and hence producing a spiral motion at the outlet. If the bend is too tight (i.e. $r/w < 1$), flow will readily separate from the inside surface with subsequent eddying and increased pressure loss. In practice, radiused bends should have an r/w value of 1.5; for low pressure loss situations r/w should be increased to 2. They should have a downstream straight duct of at least five equivalent diameters to allow the flow to stabilise again. As a general rule, the formation of an offset in a duct layout is better achieved using two angled bends ($\theta < 90°$) rather than two right-angled bends. (*Note*: in this Guide, r is taken as the mean radius of the bend to the centre line of the duct; HVCA specification DW/144[4] relates r to the throat radius of the duct.)

Table 3.6 Short radius bends with splitters; position of splitters[4]

Dimension w / mm	Number of splitters	Splitter position		
		A	*B*	*C*
400–800	1	$w/3$	—	—
800–1600	2	$w/4$	$w/2$	—
1600–2000	3	$w/8$	$w/3$	$w/2$

Note: splitters not required for bend angles less than 45°

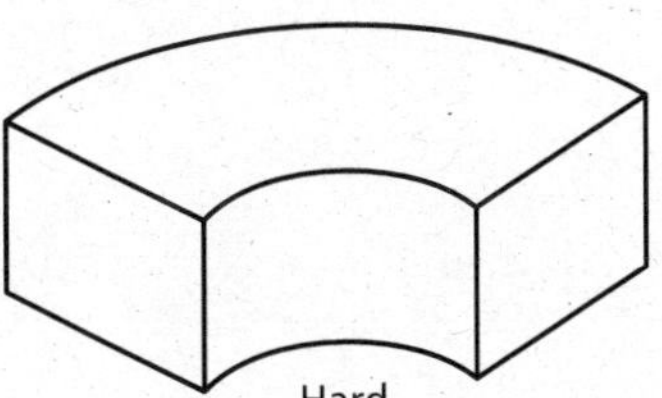

Figure 3.3 'Hard' and 'soft' bends

Splitter bends

These are tight radiused bends which use internal splitters to improve the air flow, see Figure 3.4. Standard settings for splitters are given in Table 3.6 which is taken from HVCA DW/144[4]. The flow in the air passages is as described for the radiused bend, but because multiple streams emerge at discharge, the outlet velocity profile will be more uniform than for a plain radiused bend. Hence the minimum straight length of downstream duct may be reduced to about four equivalent lengths.

Mitred elbows (with turning vanes)

Rectangular duct bends with either dimension greater than 200 mm should have properly designed turning vanes. The angle of the turning vane should be the same as that

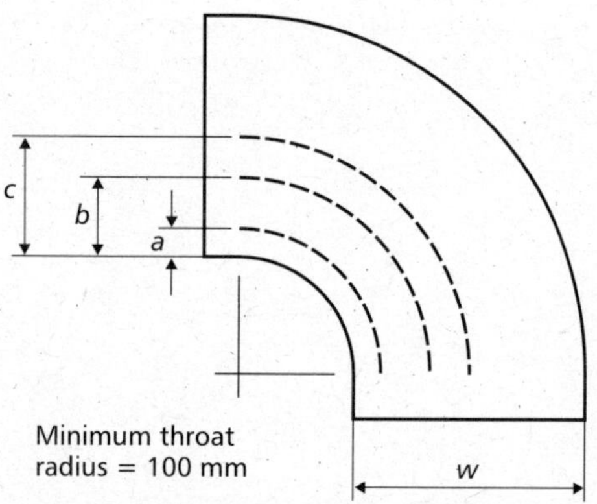

Figure 3.4 Short radius bend with splitters; position of splitters (reproduced from HVCA specification DW/144[4] by permission of the Heating and Ventilating Contractors' Association)

of the bend. Information on the structural requirements of turning vanes is given in HVCA specification DW/144[4]. The advantage of this type of bend is that it should not significantly distort the velocity profile, so that other duct fittings or components can be placed closer to the outlet, provided the inlet conditions to the bend are uniform. If the flow is not uniform at the inlet, this non-uniformity may persist down-stream of the bend.

Optimum design of turning vanes, with careful positioning, should provide a bend with less resistance to airflow than a good design of radiused bend, but this may not be achieved in practice. This is because the inside and outside corners of the bend are usually not rounded and internal and side fixings provide some obstructions. The pressure losses may then be a little higher than those in a good design of radiused bend, particularly in the case of small duct sizes. Eddies will be formed where air separates from the outside surface of a turning vane causing this type of bend to generate more noise than radiused and splitter bends.

Research by the American Sheet Metal and Air Conditioning Contractors' Association (SMACNA) on a 600 mm square elbow with blades of 114 mm radius shows the optimum spacing to be 82 mm. When the length of the blades is greater than 900 mm, it is preferable to use double thickness turning vanes to add stiffness, but there is a penalty due to increased pressure drop.

Mitred elbows (without vanes or splitters)

This type of bend is not recommended for bends with $\alpha > 30°$ because the flow becomes both distorted and very turbulent. The flow leaves the bend with higher velocities on the outside surface, and separation occurs at the inside sharp edge, leading to severe eddying. The one advantage of this eddying is that it will lead to mixing of temperature-stratified air but the pressure loss will be high, with large pressure losses resulting (see Guide C[2], section 4.10.3.5). For low velocity systems, mitred elbows can produce useful sound attenuation due to a reflection effect. Other fittings should not be placed close to the elbow.

3.3.5.4 Branches

There are many designs of branches and junctions in use. The important features are that the flow should be divided (or combined) with the minimum interference and disturbance, and that changes in duct sizes should not be made at the branch but at a short distance downstream (or upstream).

Examples of good and economic branch design are shown in Figure 3.5. A good branch design cannot be effective if the flow entering the branch is not uniform across the section.

For some of the HVCA recommended tee designs, no experimental data are available for the pressure loss, but the designer should consider their use. Section 4 of Guide C[2] provides useful information. Note that the addition of a small shoe on the branch tee can reduce pressure loss in both the branch flow and the straight flow. HVCA specification DW/144[4] suggests appropriate shoe dimensions for various sizes of duct.

3.3.5.5 Change of section

Expansion

A taper expansion of a duct causes an appreciable pressure loss due to the tendency of the flow to break away from the sides and form eddies. The greater the total included angle of divergence, the greater is the pressure loss, especially for large changes in area. There is no included angle at which dramatic differences in pressure drop occur, but for manufacturing convenience HVCA specification DW/144[4] suggests a maximum of 45°.

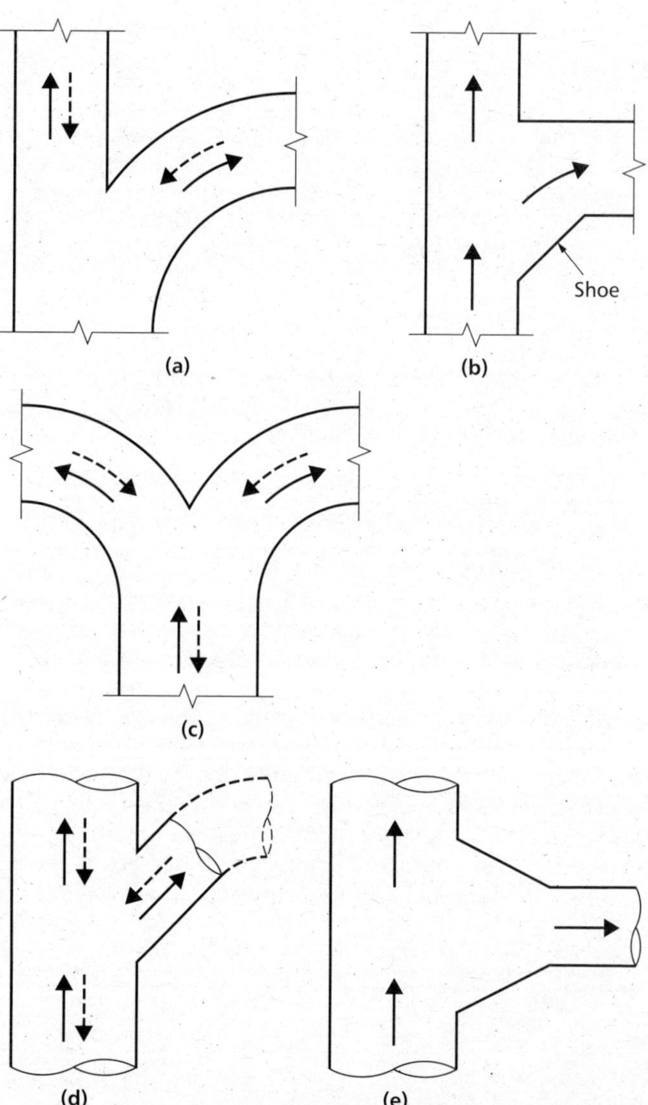

Figure 3.5 Examples of good duct design; *(a)* 90° swept branch, rectangular, *(b)* 90° branch tee with shoe, rectangular, *(c)* 90° radiused twin bend, rectangular, *(d)* 45° branch tee, circular, *(e)* 90° conical branch tee, circular

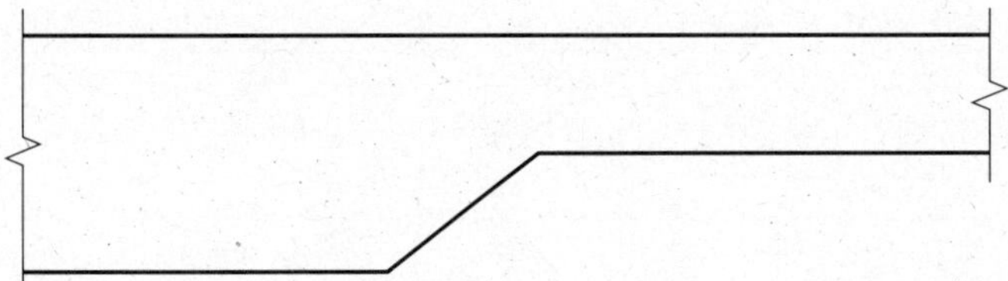

Figure 3.6 Change of section for rectangular duct; one side only inclined

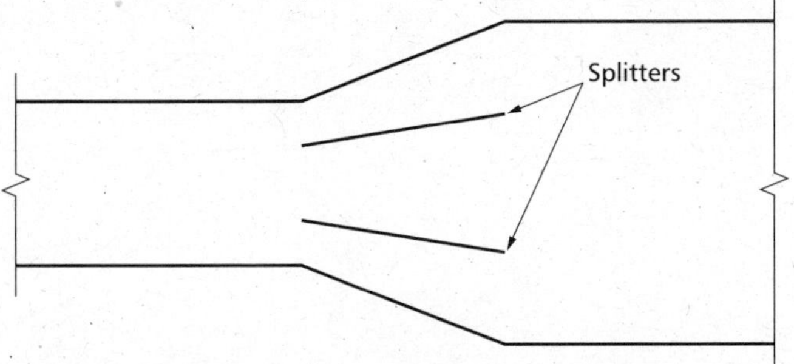

Figure 3.7 Change of section for rectangular duct with splitters

The cheapest form of taper for rectangular ductwork is to maintain the same plane for three sides and incline the fourth side only, see Figure 3.6. In any diverging section, when the plane of any side changes by more than 22.5°, DW/144 recommends the inclusion of splitter vanes, which should bisect the angle between any side and the duct centre-line, see Figure 3.7. However, it is not clear by how much the friction pressure drop is reduced by the introduction of such vanes. Certainly the inclusion of splitters would not seem worthwhile when the change in section $(A_2/A_1)>4$, see Guide C(2), section 4.10.3.17.

Contraction

Relatively little pressure drop is caused by a contraction. Again, HVCA specification DW/144(4) suggests a maximum included angle of 45°, but this is perhaps only a manufacturing convenience or, possibly, a cautious measure to prevent contraction and expansion tapers being interchanged during installation. The designer should not feel constrained in choosing the taper angle for a contraction. No splitter vanes are needed for a contraction.

Other fittings

As a general rule, fittings should avoid abrupt changes in direction and sharp edges that cause the flow to separate and form eddies, which in turn increase pressure loss and noise generation. A fitting such as a damper can create vortices which will result in a greater pressure drop than normal in a subsequent downstream fitting. Separation between the fittings by a minimum length of 5 equivalent diameters is recommended.

In the case of bends in rectangular ductwork, the combination of two bends in close proximity can give a lower pressure drop than two which are far apart (see Guide C(2), section 4.10.3.9). This is not the case for two segmented circular ducts in close proximity, but the effect of close coupling is not significant.

3.3.6 Heat gains or losses

In a duct system, the air temperature change can be significant, e.g. when passing through an untreated space. This has the effect of reducing the heating or cooling capacity of the air and increasing the energy input to the system. The heat transmission to and from the surrounding space can be reduced by insulation of the ducts. The following notes give guidance on the estimation of temperature changes in ducted air due to heat gains or losses.

The heat gain or loss rate through the walls of a run of air ducts is given by:

$$\phi = U A_s (t_{ad} - t_{as}) \tag{3.2}$$

where ϕ is the heat exchange (W), U is the overall thermal transmittance (W·m^{-2}·K^{-1}), A_s is the surface area of the duct run (m^2), t_{as} is the ambient temperature outside the duct (°C) and t_{ad} is the temperature of the air inside the duct (°C).

The temperature of the air inside the duct is given by:

$$t_{ad} = \tfrac{1}{2}(t_{ad1} + t_{ad2}) \tag{3.3}$$

where t_{ad1} is the air temperature in the upstream end of the duct run (°C) and t_{ad2} is the air temperature in the downstream end of the duct run (°C).

The duct surface area is given by:

$$A_s = P \times l \tag{3.4}$$

where A_s is the duct surface area (m^2), P is the perimeter of the duct cross section (m) and l is the length of the duct run (m).

The heat gain or heat loss rate given by equation 3.2 is equal to the heat gain or loss rate from the air in the duct, which is given by:

$$\phi = c A \rho c_p \Delta t_{ad} \times 10^3 \tag{3.5}$$

where c is the velocity of the air in the duct (m·s^{-1}), A is the cross sectional area of the duct (m^2), ρ is the density of air in the duct (kg·m^{-3}), c_p is the specific heat capacity of air in the duct at constant pressure (kJ·kg^{-1}·K^{-1}) and Δt_{ad} is the temperature difference between the ends of the duct run (K).

Δt_{ad} is given by:

$$\Delta t_{ad} = t_{ad1} - t_{ad2} \tag{3.6}$$

Equating equations 3.1 and 3.4 and rearranging gives:

$$\Delta t_{ad} = \frac{U P (t_{ad} - t_{as}) l}{c A \rho c_p 10^3} \tag{3.7}$$

or:

$$\Delta t_{ad} = \frac{4 U (t_{ad} - t_{as}) l}{c \rho c_p d_h 10^3} \tag{3.8}$$

where d_h is the hydraulic mean diameter of the duct (m).

The hydraulic mean diameter is given by:

$$d_h = 4 A / P \tag{3.9}$$

For air at 20 °C, ρ = 1.2 kg·m^{-3} and c_p = 1.02 kJ·kg^{-1}·K^{-1}. Hence, by substituting these values and combining the numerical factors:

$$\Delta t_{ad} = \frac{U (t_{ad} - t_{as}) l}{306 c d_h} \tag{3.10}$$

Ignoring the thermal resistance of the duct material, the U-value of the insulated duct is given by:

$$U = \frac{1}{(1/h_{si} + l_n/\lambda_n + 1/h_{so})} \quad (3.11)$$

where h_{si} is the heat transfer coefficient of the inside surface of the duct (W·m^{-2}·K^{-1}), l_n is the insulation thickness (m), λ_n is the thermal conductivity of the insulation (W·m^{-1}·K^{-1}) and h_{so} is the heat transfer coefficient of the outside surface of the duct (W·m^{-2}·K^{-1}).

The value of h_{si} is a function of the Reynolds number and an approximate value is given by:

$$h_{si} = 3.5\,(c^{0.8} / d_h^{0.25}) \quad (3.12)$$

For most typical applications, h_{si} may be taken as 37.5 W·m^2·K^{-1}. The value of h_{so} also depends on the conditions surrounding the duct. A typical value for unvented building voids is 10 W·m^{-2}·K^{-1}, but this can be influenced by reflective facing materials on the insulation and by draughts. Estimated values of U for insulated ducts with these values of h_{si} and h_{so} are given in Table 3.7.

The temperature change in an insulated duct can be estimated from equation 3.10 and Table 3.7. For insulation with thermal conductivity of 0.045 W·m^{-1}·K^{-1}, values of $(\Delta t_{ad} / l\,(t_{ad} - t_{as}))$ are given in Figure 3.8. The approximate values for an uninsulated duct are also shown in Figure 3.8, for typical still locations, but these temperature changes could be underestimated by about 20% if the duct is in draughty conditions.

Example 3.1

For a 600 mm × 500 mm duct with 50 mm of thermal insulation (λ_n = 0.045 W·m^{-1}·K^{-1}), an air velocity inside the duct of 9.5 m·s^{-1} and an air temperature t_{ad} = 10 °C, passing through surroundings at t_{as} = 30 °C, the change in air temperature per metre run is calculated as follows.

Cross sectional area of duct:

$$A_s = 0.6 \times 0.5 = 0.3 \text{ m}^2$$

Perimeter of duct:

$$P = 2\,(0.6 + 0.5) = 2.2 \text{ m}$$

Hydraulic diameter of duct:

$$d_h = (4 \times 0.3) / 2.2 = 0.55 \text{ m}$$

Hence:

$$d_h\,c = 0.55 \times 9.5 = 5.23 \text{ m}^2\text{·s}$$

From Figure 3.8:

$$\Delta t_{ad} / l\,(t_{ad} - t_{as}) = 0.0005 \text{ m}^{-1}$$

Hence the change in air temperature per metre of duct run is:

$$\Delta t_{ad} = 0.0005 \times 20 = 0.01 \text{ K·m}^{-1}$$

For an uninsulated duct, from Figure 3.7:

$$\Delta t_{ad} / l\,(t_{ad} - t_{as}) = 0.004 \text{ m}^{-1}$$

Therefore:

$$\Delta t_{ad} = 0.004 \times 20 = 0.08 \text{ K·m}^{-1}$$

Since this method assumes that Δt_{ad} is small, some error will be introduced if the length of ductwork is considered large, and the smaller the value of $(d_h \times c)$, the larger the error. A maximum length of 10 m is recommended. It may be noted from Figure 3.8 that as the value of $(d_h \times c)$ falls below 1.5, the rate of temperature drop in the ducts with 50 mm or less insulation increases considerably. For small ducts and low air velocities, the insulation thickness should be at least 50 mm. BS 5422[(23)] gives guidance on the assessment of the economic thickness of duct insulation. However, in the absence of such assessment, BS 5422 recommends insulation thicknesses for ducts carrying chilled and warm air as shown in Tables 3.8 and 3.9 respectively. For detailed information on the thermal insulation of ductwork, reference should be made to BS 5422[(23)] and BS 5970[(24)].

Table 3.7 Estimated U-value for insulated ducts

Thermal conductivity of insulation / W·m^{-1}·K^{-1}	U-value (/ W·m^{-2}·K^{-1}) for given thickness of insulation / mm				
	25	38	50	75	100
0.025	0.89	0.61	0.47	0.32	0.24
0.03	1.04	0.72	0.56	0.38	0.29
0.035	1.19	0.82	0.64	0.44	0.34
0.04	1.33	0.93	0.73	0.50	0.38
0.045	1.47	1.03	0.81	0.56	0.43
0.05	1.6	1.13	0.89	0.61	0.47
0.055	1.72	1.22	0.97	0.67	0.51
0.06	1.84	1.32	1.04	0.73	0.56
0.07	2.07	1.49	1.19	0.83	0.64
0.08	2.28	1.66	1.33	0.94	0.73

3.3.7 Condensation and vapour barriers

3.3.7.1 Surface condensation

Condensation of water vapour within air occurs whenever the temperature falls below the ambient dew-point. This can occur on the outside of the cold duct when the temperature of the duct air causes the duct itself to have a temperature below the dew-point of the surrounding air. Even when the ductwork is insulated, this can occur due to diffusion through the insulation of the more humid air external to the duct. In turn this can lead to corrosion of the ductwork as well as diminishing the thermal resistance of the insulation, leading to more condensation.

Vapour sealing will be required where the temperature of the air within the duct is at any time low enough to promote condensation on the exterior surface of the duct and cause moisture penetration through the thermal insulation. In this case the most important requirement is to limit penetration of the seal. The vapour barrier must be carefully installed to ensure the seal is continuous with no routes for penetration of humidity.

BS 5970[(24)] warns of the risk of condensation within the layer of insulation which is primarily used to avoid condensation on its outside surfaces. With a suitable choice of insulation material and thickness, the surface temperature of the

Table 3.8 Recommended minimum thickness of insulation on ductwork carrying chilled air[23]

Minimum air temp. inside duct / °C	Minimum thickness of insulating material (/ mm) for stated thermal conductivity λ (/ W·m^{-1}·K^{-1}) and external surface emissivity ε											
	$\lambda = 0.02$			$\lambda = 0.025$			$\lambda = 0.03$			$\lambda = 0.035$		
	$\varepsilon = 0.05$	$\varepsilon = 0.44$	$\varepsilon = 0.9$	$\varepsilon = 0.05$	$\varepsilon = 0.44$	$\varepsilon = 0.9$	$\varepsilon = 0.05$	$\varepsilon = 0.44$	$\varepsilon = 0.9$	$\varepsilon = 0.05$	$\varepsilon = 0.44$	$\varepsilon = 0.9$
15	15	8	5	18	9	6	22	11	7	25	13	8
10	26	10	9	32	17	11	39	20	13	45	23	15
5	37	19	12	47	24	15	56	28	18	64	33	21
0	48	25	16	60	31	20	72	37	24	84	43	27

Minimum air temp. inside duct / °C	Minimum thickness of insulating material (/ mm) for stated thermal conductivity λ (/ W·m^{-1}·K^{-1}) and external surface emissivity ε								
	$\lambda = 0.04$			$\lambda = 0.045$			$\lambda = 0.05$		
	$\varepsilon = 0.05$	$\varepsilon = 0.44$	$\varepsilon = 0.9$	$\varepsilon = 0.05$	$\varepsilon = 0.44$	$\varepsilon = 0.9$	$\varepsilon = 0.05$	$\varepsilon = 0.44$	$\varepsilon = 0.9$
15	29	15	10	32	17	11	36	18	12
10	52	26	17	58	29	19	64	33	21
5	75	38	24	83	42	27	92	47	30
0	96	49	31	108	56	35	120	61	39

Notes:
(a) Assumes ambient conditions of 25 °C still air, 80% relative humidity, dewpoint temperature 21.3 °C
(b) Thicknesses calculated in accordance with BS EN ISO 12241[25] based on 0.6 m vertical flat surface of rectangular duct but are also adequate for horizontal surfaces
(c) Thermal conductivity values of insulating materials quoted at mean temperature of 10 °C

Table 3.9 Environmental thickness of insulation on ductwork carrying warm air[23]

Temperature difference between air inside duct and ambient / K	Environmental thickness of insulating material (/ mm) for stated thermal conductivity λ (/ W·m^{-1}·K^{-1})				Corresponding heat loss / W·m^{-2}
	$\lambda = 0.02$	$\lambda = 0.03$	$\lambda = 0.04$	$\lambda = 0.05$	
10	19	29	38	47	7.2
25	25	38	50	63	15.3
50	32	47	63	79	26.0

Notes: *(a)* Environmental thicknesses and heat loss values calculated in accordance with BS EN ISO 12241[25] based on 0.6 m depth of vertical flat surface of rectangular duct but are also adequate for horizontal surfaces
(b) Heat loss values based on insulation with low emissivity finish ($\varepsilon = 0.5$) in ambient still air at 10 °C
(c) For intermediate temperature differences, the insulation thickness can be derived by interpolation
(d) Thermal conductivity values of insulating materials quoted at mean temperature of insulating material

ductwork can be raised sufficiently above the ambient dew point temperature to avoid surface condensation on the duct.

The extent of any vapour sealing of ductwork thermal insulation and the support method to be used should be clearly specified in advance by the designer.

The thickness of insulation to prevent surface condensation can be determined from the following approximate equations governing solid state heat transfer:

For rectangular ducts:

$$l_n = \frac{(t_{ds} - t_{ad})\,\lambda}{(t_{as} - t_{ds})\,h_{so}} \quad (3.13)$$

where l_n is the insulation thickness (m), t_{ds} is the ambient dew point temperature of the air outside the duct (°C), t_{ad} is the temperature of the air inside the duct (°C), λ is the thermal conductivity of the insulation (W·m^{-1}·K^{-1}), t_{as} is the ambient temperature outside the duct (°C) and h_{so} is the heat transfer coefficient of the outside surface of the duct (W·m^{-2}·K^{-1}).

Example 3.2

Calculate the thickness of glass wool ($\lambda = 0.045$ W·m^{-1}·K^{-1}) to prevent surface condensation on a circular duct of diameter 0.8 m, carrying cooled air at 12 °C, exposed in a ceiling void at 35 °C with relative humidity of 85%.

From a psychrometric chart, for a dry bulb temperature of 35 °C and 85% RH:

$$t_{ds} = 32.1\ °\text{C}$$

Taking h_{so} as 10 W·m^{-2}·K^{-1}, using equation 3.13, the required thickness is:

$$l_n = \frac{(32.1 - 12) \times 0.045}{(35 - 32.1) \times 10} = 0.030\ \text{m} = 30\ \text{mm}$$

Table 3.8 recommends an insulation thickness of 50 mm. Hence the glass wool thickness required for vapour resistance is less than that recommended for thermal insulation and surface condensation should not arise under these operating conditions.

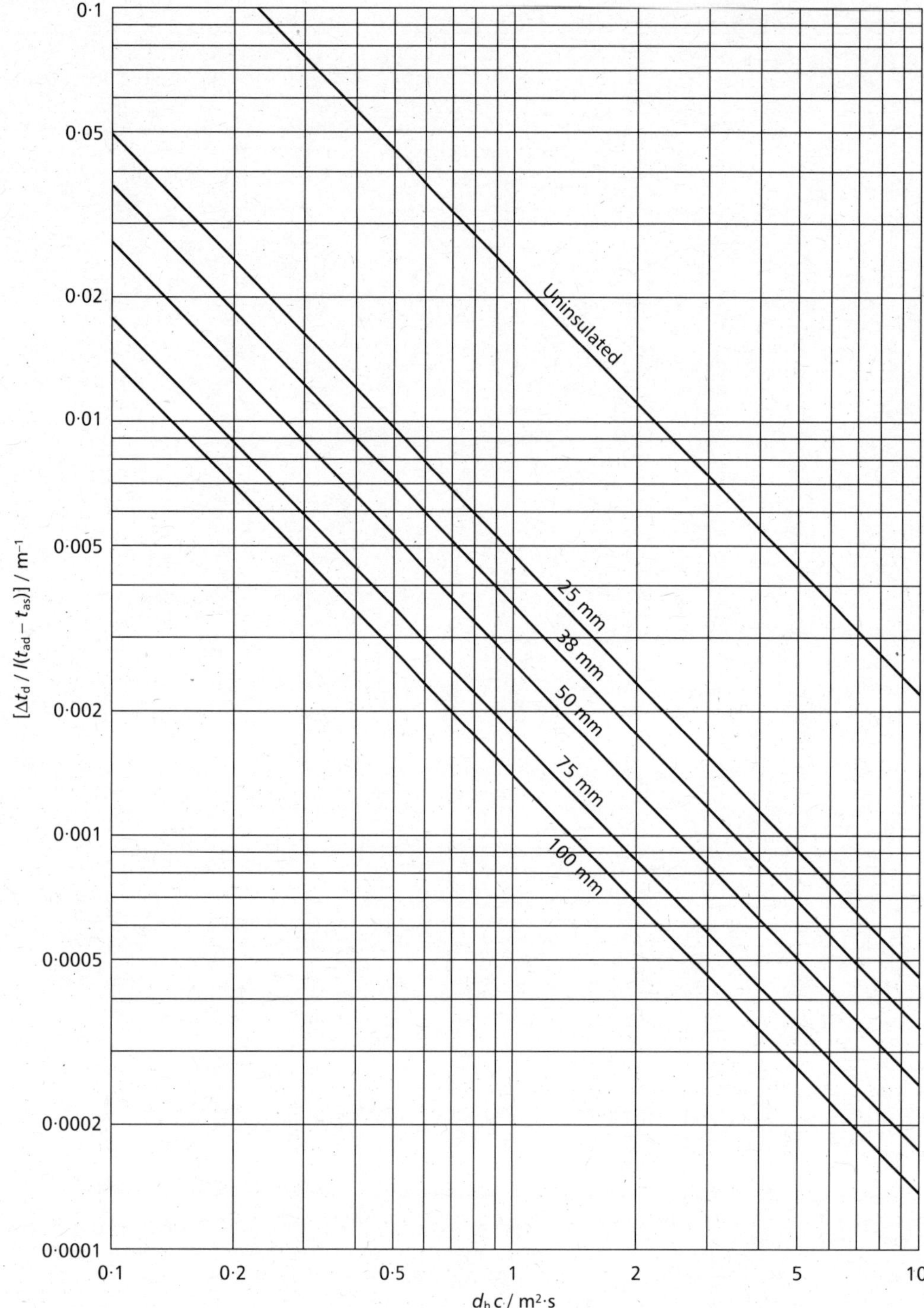

Figure 3.8 Temperature change along insulated ducts for various thicknesses of insulation

3.3.7.2 Vapour barriers

In normal circumstances the insulation thickness for heat resistance is sufficient to prevent surface condensation, but in extreme conditions the insulation thickness for vapour resistance may be larger than that for heat resistance. When cold ducts pass through areas of high dewpoint, carefully selected vapour barriers should be applied externally to the insulation. Well-installed vapour barriers with sealed joints will minimise vapour penetration and combat the risk of internal condensation in the insulation. It is good practice to provide 'nominal' vapour barriers to cold ducts or to use thermal insulation with a low value of permeability, even when the insulation thickness for vapour resistance is less than that which is recommended for thermal resistance. Although polystyrene foam provides a high resistance to vapour transfer, other thermal insulation materials, e.g. rockwool, have minimal vapour resistance (see Guide A[3], Table 3.49).

There are three main types of vapour barrier:

— *rigid barriers*: such as reinforced plastics and sheet metal, which are erected by mechanical means with sealed joints and suitable protection to resist impact damage

— *membrane barriers*: such as metal foils, plastic films and coated papers, which are easier to install and are in many cases available as backing material with heat resisting insulation, but are more easily damaged

— *coating barriers*: usually available as paints, hot melts, pastes, or powders with chemical hardeners.

Vapour barriers need to be effective and continuous. The slightest leak will permit water vapour to diffuse throughout the insulation. It is therefore imperative that cracks in vapour barriers due to poor workmanship or thermal forces are avoided. This is not normally a significant problem because Δt is often small.

A common problem is that accidental damage to barriers caused by maintenance workers is subsequently not rectified.

3.3.8 Air leakage

3.3.8.1 General

Leakage from ducted air distribution systems is an important consideration in the design and operation of ventilation and air conditioning systems. A ductwork system having air leakage within defined limits will ensure that the design characteristics of the system can be maintained. It will also ensure that energy and operational costs are not greater than necessary.

Leakage from sheet metal air ducts occurs at the seams and joints and is therefore proportional to the total surface area of the ductwork in the system. The level of leakage is similarly related to the air pressure in the duct system and, whilst there is no precise formula for calculating the level of air loss, it is generally accepted that leakage will increase in proportion to pressure to the power of 0.65.

The effect of air leakage from high pressure ductwork is critical in terms of system performance, energy consumption and the risk of high frequency noise associated with leakage. These problems are less critical with medium pressure systems, but should be considered. Low pressure ducts present the lowest risk in terms of the effect of leakage on the effective operation of the system.

It is important that ductwork should be made as airtight as possible. Conventional sheet metal ductwork is formed by seaming sheets and jointing sections; these seams and joints, penetrations made by damper spindles, control sensors, test holes, access doors etc., all give rise to air leakage. The designer should accept that some leakage will occur in conventional ductwork and make an assessment of the acceptable level in a given system. In some cases it may not be important, e.g. for a general extract system where the ducting is all in the space being served. In others it may be very important, e.g. where obnoxious or hazardous contamination is being handled. In the latter case a completely airtight system may be necessary, where fully welded ducting with air tight enclosures at all penetrations could be the basis of a special specification, outside the scope of HVCA specification DW/144[(4)].

For most ventilating and air conditioning applications, compliance with the construction and sealing requirements of DW/144 will ensure acceptably low leakage rates. For sheet metal ductwork the specification requires sealant to be applied to all longitudinal seams (except spirally wound, machine-made seams) and cross-joints; for plastic and resin bonded glass fibre ductwork similar sealing requirements are specified. The sheet metal specification also gives details of an air leakage test procedure.

Table 3.10 Ductwork air leakage limits

Ductwork pressure class	Air leakage limits / $(\mathrm{l \cdot s^{-1}})$ per $\mathrm{m^2}$ of duct surface area
Low pressure (Class A)	$0.027 \times p^{0.65}$
Medium pressure (Class B)	$0.009 \times p^{0.65}$
High pressure (Class C)	$0.003 \times p^{0.65}$

Note: p = differential pressure / Pa

Recommended acceptable leakage rates in (litres/second) per square metre of surface area are given in Table 3.10.

Appendix 3.A3 shows these limits for a range of duct static pressure differentials. These rates are in accordance with the comparable classes in prEN 12237[(9)] and prEN 1507[(10)] but these provisional European Standards do not cover the full range of high pressure ductwork.

Whilst leakage occurs at seams, joints and penetrations, the purpose of giving acceptable leakage rates in terms of surface area of ductwork is to require that the airtightness is of a consistent standard for air leakage test systems. It does not follow that the total leakage of a system which meets specified leakage requirements will always be a set percentage of the total flow rate; the percentage leakage from short runs can be substantially less than that from long runs. The design therefore plays a very important part in the likely total leakage loss from ductwork systems, since long runs not only provide more crackage and penetration, but require higher working pressures to operate. Where limitation of air leakage is important, the designer should first ensure that the duct runs are as short as possible, that the operating pressure is as low as possible, that the number of seams, joints and penetrations is kept to a minimum and that there is adequate room around the ducts for site-made joints to be effectively sealed.

Items of equipment and plant installed in ductwork systems can also leak and particular attention should be paid to the sealing of these items. Where leakage testing is required, the designer should ensure that suppliers of these items can demonstrate that their equipment meets the required airtightness standards. The designer should make adequate allowance in the fan selection for some air leakage so that the completed installation can meet its intended purpose without subsequent adjustments to the fan(s) and motor(s). Table 3.11 gives some recommendations for margins which should be included for complete installations (i.e. ductwork and equipment).

3.3.8.2 System leakage loss

There is no direct relationship between the volume of air conveyed and the surface area of the ductwork system. It is therefore difficult to express air leakage as a percentage of total air volume. Operating pressure will vary throughout the system and, since leakage is related to pressure, the calculations are complex. However, it is generally accepted that, in typical good quality systems, the leakage from each class of duct under operating conditions will be in the region of:

— low pressure (Class A): 6%

— medium pressure (Class B): 3%

— high pressure (Class C): 2%

Table 3.11 Recommended air leakage margins for design figures

Margin	Value of margin for stated class of system		
	Low pressure	Medium pressure	High pressure
Volume flow rate margin (for leakage and balancing requirements)	+10%	+5%	+5%
System total pressure loss margin:			
(a) allowance for margin on volume flow rate	+10%	+5%	+5%
(b) allowance for uncertainty in calculation	+10%	+10%	+10%
(c) combined system total pressure loss margin (sum of *(a)* and *(b)*)	+20%	+15%	+15%

3.3.8.3 Designer's calculations

The designer can calculate with reasonable accuracy the predicted total loss from a system by:

(a) calculating the operating pressure in each section of the system

(b) calculating the surface area of the ductwork in each corresponding pressure section

(c) calculating the allowable loss at the operating pressure for each section of the system (see above for indicative leakage figures).

This is illustrated in the duct sizing example shown in Appendix 3.A6.

3.3.8.4 Variable pressures in systems

Designers can achieve significant cost savings by matching operating pressures throughout the system to constructional standards and appropriate air leakage testing. The practice of specifying construction standards for whole duct systems based on fan discharge pressures may incur unnecessary costs on a project.

For example, some large systems could well be classified for leakage limits as follows:

— plant room risers: Class C

— main floor distribution: Class B

— low pressure outlets: Class A

3.3.9 Air leakage testing

3.3.9.1 General

It is normal practice for leak testing to be a requirement for all or part of high pressure ductwork installations, but it is not a regular practice for medium or low pressure ductwork installations. It is recommended as good practice that all ductwork installations of significant size (e.g. with a fan capacity greater than 1 $m^3 \cdot s^{-1}$) should be leak tested in accordance with HVCA DW/143: *A practical guide to ductwork leakage testing*[(8)]. It should be noted that air leakage testing of low and medium pressure ductwork is not obligatory under HVCA specification DW/144[(4)]; this will therefore be an individual contractual matter.

Factors which should be taken into account in deciding whether leak testing of all or part of a ductwork installation is necessary are:

— whether adequate supervision of the installation can be provided and whether a final detailed examination of the system is feasible

— whether some sections need to be checked because access will be impracticable after the installation is complete

— safety hazards which may arise from leakage of contaminated air

— whether special circumstances make necessary more stringent control of leakage than is given in the existing specification

— the cost to the client of the leakage testing and the delays caused to the completion of the installation.

The need for leak testing and the extent to which it is carried out should be assessed and, if judged to be necessary, this requirement and its extent should be included in the designer's ductwork specification.

Where it is decided that leak testing is required as part of the commissioning process, the ductwork designer should specify which sections of the ductwork system should be tested, and the test pressures and leakage criteria for those sections. DW/144 describes an appropriate leak testing procedure and gives test pressures and leakage criteria appropriate to high, medium and low pressure ductwork. These leakage rates are given in Appendix 3.A3.

To ensure that the ductwork is sufficiently airtight for the needs of the design it is recommended that:

— ductwork is sealed in accordance with the design and construction specification

— a visual check is made during erection, with particular attention to site-made joints

— where leakage testing is required, the ductwork is tested in sections as the work proceeds, and the measured air leakage rate for each section checked against the leakage criterion (the sections so chosen should be sufficiently large that the maximum permitted leakage from the sections can be accurately measured with the test equipment)

— joints between test sections that need to be remade can be visually checked

— non-ductwork items (such as attenuators, coils, fire-dampers) should be visually inspected, as the leakage from these is not covered by the relevant HVCA specification.

Ductwork constructed and installed in accordance with DW/144 should provide a level of air leakage that is appropriate to the operating static air pressure in the system. However, the environment in which systems are installed is not always conducive to achieving a predictable level of air leakage; it is therefore accepted that designers may require the systems to be tested in part or in total.

It should be recognised that the testing of duct systems adds a significant cost to the installation and incurs some extra time within the programme.

3.3.9.2 Duct pressure

Ductwork constructed to DW/144[4] will be manufactured to a structural standard that is compatible with the system operating pressure, i.e. Classes A, B and C.

3.3.9.3 Specifying air leakage testing

As stated in section 3.2.10, it is recommended as good practice that all significant installations (e.g. with a fan capacity greater than 1 $m^3 \cdot s^{-1}$) should be tested in accordance with DW/143[8].

Respecting both the cost and programme implications associated with testing ducts for leakage, the designer may, for example, indicate that a particular system is tested as follows:

— high pressure ducts: all ductwork to be tested.

— medium pressure ducts: 10% of the ductwork to be selected at random and tested

— low pressure: ductwork does not need to be tested.

In the case where a random test is selected for medium pressure ducts the following clause from DW/144 is suggested for inclusion by the designer:

> The designer shall select at random a maximum of 10% of the duct system to be tested for air leakage. The duct shall be tested at the pressure recommended in Table 17 of DW/144 for the classification for the section of the ductwork that is to be tested.
>
> The tests shall be carried out as the work proceeds and prior to the application of thermal insulation.
>
> In the event of test failure of the randomly selected section, the designer shall have the right to select two further sections at random for testing. Where successive failures are identified there shall be a right to require the contractor to apply remedial attention to the complete ductwork system.
>
> The contractor shall provide documented evidence of the calculations used to arrive at the allowable loss for the section to be tested and the client, or his agent, shall witness and sign the results of the test.

3.3.9.4 Special cases

There may be situations where special consideration needs to be given to containing air losses, e.g. a long run of ductwork may incur a disproportionate level of air loss. In such cases the designer can specify an improved standard of airtightness, e.g. 80% of allowable loss for Class B ducts. The designer should not specify a Class C test at Class C pressure for a Class B duct.

3.3.9.5 Testing of plant items

Items of in-line plant will not normally be included in an air leakage test. The ductwork installation contractor may include such items in the test if the equipment has a certificate of conformity for the pressure class and air leakage classification for the system under test.

3.3.10 Access for inspection, maintenance and cleaning

3.3.10.1 General

Examples of space allowances, access problems and good practice are shown in Appendix 3.A2.

3.3.10.2 Access/inspection openings

Due consideration should be given to access for inspection, maintenance and cleaning. Openings need to be safe and have sealed panels/covers designed so that they can be easily removed and refixed. Multiple setscrews are not recommended, and self-piercing screws are not acceptable as a method of fixing. Safety restraints should be connected to access panels located in riser ducts.

A sufficiently large area, free of services and other obstructions, is needed around panels and covers to allow them to be removed.

An access panel is required adjacent to items of in-line equipment that require either regular servicing or intermittent access. The openings need to be sized as a minimum to allow hand and/or arm access. The designer should specify the size and location of the panels where larger dimensions are required. In these cases the panels should not exceed 450 mm × 450 mm. It may be more practicable to use removable duct sections or flexible ducts/connections.

An inspection panel should be provided adjacent to items of in-line equipment that need only visual inspection of internal elements from outside the ductwork. Such inspection openings should have a minimum size of 100 mm × 100 mm for rectangular ducts and 100 mm diameter for circular ducts.

It will be the responsibility of the insulation contractor to 'dress' the insulation to the edges of the access openings without impeding the functionality of the panel, cover or door.

3.3.10.3 Provision of access panels

Access panels should be provided for the inspection and servicing of plant and equipment. Table 3.12 provides guidance. However, the ductwork system designer may choose to demonstrate that adequate provision has been made for access, such as by reference to a ductwork cleaning specialist.

In addition, the following should be noted:

— *Fire/smoke dampers*: Panels should be located to give access both to the blades and fusible links. On

Table 3.12 Summary of requirements for access to duct-mounted components

Component	Location of access openings
Dampers	Both sides
Fire dampers	One side
Heating/cooling coils	Both sides
Circular sound attenuators	One side
Rectangular sound attenuators	Both sides
Filter sections	Both sides
In-duct fans	Both sides
Air flow control device	Both sides

multiple assembly units it may be necessary to provide more than one panel; the need for such access may be determined by the external access conditions and the internal reach to the blades and their fusible links.

— *Heating/cooling coils and in-duct fans/devices*: Panel to be located on the air entry side i.e. upstream.

— *Filters*: Panel to be located in the air entry side i.e. upstream. (*Note*: dimensions of access may need to be changed to suit filter elements of the front withdrawal type.)

— *Inspection covers*: Inspection covers should be provided adjacent to regulating dampers where either the control linkage is mounted internally within the airstream or if a multi-bladed unit is an integral part of the ductwork run. It is not necessary to provide inspection covers adjacent to either single blade regulating dampers or flanged damper units.

— *Hand holes*: Hand holes to permit proper jointing of duct sections should be provided at the manufacturers' discretion, but kept to a minimum and made as small as practicable. The hand hole cover should be sealed and securely fastened.

3.3.10.4 Test holes for plant system commissioning

Test holes for in-duct airflow measurement are required, as follows:

— on both sides of the fans and heating and cooling coils (for pressure drop measurement)

— in the main ducts

— in all branches

— in centrifugal fan drive guards opposite the end of the fan spindle, for speed measurements.

The requirements for the nominal location and size of test holes are given in section 3.6. Test holes are usually best drilled on site after installation is complete. The number and spacing of holes at a particular location are given in BSRIA Application Guide AG3/89.3: *Commissioning air systems in buildings*[18].

The actual location of the test holes will be determined by the designer and/or commissioning engineer either at the drawing approval stage (to be works-drilled) or during the commissioning activity (to be site-drilled). For practical access reasons, the latter method is usually preferred.

3.3.10.5 Instrument connections

Instrument connections should be provided at locations determined during the design process.

3.3.10.6 Openings required for other purposes

It is the designer's responsibility to specify the location and size of any openings required other than those covered in this section. In the case of hinged access doors it is the designer's responsibility to indicate on the drawings the location and size of hinged access doors required, ensuring that there is an area free of services and other obstructions to enable the door to be satisfactorily opened. Unless otherwise specified by the designer, openings should not be larger than 1350 mm high and 500 mm wide. Doors should open against the air pressure. Both the opening in the duct and the access door itself need to be adequately reinforced to prevent distortion. A suitable sealing gasket should be provided, together with sufficient clamping type latches to ensure an airtight seal between the door and the duct.

For safety reasons, the manufacturer should incorporate means to prevent personnel being trapped inside the duct, e.g. by providing access doors with operating handles both inside and outside the duct.

3.3.10.7 Kitchen ventilation ductwork

For kitchen ventilation ductwork, access doors for cleaning must be provided at distances not exceeding 3 metres.

3.3.11 Noise from ductwork and HVAC plant

See section 5.

Table 3.13 lists noise transmission paths for a variety of sound sources and suggests appropriate methods of noise reduction[27].

3.3.12 Fire issues

3.3.12.1 General

The following notes summarise the main fire precautions issues relating to the design and installation of ductwork systems. Advice on fire protection systems is laid down in BS 5588: Part 9[11] and Association for Specialist Fire Protection publication *Fire rated and smoke outlet ductwork: An industry guide to design and installation*[12]. Systems are required to be tested in accordance with BS 476: Part 20[13] and BS 476: Part 22[14] for fire and smoke dampers and BS 476: Part 24 (ISO 6944)[15] for fire-rated ductwork. See also CIBSE Guide E: *Fire engineering*[29] for general guidance on fire protection.

Building Regulations in the UK require that buildings be sub-divided, with fire resisting construction depending on size and use, to inhibit the spread of fire within the building. Advice on the degree of compartmentation and fire resisting periods are given in Building Regulations Approved Document B[16].

Table 3.13 Noise reduction methods for various noise sources and transmission paths

Path	Description	Noise reduction measures
(a)	Direct sound radiated from sound source to ear	Direct sound can be controlled only by selecting quiet equipment.
	Reflected sound from walls, ceiling, and walls	Reflected sound is controlled by adding sound absorption to room and to location of equipment.
(b)	Air and structure borne sound radiated from casings and through walls of ducts and plenums is transmitted through walls and ceiling into room	Design ducts and fittings for low turbulence; locate high velocity ducts in non-critical areas; isolate ducts and sound plenums from structure with neoprene or spring hangers.
(c)	Airborne sound radiated through supply and return air ducts to diffusers in room and then to listener by path *(a)*	Select fans for minimum sound power; use ducts lined with sound absorbing material; use duct silencers or sound plenums in supply and return air ducts.
(d)	Noise is transmitted through plant/equipment room walls and floors to adjacent rooms	Locate equipment rooms away from critical areas; use masonry blocks or concrete for equipment room walls and floor.
(e)	Building structure transmits vibration to adjacent walls and ceilings from which it is radiated as noise into room by path *(a)*	Mount all machines on properly designed vibration isolators; design equipment room for mechanical dynamic loads; balance rotating and reciprocating equipment.
(f)	Vibration transmission along pipe and ductwalls	Isolate pipe and ducts from structure with neoprene or spring hangers; install flexible connectors between pipes, ducts, and vibrating machines.
(g)	Noise radiated to outside enters room windows	Locate equipment away from critical areas; use barriers and covers to interrupt noise paths; select quiet equipment.
(h)	Inside noise follows path *(a)*	Select quiet equipment.
(i)	Noise transmitted to diffuser in a room into ducts and out through an air diffuser in another room	Design and install duct attenuation to match transmission loss of wall between rooms.
(j)	Sound transmission through, over, and around room partitions	Extend partition to ceiling slab and tightly seal all around; seal all pipe, conduit, and duct penetrations.

Noise source	Transmission paths
Circulating fans; grills; diffusers; registers; unitary equipment in room	*(a)*
Induction coil and fan-powered mixing units	*(a)*, *(b)*
Unitary equipment located outside of room served; remotely located air handling equipment, such as fans and blowers, dampers, duct fittings and air washers	*(b)*, *(c)*
Compressors and pumps	*(d)*, *(e)*, *(f)*
Cooling towers; air cooled condensers	*(d)*, *(e)*, *(f)*, *(g)*
Exhaust fans; window air conditioners	*(g)*, *(h)*
Sound transmission between rooms	*(i)*, *(j)*

Fire and smoke containment and hazards are factors which influence the design and installation of ductwork systems.

A design that is required to perform a particular action as part of a fire strategy is likely to combine electrical, mechanical and builders' work components which would be influenced by the normal day-to-day operations requirements. Some of the more common components are:

— ductwork

— fire dampers

— smoke extract fans.

Ductwork is often required to transmit heat and smoke from the fire zone to the outside. The layout, jointing and potential expansion in the ductwork must be designed to withstand the calculated temperatures while maintaining integrity (to ensure containment of smoke and possibly heat), and insulation (to prevent spread of fire by radiation at high temperatures). The need for fire protection should be based on compartmentation requirements and calculated smoke temperatures. Where the fire resistant ductwork passes through a wall or floor, a penetration seal must be provided which has been tested and/or assessed with the ductwork to BS 476: Part 24[15], to the same fire rating as the compartment wall through which the fire resisting ductwork passes. Where the fire resisting ductwork passes through the fire compartment wall or floor, the ductwork itself must be stiffened to prevent deformation of the duct in a fire to:

— maintain the cross-sectional area of the duct

— ensure that the fire rated penetration seal around the duct is not compromised.

Fire dampers are provided in ductwork for fire containment by preventing flow when a pre-determined temperature is reached. The operation is usually activated by a fusible link which releases the damper at 72 °C. Generally they are required where ducts penetrate walls or floors which form fire compartments. The damper assembly should have a fire resistance rating equal to that of the fire barrier it penetrates. It should be fire tested and rated to the time/temperature curve of BS 476: Part 20[13] and Part 22[14].

Dampers would not normally be specified in ductwork used for smoke transport, although they may be required as part of the overall fire strategy in other ductwork. Higher activation temperatures can be set if there is a reason to do so. Various types of rotating or falling damper mechanisms are available, see HVCA specification DW/144[4]. Electrically controlled dampers are required in some circumstances to control the flows, depending on the location of the fire and the control system logic as determined by the requirements of the fire strategy.

Smoke extract fans must be selected to ensure reliability at the design temperature and length of exposure as predicted by the fire engineering calculations.

3.3.12.2 Main areas within a building where ductwork should be fire protected

Agreement for these areas should be sought from the Building Control Officer responsible for the building. Reference should also be made to the current Building Regulations.

Smoke extract systems

If the ductwork incorporated in a smoke extract system is wholly contained within the fire compartment, it must be capable of resisting the anticipated temperatures generated through the development of a fire. BS 476: Part 24[(15)] also requires that ductwork which is intended as a smoke extract must retain at least 75% of its cross-sectional area within the fire compartment. If the ductwork penetrates a fire resisting barrier, it must also be capable of providing the same period of fire resistance as the barrier.

Escape routes covering stairways, lobbies and corridors

All escape routes must be designed so that the building occupants can evacuate the building safely in the case of fire. Ductwork which passes through a protected escape route must have a minimum of 30 minutes fire resistance and be at least equal to the fire compartment through which the ductwork passes, either by the use of fire dampers or fire resisting ductwork.

Non domestic kitchen extract systems

Where there is no immediate discharge to atmosphere, i.e. the ductwork passes to atmosphere via another compartment, fire resistant ductwork must be used. Kitchen extract ductwork presents a particular hazard as combustible deposits such as grease are likely to accumulate on internal surfaces; therefore, all internal surfaces of the ductwork must be smooth. A fire in an adjacent compartment, through which the ductwork passes, could lead to ignition of the grease deposits, which may continue through the ductwork system possibly prejudicing the safety of the kitchen occupants. For this reason consideration must be given to the stability, integrity and insulation performance of the kitchen extract duct which should be specially tested to BS 476: Part 24[(15)] for a kitchen rating.

Particular points to note are:

- access doors for cleaning must be provided at distances not exceeding 3 metres
- fire dampers must not be used
- use of volume control dampers and turning vanes are not recommended.

Further information on kitchen extract systems is contained in HVCA specification DW/171: *Standard for kitchen ventilation systems*[(30)].

Enclosed car parks which are mechanically ventilated

Car parks must have separate and independent extract systems, designed to run in two parts, each extracting 50% of the design load. Fans require to be rated at 300 °C and the ductwork and fixings constructed from materials with a melting point not less than 800 °C. Full details of the requirements are given in Building Regulations Approved Document B[(16)].

Due to the fire risks associated with car parks, these systems should be treated as smoke extract systems and therefore maintain a minimum of 75% cross-sectional area under fire conditions in accordance with BS 476: Part 24[(15)]. Fire dampers must not be installed in extract ductwork serving car parks.

Basements

Ductwork from basements must be fire rated except for car parks as above. If basements are compartmented, each separate compartment must have a separate outlet and have access to ventilation without having to gain access (i.e. open a door to another compartment). Basements with natural ventilation should have permanent openings, not less than 2.5% of the floor area and be arranged to provide a through draft with separate fire ducts for each compartment. See Approved Document B[(16)] for full details.

Pressurisation systems

Pressurisation is a method of restricting the penetration of smoke into certain critical areas of a building by maintaining the air at higher pressures than those in adjacent areas. It applies particularly to protected stairways, lobbies, corridors and firefighting shafts serving deep basements, as smoke penetration to these would inhibit escape. As the air supply providing pressurisation must be maintained for the duration of a fire, fire dampers cannot be used in the ductwork to prevent spread of fire. Any ductwork penetrating fire resisting barriers must be capable of providing the same period of fire resistance.

Good practice in such systems requires:

- *Holes in compartment walls and floors*: All builders' work openings through the compartment walls and floors surrounding the pressurised space (e.g. penetrations for building services) must be made good and sealed.
- *Builders' shafts*: If constructed of brick or blockwork, the inside surfaces of shafts used as part of the system should have a smooth rendered finish to ensure low resistance to airflow and provide a good seal against leakage. The shafts must be pressure tested and be proven to have a leakage factor of less than 10%.
- *Correctly-sized shafts and ducts*: Since most systems use a very basic shaft layout with simple spigot connections to discharge grilles, it is important to size the shafts and ducts for relatively low air velocity to ensure that correct air distribution is achieved at each grille.
- *Ductwork arrangements*: Good working practice must be employed in the layout of the ductwork system. The system must be designed for correct

operation of the pressurisation system, not simply to fit the building constraints.

— *Position of air intake*: If at roof level, the intake should be positioned so that it is unlikely to be affected by smoke and should be lower than any shaft or duct which may discharge smoke in the event of a fire. Changes to plant layout during construction should not compromise the air intake position.

— *Position of discharge*: For buildings over three stories in height there should be a discharge grille for every three floors.

Hazardous areas

There are other areas within the building where the Building Control Officer could state a requirement for fire resisting ductwork, e.g. areas of high fire risk, boiler houses, plant rooms, transformer rooms.

3.3.12.3 Methods of fire protection of ductwork

There are three methods of fire protection, related to ductwork systems as given in BS 5588 Part 9[11]. These are described in Appendix 3.A4.

Fire resistance and DW/144

It should be noted that ductwork constructed to HVCA specification DW/144[4] has no tested fire resistance. General purpose ventilation/air conditioning ductwork and its ancillary items do not have a fire rating and cannot be either utilised in, or converted into, a fire rated ductwork system unless the construction materials of the whole system (including supports and penetration seals) are proven by test and assessment in accordance with BS 476: Part 24[15].

In the case where galvanised sheet steel ductwork is clad by the application of protective materials, the ductwork construction must be type tested and comply with the protective material manufacturers recommendations, e.g. gauge of ductwork, frequency of stiffeners and non-use of low melting point fasteners or rivets. Sealants, gaskets and flexible joints should be as tested and certified in accordance with BS 476: Part 24, and comply with the manufacturers' recommendations.

Methods of fire protection for galvanised steel ductwork, as described in DW/144 are given in Appendix 3.A4.

Design considerations

Where ducting penetrates a fire wall or barrier, it is usual to install a fusible link fire damper which has the same fire rating as the wall itself. An alternative in some circumstances is to use fire rated ducting provided this does not link two different fire zones. For example, it is not permitted to install fire dampers in kitchen extract ducting and, once the ducting has left the kitchen area, it will have to be fire rated up to the point of discharge from the building. No openings into the duct will be permitted nor connections to other areas, not even another kitchen.

In instances where ducting links an escape route to an adjacent area, a fusible link fire damper will not be sufficient. There will be the possibility that 'cool' smoke will fail to melt the fusible link and thereby enter the escape route and render it unusable. In these instances an additional mechanism will be required that will close the damper on a signal from the building fire detection system. The dampers may be re-opened manually or mechanically. Where the damper is not within easy reach, or where there are a significant number of them, motors will be a better, but more costly, option. In planning the design, adequate space for the installation and maintenance of these items must be allowed.

It is usual to route ducting along corridors with branches into the treated area as this has advantages from the point of view of maintenance access, potentially deeper ceiling void, proximity to risers etc. However, where there is a need for a large number of dampers that are released by the fire alarm system, the designer may consider it better to run the ductwork through the treated area in order to reduce the complication and cost of numerous dampers on several branch ducts.

Fire rating

Where ductwork is required to be fire rated, it is specified according to stability, integrity and insulation. Stability is the ability of a duct to stay in place for the specified period of time when exposed to a fire. Ductwork supports must match the stability of the ductwork. This can be achieved by oversizing them or by applying a protective covering. Integrity is the ability of the duct to prevent the passage of fire either into or out of the duct. Insulation is usually called for if the Building Control Officer believes that a duct carrying hot smoke may become sufficiently hot to compromise an escape route.

Fire rated ductwork can be either single or double skin. Double skin ducting is used to encase insulation where this is required, though the more usual alternative is to add insulation to a fire rated duct. It is important that adequate space is allowed if a duct is to be insulated. Site modifications to fire rated ducting are much more difficult than to normal ducting as the duct and fittings are manufactured off-site and site changes may well compromise the rating. Any holes needed for pitot tube measuring instruments need to be cut at the manufacturing stage as site drilling is not allowed.

3.3.13 Supports and fixings

3.3.13.1 General

Supports are an essential part of the ductwork system and their supply and installation are normally the responsibility of the ductwork contractor. The choice between available methods of fixing will depend on the type of building structure and on any limitations imposed by the structural design. Unless the designer has specified the requirements in detail, the load to be carried will be understood to be limited to the ductwork and its associated thermal and/or acoustic insulation. However, where the duct is large enough to allow human access for cleaning, the duct and its supports should be sufficiently strong to withstand the additional load and the type and location of access components should allow the person carrying out the cleaning to enter and exit the duct. The range of supports available includes an increasing range of proprietary types. Figure 3.9 (page 3-25) illustrates various types of bearers and hangers[4].

Floor supports and supports for ductwork external to the building have been excluded, as these are individually designed to suit the circumstances, and also may be required to meet local authority standards.

With a proprietary device, unless the designer has specified the requirements in detail, it will be the responsibility of the ductwork installer to ensure that it meets the requirements, with a sufficient margin of overload, and that it is installed in accordance with the manufacturers' recommendations.

3.3.13.2 Fixing to building structure

The fixing to the building structure should be of a strength and durability compatible with those of the ductwork support attached to it. A fixing to concrete or brickwork must be made in such a way that it cannot loosen or pull out through normal stressing or through normal changes in the building structure.

3.3.13.3 Horizontal ductwork

The hanger is normally mild steel plain rod or studding or flat strap, pre-treated by hot-dip galvanising, sherardising, electro-deposited zinc plating or by other acceptable anti-corrosion treatment. Other materials, such as multi-stranded wire, may also be acceptable. Provided the integrity of the ductwork is maintained, hangers may be attached to the corners of either the flanges or stiffeners, as an alternative to the use of a bottom bearer. Details of the construction of supports are given in DW/144[4].

3.3.13.4 Vertical ducts

The design of supports for vertical ducts is dictated by site conditions and they are often located to coincide with the individual floor slabs. The designer must specify the particular requirements if the spacing exceeds four metres. Vertical ducts should be supported from the stiffening angle or the angle frame, or by separate supporting angles fixed to the duct.

A typical method of supporting vertical rectangular and circular ducts is shown in Figure 3.10. The same methods are applicable to flat oval ducts.

The support bearer, which, depending on duct/structural opening size, could be either channel or angle section, may be utilised in any of the following arrangements:

- Fixed directly to duct skin with sealed fixings (flat face only of either rectangular or flat oval ductwork).
- Supporting the underside of a flat bar clip in halves (circular or flat oval ductwork).
- Supporting the underside of either the stiffening frame or the flanged joint of any duct section.
- Supporting either a stiffening frame or a flanged joint below using drop rods/studs.

3.3.13.5 Insulated ducts with vapour sealing

Vapour sealing may be required where the temperature of the air within the duct can fall low enough to promote condensation on the exterior surface of the duct. This can cause moisture penetration through the thermal insulation. In this case, the most important requirement is to limit penetration of the seal by the support. The extent of any vapour sealing of ductwork thermal insulation, and the method to be used, must be clearly specified in advance by the designer.

3.3.13.6 Heat transfer

It is not normally necessary to make special arrangements for the limitation of heat transfer via the duct supports. However, there may be special cases where the temperature difference justifies a heat barrier to conserve heat or to prevent condensation. Such requirements must be specified by the designer.

3.3.13.7 Fire rated ductwork

Ductwork supports illustrated in DW/144[4] cannot be used on fire rated ductwork systems. Oversizing can be an acceptable method of achieving fire rating of supports.

3.3.14 Overseas work

Ductwork manufactured in accordance with HVCA specification DW/144[4] should meet most requirements for construction and air tightness for overseas work. Some countries have their own standards such as the

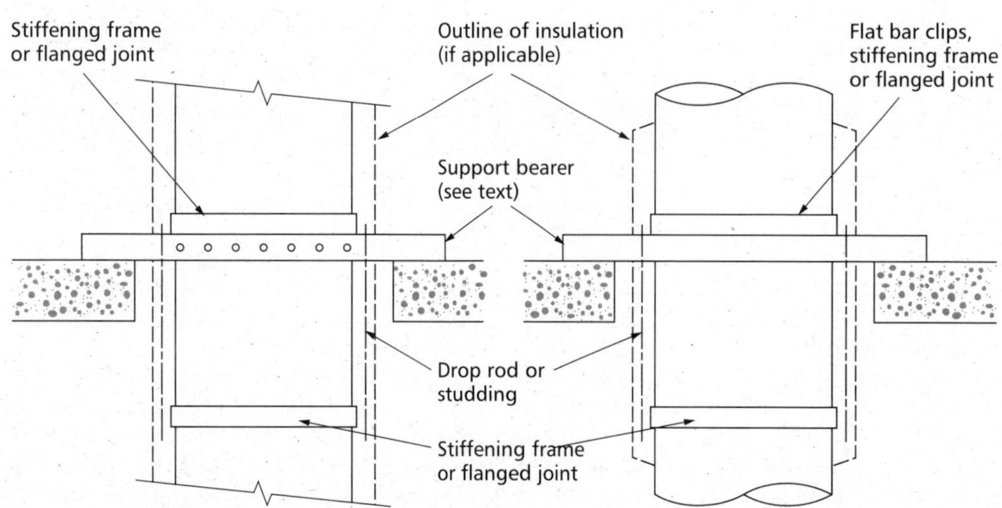

Figure 3.10 Vertical duct supports; *(a)* rectangular ducts, *(b)* circular ducts (reproduced from HVCA specification DW/144[2] by permission of the Heating and Ventilating Contractors' Association)

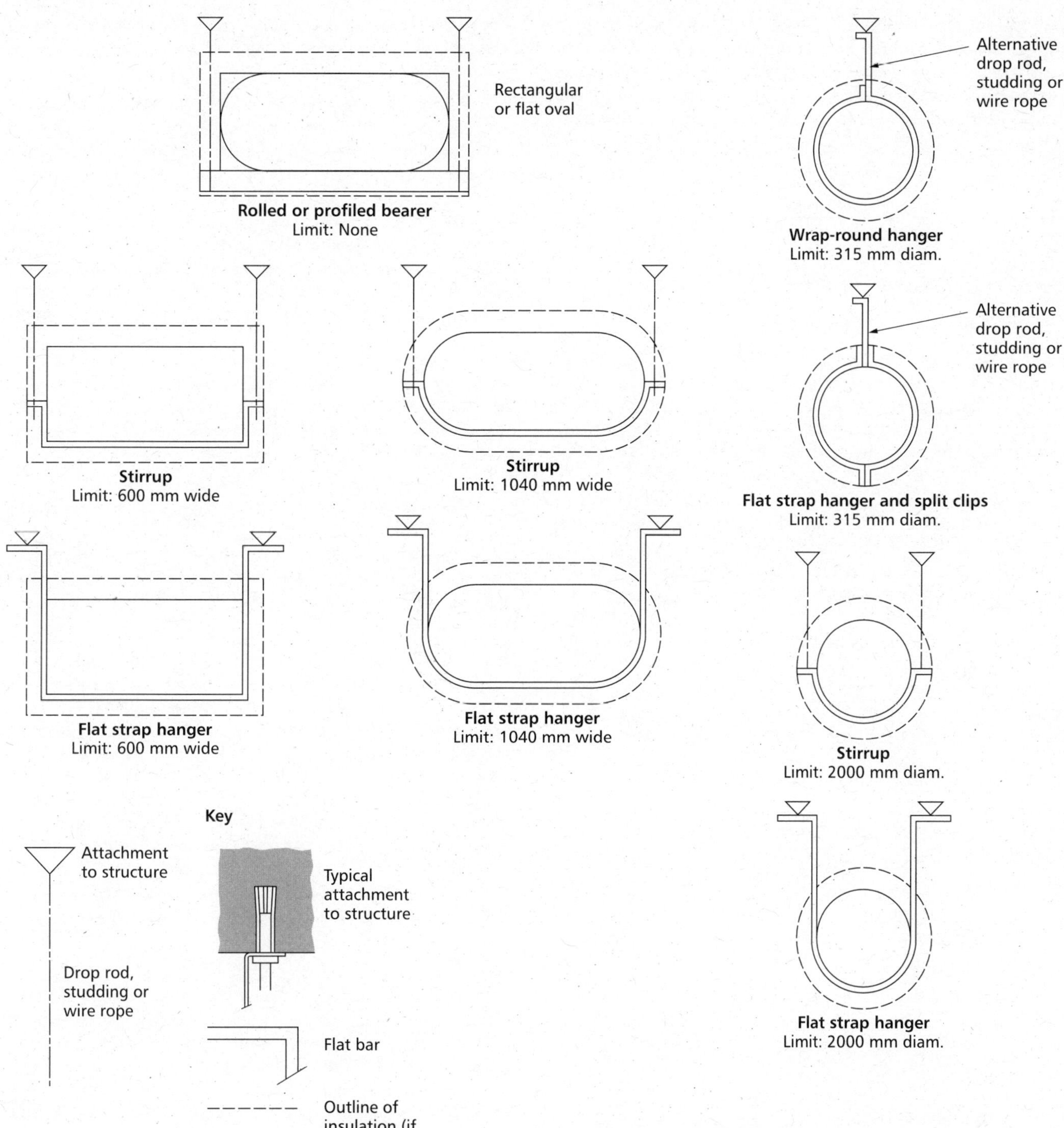

Figure 3.9 Arrangements of bearers and hangers (reproduced from HVCA specification DW/144[4] by permission of the Heating and Ventilating Contractors' Association)

SMACNA[27, 31–33] in the USA, which may be used by other countries in preference to DW/144. Whichever standards are adopted, the designer should confirm that the installation will be adequately supervised.

At an early stage it should be decided whether it is appropriate to manufacture ductwork on site or to transport it from the UK as partly constructed ductwork and finish fabrication on site. Transport charges are based on the 'shipping tonne' or one cubic metre. Complete lengths of ductwork occupying one cubic metre are comprised almost entirely of fresh air, but will still attract freight charges based on the shipping tonne. It is not always practicable to fit smaller ductwork inside larger ductwork without the risk of some damage, although it may be appropriate for circular and flat oval spirally-wound ductwork.

The designer should thoroughly check the local requirements and also availability of materials and services which could affect the construction and installation of ductwork systems. Examples of such conditions are sandstorms, monsoons, termites and other infestation. Where contract sites are close to coastal areas, particularly in the Middle East, special consideration must be given to the selection of suitable materials and to the application of suitable corrosion protection finishes for exposed ductwork. This may also apply to duct ancillary equipment such as louvres, damper linkages etc.

Greater use of bendable and flexible ducting than is normal in the UK may need to be considered, in order to offset the risk of inaccurate setting out of building structures, unforeseen obstacles etc., which could otherwise lead to lengthy delays. It is important that the standard of workmanship should be good, as any subsequent rectification may prove very expensive. The satisfactory installation of ductwork depends on effective channels of communication and good supervision wherever it is erected.

3.4 System selection

3.4.1 Introduction

In most ductwork installations, the constraints imposed by the building structure, and the location of fans, plant items and terminals will lead to an overall ductwork layout that is not ideal. The system selection should be based on the most economical and cost-effective solution, taking account of the whole life cost of the installation.

The full range of ductwork forms and materials should be considered when selecting the components for the particular system. The designer should be prepared to use the full range of materials and fittings available and not feel constrained by particular methods or materials.

The potential impact of noise on the environment served by the ductwork, and restrictions applied by any requirements for fire protection will also have a direct effect on system selection.

3.4.2 Duct sizing criteria

The criteria to be used when designing a ductwork installation include:

- system pressurem
- velocity
- noise levels
- energy
- specific fan power
- ductwork distribution
- terminal devices
- capital cost
- operating, maintenance, cleaning and replacement costs.

Recommended duct sizes are given in Appendix 3.A1 for rectangular, circular and flat oval duct. Rectangular ducting is available in any reasonable size since it is normally manufactured to order.

The smaller the ductwork, the greater the fan power required and hence the higher the energy consumption. Increasing the duct size can have a large effect on decreasing fan power since the smaller friction drops of the basic circuit will require smaller friction drops through control dampers for the same value of control authority, thus leading to a further saving. The optimum size from the point of view of life cycle costing must consider the length of the system, the capital cost, the mean pressure drop, the running time at full and partial load, the efficiency of the fan and motor combination, anticipated electrical tariffs and costs of cleaning and maintenance of the ductwork system.

Larger ductwork requires more space and has a greater first cost, but it has the advantage of lower noise generation and, more importantly, a lower pressure drop. This results in lower fan power and energy costs. Past experience may not necessarily be a guide now that designers and clients are more energy conscious. Building Regulations Approved Document L[1] introduced a limiting value of 'specific fan power', i.e. the electrical fan power per unit volume flow ($W \cdot s \cdot litre^{-1}$). Even where this new criterion does not result in larger duct sizes, any duct run requiring damper control should require special consideration. Taking a control authority of 0.5 as an example, the basic damper pressure drop (when fully open) would need to be equal to that of the rest of that ductwork circuit. Thus a halving of the ductwork resistance would result in the choice of a control damper of half the resistance.

The basic equations for calculating pressure losses in ductwork and ductwork fittings, along with pressure loss factors, are given in Guide C[2], section 4. Relevant figures and tables have been included in this Guide. A worked example is provided in this Guide as Appendix 3.A5.

In a complex ductwork system, the duct sizes should be chosen in such a way that each circuit is inherently balanced. There is little point in choosing a duct of large size for a branch which will then require a balancing diameter to produce a large pressure drop. Where there is a mixture of short and long branches there is unlikely to be sufficient flexibility in the choice of sizes to give equal pressure drops to provide full equalisation without exceeding the maximum velocity on the short runs (so risking noise problems). It is better in this case to have somewhat larger ducts on the long runs to reduce their resistance. Better still is a design where the branches are all of approximately the same length.

Even for a small system, it must be remembered that the fan pressure rise required must equal the system pressure drop for the whole air circuit. For a supply-only system, the total pressure drop of the system must include the pressure drop through the extract grille or, if by leakage, the pressure drop through the door gaps and vents. Similarly an extract system pressure drop calculation must include the pressure drop via the inward leakage routes.

For very simple linear systems, the following methods have been cited as a starting point for any design. However the designer should not feel constrained by any of them. The final design constraints to be satisfied are:

- no objectionable noise generation
- no excessive pressure drop
- compliance with Building Regulations[1] concerning specific fan power
- all air routes (circuits) to be in balance at the design stage.

The architect may wish to add another, namely that the size be minimised, but this might be incompatible with the above constraints.

3.4.3 Principles of design

3.4.3.1 General

Duct sizing and pressure loss calculations are normally carried out as a combined exercise to quantify the ductwork dimensions and provide data for specifying the fan duty. The duct sizing process and pressure loss calculations require the specification of system requirements, including:

- system type, i.e. low, medium, high pressure or industrial
- volume flow rates in all parts of the ductwork
- positions of fans, other plant items, supply and extract terminals
- special operating requirements, e.g. minimum conveying velocities in extract systems
- ductwork type, i.e. circular, rectangular, flat oval
- layout of the duct runs, including fittings, dampers and plant items
- duct material.

The purpose of duct sizing is to determine the cross-sectional dimensions of the various parts of the duct system, taking into account that the system, fans and other plant items should be:

- economical in installed and operating costs
- compatible with the space limitations imposed by the structure and other services
- sufficiently quiet in operation
- easily regulated after installation to achieve the design airflow at each terminal.

In practice, duct sizing seeks to obtain an economical and practical solution to these objectives by either simplified manual procedures or computer programs. The computer programs can vary in complexity from computerisation of manual procedures to overall design including optimisation, damper settings and noise assessment.

Before commencing duct sizing, a schematic of the air distribution system must be prepared. This should indicate the airflow directions and contain the following information:

(a) system identification for each section

(b) air volume flow rates in each section

(c) the length of all straight sections

(d) descriptions of fittings, dampers, plant items and terminals.

Items *(a)* and *(b)* are not needed specifically for sizing purposes but are needed to determine the system pressure loss and hence the fan duty specification.

An example schematic is shown in Figure 3.11.

3.4.3.2 Manual duct sizing methods

Simple design methods include the following:

- velocity method
- constant pressure drop (or equal friction loss) method
- static regain method.

The most common method is based on constant pressure drops with maximum duct velocities as set out in Tables

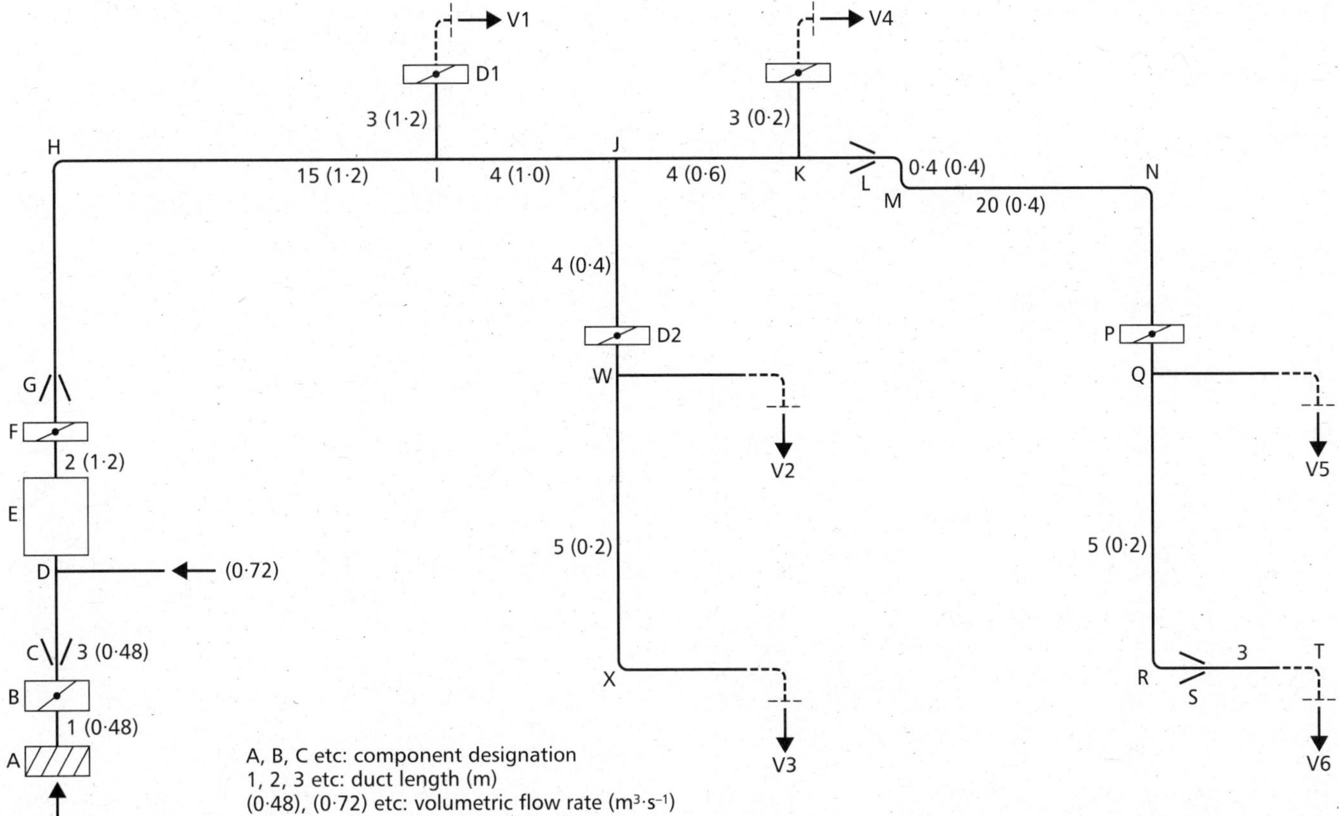

Figure 3.11 Example schematic of ductwork layout, showing lengths (m) and flow rates ($m^3 \cdot s^{-1}$) (see Appendix 3.A6 for calculation procedure)

3.2 and 3.3 for low, medium and high pressure systems. These methods are simple procedures which use ductwork data charts to determine duct dimensions. The overall cost-effectiveness, ease of system regulation and noise can be taken into account by imposing limits on some of the design parameters. It is recommended that the calculated duct size is rounded to the nearest recommended duct size (see Appendix 3.A1) before the system resistance calculation is carried out. A brief description of these methods is given below.

Velocity method

This method is based on the selection of duct velocities by the designer using limiting noise generation and/or pressure drop. In a typical system the velocity at the fan connection is chosen, and this is progressively reduced in the duct run from the fan to the terminals. Tables 3.2 and 3.3 give some guidance on suitable maximum air velocities. In practice, this is only used on simple layouts or sections of systems, as the procedure depends on experienced but subjective judgements. It is difficult to produce a coherent selection of sizes for a complex layout on this basis. In industrial systems where minimum transport velocities are required this method may be employed more frequently.

Constant pressure drop (equal friction loss) method

The basis for this method is to select a constant pressure loss per unit length for the duct runs and then to size the ducts at this rate, using Figure 3.12. The method is used for the sizing of very simple low pressure supply and extract systems, some medium pressure systems and also for variable air volume (VAV) systems. For low pressure systems, typical values used for the constant pressure loss rate are in the range 0.8–1.2 Pa·m^{-1} with duct velocities not exceeding 10 m·s^{-1}. At large volume flow rates in low pressure systems the 10 m·s^{-1} duct velocity limit should override the constant pressure loss rate chosen, leading to somewhat lower pressure loss rates in the large ducts.

The sizing process involves:

(*a*) the selection and use of a vertical constant pressure loss line on Figure 3.12, appropriate to the design requirement

(b) reading-off the circular duct diameter for the actual volume flow rate

(*c*) if a rectangular or flat oval duct is required, taking the dimensions from Tables 3.A1.1 or 3.A1.2 (see Appendix 3.A1), as appropriate, for the equivalent circular diameter.

The friction loss method gives a reducing velocity from the fan to the terminals but does not ensure that the branch flow rates are inherently balanced. Provision for site regulation needs to be included in the design. Adopting different pressure loss rates for the individual branches of a system can be used to produce a more nearly equal resistance to each duct run and so assist site commissioning. This modification can be introduced during the pressure loss calculation.

Initially, all parts of the system should be sized to the same pressure loss rate and the adjustments to individual branch sizes only carried out after the pressure losses in the initial system design have been computed. These adjustments are most quickly and conveniently carried out by computer.

Static regain method

When the velocity in a duct is reduced without excessive losses occurring, the static pressure increases. In high pressure systems, this increase can be significant and is the basis for the static regain duct-sizing method. The principle is to size ducts between branch take-offs so that the recovery in static pressure after one branch take-off due to reduction in velocity is equal to the static pressure loss due to friction and fittings in the subsequent duct run. The method seeks to equalise the static pressures at the branch take-offs, and where these take-offs serve high pressure terminals an inherently balanced system can be achieved.

The static regain method is used primarily for those parts of a high pressure system where the initial duct velocity pressure is sufficient to give static pressure regain without unnecessarily low duct velocities at the end of the run. In practice, only the duct mains serving multiple terminal branches are sized by this method, while the smaller branches to terminals are sized by the equal friction method (see *Constant pressure drop method* above) to minimise their size and cost. High pressure terminals on the same system normally all have roughly the same pressure loss. If this value is high compared to the branch duct pressure loss, then variations in the latter between different branches arising from the use of the equal friction sizing method will not significantly unbalance the system. The static regain method uses duct static pressure losses rather than total pressure losses in the sizing procedure. For the application of the method it also needs these static pressure losses to be expressed in terms of lengths of straight duct which have the same loss.

The static regain is due to the drop in velocity pressure. However it must be emphasised that there is still a drop in total pressure Δp_t, due to friction.

For the branch shown in Figure 3.13, subscript 'c' denotes 'combined' flow, subscript 'b' denotes 'branch' flow and subscript 's' denotes 'straight' flow.

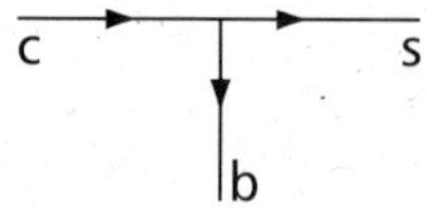

Figure 3.13 Schematic of duct branch

Pressure drop across the branch is given by:

$$\Delta p_t = p_{tc} - p_{ts} = \zeta_{c-s}\ {}^1\!/_2\ \rho\ c_c^{\,2} \qquad (3.14)$$

where Δp_t is the loss of total pressure across the branch (Pa), p_{tc} is the total pressure on the upstream side of the branch (Pa), p_{ts} is the total pressure on the downstream side of the branch (Pa), ζ_{c-s} is the pressure loss factor for the branch, ρ is the density of air (kg·m^{-3}) and c_c is the air velocity on the upstream side of the branch (m·s^{-1}).

Static regain is given by:

$$p_s - p_c = {}^1\!/_2\ \rho\ (c_c^{\,2} - c_s^{\,2}) \qquad (3.15)$$

The air velocities are given by:

$$c_c = q_c / A_c \qquad (3.16)$$

$$c_s = q_s / A_s \qquad (3.17)$$

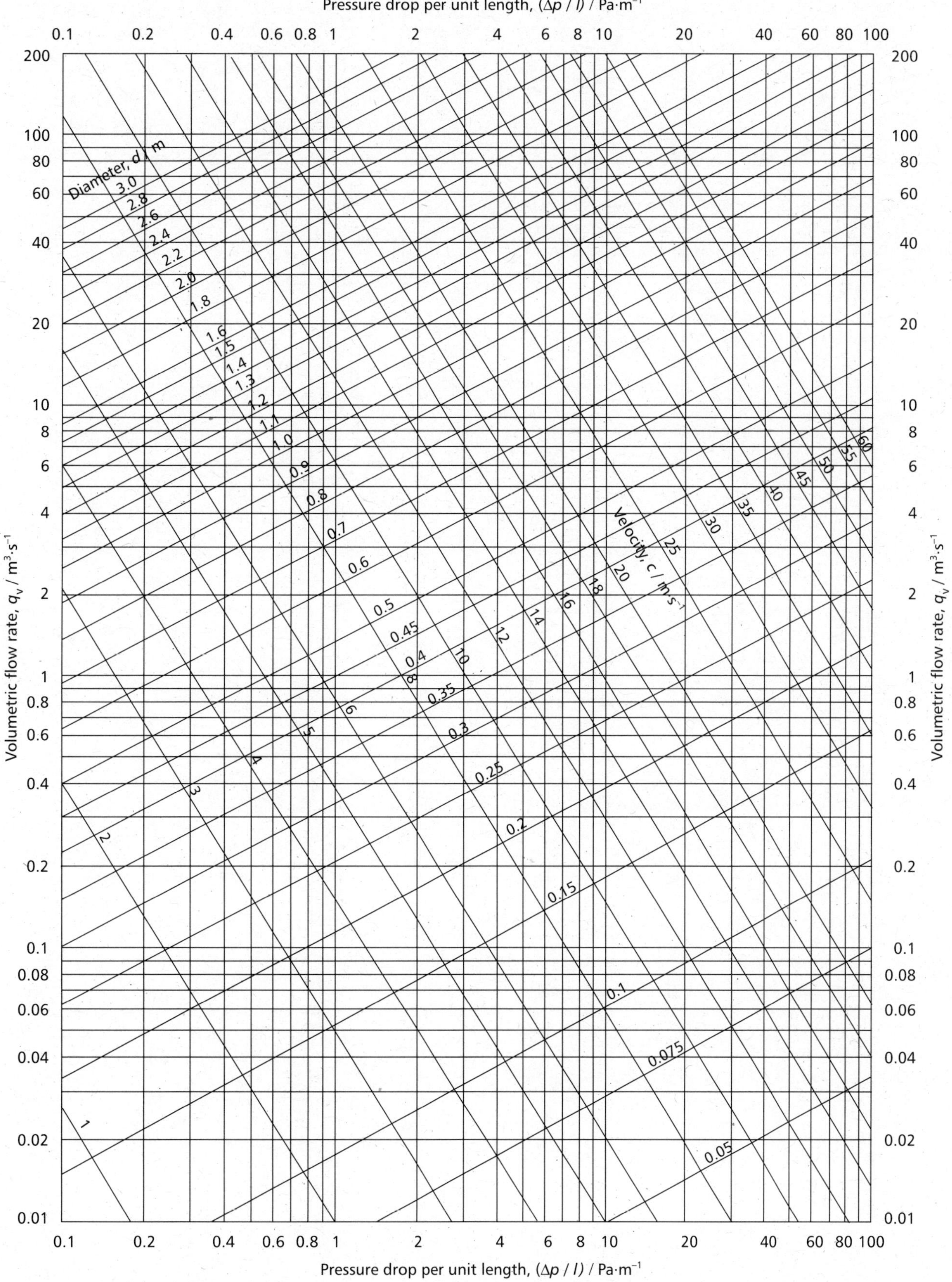

Figure 3.12 Pressure drop for air in galvanised circular ducts ($\rho = 1.2$ kg·m^{-3}; $T = 293$ K)

where q_c and q_s are the flow rates on the upstream and downstream sides of the branch, respectively (kg·s^{-1}), A_c and A_s are the cross-sectional areas of the inlet to and outlet (straight flow) from the branch, respectively (m^2).

(In general, $A_c = A_s$, but the cross-sectional area could increase between inlet and outlet if required.)

It must be emphasised that the fan must produce a rise in *total pressure* equal to the drop in *total pressure* of the ductwork system. The deliberate use of 'static regain' does not directly influence this, except that the downstream duct sizes are larger than might otherwise have been the case.

The value of air pressure in the duct ('static pressure', p) is only of consequence in duct air leakage calculations, and for ensuring approximately equal pressures behind any air outlets immediately on the duct itself.

Sizing ductwork by the static regain method is normally carried out using a computer program.

Choice of duct sizing method

Use of the static regain method on low and medium pressure systems is limited, and its worth depends on the equivalent length of the index run; the shorter the index run, the more favourable the case for the static regain method. This is because in a low pressure system, the loss of velocity pressure is small and in a large installation its recovery is not significant in comparison with the friction loss in the system.

The equal friction loss method is easier to use in design and results in smaller duct sizes. Ducts sized using this method can cost up to 8% less than those sized by the static regain method. However, the savings will be at least partly offset by higher commissioning costs, especially where the index run is relatively short but with numerous branches and outlets. This reduction in duct size may not be an option under Building Regulations Approved Document L[(1)] which limits specific fan power to 2 $W \cdot s \cdot l^{-1}$.

Similar considerations apply for high pressure systems but, because of the higher potential loss of velocity pressure and the greater need to equalise static pressures at terminals (to avoid generation of noise at terminal dampers), there will be more occasions when the static regain method is worthwhile. The additional cost of ductwork will probably be less than 1%.

3.4.3.3 Calculation of system pressure loss

The pressure loss in a ductwork system is made up of the pressure losses at plant items and terminal equipment, the friction loss in the straight ducts plus the losses due to duct fittings.

The losses due to both straight duct and fittings are directly related to the duct sizes, so that the determination of the system pressure loss follows the duct sizing process. The calculation as described, using data given in section 4.10 of CIBSE Guide C[(2)], gives the 'total pressure' loss and this can be used to assess the required fan total pressure for the system. The total pressure loss of plant items and fittings is related to the static pressure loss as follows:

$$\Delta p_t = \Delta p + p_{vi} - p_{vo} \tag{3.18}$$

where Δp_t is the total pressure loss (Pa), Δp is the static pressure loss (Pa), p_{vi} is the inlet velocity pressure (Pa) and p_{vo} is the outlet velocity pressure (Pa).

In the case of plant items and fittings where the inlet and outlet connection areas and flow rates are equal, then $p_{vi} = p_{vo}$ and the total and static pressures are identical.

The advantage of using total pressure losses is that the friction and fitting losses are such that the total pressure always decreases in the direction of airflow so that the losses can simply be added. The total pressure loss of the terminals must be included in the overall total system pressure loss. The required fan total pressure for the system is equal to the system pressure loss but it is prudent to allow a margin on the calculated total pressure loss to take account of:

— differences between the design concept and the actual installation

— the effect of system leakage on the fan duty.

Suitable air leakage margins are given in Table 3.11.

The first step in the manual calculation of the total pressure loss in a system is to identify the 'index' duct run. This is the duct run that has the greatest total pressure loss. Normally the index run will be that which links the fan and the most distant terminal. However, this is not automatically true because it is possible for shorter runs to have higher pressure losses if they contain plant items, high pressure loss terminals or a high proportion of duct fittings. Some judgement is necessary when identifying the index run.

The second step is to compute the index run total pressure loss. This calculation should (for a supply system) typically include pressure losses at the following items:

— *entry*: intake opening, louvres, bird screens

— *suction duct*: straight duct sections, duct fittings, control and fire dampers, mixing chambers

— *plant*: filters (dirty condition), heaters, cooling coils, humidifiers, eliminators, attenuators

— *fan*: inlet vanes, inlet duct connection, outlet duct connection, flexible connections

— *supply duct*: straight duct sections, attenuators, duct fittings, balancing and fire dampers, zone plant items, control boxes, flexible ducting, terminals.

Extract systems will probably include many of the same items, but in a different order. Where the connections to equipment are different in size, or where multiple connections occur, the manufacturer's pressure loss data should be checked to ensure that they are the total pressure losses.

3.4.4 Ductwork sizing process

Duct sizing is an iterative process following identification of the duct runs. It requires determining the air flow requirements in the main ducts and subsidiary branches to assess the size of each. These then need to be checked against the original design parameters. A balance needs to be obtained between the duct sizes required to achieve the design outputs and the space allocated for the ductwork system. Within an overall ductwork installation, there may be different ductwork standards, resulting in a mixture of high, medium and low pressure systems. Proper sealing of ductwork will mean reduced air leakage and therefore reduced ductwork size.

Materials, equipment, fittings and construction methods need to be chosen with respect to whole life costs, not just the initial or installation cost. It can be beneficial and cost effective to standardise the types and sizes of the ducts and fittings used in the installation.

The areas served by the risers are likely to dictate the size of the horizontal branches. The depth of horizontal ductwork will also have a significant influence on the depth of false ceilings or floors and the overall floor-to-floor height.

The depth of the horizontal element is a function of the number of the vertical risers:

— maximum number of, or space in, vertical risers equates to the minimum horizontal element depth

— minimum number of, or space in, vertical risers equates to the maximum horizontal element depth.

It is essential that ductwork is sized correctly for air velocity, particularly to avoid noise. Where noise is likely to be a problem, providing two smaller ducts in parallel (rather than a single large duct) will reduce the air velocity and hence the noise. However, energy can be wasted by reducing the duct size since this will result in increased fan power. A worked example of the duct sizing process is provided in Appendix 3.A6.

3.4.5 Computer-based sizing methods

Computer programs have been produced which cover one or more of the following design aspects:

— duct sizing

— pressure losses in ductwork systems

— total fan pressure

— duct heat losses or gains and terminal temperatures

— acoustic analysis, with attenuation calculations from fan to terminals

— leakage analysis.

The computer-based sizing methods use tabulated data and equations from CIBSE Guide[(2)], the 2001 edition of which provides extended and updated data for ductwork sizing. Users of computer-based sizing methods are advised to ensure that the reference data and equations used by the computer program are based on the 2001 edition of CIBSE Guide C.

3.4.6 Ductwork connections

3.4.6.1 Fan connections

The fan performance figures given by manufacturers in their catalogue data are based on tests carried out under ideal conditions, which include long uniform ducts on the fan inlet/outlet. These standard test conditions are unlikely to occur in practice. An objective of good ductwork design should therefore be to ensure that, as far as practicable, the fan performance will not be de-rated by the system. Ensuring that the fan inlet flow conditions comprise uniform axial flow velocities with low levels of turbulence can help to achieve this.

Where the outlet duct is larger than the fan discharge connections, there should be a gradual transition as illustrated in Figure 3.14 with a following section of straight duct having a length equivalent to three duct diameters. Figure 3.14 also gives examples of good and bad centrifugal fan outlet connections which apply equally to axial flow fans.

The design of the fan inlet connection must be carefully considered to avoid swirl in the air stream. When the air spins in the same direction as the impeller, the performance and power consumption of the fan are reduced. When the air spins in the opposite direction to the impeller, the power consumption and noise will increase with hardly any pressure increase. Air stream swirl is usually induced by large variations across the fan inlet eye caused by the air passing round a tight bend immediately before the eye. The two forms of connection to centrifugal fans likely to cause swirl are shown in Figure 3.15.

For any condition in which a centrifugal fan is located within a free inlet the clear distance between the suction opening and the nearest wall should not be less than the diameter of the inlet. If two fans with free inlets are positioned within the same chamber their adjacent suction openings should be at least 1.5 diameters apart. Examples of good and bad practice in duct inlet connections to centrifugal fans are shown in Figure 3.16 and to axial fans in Figure 3.17.

3.4.6.2 Plant connections

Airflow across air treatment components such as filters, heat exchangers and humidifiers will be influenced by the pattern of the approaching airstream and, if unsatisfactory conditions are created, the performance of the components will be reduced. Examples of good and bad practice are shown in Figure 3.18.

3.4.6.3 Air inlets

The location of the air inlet is an important part of the design process. It should be located to avoid possible contamination from external sources and be sufficiently remote from the exhaust to avoid recirculation of vitiated air. Should there be a risk of pollution at the air intake reference should be made to CIBSE TM21: *Minimising pollution at air intakes*[(34)].

3.4.6.4 External louvres and cowls

The usual starting point for sizing external louvres is the actual opening in the wall. The size of the structural openings required for external louvres should be large enough to prevent excessive air velocity and pressure loss through the louvre. The preliminary size of the opening can be calculated by dividing the airflow rate by a nominal velocity of 2 $m \cdot s^{-1}$ to give an overall face area for the louvre, and adding an allowance for the framing. The framing allowance will depend on the material used, but an initial allowance of 100 mm all round should suffice.

The final size of opening can be fixed only when details of the louvre and related factors are settled, such as:

— louvre frame or flange

— blade thickness and shape

— bird and security screens

— duct connection requirements.

Recommendations on the clearance which should be provided between a cowl and an external vertical duct opening are illustrated in Figure 3.19 (see also Guide C[(2)], sections 4.10.5.18 to 4.10.5.22). Where adequate clearance cannot be provided, fitting an inverted cone deflector under the cowl can reduce the resistance.

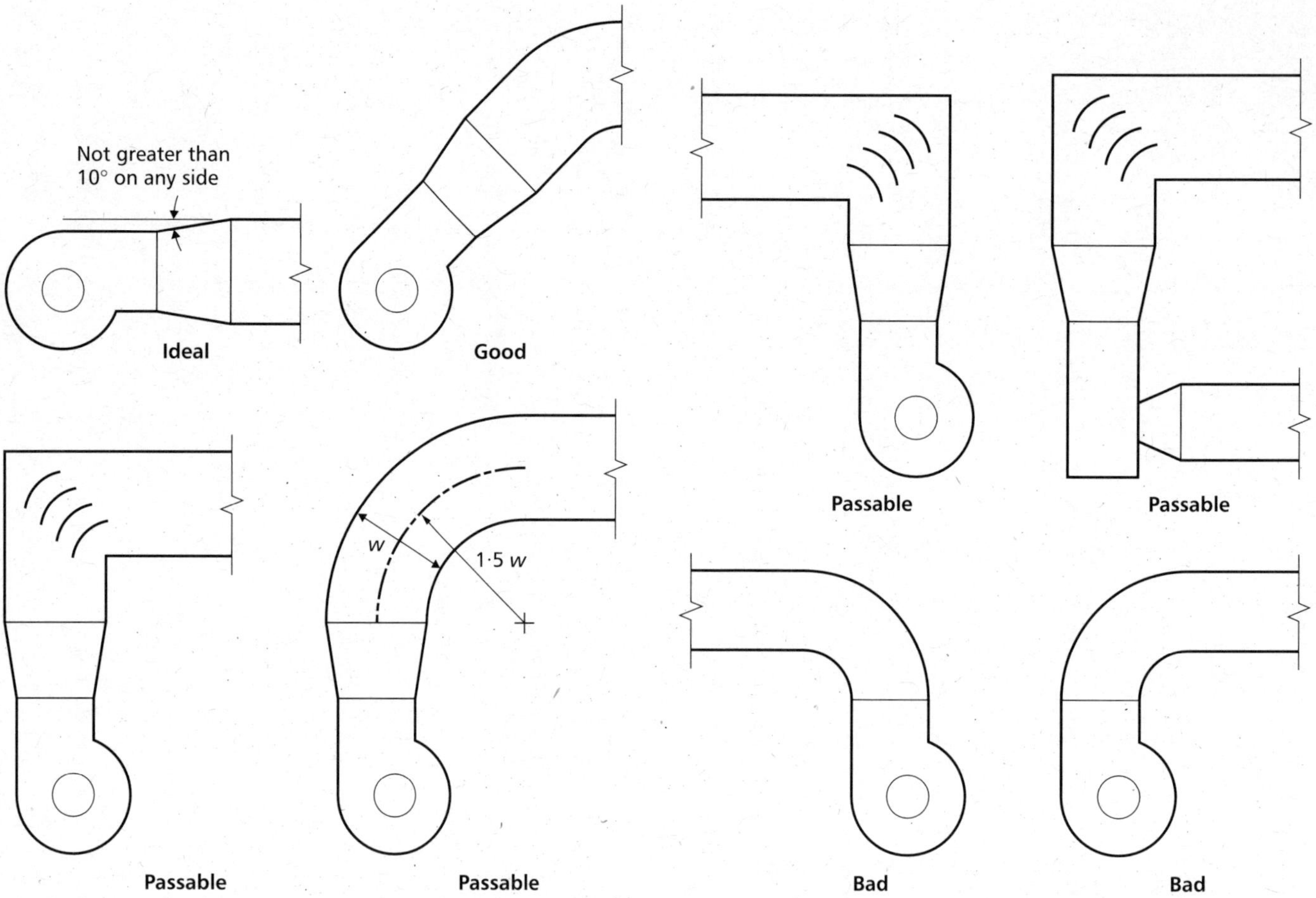

Not greater than 10° on any side

Ideal

Good

Passable

Passable

w

1·5 w

Passable

Passable

Bad

Bad

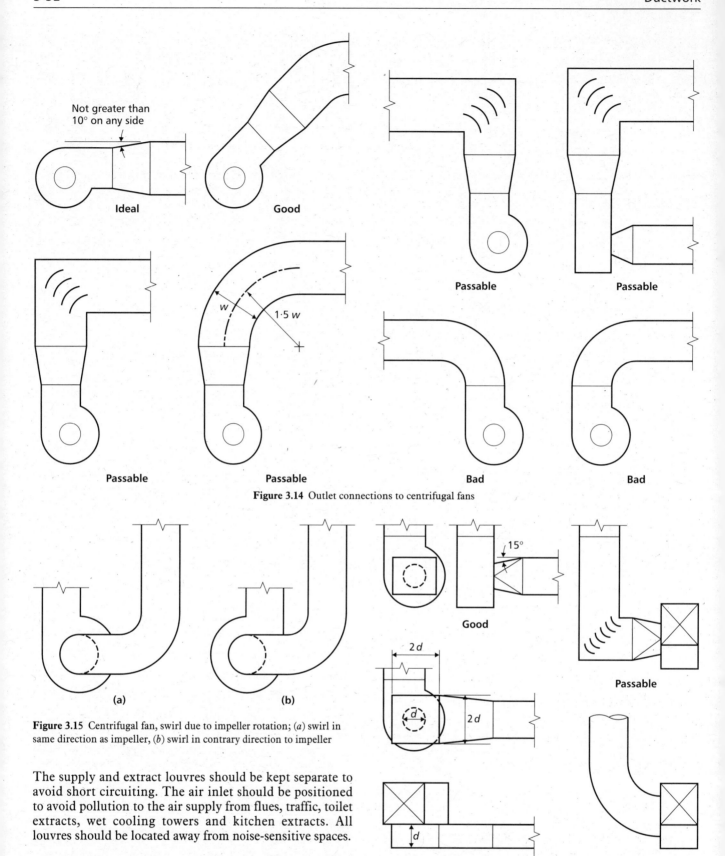

Figure 3.14 Outlet connections to centrifugal fans

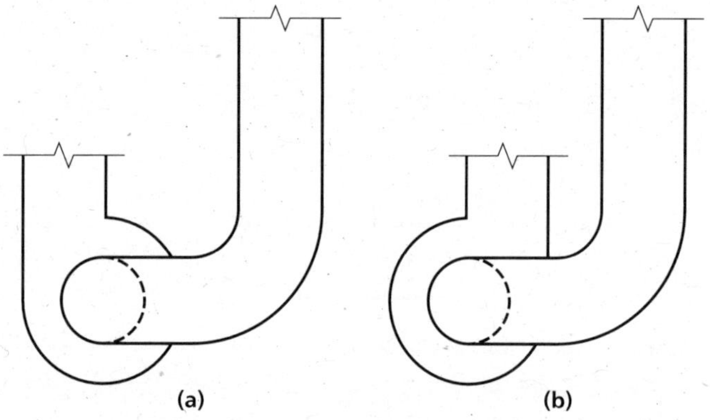

(a)

(b)

Figure 3.15 Centrifugal fan, swirl due to impeller rotation; (*a*) swirl in same direction as impeller, (*b*) swirl in contrary direction to impeller

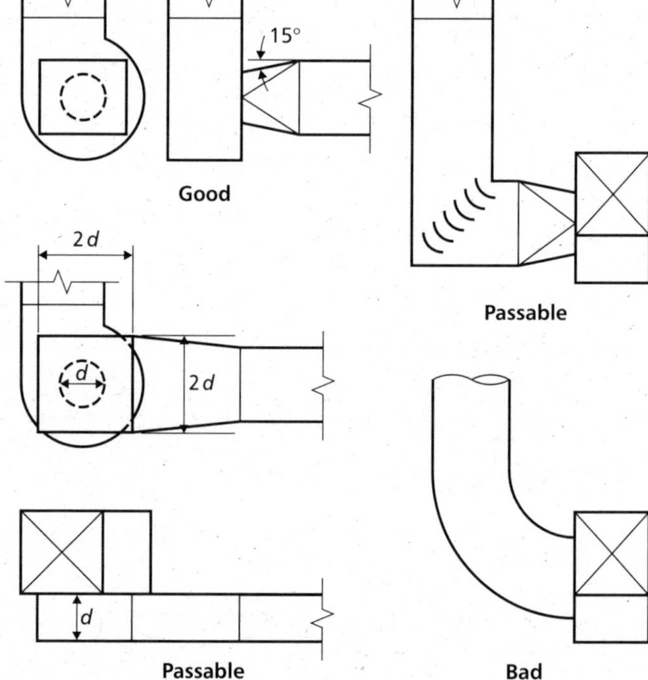

Figure 3.16 Centrifugal fans; inlet connections

The supply and extract louvres should be kept separate to avoid short circuiting. The air inlet should be positioned to avoid pollution to the air supply from flues, traffic, toilet extracts, wet cooling towers and kitchen extracts. All louvres should be located away from noise-sensitive spaces.

The impact on indoor air quality of the siting of fresh air inlets in relation to local sources of pollution, and in relation to the risk of re-admitting exhaust air, are discussed in detail in CIBSE TM 21: *Minimising pollution at air intakes*(34).

Research(35) has identified that there are benefits in introducing air at high level due to reduced load from combustion products such as carbon monoxide and oxides of nitrogen. The study found that ozone concentration increased when air was supplied at high level, but the concentration level would substantially decrease as the ozone passes through points of earthing such as sheet metal (particularly galvanised) ductwork and air handling units.

3.4.6.5 Flexible ducts

Flexible duct connections may be appropriate in the following applications, however their installation needs to be closely monitored since they can be prone to damage:

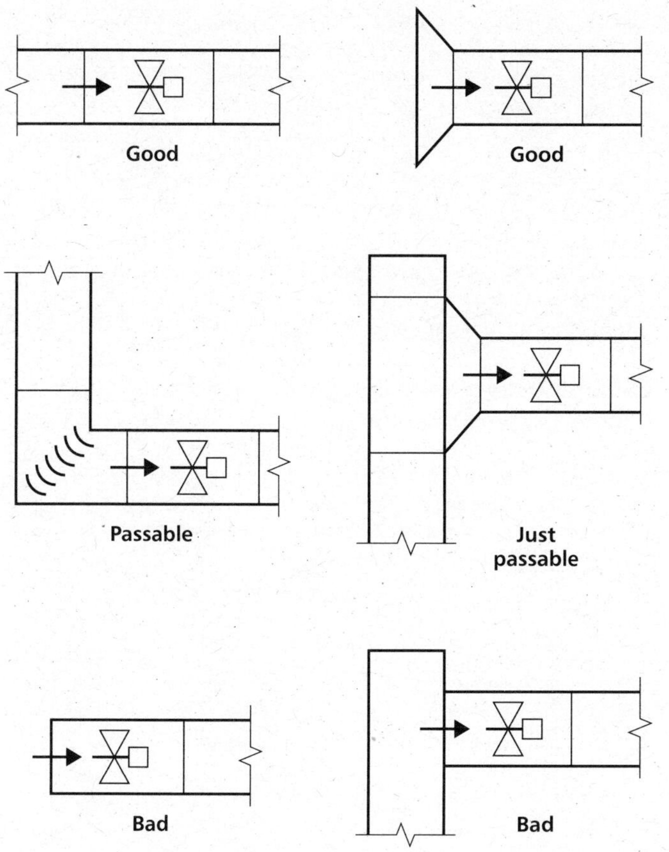

Good
Good
Passable
Just passable
Bad
Bad

Figure 3.17 Axial fans; inlet connections

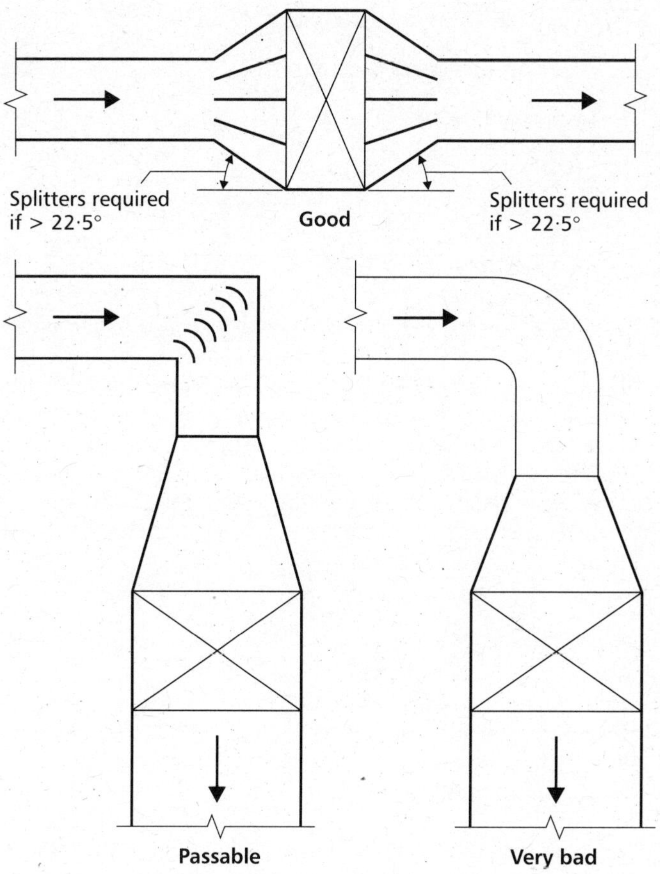

Splitters required if > 22·5°
Good
Splitters required if > 22·5°
Passable
Very bad

Figure 3.18 Plant connections

H
0·25d
d
Bad
0·3d
0·5d
d
Passable
0·75d
d
Good

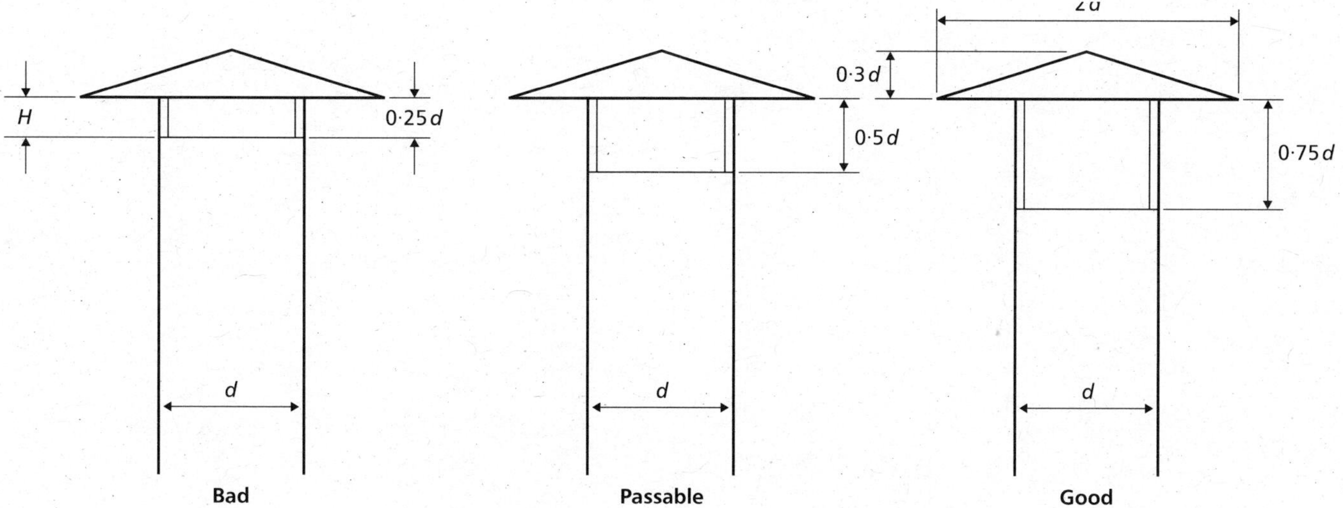

Figure 3.19 Discharge cowls; good and bad design

— terminal units

— fan coil units

— constant volume/variable air volume units

— grilles and diffusers

— plenum boxes

— distribution ducts between the above items.

Flexible ducts can be abused to overcome poor installation, e.g. where grilles do not line up. This can result in poor airflow at the grille and/or excessive noise. The following advice should be noted when using flexible ductwork (particularly metal types):

— lengths should be as short as possible

— flexible ductwork should be almost fully extended.

Flexible ductwork is available in a range of materials including metal, PVC and fabric, both with or without thermal insulation.

The designer should consider the following when selecting a particular type of flexible duct:

— temperature range

— fire rating

— resistance to airflow

— airtightness characteristics
— length restrictions if applicable
— support requirements
— flexibility
— insulation values
— system pressure.

Flexible ducts are also available in twin-wall format where the inner liner is perforated to provide acoustic properties or plain for thermal insulation. Pressure losses from flexible ducts can be high so lengths should be kept to a minimum, consistent with the particular application. Flexible ducts should be fastened at each end using a proprietary band. Care should be taken not to damage the flexible duct and to ensure that the required airtightness of the system is maintained.

Flexible ducts: metal

Flexible ducts made of coated steel, stainless steel or aluminium are normally helically-wound with a lock seam to form a corrugated duct capable of being bent without deforming the circular section. Bending is done by closing the corrugations in the throat and slightly opening the corrugations at the back of the bend. Some re-adjustment is possible but small radius bends cannot be straightened without leaving some distortion of the corrugations. Repeated bending is not recommended. The ducts should be mechanically fastened at each end and particular care taken to ensure that the airtightness of the system is maintained.

Flexible ducts: fabric

Fabric flexible ducts made from various materials including PVC/polyester laminate and aluminium/polyester laminate encapsulating a high tensile steel wire helix; these are a very flexible form of construction.

Flexible ducts: textile

Textile ducts can offer advantages over other forms of ductwork installations. The initial capital cost is usually lower than metal air distribution systems. They have no internal stiffening and, due to their simplicity in construction and installation, they are low in weight. They are also easily removed and washed where cleanliness is important, but it may be necessary to have a spare duct available to allow washing to take place.

Textile ducts are produced from 100% permeable material and use thermal displacement with the air flowing through the entire surface due to the pressure difference. They can offer particular advantages when supplying cooled air, e.g. they are draught-free, there is no condensation on ductwork surfaces and noise levels are very low.

Textile ductwork originated in the food-processing industry, but is now used widely in other process industries, warehouses, retailing, laboratories, sports halls, swimming pools and offices. The materials used are specifically manufactured to provide high fire resistance and to ensure compliance with fire regulations.

Care is needed to avoid material and seams from splitting when the duct is dirty. It may be necessary to ensure that the fan pressure cannot exceed the maximum ductwork design pressure.

Flexible ductwork for making final connections

The use of flexible ductwork to supply diffusers is very convenient. However, such ductwork produces much greater pressure drops than those for the equivalent smooth galvanised steel ductwork.

Flexible ductwork naturally has an equivalent roughness which is appreciably more than that for galvanised steel ductwork, i.e. 1.0–4.6 mm compared to 0.15 mm (see Guide C[2], Table C4.1). This alone causes a much greater pressure drop. Furthermore, if the flexible duct is not fully extended the pressure loss can be even greater. ASHRAE[36] suggests that if extended to only 70% of its fully extended length, the pressure loss can be increased by a factor of four.

Based on a worst case of roughness k = 4.6 mm and extended to only 70% of full length, Table 3.14 has been derived as guidance to give the multiplying factor to be applied to the equivalent rigid circular galvanised duct.

Table 3.14 Correction factors to be applied to the pressure drop of a rigid duct, for flexible duct having a roughness of 4.6 mm and extended to only 70% of full length.

Air velocity, c / m·s^{-1}	Correction factor for stated duct diameter, d / mm		
	100	200	500
2.5	6.7	7.5	8.3
4.5	7.4	8.0	8.7
6.0	7.7	8.2	8.9

Supports for flexible ductwork

Flexible ducts have a higher resistance factor than conventional ductwork and should be supported in such a way that excessive sagging and consequent kinking of the duct is avoided.

Test holes

It is not practicable to make test holes or take test readings in metal or fabric flexible ducts. Where readings are required, the test holes should be made in rigid ductwork.

Flexible joint connections

For details of methods of flexible joint connections, see HVCA specification DW/144[4].

3.4.7 Flow regulation

One of the basic requirements for an effective system is having the necessary dampers in the correct position. The main requirements for siting dampers are as follows:

— There should be a main damper for the air handling unit, preferably following it; an alternative is to use adjustable inlet guide vanes on the fan.

— There should be dampers on all terminals and in all branch and sub-branch ducts; damper positions are shown on a basic schematic drawing, see Figure 3.20.

— Terminals should ideally have dampers in the connecting duct. Where this is not possible, the terminal should have a built-in damper which can be set without disturbing the terminal unit itself. (For example, with some terminal diffusers the cone must be removed to operate the damper key, therefore altering the discharge resistance and making it difficult to finalise the damper setting.)

— As flow measurements and adjustments of the terminal take place at the same time, it is important to position the terminal and its damper as close together as possible, but allowing sufficient distance to reduce noise generation or at least allow attenuation.

Factors influencing damper selection are as follows:

— Built-in terminal dampers are not suitable where large pressure differences have to be accommodated. Nearly-closed dampers both create noise and alter the throw pattern of the terminal.

— For rectangular ducts, the opposed blade damper gives the best results because it produces the least downstream distortion when partly closed and it has a wider setting range than louvre or butterfly dampers.

— For circular ducts, the variable iris damper is a good choice, providing there is sufficient space round the duct for the damper housing, with the butterfly damper being the next best. Louvre and butterfly dampers can be noisy in high velocity systems.

— Dampers need to be accessible, not obstructed by projecting bolts or screws.

— All dampers should have a means of fixing in position, i.e. a sector plate with locking screw, with a means of marking so that the correct setting can be permanently marked after the regulation is complete.

Further information on actuators and pressure, velocity, flow and air quality measurement sensors is available in CIBSE Guide H: *Building control systems*[37].

Section 3.6 lists additional points to consider for particular types of ductwork.

3.4.8 Passive stack ventilation

A passive stack system comprises vents connected to individual near-vertical circular or rectangular ducts which rise to ridge or tile terminals. Moist air is drawn through the ducts by a combination of stack and wind effects. The ducts should have no more than two bends at greater than 30° to the vertical to minimise the resistance to air flow, and be insulated where they pass through cold spaces to reduce the risk of condensation. Typical applications are in kitchens and bathrooms where ducts are normally 80–125 mm in diameter. This technique has

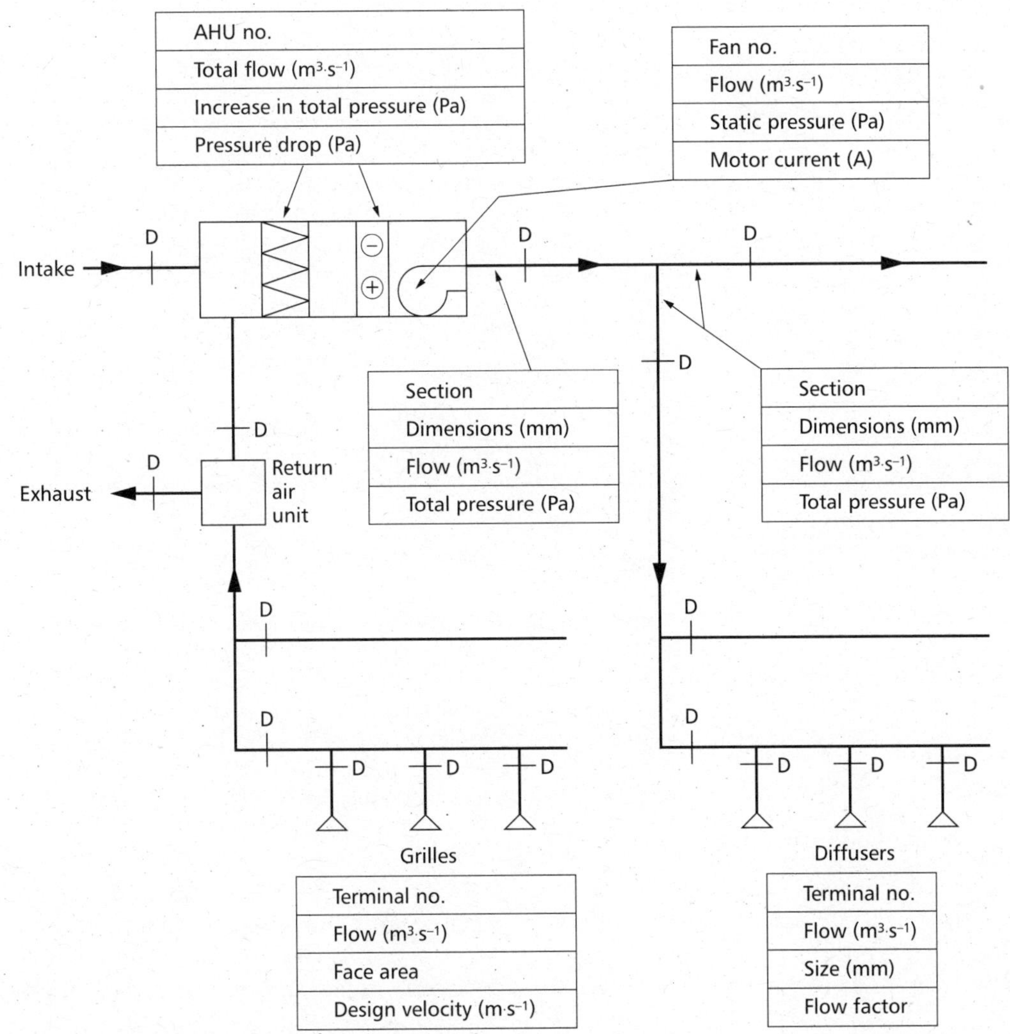

Figure 3.20 Basic schematic for system regulation showing damper positions (reproduced from BSRIA AG3.89[18] by permission of the Building Services Research and Information Association)

also been applied to complete buildings such as communal residences, schools and other education buildings.

Standard passive stack ventilation (PSV) systems have a simple inlet grille to the duct. Humidity-sensitive vents are available that can provide increased flows when humidity is high. Acoustic treatment may be required to reduce ingress of external noise. Fire dampers are required where ducts pass through a fire-separating wall.

The normal strategy in domestic applications is to extract air directly at source from wet zones. Replacement air enters via trickle or similar ventilators located in the 'dry' rooms such as living areas and bedrooms, using natural ventilation or make-up induced by the negative pressure. Passive stack ventilation can be combined with extract fans in hybrid systems, the fan being located in the kitchen.

Advantages of passive stack ventilation include:

— no direct running costs

— the system will last the lifetime of the building

— silence in operation

— requires no electrical connection.

Disadvantages include:

— the ventilation rate can be highly variable

— the ventilation rate may be inadequate in poorly ventilated buildings

— existing house layouts may make it difficult to accommodate duct runs

— site installation must be of good quality to avoid flow restrictions and excessive pressure drops

— uncontrolled systems waste energy due to continuous operation.

Effective commissioning of PSV systems is important. Further information on PSV systems is provided section 2.

3.5 Ductwork materials and fittings

3.5.1 Ductwork materials

The choice of materials to be used for the manufacture of a duct will take account of:

— the nature of the air or gas being conveyed through the duct

— the environment in which the duct will be placed and will operate

— the initial cost of the installation and the subsequent operation, maintenance and cleaning cost.

Galvanised steel sheet is generally suitable and economical for normal ventilation and air conditioning systems. That is those in which air is used for the creation of a comfortable environment within a space or building, and where no external, harmful conditions such as exposure to the weather or other aggressive atmospheres exist. For any other application, the composition of air and gas within and outside the duct must be assessed to verify that the material chosen will not be harmed by corrosion, deformation due to heating or softening and other chemical or physical change to the material. If the choice of material is not obvious, then specialist advice should be sought.

Materials most suitable for the formation of ductwork are:

(a) Metal:

— steel

— galvanised steel

— black steel

— stainless steel

— aluminium

— copper

(b) Non-metal:

— resin bonded glass fibre

— glass reinforced plastic (GRP)

— polypropylene

— polyester (textile or fabric ducting)

— polyvinyl chloride (PVC)

— polyisocyanurate

— concrete

— synthetic rubber.

Factors influencing the selection of a material for a particular application are summarised in Table 3.15 (based on information published by SMACNA[31]).

Builders' work ducts are constructed from various materials such as brick, concrete, and building boards. These will leak more than sheet metal ducts. Whilst solid concrete is impermeable to air, brickwork, concrete panels and concrete blockwork are not. Other common sources of leakage are where the shaft walls meet the floor slab and around metal ducts, pipes and electrical services passing into and out of the shaft. These sources of leakage may need to be sealed to comply with fire requirements.

Builders' work ducts may be used for systems where the pressure differentials across the duct walls are low, the obvious holes are blocked up and leakages are acceptable. High rates of leakage are likely. In systems where air leakage is more critical and pressure differentials across the walls are higher, builders' work ducts should not be used, particularly when the maintenance of room supply/extract air differential pressure is important. Brickwork ducts should also be rendered and adequate supervision and inspection during construction are vital to a successful installation. Acoustic or thermal insulation materials applied to inside surfaces should not be relied upon to provide air tightness. Access doors and panels into the duct should open against the air pressure.

3.5.2 Weights and thicknesses of ductwork materials

The weight of ductwork, in newtons, can be derived from the mass by multiplying the mass in kilograms by 9.81.

Table 3.15 List of materials suitable for formation of ductwork

Material	Applications	Advantages	Limiting characteristics	Remarks
Galvanised steel	Most air handling systems	High strength, rigidity, durability, rust resistance, availability, non-porous, 'workability', 'weldability'	Weight, corrosion resistance for corrosive products or temperatures above 200 °C, ability to be painted	Widely used and available
Carbon steel (black iron)	Breeching, flues, stacks, hoods, high temperature systems, kitchens	High strength, rigidity, ability to be painted, non-porous	Corrosion resistance, weight	Steel when no minimum content specified
Aluminium	Moisture laden air (salt free), louvres, special exhausts, ornamental	Weight, resistance to corrosion due to moisture	Low strength, cost, difficult to weld, high thermal expansion	Various alloys available
Stainless steel	Kitchen exhaust, moisture laden air, fume exhaust	High corrosion resistance, high polish possible	Labour, cost, 'workability', availability	Various alloys available
Copper	Ductwork exposed to outside chemical attack, ornamental	Can be soldered, durable, resists corrosion, non-magnetic	Cost, electrolysis, stains, thermal expansion	Common for ornamental ductwork
Glass fibre re-inforced plastic (GRP)	Chemical exhaust, scrubbers, underground ducts	Corrosion resistance, easily modified	Cost, weight, chemical and physical properties, fabrication	
Polyvinyl chloride (PVC)	Exhaust systems, underground ducts	Corrosion resistance, weight, easily modified	Cost, fabrication, thermal shock, weight, code acceptance	
Polyester (textile/fabric ducts)	Food and other process industries, warehousing, retail, sports/leisure, offices	Cost, weight, ease and speed of installation, low noise, not subject to condensation	Non-rigid, unsuitable for fire ductwork, damage during removal and/or replacement	

This weight is normally insignificant, even when insulated, compared with most building materials, and its influence on structural calculations is usually negligible. However, if the weight of the ducting is requested, e.g. where it is to be suspended from a lightweight factory roof, Tables 3.16, 3.17, 3.18 and 3.19 may be used as a guide. Fittings may be taken as equivalent to the same length of straight duct. The weight of textile ducts may be taken as 230 $g \cdot m^{-2}$, plus supports and hangers. Standard thicknesses for galvanised and aluminium sheet are given in Table 3.20.

Table 3.16 Weight of galvanised steel ductwork[4]

Thickness / mm	Weight per unit surface area of duct / $kg \cdot m^{-2}$
0.5	3.9
0.6	4.7
0.7	5.4
0.8	6.2
0.9	7.0
1.0	7.8
1.2	9.4
1.6	12.5
2.0	15.6
2.5	19.6

Table 3.17 Weight of aluminium ductwork

Thickness / mm	Weight per unit surface area of duct / $kg \cdot m^{-2}$
0.5	1.6
0.6	1.92
0.7	2.24
0.8	2.56
0.9	2.88
1.0	3.2
1.2	3.84
1.6	5.12
2.0	6.4
2.5	8.2

Table 3.18 Weight of stiffeners and joints

Angle section / (mm × mm × mm)	Weight per unit length / $kg \cdot m^{-1}$	
	Steel	Aluminium
25 × 25 × 3	15	7
30 × 30 × 3	17	8
40 × 40 × 4	28	12
50 × 50 × 5	42	17

Note: values include 0.3 $kg \cdot m^{-1}$ for fastenings and sealant

3.5.3 Fittings, dampers and ancillaries

A wide range of fittings are available from the manufacturers of all types of ductwork, who can also provide design information. Examples of standard components for sheet metal ductwork are provided in DW/144[4]. See also section 3.6.2.3.

Table 3.19 Weight of ductwork insulation

Material	Weight per unit surface area of duct, including adhesive / $kg \cdot m^{-2}$
Glass fibre, polystyrene or mineral wool (per 25 mm thickness)	20
Aluminium cladding (0.8 mm thick) with fastenings	25
Hard setting cement (12 mm thick)	220

Table 3.20 Standard thicknesses for ductwork[4]

Standard thickness / mm	
Galvanised steel*	Aluminium
0.5	0.5
0.6	0.6
0.7	0.7
0.8	0.8
0.9	0.9
1.0	1.0
1.2	1.2
1.6	1.6
2.0	2.0
2.5	2.5
—	3.0

* 0.5 mm is a standard thickness for galvanised sheet only; 2.5 mm is a standard thickness for hot-rolled sheet only

3.5.4 Protective coverings

3.5.4.1 General

Unless otherwise stated, all sheet metal ductwork will be manufactured in pre-galvanised sheet steel, aluminium or stainless steel as specified, with a primer coating where applicable. Any variations or additions to this basic specification and any special coatings and/or paint finishes to be provided by the ductwork contractor must be advised by the designer.

3.5.4.2 Galvanising after manufacture

Galvanising after manufacture is not recommended for general use, as distortion of the duct or fitting is probable, thus making if difficult to achieve an airtight joint. Galvanising after manufacture is, however, an acceptable protective finish for circular pressed fittings and external ductwork exposed to atmosphere. Where galvanising after manufacture is specified, it should be carried out according to BS EN ISO 1461(38). No paint protection is required.

3.5.4.3 Metal spraying

Zinc or aluminium spraying should be to BS EN 22063(39).

3.5.4.4 Ducts made from pre-galvanised sheet or coil

Ducts and profile sections made from pre-galvanised sheet or coil will have no need for paint or further protection where located inside a building. This also applies to exposed cut edges, which will be protected by the zinc coating giving sacrificial protection, this also extends to surface scratches.

3.5.4.5 Ducts made from other types of mild steel sheet

Where ducts need to be made from mild steel sheet or coil other than those listed above, protective requirements should be specified by the designer.

3.5.4.6 Untreated steelwork profiles and sheet

Any plain mill finish unprotected mild steel such as rolled steel sections and sheet used for flanging, stiffeners, supports and duct walls must be treated. Treatment would be an appropriate primer such as zinc rich, zinc chromate, red oxide or aluminium paint.

3.5.5 Connections to building openings

Openings in brick, block, concrete walls and dry lining partitions should have inset frames to provide a suitable means of fixing grilles, louvres, masking flanges or the flanged ends of ductwork. The inset frames should be constructed to maintain the structural integrity of the wall and cavities should be suitably lined, where applicable.

Openings in cladding walls and roofs should have flanged sleeves/frames to provide a suitable means of fixing. Horizontal and vertical openings that are exposed to the outside atmosphere should be provided with a suitable weathering finish at the external face, especially if profiled cladding is involved.

3.5.6 Sensors

Sensors intended to provide automatic control of fan performance should be located to ensure responsive, stable and reliable regulation across the full range of fan operation. Indicative positioning should be specified by the designer, based on the distribution ductwork system layout and the calculated system resistance characteristics. The performance of the extract system must follow that of the supply system. Limitations of instrument accuracy at low velocities may make it impossible to achieve repeatable measurements of fan performance at minimum volume.

Sensors should be at least as long as half the width of the duct. If this is not possible, averaging element capillary sensors should be used. Duct mounted frost thermostats should be of the capillary type located within 100 mm of the heater battery surface and arranged to sense the temperature across the full width and height of the duct. Other sensors possibly required in ducts will be smoke detectors to form part of the fire detection system.

The setting of the automatic control system should be finalised by the controls specialist in liaison with the commissioning specialist. When cleaning or undertaking other work within ducts it is essential that sensor probes are withdrawn to prevent them from being damaged.

3.6 Testing and commissioning

3.6.1 Introduction

All ductwork systems should be tested and commissioned and those of significant size (e.g. with a fan capacity above 1 $m^3 \cdot s^{-1}$) should also be leak tested, see section 3.2.10. The needs of on-site regulation should be planned and provided for in the design stage, otherwise balancing the system within acceptable limits may not be possible. The designer must accept the implications of the commissioning procedures to which the air distribution system will be subjected. Inadequate commissioning will result in poor environmental performance, energy wastage, draughts and noise. The designer's objectives must be to design an air distribution system where arrangements of ductwork and the selection and disposition of the components, particularly the means of air regulation, will promote a balanced and stable air flow.

The measuring, regulating and apportioning of air flow in a distribution system is a means to an end. The objective is to ensure that the performance of the commissioned installation is adequate to maintain the specified environmental conditions of the space with optimum efficiency.

Procedures for commissioning air handling systems are given in CIBSE Commissioning Code A(17) and BSRIA Application Guide 3/89.3(18). Table 3.21 shows a summary of the flow measuring techniques recommended by BSRIA for various ducts and terminals.

Table 3.21 Flow measurement techniques (reproduced from BSRIA Application Guide AG3/89.3[18] by permission of the Building Services Research and Information Association)

Position	Measurement technique	Instruments
Main duct (total flow at fan)	● Velocity traverse in duct	Pitot tube with micromanometer
	❍ Wilson flow grid	Micromanometer
Branch ducts	● Velocity traverse in duct	Pitot tube with manometer
Terminal connecting ducts	● Velocity traverse or single point reading in duct	Pitot tube with micromanometer or mini-rotating vane anemometer where velocity < 4 m·s^{-1}
Grilles	● Velocity traverse across face	Rotating vane anemometer
	● Hood	Rotating vane anemometer or integral hood assembly
Ceiling diffusers	● Flow hood	Rotating vane anemometer or integral hood assembly
	● Velocity in connecting duct	Pitot tube/manometer or mini-rotating vane anemometer
	● Static pressure in connecting duct	Diaphragm pressure gauge or pitot tube
	❍ Average peripheral velocity and area	Mini-rotating vane anemometer or thermal anemometer
Slots and linear diffusers	● Face velocity (for slots of equal width and same louvre setting)	Mini-rotating vane anemometer or thermal anemometer
	● Flow hood	Rotating vane anemometer or integral hood assembly
	❍ Velocity in connecting duct	Pitot tube/manometer or mini-rotating vane anemometer
Perforated ceiling	● Velocity in connecting duct to ceiling void	Pitot tube/manometer or mini-rotating vane anemometer
Perforated panel diffuser	● Velocity in connecting duct	Pitot tube/manometer or mini-rotating vane anemometer
	● Flow hood	Rotating vane anemometer or integral hood assembly
	❍ Face velocity (no deflection)	Rotating vane anemometer or integral hood assembly
Decorative terminals	● Velocity in connecting duct	Pitot tube/manometer or mini-rotating vane anemometer
Induction units	● Static pressure in nozzle plenum	Diaphragm pressure gauge
High velocity nozzles	● Jet velocity	Pitot tube/manometer or mini-rotating vane anemometer
	● Static pressure in connecting duct; previous calibration or maker's data	Diaphragm pressure gauge
Fan coil units	● Velocity in connecting duct	Pitot tube/manometer or mini-rotating vane anemometer
Extract openings (grilles)	● Face velocity	Pitot tube/manometer or electronic hood
Slots, perforated panels, decorative openings	● Velocity in connecting duct	Pitot tube/manometer or mini-rotating vane anemometer
Combined lighting units, adjustable exhaust valves	● Manufacturer's recommended technique ● Velocity in connecting duct	Pitot tube/manometer or mini-rotating vane anemometer

Note: ● indicates preferred measuring technique for stated location
❍ indicates second choice (i.e. more difficult to use in practice or subject to a greater possibility of error)

Before system regulation starts, the building needs to be complete, with windows and doors open or shut according to their normal state. The air distribution system needs to be complete with leakage testing satisfactorily concluded. A reasonable standard of system cleanliness should be achieved before system start up.

Each system should be considered on its own merits and a detailed commissioning method statement produced and agreed prior to commissioning. It is important that the designer provides full information on all relevant aspects of the design, particularly VAV systems, in sufficient detail for the commissioning specialist to produce a comprehensive method statement. The commissioning specialist should review the recommendations of the equipment suppliers with regard to the inclusion of their equipment in the commissioning process for the air distribution system.

3.6.2 Design provisions to facilitate commissioning

3.6.2.1 Good ductwork design

The duct sizing procedure (sections 3.4.2 and 3.4.3) should take into account the requirements of system balancing. The position and number of regulating dampers included in the design should be sufficient for this purpose.

3.6.2.2 Communication

The designer should pass on the design intent to the commissioning engineer by indicating which parts of the system are high, medium and low pressure, and by providing:

— relevant parts of the specification

— schematic drawings as listed in Table 3.22 (see also Figure 3.20, which shows a basic schematic for system regulation including damper positions).

— equipment schedules

— controller and regulator schedule

— fan performance curves

— wiring diagrams for electrical equipment, including interlock details

— manufacturers' operating and maintenance instructions.

Table 3.22 Information to be provided in schematic drawings

Items of system	Information to be provided
Fans	Fan total pressure Volume flow rates Motor current
Plant items	Type and identification numbers from equipment schedules Volume flow rates Pressure losses Dry bulb temperatures } for coils and Wet bulb temperatures } humidifiers Humidity } as appropriate
Dampers (including motorised) and fire dampers	Identification numbers from equipment schedules Location Volume flow rates
Main and branch ducts	Location Dimensions Volume flow rates
Terminals	Identification numbers from equipment schedules Location Dimensions Volume flow rates and velocities Operating pressures
Test holes and access panels	Location
Controllers	Set points

Notes:
(1) Fan total pressure is the difference between the total pressure (static pressure + velocity pressure) at the fan outlet and the total pressure at the fan inlet.
(2) Where volume flow rates are variable, maximum and minimum values should be provided.

The information listed above should also be included in the building's log book.

3.6.2.3 Provision and siting of dampers

Note: it is important to have a means of recording the positions of volume control dampers which have been set during commissioning; spray paint over the quadrant is effective for smaller sizes of dampers.

Low and medium pressure systems

Manually operated balancing dampers are generally needed:

(a) in the main duct downstream of the fan

(b) in the branch or zone ducts

(c) in sub-ducts serving four or more terminals

(d) at terminals not covered by *(c)* above.

Dampers integral with terminals should only be used for final trimming of air volumes, or noise and air distribution problems may result.

High pressure systems

Where pressure reduction in a high pressure system is essential, it is recommended that:

— throttling dampers should not be used in high pressure and high velocity sections because of duct leakage and noise problems; if this cannot be avoided, then additional attenuators and external sound barrier mats may be needed at the damper and downstream to limit noise break-out

— orifice plates or proprietary pressure-reducing valves should be used as first choice in main branches

— where dampers are required they should be confined to areas of relatively low duct velocities; iris type in circular ducts, streamlined blade construction in rectangular ducts.

Variable volume systems

Rather than using throttling dampers in the main duct, system static pressure control in VAV systems should be effected by:

— variable speed motors on the fan(s) or,

— inlet guide vanes with centrifugal fans or,

— variable pitch blades on axial-flow fans.

Motorised dampers

Motorised dampers for throttling airflow should be opposed-blade type opening through a full 90°; for mixing purposes they should be parallel-blade type opening only through 60°.

Throttling dampers should be sized to have an authority of 5–8% of the fan total pressure. Mixing dampers should be sized to have a face velocity of 4–10 $m \cdot s^{-1}$. To obtain maximum benefit from outside air cooling, fresh air/recirculation air dampers must have a good shut-off; this means they should:

- be rigid with accurate square connections
- be provided with end and edge seals of flexible material
- not be distorted during fitting.

3.6.2.4 Inspection and access openings

See section 3.3.10: Access for inspection, maintenance and cleaning.

3.6.3 Test holes

3.6.3.1 General

Except in special circumstances, it is not usual practice to install air flow measuring devices permanently in air ducts. The normal procedure is to make velocity traverses across the duct at appropriate locations using a pitot tube. The small test holes for using a pitot tube are usually made by the commissioning specialist.

Test holes for in-duct measurement are needed on the main duct following the air handling plant. The basic locations for siting test holes for flow measurement are shown in Figure 3.21 as 'principal measuring points'. If there is insufficient space, an alternative is to provide test holes in principal branches so that the total flow from the fan can be obtained by summation. These points are shown in Figure 3.21 as 'secondary measuring points'.

Test holes for in-duct airflow measurement are required:

- on both sides of the fans and heating and cooling coils (for pressure drop measurement)
- in the main ducts
- in all branches
- in centrifugal fan drive guards opposite the end of the fan spindle, for speed measurements.

The number and spacing of holes at a particular location are given in BSRIA Application Guide 3/89.3[(18)]; these recommendations are summarised in Table 3.23 and Figure 3.22.

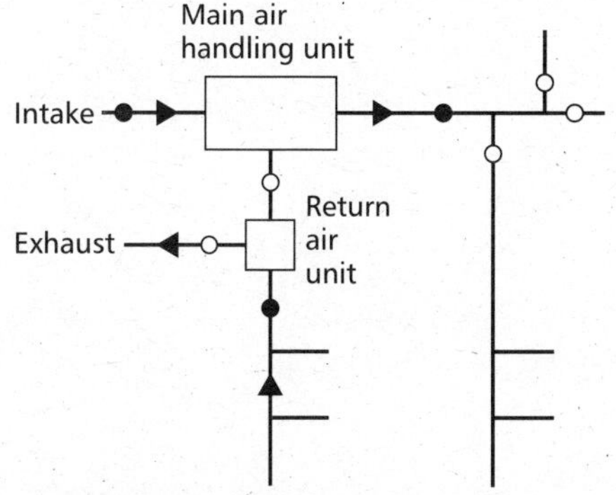

Figure 3.21 Basic test hole positions for flow measurement in duct systems (reproduced from BSRIA Application Guide AG3/89.3[(18)], by permission of the Building Services Research and Information Association)

Table 3.23 Test hole positions; special requirements for measurement of total airflow from the fan (reproduced from BSRIA Application Guide AG3/89.3[(18)], by permission of the Building Services Research and Information Association)

Type of fan	Position of test holes*	
	Upstream	Downstream
Centrifugal	4 *d*	10 *d*
Axial:		
— single stage	4 *d*	Not advised
— single stage with guide vanes	4 *d*	10 *d*
— two-stage, contra-rotating	4 *d*	10 *d*

* *d* = diameter (equivalent diameter for non-circular ducts) of duct following the fan

The location chosen for the measurement point should be:

- at least 1.5 duct diameters upstream of sources of turbulence such as dampers and bends; if this is not possible then well downstream of these sources
- where there is enough space round the duct to insert the pitot tube and take readings
- where the duct has a constant cross sectional area.

Minimum distances of test holes from sources of turbulence are given in Figure 3.22.

3.6.3.2 Test hole specification

The main test hole locations are shown in Figure 3.21. Usually the installer will not have drilled the test holes, this being left to the commissioning specialist. However, the designer and the installer should have taken account of the location of test holes to ensure access. It is sometimes appropriate to use resealable test holes, included in the ductwork prior to installation.

Figure 3.22 shows the minimum distance of test holes from sources of turbulence[(18)]. Figure 3.23 gives the dimensions of a standard test hole for a pitot tube for in-duct measurement[(18)].

For rectangular ducts the number of test holes depends on the duct dimensions. For circular ducts, a single test hole is required for ducts less than 150 mm in diameter, and two holes spaced at 90 degrees are required for larger ducts. The appropriate position, number and spacing of test holes are given in BSRIA Application Guide AG 3/89.3[(18)].

3.7 Maintenance and cleaning

3.7.1 Introduction

The purpose of an air distribution system is to provide healthy, fresh and clean air into the building. The designer should be aware that the air distribution system may become a major odour source. It is possible to eliminate nearly all the odour emissions from the system, in both new and renovated buildings.

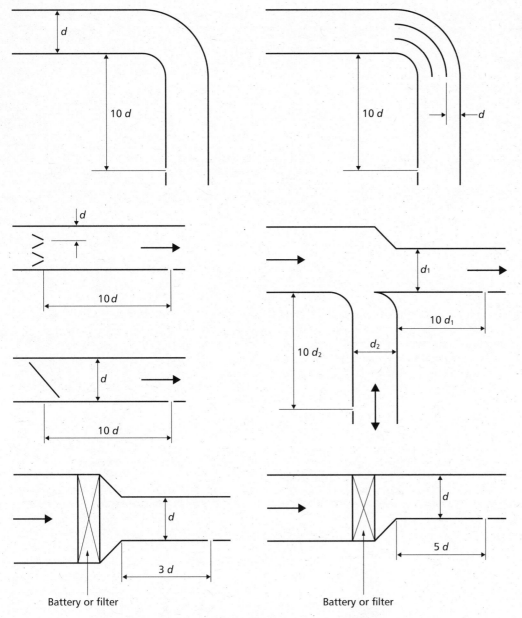

Figure 3.22 Minimum distance of test holes from sources of turbulence (reproduced from BSRIA Application Guide AG3/89.3[18], by permission of the Building Services Research and Information Association)

3.7.2 Legislation

The EU Workplace Directive has been implemented in the UK by the Workplace (Health, Safety and Welfare) Regulations 1992[40]. The Health and Safety Commission's Approved Code of Practice and Guidance L24[41] states that: 'Mechanical ventilation systems (including air conditioning systems) should be regularly and properly cleaned, tested and maintained to ensure that they are kept cleaned and free from anything which may contaminate the air'. This has applied to all workplaces since January 1996. Additionally, provision for access space for maintenance of the ventilation systems will need to be considered at the design stage.

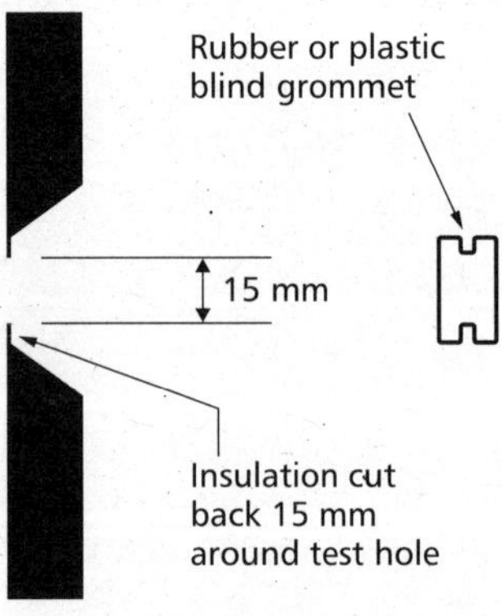

Figure 3.23 Dimensions of standard test holes (reproduced from BSRIA Application Guide AG3/89.3[18], by permission of the Building Services Research and Information Association)

3.7.3 Maintenance

Ductwork systems should be clean on completion. HVCA DW/TM2: *Guide to good practice — internal cleanliness of new ductwork installations*[42] states that: 'where specific levels of cleanliness are required, ductwork shall be cleaned after installation by a specialist cleaning contractor.'

During use over a number of years, a slow build-up of deposits can occur, particularly at points where the air velocity reduces. More rapid build-up of dirt will result when filters are faulty or damaged, poorly installed or badly maintained.

See section 3.7.12 for information on ductwork cleaning methods.

Special requirements apply to cleaning and maintenance of ductwork in applications such as food preparation (see HVCA DW/171: *Standard for kitchen ventilation systems*[30]), process industries and plant rooms.

Table 3.24 Summary of recommendations for maintenance of ductwork[(43)]

Item	Frequency	Action
General: — access doors — flexible connections — insulation — anti-vibration mounts — internal cleanliness	12–monthly	Visual inspection for damage, security of fittings, deterioration and internal condition
Dampers: — volume control dampers — fire and smoke dampers — linkages — controls — electrical	6–monthly	Visual inspection, check action of moving parts and lubricate, check security of locking devices, check fusible links. Check for damage to electrical connections, tighten where required. Check integrity of electrical installation
Acoustics: — attenuators — support fixings	12–monthly	Inspect visually internally and externally. Repair sound insulation as required. Check all fixings are secure. Clean, de-rust, repaint as required
Grilles and diffusers	12–monthly	Examine, check mounting fittings, clean
Louvres, bird and insect screens	6–monthly	Clean, remove debris, check for damage, repair or replace

Detailed maintenance requirements for ductwork are set out in HVCA Standard Maintenance Specification, volume 2: *Ventilation and air conditioning*[(43)]. In summary these requirements are shown in Table 3.24.

When undertaking maintenance work within ducts, it is essential that sensor probes are withdrawn to protect them from being damaged.

3.7.4 Design for cleaning

To enable cleaning to be carried out safely and efficiently, it is important that the air distribution system is designed and installed so that all internal surfaces and components can be accessed. Components (e.g. dampers, sensors, air flow measuring devices) should be installed so that they can be cleaned in-situ or removed for cleaning. If removal is not possible, service access should be provided according to Table 3.25. Access should be provided which is not obstructed by suspended ceilings, electric cables, lighting, pipes or other ducts.

Abrupt bends, area reductions and sharp objects inside duct joints such as projecting screws should be avoided to prevent injury to maintenance and cleaning personnel. Stiffeners and other equipment inside the ductwork should not obstruct the cleaning process. Access doors and covers should be easy to open and be constructed and installed to match the type and location of any thermal, acoustic or fire insulation.

A ductwork component which can be dismounted for cleaning can also be regarded as an access door on condition that its dimensions are in accordance with Table 3.26 or sufficient for the specified and documented cleaning method. Access to duct-mounted components should be provided in accordance with Table 3.25, unless the component is easily removable for cleaning, or can be cleaned through the ductwork without obstructions.

The location of and distance between openings depends on the quality of supply and extract air and also on the defined or available cleaning method. Unless the cleaning method is known or can be fixed at the design stage, the distance between the openings should not exceed 10 m, or not more than two ≥ 45° bends.

Designers should take specialist advice and stipulate their requirements for the periodic internal cleaning and maintenance of ductwork.

3.7.5 Air quality and health issues

The air quality within a building is influenced by contaminants in the form of particles and gases that are generated within the building envelope and those brought in from outdoors. Contaminant particles may enter the building with the outdoor air. These can include carbon produced by combustion and vehicles, and particles of biological origin. Contaminant gases produced within a building include the volatile organic compounds (VOCs) emitted by

Table 3.25 Requirements for access to duct-mounted components

Component	Location of access opening(s)
Dampers	Both sides
Fire dampers	One side
Heating/cooling coils	Both sides
Circular sound attenuators	One side
Rectangular sound attenuators	Both sides
Filter sections	Both sides
In-duct fans	Both sides
Air flow control device	Both sides

Table 3.26 Openings for ducts; recommended minimum dimensions

Duct type and size	Access opening size	
	A / mm	B / mm
Circular ducts (diam. d mm):		
— $200 < d \leq 315$	300	100
— $315 < d \leq 500$	400	200
— $500 < d$	500	400
— inspection opening	600	500
Rectangular (side length s mm):		
— $s < 200$	300	100
— $200 < s \leq 500$	400	200
— $s > 500$	500	400
— inspection opening	600	500

some construction materials, fabrics and adhesives, and fumes emitted by photocopiers and laser printers. Gases admitted from outdoors include vehicle exhaust gases. Biological agents such as bacteria, fungal spores and pollen grains can enter the building from outside. Particles generated indoors can include human skin scales, bacteria, viruses and fungi, faecal matter from the house dust mite and paper dust. Settled deposits in ductwork may cause contamination of air supply by release of chemicals such as odorous VOCs, produced either micro-biologically or chemically.

Designers do not normally consider the health effects of microbes in ductwork systems, since their focus is the attainment of specified operating conditions, generally for comfort purposes. It is important to be aware of the potential health issues arising from microbial material in ductwork. There are currently no environmental health criteria setting safe microbial exposure. Possible harmful health effects on the occupants of buildings from micro-bial growth within the fabric include allergies, infection and toxicosis. Further information about these is provided in CIBSE TM26: *Hygienic maintenance of office ventilation ductwork*[44].

Ultraviolet (UV) light can be very effective in de-activating pathogens and other airborne bacteria, viruses and moulds. Where a high quality air supply is required, such as in health care facilities and situations where there is a high occupation density, UV lamps can be installed in the duct-work. Medium pressure lamps, e.g. 3.5 kW and 300 mm in length, run very hot and must be switched off when the fan is not operating. Provision of UV lamps will also have implications for maintenance.

3.7.6 New ductwork construction

The designer should specify the requirements for:

— cleanliness levels for ductwork leaving the factory

— protection during transit

— protection during site storage

— protection of ductwork risers

— inspection and cleaning during installation and before handover.

HVCA publication DW/TM2: *Guide to good practice – internal cleanliness of new ductwork installations*[42], provides for three grades of pre-commission cleanliness. The designer should determine which is appropriate for the specific installation and state this in the design specification.

In manufacturing ducts, attention should be paid to the grease used in production. The ductwork should leave the factory as clean and dry as possible. Any remaining grease film is a potential base for microbial growth.

The whole ductwork installation should be inspected and, where necessary, cleaned before handover. The preferred cleaning method should be specified in the hand-over documents, including guidelines on access to all points to be cleaned.

3.7.7 Installation

During installation the installer should ensure that dust and debris are prevented from entering the ductwork system, to ensure that the installation is clean prior to commissioning. The commissioning process should include an inspection of ductwork cleanliness. Where this is not the case, it may be necessary to employ a specialist ductwork cleaning company. The commissioning should not commence until cleanliness has been inspected and certified. The installation should be in a clean state at handover.

3.7.8 Existing ductwork

The normal operation of ductwork systems will introduce dirt both from the external air brought into the system and from recirculated air containing dust and other particles. The filtration system (where provided) should be designed to remove dirt and dust. However, the level of filtration, the standard of filter medium used and the adequacy of seals and fittings around the filtration equip-ment can all lead to increased levels of dust and dirt. These in turn can have an effect on plant performance such as reducing the efficiency of the fan and heat transfer equipment. The function of the air movement system can determine the requirements for cleaning. Certain process applications, e.g. food and pharmaceuticals, are likely to have considerably higher standards of ductwork clean-liness than that serving an office building.

3.7.9 Dust deposition

Dust will generally be deposited mainly over the lower surfaces of air distribution ducts, with the deposition increasing with distance from the air handling unit. There may be additional deposition where the local flow of air is slowed. This will happen at points where there is a resis-tance to the flow of air including the filters, heating and cooling coils, corner vanes and changes in the direction of ducting, changes in cross sectional area and at surface imperfections and jointing cracks between duct sections. Once it is deposited, a physical disturbance or a change in the flow speed would be required to re-entrain significant amounts of the dust into the air.

3.7.10 Moisture

It is important to take precautions to avoid the generation or ingress of moisture, as the presence of moisture or free water droplets on the surfaces of ducts is well known as a potential cause of microbial contamination. This is normally avoided by the system design and control, but unwanted moisture can arise under some circumstances, for example:

— where the metal duct surface temperature falls below the dew-point of the air flowing through it

— downstream of cooling coils operated below the dew-point (a spray eliminator is usually installed downstream of cooling coils used for dehumid-ification, but 'normal' cooling coils may also operate unintentionally under these conditions)

— where there is a leak of water from a heating or cooling coil, or from water pipework outside the air duct

— as a (temporary) residue from any wet cleaning process

— by ingress of rain water.

3.7.11 Inspection

Inspection of the ventilation system will usually start with a visual check of the outside air intake which can be a source of pollution and contamination. A smoke test can quickly determine if outside air is entering the system. Further items to check will be dampers, protective devices against weather, insect and rodents, the hygiene of coils, fans and insulation, the presence of water and condition of condensate drain pans and humidifier reservoirs.

Checking the need for cleaning should be done periodically. Eurovent includes recommendations on indoor air quality (IAQ)[45].

The Heating and Ventilating Contractors' Association (HVCA) recommends an annual check on the internal cleanliness through sampling points[43]. This is in accordance with BS 5720[46]. Local exhaust ventilation may be intended to control substances hazardous to health, including biological agents. The Health and Safety Executive (HSE) recommends examination and testing of such systems at least every 14 months and more frequently for certain processes[47].

Ventilation ductwork may be inspected optically using visual inspection instruments (e.g. borescopes) or by remote control inspection vehicles using closed-circuit television (CCTV) to record the internal condition of the ducts. Visual inspection (e.g. video) should be combined with quantitative methods of measuring dirt or micro-organisms.

Special attention is required to the cleanliness of:

— air filters

— sound attenuators

— humidifiers

— components for measurement or control.

The condition of all these items is generally a good indicator of the need for cleaning. It is recommended to start inspection from these components. After cleaning, all these components should be inspected to ensure that no damage has occurred and the cleanliness and functionality are as intended.

The need for cleaning following an inspection of the ductwork will depend on the level of dirt identified at the inspection and the particular requirements of the building, including the specific operations undertaken within the facility. Some buildings will be more sensitive to a build-up of dirt and dust in the ductwork and are likely to need a more frequent inspection regime and subsequent cleaning.

Checking the results of cleaning should be combined with checking the functions of the system after cleaning, and readjustments made where required.

3.7.12 Cleaning methods

There are several methods by which cleaning contractors can remove dust, debris and other surface contaminants:

— vacuum

— steam

— compressed air

— rotary brush.

Cleaning methods are more fully described in HVCA Guide to Good Practice TR17[48] and BSRIA Technical Note TN18/92[49]. Methods will vary according to the air distribution system. On the basis that the contaminants are dry, dry methods of cleaning are adequate for supply air and general extract systems. Wet methods are needed for air ducts in commercial kitchens and similar installations where extract air contains smoke, grease and other impurities.

The cleaning process involves loosening dirt adhering to ductwork surfaces and its subsequent removal. The loosening can be remotely by compressed air or rotary brushing equipment in conjunction with removal by industrial vacuum collector. Dust may alternatively be removed directly by a technician crawling along the ducts using a hand-held vacuum cleaner. When cleaning within ducts it is essential that sensor probes are withdrawn to prevent them from being damaged.

Dust resulting from cleaning, particularly that which may contain biologically active material, should be disposed of safely.

When cleaning is complete, the ductwork system may require rebalancing. Most cleaning contractors leave dampers and other control devices in their 'as found' positions. Based on system performance, the property operator will then need to decide whether rebalancing is required. It is recommended that a commissioning specialist be appointed to undertake this task.

References

1 The Building Regulations 2000 Approved Document L: *Conservation of fuel and power* (London: The Stationery Office) (2001)

2 *Reference data* CIBSE Guide C (London: Chartered Institution of Building Services Engineers) (2001)

3 Hayden G W and Parsloe C J *Value engineering of building services* BSRIA Applications Guide AG15/96 (Bracknell: Building Services Research and Information Association) (1996)

4 *Specification for sheet metal ductwork* HVCA DW/144 (London: Heating and Ventilating Contractors' Association) (1998)

5 *Space requirements for plant access, operation and maintenance* Defence Estates Organisation (Works) Design and Maintenance Guide 08 (London: The Stationery Office) (1996)

6 *Spatial allowances for building services distribution systems* BSRIA Technical Note TN10/92 (Bracknell: Building Services Research and Information Association) (1992)

7 BS 8313: *Code of practice for accommodation of building services in ducts* (London: British Standards Institution) (1997)

8 *A practical guide to ductwork leakage testing* HVCA DW/143 (London: Heating and Ventilating Contractors' Association) (2000)

9 prEN 12237: *Ventilation for buildings. Requirement for testing for strength and leakage of circular metal air ducts* (draft) (London: British Standards Institution) (1995)

10 prEN 1507: *Ventilation for buildings. Requirement for testing for strength and leakage of rectangular sheet metal air ducts* (draft) (London: British Standards Institution) (1994)

11 BS 5588: *Fire Precautions in the design and construction of buildings*; Part 9: 1999: *Code of practice for ventilation and air conditioning ductwork* (London: British Standards Institution) (1999)

12 *Fire rated and smoke outlet ductwork* ('The Blue Book') (Aldershot: Association for Specialist Fire Protection) (2000)

13 BS 476: *Fire tests on building materials and structures*; Part 20: 1987: *Method for determination of the fire resistance of elements of construction (general principles)* (London: British Standards Institution) (1987)

14 BS 476: *Fire tests on building materials and structures*; Part 22: 1987: *Methods for determination of fire resistance for non-load bearing elements* (London: British Standards Institution) (1987)

15 BS 476: *Fire tests on building materials and structures*; Part 24: 1987: *Method for determination of the fire resistance of ventilation ducts* (London: British Standards Institution) (1987)

16 Building Regulations 1991 Approved Document B: *Fire safety* (London: The Stationery Office) (2000)

17 *Air distribution systems* CIBSE Commissioning Code A (London: Chartered Institution of Building Services Engineers) (1996)

18 *Commissioning air systems* BSRIA Application Guide AG 3/89.3 (Bracknell: Building Services Research and Information Association) (2001)

19 Building Regulations 2000 Statutory Instrument 2000 No. 2531 (London: The Stationery Office) (2000)

20 *Environmental design* CIBSE Guide A (London: Chartered Institution of Building Services Engineers) (1999)

21 Health and Safety at Work etc. Act 1974 (London: Her Majesty's Stationery Office) (1974)

22 The Construction (Design and Management) Regulations 1994 Statutory Instrument 1994 No. 3140 (London: Her Majesty's Stationery Office) (1994)

23 BS 5422: 2001 *Method for specifying thermal insulating materials for pipes, tanks, vessels, ductwork and equipment operating within the temperature range –40 °C to +700 °C* (London: British Standards Institution) (2001)

24 BS 5970: 2001 *Code of Practice for thermal insulation of pipework and equipment in the temperature range –100 °C to +870 °C* (London: British Standards Institution) (2001)

25 BS EN ISO 12241: 1998 *Thermal insulation for building equipment and industrial installations. Calculation rules* (London: British Standards Institution) (1998)

26 BS 848: *Fans for general purposes*; Part 2: 1996 *Methods of noise testing*; Part 2.6: 2000 (ISO 10302: 1996) *Methods of noise testing. Airborne noise emitted by small air-moving devices* (London: British Standards Institution) (dates as indicated)

27 *HVAC systems duct design* (Chantilly, VA: Sheet Metal and Air Conditioning Contractors' National Association (SMACNA)) (1990)

28 Iqbal M A, Willson T K and Thomas R J *Control of noise in ventilation systems* (London: E & F N Spon) (1977)

29 *Fire engineering* CIBSE Guide E (London: Chartered Institution of Building Services Engineers) (1997)

30 *Standard for kitchen ventilation systems* HVCA DW/171 (London: Heating and Ventilating Contractors' Association) (2000)

31 *HVAC duct construction standards (metal and flexible)* 2nd ed. (Chantilly, VA: Sheet Metal and Air Conditioning Contractors' National Association (SMACNA)) (1995)

32 *Thermoplastic duct (PVC) construction manual* (Chantilly, VA: Sheet Metal and Air Conditioning Contractors' National Association (SMACNA)) (1995)

33 *HVAC duct systems inspection guide* (Chantilly, VA: Sheet Metal and Air Conditioning Contractors' National Association (SMACNA)) (1989)

34 *Minimising pollution at air intakes* CIBSE TM21 (London: Chartered Institution of Building Services Engineers) (1999)

35 *Location of fresh air intakes* BSRIA TN 12/2000 (Bracknell: Building Services Research and Information Association) (2000)

36 *Space air diffusion* Chapter 32 in ASHRAE Handbook: *Fundamentals* (Atlanta, GA: American Society of Heating, Refrigerating and Air-Conditioning Engineers) (2001)

37 *Building control systems* CIBSE Guide H (London: Chartered Institution of Building Services Engineers) (2000)

38 BS EN ISO 1461: 1999 *Hot dipped galvanised coatings on fabricated iron and steel articles. Specification and test methods* (London: British Standards Institution) (1999)

39 BS EN 22063: 1994 *Metallic and other inorganic coatings* (London: British Standards Institution) (1994)

40 The Workplace (Health, Safety and Welfare) Regulations 1992 Statutory instrument 1992 No. 3004 (London: Her Majesty's Stationery Office) (1992)

41 *Workplace health, safety and welfare Workplace (Health, Safety and Welfare) Regulations 1992 – Approved Code of Practice and guidance* Health and Safety Commission Legislation series L24 (Sudbury: HSE Books) (1994)

42 *Guide to good practice – internal cleanliness of new ductwork installations* HVCA DW/TM2 (London: Heating and Ventilating Contractors' Association) (1991)

43 *Standard maintenance specification for mechanical services in buildings – Vol. 2: ventilating and air conditioning* (London: Heating and Ventilating Contractors' Association) (1991)

44 *Hygienic maintenance of office ventilation ductwork* CIBSE TM26 (London: Chartered Institution of Building Services Engineers) (2000)

45 *Recommendation concerning indoor air quality* Eurovent REC 08 (Vienna: Eurovent) (January 1999)

46 BS 5720: 1979 *Code of practice for mechanical ventilation and air conditioning in buildings* (London: British Standards Institution) (1979)

47 *The maintenance, examination and testing of local exhaust ventilation* HSG54 (Sudbury: HSE Books) (1998)

48 *Guide to good practice – cleanliness of ventilation systems* HVCA TR17 (London: Heating and Ventilating Contractors' Association) (2002)

49 *Ventilation system hygiene - a review* (8th ed.) BSRIA TN18/92 (Bracknell: Building Services Research and Information Association) (1996)

Bibliography

General

Burberry P *Distribution and sizing: Ducts, pipes and trunking* Architects Journal 5 March 1986

Specification for plastics ductwork DW/154 (London: Heating and Ventilating Contractors' Association) (2000)

Guide to good practice for glass fibre ductwork DW/191 (London: Heating and Ventilating Contractors' Association) (1974)

Air leakage rates in sheet metal air distribution systems Document 212 (Vienna: Eurovent) (1981)

BS 476: *Fire tests on building materials and structures*; Part 6: 1989 *Method of test for fire propagation for products*; Part 7: 1997 *Method of test to determine the classification of the surface spread of flame of products* (London: British Standards Institution) (dates as indicated)

BS 848: *Fans for general purposes*; Part 1: 1997: *Performance testing using standardized airways*; Part 2: 1985: *Methods of noise testing*; Part 2, section 2.6: 2000: *Airborne noise emitted by small air-moving devices* (London: British Standards Institution) (dates as indicated)

BS 5720: 1979 *Code of practice for mechanical ventilation and air conditioning in buildings* (London: British Standards Institution) (1979)

BS EN 22063: 1994 *Metallic and other inorganic coatings. Thermal spraying. Zinc, aluminium and their alloys* (London: British Standards Institution) (1994)

Ductwork construction

Stephen R K *Passive stack ventilation systems - design and installation* BRE Information Paper 13/94 (Garston: Building Research Establishment) (1994)

HVAC systems — duct design (Chantilly, VA: Sheet Metal and Air Conditioning Contractors' National Association) (1990)

HVAC duct systems inspection guide (Chantilly, VA: Sheet Metal and Air Conditioning Contractors' National Association) (1989)

Thermoplastic duct (PVC) construction manual (Chantilly, VA: Sheet Metal and Air Conditioning Contractors' National Association) (1995)

Woods practical guide to fan engineering 3rd. edition (Colchester: Woods of Colchester) (1978)

Industrial ventilation — a manual of recommended practice 24th. edition (Lancing, MI: American Conference of Industrial Hygienists) (2001)

Airflow in ducts

Flow of fluids in pipes and ducts Section 4 in CIBSE Guide C: Reference data (London: Chartered Institution of Building Services) (2001)

Jackson K R Branch losses in high velocity systems *JIHVE* **37** 208–214 (1969)

Eschman R and Lang W E A critical assessment of high velocity duct design information *ASHRAE Trans.* **76** 157 (1970)

Appendix 3.A1: Recommended sizes for ductwork

Table 3.A1.1 Recommended sizes for rectangular ductwork, including equivalent diameter, hydraulic diameter, cross sectional area and perimeter (based on BS EN 1505[A1.1])

Longer side / mm	Parameter*	Shorter side / mm: 100	150	200	250	300	400	500	600	800	1000	1200	Parameter*
150	d_e	134	165										d_e
	P	0.5	0.6										P
	d_h	120.00	141.55	180.82									d_h
	A	0.015	0.0225	0.03									A
200	d_e	154	190	220									d_e
	P	0.6	0.7	0.8									P
	d_h	133.33	171.43	200.00									d_h
	A	0.02	0.03	0.04	0.05								A
250	d_e	171	212	246	275								d_e
	P	0.7	0.8	0.9	1.0								P
	d_h	142.86	187.50	222.22	250.00								d_h
	A	0.025	0.0375	0.05	0.0625	0.075							A
300	d_e	185	231	269	301	330							d_e
	P	0.8	0.9	1.0	1.1	1.2							P
	d_h	150.00	200.00	240.00	272.73	300.00							d_h
	A	0.03	0.045	0.06	0.075	0.09	0.12						A
400	d_e	211	264	308	346	387	441						d_e
	P	1.0	1.1	1.2	1.3	1.4	1.6						P
	d_h	160.00	218.18	266.67	307.69	342.86	400.00						d_h
	A	0.04	0.06	0.08	0.1	0.12	0.16	0.2					A
500	d_e		291	341	385	424	492	551					d_e
	P		1.3	1.4	1.5	1.6	1.8	2.0					P
	d_h		230.77	285.71	333.33	375.00	444.44	500.00					d_h
	A		0.075	0.1	0.125	0.15	0.2	0.25	0.3				A
600	d_e		316	371	419	462	537	603	661				d_e
	P		1.5	1.6	1.7	1.8	2.0	2.2	2.4				O
	d_h		240.00	300.00	352.94	400.00	480.00	545.45	600.00				d_h
	A			0.12	0.15	0.18	0.24	0.3	0.36	0.48			A
800	d_e			421	477	527	616	693	761	881			d_e
	P			2.0	2.1	2.2	2.4	2.6	2.8	3.2			P
	d_h			320.00	380.95	436.36	533.33	615.38	1538.46	800.00			d_h
	A				0.2	0.24	0.32	0.4	0.48	0.64			A
1000	d_e				527	583	683	770	848	984	1101		d_e
	P				2.5	2.6	2.8	3.0	3.2	3.6	4.0		P
	d_h				400.00	461.54	571.43	666.67	750.00	888.89	1000.00		d_h
	A				0.25	0.3	0.4	0.5	0.6	0.8	1.0	1.2	A
1200	d_e					632	741	837	924	1075	1205	1322	d_e
	P					3.0	3.2	3.4	3.6	4.0	4.4	4.8	P
	d_h					480.00	600.00	705.88	800.00	960.00	1090.91	1200.00	d_h
	A					0.36	0.48	0.6	0.72	0.96	1.2	1.44	A

* d_e = equivalent diameter / mm; P = perimeter / m; d_h = hydraulic diameter / mm; A = cross sectional area / m^2

Table continuees

Table A1.1 Recommended sizes for rectangular ductwork, including equivalent diameter, hydraulic diameter, cross sectional area and perimeter (based on BS EN 1505[(A1.1)]) — *continued*

Longer side / mm	Parameter*	Shorter side / mm: 100	150	200	250	300	400	500	600	800	1000	1200	Parameter*
1400	d_e						*794*	*898*	*992*	*1118*	*1299*	*1427*	d_e
	P						3.6	3.8	4.0	4.4	4.8	5.2	P
	d_h						*622.22*	*736.84*	*840.00*	*1018.18*	*1166.67*	*1292.31*	d_h
	A						0.56	0.7	0.84	0.112	0.14	0.168	A
1600	d_e						*843*	*954*	*1054*	*1231*	*1385*	*1523*	d_e
	P						4.0	4.2	4.4	4.8	5.2	5.6	P
	d_h						*640.00*	*761.90*	*872.73*	*1066.67*	*1230.77*	*1371.43*	d_h
	A							0.8	0.96	1.28	1.6	1.92	A
1800	d_e							*1006*	*1112*	*1256*	*1465*	*1612*	d_e
	P							4.6	4.8	5.2	5.6	6.0	P
	d_h							*782.61*	*900.00*	*1107.69*	*1285.71*	*1440.00*	d_h
	A							0.9	1.08	1.44	1.8	2.16	A
2000	d_e							*1053*	*1166*	*1365*	*1539*	*1695*	d_e
	P							5.0	5.2	5.6	6.0	6.4	P
	d_h							*800.00*	*923.08*	*1142.86*	*1333.33*	*1500.00*	d_h
	A							1.0	1.2	1.6	2.0	2.4	A

* d_e = equivalent diameter / mm; P = perimeter / m; d_h = hydraulic diameter / mm; A = cross sectional area / m^2

Table 3.A1.2 Recommended sizes for circular ducting (based on BS EN 1506[(A1.2)])

Diameter, d / mm	Perimeter, P / m	Hydraulic diameter, d_h / mm	Cross sectional area, A / m^2
63	0.198	63	0.004
80	0.251	80	0.006
100	0.314	100	0.010
125	0.393	125	0.156
150	0.470	150	0.023
160	0.502	160	0.026
200	0.628	200	0.040
250	0.785	250	0.063
315	0.990	315	0.099
355	1.115	355	0.126
400	1.257	400	0.160
450	1.413	450	0.203
500	1.571	500	0.250
560	1.760	560	0.314
630	1.079	630	0.397
710	2.229	710	0.504
800	2.512	800	0.640
900	2.826	900	0.810
1000	3.142	1000	1.000
1120	3.517	1120	1.254
1250	3.927	1250	1.563

References

3.A1.1 BS EN 1505: 1998 *Ventilation for buildings. Sheet metal air ducts and fittings with rectangular cross-section. Dimensions* (London: British Standards Institution) (1998)

3.A1.2 BS EN 1506: 1998 *Ventilation for buildings. Sheet metal air ducts and fittings with circular cross section. Dimensions* (London: British Standards Institution) (1998)

3.A1.3 *Specification for sheet metal ductwork* HVCA DW/144 (London: Heating and Ventilating Contractors' Association) (1998)

Table 3.A1.3 Recommended sizes for flat oval ducting (from HVCA DW/144[(A1.3)])

Perimeter / m	Width of duct (major axis) / mm for stated depth of duct (minor axis) / mm										
	75	100	125	150	200	250	300	350	400	450	500
0.718	320										
0.798	360	350	330	320							
0.878	400	390	370	360							
0.958	440	430	410	400							
1.037	480	470	450	440							
1.117	520	505	490	480							
1.197		545	530	520							
1.277				555	525						
1.436				635	605	580					
1.596				715	690	660	630				
1.756				800	770	740	710	685	655		
1.915				880	845	825	790	765	735	705	680
2.075				960	930	900	875	845	815	785	755
2.238				1040	1010	985	955	925	895	865	835
2.394				1120	1090	1065	1035	1005	975	945	915
2.553				1200	1170	1145	1115	1085	1055	1025	1000
2.873					1335	1305	1275	1245	1215	1190	1160
3.192						1465	1435	1405	1375	1350	1320
3.511						1625	1595	1570	1540	1510	1480
3.830						1785	1760	1730	1700	1670	1640

Appendix 3.A2: Space allowances

3.A2.1 Space allowances for ductwork

Figure 3.A2.1 shows the recommended space allowances for rectangular, circular and flat oval ductwork(3.A2.1). Figure 3.A2.2 shows recommended space allowances for vertical risers, both insulated and uninsulated(3.A2.2). Access to ducts is governed by the space required to install and insulate the ductwork and this is determined by the clearance from firm objects, the jointing method, and whether or not the ducts are to be insulated after installation. See BS 8313(3.A2.3) for details.

Duct clearances can be reduced with care, providing correct jointing, insulation and maintenance of vapour barriers is achieved. Consideration should also be given to how the ductwork will be tested and, eventually, replaced. See also BSRIA Technical Note TN10/92: *Space allowances for building services distribution systems*(3.A2.1).

3.A2.2 Ductwork access: common problems

3.A2.2.1 Fire dampers

Access to fire dampers must not be obstructed by other services. Clear access must be ensured for inspection and testing. Figure 3.A2.3 illustrates two common problems.

3.A2.2.2 Ceiling-mounted terminal units

A typical installation is shown in Figure 3.A2.4. The ceiling grid immediately beneath the terminal unit should be demountable to facilitate access for removal and replacement of filters, fans, motors or the complete unit, if necessary. Access should be provided which is at least equal to the full plan dimensions of the unit (including control and commissioning valves) plus a minimum allowance of 100 mm on all sides.

3.A2.2.3 False ceilings and raised floors

Table 3.A2.1 shows typical floor-to-floor heights and the heights/depths of typical false floors/ceilings(3.A2.4). Figure 3.A2.5 illustrates some specific points.

References

3.A2.1 *Space allowances for building services distribution systems — detail design stage* BSRIA Technical Note TN10/92 (Bracknell: Building Services Research and Information Association) (1992)

3.A2.2 *Space requirements for plant access, operation and maintenance* Defence Estates Organisation (Works) Design and Maintenance Guide 08 (London: The Stationery Office) (1996)

3.A2.3 BS 8313: 1997 *Code of practice for accommodation of building services in ducts* (London: British Standards Institution) (1997)

3.A2.4 Burberry P *Architects Journal* 26 February 1986

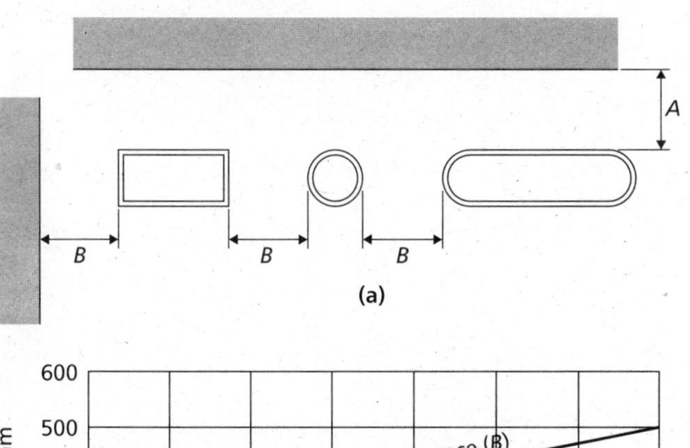

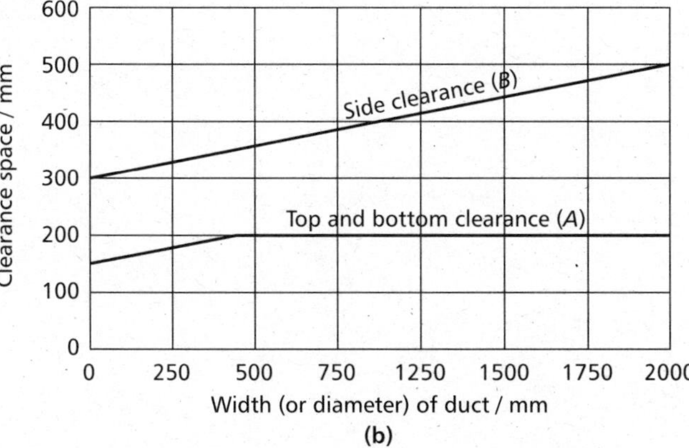

Figure 3.A2.1 Space allowance for rectangular, circular and flat oval ductwork (a) schematic, (b) recommended clearances (reproduced from BSRIA Technical Note TN10/92 (A2.1) by permission of the Building Services Research and Information Association)

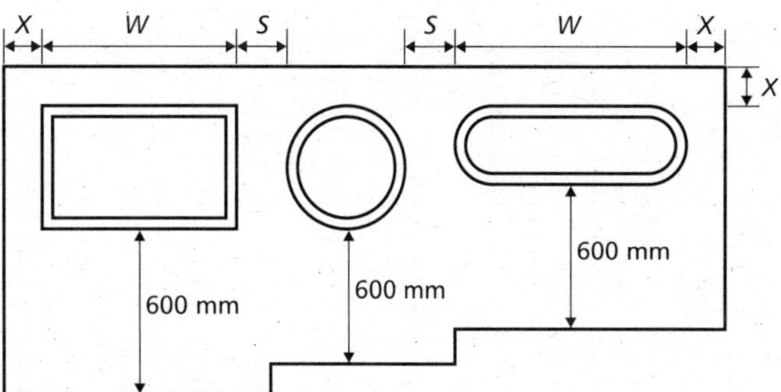

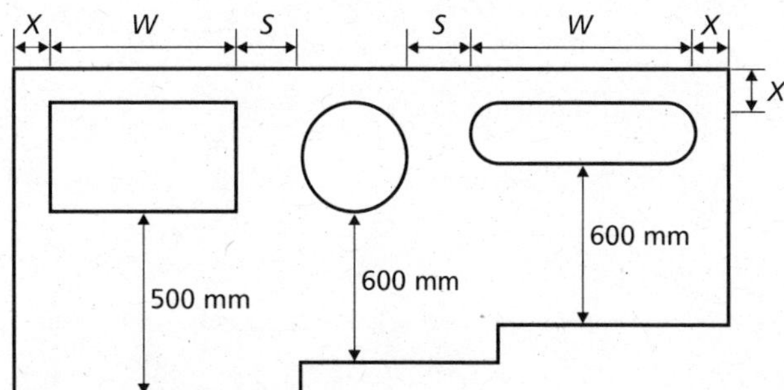

Figure 3.A2.2 Space allowance for rectangular, circular and flat oval ductwork; (a) insulated, (b) uninsulated (reproduced from MoD Design and Maintenance Guide 08(3.A2.2); © Crown copyright material is reproduced with the permission of the Controller of HMSO and Queen's Printer for Scotland)

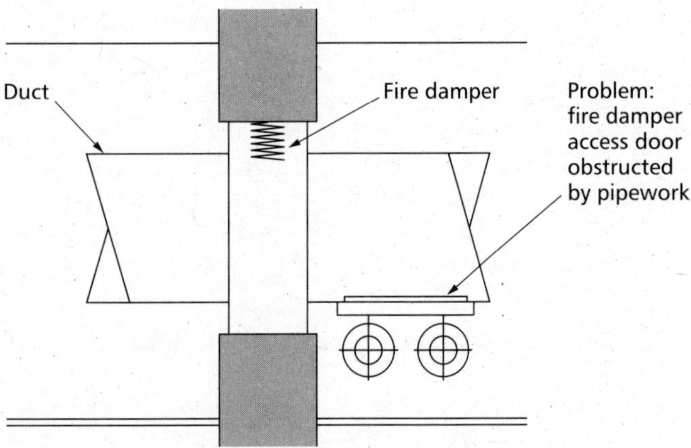

Figure 3.A2.3 Common problems with access to fire dampers (reproduced from MoD Design and Maintenance Guide 08[A2.1]; © Crown copyright material is reproduced with the permission of the Controller of HMSO and Queen's Printer for Scotland)

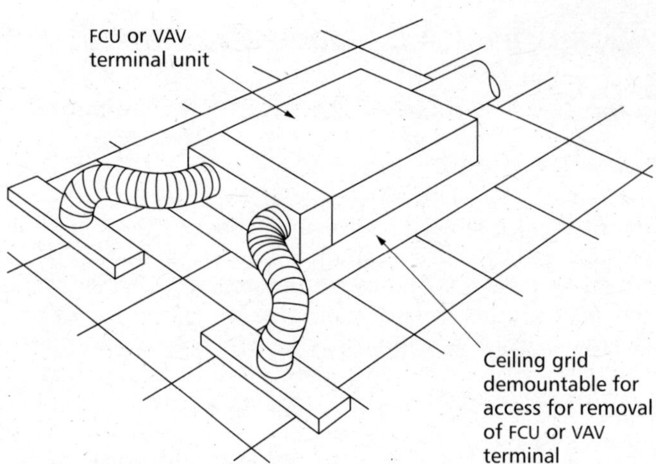

Figure 3.A2.4 Typical ceiling-mounted terminal unit (reproduced from MoD Design and Maintenance Guide 08[A2.1]; © Crown copyright material is reproduced with the permission of the Controller of HMSO and Queen's Printer for Scotland)

Table 3.A2.1 Typical floor-to-floor heights and heights/depths of typical false floors/ceilings[3.A2.4] for offices

Office type	Typical floor-to-floor height / m	Typical false ceiling height / m	Typical false floor depth* / m
Average quality office, refurbished office; average requirements for IT and engineering services	3.6–3.8	0.5–0.6	—
High quality office, minimal perimeter systems; above average requirements for IT and engineering services	3.9–4.2	0.8–1.0	0.4–0.6

* Option to reduce false ceiling height

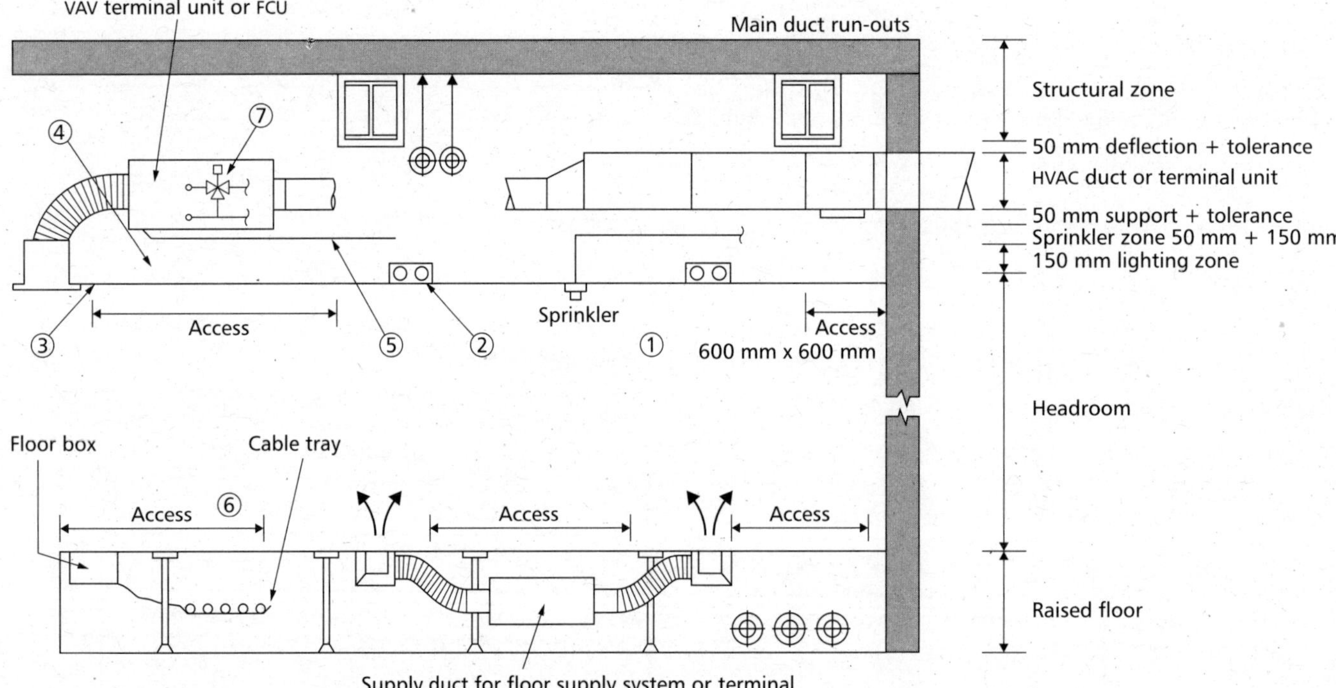

Figure 3.A2.5 False ceilings and raised floors (reproduced from MoD Design and Maintenance Guide 08[3.A2.2]; © Crown copyright material is reproduced with the permission of the Controller of HMSO and Queen's Printer for Scotland)

Appendix 3.A3: Maximum permissible air leakage rates

Table 3.A3.1 shows maximum leakage rates for different static pressure differentials. This information is taken from HVCA specification DW/144(3.A3.1), Table 17. The information is shown graphically in Figure A3.3.1.

Reference

3.A3.1 *Specification for sheet metal ductwork* HVCA DW/144 (London: Heating and Ventilating Contractors' Association) (1998)

Table 3.A3.1 Maximum permissible air leakage rates (reproduced from HCVA DW144(3.A3.1) by permission of the Heating and Ventilating Contractors' Association)

Static pressure differential / Pa	Maximum permissible leakage of ductwork / $(l \cdot s^{-1})$ per m^2 of surface area		
	Low pressure (Class A)	Medium pressure (Class B)	High pressure (Class C)
100	0.54	0.18	—
200	0.84	0.28	—
300	1.10	0.37	—
400	1.32	0.44	—
500	1.53	0.51	—
600	—	0.58	0.19
700	—	0.64	0.21
800	—	0.69	0.23
900	—	0.75	0.25
1000	—	0.80	0.27
1100	—	—	0.29
1200	—	—	0.30
1300	—	—	0.32
1400	—	—	0.33
1500	—	—	0.35
1600	—	—	0.36
1700	—	—	0.38
1800	—	—	0.39
1900	—	—	0.40
2000	—	—	0.42

Note: Recommended 'mean' test pressures are shown in italic type with the actual selection being left to the test operator.

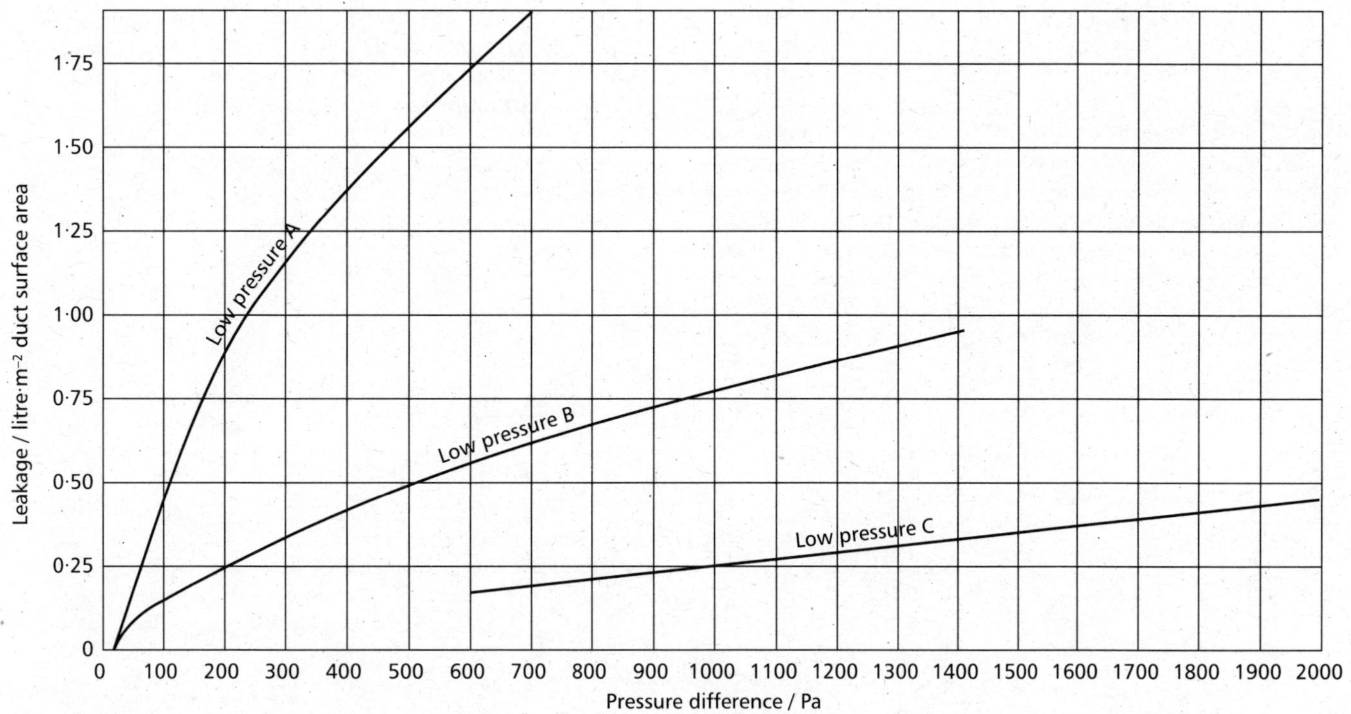

Figure 3.A3.1 Permitted leakage rates at various pressures (reproduced from HCVA DW144(3.A3.1) by permission of the Heating and Ventilating Contractors' Association)

Appendix 3.A4: Summary of fan types and efficiencies

See section 2, Table 2.53 (p2-130).

Appendix 3.A5: Methods of fire protection

The following information is taken from HVCA specification DW/144[(3.A4.1)], Appendix D.

3.A5.1 Protection using fire dampers

The fire is isolated in the compartment of origin by the automatic or manual actuation of closures within the system. Fire dampers should, therefore, be sited at the point of penetration of a compartment wall or floor, or at the point of penetration of the enclosure of a protected escape route.

Fire dampers should be framed in such a way as to allow for thermal expansion in the event of fire, and the design must provide for the protection of any packing material included.

Standard types of fire dampers and frames are described in section 22 of HVCA specification DW/144[(3.A4.1)].

3.A5.2 Protection using fire resisting enclosures

Where a building services shaft is provided through which the ventilation ductwork passes, and if the shaft is constructed to the highest standard of fire resistance of the structure which it penetrates, it forms a compartment known as a 'protected shaft'. This allows a complicated multiplicity of services to be transferred together through a shaft transversing a number of compartments and reaching remote parts of the building, without requiring further internal divisions along its length. The provision of fire dampers is then required only at points where the ventilation duct leaves the confines of the protected shaft. However, if there is only one ventilation duct and there are no other services within the protected shaft, between the fire compartment and the outside of the building, no fire dampers will be required.

3.A5.3 Protection using fire resisting ductwork

In this method of fire protection, the ductwork itself forms a protected shaft. The fire resistance may be achieved by the ductwork material itself, or through the application of a protective material. This is provided that the ductwork has been tested and/or assessed to BS 476: Part 24[(3.A5.2)] with a fire resistance, when tested from either side, that should not be less than the fire resistance required for the elements of construction in the area through which it passes. It should also be noted that the fire resisting ductwork must be supported with suitably sized and designed hangers, which reflect the reduction in tensile strength of steel in a fire condition, i.e.:

— fire resisting ductwork rated at 60 minutes (945 °C): tensile strength is reduced from 430 $N{\cdot}mm^{-2}$ to 15 $N{\cdot}mm^{-2}$

— fire resisting ductwork rated at 120 minutes (1049 °C): tensile strength is reduced to 10 $N{\cdot}mm^{-2}$

— fire resisting ductwork rated at 240 minutes (1153 °C): tensile strength is reduced to 6 $N{\cdot}mm^{-2}$.

Where the fire resisting ductwork passes through a fire compartment wall or floor, a penetration seal must be provided which has been tested and/or assessed with the ductwork to BS 476: Part 24, to the same fire rating as the compartment wall through which the fire resisting ductwork passes. It should also be noted that where the fire resisting ductwork passes through the fire compartment wall or floor, the ductwork itself must be stiffened to prevent deformation of the duct in a fire to:

— maintain the cross-sectional area of the duct

— ensure that the fire rated penetration seal around the duct is not compromised.

References

3.A4.1 *Specification for sheet metal ductwork* HVCA DW/144 (London: Heating and Ventilating Contractors' Association) (1998)

3.A4.2 BS 476: *Fire tests on building materials and structures*; Part 24: 1987: *Method for determination of the fire resistance of ventilation ducts* (British Standards Institution) (1987)

Appendix 3.A6: Example calculations

3.A6.1 Ductwork sizing and pressure drop calculations

Ductwork sizing is so inter-related to pressure drop that the two calculations must be handled together, as will be seen in the following worked example. The ductwork sizing example is in four parts, as follows:

- The first part leads through the ductwork with explanations of the reasons for the first choice of size for each section of ductwork. Some of the sizes could or should be changed later in the light of subsequent calculations. The simple example, see Figure 3.A6.1, is designed to incorporate several different components and illustrate the consequences and choices which can be made. Only the supply ductwork is shown.
- The second part includes the calculations of pressure drop, using data contained in CIBSE Guide C[(3.A6.1)], section 4. A separate but similar calculation would be required for the return ductwork.
- Amendment of some duct sizes in the light of the pressure drop calculations.
- Consideration of the outdoor air supply duct.

3.A6.1.1 System design data

Figure 3.A6.1 illustrates a simple supply system to a suite of six private offices, each requiring 0.2 $m^3 \cdot s^{-1}$ of air. The main ductwork will be in the ceiling void of the corridors. Branches will be in ceiling voids within the offices. Outdoor air will constitute 40% of the total air being treated in the air handling unit (AHU). The main air supply has a winter design temperature of 30 °C.

For initial estimates only, the discharge diffusers will be assumed to give a pressure drop of 20 Pa for a flow of 0.2 $m^3 \cdot s^{-1}$.

It is anticipated that the interior of the building will have a positive pressure of 15 Pa to allow exhaust air to be extracted naturally.

3.A6.1.2 Preliminary sizing and explanation

From CIBSE Guide C[(A6.1)], Appendix 4.A1, properties of air are as follows:

- at 10 °C: $\rho = 1.24$ kg·m^{-3}; $\eta = 17.63 \times 10^{-6}$ kg·m^{-1}·s^{-1}; $c_p = 1.018$ kJ·kg^{-1}·K^{-1}
- at 30 °C: $\rho = 1.16$ kg·m^{-3}; $\eta = 18.55 \times 10^{-6}$ kg·m^{-1}·s^{-1}; $c_p = 1.030$ kJ·kg^{-1}· K^{-1}.

The minimum size of ductwork is constrained by acoustic considerations which limit air speeds. Otherwise life cycle costing should be the important factor, see section 3.4.2. Thus, the limiting air velocities used as a starting point for duct sizing are as follows:

- *at external louvres*: air velocity, c = 2.5 m·s^{-1} (from CIBSE Guide C, Table 4.35)
- *in the AHU*: air velocity, c = 2 m·s^{-1} (face velocity; see Table 3.2)

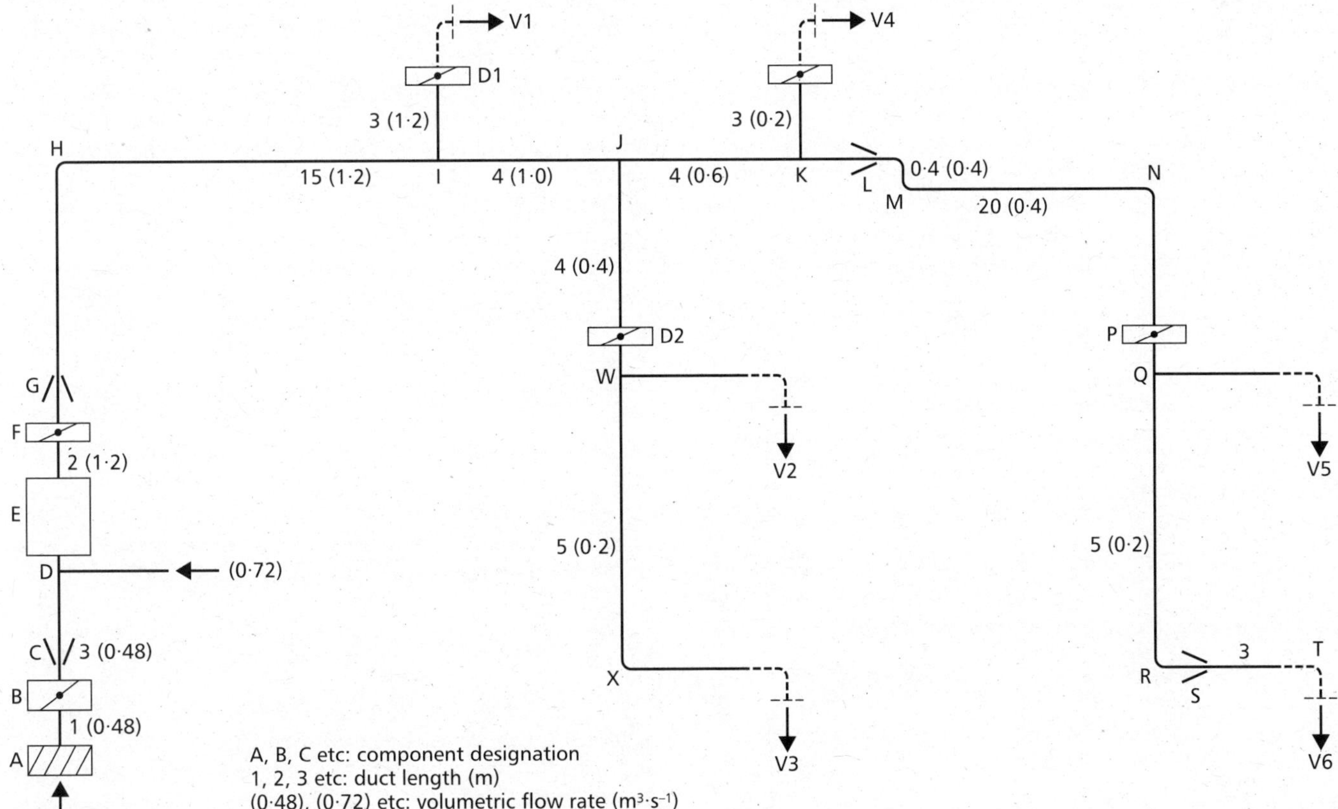

Figure 3.A6.1 Duct layout with lengths (m) and flow rates ($m^3 \cdot s^{-1}$)

— *in main duct*: air velocity, $c = 6$ m·s^{-1} (Table 3.2)

— *in branch duct*: air velocity, $c = 5.5$ m·s^{-1} (Table 3.2)

— *in final duct*: air velocity, $c = 3$ m·s^{-1} (Table 3.2)

External louvres and mesh (A)

The pressure drop through louvres can be considerable. CIBSE Guide C, Table 4.35, recommends a maximum velocity of 2.5 m·s^{-1} through the free area in a 'normal' situation. Provisionally assuming a 90% free area, this implies a maximum face velocity of 2.25 m·s^{-1}.

For a total required airflow rate of 1.2 m^3·s^{-1}, 40% of which is outdoor air, the airflow rate at the inlet is:

$$q = 0.4 \times 1.2 = 0.48 \text{ m}^3\cdot\text{s}^{-1}$$

Hence:

$$A_{min} = q / c = 0.48 / 2.25 = 0.213 \text{ m}^2$$

From Appendix 3.A1, Table 3.A1.1, a rectangular duct measuring 500 mm × 500 mm has a cross-sectional area, $A = 0.25$ m^2.

Substituting back into the previous equation gives velocity, $c = 1.92$ m^3·s^{-1}

(*a*) *External louvres*

CIBSE Guide C, section 4.10.3.32, gives tentative guidance on the friction factor for louvred duct entries. Provisionally assuming louvre ratios, as defined in Guide C, of $(h_i / h) = 0.7$ and $(x / x_1) = 0.9$, and louvres with vertical flat ends (case a), Guide C gives the pressure loss factor, $\zeta = 4.8$.

After selection of an appropriate louvre, the correct figure for pressure drop should be obtained from the manufacturer.

For a typical winter day, outdoor air might have a temperature of 10 °C, hence $\rho = 1.24$ kg·m^{-3}.

(*b*) *Bird mesh*

Provisionally assume a free area of 70%. CIBSE Guide C, section 4.10.3.29 suggests pressure loss factor, $\zeta = 0.58$

Outdoor air inlet damper (B)

Provisionally assuming for the moment that it will be an opposed blade damper with 3 blades, CIBSE Guide C, section 4.10.3.16, suggests pressure loss factors based on the value of parameter x, given by:

$$x = n\, w / [2\,(h + w)]$$

where n is the number of blades, and w and h are the duct width (m) and height (m) respectively. Hence:

$$x = (3 \times 500) / [2 \times (500 + 500)] = 0.75$$

For the damper fully open ($\theta = 0°$), Guide C gives the pressure loss factor $\zeta = 0.52$.

After selection of an appropriate damper, the correct value should be obtained from the manufacturer.

Before continuing with the next item of ductwork, it is necessary to look ahead to the requirements of the air handling unit (E).

This will be handling airflow rate, $q = 1.2$ m^3·s^{-1}. In section 4.2, life cycle costing studies recommend a maximum face velocity of 2 m·s^{-1} for an air handling unit. Hence:

$$A_{min} = q / c = 1.2 / 2.0 = 0.6 \text{ m}^2$$

For this cross-sectional area, Appendix 3.A1, Table 3.A1.1, suggests a rectangular duct measuring 1000 mm × 600 mm, giving $c = 2.0$ m.s^{-1}.

In anticipation of the tee at D, requiring 1000 mm × 600 mm, an expansion taper is included at C. (Clearly there would be a case both for simplicity and a lowering of face velocity if the louvre size had been chosen as 1000 mm × 600 mm in the first place.)

After the AHU, the air has a temperature of 30 °C, for which $\rho = 1.16$ kg·m^{-3}.

Expansion (C)

HVCA specification DW/144[3.A6.2] suggests a maximum taper included angle of $\theta = 45°$.

For expansion from (500 × 500) to (1000 × 600):

$$A_2 / A_1 = (1.0 \times 0.6) / (0.5 \times 0.5) = 2.4$$

For such small expansions, CIBSE Guide C, Table 4.79, shows that the angle of the taper is not very important, so a value of $\theta = 45°$ is chosen.

CIBSE Guide C, section 4.10.3.17, shows the determination of ζ to be quite complex. For a quick calculation, a speculative value might provisionally be taken from the table, especially as this is not a large expansion. Nevertheless a full calculation is demonstrated here. A typical winter temperature of 10 °C is chosen, but this is not critical.

Based on 500 × 500, $d_h = 500$ mm (from Appendix 3.A1, Table 3.A1.1). At (C), the airflow rate is: $q = 0.48$ m^3·s^{-1}. Hence, velocities before and after the expansion taper are: $c_1 = 1.92$ m·s^{-1} and $c_2 = 0.8$ m·s^{-1}. The Reynolds number is then given by:

$$Re_1 = \rho\, c\, d / \eta = (1.24 \times 1.92 \times 0.5) / 17.63 \times 10^{-6}$$
$$= 0.68 \times 10^5$$

Approximately, taking $A_2 / A_1 = 2$, and $Re = 1 \times 10^5$, Guide C, Table 4.79 gives $\zeta = 0.330$. (More accurately, by graphical interpolation, $\zeta = 0.50$.)

Tee, with shoe on the branch (D)

Note that for all tees, the value of ζ is to be used with the velocity pressure of the combined flow. CIBSE Guide C, section 4.10.3.22 applies. The velocity for the combined flow is given by:

$$c_c = 1.2 / (1.0 \times 0.6) = 2.0 \text{ m}\cdot\text{s}^{-1}$$

For converging flow, the ratio of straight flow rate to combined flow rate is:

$$q_s / q_c = 0.48 / 1.2 = 0.4$$

From CIBSE Guide C, Table 4.88, the pressure loss factor for straight flow is: $\zeta_{s-c} = 0.22$.

Assume that the branch, carrying 0.72 $m^3 \cdot s^{-1}$, has a size 300 mm × 400 mm; hence $c = 6$ $m \cdot s^{-1}$. Therefore, ratio of branch flow rate to combined flow rate is:

$$q_b / q_c = 0.72 / 1.2 = 0.6$$

Hence, from CIBSE Guide C, Table 4.89, the pressure loss factor for branch flow (not required at the moment) is: $\zeta_{b-c} = 1.03$.

(Note that without a shoe, CIBSE Guide C, section 4.10.3.21, shows that the pressure loss factor for straight flow would have 0.46, i.e. twice that for a tee with a shoe on the branch.)

Air handling unit (ahu) (E)

The air handling unit, including heater battery, filter and fan, may be regarded as a 'black box' which must provide a pressure rise, external to itself, equal to the total pressure drop around the whole air circuit, supply and return.

Control damper, opposed blade, 3 blades (F)

As a first estimate, using CIBSE Guide C, section 4.10.3.16 (see above, section A6.1.2.2), parameter x is given by:

$$x = (3 \times 0.6) / [2 \times (0.6 + 0.6)] = 0.75$$

For the damper fully open ($\theta = 0$), hence $\zeta = 0.52$.

After selection of the damper, the correct value must be obtained from the manufacturer.

Duct (G–H–I)

For a building containing private offices, Table 3.2 gives the maximum permitted velocity in a main duct as 6 $m \cdot s^{-1}$. This also accords with figures derived from life cycle costing.

Again, using the expression $A = q / c$, the required cross-sectional areas of the duct is:

$$A = 1.2 / 6.0 = 0.2 \text{ m}^2$$

Appendix 3.A1, Table 3.A1.1, suggests either 600 mm by 400 mm, or 500 mm by 400 mm ductwork. For this example 500 mm by 400 mm is chosen, and the orientation such as to make the following bend (H), an 'easy' bend, i.e. $w = 400$ mm, $h = 500$ mm.

From the same table, the equivalent diameter is:

$$d_e = 492 \text{ mm}$$

Contraction (G)

For reduction from (1000 × 600) to (400 × 500), the ratio of cross-sectional areas is:

$$A_2 / A_1 = (400 \times 500) / (1000 \times 600) = 0.333$$

The maximum taper recommended in HVCA specification DW/144(3.A6.2) is an included angle $\theta = 45°$.

CIBSE Guide C, section 4.10.3.18, shows that for contractions the included angle is not important and ζ is small. Note that ζ is to be used with the outlet velocity, c_2. An included angle of 45° is chosen hence, from CIBSE Guide C, Table 4.80, by interpolation: $\zeta = 0.055$.

The outlet velocity is:

$$c_2 = q / A_2 = 1.2 / (0.4 \times 0.5) = 6.0 \text{ m·s}^{-1}$$

Bend, with splitter vanes (H)

CIBSE Guide C section 4.10.3.2 applies. For $400 < w < 800$, Table 3.5 (based on HVCA specification DW/144(3.A6.2)) recommends a single splitter vane. The HVCA standard radius for bends is r = w, and this radius will be used. Hence:

$$h / w = 500 / 400 = 1.25$$

From CIBSE Guide C, Table 4.63, $\zeta = 0.05$.

Note that this value is considerably less than would have been the case without the vane. CIBSE Guide C, Table 4.60 would then apply, giving $\zeta = 0.23$. Note also that, although the DW/144(3.A6.2) standard bend radius is $r = w$, a worthwhile reduction in friction losses would be achieved by increasing the curvature to $r = 1.5\ w$.

Typical branch (I–D1–V1)

The 'index run', i.e. the pipe run likely to give the highest pressure loss, would appear to be the run from G to R to V6. In reality, it would depend upon the route taken by the return duct from the room supplied at V6.

Thus at the next few tees, it is necessary to consider only the pressure loss factors for straight flow, ζ_{c-s}. Since the pressure drop incurred by tees depends upon the relative size of the branch, it is worth digressing at this point to consider the branches to the final run outs.

In this example, each final branch has the same flow. It is more convenient for the branches to be circular, especially as it is convenient to make the final connection to a diffuser by a flexible duct. However the length of such flexible ducts should be kept to a minimum as their pressure loss is high.

Taking a typical branch, I–D1–V1, assumed now to be within the office space, noise is the most important criterion, therefore velocity $c < 3$ $m \cdot s^{-1}$ (see Appendix 3.A1, Table 3.A1.1). Generally, even lower velocities are used, a velocity $c = 2.5$ $m \cdot s^{-1}$ will be assumed. Hence, the branch duct area is:

$$A = q / c = 0.2 / 2.5 = 0.08 \text{ m}^2$$

For a circular duct, this gives a minimum diameter d_{min} = 319 mm. This is so close to a standard size of 315 mm that the difference might be considered trivial. Furthermore this is a branch which provides an air route of minimum length and resistance. It is tempting to have the smaller diameter for this first branch and larger branches for the others, but this might lead to confusion for the installers. As the branch ducts are short it might be thought that the pressure drop will be small. However, the use of a short length of flexible ductwork for the final connection to the diffuser can add a disproportionate pressure drop. For these reasons, d = 315 mm is chosen for the branch diameter.

For d_b = 315 mm, the branch cross-sectional area is A_b = 0.0779 m^2. Hence, the ratio of the cross-sectional area of the branch to that of the main duct flow is:

$$A_b / A_c = 0.0779 / (0.5 \times 0.4) = 0.390$$

The air velocity in the branch is:

$$c_b = q_b / A_b = 0.2 / 0.0779 = 2.57 \text{ m·s}^{-1}.$$

Tee (with shoe) (I)

For the rectangular main duct (500 × 400): A_c = 0.2 m^2, q_c = 1.2 m^3·s^{-1}, hence c_c = 6 m·s^{-1}

For the circular branch (d = 315 mm): A_b = 0.0779 m^2, q_b = 0.2 m^3·s^{-1}.

Hence:

$$A_b / A_c = 0.0779 / 0.2 = 0.39$$

$$q_b / q_c = 0.2 / 1.2 = 0.166$$

$$q_s / q_c = 1.0 / 1.2 = 0.833$$

For 'straight' flow, CIBSE Guide C, Table 4.113 for diverging flow, gives, by interpolation: ζ_{c-s} = 0.012.

For flow through the branch, Guide C Table C 4.114 for diverging flow, gives, by interpolation: ζ_{c-b} = 0.830

(Note that the pressure drop to the branch is less than it would be without the shoe, but is still considerably greater than that for the straight, which is to be expected.)

Branch (J–X)

This is required to carry 0.4 m^3·s^{-1} with a limiting speed of 5.5 m·s^{-1}. This implies a diameter of 304 mm. There would seem little option but to choose circular ductwork the next size up, i.e. 315 mm, though rectangular ductwork 300 mm × 250 mm could be chosen.

Ducts (I–J and J–K)

The straight runs I–J and J–K are short enough not to justify the complication of reductions in size, so, for convenience, the duct dimensions will remain the same as for ductwork run (G–H–I), i.e. 500 mm × 400 mm.

Tee (with shoe) (J)

For the rectangular main duct (500 mm × 400 mm): A_c = 0.2 m^2, q_c = 1.0 m^3·s^{-1}, hence c_c = 5 m·s^{-1}.

For the circular branch (d = 315 mm): A_b = 0.0779 m^2, q_b = 0.4 m^3·s^{-1}.

Hence:

$$A_b / A_c = 0.0779 / 0.2 = 0.39$$

$$q_b / q_c = 0.4 / 1.0 = 0.4$$

$$q_s / q_c = 0.6 / 1.0 = 0.6$$

For 'straight' flow, CIBSE Guide C, Table 4.113 for diverging flow, gives, by interpolation: ζ_{c-s} = 0.064.

(Note that, since A_b / A_c is very close to the break point between two lines of data, an interpretation could be made such as to take the average of the two values for q_b / q_c = 0.4; this would give ζ_{c-s} = 0)

Tee (without shoe) (K)

For the rectangular main duct (500 mm × 400 mm): A_c = 0.2 m^2, q_c = 0.6 m^3·s^{-1}, hence c_c = 3 m·s^{-1}.

For the circular branch (d = 315 mm): A_b = 0.0779 m^2, q_b = 0.2 m^3·s^{-1}.

Hence:

$$A_b / A_c = 0.0779 / 0.2 = 0.39$$

$$q_s / q_c = 0.4 / 0.6 = 0.667$$

For 'straight' flow, CIBSE Guide C, Table 4.108 for diverging flow, gives, by interpolation: ζ_{c-s} = 0.045.

Duct (L–M–Q)

This main branch could tolerate velocities up to 5.5 m·s^{-1}. The ductwork could conveniently be circular.

Hence, for q = 0.4 m^3·s^{-1}:

$$A_{min} = q / c = 0.4 / 5.5 = 0.0727 \text{ m}^2$$

$$d_{min} = 304 \text{ mm}$$

A diameter of 315 mm could easily be chosen here, but since this is the index run, it is advisable to minimise pressure losses along this run as this will make subsequent balancing easier. Therefore the next size up is selected: d = 355 mm.

Hence:

$$A_c = 0.100 \text{ m}^2$$

Contraction, rectangular to circular (L)

For reduction from rectangular (500 mm × 400 mm) to circular (d = 355 mm), with a maximum taper angle of θ = 45°, CIBSE Guide C, section 4.10.4.2 applies.

$$A_2 / A_1 = 0.1 / 0.2 = 0.5$$

For an included angle of 45°, from CIBSE Guide C, Table 4.80, by interpolation: ζ = 0.055.

The outlet velocity is:

$$c_2 = q / A_2 = 0.4 / 0.1 = 4.0 \text{ m·s}^{-1}$$

CIBSE Guide C, section 4.10.3.18, shows that for contractions the included angle is not important and ζ is small. Note that ζ is to be used with the outlet velocity, c_2.

Segmented bends in close proximity (M)

CIBSE Guide C, section 4.10.5.4 applies. Separation of bends, l = 400 mm, so (l / d) = 400 / 355 = 1.1; (r / d) = 1 for each bend. The Reynolds number is given by:

$$Re = \rho \, c \, d / \eta = 1.16 \times 4.0 \times 0.355 / (18.55 \times 10^{-6})$$
$$= 0.888 \times 10^5$$

From CIBSE Guide C, Table 4.122, by interpolation, C_2 = 1.90. (Note that the caption to Table 4.122 refers in error to 'ζ_2'.) This means that the interaction of the bends due to their close proximity is such as to give a pressure drop less than two isolated bends. For such combinations of bends, from CIBSE Guide C, section 4.10.5.4, the pressure loss factor for the combination (ζ) is related to the pressure loss factor for a single bend (ζ_1), i.e.:

$$\zeta = C_2 \, \zeta_1$$

From CIBSE Guide C, Table C 4.119, for a single bend: ζ_1 = 0.305. Hence:

$$\zeta = 1.90 \times 0.305 = 0.580$$

90° segmented bend (N)

By interpolation, from CIBSE Guide, Table 4.119, for (r / d) = 1, R_e = 0.9 × 105, d = 355 mm:

$$\zeta = 0.305$$

Fire damper (P)

This should have a totally clear area when open, presenting a small resistance. Provisionally, until manufacturer's data are available, assume ζ = 0.12.

Tee (without shoe) (Q)

For the circular main duct (d_c = 355 mm): A_c = 0.10 m^2, q_c = 0.4 m^3·s^{-1}.

For the circular branch (d_b = 315 mm): A_b = 0.0779 m^2, q_b = 0.2 m^3.s^{-1}.

Hence:

$$A_b / A_c = 0.0779 / 0.10 = 0.78$$
$$q_b / q_c = 0.2 / 0.4 = 0.5$$

CIBSE Guide C, Table C 4.133 for diverging flow, gives: ζ_{c-s} = 0.

Duct (Q–R)

Logically, the diameter could be reduced to 315 mm. However, since this is the index run, it is better to minimise pressure loss, therefore it is better to maintain the duct diameter as 355 mm until after the final bend R.

90° segmented bend (R)

The air velocity is given by:

$$c = q / A = 0.2 / 0.1 = 2.0 \text{ m·s}^{-1}$$

Hence, the Reynolds number is:

$$Re = \rho \, c \, d / \eta = 1.16 \times 2.0 \times 0.355 / (18.55 \times 10^{-6})$$
$$= 0.44 \times 10^5$$

From CIBSE Guide, Table 4.119:

$$\zeta = 0.35$$

Symmetrical contraction (S)

For reduction from d_1 = 355 mm to d_2 = 315 mm, ratio of cross-sectional areas is:

$$A_2 / A_1 = (315 / 355)^2 = 0.79$$

CIBSE Guide C, section 4.10.5.9 applies. For an included angle θ = 45°, CIBSE Guide C, Table 4.126 gives, by extrapolation: ζ = 0.055.

The outlet velocity is:

$$c_2 = q / A_2 = 0.2 / 0.0779 = 2.57 \text{ m·s}^{-1}$$

90° segmented bend (T)

The Reynolds number is given by:

$$Re = \rho \, c \, d / \eta = 1.16 \times 2.57 \times 0.315 / (18.55 \times 10^{-6})$$
$$= 0.51 \times 10^5$$

By interpolation, from CIBSE Guide C, Table 4.119, for (r / d) = 1, Re = 0.51 × 10^5 and d = 315 mm:

$$\zeta = 0.36$$

Diffuser (V)

Provisionally, take:

$$\Delta p = 20 \text{ Pa}$$

3.A6.1.3 Calculation of pressure drop

For each duct fitting, along what is believed to be the index run, the pressure drop is given by:

$$\Delta p_t = \zeta \, {}^1\!/_2 \, \rho \, c^2$$

Appropriate values have already been obtained in section 3.A6.1.2 above, and a table of the calculations is shown as Table 3.A6.1.

For the straight lengths of duct, Figure 3.12 is used to obtain the pressure drop per unit length. The calculations are shown in Table 3.A6.2.

The pressure drops obtained in Tables 3.A6.1 and 3.A6.2 are summed to give a drop in total pressure of 70.4 Pa.

3.A6.1.4 Amendment to duct sizes to improve balance

Although the duct sizing has, by normal criteria, been on the generous side, the pressure drop along the index run is nevertheless dominated by the pressure drop along G–I and L–Q. If the design is left as it is, then branch run (I–D1–V1) will require considerable additional resistance by closing damper D1, which could cause additional noise generation. Furthermore, the system pressure drop will consequently always be greater and incur constant additional fan power and energy costs. Consideration should always be given to the alternative solution of reducing the pressure loss in the index run by increasing the duct size along the 'problem' runs. To illustrate this, the duct size from L–S could be increased to the next size up.

Table 3.A6.3 illustrates the effect of increasing the diameter of duct run (L–S) from 355 mm 400 mm. The effect is to reduce friction pressure drop by 10.8, some 16% of the total pressure drop, which would be worth achieving.

Table 3.A6.4 gives a break-down of the pressure drop incurred along the index run to V6 with the increased duct sizes. The drop in total pressure is now 59.7 Pa.

Before finally accepting these design sizes, it is worth checking on the pressure drop incurred by the airflow along the shortest duct run, namely E to V1, see Table 3.A6.5.

Note that the pressure drops along the index run (see Table 3.A6.4) and along the shortest run (see Table

Table 3.A6.1 Calculation of pressure drops for fittings in the index run of supply ductwork (E–V6)

Item	Description	Guide C table ref.	Appropriate air velocity	Air velocity / m·s^{-1}	($\frac{1}{2}\rho c^2$) / Pa	Pressure loss factor, ζ	Pressure drop, Δp / Pa
A_1	Louvre	4.104	—	1.92	2.29	4.8*	11.0
A_2	Mesh screen	4.102	—	1.92	2.29	0.58	1.3
B	Outdoor air inlet damper	4.78	—	1.92	2.29	0.52*	1.2
C	Expansion taper	4.79	c_1	1.92	2.29	0.33	0.8
D	Tee, shoe, converging (straight flow)	4.88	c_c	2.0	2.48	0.22	0.5
D	Tee, shoe, converging (branch flow)	4.89	c_c	2.0	2.4	1.03	2.5
E	Air handling unit (AHU)	—	—	—	—	—	—
F	Damper	4.78		2.0	2.32	0.52*	1.2
G	Contraction taper (rect.)	4.80	c_2	6.0	20.9	0.055	1.1
H	90° bend with vane (rect.)	4.63	—	6.0	20.9	0.05	1.0
I	Tee, shoe, diverging	4.108	c_c	6.0	20.9	0.012	0.3
J	Tee, shoe	4.108	c_c	5.0	14.5	0	0
K	Tee	4.108	c_c	3.0	5.22	0.045	0.2
L	Contraction taper (rect. → circ.)	4.80	c_2	4.0	9.28	0.055	0.5
M	Double bend	4.122	—	4.0	9.28	0.58	5.4
N	Bend	4.119	—	4.0	9.28	0.305	2.8
P	Fire damper	—	—	4.0	9.28	0.12*	1.1
Q	Tee	4.133	c_c	4.0	9.28	0	0
R	Bend	4.119	—	2.0	2.32	0.35	0.8
S	Contraction (circ.)	4.126	c_2	2.57	3.83	0.055	0.2
T	Bend	4.119	—	2.57	3.83	0.36	1.4
V6	Diffuser	—	—	—	—	—	20.0*
						Total (E–V6):	36.0
I	Tee (branch flow)	4.108	c_c	6	20.9	0.83	17.3

* provisional value to be replaced with manufacturer's data following selection of equipment

Note: items A, B and C have not been added into the total, as the outdoor air supply is not in series with the return ductwork and will have to be considered separately later. Similarly, although the pressure drops across tee D have been illustrated, this would constitute part of the calculations for the return air ductwork.

Table 3.A6.2 Calculations for straight ductwork in the index run of supply ductwork (E–V6)

Run	Air velocity, c / m·s^{-1}	Duct length / m	Flow rate, q / m^3·s^{-1}	Dimensions / (mm × mm)	Equiv. diam., d_e / mm	$\Delta p / l$ Pa·m^{-1}	Pressure drop, Δp / Pa
A–B	1.92	1	0.48	500 × 500	545	0.09	0.1
C–D	0.8	3	0.48	1000 × 600	848	0.01	0
E–G	2.0	2	1.2	1000 × 600	848	0.01	0
G–I	6.0	15	1.2	500 × 400	492	1.0	15.0
I–J	5.0	4	1.0	500 × 400	492	0.75	3.0
J–K	3.0	4	0.6	500 × 400	492	0.29	1.2
K–L	2.0	1	0.4	500 × 400	492	0.13	0.1
L–Q	4.0	20.4	0.4	—	355	0.6	12.2
Q–S	2.0	5	0.2	—	355	0.16	0.8
S–T	2.57	3	0.2	—	315	0.34	1.0
T_1–T_2	2.57	0.4	0.2	—	315	8 × 0.35*	1.1
						Total (E–T_2):	34.4

* Flexible duct giving estimated pressure drop of 8 times that of smooth duct

Note: pressure drops along A–B and C–D have not been added into the total, as the fresh air supply is not in series with the return ductwork, and will have to be considered separately later.

Table 3.A6.3 Effect of a increasing diameter for duct run L–S

Item	Description	Length, l / m	$\Delta p / l$ Pa·m^{-1}	Pressure loss factor, ζ	($\frac{1}{2}\rho\, c^2$) / Pa	New pressure drop, Δp / Pa	Old pressure drop, Δp / Pa	Reduction / Pa
L–Q	Duct	20.4	0.28	—	—	6.1	12.2	6.1
Q–S	Duct	5	0.075	—	—	0.4	0.8	0.4
L	Contraction	—	—	0.055	5.88	0.3	0.5	0.2
M	Double bend	—	—	0.532	5.88	3.1	5.4	2.3
N	Bend	—	—	0.28	5.88	1.6	2.8	1.2
P	Fire damper	—	—	0.12*	5.88	0.7	1.1	0.4
Q	Tee	—	—	0.05	5.88	0.3	0	–0.3
R	Bend	—	—	0.282	1.47	0.4	0.9	0.5
S	Contraction	—	—	0.055	10.4	0.2	0.2	0
							Total saving:	10.8

* provisional value to be replaced with manufacturer's data following selection of equipment

Table 3.A6.4 Table of final calculations for ductwork and fittings in the index run (E–V6)

Item	Description	Dimensions / (mm × mm)	Length, l / m	$\Delta p / l$ / Pa·m^{-1}	Air vel., c / m·s^{-1}	($\frac{1}{2}\rho\, c^2$) / Pa	Press. loss factor, ζ	Press. drop, Δp / Pa
E–G	Duct	1000 × 600	2	0.01	2	2.4	—	0
F	Damper	1000 × 600	—	—	2	2.4	0.52*	1.2
G	Contraction taper (rect.)	—	—	—	6	20.9	0.055	1.1
H	90° bend, with vane (rect.)	500 × 400	—	—	6	20.9	0.05	1.0
G–I	Duct	500 × 400	15	1.0	6	20.9	—	15.0
I	Tee, shoe, diverging	500 × 400	—	—	6	20.9	0.012	0.3
I–J	Duct	500 × 400	4	0.75	5	14.5	—	3.0
J	Tee	500 × 400	—	—	5	14.5	0	0
J–K	Duct	500 × 400	4	0.29	3	5.22	—	1.2
K	Tee	500 × 400	—	—	3	5.22	0.045	0.2
K–L	Duct	500 × 400	1	0.13	2	2.32	—	0.1
L	Contraction taper (rect. → circ.)	400	—	—	3.18	5.88	0.055	0.3
M	Double bend (circ.)	400	—	—	3.18	5.88	0.536	3.1
N	Bend (circ.)	400	—	—	3.18	5.88	0.282	1.6
P	Fire damper (circ.)	400	—	—	3.18	5.88	0.12*	0.7
L–Q	Duct (circ.)	400	20.4	0.3	3.18	5.88	—	6.1
Q	Tee, without shoe (circ.)	400	—	—	3.18	5.88	0.05	0.3
R	Bend (circ.)	400	—	—	1.59	1.5	0.282	0.4
Q–S	Duct (circ.)	400	5	0.075	1.59	1.5	—	0.4
S	Contraction (circ.)	400 → 315	—	—	2.57	3.96	0.055	0.2
T	Bend (circ.)	315	—	—	2.57	3.96	0.36	1.4
S–T	Duct (circ.)	315	3	0.34	2.57	3.96	—	1.0
T–T	Flexible duct (circ.)	315	0.4	2.8*	2.57	3.96	—	1.1
V6	Diffuser	—	—	—	—	—	—	20.0*
							Total (E–V6):	59.7
I	Tee (branch flow)	315	—	—	6	20.9	0.83	17.3

* provisional value to be replaced with manufacturer's data following selection of equipment

3.A6.5) are now almost in balance, being 59.7 and 61.2 Pa respectively. This is due to the decision to employ larger size ductwork along the index run, and also to the fact that flow round to the branch at tee I is considerably more than along the straight, despite the shoe. Normally the control damper D1 would need to provide an additional pressure drop, but in this instance it is not necessary. Similar calculations should be carried out for each air route.

Assuming that all the air flow runs can be adjusted to have the same loss of total pressure, the 'design flow rates' should then occur. Note that the total pressure drop for the circuit is only that for one circuit as all the routes are in parallel.

At this stage the return ductwork has been neither designed nor sized. The exercise is similar to the above calculations for the supply ductwork. In this example, only 60% of the total air flow is to be recirculated. The pressure

Table 3.A6.5 Final pressure drops for shortest run (E–V1)

Item	Description	Length, l / m	Dimensions / (mm × mm)	Pressure drop, Δp / Pa
D–G	Straight duct	2.0	1000 × 600	0
G–I	Straight duct	15.0	500 × 400	15.0
I–V1	Straight duct	3.0 + 0.4	315 (diam.)	2.1
G	Contraction	—	—	1.1
H	Bend	—	500 × 400	1.0
I	Tee (branch flow)	—	500 × 400	17.3
T	Bend	—	315 (diam.)	1.4
F	Damper	—	1000 × 600	1.2*
D1	Damper	—	315 (diam.)	2.1*
V1	Diffuser	—	—	20.0*
			Total (supply run) (E–V1):	61.2

* provisional value to be replaced with manufacturer's data following selection of equipment

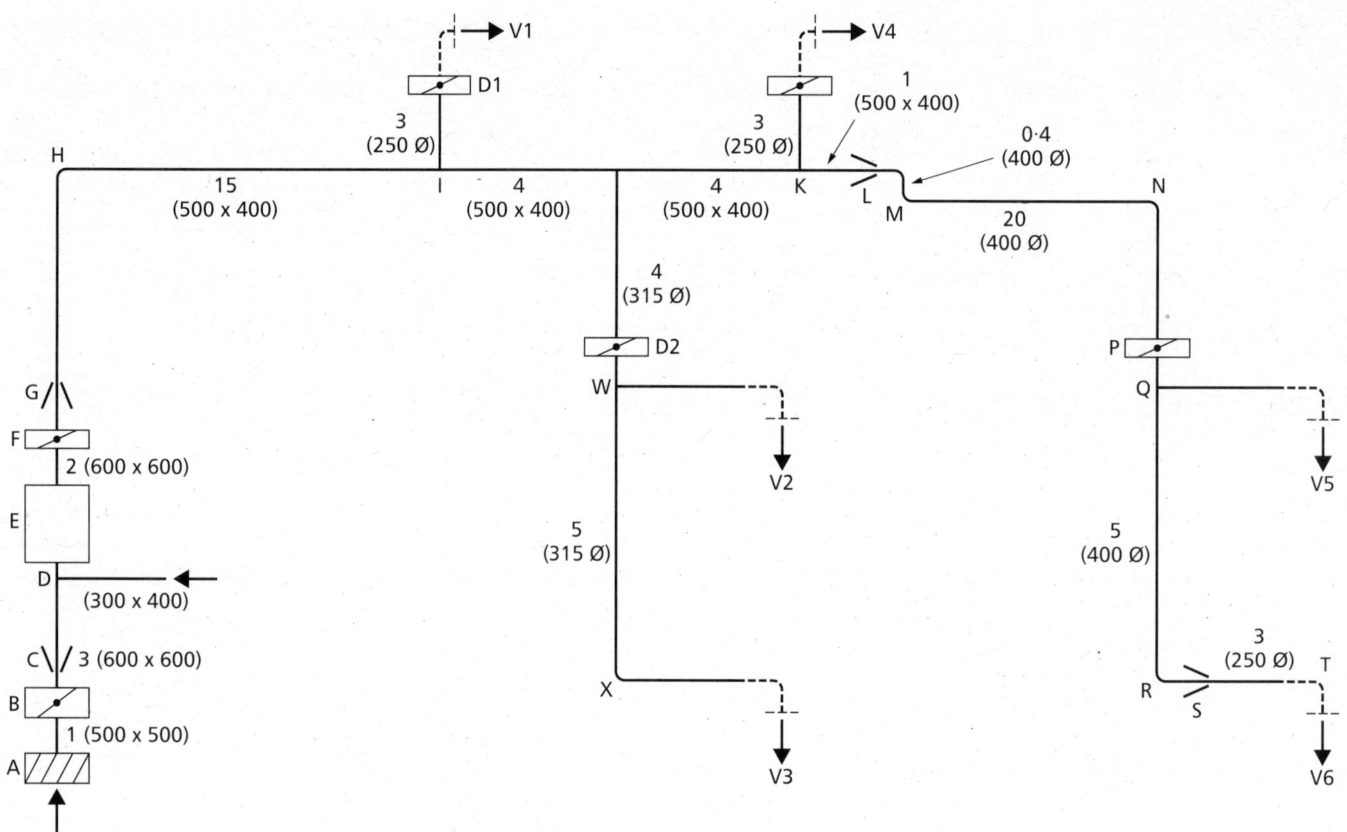

Figure 3.A6.2 Final duct layout with lengths (m) and sizes (mm)

drops calculated would in general be very similar, except to note that the pressure drop through an extract grille will, or should be, considerably less than that through a supply diffuser. For the purposes of this example, a return airflow of 0.72 $m^3 \cdot s^{-1}$ is assumed, incurring a pressure drop of 50 Pa. This would give rise to a total pressure drop for the circuit of (60 + 50) Pa = 110 Pa.

Note that a cost–benefit analysis of enlarging duct L–S might not in isolation justify such enlargement. However, the 'knock-on' effects should not be overlooked; i.e. the pressure drop on the other four air routes would be affected such that dampers in non-index run routes might require less trimming. It has already been shown that, for example, damper D1 will require no measurable trimming.

The final duct layout using the amended duct sizes is shown in Figure 3.A6.2.

3.A6.1.5 Outdoor air supply

Note that, up to this point, the effect of the outdoor air inlet has not been considered because it does not constitute part of the main airflow loop. A few assumptions will now be made to illustrate the effect.

Suppose that the air leaks from each room to the external air resulted in the air within each room having a pressure of 15 Pa above the pressure outside the building. The pressure drop in the return ductwork (Δp_t) was found to be 50 Pa (see section 3.A6.1.4). Thus, the total pressure just before the air handling unit (E), will be (–50 + 15) Pa =–35 Pa.

Table 3.A6.6 draws together the fresh air inlet duct calculations from Tables 3.A6.1 and 3.A6.2. This shows that, for the design flow of outdoor air, the pressure drop is 15.0 Pa. This needs to be 35 Pa so that the right quantity of outdoor air is drawn in. This can be achieved either by closing down damper B considerably, or by selecting a smaller louvre and mesh screen.

These considerations of the outdoor air supply duct have no bearing on the fan selection which follows.

Table 3.A6.6 Pressure drops for outdoor air supply (A–E)

Item	Description	Length, l / m	Dimensions / (mm × mm)	Pressure drop Δp / Pa
A–B	Straight duct	1.0	500 × 500	0.1
C–E	Straight duct	3.0	1000 × 600	0
A	Louvre/mesh screen	—	500 × 500	12.3
B	Outdoor air inlet damper	—	500 × 500	1.2
C	Expansion taper	—	—	0.8
D	Tee, shoe, converging (straight flow)	—	—	0.5
			Total (A–E):	15.0

3.A6.2 Choice of fan or air handling unit (AHU)

3.A6.2.1 Fan specification

The air handling unit will be required to provide, external to the unit, an increase in total pressure of 110 Pa for a volumetric airflow rate of 1.2 $m^3 \cdot s^{-1}$.

The question of margins or safety factors sometimes arises. There is little point in adding a margin to both the air flow and to the pressure drop since an increased air flow in the calculations automatically causes a larger pressure drop. For low pressure ductwork, air leakage is likely to be trivial so there is no need to add a safety margin. However, although the accuracy of the pressure drop data has improved considerably over recent years, the published values are not precise. Therefore a margin of 10% could be added.

If a margin of 10% is added to the estimated pressure loss calculation of the ductwork, the air handling unit would be required to provide a rise in total pressure of 121 Pa for a flow of 1.2 $m^3 \cdot s^{-1}$.

Within the air handling unit there will be a considerable pressure drop through the filter and through the heat exchanger (also know as the 'heating coil'). However, for packaged units it is the responsibility of the supplier to select the fan so as to meet the pressure drop of the components within the unit and the ductwork.

If the fan is selected independently of any packaged air handling unit, then it is to be hoped that matching the system characteristic to the fan performance characteristic will result in an operating point somewhere near the point of maximum efficiency. If not, further amendments to the duct sizes might prove advisable. If the estimated level of the fan noise is found to be excessive, then the inclusion of sound attenuators may be necessary; this would add appreciably to the pressure drop and may require a different fan to be chosen.

3.A6.2.2 Specific fan power

Building Regulations Approved Document L[(3.A6.3)] imposes a limit on 'specific fan power'. This is defined as the sum of the design total circuit-watts, including all losses through switchgear and controls such as inverters, of all fans that supply air and exhaust it back outdoors (i.e. the sum of the supply and extract fans), divided by the design ventilation rate through the building.

For AC/MV systems in new buildings, the SFP should be no greater than 2 $W \cdot s \cdot litre^{-1}$, i.e. 2 $kW \cdot s \cdot m^{-3}$.

It is impossible at this stage to predict the electrical power consumption of the AHU, which has yet to be selected. However, since the total outside air requirement is 1.2 $m^3 \cdot s^{-1}$, the SFP will limit the consumption to 2.4 kW.

To illustrate the consequences, the following assumptions will be made:

— fan total efficiency, $\eta_f = 80\%$

— fan motor efficiency, $\eta_m = 85\%$

— pressure drop across the filter and heat exchanger = 200 Pa

From section 3.A6.1.4, the pressure drops for the supply and return ductwork are 60 Pa and 50 Pa, respectively. Therefore, the total pressure rise (including 10% margin) required is given by:

$$[(\Delta p_{t(supply)} + \Delta p_{t(return)}) \times 1.1] + \Delta p_{t(other\ components)}$$
$$= (110 \times 1.1) + 200 = 321 \text{ Pa}$$

The air power required is:

$$q\,\Delta p = 1.2 \times 321 \text{ m}^3\cdot\text{s}^{-1}\cdot\text{Pa} = 385 \text{ W}$$

Total electrical power required for fans:

$$P_e = (q\,\Delta p) / \eta_f\,\eta_m = 385 / (0.8 \times 0.85) = 0.566 \text{ kW}$$

Specific fan power:

$$\text{SFP} = P_e / q = 0.566 / 1.2 = 0.472 \text{ kW}\cdot\text{s}\cdot\text{m}^{-3}$$

This is well within the limit imposed by Approved Document L2, as would be expected for the very simple system used in the example. A larger, more realistic system, with more tortuous duct runs and sound attenuators, would incur much greater pressure losses, necessitating a more powerful fan and motor, and thus lead to a higher specific fan power.

3.A6.3 Air leakage

Up to this point, only total pressure and drops in total pressure of the air have been considered. However, air leakage depends upon the actual pressure (static pressure) of the air in the duct relative to that outside the duct. It is impossible to predict this value, though it can be measured after installation. The following illustrates the calculation of the permissible air leakage.

Air leakage is given by:

$$q_L = C\,A_s\,p^{0.65} \quad (3.A6.1)$$

where q_L is the air leakage rate ($litre \cdot s^{-1}$), C is a constant ($litre \cdot s^{-1} \cdot m^{-2} \cdot Pa^{-0.65}$) and p is the static pressure in the duct relative to the air outside the duct (Pa).

For low pressure ductwork, C = 0.025 $litre \cdot s^{-1} \cdot m^{-2} \cdot Pa^{-0.65}$.

It is possible to calculate the leakage progressively along the duct in accordance with the change in pressure of the duct air. However, for simplicity, the pressure at the mid-length position only of each length of duct will be considered.

The mean pressure in a duct will be approximately equal to the pressure half way along the duct, and is given by:

$$p = p_{t1} - \tfrac{1}{2}\,\Delta p - \tfrac{1}{2}\,\rho\,c^2 \quad (3.A6.2)$$

where p is the mean pressure in the duct (Pa), p_{t1} is the total pressure at the beginning of the duct (Pa), Δp is the pressure loss along the duct (Pa), ρ is the density of the air in the duct ($kg \cdot m^{-3}$) and c is the air velocity in the duct ($m \cdot s^{-1}$).

The drop in total pressure along the supply air ductwork is 59.7 Pa (see section 3.A6.1.4). This means that the total pressure at the exit from the AHU will be 59.7 Pa above that of the room. That is the starting point for the calculations shown in Table 3.A6.7. However, to illustrate the procedure, the leakage from duct run J–K is calculated as follows.

Surface area of duct = duct length × perimeter. Hence:

$$A_s = 4 \times [2 \times (0.5 + 0.4)] = 7.2 \text{ m}^2$$

The pressure loss up to and just past tee J is the sum of the first eight items of Table 3.A6.4, i.e.:

$$\Delta p = 21.6 \text{ Pa}$$

Total pressure at start of duct run J–K is the total pressure at E minus the pressure drop up to tee J:

$$p_{t1} = 59.7 - 21.6 = 38.1 \text{ Pa}$$

From Table 3.A6.4, $^1/_2\, \rho\, c^2$ for duct run J–K is 5.22 Pa. The pressure drop halfway along J–K is (0.5 × 1.2) Pa. Therefore, using equation 3.A6.2, the mean static pressure half way along duct run J–K is:

$$p = 38.1 - 0.6 - 5.22 = 32.3 \text{ Pa}$$

Hence, using equation 3.A6.1, the air leakage is:

$$q_L = 0.025 \times 7.2 \times 32.3^{0.65} = 1.72 \text{ l·s}^{-1}$$

In Table 3.A6.7, note that although the value of total pressure has been dropping consistently along the duct, in this portion of duct J–K, the actual pressure of the air is greater than in the preceding section. This is due to an accidental element of 'static regain'. At tee I, the main duct section has not changed although less air flows along the main duct after the branch. Thus in this section the air velocity, and thus the value of ($^1/_2\, \rho\, c_2$), has diminished. This occurs at every tee, as shown in Table 3.A6.7 for runs K–L and Q–S.

Table 3.A6.7 suggests that the maximum leakage would be 20.8 l·s^{-1}. Therefore the permissible fraction lost through air leakage is 1.7% of the original flow rate of 1.2 m^3·s^{-1} (i.e. 1200 l·s^{-1}). This does not justify specifying a higher flow rate, nor a recalculation of the pressure drop.

Note that the air in much of the return ductwork will be found to have negative static pressure, i.e. the pressure in the duct will be lower than the surroundings, so there will be air leaks into the ductwork.

3.A6.4 Drop in air temperature along the duct

3.A6.4.1 Uninsulated ductwork

Table 3.A6.8 shows the calculation of heat loss from the index run assuming uninsulated ductwork having a thermal transmittance (U-value) of 7.89 W·m^{-2}·K^{-1}. The air temperatures inside and outside the duct are:

— temperature of air inside the duct at beginning of run, t_{ad1} = 30 °C

— temperature of air surrounding the duct, t_{as} = 20 °C.

Table 3.A6.7 Leakage calculations for the supply duct along the index run

Item	Length / m	Dimensions / (mm × mm)	Duct surface area, A_s / m^2	Total pressure at start of run, p_{t1} / Pa	Pressure loss, Δp / Pa	($^1/_2\,\rho\,c^2$) / Pa	Mean static pressure, p / Pa	Leakage, q_L / l·s^{-1}
(*a*) Main duct run								
E–F	2	1200 × 600	7.2	59.7	0	2.4	57.3	2.50
G–I	15	500 × 400	27	57.4	16	20.9	29.8	5.96
I–J	4	500 × 400	7.2	41.1	3.0	14.5	25.1	1.46
J–K	4	500 × 400	7.2	38.1	1.2	5.22	32.3	1.72
K–L	1	500 × 400	1.8	36.7	0.1	2.32	34.3	0.45
L–Q	20.4	400	25.6	33.2	7.7	5.88	23.5	4.98
Q–S	5	400	6.3	24.5	0.4	1.5	22.8	1.20
S–V6	3	315	2.97	23.5	1.0	3.96	19.0	0.50
(*b*) Branch duct runs								
I–V1	3	315	2.97	24.1	1.0	3.96	19.6	0.51
Similar calculations for remaining branches								1.51*
							Total:	20.79

* Notional value for sum of air leakage from remaining branches, for purposes of example calculation

Table 3.A6.8 Heat loss calculations for uninsulated supply duct along the index run (U = 7.89 W·m^{-2}·K^{-1})

Item	Length / mm	Dimensions / (mm × mm)	Flow rate, q / m^3·s^{-1}	Duct surface area, A_s / m^2	Temp. at start of run, t_{ad1} / °C	Temp. diff. ($t_{ad} - t_{as}$) / K	Heat flux, ϕ / W	Temp. diff.* ($t_{ad1} - t_{ad2}$) / K
E–F	2	1000 × 600	1.2	6.4	30	9.83	496	0.34
G–I	15	500 × 400	1.2	27	29.66	8.95	1917	1.33
I–J	4	500 × 400	1.0	7.2	28.33	8.14	464	0.32
J–K	4	500 × 400	0.6	7.2	28.01	7.70	437	0.61
K–L	1	500 × 400	0.4	1.2	27.40	7.33	69	0.15
L–Q	20.4	400 (diam.)	0.4	25.6	27.25	5.77	1210	2.52
Q–S	5	400 (diam.)	0.2	6.3	24.73	4.30	214	0.89
S–T	3	315 (diam.)	0.2	3.0	23.84	3.64	87	0.36
T	—	—	—	—	23.48	—	—	—
						Totals:	4984	6.52

* Temperature difference between beginning and end of duct run

Table 3.A6.8 shows that, along the index run E–V6, the heat loss is 4.98 kW, possibly being dissipated into a region that does not require heating. If the ductwork were situated in ceiling voids, which consequently became over-heated, then the heat loss would be less due to the higher temperature outside the duct. Of greater importance is that the temperature of the air at the end of the run will be significantly below the desired supply temperature of 30 °C. Table 3.A6.8 shows that the temperature of the supply air to zone V6 will be 23.5 °C, which will be inadequate. Clearly, it is recommended that ductwork carrying heated or cooled air should be insulated.

3.A6.4.2 Insulated ductwork

Table 3.8 gives recommended thickness of insulation for ductwork depending on the thermal conductivity (λ) of the insulation material. In the following example, $\lambda = 0.035$ W·m^{-1}·K^{-1}. The duct air temperature is nominally 30 °C and the temperature of the surrounding air is 20 °C, i.e. $(t_{ad1} - t_a) = 10$ K.

From Table 3.8, the recommended thickness for a duct carrying air at a temperature 10 K greater (or less) than the surroundings, and for a thermal conductivity $\lambda = 0.035$ W·m^{-1}·K^{-1}, is 50 mm. From Table 3.7, the overall thermal transmittance is $U = 0.64$ W·m^{-2}·K^{-1}.

For simplicity, it is assumed that the temperature drop along a section is trivial.

Taking duct run I–J as an example:

Surface area of duct = duct length × perimeter. Hence:

$$A_s = 4 \times [2 \times (0.5 + 0.4)] = 7.2 \text{ m}^2$$

The thermal transmittance is related to the surface area of the ductwork, not to the outer surface area of the insulation. The air has already cooled such that at (I) its temperature is 29.85 °C. In the first instance, it is assumed that this remains constant through I–J. Hence, using equation 3.2, the heat loss is given by:

$$\phi = U A_s (t_{ad} - t_{as}) = 0.64 \times 7.2 (29.85 - 20) = 45.3 \text{ W}$$

The temperature drop along duct run I–J is:

$$t_{ad1} - t_{ad2} = \phi / (q_m\, c_p) = \phi / (q\, \rho\, c_p)$$

where t_{ad1} is the temperature at the beginning of the duct run (°C), t_{ad2} is the temperature at the end of the duct run (°C), ϕ is the heat flux (W), q_m is the mass flow rate (kg·s^{-1}), c_p is the specific heat capacity of air (J·kg^{-1}·K^{-1}), q is the volumetric flow rate (m^3·s^{-1}) and ρ the density of the air (kg·m^{-3}).

Therefore:

$$t_{ad1} - t_{ad2} = 45.3 / (1.0 \times 1.16 \times 1.030 \times 103) = 0.04 \text{ K}$$

The temperature at (J) is:

$$t_{a2} = 29.85 - 0.04 = 29.81 °\text{C}$$

Hence, mean temperature in duct I–J = ½ (29.85 + 29.81) = 29.83°C.

In principle, the heat loss ϕ should be re-calculated at the mean temperature, but in this instance the difference is trivial and may be ignored.

Note that though the heat loss from the next duct run J–K is the same (i.e. 45 W), the temperature drop is greater (0.06 K as opposed to 0.04 K). This is because, although the air temperature in the duct is almost the same, the airflow through section J–K is appreciably less (i.e. 0.6 m^3·s^{-1} as opposed to 1.0 m^3·s^{-1}).

In summary, Table 3.A6.9 shows that the total heat loss from the index run is 522 W, the temperature drop is 0.83 K and the supply air temperature to V6 is 29.2 °C. This is sufficiently close to the required supply temperature at V1 of 29.8 °C for there to be no significant control problems. However the delivered heat to zone V6 is reduced by 8%, therefore there is a case for increasing the design outlet temperature of the air handling unit from 30 °C to 30.5 °C.

3.A6.5 Effects on airflows when closing down one branch

Figure 3.A6.3 shows a simplified duct network where boxes 1, 2 and 3 represent the ductwork circuits for supplying three zones. Box 5 represents the return ductwork. D is a damper which is initially open, but which will be closed down.

The design conditions are as follows:

— *duct system 1*: $q = 0.2$ m^3·s^{-1}; $\Delta p = 70$ Pa

— *duct system 2*: $q = 0.2$ m^3·s^{-1}; $\Delta p = 50$ Pa

— *duct system 3*: $q = 0.2$ m^3·s^{-1}; $\Delta p = 40$ Pa

— *duct system 4*: $q = 0.4$ m^3·s^{-1}; $\Delta p = 20$ Pa

Table 3.A6.9 Heat loss calculations for insulated supply duct along the index run ($U = 0.64$ W·m^{-2}·K^{-1})

Item	Length / mm	Dimensions / (mm × mm)	Flow rate, q / m^3·s^{-1}	Duct surface area, A_s / m^2	Temp. at start of run, t_{ad1} / °C	Temp. diff. $(t_{ad} - t_{as})$ / K	Heat flux, (ϕ / W	Temp. diff.* $(t_{ad1} - t_{ad2})$ / K
E–F	2	1000 × 600	1.2	6.4	30	9.99	41	0.03
G–I	15	500 × 400	1.2	27	29.97	9.91	171	0.12
I–J	4	500 × 400	1.0	7.2	29.85	9.83	45	0.04
J–K	4	500 × 400	0.6	7.2	29.81	9.78	45	0.06
K–L	1	500 × 400	0.4	1.2	29.75	9.74	7	0.02
L–Q	20.4	400	0.4	25.6	29.73	9.56	157	0.33
Q–S	5	400	0.2	6.3	29.40	9.32	38	0.16
S–T	3	315	0.2	3.0	29.24	9.20	18	0.07
T	—	—	—	—	29.17	—	—	—
						Total:	522	0.83

* Temperature difference between beginning and end of duct run

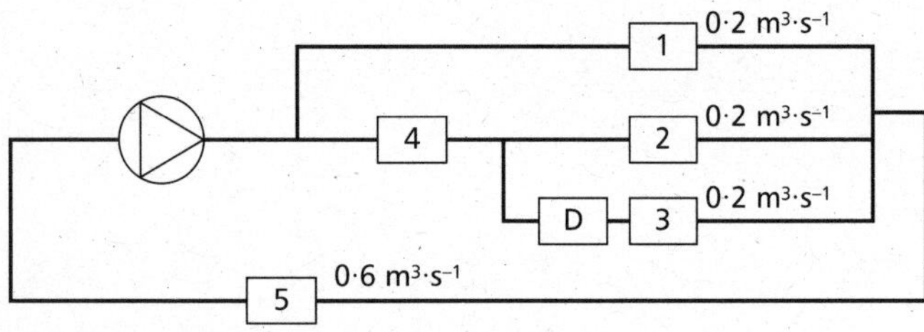

Figure 3.A6.3 Simplified duct network

— *duct system* 5: $q = 0.6$ m^3·s^{-1}; $\Delta p = 20$ Pa

— *damper D*: $q = 0.2$ m^3·s^{-1}; $\Delta p = 10$ Pa

From the above design requirement, the fan must produce a pressure rise of 70 Pa for a volume flow of 0.6 m^3·s^{-1}.

We can use the approximate simplification that the pressure drop of the system is proportional to the square of the velocity, and thus proportional to the square of the flow rate. (*Note*: not true where there are HEPA filters in the system). Thus pressure drop at any flow rate is easily obtained using:

$$\Delta p \propto q^2 \qquad (3.A6.3)$$

where Δp is the pressure drop (Pa) and q is the volumetric flow rate (m^3·s^{-1}).

Hence, from such values the 'system characteristic' can be constructed as shown in Figure 3.A6.4.

A fan would be chosen such that the intersection of the fan characteristic and the system characteristic gives the design requirement, as shown, of 0.6 m^3·s^{-1} and a total pressure drop Δp_t of 70 Pa.

The following illustrates what happens to the flow in the various branches of the system when the resistance of one branch is changed as a result of closing damper D.

The problem can be resolved using either circuit resistances or capacities. Since valve manufacturers always give valve capacities, the following uses the capacity method for consistency. (See also Guide C, section 4, Appendix 4.A5.)

Capacity K is given by the relationship:

$$q = K \, \Delta p_p \qquad (3.A6.4)$$

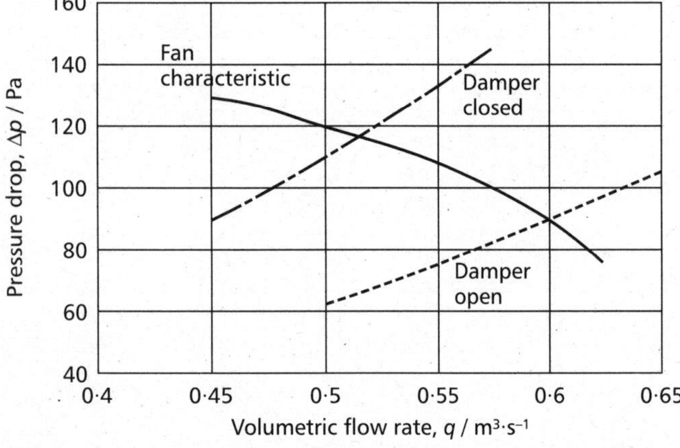

Figure 3.A6.4 System characteristic for simplified duct network; (*a*) characteristic with damper D open and (*b*) characteristic with damper D closed

where K is the capacity (m^3·s^{-1}·Pa$^{-0.5}$)

Using equation 3.A6.4, the capacity of each leg of the network can be calculated, as follows:

$$K_1 = q_1 / \Delta p_{p1} = 0.2 / \surd 70 = 0.02390 \text{ m}^3\cdot\text{s}^{-1}\cdot\text{Pa}^{-0.5}$$

$$K_2 = q_2 / \Delta p_{p2} = 0.2 / \surd 50 = 0.02828 \text{ m}^3\cdot\text{s}^{-1}\cdot\text{Pa}^{-0.5}$$

$$K_3 = q_3 / \Delta p_{p3} = 0.2 / \surd 40 = 0.03162 \text{ m}^3\cdot\text{s}^{-1}\cdot\text{Pa}^{-0.5}$$

$$K_4 = q_4 / \Delta p_{p4} = 0.4 / \surd 20 = 0.08944 \text{ m}^3\cdot\text{s}^{-1}\cdot\text{Pa}^{-0.5}$$

$$K_5 = q_5 / \Delta p_{p5} = 0.6 / \surd 20 = 0.13416 \text{ m}^3\cdot\text{s}^{-1}\cdot\text{Pa}^{-0.5}$$

With damper D closed, no flow will pass through leg 3.

K_2 and K_4 are in series, giving an effective capacity of $K_{2,4}$, i.e:

$$\frac{1}{K_{2,4}^{\ 2}} = \frac{1}{K_2^{\ 2}} + \frac{1}{K_4^{\ 2}} = \frac{1}{0.02828^2} + \frac{1}{0.08944^2}$$

Hence:

$$K_{2,4} = 0.02696 \text{ m}^3\cdot\text{s}^{-1}\cdot\text{Pa}^{-0.5}$$

$K_{2,4}$ and K_1 are in parallel, i.e:

$$K_{1,2,4} = K_{2,4} + K_1$$
$$= 0.02696 + 0.02390 = 0.05086 \text{ m}^3\cdot\text{s}^{-1}\cdot\text{Pa}^{-0.5}$$

The total system capacity K_0 is the result of $K_{1,2,4}$ in series with K_5, i.e:

$$\frac{1}{K_0^{\ 2}} = \frac{1}{K1_{1,2,4}^{\ 2}} + \frac{1}{K_5^{\ 2}} = \frac{1}{0.05086^2} + \frac{1}{0.13416^2}$$

Hence:

$$K_0 = 0.04756 \text{ m}^3\cdot\text{s}^{-1}\cdot\text{Pa}^{-0.5}$$

Had the capacity been calculated for the original system, it would have been found to be 0.0717 m^3·s^{-1}·Pa$^{-0.5}$.

A new system characteristic can now be determined from equation 3.A6.4 using the calculated value of K_o, e.g. for $q = 0.55$ m^3·s^{-1}:

$$\Delta p = (0.55 / 0.04756)^2 = 133.7 \text{ Pa}$$

With the damper closed, the system has a new system characteristic, see Figure 3.A6.4. The intersection with the fan characteristic now gives a flow of 0.516 m^3·s^{-1} and a pressure drop of $\Delta p = 117.7$ Pa.

It is now necessary to ascertain the proportions in which this total flow is apportioned between supply legs 1 and 2.

Knowing the flow through leg 5 (being either the return ductwork, or extract to the outside and inlet from the outside), the pressure loss through leg 5 can be calculated using equation 3.A6.4:

$$0.55 = 0.13416 \surd \Delta p_5$$

Hence:

$$\Delta p_5 = (0.55 / 0.13416)^2 = 16.8 \text{ Pa}$$

The remainder is the pressure drop existing across leg 1, and across leg 4/2:

$$\Delta p_1 = \Delta p_o - \Delta p_5 = 117.7 - 16.8 = 100.9 \text{ Pa}$$

The flow through leg 1 can now be determined using equation 3.A6.4:

$$q_1 = 0.02390 \sqrt{100.9} = 0.2401 \text{ m}^3\cdot\text{s}^{-1}$$

The rest of the flow passes along leg 4/2, i.e:

$$q_4 = q_o - q_5 = 0.516 - 0.240 = 0.276 \text{ m}^3\cdot\text{s}^{-1}$$

The flow rates resulting from closure of damper D are shown on Figure 3.A6.5.

It should be noted that, although the supplies to legs 1 and 2 were initially equal, this is no longer the case once any change is made to any other branch.

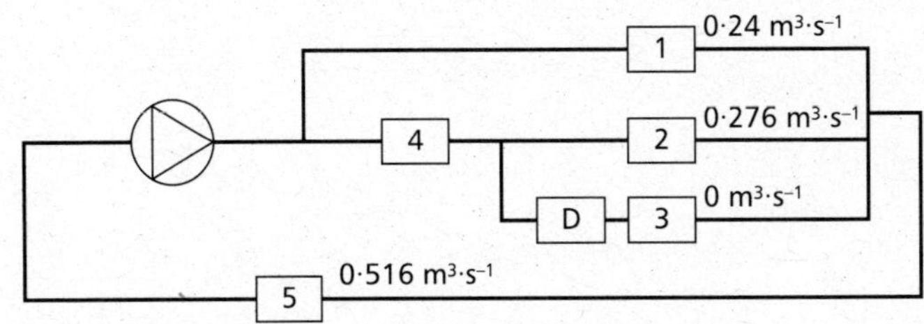

Figure 3.A6.5 Duct network with damper D closed

References

3.A6.1 *Reference data* CIBSE Guide C (London: Chartered Institution of Building Services Engineers) (2001)

3.A6.2 *Specification for sheet metal ductwork* HVCA DW/144 (London: Heating and Ventilating Contractors' Association) (1998)

3.A6.3 The Building Regulations 2000 Approved Document L: *Conservation of fuel and power* (London: The Stationery Office) (2001)

4 Refrigeration and heat rejection

4.1 Introduction

4.1.1 General

This section gives guidance on the selection of refrigeration and heat rejection systems and equipment currently available for the built environment. Before using these systems and equipment however, the designer should consider carefully the use of alternative free cooling and low energy techniques in the interest of minimising the overall global warming impact and use of environmentally harmful refrigerants arising from the manufacture and operation of refrigeration and heat rejection equipment. Reasons for choosing such alternatives should be recorded and substantiated by the designer, see CIBSE Guide F: *Energy efficiency in buildings*[1] and Action Energy publications[2–8].

Whilst the process for each application and design will be unique, the route to final selection of a system will follow a common fundamental path and format involving problem definition, idea generation, analysis and selection of the preferred solution. As an aid to this iterative process of system selection a flowchart is given in Figure 4.1.

It should be noted that the guidelines given in this section are to be used by practicing engineers who hold a basic knowledge of the fundamentals of refrigeration and heat rejection. As such, mathematical derivations of formulae are not given. References are given where appropriate to enable further detailed investigations of the systems covered.

4.1.2 Overview of section 4

CIBSE Guide B section 4 has its origins in the 1986 edition of CIBSE Guide B14[10]. It has been comprehensively revised to take account of developments in the intervening years, in particular to incorporate guidance on health and safety issues, new regulations, and low energy techniques and alternatives to CFC and HCFC refrigerants which have emerged over the past two decades. More detailed information on low energy cooling and ventilation strategies can be found in section 2 and CIBSE Guide H[11], and more information on replacement refrigerants is given in Guidance Note GN1[12].

The contents of this section are as follows:

— section 4.2 describes an integrated approach to design that addresses issues of location, orientation and structural form and discusses their impact on the refrigeration and heat rejection strategy for the building

— section 4.3 describes the basic requirements for refrigeration and heat rejection

— section 4.4 provides details of the basic forms of refrigeration and heat rejection and gives help in the selection of suitable equipment

— section 4.5 provides information about a wide range of equipment used in refrigeration and heat rejection systems.

4.2 Strategic design decisions

4.2.1 Introduction

This section addresses the general requirements for the application of refrigeration and heat rejection in buildings. It reviews the factors to be considered in deciding the appropriate design strategy for the building and the client, and highlights points relevant to specific requirements. The design process must be based on a clear understanding of client and end user needs and expectations and must be followed by correct installation and effective commissioning, handover and building management.

For the purpose of this chapter, refrigeration is defined as the process of removing heat and heat rejection is defined as the discharge of heat to waste or atmosphere or to a system permitting reclaim or recovery.

Key factors to be considered in determining a refrigeration and heat rejection strategy are summarised as follows:

— end user requirements

— energy efficiency and environmental issues

— interaction with building fabric, services and facilities

— choice of refrigeration and heat rejection strategy

— associated systems

— whole life costs

— procurement issues

— commissioning

— operation

— maintenance

— future needs

An appreciation of the above issues is an essential part of the briefing process. Further advice on briefing in general can be obtained from BSRIA Application Guide AG 11/98: *Project management handbook for building services*[13].

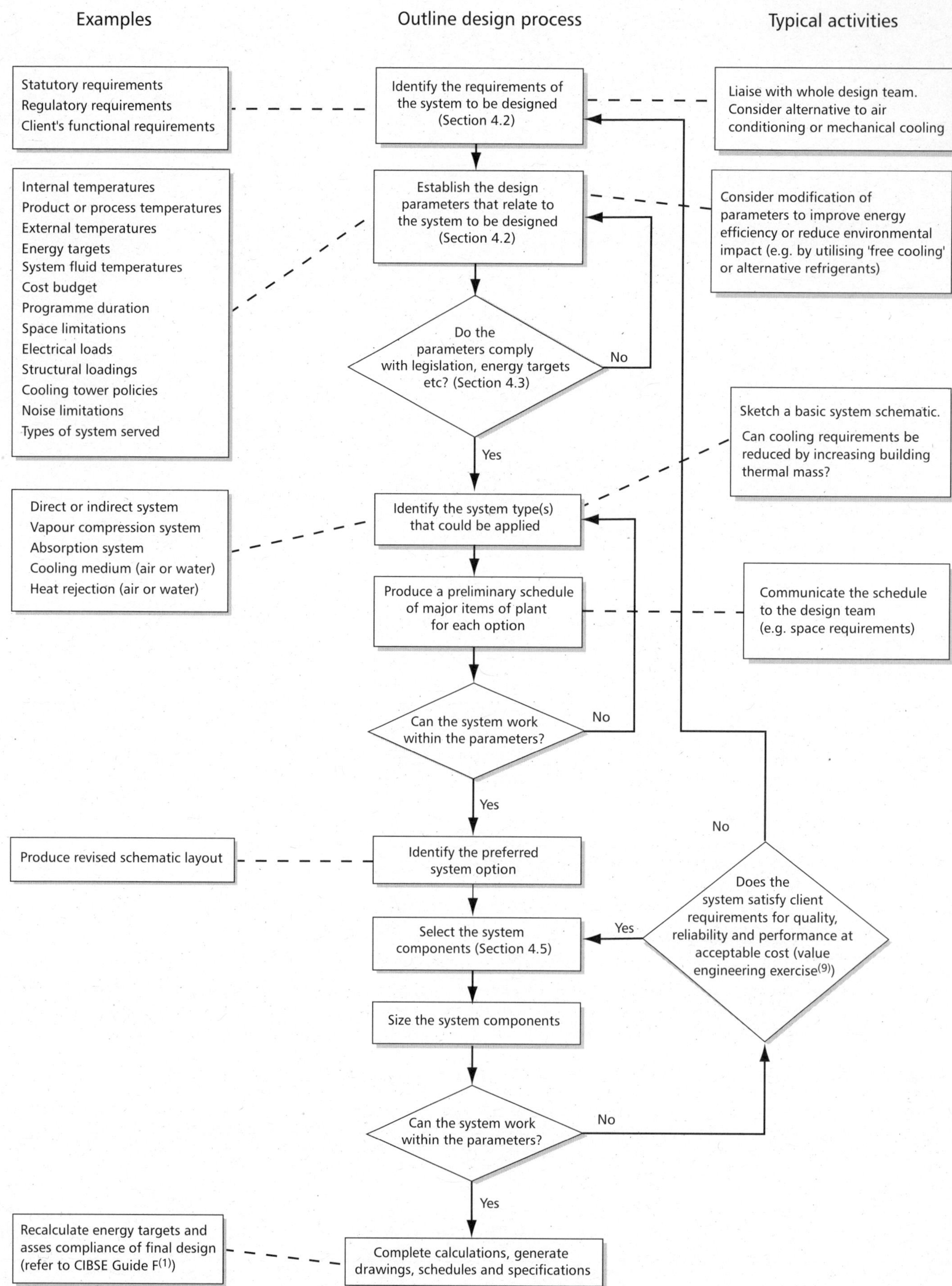

Figure 4.1 'First-pass' flow chart for design process: refrigeration and heat rejection

4.2.2 End-user requirements

The key end-user requirements that need to be clarified before a refrigeration and heat rejection strategy can be chosen are summarised in Table 4.1.

Ideally, where the issues highlighted in 4.2.1 have not been covered by a standard specification document, the design team should expect to agree requirements with the client at the onset of the project to optimise the choice of refrigeration and heat rejection strategy and, ultimately, the system to be developed. If the client is unable to advise on the precise needs the design team must, as a minimum, make the client aware of any limitations of the chosen design in these respects. Requirements may subsequently be adjusted over the course of the project to meet financial constraints or changing business needs. The design team must also be able to advise the client on the impact of any such changes on the final plant performance and life cycle costs.

The designer should review the need for cooling in relation to the end-user requirements (Table 4.1) and the key factors listed in Section 4.2.1. Refrigeration and heat rejection systems should only be specified where there is a clear and proven need to meet cooling requirements that cannot be met by simpler and less energy intensive means.

Table 4.1 Establishing end-user requirements

Issue	Requirement/comments
Client brief	— To be developed in the context of the other issues
Building occupants activities/processes	— Understanding of the business process(es) to be undertaken in the building and their specific cooling requirements including any requirement for tight temperature and humidity control — Cooling load profile: hourly and daily load variation — Anticipated diversity of cooling loads
Energy/environmental targets	— Compatibility with statutory requirements (e.g. Building Regulations) and client company environmental policy (e.g. refrigerant policy, BREEAM certification), see section 4.2.3 — Anticipate future statutory energy/environmental targets or requirements
Integrated design	— Integration with building fabric, services and facilities. Requires co-ordinated approach with the client, architect and other professionals from the outline design, see section 4.2.4
Investment criteria	— Constraints imposed by 'letability' requirements
Whole life costs	— Understanding of the client's priorities towards capital costs and issues of whole-life costs, see section 4.2.8 — Has the client been involved in discussions of acceptable design risk? — Importance of part-load performance
Provision of controls	— Required basis of control, e.g. temperature, humidity — Required closeness of control — Ability and willingness of the occupants to understand and operate controls: controls for unit air conditioners may be in the occupied space but controls for central chiller plant may be hidden from the user and only accessible to facilities or engineering staff — Ability and willingness of the building operator to maintain controls
Reliability	— The business process(es) to be undertaken in the building may demand specific levels of reliability of the refrigeration and heat rejection systems (dealer floors and call centres may represent very high value operations to the owner and IT/telecommunications centres may be 'mission critical' operations which require completely separate back-up cooling and power supply systems), see section 4.2.7
Maintenance requirements	— Understanding of the client's ability to carry out, or resource, maintenance, see section 4.2.12 — Client willingness for maintenance to be carried out in occupied space (e.g. unit and multi-split air conditioning systems) — Any requirement for 'standard' or 'familiar' components
Aesthetic and noise considerations	— The need for system concealment (visible plant on the roof or at ground level) — Restriction on placement of cooling towers — Restriction on location of noisy plant (e.g. proximity to conference rooms and neighbouring buildings) — Restrictions imposed by local authorities, building listing etc. (particularly related to plant on roofs or mounted on walls)
Security	— Restrictions on size and location of any openings
Space allocation	— Restrictions on space allocated for refrigeration and heat rejection equipment may have a significant effect on the choice of plant, its energy efficiency and on the ability to maintain it adequately and safely
Procurement issues	— Time constraints — Programming constraints, particularly for refurbishment projects
Future needs	— Adaptability, i.e. the need to cope with future change of use — Flexibility, i.e. the need to cope with future changes in work practices within the current building — Acceptable design margins: it is important to distinguish, in collaboration with the client, between design that is adequate for current cooling requirements and design which makes sensible agreed allowances for future changes in cooling requirements

4.2.3 Energy efficiency and environmental issues

The UK is committed to significantly reducing carbon emissions by the year 2010, with a target of a 20% cut based on 1990 levels. As well as sponsoring Action Energy to promote energy efficiency, the government has also introduced the Climate Change Levy, effectively a specific tax on energy use, and Enhanced Capital Allowances for certain energy efficient measures including some specific refrigeration plant, see *www.eca.gov.uk* for lists of eligible equipment. Approved Document L2 (2002) (ADL2) of the Building Regulations 2000 in England and Wales[14] requires that refrigeration equipment and fans and pumps are reasonably efficient and appropriately sized. Guidance on specific requirements is given in Section 4.3.5.

Buildings account for around 45% of the energy consumption and greenhouse gas emissions in the UK and are therefore a key target for action to improve energy efficiency and reduce carbon emissions. The need for refrigeration and heat rejection is increasing in response to a warmer climate and through higher comfort expectations and more sophisticated building usage such as greater use of information and communication technology. Recent studies under the government's Energy Efficiency Best Practice programme suggest that there is likely to be a significant increase in energy consumption related to air conditioning.

These factors should stimulate a greater interest in energy efficiency measures amongst building owners and operators, and energy efficiency will be become a crucial strategic design issue for refrigeration and heat rejection systems.

Most refrigeration and heat rejection plant is electrically driven and therefore such plant contribute to power station greenhouse gas emissions. Heat driven refrigeration plant, such as absorption chillers, will also contribute to primary energy consumption and greenhouse gas emissions, unless driven by waste heat.

The chosen refrigeration and heat rejection strategy will influence, and will be influenced by, energy efficiency and environmental issues and any specific targets. The design team should ensure that agreement is reached with the client on any specific energy and environmental targets at an early stage in the design process. Checks should be carried out continuously by the design team to ensure that the implications of any changes made during design, construction, or subsequent installation are understood and mutually acceptable.

Documents are available to assist in setting energy and environmental targets, including:

— CIBSE TM22: *Energy Assessment and Reporting Methodology*[15], which provides energy benchmarks and target assessment methods for dealing with banks and similar agencies, hotels, offices and mixed use buildings.

— The series of Energy Consumption Guides[16], published by Action Energy, which provide energy benchmarks and targets for industrial buildings and sites, offices, public houses, hotels, hospitals, domestic properties, nursing and residential homes, and other non-domestic sectors.

— The Building Research Establishment Environmental Assessment Method (BREEAM)[17], which provides an environmental assessment methodology for industrial units, offices, superstores and supermarkets and housing.

Specific energy consumption targets may be difficult to achieve where for example there is an overriding requirement for close control of temperature and humidity. In these cases the design team may need to agree with the client a relaxation of specific energy consumption targets where it can be proven that the need for tight control is an unavoidable requirement of the building use. Specific guidance on achieving energy targets is also given in CIBSE Guide F: *Energy efficiency in buildings*[1]. It should be noted that tight control of temperature and humidity are not needed to achieve human comfort but could be needed for the preservation of artefacts, or the production or storage of some products or materials.

Refrigeration systems often use a refrigerant fluid that is harmful to the environment. Refrigerant may be released accidentally during installation, maintenance, repair or decommissioning procedures or through leaks from the system. Chlorofluorocarbon (CFC) refrigerants which are very damaging to the ozone layer have been phased out for new systems but may occasionally be found in existing systems. Many replacement refrigerants including hydrochlorofluorocarbons (HCFCs) (themselves now being phased out) and hydrofluorocarbons (HCFs) are also harmful to the environment and their use is subject to certain regulations, standards and codes of practice, see sections 4.3.4 and 4.4.5.

Refrigerant leakage can also have an adverse impact on energy efficiency as operating a vapour compression system with either too much or too little refrigerant can cause a significant reduction in the cooling performance and energy efficiency of the system, see section 4.4.4.4.

Refrigeration and heat rejection systems also use other potentially environmentally harmful substances including water treatment chemicals required to minimise microbiological contamination and corrosion, see section 4.5.5.

4.2.4 Interaction with building fabric, services and facilities

The cooling requirements to be met by a refrigeration and heat rejection system will include the ventilation, air-conditioning and other internal cooling loads within the building. These loads will be based on estimates of:

— Internal gains determined by the occupants, e.g. occupancy itself, lighting, small power loads and any business related process

— Internal gains determined by the fabric, e.g. insulation, glazing, thermal mass.

Although the architect is, traditionally, associated with fabric related decisions, the building services engineer must be involved at an early stage and advise on their implications for the building services and, ultimately, on the requirements for cooling and heat rejection. The services engineer must therefore be involved in the decision making process as far is as practical and at as early a stage in the process as possible.

Approved Document L2 (2002) (ADL2) of the Building Regulations 2000[14] requires that buildings with air conditioning and mechanical ventilation are designed and constructed such that the form and fabric of the building do not result in a requirement for excessive installed capacity, see section 4.3.5.

As a minimum the building services engineer should be able to enter into a dialogue with the architect on building fabric related issues that will impact on the cooling requirements of the ventilation and air conditioning systems, including the following:

- location
- pollution
- orientation
- form
- insulation
- infiltration
- shading
- window choice
- glazing
- thermal mass.

Specific guidance on these issues is given in CIBSE Guide A[18] and in section 2 of this Guide. Some of these issues now have statutory requirements. For example, ADL2 requires that non-domestic buildings should be reasonably airtight, and that buildings of greater than 1000 m^2 are to be pressure tested in accordance with CIBSE TM23: *Testing buildings for air leakage*[19].

The design strategy for the windows and glazing will impact on the provision of daylight, which will in turn interact with the cooling load created by the use of electric lighting. More specific guidance is given in CIBSE Lighting Guide LG10: *Daylighting and window design*[20]. Heat gains from the lighting should be minimised through:

- selection of appropriate light levels and differentiating between circulation spaces and workstations
- selection of efficient luminaires
- installation of appropriate controls to minimise unnecessary electric light usage
- use of ventilated luminaires to minimise heat gains to the occupied space.

Small power loads arising from IT and office equipment are an increasingly significant component of internal heat gains. It is important that a realistic estimate is made of the anticipated diversity in use of such equipment. The designer should also encourage the client to reduce small power heat gains through:

- the selection of low energy equipment and the use of power cut-off mechanisms
- the location of shared equipment, eg photocopiers, printers and vending machines, in spaces that can be readily cooled (eg through the use of opening windows or simple extract ventilation).

The choice of cooling distribution system and terminal units can also affect the requirement for cooling as well as the size and efficiency of the cooling or heat rejection system. For example, the use of chilled ceilings or beams can allow secondary chilled water temperatures of 14 °C or higher, which makes the use of simpler heat rejection systems or other 'free-cooling' strategies practical for a greater proportion of the year than possible with conventional chilled water based systems. By treating cooling loads that require low temperatures (e.g. dehumidification systems) separately the refrigeration efficiency can also be raised. Further guidance on these and other cooling distribution systems and terminals is given in section 2 of this Guide.

The designer must at an early stage agree with the architect and structural engineer any specific requirements relating to the refrigeration and heat rejection systems and the safety of those installing and maintaining it. These include ensuring that there is:

- sufficient space for the plant itself, and for installation and subsequent maintenance procedures: manufacturers' literature for plant and equipment should be consulted for the space requirements around plant for procedures such as the withdrawal of heat exchange coils, compressors etc.
- Sufficient access for replacement and damaged parts to be brought into and out of the plant room: adequately sized doorways, access stairs or demountable structural openings may need to be provided; in addition it may be advantageous for lifting beams to be built into the structure in order to move equipment easily into and out of plant rooms
- adequate structural strength to support heavy items of plant such as cooling towers, chillers and water tanks: these items may be located on the building roof which may need to be specially strengthened.

4.2.5 Choice of refrigeration and heat rejection strategy

The selection of an appropriate strategy should take into account all of the strategic design decisions discussed in section 4.2. It is important that the requirement for cooling is minimised as this should reduce the energy consumption of the building, minimise maintenance costs (e.g. specialist refrigeration maintenance and water treatment costs), and in many cases reduce the life cycle costs of the building.

The requirement for cooling can also be minimised by selecting an appropriate building ventilation strategy that maximises the use of ambient air for ventilation and cooling instead of providing a full air conditioning system. Figure 4.2 shows a decision flow chart that may assist this selection process.

The choice of refrigeration or heat rejection strategy should take account of the following guidelines:

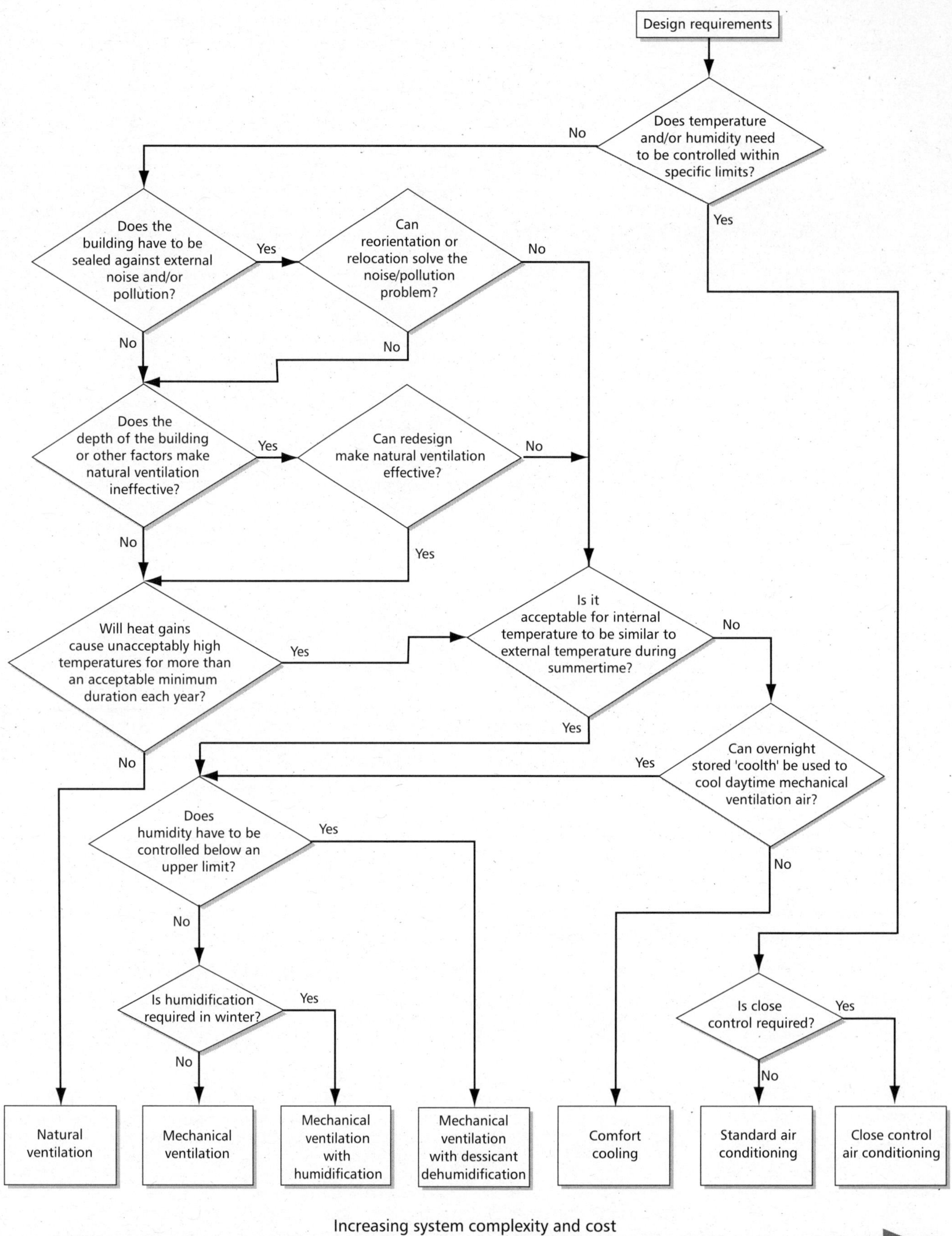

Figure 4.2 Decision flow chart

- The need for refrigeration can be minimised by using simpler heat rejection or 'free cooling' strategies during cool weather, such as cooling towers, dry air coolers or refrigerant migration (thermosyphon) chillers (see section 4.4.9).
- The decision to use simple heat rejection or free cooling in cool weather, in addition to a separate refrigeration system for use in hot weather, requires careful assessment of life cycle costs;
- 'Free cooling' systems can be particularly appropriate for buildings where cooling requirements are high and unrelated to ambient temperature, for example computer suites and telecommunication switching centres.

Where the need for a refrigeration system is unavoidable the overall global warming impact of the system (due to energy use and refrigerant emissions) should be minimised through the following guidelines:

- Ensure good refrigeration efficiency through the selection of an efficient machine and by minimising the refrigeration 'lift' (the difference between the temperature of the cooling medium, usually air or chilled water, and that of the heat sink, usually ambient air).
- Where multiple refrigeration machines are installed, machine sizing should be related to the cooling demand profiles in preference to installing a number of equal-sized machines. Good control provisions in such cases are essential, see also section 4.5.3.3.
- Where a vapour compression system is used minimise the direct global warming effect from possible refrigerant emissions by selecting a refrigerant with a low global warming potential and by selecting a machine with a low specific refrigerant charge (kg of refrigerant per kW cooling capacity), see section 4.4.5.
- Where there is a source of waste or reclaim heat of suitable temperatures, for instance where there is a case for using a CHP system, then consider the use of heat driven absorption cycle chillers.

4.2.6 Associated systems

Associated systems may include chilled water and condenser cooling distribution pipework and pumps, fans and pumps in heat rejection systems and ventilation air distribution fans. The fans and pumps in a typical air conditioned office building may consume between two and three times the electrical energy consumed by the chillers. It is therefore important that the design and energy efficiency of these associated systems is given as much attention as the main refrigeration and heat rejection systems.

Approved Document L2 (2002)[14] requires that fans and pumps are reasonably efficient and are appropriately sized.

Most air conditioned buildings experience varying cooling loads depending on the season and time of day. Significant savings in chilled water pumping energy and fan energy can be made by using variable speed drives to vary the flow rate with the load. Actual energy savings are around 40% at 80% flow and 80% energy savings at 50% flow (the actual savings are always lower than the theoretical, cubed law, power savings predicted by the fan and pump laws). It is also important not to oversize fans and pumps, especially when manual flow regulating valves and dampers are used as these simply increase system pressure. Although the use of variable speed drives can avoid the energy penalty associated with manual flow regulating valves excessive oversizing should still be avoided because of the capital cost implications of oversized components.

Water treatment to prevent scaling, microbiological contamination and corrosion is recommended for chilled water distribution systems and is a legal requirement for any evaporative heat rejection system. The capital and running costs of water treatment may be significant and must be taken into account in calculating life cycle costs to assess the economics of alternative refrigeration and heat rejection systems.

4.2.7 Reliability

The reliability, security of supply, maintenance, and back-up of the refrigeration or heat rejection system is a major design consideration the importance of which will depend upon the nature of the end user's business operation.

A distinction must be made between 'mission critical' operations such as telecommunications centres and internet site providers (ISPs), and standard office comfort cooling applications. The financial consequences of the loss of cooling to a dealer floor may considerable. Uninterruptible power supply (UPS) systems may require 1 kW/m^2 of cooling and may be unable to operate for more than 5–10 minutes after a failure of the cooling system.

The use of over sized equipment is not recommended for energy efficiency and control reasons. It is also now a requirement of Approved Document L2 (2002)[14] that refrigeration equipment and fans and pumps used to condition general office space are appropriately sized to have no more capacity than is necessary for the task. This excludes the capacity of any 'off line' standby equipment.

For standard comfort air conditioning the loss of some or even all cooling capacity may not be a serious problem. However, 'mission critical' systems may require two independent chiller and chilled water distribution systems and controls with a back-up generator fed electricity supply to guarantee the availability of cooling.

Large air conditioned buildings with central chiller plant are often designed with multiple chillers. Multiple chillers offer operational flexibility, some standby capacity, and less disruptive maintenance. The chillers can be sized to handle a base load and increments of a variable load and, with a suitable sequencing control strategy, may achieve better energy efficiency than a single chiller installation. It is usual in these situations to provide 'run' and 'standby' pumps. Section 4.5.3.3 provides guidance on piping and control arrangements for multiple chiller installations.

The designer should be aware that the time taken to achieve normal temperatures is affected by the pull-down time (the time taken for the system to achieve normal operating temperatures) which might be quite long for some large chilled water systems. Designers should also be aware that some chillers have a long start-up time which may affect the time necessary to bring on stand-by plant. The designer should specifically obtain this information from the manufacturer.

It is recommended that the designer should consider undertaking a risk analysis assessment of the system to determine the level of reliability and back-up or redundancy that should be provided by the design. It should indicate the failure scenarios, which would dictate client action such as training, keeping spares, provision and safe keeping of original equipment manufacturer's O&M manuals. Carrying out a risk assessment in the early design stages will help the designer to reduce or, at least, identify the risk. Further guidance may be found in a paper by Tozer(21) and annex F of BS EN 378-1(22).

4.2.8 Whole-life costs

It is now a requirement of public sector purchasers that they move to whole-life cost-based procurement(23). The government's Private Finance Initiative(24) (PFI) has already stimulated a marked increase in interest in whole-life costing and there has been a growth in the availability of data to support the activity(25–28).

The designer should carry out a whole-life cycle costing exercise during the preliminary design stage in order to evaluate the full impact of plant selection on the end user. The elements of life costs include:

— acquisition

— installation

— commissioning

— energy

— running costs

— maintenance

— repair

— disposal.

While energy efficiency is an important criterion to those involved in selecting particular plant, the actual cost of running the plant across its full life can be a major consideration to the end user and one that should be factored into the final basis of selection. It is important that the designer ascertains the capability and willingness of the client to maintain an efficient, but more complicated system. For example, a simple system that requires only one service visit per year may be more suitable for some clients than a highly efficient but complicated system that requires three-monthly service visits.

Minimising the environmental impact of building cooling systems is linked inextricably to life cycle costs. For example, systems with the least whole-life cost are likely to be those with the lowest energy consumption and therefore the least impact on global warming, see section 4.2.3.

An assessment of whole-life costs should take account of the availability of enhanced capital allowances (ECAs). The Government's Enhanced Capital Allowance Scheme is devised to encourage businesses to invest in low carbon technologies. It enables businesses to claim 100% first year capital allowances on investments in energy saving technologies and products. The list which includes a range of refrigeration components and systems, including variable speed drives, is subject to constant update and can be consulted at (www.eca.gov.uk). See also section 4.3.5.1.

4.2.9 Procurement issues

When specifying components and plant the designer should take account of the need for, and likely availability of, replacement parts and spares. Refrigeration and heat rejection plant is commonly the most expensive single item of plant and it is important that spares and replacement parts are readily available at reasonable cost for the anticipated lifetime of the equipment.

The future availability of replacement refrigerant for topping up and servicing should be considered because many refrigerants are subject to ozone and global warming related regulations. CFCs have already been phased out and HCFCs are currently in the process of being phased out for use in new equipment, and have a limited availability for servicing existing systems. The long term availability of HFC refrigerants depends on whether safe, practical and economic replacements with lower global warming potential will become available, see section 4.3.4 and 4.4.5. The designer should keep up to date with current and developing regulations and standards.

Some components and systems are already subject to specific health and safety related regulations. These include cooling towers, refrigerants and most pressure systems (which covers most vapour compression refrigeration systems). Health and safety related regulations are constantly being updated and their scope widened. In many cases the implications can include increased cost of ownership. The designer should keep up to date with current and developing regulations and standards and ensure that the most up to date information is used when carrying out life cycle cost studies and when specifying equipment to procure.

4.2.10 Commissioning

Commissioning is defined as the advancement of an installation from static completion to full working order to the specified requirements. Approved Document L2 (2002)(14) requires that all building services systems are commissioned. The designer or procurer has to show that the design is commissionable, and show that the systems have been commissioned, within reason, to the design specification.

In order to ensure that the design is commissionable the designer should consider how the system should be commissioned at an early stage in the design process, and ensure that the necessary components and facilities are provided in the design to allow commissioning to be properly carried out. The designer should seek the assistance of a commissioning engineer where there is insufficient in-house experience. The designer must make sure that a clear description of how the system is intended to operate and the design parameters are clearly stated and recorded either in the design specification or the system design drawings. The requirement for subsequent recommissioning during the lifetime of the system should also be considered and this should take into account the resources available to the client.

It is particularly important for the success and feasibility of commissioning that the refrigeration system cooling capacity, controls and safety devices permit stable operation over the specified range of cooling load conditions. Oversizing should also be avoided and stand-by arrangements should be consistent with the design risk.

Key requirements for successfully commissioning a refrigeration and heat rejection system are given in section 4.3.6.2.

4.2.11 Operation

The operational efficiency of the system depends to a certain degree on the ability and commitment of the end user. This is because the end user is ultimately responsible for such items as the implementation of a planned preventative maintenance scheme (see section 4.2.12) and monitoring the system for faults or failures of plant or system components. For example, the correct setting of time-clocks or other controls with respect to the occupancy or process time periods will contribute significantly to overall efficiency.

It is therefore important to ensure that the relevant responsible person for the end user understands the system, and is also made aware of their responsibilities with regard to the operation of the plant. This is now a requirement of Approved Document L2 (2002)[(14)] which requires that the owner and/or operator of the building is provided with a log book giving details of the installed building services and controls, their method of operation and maintenance, and other details that show how energy consumption can be monitored and controlled. This information should be provided in summary form, suitable for day-to-day use and should be in addition to the more detailed information provided as part of the Operation and Maintenance Manuals and Health and Safety file.

CIBSE TM31[(29)] provides specific guidance on the preparation of building log-books.

The need for specific user training should be considered in cases where the plant and systems are particularly complex or unusual.

Approved Document L2 (2002)[(14)] also requires that sufficient sub-metering is provided so that the owner and/or operator can monitor and control energy use, see section 4.3.5.

4.2.12 Maintenance

The designer should consider maintenance requirements and ensure that the plant and systems are capable of being maintained effectively and safely by the user and/or operator. This includes ensuring that sufficient space is available around the plant for maintenance and the replacement of parts, and that adequate lighting levels are provided. The designer should liaise with the client at an early stage to ensure that the maintenance requirements of the selected plant and systems are within the capabilities of the intended user/operator.

The designer should be aware that some systems require very different or specific maintenance compared to standard equipment. For example evaporative cooling towers and condensers require meticulous water treatment and maintenance which some users and/or operators may be unwilling or incapable of providing.

It is the designer's responsibility under the Construction (Design and Management) Regulations[(30)] (CDM Regulations) to ensure that future maintenance of the plant can be carried out safely.

Requirements for the maintenance of refrigeration and heat rejection systems are given in Section 4.3.7.

4.2.13 Future needs

The future needs of the client should be discussed and agreed at the initial design stage. Future needs may relate to potential changes or additions to the cooling load of business processes in the building (for example telecommunications and IT equipment), occupancy densities or to the floor area covered by an air conditioning system.

Future needs may be simply allowed for by the provision of sufficient additional space for the installation of separate refrigeration and heat rejection plant. Alternatively, it may extend to the installation of the additional plant, pipework, controls etc. at the initial construction phase, sized to cater for any foreseeable requirements.

Initial oversizing of an individual refrigeration plant is not recommended in office applications; it will be difficult to justify under the requirements of Approved Document L2 (2002)[(14)], as it would inevitably operate at a relatively low load, is likely to significantly reduce the energy efficiency of the plant as well make control more difficult. Additional refrigeration capacity could be provided by an additional chiller in a multiple chiller installation. The excess capacity could then be left off-line until required. Careful design of the piping and pumping arrangements, including provision of inverter-driven pumps, should reduce the impact on pumping power and flow control, see 4.5.3.3.

As part of the consideration of future needs the designer should be aware of new requirements likely to be required by future revisions of the Building Regulations. In particular the Energy Performance of Buildings Directive[(31)] requires energy certification of buildings and regular inspection of air conditioning systems, including an assessment of the energy efficiency of refrigeration and heat rejection systems.

4.3 Requirements

4.3.1 Introduction

This section outlines the general limiting requirements, including relevant regulations, that need to be considered by the designer when selecting refrigeration and heat rejection plant and equipment with regard to:

(*a*) the provision of a safe, comfortable and healthy working internal environment with due consideration of the external environment and relevant regulations

— safety

— noise and vibration

— pollution

— building regulations

— commissioning

— maintenance

— decommissioning

(*b*) the building fabric

— building structure and layout

— plant space available

— aesthetics

(*c*) the specific requirements of the individual building, plant and equipment installed therein.

4.3.2 Safety

The designer has a responsibility to ensure that the design of the refrigeration and heat rejection system as a whole takes into account all the necessary provisions for safe operation and maintenance, as well as the necessary monitoring, warning and automatic protection features to ensure that the system remains safe during normal operation and during times of component failure.

4.3.2.1 UK Health and Safety Legislation

The designer should take account of the requirements of the Health and Safety at Work etc Act 1974 and all related regulations. UK health and safety regulations with specific requirements for refrigeration and heat rejection systems include:

— Management of Health and Safety at Work Regulations 1999[(32)]: require employers to assess the risks to the health and safety of their employees, and to take appropriate measures to prevent or control those risks.

— Pressure Systems Safety Regulations 2000[(33)]: require that all refrigeration systems with an input power greater than 25 kW are maintained properly and subject to a written scheme for regular safety inspections.

— Pressure Equipment Regulations 1999 (Pressure Equipment Directive)[(34)]: concerns the design, manufacture and supply of equipment. It covers all pressure equipment including refrigeration compressors, pipework, heat exchangers and safety devices. Essentially the requirements are that equipment is manufactured and installed to meet certain requirements and is subject to conformity assessment procedures.

— Control of Substances Hazardous to Health (COSHH) Regulations 1999[(35)]: require employers to ensure that exposure of their employees to substances hazardous to health is either prevented or, where this is not reasonably practicable, adequately controlled. COSHH would normally cover exposure to refrigerants in plant rooms and the control of legionella bacteria in water systems including cooling towers and evaporative condensers.

— Construction (Design and Management) (CDM) Regulations 1994[(35)]: require designers to prepare a health and safety file for the client on how to manage the safety risks when the plant is maintained, repaired, renovated or decommissioned.

— The Notification of Cooling Towers and Evaporative Condensers Regulations 1992 (SI 1992/2225)[(36)]: requires that the local authority is notified of all cooling towers and evaporative condensers.

Specific guidance on meeting the requirements of these regulations for vapour compression refrigeration systems is given in The Institute of Refrigeration Safety Codes[(37–39)]. The codes also give guidance on health and safety risk assessments for refrigeration systems. Guidance on compliance with the regulations with respect to the risk of exposure to legionella bacteria is given in HSC Approved Code of Practice and Guidance L8: *Legionnaires' disease: The control of legionella bacteria in water systems*[(40)].

4.3.2.2 Refrigerants

Refrigerants, their mixtures and combination with oils, water or other materials present in the refrigerating system can present risks to both people and property. Depending on the refrigerant used, the following risks can be caused by the escape of refrigerant from refrigeration systems:

— fire

— explosion

— toxicity

— caustic effects

— freezing of skin

— asphyxiation

— panic.

Other risks related to refrigerants include bursting or explosion due to over pressure or failure of some part of the refrigeration system. These risks can be caused by poor system design, maintenence or operation and in the worst case can lead can lead to significant property damage and danger to people.

The risks associated with the escape of refrigerant and the risks of systems bursting or exploding due to over pressure of refrigerant or equipment failure should be minimised by complying with relevant regulations, codes and standards, some of which have been detailed in 4.3.2.1. In addition, it is CIBSE policy that the requirements of BS EN 378: *Refrigerating systems and heat pumps. Safety and environmental requirements*[(22)] should also be complied with. The guidance given in CIBSE GN1[(12)] should also be followed. The Institute of Refrigeration Safety Codes[(37–39)] provide specific guidance on the requirements of BS EN 378.

Safety requirements specific to particular refrigerants are given in section 4.4.

4.3.2.3 *Legionella*

Any system that contains water at between 20 °C and 45 °C is at risk of supporting colonies of *Legionella* bacteria. If the system has the means of creating and disseminating breathable water droplets or aerosols it is at risk of causing exposure to *Legionella* bacteria, the cause of a potentially fatal disease in humans. Cooling and heat rejection systems that incorporate a cooling tower or evaporative condenser are thus at particular risk of supporting the bacteria that could cause *Legionella* infection.

Relevant regulations (see 4.3.2.1) that must be complied with include:

- Management of Health and Safety at Work Regulations 1999[32]
- Control of Substances Hazardous to Health Regulations 1999[35] (COSHH)
- The Notification of Cooling Towers and Evaporative Condensers Regulations 1992[36].

Practical guidance on complying with these regulations is given by the HSC Approved Code of Practice and Guidance L8[40] and CIBSE TM13[41].

The regulations impose specific legal duties on employers and building owners/operators to identify and assess all potential sources of *Legionella*, prepare a scheme for preventing or controlling the risk, implement, manage and monitor precautions and keep records of the precautions.

Designers and installers have legal responsibilities to minimise the risk of *Legionella* infection through the design, construction and commissioning of cooling and heat rejection systems. These include the design and construction of cooling towers and evaporative condensers, their location, water treatment systems and water distribution system design, see section 4.5.5.4.

Other forms of heat rejection equipment such as dry air coolers normally have no risk of causing *Legionella* infection. However, if rain water is allowed to collect in idle equipment in warm conditions then there is a risk of *Legionella* bacteria multiplying and being distributed in an aerosol when fans are restarted. Care should be taken when designing, installing and maintaining systems to ensure that water drains away freely. This includes making sure that components are properly levelled and that drains are free falling and kept clear and that there is adequate access for cleaning.

4.3.2.4 Operation and maintenance

The design of the system and selection of components should allow the system to be operated and maintained safely. The designer should also ensure that the operation and maintenance requirements are within the capabilities and resources of the intended owner and operator.

The Construction (Design and Management) Regulations 1994[30] require that designers consider the need to design in a way which avoids risks to health and safety or reduces these risks as far as practicable so that the project can be constructed and maintained safely. This would include, for example, provision of safe access to cooling towers and evaporative condensers to allow their regular inspection and cleaning, and sufficient space and lighting around refrigeration plant to allow regular refrigerant leak checks. The regulations require the designer to provide the client with a health and safety file on how to manage the safety risks when the plant is maintained, repaired or decommissioned. This document is in addition to the operation and maintenance (O&M) manuals and to the building log book recommended in Building Regulations Approved Document L2[14].

Operation and maintenance procedures should comply with relevant UK health and safety regulations which are summarised in section 4.3.2.1 and BS EN 378-4[22]. In particular the Pressure Systems Safety Regulations 2000[33] require that systems are maintained properly and that all refrigeration systems with an input power greater than 25 kW are subject to a written scheme for regular safety inspections. The Institute of Refrigeration's Safety Codes [37–39] provide guidance on complying with relevant UK regulations and BS EN 378[22] as well as practical guidance on what constitutes a suitable maintenance and inspection schedule. Additional specific guidance for systems that use ammonia as refrigerant is given in the Health and Safety Executive Guidance Note PM81[42].

The Control of Substances Hazardous to Health Regulations 1999[35] (COSHH) (see section 4.3.2.1) include the risk of exposure to refrigerants in plant rooms and elsewhere in buildings. In general plant rooms should be adequately ventilated and provided with refrigerant gas detectors linked to alarms at the occupational exposure limit concentrations. Specific requirements are given in BS EN 378[22] and are summarised in section 4.4.

4.3.3 Noise

Refrigeration and heat rejection plant produces noise pollution in the form of:

- *mechanical vibration*: which can be transmitted through the building structure and generate noise in occupied rooms
- *airborne noise*: which can be a nuisance to the occupants of the building, to neighbouring buildings and also to operatives inside plant rooms.

Dealing with noise pollution is an important aspect of design and requirements for its control are given in section 5 of this Guide. Designers and employers should be aware that they have specific requirements under the Noise at Work Regulations 1990[43] relating to the exposure of employees to noise in the workplace. This is especially relevant to noise levels in refrigeration system plant rooms and requires a risk assessment and the implementation of measures to protect people from hazardous noise levels.

There are several approaches to preventing noise problems and these are outlined below:

- Selection of quieter plant: this is the simplest option but may not be practicable or economic.

The size, speed and design of the fans on air cooled chillers and other heat rejection equipment can also have a significant impact on noise.

— Location of plant: noisy plant such as refrigeration compressors should be located in appropriately designed and constructed plant rooms or well away from occupied areas.

— Plant rooms containing very noisy equipment should be constructed with high mass floor, walls and roof and particular care should be taken to seal any potential noise leakage paths.

— Scheduled maintenance programmes should be adhered to with particular care to ensure that moving parts are adequately lubricated and that worn or loose parts are replaced or tightened.

— Air borne noise from plant such as chillers and cooling towers can be partially blocked using barriers, with or without sound absorbing material, placed between the noise producing plant and the occupied areas.

— Airborne noise from cooling towers can also be reduced by fitting an acoustically lined vent cowl.

— Where barriers are not sufficient plant can be enclosed inside an acoustic enclosure with silencers at the fan outlets and air intakes.

— Noise resulting from vibration can be reduced by placing plant on suitable anti-vibration mounts.

Where plant is enclosed in structures such as an acoustic enclosure the designer must ensure that adequate access space is provided around the plant to allow for maintenance procedures to be safely carried out. Space should also be provided to ensure that the plant receives adequate airflow for cooling and heat rejection.

Enclosing plant or fitting silencers to air inlets and outlets may have a detrimental effect on energy efficiency and this should be taken into account.

The method of control of plant can affect noise levels. For instance where fans are speed controlled to suit the heat rejection load and ambient temperature they are likely to operate for much of the time at reduced speed and hence produce less noise than at the design load. The designer and contractor should consult the manufacturer or supplier at an early stage, so that all available options may be considered.

Particular care is needed when installing small refrigerant condensers on the outside walls of buildings as is common with split or multi-split air conditioning systems. Close proximity to windows and neighbouring buildings should be avoided. The start up noise from compressors should be considered as well as the general noise when operating compressors and fans.

Where structure borne noise is a particular issue, such as in residential type buildings, absorption chillers should be considered instead of vapour compression plant. However, energy efficiency issues should be taken into account, see section 4.4.5. The relatively low efficiency of absorption chillers also means that significantly larger heat rejection systems or cooling towers are required, taking up more space and possibly increasing noise levels outside the building compared with vapour compression chillers.

4.3.4 Pollution

Many refrigerants, oils and other chemicals used in refrigeration systems may cause pollution to the environment. The system designer and the equipment specifier should be aware of any environmentally damaging substances or materials used in the refrigeration and heat rejection equipment. A major factor is the emission of environmentally damaging refrigerants, such as ozone-depleting CFCs and HCFCs, into the atmosphere due to leakage or spillage during servicing. The designer should be sure of the validity and reasoning behind the selection of potentially environmentally damaging materials.

The requirements of the following regulations must be met:

— EC Regulation No 2037/2000[44] on ozone depleting substances: as well as phasing-out and controlling use of CFCs and HCFC refrigerants this regulation also includes legal requirements for the minimisation and avoidance of refrigerant emissions and leakage, see section 4.3.4.1.

— Environmental Protection Act 1990[45]: Section 33 of the Act states that it is illegal to 'treat, keep or dispose of controlled waste in a manner likely to cause pollution to the environment or harm human health'. Most refrigerants and oils come under the category of controlled waste. Section 34 places a duty of care on all those who handle controlled waste to ensure that it is legally and safety dealt with. This includes preventing its escape.

It is also considered good practice and CIBSE policy that the requirements of BS EN 378[22] are complied with as well as the above statutory regulations. The guidance given in CIBSE GN1[12] should also be followed.

The UK is party to a number of international agreements including the Montreal Protocol[46] and the Kyoto Protocol[47]. The Montreal Protocol is implemented through EC Regulation 2037/2000[44], see section 4.3.4.1. The Kyoto Protocol addresses the issue of the emission of man-made greenhouse gases including many refrigerants. Details of the Kyoto Protocol and UK policy are detailed in section 4.3.4.2.

Whilst the designer should consider the impact of the choice of substances used within a system, consideration should also be given to ways in which the severity of pollution could be reduced in the event of a leak. This can be by means of a simple refrigerant gas detection system which raises an alarm. Alternatively it may involve the use of a complex system that will initiate automatic shut down in the event of a leak, thus minimising the volume of material leaked.

4.3.4.1 Ozone depleting substances

Chlorofluorocarbons (CFCs) and hydrochlorofluorcarbons (HCFCs) have been widely used as refrigerants. It is now accepted that the emission of CFCs and HCFCs contribute to depletion of the ozone layer (as well as being powerful greenhouse gases).

The Montreal Protocol[46] is an international treaty to protect the stratospheric ozone layer through controls on the consumption and production of ozone-depleting substances, including refrigerants containing chlorine and/or bromine. The original Protocol was agreed on 16 September 1987 and entered into force on 1 January 1989. The protocol has since been amended and has now been ratified by over 170 countries, including the European Union and the United States. Countries with developing country status have longer to comply with the CFC and HCFC phase-outs. The requirements of the current version of the Montreal Protocol are detailed in Table 4.2.

Within the European Union the Montreal Protocol is enforced through EC Regulation No 2037/2000 on ozone depleting substances[44] (as amended by Regulations 2038/2000 and 2039/2000). This regulation is law throughout the European Union and is in addition backed up in the UK by Statutory Instrument 2002 No 528 The Environmental Protection (Controls on Ozone-Depleting Substances) Regulations 2002[48]. The regulation requires a faster phase-out of HCFCs than the Montreal Protocol and has other requirements related to prevention of leakage and the use of recycled CFCs and HCFCs. The principal requirements are detailed in Table 4.3.

4.3.4.2 Greenhouse gases

It is now generally accepted that man-made emissions of greenhouse gases, especially carbon dioxide from the burning of fossil fuels, are causing global warming. An international agreement, the Kyoto Protocol, was agreed in 1997 to address this issue. Under the Kyoto Protocol many of the developed countries agreed to targets to reduce their emissions of a basket of six greenhouse gases (carbon dioxide, methane, nitrous oxide, hydrofluorocarbons (HFCs), perfluorocarbons and sulphur hexafluoride) by 5.2% below 1990 levels over the period 2008 to 2012. Although CFCs and HCFCs are powerful greenhouse gases their phase-out is being addressed by the Montreal Protocol. The European Union agreed to an 8% target

Table 4.2 The Montreal Protocol

Product	Date and restriction imposed			
	Developed countries		Developing countries	
CFCs	1/1/1996	Consumption banned	1/1/2010	
HCFCs	1/1/1996	Freeze consumption at 2.8% of 1989 CFC consumption plus 1989 HCFC consumption (in ODP tonnes)	1/1/2010 1/1/2040	Freeze consumption at 2015 level Consumption banned
	1/1/2004	Consumption limited to 65% of 1996 level		
	1/1/2010	Consumption limited to 35% of 1996 level		
	1/1/2015	Consumption limited to 10% of 1996 level		
	1/1/2020	Consumption limited to 0.5% of 1996 level		
	1/1/2030	Consumption banned		

Note: 'Consumption' means production plus imports minus exports (all values are in ODP tonnes). Recycled and reused product is excluded from the above controls and some exceptions are possible for limited 'essential uses'.

Table 4.3 EC Regulation 2037/200 on ozone depleting substances

Substance/measure	Date	Restriction imposed
CFCs	1//1/1995	Production banned (earlier regulation)
	1/10/2000	Supply to market banned
	1/1/2001	Use for maintaining or refilling existing systems banned
HCFCs: restrictions to quantity placed on the market	1/1/2001	Quantity of HCFCs plus 2% of the quantity of CFCs placed on the market in 1989 (in ODP tonnes)
	1/1/2002	85% of the 2001 limit
	1/1/2003	45% of the 2001 limit
	1/1/2004	30% of the 2001 limit
	1/1/2008	25% of the 2001 limit
	1/1/2010	Supply to market banned
HCFCs: end use controls (refrigeration and air conditioning systems)	1/1/2000	Banned for use in new refrigeration systems for the following applications: — domestic refrigerators and freezers — road public transport and rail transport air conditioning — public and distribution cold stores and warehouses — equipment of 150 kW (shaft power) and over
	1/1/2001	Banned in all new refrigeration and air conditioning systems, except for the following temporary exceptions: — ban is delayed until 1/7/2002 for fixed air conditioning equipment with a cooling capacity less than 100 kW — ban is delayed until 1/1/2004 for reversible air conditioning systems and heat pumps
	1/1/2010	Ban on use of virgin HCFCs for servicing and topping-up existing systems.
	1/1/2015	Ban on use of all HCFCs, including recycled materials (from 2015 recovered HCFCs must be destroyed by an environmentally acceptable technology).
Recovery and destruction	All CFCs and HCFCs used in refrigeration and air conditioning equipment must be recovered during servicing or maintenance, or prior to dismantling or disposal of the equipment. After 1/1/2001 recovered CFCs must be destroyed by an environmentally acceptable technology. Recovered HCFCs may be destroyed or reused until 2015.	
Leakage prevention	All precautionary measures practicable must be taken to prevent and minimise leakage of CFCs and HCFCs. Fixed refrigeration and air conditioning equipment containing more than 3 kg of CFCs or HCFCs must be checked annually for leakage.	

shared between its member states and under this the UK's national target is 12.5%.

The UK Government published and presented to Parliament on 17th November 2000 the UK's climate change programme[49]. The programme sets out the UK strategy for tackling climate change and includes specific measures related to the use of HFCs:

- HFCs should only be used where other safe, technically feasible, cost effective and more environmentally acceptable alternatives do not exist
- HFCs are not sustainable in the long term: the Government believes that continued technological developments will mean that HFCs may eventually be able to be replaced in the applications where they are used
- HFC emission reduction strategies should not undermine commitments to phase out ozone depleting substances under the Montreal Protocol
- HFC emissions will not be allowed to rise unchecked.

The programme explains a range of policies to reduce HFC emissions including strengthening existing voluntary agreements with industry, and where appropriate for industry to use alternative refrigerants with zero or low global warming potential (GWP) such as ammonia and hydrocarbons.

For refrigeration systems the issue of greenhouse gas emissions is complex because there is the direct impact of the emission of greenhouse gas refrigerants and the indirect impact of the use of energy, with its associated carbon dioxide emissions, to operate the refrigeration system. Total equivalent warming impact (TEWI) is a way of assessing the overall impact of refrigeration systems from the direct and indirect emissions, see section 4.3.5.2. Designers should seek to minimise TEWI through the selection of an appropriate refrigeration machine and refrigerant and by optimising the selection of components and system design for the best energy efficiency.

The direct global warming impact of a gas is measured by the relative global warming potential of one kilogram of the gas relative to one kilogram of carbon dioxide. It is usual to base this on a 100 year time horizon, although in reality many greenhouse gases have atmospheric lifetimes longer than this. Global warming potentials of a range of common refrigerants are shown in Table 4.4.

Table 4.4 Global warming potentials of common refrigerants

Refrigerant	Global warming potential 100-year time horizon (GWP100)
R11 (CFC-11)	4000
R12 (CFC-12)	8500
R22 (HCFC-22)	1700
R123 (HCFC-123)	93
R134a (HFC-134a)	1300
R404A (HFC-404A)	3800
R407C (HFC407C)	1600
R410A (HFC-410A)	1900
R417A (HFC-417A)	1950
R290 (propane)	3
R600a (isobutane)	3
R717 (ammonia)	0

Source : BS EN378[22] (values vary slightly depending on source of data)

4.3.4.3 Other pollutants

Other refrigerants and substances used in refrigeration and heat rejection systems are potentially harmful to the environment and to human health and are therefore subject to the requirements of the Environmental Protection Act and should be disposed of as controlled waste or in some cases as special waste. These pollutants include the following:

- *Ammonia*: used as a refrigerant in some vapour compression and absorption chillers. Ammonia is highly toxic to people and to aquatic organisms and fish so should never be discharged to surface water courses. However, ammonia is safe to discharge to the atmosphere as long as it is in a safe location away from people and buildings.
- *Lithium bromide and water*: used in many absorption chillers and is corrosive.
- *Corrosion inhibitors*: used specifically in absorption chillers (which may also contain alcohol) but may also be used in water based cooling systems.
- *Water treatment chemicals*: cooling towers and evaporative condensers use special water treatment chemicals including biocides and these may not be accepted into public sewers.

4.3.5 Energy efficiency

It is CIBSE policy that the energy efficiency of refrigeration and heat rejection systems is optimised. Building Regulations Approved Document L2[14] also includes specific energy efficiency provisions (see section 4.3.6), particularly for air conditioning systems in office buildings. The Energy Performance of Buildings Directive[31] will also require specific energy efficiency targets to be set for the design of most non-domestic buildings and periodic inspections and assessment of air conditioning systems. Information about the energy efficiency of specific types of vapour compression and absorption refrigeration systems is given in sections 4.4.4 and 4.4.5 and strategic design guidance on energy efficiency issues is given in section 4.2.3. Information and guidance on achieving energy targets is also given in CIBSE Guide F: *Energy efficiency in buildings*[1].

4.3.5.1 Climate change levy

The Climate Change Levy came into force in the UK in 2001 as a mechanism to encourage non-domestic building users to improve the efficiency of their systems. The levy was originally set at 0.15 p/kW·h for gas and 0.43 p/kW·h for electricity. At the time of writing the levy is offset by a cut in employers National Insurance Contributions and 100% first-year Enhanced Capital Allowances against tax for designated energy-saving equipment as an incentive for purchasers of equipment to choose more efficient equipment. Qualifying refrigeration related equipment includes:

- evaporative condensers

- liquid pressure amplification systems
- automatic air purgers
- automatic leak detection systems
- absorption chillers driven by qualifying combined heat and power (CHP) plant
- efficient compressors
- variable speed motor drives
- pipe insulation.

The list of qualifying equipment from particular manufacturers is subject to constant update and can be viewed at (www.eca.gov.uk).

4.3.5.2 Total equivalent warming impact (TEWI)

Total equivalent warming impact (TEWI) is a way of assessing the overall impact of refrigeration systems from the direct refrigerant related and indirect fuel related emissions. Designers should seek to minimise TEWI through the selection of an appropriate refrigeration machine and refrigerant and by optimising equipment selection and system design for the best energy efficiency.

TEWI sums all emissions of greenhouse gases in tonnes or kilograms of CO_2 equivalent over the lifetime of the plant. It may be calculated using the following formula:

$$\text{TEWI} = Q\,\beta\,L + \frac{M\,L\,(l_1 + l_2 + s_1 + s_2)}{100} + M\,(1 - \alpha) \tag{4.1}$$

where TEWI is the total equivalent warming impact (kg CO_2), Q is the annual energy consumption (kW·h), β is the CO_2 emission factor for electricity (kg CO_2/ kW·h) (see Table 4.8), L is the life of the plant (years), M is the refrigerant charge (kg), l_1 is the annual leak rate (% of refrigerant charge), l_2 is the annual purge release factor (% of refrigerant charge), s_1 is the annual service release (% of refrigerant charge), s_2 is the probability factor for catastrophic failure (% refrigerant charge loss/year) and α is the refrigerant recovery efficiency factor.

For valid comparison between different refrigeration systems the annual energy consumption should include all of the circulation pumps, fans and related components that make up the whole refrigeration system.

Further guidance on the calculation of TEWI, including sample worksheets, is provided by the British Refrigerating Association (BRA)[50]. The BRA also provides sectorial release factors for calculating TEWI for new refrigeration systems that are manufactured, installed and maintained to current best practice standards. These factors are reproduced in Table 4.5.

4.3.6 Building Regulations

Approved Document L of the Building Regulations for England and Wales[14], and the equivalent for Scotland and Northern Ireland[51,52], provides guidance on building design to reduce energy consumption and carbon emissions.

Table 4.5 TEWI sectorial release factors for new systems to best practice standards[50]

Sector	Lifetime, L (years)	Sectorial release factors				
		α	l_1	l_2	s_1	s_2
Commercial DX	10	0.95	5	n/a	0.25	n/a
Liquid chillers (flooded) and industrial plant	10	0.95	2	0.5	0.25	n/a
White goods:						
— commercial	10	0.6	0	0	0	0
— domestic	10	0.3	0	0	0	0

These provisions include:

- testing insulation continuity and air tightness of buildings
- commissioning of systems
- the provision of energy meters and information on their use that enable building occupiers to maintain and operate the building effectively
- designing systems which comply with specific performance targets
- checking that systems as built meet the design intent
- provision of simplified operating and maintenance log books.

The Building Regulations Approved Document L2 (2002) (ADL2)[14] provides practical guidance with respect to the requirements of the regulations.

4.3.6.1 Efficiency of air conditioning and mechanical ventilation systems

Since ADL2 has included provisions that address the efficiency of air conditioning and mechanical ventilation (AC/MV) systems in offices, and of mechanical ventilation systems in other types of buildings. The energy efficiency targets for these systems currently do not apply to whole systems or the parts of systems used for process cooling applications, including sports facilities, restaurants and kitchens, large dedicated conference rooms and dedicated computer or communications rooms.

AC/MV systems in office buildings

There are three calculation methods that could be used depending on how the proposer chooses to demonstrate compliance:

- *Elemental method* (see ADL2[14], paragraphs 1.60 to 1.68 and Appendix G): to show compliance the building envelope has to provide certain minimum levels of insulation including maximum allowable areas of glazing, and the building services systems each have to meet defined minimum standards of energy efficiency. For offices, air conditioning systems have to meet a standard of efficiency defined as the carbon performance rating (CPR). The maximum values of CPR for new AC/MV systems are shown in Table 4.6. The CPR takes into account the size and method of control of the refrigeration plant and the air/water distribution system.

Refrigeration plant size is taken as a measure of the 'quality' of design, including details of the building fabric (solar gain etc.), the plant and system efficiency selected, and design assumptions about internal gains etc. Refrigeration system efficiency can be balanced against the distribution system efficiency as long as the target is met. The elemental method is only suitable for standard buildings; it is unsuitable for innovative buildings or innovative building services systems.

— *Whole building method (for offices)* (see ADL2[14], paragraphs 1.69 to 1.73 and Appendix G): to show compliance the building envelope has to provide certain minimum levels of insulation and air tightness and the whole building must meet specified maximum values of whole building carbon performance rating (Table 4.7). This method allows more design flexibility than the elemental method and allows trade-offs between the heating, lighting, ventilation and air conditioning system efficiencies.

— *Carbon emissions calculation method* (CECM): this method of compliance uses any suitably approved calculation method or software to demonstrate that the overall design would not produce any more carbon emissions than if it had been designed to comply with the elemental method (ADL2[14], paragraph 1.74). Design is largely unrestricted within this constraint, for example allowing trade-offs between glazed areas and system efficiency, although some minimum specified insulation and air tightness standards still apply. CIBSE TM32[53] has been developed to simplify its application.

ADL2[14] provides values for carbon emission factors to be used when calculating the carbon performance rating of different heating and ACMV systems. These are reproduced in Table 4.8.

AC/MV systems in other buildings

ADL2[14] currently only includes a simple provision for the minimum efficiency of mechanical ventilation systems in other buildings. Specific fan power* (SFP) should be no more than 2 W/(litre·s^{-1}) in new construction or 3 W/(litre·s^{-1}) in existing buildings where a new AC/MV is being installed or where an existing AC/MV system is being substantially altered.

4.3.6.2 Inspection and commissioning of the building services

ADL2[14] defines inspection as establishing at completion of the installation that the specified and approved provisions for efficient operation have been put in place. Commissioning means the advancement of these systems from the state of static completion to working order to the specified requirements of the approved design. For each system this includes setting-to-work, adjustment to achieve the specified performance, the calibration, setting-up and testing of the associated automatic control systems, and recording of the system settings and the performance test results that have been accepted as satisfactory.

* Specific fan power (SFP) is defined as the sum of the design total circuit watts, including all losses through switchgear and controls such as inverters, of all fans that supply air and exhaust it back to outdoors (i.e. the sum of supply and extract fans) divided by the design ventilation rate through the building.

Table 4.6 Elemental method: maximum allowable AC/MV carbon performance ratings (CPR) for offices

System	Maximum CPR for a new system installed in an office / (kg C·m^{-2} per year)	
	New office building	Existing office building
Air conditioned	10.3	11.35
Mechanically ventilated	6.5	7.35

Table 4.7 Whole building method: maximum whole-office CPR

System	Maximum allowable CPR for a new system installed in an office / (kg C·m^{-2} per year)	
	New office	Refurbished office
Naturally ventilated	7.1	7.8
Mechanically ventilated	10.0	11.0
Air conditioned	18.5	20.4

Table 4.8 Carbon emissions calculation method: carbon emission factors

Fuel	Carbon emission factor	
	(kg C / kW·h)	(kg CO_2 / kW·h)
Natural gas	0.053	0.194
Oil	0.074	0.271
Coal	0.086	0.315
Electricity (average)	0.113	0.414

The principal requirement of ADL2[14] is that the designer or procurer must provide a report that shows that the work complies with ADL2 and has been completed to a reasonable standard. The report must be produced by a competent person who's suitability should be agreed by the building control authority. The report should include:

— A commissioning plan that shows that every system has been properly inspected and commissioned. A way of demonstrating compliance would be to follow the guidance in the CIBSE Commissioning Codes and BSRIA commissioning guides, see below. Guidance is also provided by the Commissioning Specialists Association[54].

— The results of the commissioning tests, confirming that the performance is reasonably in accordance with the approved design.

The following are key recommendations for successfully commissioning a refrigeration and heat rejection system:

— The refrigeration and heat rejection systems must be inherently commissionable and this includes providing sufficient space for access to equipment (for maintenance as well as commissioning). The requirement for commissioning should be included in the brief at the outset of the project and followed through to installation and handover.

— It is recommended that specialist commissioning advice is sought early in the design process.

— The contractor and client must allow sufficient time for the complete commissioning process to be integrated into the overall programme.

— Suitably qualified persons must carry out the commissioning. Particular attention must be given to the safe handling of all refrigerants, but especially ammonia and hydrocarbons.

— Maximise off-site pre-commissioning and performance testing where appropriate.

— Post occupancy checks should be carried out to confirm the performance of refrigeration plant and systems. This should include refrigerant leak detection and operation at part and full load.

— Refrigeration plant is often packaged and in this case a representative of the equipment supplier or manufacturer should be involved in the commissioning process to liaise with contractors supplying related components such as chilled water pumps.

Experience has shown that the commissioning of chillers should include a check of the low chilled water flow rate cut-outs (to prevent nuisance trips when strainers are dirty), and chiller power on/off tests (some chillers lock-out after a power failure and require a manual restarting sequence).

For further guidance see CIBSE Guides F[(1)] and H[(11)], CIBSE Commissioning Code R: *Refrigerating systems*[(55)] and BSRIA Application Guide AG02/89: *Commissioning of water systems in building*[(56)] and the Commissioning Specialists Association Technical Memorandum No. 1: *Standard specification for the commissioning of mechanical engineering services installations for buildings*[(54)].

4.3.6.3 Building log-book

The building owner should be provided with a log book, in which the installed plant and its function are described in simple language for the everyday use of the owner. The log book should be in addition to the more detailed information provided in the operation and maintenance manuals and the health and safety file.

Information that should be provided in the building log book includes:

— a description of the building and its building services systems, including intended purpose

— a simple description of the operation and control strategies of the building services systems

— the location(s) of relevant plant and simplified system schematics

— input power and output ratings of the services plant

— a summary of the commissioning report

— maintenance instructions

— details of sub-meters and advice on their use

— results of air tightness testing.

A suitable template for the production of the building logbook is available as CIBSE TM31: *Building log books* [(29)].

4.3.6.4 Installation of energy meters

Adequate energy meters should be provided for the owner or occupier to measure their actual energy consumption. Sub-metering should be provided for significant individual items of plant such as chiller installations of greater than 20 kW rated input power, fan and pump motor control centers with a rated input power greater than 10 kW, or sub-tenanted areas of over 500 m^2. In some cases, such as the provision of chilled water service to tenants, heat metering may be required to measure the energy supplied.

The owners or occupiers should also be provided with instructions and a metering strategy, showing how to use the meters to account for at least 90% of the energy used with the building and how the results can be used to compare operating performance with published benchmarks. Guidance on metering strategies is given in ActionEnergy General Information Leaflet GIL 65: *Sub-metering new build non-domestic buildings*[(57)].

4.3.6.5 EU Directive on the energy performance of buildings

The Energy Performance of Buildings Directive[(31)] focuses on the ongoing performance of buildings after occupation and further development of the Building Regulations may also be needed to support the aims of the Directive.

The Directive requires a number of specific procedures to be developed in EU countries:

— development of a methodology for calculating the energy performance of buildings

— minimum requirements for the energy performance of new buildings, and existing buildings undergoing major renovation

— energy certification of buildings

— regular inspection and assessment of boilers and air conditioning systems.

When the Directive is enacted, regular inspection of air conditioning systems with a rated output of greater than 12 kW will be required. The inspections should include an assessment of the of the air conditioning system efficiency and the sizing compared to the cooling requirements of the building. Appropriate advice should be provided to the users on possible improvement or replacement of the air conditioning system and on alternative solutions.

4.3.7 Maintenance

It is the designer's responsibility under the Construction (Design and Management) Regulations[(30)] (CDM Regulations) to ensure that future maintenance of the plant can be carried out safely. Attention is drawn to the people working on refrigeration plant and their responsibilities within the provisions of the Health and Safety at Work etc. Act 1974[(58)]. In particular, people who are responsible for maintenance shall be 'competent' (i.e. they have the necessary training and knowledge for their task to achieve 'competence'). One way of demonstrating competence is by registration with an accredited registration organisation such as the Air Conditioning and Refrigeration Industry Board* (ACRIB) and thereby obtaining a refrigerant handling certificate.

European and UK legislation and standards must be observed. The Institute of Refrigeration (IoR) codes for safety in the design, construction and installation, commissioning, inspection, maintenance and decommissioning of vapour compression refrigerating systems[37–39], amplify the requirements of BS EN 378-4[22] and take account of relevant UK regulations, see Section 4.3.2.

The designer should be aware that some systems require very different or specific maintenance compared to standard equipment. Examples include:

— Evaporative cooling towers and condensers require meticulous water treatment and maintenance which some users and/or operators may be unwilling or incapable of providing. It is possible to subcontract maintenance of these systems to specialist maintenance companies or to the equipment manufacturer.

— Chillers using ammonia as a refrigerant should only be maintained by specialist contractors or the manufacturer.

— The Pressure Systems Safety Regulations 2000[33] specify that all vapour compression refrigeration equipment with more than 25 kW compressor input power require regular periodic inspection by a competent person in accordance with a written scheme of inspection, see section 4.4.5.2.

4.3.8 Building structure and layout

The design and specification of refrigeration and heat rejection systems should take account of specific building structure and layout requirements. These include:

— *Acceptable structural loads*: roof and floor structures must be strong enough for the specified refrigeration and heat rejection plant. Inadequate strength will result in a need for strengthening or may limit the type or size of plant.

— *Available space inside the building*: space for plant rooms inside a building may be restricted due to commercial requirements to maximise the lettable area.

— *Available roof space*: competing space requirements from other equipment (such as mobile phone masts and other telecommunications equipment) may restrict the space for heat rejection plant. This may cause heat rejection plant to be installed too close together which could reduce cooling capacity and efficiency.

— *Building layout constraints*: may make access to plant areas difficult for maintenance or for replacement of large items of plant such as chillers. Knock-out panels may have to be incorporated into roofs and walls to allow access for future plant replacement.

* Air Conditioning and Refrigeration Industry Board, 76 Mill Lane, Carshalton, Surrey SM5 2JR (acrib@acrib.org.uk)

These building structural and layout requirements should be taken into account at an early stage in the design process as they will affect the ability of the designer to meet the legal requirements of the Construction (Design and Management) Regulations[30] (CDM). Access for both installation and maintenance of the refrigeration and heat rejection plant is affected by the building layout as well as the building structural design, and will have an impact on the type of system and size of plant that can be installed.

More energy efficient plant may be smaller and lighter than less efficient alternatives and will reduce the impact of the above requirements. For example, a more energy efficient chiller will have a lower heat rejection load than a less efficient chiller, and will require less roof space and have a lower weight.

4.3.9 Aesthetics

Local authority planning consent and architectural considerations may require that external plant meets certain visual requirements. This may call for concealment or screening of plant on building roofs. For example, this might affect cooling towers, chillers and other heat rejection equipment. These conditions may be in addition to any requirements for noise reduction. Listed buildings will have additional requirements.

The designer and contractor should liaise with the architect at an early stage in the project to ensure that any planning, listed building and architectural requirements are known at the outline design stage. Any requirement for screening or concealment of plant should be assessed for the effect on plant air flow requirements and space for commissioning and maintenance.

4.4 System selection

4.4.1 Introduction

System selection should be based on the requirements of the refrigeration and heat rejection strategy determined from the guidance given in section 4.2, taking into account the general limiting requirements, including relevant regulations, detailed in section 4.3.

It is assumed that the requirement for some form of building cooling system has been determined taking into account the guiding principles of strategic design outlined in section 4.2. The designer should select a system to satisfy this cooling demand whilst avoiding or minimising the requirement for refrigeration, taking into account economic and environmental considerations. For example, a simpler heat rejection system may meet part or all of the cooling load without the need to operate a refrigeration system, an example of 'free cooling'.

Sections 4.4.2 to 4.4.10 consider systems, including methods of free cooling, which are currently available to implement the strategies set out in section 4.2 and meet the regulatory and other requirements defined in section 4.3. Details of the constituent items of systems are given in section 4.5.

The level of information provided here is not intended to give step-by-step guidance, but to provide a summary of key issues and performance targets which need to be addressed during design. The guidance contained in this section should be read in conjunction with CIBSE Guides A[18] and F[1].

4.4.2 Refrigeration and heat rejection systems

Guidance on selecting cooling systems is given in Table 4.9 which summarises and classifies the main types of systems according to BS EN 378-1[22]. This is intended as an aid to understanding the types of equipment referred to later in section 4.4s and 4.5.

Type (*a*) systems have the disadvantage that components that contain refrigerant are installed in the space or room being cooled. Distributed versions of (*a*) may contain large quantities of refrigerant. Most conventional chilled water based systems are based on systems (*d*) or (*e*) and use terminal units such as fan coil units, induction units or chilled beams and panels. With these systems the components that contain refrigerant are outside the space being cooled and this avoids the risk of refrigerant leaks into occupied areas.

Table 4.10 summaries the main types of heat rejection system and provides guidance on selection and cross-references to further information in section 4.5.

4.4.3 Free cooling

The aim of 'free cooling' is to minimise or eliminate the need to provide and operate a refrigeration system. Most buildings or processes that require cooling throughout the year have the potential to use free-cooling during cool weather. In summary:

— Free cooling can minimise or eliminate the need to operate a refrigeration system.

— Free cooling opportunity can be increased through selection of an appropriate cooling system.

— Air and chilled water transport energy consumption may be quite high.

Free cooling usually requires the transport of air or water as a cooling medium and may also require the use of additional fans and pumps for heat rejection at a dry air cooler or cooling tower. The designer should ensure that the overall energy used by a free cooling system is less than would be consumed had a refrigeration system been operated. Free cooling systems generally involve moving relatively large amounts of tempered or ambient air and cool water, compared with the smaller amounts of cold air or water distributed when a refrigeration system is operated.

The designer can maximise the opportunity for free-cooling by selecting a cooling system that requires air or chilled water at a relatively high temperature. For example, chilled ceilings and beams generally require chilled water at between 13 °C and 18 °C, although higher temperatures than these can be used at part load or if comfort conditions are slightly relaxed. Displacement ventilation systems typically supply air at 19 °C to the conditioned space which increases the proportion of the year that full fresh air can be used and reduces refrigeration requirements in hot weather. Further guidance on these systems is given in section 2 of this Guide.

In some systems the potential for free cooling may be increased by separating the latent and sensible loads. Free cooling may satisfy the sensible cooling load at quite high ambient temperatures, while a separate refrigeration system is provided for dehumidification as this function usually requires a lower coolant temperature.

Free cooling systems may be classified as follows:

— environmental free cooling

— chilled water free cooling

— condenser water/chilled water heat recovery

— refrigerant migration chillers (thermosyphon chillers)

4.4.3.1 Environmental 'free cooling'

Environmental cooling may be used directly for cooling a building or building related process (i.e. 'free-cooling'), or if it is not cold enough then it may be used as a heat sink for heat rejected from a refrigeration plant. Sources of environmental cooling include:

— ambient air

— ground water

— rivers or lakes

— sea water

— ambient air.

Fresh-air free cooling using ambient air is the simplest form of free cooling. It relies on delivering a sufficient quantity of fresh air to meet all or part of the cooling load when the ambient air temperature is sufficiently low. The fan energy may be quite high and this needs to be assessed in relation to the refrigeration plant energy savings.

Fresh-air free cooling is unlikely to reduce the peak cooling load or size of chiller required in hot weather because the maximum cooling requirement usually coincides with maximum outside temperature, unless some form of night cooling and stored cooling is utilized. Guidance on night cooling and stored cooling in the building fabric is given in section 2.4.7. The effectiveness of fresh-air free cooling is also improved by enthalpy control, especially when humidity control is required (see section 2.4.6.3).

Some unit air conditioners are also designed to make use of free air cooling. Such units incorporate a damper that can be automatically adjusted to allow 100% outside air free cooling, mechanical cooling with full recirculation, or incremental free cooling plus mechanical cooling. The y are controlled such that when the return air temperature is greater than the cooling set-point and the outside air temperature is less than the return air temperature (by, say, 2 K), the evaporator fans will continue to run and the damper will modulate between 0 and 100% in order to utilise ambient air to maintain the space conditions.

Table 4.9 Types of cooling system

System type	Description	Area to be cooled	Refrigerating or heat rejection system	Comments
(*a*) Direct system (direct expansion or 'DX' system)	The refrigeration system evaporator is in direct communication with the space to be cooled.	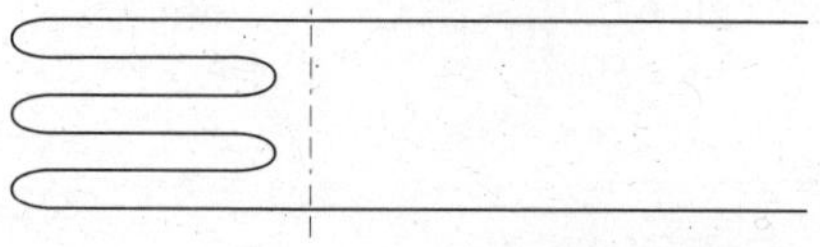		Most efficient cooling system but risk of refrigerant leaks in the occupied areas of the building. May have a relatively high refrigerant charge.
(*b*) Indirect open system	A refrigeration or heat rejection system cools a heat transfer medium which is in direct communication with the space to be cooled.	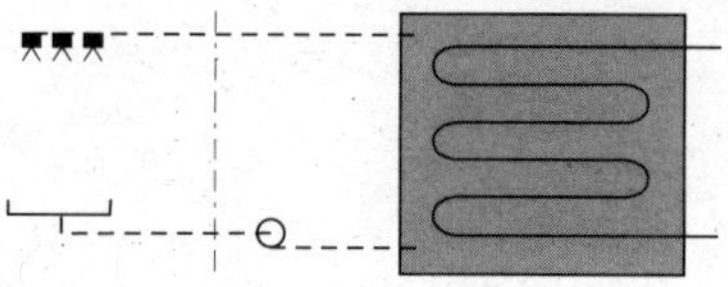		May use an air washer or spray coil to cool air. Hygiene risks mean that these systems are not widely used.
(*c*) Indirect vented open system	Similar to (*b*) but with open or vented tank.	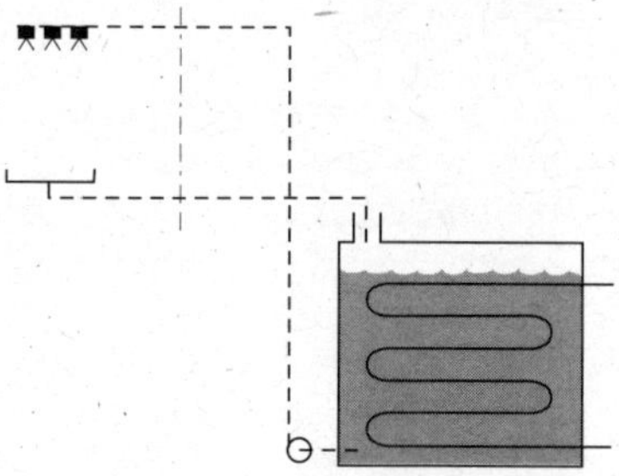		
(*d*) Indirect closed system	A refrigeration or heat rejection system cools a heat transfer medium which passes through a closed circuit in direct communication with the space to be cooled.	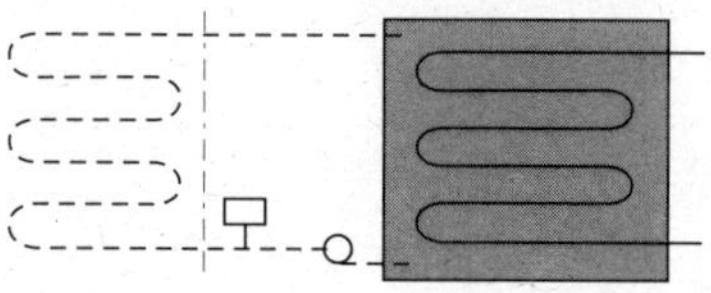		Widely used with chilled water as heat transfer medium. Lower energy efficiency than (*a*), (*b*) or (*c*) due to additional heat transfer process. Safer than (*a*) because it keeps refrigerant-containing parts out of occupied areas.
(*e*) Indirect vented closed system	Similar to (*d*) but with open or vented tank.	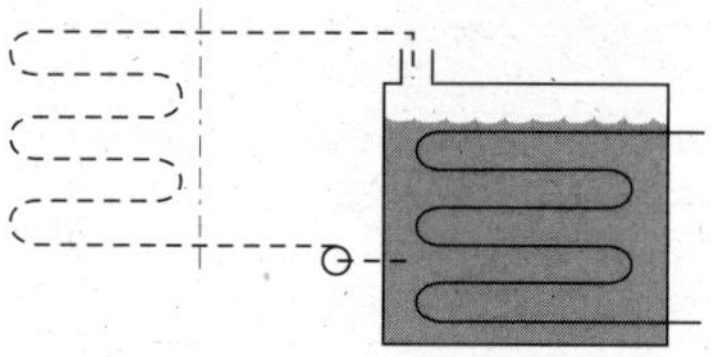		
(f) Double indirect system (open or closed)	A combination of (*b*) and (*d*) where the cooled heat transfer medium passes through a second heat exchanger.	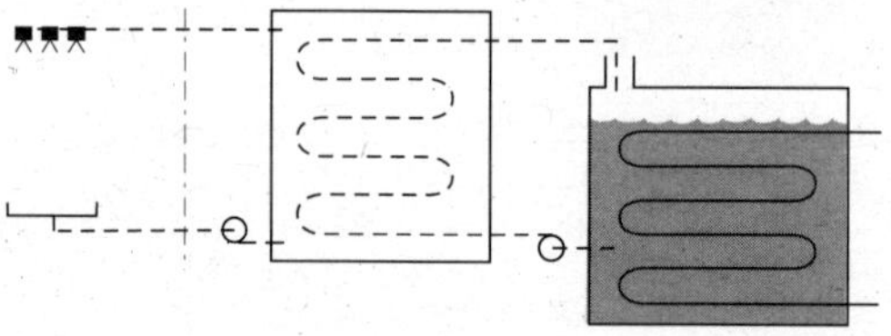		Two additional heat transfer processes make it least efficient system. Highest safety where toxic and/or flammable refrigerants are used, but little justification for its use.

Pipework containing refrigerant: ———— Pipework containing heat transfer medium: - - - - - - - -

Ground water cooling

Ground water cooling at between 11 °C and 13 °C is available in many areas of the UK all year round and is practical for free-cooling buildings in conjunction with chilled ceilings and beams or displacement ventilation systems. Chilled ceilings and beams typically require chilled water at between 14 °C and 17 °C and displacement ventilation uses air at around 19 °C and are therefore suitable for use with ground water cooling without the need for refrigeration plant, except perhaps for dehumidification purposes. Further guidance on ground water cooling and chilled ceilings and beams and displacement ventilation is given in sections 2.4.15, 2.4.8 and 2.4.2.5.

River, lake and sea water cooling

Opportunities for free cooling with river and lake water are fairly limited in the UK due to relatively high water temperatures during much of the year. For this reason these sources of cooling are more suitable for rejecting heat from refrigeration plant condensers. However, compared with the use of cooling towers and evaporative condensers, river and lake cooling may offer little advantage.

Sea water may be used for rejecting heat from refrigeration plant and is used in the UK for some large power station cooling systems. Rejection of condenser heat to sea water is fairly common in coastal cities such as Hong Hong.

Table 4.10 Types of heat rejection system

System type	Description	Heat rejection system	Section	Comments
(*a*) Air cooled condenser	Fans induce air flow over finned tubing in which refrigerant condenses.		4.5.5.3	Convenient and common for chillers up to a few 100 k W. Free of hygiene risks and do not require water piping. Can be adapted to provide free cooling with thermosyphon systems.
(*b*) Dry air cooler	Similar to (*a*) but aqueous glycol solution of water is passed through the tubes instead of refrigerant.		4.5.5.4	Less efficient than (*a*) because an additional heat transfer process, and pumps, are required to reject heat from a refrigeration plant. May cool water sufficiently in winter to avoid need to operate a refrigeration plant – 'free cooling'.
(*c*) Cooling tower	Water is sprayed over a packing material. Airflow over the packing evaporates some of the water causing the water to be cooled.		4.5.5.5	More efficient than (*a*) or (*b*) because less air is required and water is cooled to a few degrees above the wet bulb temperature. May cool water sufficiently to avoid need to operate a refrigeration plant – 'free cooling'. High maintenance requirement.
(*d*) Evaporative condenser	Water is sprayed over tubing in which refrigerant condenses. Airflow across the tubing evaporates some of the water causing the water and the tubes to be cooled.		4.5.5.6	Most efficient method of rejecting heat from a refrigeration plant. Similar maintenance requirements as (*c*). Can be adapted to provide free cooling with thermosyphon systems.

Pipework containing refrigerant: ———— Pipework containing heat transfer medium: - - - - - - - -

Special provision is needed to prevent corrosion and fouling of heat exchangers.

Further guidance on these forms of environmental cooling are given in section 2.4.22.

4.4.3.2 Chilled water free cooling

If a cooling load exists when the ambient air temperature is low then cooling of chilled water can be provided by circulating the chilled water through separate dry air coolers or the main air supply cooling coil or dehumidification coil, see Figure 4.3. Automatic control valves bypass the refrigeration system (if one is installed). Precautions must be taken to prevent freezing in cold weather which may require the use of a water-glycol mixture. This will alter the viscosity and other physical parameters including specific heat capacity and pressure drop through the system. Approprate allowances must be made for these effects when selecting components including the pumps and dry air coolers. Higher pressure drop will also increase pumping energy consumption. Packaged air cooled chillers are also available with integral free cooling coils and diverter valves, see Figure 4.4.

Cooling towers may also be used for chilled water free cooling although maintenance requirements are much higher than other methods. Section 4.5.5.4 gives specific information on cooling towers and section 4.3.2.3 gives guidance on minimising the risk of *Legionella*. The most thermodynamically efficient system is a direct system (some times known as a 'strainer cycle') in which the chilled water is directly circulated through the cooling tower, see Figure 4.5. Cooling towers continully wash dirt and other pollutants from the atmosphere and very effective filtration is vital to prevent excessive dirt contamination or blockage of the building cooling system. There is also a high risk of corrosion. In systems that use the same cooling towers for rejecting heat from a refrigeration system in warm weather special consideration is needed for the hydraulic balance between the two systems.

Indirect cooling tower based systems use a plate heat exchanger to separate the cooling tower water from the building cooling system, see Figure 4.6. A temperature difference of around 2 °C to 3 °C across the plate heat exchanger, depending on its selection, will reduce the availability of free cooling compared to a direct system. The advantage, however, is that the building cooling

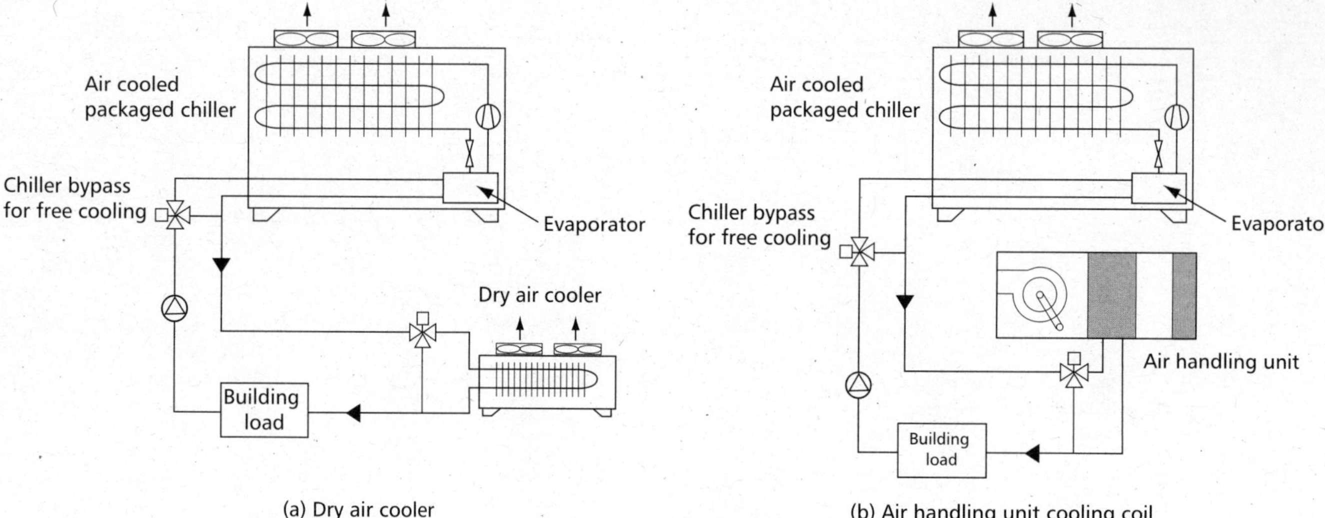

Figure 4.4 Chilled water free cooling

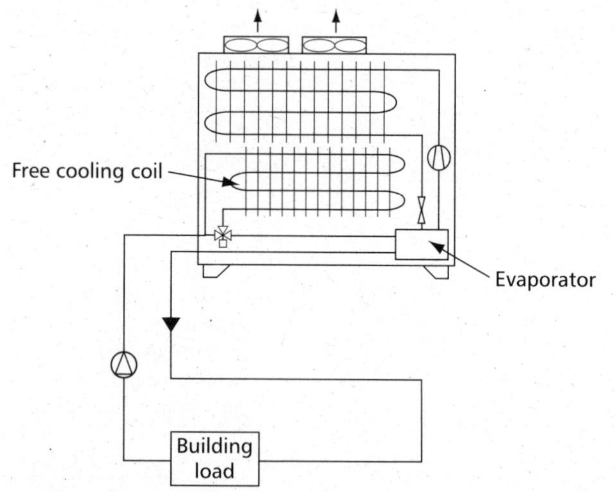

Figure 4.4 Chilled-water free cooling using an integral free-cooling coil in a packaged chiller

system is kept clean and the two circuits are hydraulically independent. The volume of water that requires regular chemical biocide treatment will also be lower which will reduce the overall running costs.

Further guidance on these free cooling systems is given in BSRIA Research Report RR16/96: *Free cooling systems — design and application guide*(59).

4.4.3.3 Condenser water/chilled water heat recovery

A disadvantage of the free-cooling systems described above in section 4.4.3.2 is that free cooling availability is limited to those periods when the return water temperature from the cooling tower or dry air cooler is lower than the required chilled water supply temperature. However, by locating the free-cooling plate heat exchanger in series with the chilled water return the warmest water in the building cooling system is in contact with the water from the cooling tower or dry air cooler(60). This extends the availability of free cooling compared to the systems shown in 4.4.3.2. Such a system is shown schematically in Figure 4.7. The system is able to operate in a mixed operating mode with the chillers able to top up the cooling to meet the building load. Free cooling can be exploited whenever the cooling tower or dry air cooler water in the heat exchanger is cooler than the building return water temperature. However, at some point the increased pumping energy from circulating water through the plate heat exchanger will be greater than the chiller energy savings and the system should then be switched to chiller only operating mode.

The opportunity of free cooling with series condenser water/chilled water free cooling systems is dependent on the chilled water return temperature. With conventional constant flow rate chilled water cooling systems, employing three-port valve control of cooling terminals and coils, the chilled water return temperature falls at part load which reduces free cooling opportunity. However, in systems with variable flow chilled water distribution systems, employing two-port valve control of cooling terminals and coils, the return water temperature actually rises at part load. Such systems can therefore be used in conjunction with series condenser water/chilled water systems to maximise free cooling opportunities.

4.4.3.4 Refrigerant migration chillers (thermosyphon chillers)

Refrigerant migration or 'thermosyphon' chillers achieve free cooling through bypassing the chiller compressor and expansion valve when the condenser temperature is lower than the evaporator temperature(61). Refrigerant flows to the air cooled or evaporative condenser due to the pressure difference produced by the temperature difference between the chilled water and the ambient air. Condensed refrigerant then returns to the evaporator through gravity circulation. This requires the condenser to be elevated above the chiller and for the refrigerant pipes to be carefully designed to minimise pressure drops. The compressor is operated when insufficient cooling is provided by thermosyphon free cooling.

Ideally to maximise the opportunity for thermosyphon free, cooling the system should comprise several individual chillers, including any standby chillers, connected in series on the chilled water side. This ensures that even when one or two compressors need to be operated the other chillers in the system can continue to operate in free cooling mode. Figure 4.8 shows a typical thermosyphon chiller system. It should be noted that the lead chiller is always last inline to receive return chilled water. No attempt is made to equalize compressor run hours. Annual system COSP (coefficient of system performance, see section 4.4.4.5) has been predicted to be

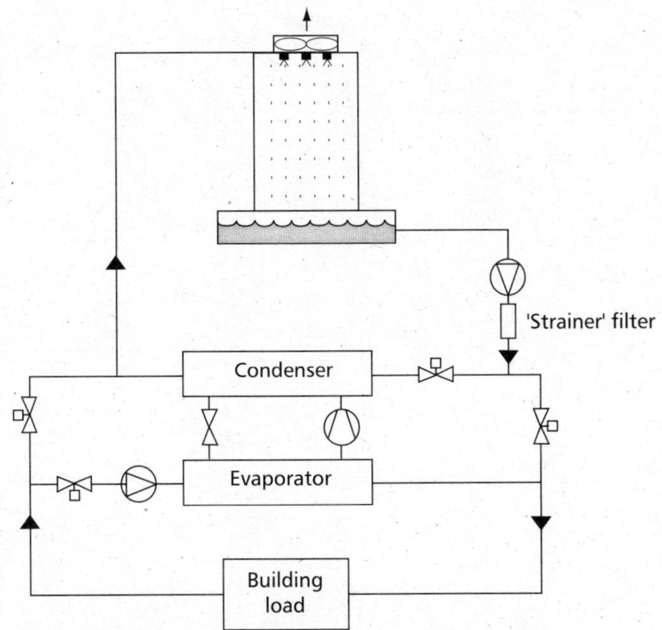

Figure 4.5 Direct cooling tower-based free cooling system

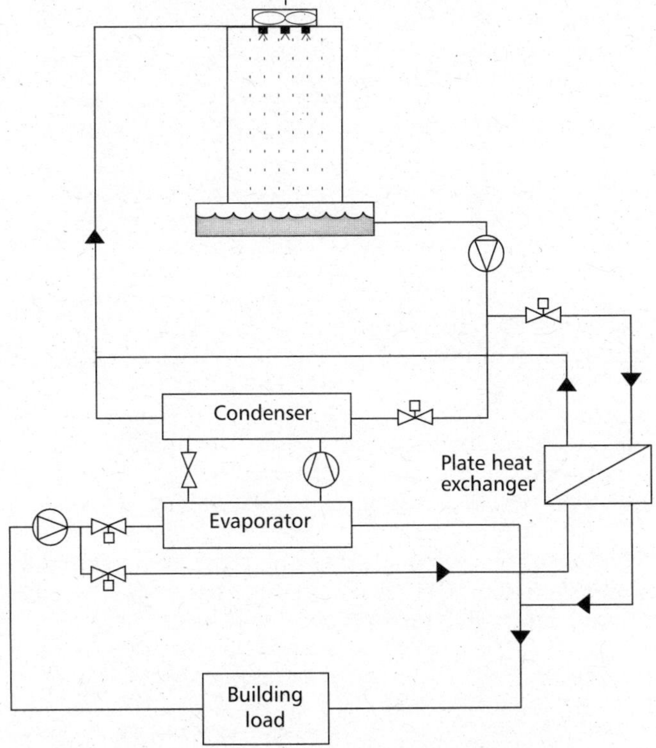

Figure 4.6 Indirect cooling tower-based free cooling system

10.5 for a thermosyphon chiller system utilising air cooled condensers installed in a data processing centre with a year-round cooling load[62]. The use of evaporative condensers would result in a higher annual COSP.

The duration of the thermosyphon operating mode and the system COSP can be maximised by using specially treated heat exchanger surfaces on the refrigerant side of the evaporator to improve the heat transfer coefficient. This allows the initiation of refrigerant boiling at very low temperature differences and maximises the time that thermosyphon cooling is available.

For further guidance see section 2 and BSRIA Research Report RR16/96: *Free cooling systems — design and application guide*[59].

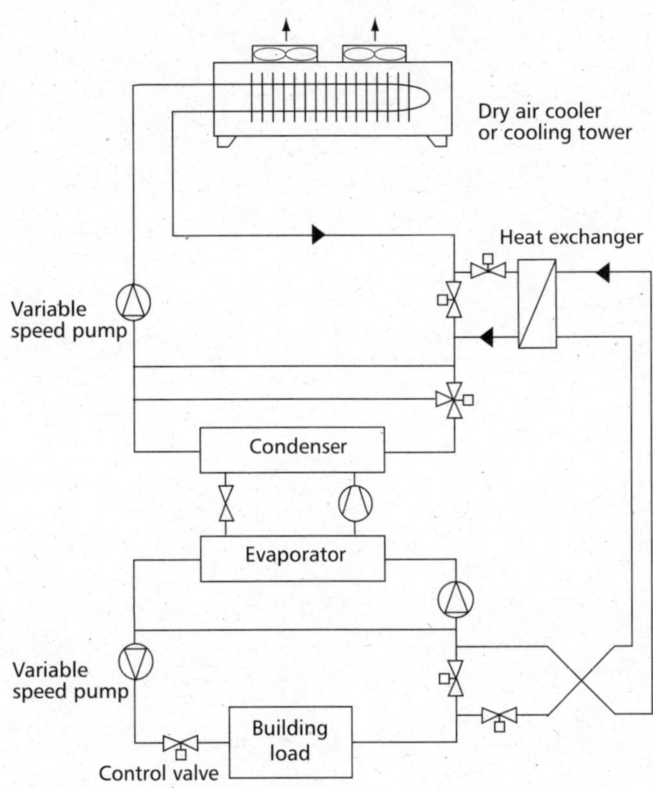

Figure 4.7 Series condenser water/chilled water free cooling system

4.4.4 Vapour compression refrigeration

The vapour compression refrigeration cycle employs a volatile refrigerant fluid which vaporises or evaporates in a heat exchanger, cooling the surroundings through the absorption of heat. The vapour is then restored to the liquid phase by mechanical compression. The mechanical vapour compression refrigeration cycle is currently the dominant technique for refrigeration and air conditioning applications.

Figure 4.9 shows the basic components in a vapour compression circuit and Figure 4.10 illustrates the complete refrigeration cycle on a pressure–enthalpy diagram. The cycle shown is simplified and in particular ignores the effect of pressure drops in pipes and heat exchangers.

The stages in the cycle are as follows:

- *Stage 1 to 2*: low pressure liquid refrigerant in the evaporator absorbs heat from the medium being cooled (usually water or air) at constant pressure while evaporating to become dry saturated vapour.
- *Stage 2 to 3*: the refrigerant vapour absorbs more heat while in the evaporator and while in the pipework joining the evaporator to the compressor, to become a superheated vapour.
- *Stage 3 to 4*: the superheated vapour is compressed, increasing its temperature and pressure.
- *Stage 4 to 5*: the hot superheated vapour enters the condenser where the first part of the process is desuperheating.
- *Stage 5 to 6*: the hot vapour is condensed back to a saturated liquid at constant temperature and

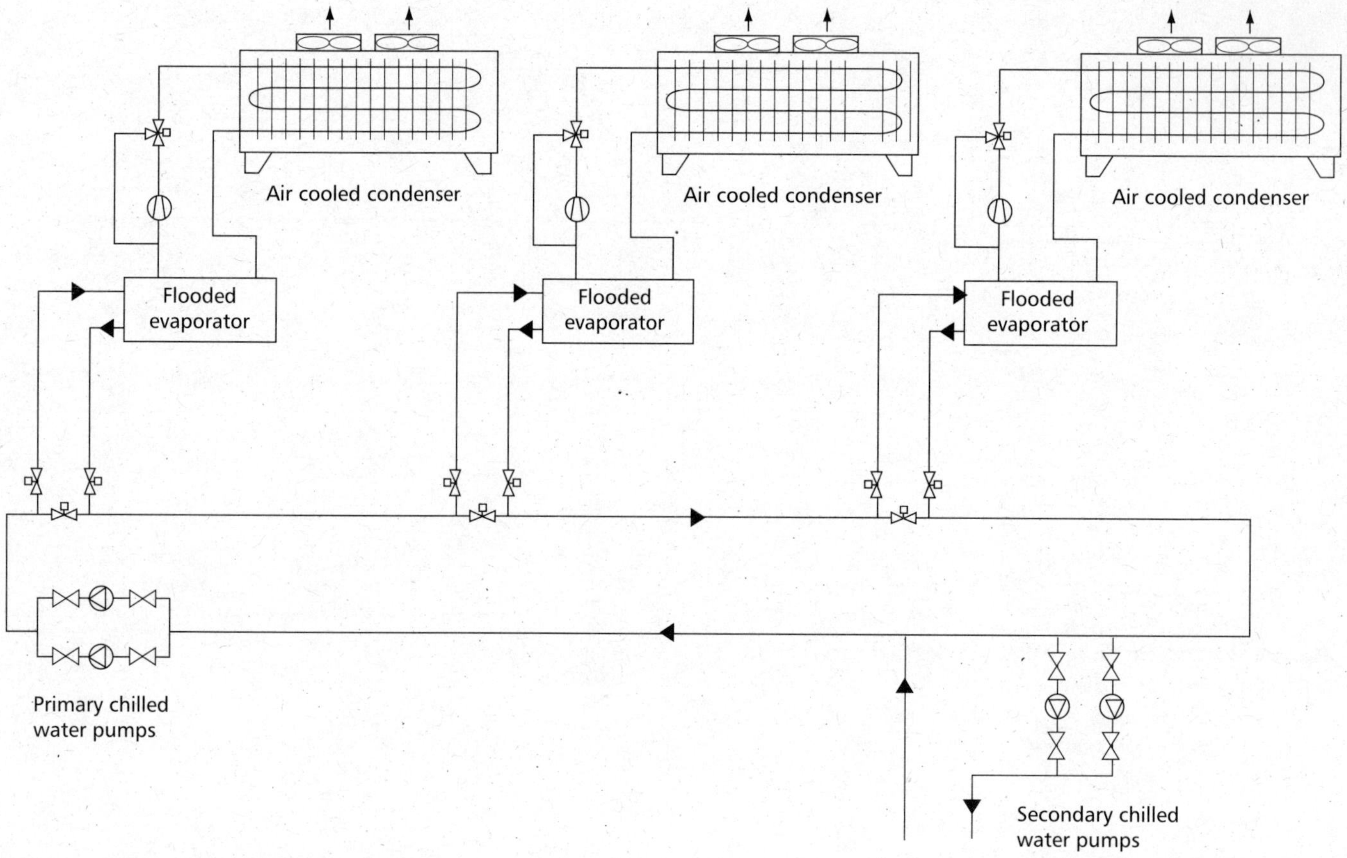

Figure 4.8 Typical thermosyphon chiller system

pressure through being cooled by a coolant (usually air or water);

— *Stage 6 to 7*: further cooling may take place to sub-cool the liquid before it enters the expansion valve (this may occur in the condenser, a second heat exchanger or in the pipework connecting the condenser with the expansion valve).

— *Stage 7 to 1*: the high pressure sub-cooled liquid passes through an expansion device causing a reduction in its temperature and pressure at constant enthalpy.

Where a vapour compression system is intended to provide useful heating (from the heat rejected at the condenser) it is usually known as a heat pump. Heat pumps may also provide cooling. Figure 4.11 shows a reversible (refrigerant changeover) air-to-air heat pump that may be used for either heating or cooling. Water-to-water heat pumps employ a water changeover valve arrangement instead.

Modern vapour compression plant may use one of a variety of compressor types depending partly on the cooling capacity required. Information on compressors and other system components is given in section 4.5.2.

The designer or specifier should take into account a number of factors when specifying a mechanical vapour compression plant including:

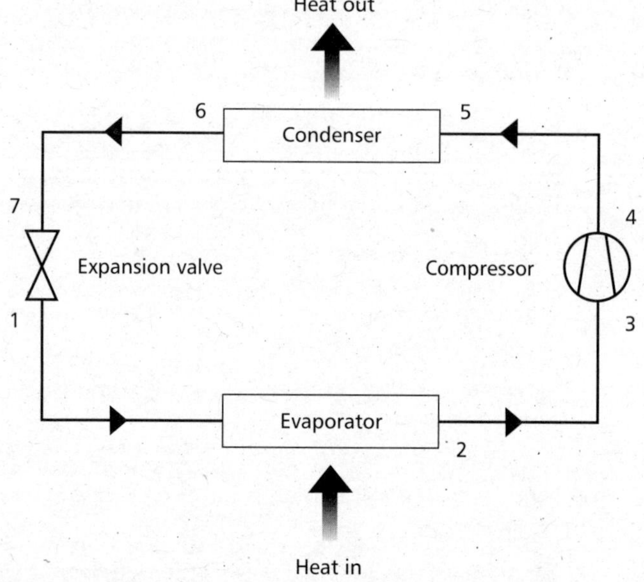

Figure 4.9 Vapour compression cycle: principal system components

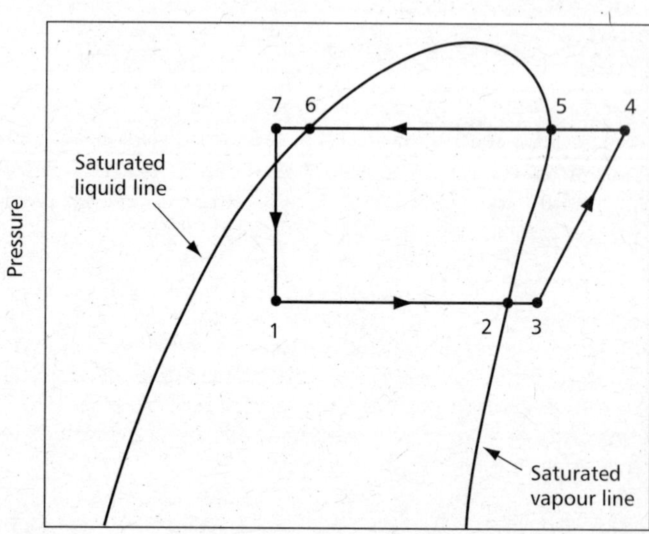

Figure 4.10 Vapour compression cycle : simple pressure–enthalpy diagram

— refrigerant type
— safety requirements
— environmental requirements
— energy efficiency (coefficient of performance).

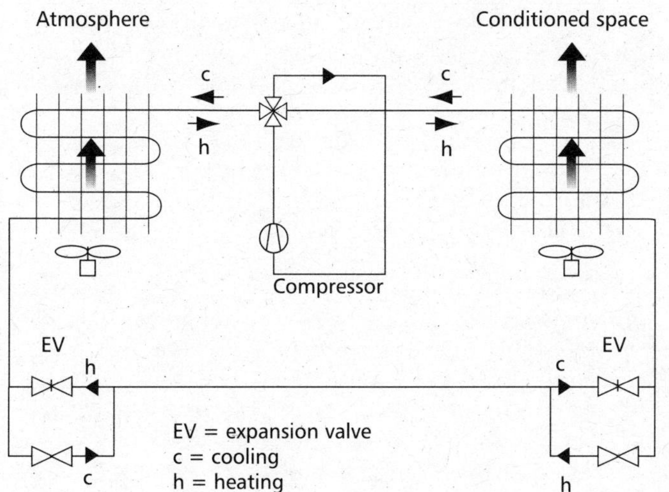

Figure 4.11 Reversible heat pump system for heating or cooling

4.4.4.1 Refrigerant selection

A wide range of fluids may be used as refrigerant in vapour compression systems. The basic requirement is that the fluid evaporates at the required cooling temperature at a reasonable pressure, and that it condenses at the temperature of a readily available cooling medium. However, commercial vapour compression refrigeration systems should be safe, practical and economic and generally the refrigerant should possess as many of the properties listed in Table 4.11 as possible.

No single refrigerant satisfies all of the desired refrigerant properties and a range of refrigerants are commercially available for standard refrigeration and air conditioning applications. Some key properties of these refrigerants are summarised in Appendix 4.A1 and pressure–enthalpy charts are shown in Appendix 4.A2. The designer should be aware of the key properties of different refrigerants and clarify with the equipment supplier or manufacturer the most suitable refrigerant selection for a particular application taking into account the following factors (see also section 4.2.2):

— *equipment size*: capacity required per machine, since the capacity of a compressor is affected by the type of refrigerant

Table 4.11 Key refrigerant section criteria

Refrigerant property	Selection criteria
Low toxicity	A desirable property especially for systems that may be installed in occupied parts of buildings, such as split and multi-split air conditioners. See section 4.4.4.2.
Zero ozone deletion potential	Ozone depleting substances are no longer acceptable as refrigerants. See section 4.3.4.1.
Low global warming potential	Substances with high global warming potential are likely to be restricted or phased out by some governments and some corporate environmental policies already restrict the use of refrigerants with high global warming potential. See section 4.3.4.2.
Non-flammable	A desirable property especially for systems that contain large quantities of refrigerant and are located in occupied parts of buildings. See section 4.4.4.2.
Chemically stable and compatible with conventional materials and compressor lubricants	Substances without these properties are unlikely to be used as commercial refrigerants.
Suitable pressure/temperature relationship	Excessively high operating pressures require the use of strong components, pipework and heat exchangers which increases the cost and weight of systems and increases the likelihood of leakage. Operating pressures below atmospheric pressure increase the risk of contamination and ingress of air. High pressure ratios reduce system energy efficiency.
High latent heat	This determines the mass flow of refrigerant that has to be circulated and although is a highly desirable property it can be offset by other properties.
High critical temperature	The critical temperature (the temperature above which a substance behaves like a permanent gas and cannot be liquefied) should normally be well above the required heat rejection temperature. Also, as the critical temperature is approached the latent heat of vapourisation decreases which tends to reduce the efficiency of the system. See section 4.4.4.5.
Low vapour specific heat ratio	The specific heat ratio determines the index of compression and hence the temperature rise during compression. Low indices of compression give low discharge temperatures which are desirable to minimise breakdown of refrigerant and lubricant.
Low temperature glide* (for blends)	This can either improve or reduce heat transfer coefficients in the evaporator and condenser, depending on their design. High glide can cause handling difficulties and cause preferential leakage (increasing the cost of maintenance). Refrigerants with a high glide are generally unsuitable for use in flooded evaporators due to large concentration changes in the evaporator leading to reductions in performance. High glide causes a reduction in the refrigerant temperature at the evaporator inlet for a given chilled water supply temperature. This may cause a risk of icing in systems supplying water at 6 °C or below and may require an anti-freeze additive.

*Non-azeotropic blends exhibit a change ('glide') in temperature during the evaporation and condensation process. The temperature of the evaporating refrigerant rises along the evaporator, and the temperature of the condensing vapour decreases along the condenser. The extent of the temperature glide is mainly dependent on the boiling points and proportions of the individual constituents.

— *type of compressor*: reciprocating, centrifugal, screw or scroll

— *operating temperature range*: air conditioning, process cooling

— *economics*: first cost of the equipment and refrigerant, cost of servicing, refrigerant handling requirements and eventual cost of refrigerant disposal

— *environmental and safety factors*: acceptability to the client (for example in relation to environmental policies and green labelling and certification), future refrigerant availability (government environmental regulation), safety requirements of relevant codes and standards (see section 4.4.4.2).

At the time of writing the following refrigerant types are in common use in vapour compression refrigeration systems (although not all are available for use in new plant):

— *chlorofluorocarbons* (CFCs): containing chlorine, fluorine and carbon

— *hydrochlorofluorocarbons* (HCFCs): containing only hydrogen, chlorine, fluorine and carbon

— *hydrofluorocarbons* (HFCs): containing only hydrogen, fluorine and carbon

— *ammonia*

— *hydrocarbons* (HCs): containing only hydrogen and carbon.

Chlorofluorocarbons (CFCs)

CFCs have many of the desirable refrigerant properties above except for their ozone depletion and global warming potentials. Because CFCs have high ozone depletion potentials the supply of virgin CFCs has now been phased out except in developing countries, see section 4.3.4.1. However, some existing refrigeration systems may still contain CFCs, particularly R12 (CFC-12) in domestic refrigerators and some heat pumps and R11 (CFC-11) in some large centrifugal chillers. At the end of use of these systems it is a legal requirement for the CFC refrigerant to be recovered and destroyed by an environmentally acceptable technology, see section 4.3.4.1.

Hydrochlorofluorocarbons (HCFCs)

Many HCFCs have most of the desirable refrigerant properties above except for their ozone depletion and global warming potentials. Although HCFCs have lower ozone depletion potentials than CFCs the supply and use of HCFCs is being phased out, see section 4.3.4.1. However, HCFCs are expected to continue to be available in non-EU and developing countries for some time. HCFCs such as R502 and R22 (HCFC-22) will also continue to be used in many existing air conditioning and refrigeration systems until the systems are replaced. R123 (HCFC-123) has been used in some centrifugal chillers as an interim replacement for R11 (CFC-11) although concerns about its toxicity have limited its use.

Hydrofluorocarbons (HFCs)

HFCs have many of the desirable refrigerant properties above and are widely used as replacements for CFCs and HCFCs in new systems and in some existing systems, on account of their good refrigeration properties and zero ozone depletion potentials. However, no single HFC exactly matches the refrigeration properties of commonly used CFC and HCFC refrigerants and refrigerant producers have developed a range of HFC blends to match the properties of these individual CFCs and HCFCs. Some blends have quite high glide temperatures which can potentially increase the cost of maintenance. However, HFCs have global warming potentials similar to most CFCs and HCFCs and as a result there is political pressure in Europe to minimise or phase out the use of HFCs. Section 4.3.4.2 summarises UK government policy on the use of HFCs.

HFCs are not soluble or miscible with conventional mineral based oils. Many systems rely on the solubility and miscibility of the oil and refrigerant for effective oil transport in the system and return of oil to the compressor. Most equipment manufacturers specify a synthetic polyolester oil for use with HFC refrigerants. Polyolesters are more hygroscopic than traditional lubricants which means that greater care is needed in transport, storage and charging to avoid excessive moisture contamination.

At the time of writing the following HFCs are commercially available and used in refrigeration and air conditioning systems:

— R134a (HFC-134a) is a non-flammable pure fluid, similar in refrigeration capacity and operating pressures to R12, see Appendix 4.A1. It has replaced R12 in many applications including car air conditioning, centrifugal chillers and domestic refrigerators and freezers. Many manufacturers also specify it for same large screw compressor based chillers. Its operating pressures are relatively low which make it attractive for very large chillers (due to the potential materials and weight savings) but this is countered by a relatively low refrigeration capacity compared to R22 and its HFC based alternatives. This means that chillers with relatively large cooling capacities are physically quite large compared to systems using R22 or similar HFC alternatives, requiring approximately 60% larger compressors and pipework.

— R404A is a blend of HFC-125, HFC-143a and HFC-134a. Its use is mainly as a substitute for R502 in commercial refrigeration systems (for example cold stores and supermarket refrigeration systems) because its relatively low discharge temperature makes it a good choice for low temperature systems. However, its relatively low critical temperature makes its use for air conditioning systems less suitable than other HFCs. It also has a relatively high global warming potential compared with other HFCs, see Appendix 4.A1.

— R407C is a blend of HFC-32, HFC-125 and HFC-134a. Its operating pressures and refrigeration capacity are similar but not identical to those for R22 and it is therefore quite often used as a replacement for R22. However, R407C is a blend with a relatively high temperature glide (around 6 K) which may increase the cost of maintenance and refrigerant handling, and is not recommended for systems with flooded evaporators.

— R410A is a blend of HFC-32 and HFC-125 but has a low temperature glide (< 1 K) which makes refrigerant handling and system maintenance easier than for R407C. R410A operates at relatively high pressures and stronger pipe and other components are required than for R134a and R407C. However, R410A has a relatively high refrigeration capacity which is liked by equipment manufacturers because it reduces the size of compressors, pipework and other components. R410A is less favourable for large systems on account of the stronger compressor casing and pipework compared to other refrigerants. R410A is also less suitable for systems with high condensing temperatures (such as is necessary in hot climates) because of its relatively low critical temperature.

— R125 (HFC-125) is a non-flammable pure fluid. It has a particularly low critical temperature which generally makes it unsuitable for air cooled equipment in normal climates. However, it has a relatively high refrigeration capacity and some equipment manufacturers offer it for water cooled screw compressor chillers, especially for low temperature applications.

— R417A is a blend of HFC-125, HFC-134a and R600a (isobutane), although it is non-flammable due to the small percentage proportion of R600a. In some respects R417A is similar to R407C. However, R417A offers potential compatibility with mineral oils and may therefore be suitable for us as a replacement for R22 in existing systems without the need to change the oil type.

Ammonia

Ammonia is an effective and tried and tested refrigerant without any harmful ozone depletion or global warming effects. However, ammonia is highly toxic and mildly flammable which means that special safety precautions are necessary, see section 4.4.4.2. Ammonia is widely used in industrial refrigeration systems and is increasingly being used in chillers for air conditioning in the USA and parts of Europe including the UK. It is not suitable for use in direct systems (for example splits and multi-split air conditioners) due to the risk of leakage into the occupied space and its non-compatibility with standard copper pipes and copper based alloys. Ammonia chillers generally use steel or stainless steel pipework and valves.

Hydrocarbons

Hydrocarbons such as propane (R290) and isobutene (R600a) have good refrigeration properties and are compatible with standard materials and components. However, because hydrocarbons are highly flammable specific safety precautions are necessary, see section 4.4.4.2. Generally systems with small refrigerant charges are most suitable for hydrocarbon refrigerants. Many European domestic refrigerator and freezer manufactures have switched entirely from R12 or R134a to R600a (isobutane). Hydrocarbons are also increasingly used in small commercial display cabinets and vending machines.

Other refrigerants: carbon dioxide (R744) and water (R718)

Although interest is growing in the use of carbon dioxide in the low temperature stage of cascade systems for low temperature industrial cooling systems, its low critical temperature of 31.3 °C makes it unsuitable for air conditioning applications where heat is rejected at the ambient temperature. There is some interest in using carbon dioxide as a volatile secondary coolant but at the time of writing no commercial systems are available.

Water vapour may be used as a refrigerant in applications above 0 °C but its extremely high specific vapour volume (around two orders of magnitude greater than conventional refrigerants) has to date largely made it impractical and uneconomic.

4.4.4.2 Safety

The designer has a responsibility to ensure that the design of the refrigeration system takes into account all the necessary provisions for safe installation, commissing operation, maintenance and decommisioning of the system. The requirements of relevant UK health and safety related legislation are outlined in section 4.3.2.1. The selection of the system type and refrigerant should minimise hazards to persons, property and the environment. Specific requirements are detailed in BS EN 378[22], and theses are amplified in the Institute of Refrigeration safety Codes[37–39]. Guidance on policy and refrigerant replacement issues are given in CIBSE GN1[12] and specific requirements for commissioning systems are given in CIBSE Commissioning Code R[55].

The purpose of BS EN 378[22] is to minimise possible hazards to persons, property and the environment from refrigerating systems and refrigerants. It stipulates specific requirements for different refrigerants, types of refrigeration systems, locations and type of building.

BS EN 378[22] classifies refrigerants into groups according to their influence on health and safety and these groupings are maintained in the the Institute of Refrigeration Safety Codes. Building occupancies are classified according to the safety of the occupants, who may be directly affected in case of abnormal operation operation of the refrigerating system (such as catastrophic leakage). Refrigerating systems are classified according to the method of cooling the space and heat rejection and broadly follows the classification given in Table 4.9.

Occupancy categories

Building occupancy categories are classified as:

— *Category A*: rooms, parts of buildings, or buildings where:

(*a*) people may sleep

(*b*) people are restricted in their movement, and

(*c*) an uncontrolled number of people are present or to which any person has access without being personally acquainted with the necessary safety precautions

Examples of these are hospitals, courts or prisons, theatres, supermarkets, schools, lecture halls, public transport termini, hotels, dwellings, restaurants.

— *Category B*: rooms or parts of buildings where only a limited number of people may be assembled, some being necessarily acquainted with the general safety precautions of the establishment. Examples of these are business or professional offices, laboratories, places for general manufacturing and where people work.

— *Category C*: rooms, parts of buildings, buildings where only authorized persons have access, who are acquainted with the general and special safety precautions of the establishment and where manufacturing, processing or storage of material or products takes place. Examples of these are manufacturing facilities, e.g. for chemicals, food, beverage, ice-cream, refineries, cold stores, dairies, abattoirs, non-public areas in supermarkets.

Category C areas can exist in category A and B buildings as long access to category C areas is restricted to authorised persons who are acquainted with any special safety requirements. Category C areas should also be separated from category A and B areas by sealed partitions, floors and ceilings.

Refrigerant safety groups

Refrigerant safety groups are classified according to the lower flammability limit (at atmospheric pressure and room air temperature), and according to toxicity, see Table 4.12.

Individual refrigerants are classified according to a simplified grouping, L1, L2 or L3:

L1 = A1 (for example CFCs, HCFCs and HFCs)

L2 = A2, B1, B2 (for example ammonia)

L3 = A3, B3 (for example hydrocarbons).

Maximum charge of refrigerant

BS EN 378[22] limits the hazards from refrigerants by stipulating the maximum charge of refrigerant for given occupancy categories and refrigerant safety groups. Table 4.13 summarises maximum refrigerant charge and other restrictions for chillers (indirect closed systems) and direct (DX) systems. The latest version of BS EN 378 should always be consulted for full details. Maximum refrigerant charge is related to the 'practical limit' or maximum allowable short term refrigerant concentration should the entire charge be released into the space or the room occupied by the system (does not apply to systems located out of doors). Table 4.14 shows the practical limit and the corresponding maximum refrigerant charge for a range of common refrigerants.

For L1 refrigerants the practical limit is less than 50% the concentration of refrigerant that can cause suffocation from oxygen displacement, narcosis or cardiac sensitisation, whichever is the most critical. The limits relate to the maximum short term exposure following a sudden release and are not safe limits for regular day-to-day exposure. The HSE stipulates occupational exposure limits based on long term exposure in the work place, see Health and Safety Executive EH40 *Occupational exposure limits*[63]. The designer and plant operator should ensure that suitable measures, such as refrigerant gas detectors and alarms, are in place to prevent these exposure limits from being exceeded.

For L2 refrigerants the practical limit refers to the toxicological or flammability limits, whichever is the lowest. For L3 refrigerants the practical limit is 20% of the lower flammability limit.

Table 4.12 Refrigerant safety groups

Flammability	Increasing toxicity >	
	Occupational exposure limit ≥ 400 ppm V/V	Occupational exposure limit < 400 ppm V/V
Lower flammability limit < 3.5% V/V in air	A3	B3
Lower flammability limit ≥ 3.5% V/V in air	A2	B2
Not flammable in air	A1	B1

Specific requirements for ammonia

Ammonia is highly toxic through direct contact and inhalation of concentrations above 1000 ppm. However, it has a highly pungent smell (detetectable by nose down to about 10 ppm) which makes voluntary exposure highly unlikely. At these lower concentrations ammonia has no known long term or accumulative health effects although its pungency can induce panic and alarm. Ammonia is flammable at concentrations between 16% and 27% by volume, although in practise such high concentrations are only likely in the event of the most flagrant contravention of safety guidelines.

It is essential that relevant health and safety regulations, safety standards and codes and other industry guidance documents are complied with. These include:

— relevant UK regulations (see section 3.2.1)

— BS EN 378[22]

— Institute of Refrigeration's *Safety code for refrigerating systems utilizing ammonia refrigerant*[39]

— Health and Safety Executive Guidance Note PM81: *Safe management of ammonia refrigeration systems*[42]

— Institute of Refrigeration Guidance Note 10: *Working with ammonia*[64].

In addition to meeting the specific requirements of these standards and codes it is highly recommended that the following additional guidelines are followed:

— Ammonia systems installed for air conditioning in buildings occupied by humans should be installed either in a special plant room within the building or inside a special enclosure which may be on the building roof. The advantages of such a plant room or enclosure are that any spilled or leaked liquid ammonia can be contained and that external gas discharge rates can be controlled.

— The total quantity of ammonia used should be minimised through appropriate design such as the use of multiple chillers for large systems and the

Table 4.13 Summary of BS EN 378[22] requirements for maximum refrigerant charge (latest version of BS EN 378 should be consulted for full details)

Refrigerant	System type	Occupancy category A (e.g. residential, hotels, supermarkets etc.)		Occupancy category B (e.g. offices, shops, workplaces etc.)		Occupancy category C (e.g. manufacturing facilities, plant rooms or other areas with access limited to authorized persons)	
		Max. charge (per system)	Restrictions	Max. charge (per system)	Restrictions	Max. charge (per system)	Restrictions
L1 refrigerants (e.g. CFCS, HCFCS and HFCS)	DX	Practical limit × room vol.	Maximum charge limit may be relaxed*	No limit	If located below ground or on an upper floor without emergency exits then maximum charge is practical limit × room volume	No limit	If located below ground or on an upper floor without emergency exits then maximum charge is practical limit × room volume
	Chillers	No limit	Must be in open air or 'special machinery room'†	No limit	Must be in open air or 'special machinery room'†	No limit	Must be in open air or 'special machinery room'†
L2 refrigerants (e.g. ammonia)	DX	Practical limit × room vol. (2.5 kg limit)	Must be a sealed system. Not allowed if people are restricted in their movement	10 kg	—	10 kg	50 kg if occupancy less than 1 person per 10 m^2 and there are emergency exits
	Chillers	No limit	Must be in open air or 'special machinery room'† with an exit to open air and no direct access to cat. A	No limit	Must be in open air or 'special machinery room'† with no direct access to occupied rooms	No limit	—
L3 refrigerants (e.g. HCS)	DX	Practical limit × room vol. (1.5 kg limit)	Cannot be used for air conditioning or heating for human comfort. Refrigeration system must not have any sources of ignition (e.g. requires sealed electrics)	Practical limit × room vol. (2.5 kg limit)	Cannot be used for air conditioning or heating for human comfort. Practical limit × room vol. up to a maximum of 1 kg if below the ground	10 kg	Cannot be used for air conditioning or heating for human comfort. 1 kg limit if below ground level
	Chillers	5 kg	Must be in open air or 'special machinery room'†. 1 kg limit if below ground level	10 kg	Must be in open air or 'special machinery room'†. 1 kg limit if below ground level	No limit	Must be in open air or 'special machinery room'†. 1 kg limit if below ground level

* The total volume of all rooms cooled or heated by air from one system is used as the volume for calculation, provided the air supply to each room cannot be restricted below 25% of its full supply. If the space has a mechanical ventilation system that is always operating during operation then the effect of air change may be considered in calculating the volume. Other methods of ensuring safety in the event of a major release are permitted if they prevent concentrations exceeding the practical limit, or give adequate warning to occupants so that they may avoid excessive exposure time.

† Special machinery room is a plant room with special requirements. These include tight fitting and self-closing doors with at least 0.5 h fire resistance; all fabric elements and service entry points sealed; minimum specifications for ventilation; and refrigerant detectors. Additional requirements for ammonia include an at least one emergency exit opening into the open air or an escape passage way; mechanical ventilation and a remote switch for isolating all electrical equipment inside the plant room should ammonia be released into the plant room.

Table 4.14 Maximum refrigerant charge derived from practical limits

Refrigerant	Practical limit (/ kg•m^{-3})	Maximum refrigerant charge (/ kg) for a direct system serving or installed in a 100 m^3 room
R12	0.50	50
R22	0.30	30
R123	0.10	10
R134a	0.25	25
R407C	0.31	31
R410A	0.44	44
R717 (ammonia)	0.00035	0.035
R290 (propane)	0.008	0.8
R600a (isobutane)	0.008	0.8

use of compact heat exchangers such as plate heat exchangers.

— Relief valves should discharge in a safe place away from any building, such as a vertical pipe on the building roof.

— An acceptable way of disposing of large quantities of spilt or leaked ammonia is through controlled atmospheric dispersion, ideally through a high fan-assisted stack away from people and other buildings.

— The practice of spraying water onto pools of liquid ammonia is highly hazardous and should be avoided.

Further information on minimising ammonia hazards, including predicting gas concentrations in dispersing ammonia plumes is given in BRE Information Paper IP18/00[65].

Specific requirements for hydrocarbons

Hydrocarbon (HC) refrigerants are highly flammable. However, they have very good refrigeration properties and may be used in a very wide range of refrigeration equipment.

It is essential that relevant health and safety regulations, safety standards and codes and other industry guidance documents are complied with. These include:

— relevant UK regulations (see section 4.3.2.1)

— BS EN 378[22]

— Institute of Refrigeration's *Safety code for refrigerating systems utilizing group A3 refrigerants*[38]

— ACRIB's *Guidelines for the use of hydrocarbon refrigerants in static refrigeration and air conditioning systems*[66]

The above standards and codes are designed to minimise hazards associated with the use of flammable hydrocarbon refrigerants and bring the degrees of risk in line with other types of refrigerant. It is also essential that safe working practices are adhered to during maintenance and servicing as refrigerant grades of hydrocarbons are odourless. In particular the following precautions are essential during maintenance and servicing:

— Hydrocarbon vapour detectors should be used during maintenance and servicing to alert the technician to the presence of potentially flammable atmospheres.

— No source of ignition should be present and special precautions should be taken prior to any brazing or welding.

— Any person who is involved with working on or breaking into a refrigeration circuit should hold a current certificate from an industry accredited authority which certifies their competence to handle refrigerants (including hydrocarbons) safely in accordance with an industry recognised assessment specification.

Refrigerant detection

Refrigerant detectors and alarms are required in all refrigeration equipment plant rooms to prevent the exposure of workers to refrigerant concentrations higher than the HSE occupational exposure limits (see HSE EH40[63]) and to warn of higher toxic concentrations. Detectors are also required in plant rooms that contain hydrocarbon or ammonia systems to start emergency ventilation and shutdown any electrical equipment that is not suitable for operation in explosive atmospheres. Refrigerant detectors can also be used as a means of detecting refrigerant leaks although their effectiveness is affected by how well the plant room is ventilated. Refrigerant detectors are unlikely to be effective for detecting leaks from equipment installation outside.

The location of refrigerant detectors should take account of the density of the refrigerant. HCFCs, HFCs and hydrocarbons are heavier than air and refrigerant detectors should therefore be located at low level. Ammonia vapour is lighter than air and detectors are therefore usually located above the refrigeration equipment.

Common types of detector include semiconductor sensors and infrared analysers. Electrochemical sensors are also used for ammonia detection. Semiconductor and electrochemical sensors are sensitive to other gases, including some cleaning chemicals, whilst infrared systems are more selective but are also more expensive. Detectors may be discrete single-point devices or aspirated systems that may have several sensing points connected to the sensor by air sampling tubes and a small air pump. All types of detector require periodic recalibration and electrochemical sensors have a short lifetime.

4.4.4.3 Environmental impacts

The selection of a refrigerant and refrigeration system type should take account of the environmental impact of the refrigerant and the systems, and legal requirements. These are mainly related to the leakage of refrigerant to the atmosphere and the end of life disposal of refrigerants and compressor oil. It is a legal requirement that all used refrigerant and oils are recovered for recycling or disposal using an environmentally acceptable method. Legal and other environmental related requirements are detailed in section 4.3.4.

The selection of a refrigeration system and refrigerant should aim to minimise the total global warming impact (TEWI) of the system over its expected lifetime. TEWI takes account of the direct global warming potential of the refrigerant and the global warming impact of the energy used to drive the system. Section 4.3.5.2. provides guidance on TEWI assessment.

4.4.4.4 Refrigerant leakage

Refrigerant leakage is the unwanted loss of refrigerant from a system and may, for example, be caused by defective gaskets, seals, joints, pipes and hoses. Refrigerant leakage may be gradual, which can be continuous or intermittent, or catastrophic due to sudden component failure or accident. Refrigerant losses may also occur during servicing and maintenance, and may be deliberate, accidental or unavoidable.

The consequences of refrigerant leakage include:

— *Environmental impact*: CFCs and HCFCs damage the ozone layer and most refrigerants contribute to global warming

— *Higher running costs and reduced cooling performance*: refrigerant loss will cause a gradual reduction in refrigeration capacity and energy efficiency (coefficient of performance (COP), see section 4.4.4.5).

— *Health and safety hazards*: some refrigerants are toxic and/or flammable and many other are toxic at high concentrations

— *Higher servicing costs*: locating and repairing leaks and replenishing leaked refrigerant increases operating costs.

— *Unreliability*: loss of refrigerant may cause a refrigeration system to trip-out due to low pressure and can cause reduced lubrication and cooling of compressors and motors possibly causing their failure.

— *Legal requirements*: knowingly allowing CFC and HCFC refrigerants to leak is an offence that could result in a large fine (see section 4.3.4).

Leakage will cause a gradual deterioration in the system coefficient of performance (COP) and cooling performance. Some systems are buffered, that is they hold a significant reserve of refrigerant, and will show a delayed effect before the effects of leakage becomes apparent. Figure 4.12 shows the effect of refrigerant leakage on the coefficient of performance of one example unbuffered chiller[(67)] and Figure 4.13 shows the effect on refrigeration capacity.

Refrigerant leakage can be minimised through good design and working practices. In particular it is recommended that the following guidelines are followed:

— *Minimise the use of refrigeration*: it is important that a genuine requirement for mechanical refrigeration has been established by properly evaluating end-user requirements (section 4.2.2) and that options for free cooling have been considered (sections 4.2.5 and 4.4.3).

— *Minimise the quantity of refrigerant*: the quantity of refrigerant used should be minimised by selecting equipment with a low specific refrigerant charge (kg of refrigerant per kW nominal refrigeration capacity).

— *Use small systems in combination*: using several self-contained refrigeration systems with a lower individual refrigerant charge, rather than a single large system, reduces the total amount of refrigerant that can be released from a single leak. Compact refrigeration equipment generally has a lower charge than larger or extensive distributed systems (such as multi-split or VRF systems).

— *Avoid large reserves*: avoid unnecessarily large reserves of refrigerant in 'buffered' systems, for example in liquid receivers, pumped recirculation systems or oversized liquid lines.

— *Minimise the number of joints, seals and valves*: brazed or welded joints are much more likely to be leak tight than demountable joints. Valves are a potential source of leaks although sufficient should be provided to minimise refrigerant loss during servicing and maintenance.

— *Select a refrigerant to minimise the impact of leakage*: different refrigerants have differing impacts on ozone depletion, global warming and health and safety. For example, ammonia has a zero global warming potential and hydrocarbons have very low global warming potentials, whereas HCFCs and HFCs generally have high global warming potentials, see Appendix 4.A1.

Further guidance is given by the Institute of Refrigeration's *Code of practice for the minimization of refrigerant emissions from refrigerating systems*[(67)], Action Energy Good Practice Guide GPG178[(68)] and BRE Information Paper IP1/94[(69)].

4.4.4.5 Coefficient of performance

The energy efficiency of a refrigeration system is defined as the coefficient of performance (COP):

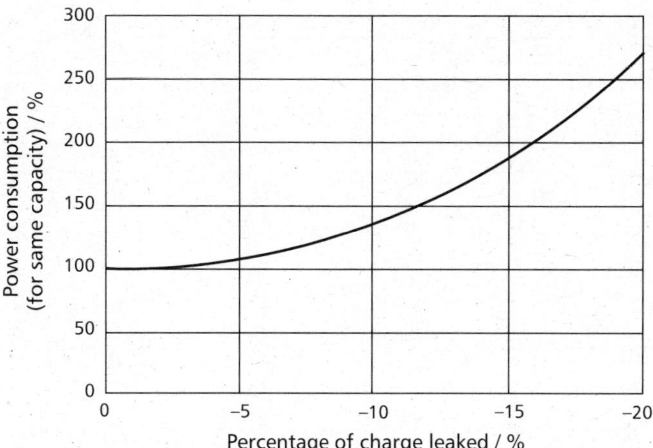

Figure 4.12 Effect of refrigerant leakage on coefficient of performance: unbuffered chiller[(68)]

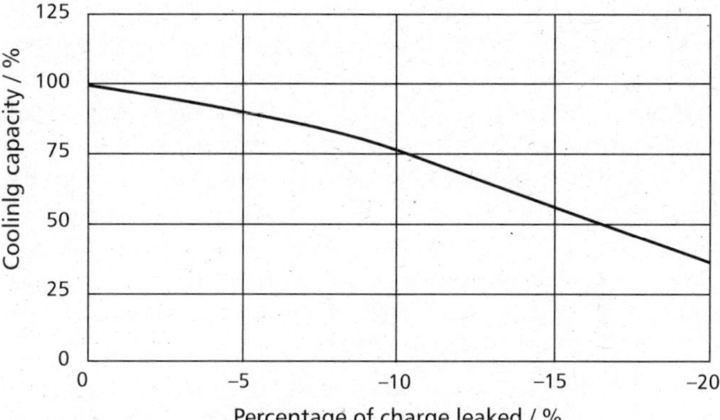

Figure 4.13 Effect of refrigerant leakage on refrigeration performance (cooling capacity): unbuffered chiller[(68)]

$$\mathrm{COP} = \frac{\text{Refrigeration effect (kW)}}{\text{Power input of the compressor (kW)}} \tag{4.2}$$

In practice the coefficient of system performance (COSP) is more useful for comparing different systems. COSP includes the power consumed by ancilliary equipment associated with the refrigeration system, including condenser fan motors, condenser water pumps, electrical controls and cooling tower fans and pumps. COSP does not include the power consumed by the chilled water pumps or ventilation pumps.

$$\mathrm{COP} = \frac{\text{Refrigeration effect (kW)}}{\text{Power input of the compressor and ancilliary motors and controls (kW)}} \tag{4.3}$$

The designer should seek to achieve the highest possible COSP consistent with a practicable and economic system. A plant operating with a COSP of 4 will use 25% less power to achieve the same cooling than one operating with a COSP of 3. COSP depends on many factors although the temperature lift of the system is usually the most important factor. Temperature lift is the difference between the condensing and evaporating temperatures and is affected by factors such as the mode of heat rejection. Other factors include the compressor efficiency, motor efficiencies and the choice of refrigerant.

The COSP of a range of vapour compression chiller types with air-cooled and water-cooled condensers is shown in

Table 4.15 COSP for a range of vapour compression chiller types

Type	Cooling capacity / kW	Coefficient of system performance (COSP)*	
		Water-cooled condensers	Air-cooled condensers
Reciprocating	< 120	2.6	3.2
	> 120	2.8	3.4
Scroll	< 250	2.8	3.4
Screw	< 1800	2.6	3.6
Centrifugal	< 800	2.2	3.8
	> 800	2.3	4.0

*Values are typical for a packaged water chiller operating at chilled water temperature of +6 °C and dry bulb air temperature of 28 °C

Table 4.15. The values shown are COSP values and are lower than COP values that might be quoted by a manufacturer.

The designer should seek to minimise the temperature lift by increasing the evaporating temperature and/or by reducing the condensing temperature. This is usually effected by maximising the size and efficiency of the heat absorption and rejection heat exchangers. A reduction in condensing temperature of 1 K or an increase in the evaporating temperature of 1 K reduces energy use by 2–4%. Guidance on optimising COP and COSP is given by CIBSE Guide F[(1)].

The vapour compression cycle approximates to the reversed Rankine and Carnot cycles. The theoretical cop of the Carnot cycle is given by:

$$\mathrm{COP} = \frac{T_1}{T_2 - T_1} \quad (4.4)$$

where T_1 is the evaporating temperature (K) and T_2 is the condensing temperature (K).

The COP of a practical vapour compression system is considerably lower than the COP of the theoretical Carnot cycle. However, equation 4.4 can be used by the designer to predict the relative change in COP from changes in the evaporating and condensing temperatures.

4.4.5 Absorption refrigeration

The term 'sorption' includes both absorption and adsorption, both being systems where refrigeration is effected by evaporation of a refrigerant, the vapour being absorbed or adsorbed by a liquid absorbent or solid adsorbent medium respectively, from which it is subsequently expelled at a higher partial pressure by heating and then liquefied by cooling. The number of fully developed adsorption systems is, however, relatively small. (For further details see IEA Heat Pump Programme Annex 24[(70)].)

The working principle of an absorption cycle is similar to that of a mechanical vapour compression system, the only major difference being the replacement of the compressor by a heat operated absorber–generator, see Figures 4.14 and 4.15.

The COP of absorption systems is generally inferior to that of vapour compression systems but advantages can accrue where thermal energy (e.g. from a CHP system) is used to power the generator, or where quiet vibration-free operation is a criterion. The COP of vapour compression

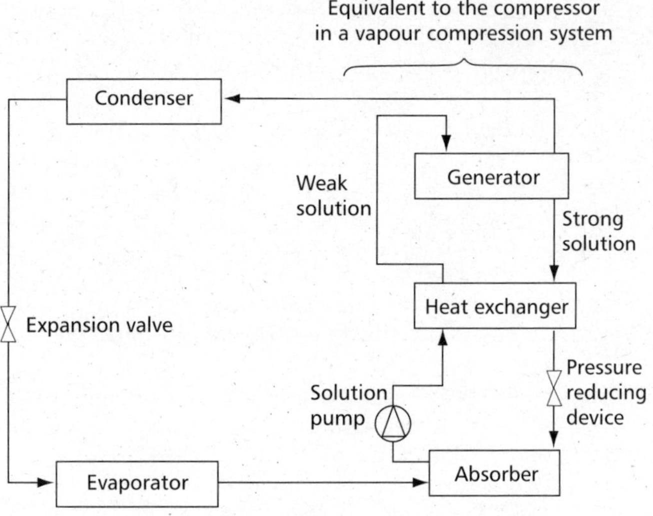

Figure 4.14 Single effect absorption system (lithium bromide)

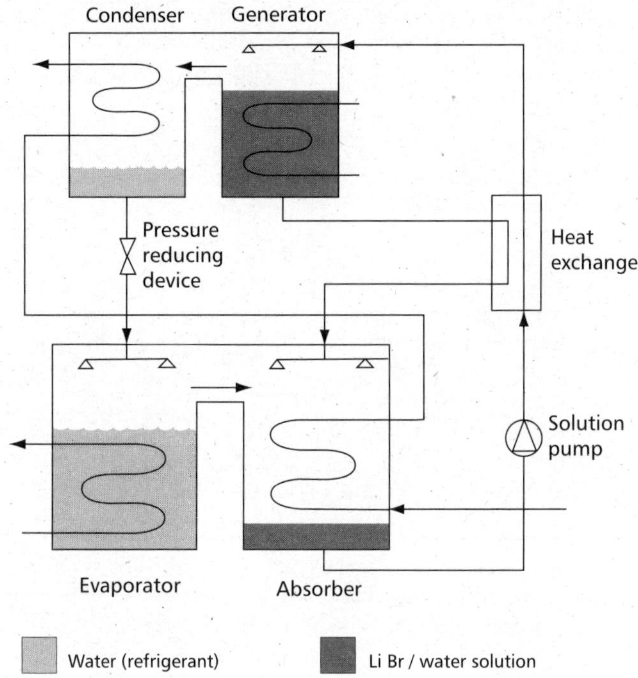

Figure 4.15 Single effect absorption chiller[(71)]

machines is measured in terms of cooling to electrical power input whereas, for absorption machines, COP is measured in terms of cooling to thermal energy input whereas, for absorption machines, cop ismeasured interms of cooling to thermal energy input. For definitions of COP for vapour compression and absorption systems, see sections 4.4.4.5 and 4.4.5.5 respectively.

In air conditioning systems, the absorption process is commonly employed in packaged equipment for the production of chilled water using hot water, gas or steam as the heat energy source. Figures 4.15 and 4.16[(71)] show schematics of the two types of absorption chillers currently available.

The double effect lithium bromide absorption cycle incorporates two generators. The solution is pumped through the solution heat exchangers to the first effect generator and then the second effect generator. As the high temperature condenser heat is used to drive the low temperature generator, it provides a higher efficiency system.

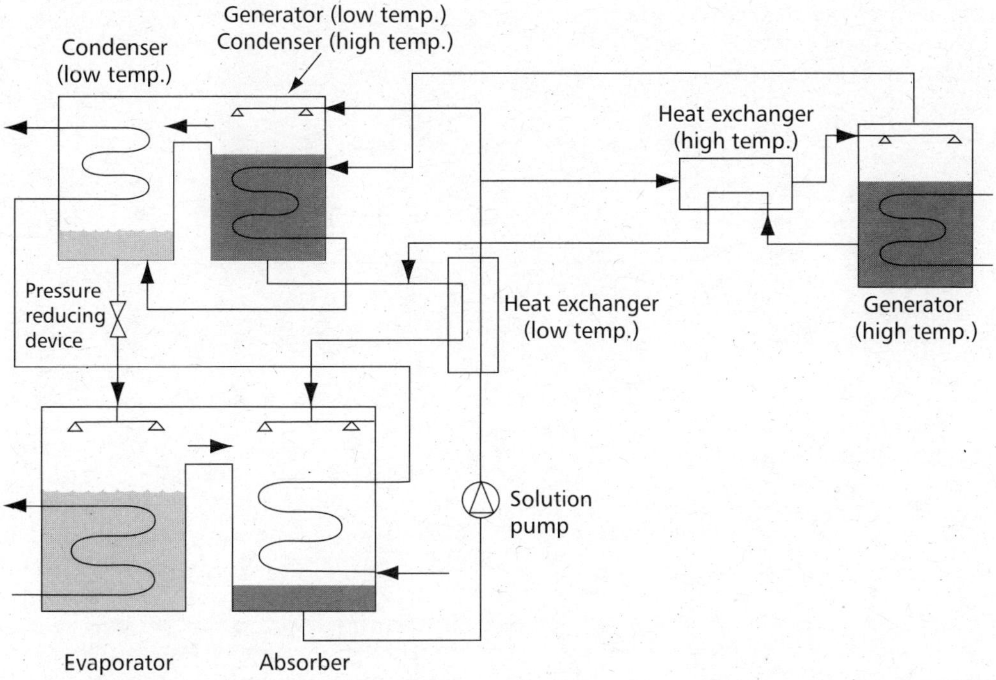

Figure 4.17 Double effect absorption chiller[71]

The stages in the process are as follows:

- in the evaporator the refrigerant extracts heat by evaporation (q_r = heat of evaporation)
- the refrigerant vapour is absorbed and condensed into the solution in the absorber, thereby making the solution weaker ($q_r + q_l$ = heat of evaporation plus solution)
- the weak solution is pumped to high pressure and transferred to the generator
- the addition of heat ($q_r + q_l$ = heat of evaporation plus solution) in the generator raises the temperature of the solution, separating and evaporating the refrigerant, thus making the solution stronger
- the strong solution is returned to the absorber through the pressure reducing device so maintaining the pressure difference between the high and low sides of the system
- the refrigerant vapour driven out of solution at high pressure in the generator flows to the condenser where it is liquefied by removal of heat at constant pressure (q_r = heat of evaporation)
- the condensed liquid is fed through a pressure reducing device into the evaporator where the cycle re-commences.

The heat generated due to the absorption ($q_r + q_l$) and condensation (q_r) is usually removed by passing cooling water through these vessels in series in water-cooled systems or by air coils in air-cooled systems. Utilisation of waste heat, heat recovery, peak demand shaving and co-generation have been the major factors that have influenced the choice of absorption technology in the current market.

The choice between single effect (Figure 4.15) and double effect (Figure 4.16) absorption chillers is usually based on the temperature of the driving energy source as double effect absorption chillers require a higher temperature heat source than single effect chillers, see Table 4.16.

Although absorption chillers are much less efficient than vapour compression refrigeration systems the fact that their only major requirement is heat gives them greater flexibility. The carbon emissions resulting from the operation of an absorption chiller are also not as bad as the COP would appear to indicate because of the lower carbon overhead of gas or heat compared to delivered electricity. An effective application of absorption chillers is in conjunction with combined heat and power (CHP) systems. Absorption chillers can be used with CHP systems in the following ways:

(*a*) Single-effect chillers:
- hot water driven (80–130 °C)
- steam driven (1 bar)

(*b*) Double-effect chillers:
- steam driven (3–9 bar)
- exhaust gas driven (280–800 °C).

Table 4.16 Absorption chiller range[71]

Heat source	Single effect			Double effect		
	Refrigerant	Condenser type	COP	Refrigerant	Condenser type	COP
Direct fired natural gas	Ammonia	Air cooled	0.5	Water	Water cooled	1.0
Hot water (80–130 °C) or steam (0.2–1.0 bar)	Water	Water cooled	0.7	—	—	—
Steam (3–9 bar)	—	—	—	Water	Water cooled	1.2
Engine exhaust gases (280–800 °C)	—	—	—	Water	Water cooled	1.1

Although single-effect absorption chillers can be driven by low pressure steam, the most common application is to use engine jacket cooling water. Many CHP systems, such as those commonly used in hospitals and industrial applications, use steam at approximately 8–15 bar and these are very suitable for steam driven double-effect absorption chillers designed to use steam at 8 bar. Where reciprocating engines or gas turbines are used the hot gas exhaust, which is typically at 280–800 °C, can be used directly with hot gas driven double-effect absorption chillers. Further guidance on using absorption chillers with CHP, including sizing the chillers, is given by the Action Energy Good Practice Guide 256[(72)].

Triple-effect absorption chillers are being developed by a number of commercial manufacturers. Basically they use the heat three times in the same way as the double-effect cycle and gas-fired machines are expected to have COPs in the order of 1.52.

GAX absorption chillers

In generator absorber heat exchanger (GAX) absorption chillers part of the thermal load on the generator is met by direct heat transfer from the absorber. Figure 4.17 shows this internal heat transfer process. The degree of internal heat transfer or temperature overlap depends on the temperature of the evaporator which should be as high as possible.

Although COP improvements in the order of 22% have been shown compared with a conventional single effect gas-fired chiller, the additional heat transfer process adds complexity and cost to the chiller and in practice it may be more economic to use a double effect machine.

Rotary (Interotex) absorption chiller

The interotex absorption chiller, commonly known as the 'rotex' machine, is basically a double effect machine that uses process intensification through rotational force to improve heat and mass heat transfer. The active components of the machine rotate at a high speed (typically 550 rpm) subjecting the liquid films to very high gravitational forces thus providing reduced film thicknesses and enhanced transfer coefficients.

A cooling COP of around 1 has been recorded based on a chilled water temperature of 7 °C and a temperature lift of 45 °C from a prototype type machine[(73)]. The concept is more complex than a conventional double effect absorption chiller and its practicality and economic viability has yet to be proven.

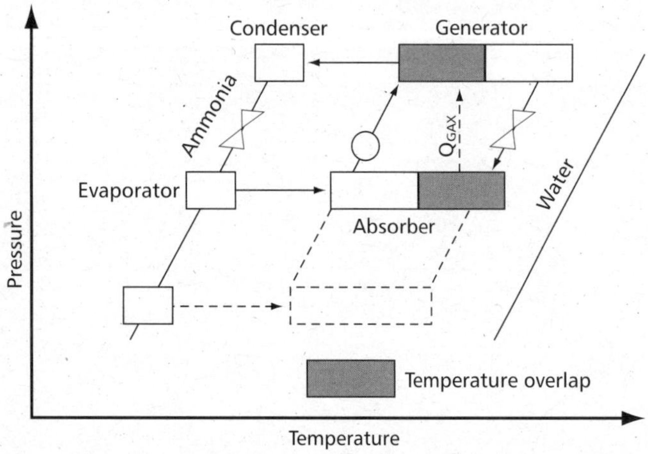

4.4.5.1 Refrigerant selection

Commercially available absorption chillers generally use water–lithium bromide (LiBr) or ammonia–water solutions depending on the cooled fluid temperature and the required cooling duty:

- for chilled water temperatures >5 °C, a water/LiBr absorption machine is typically used with a water-cooled condenser, although dry coolers have been used in the UK
- for chilled water temperatures < 5 °C, an ammonia/water machine may be used; this can be either small air-cooled modules or water-cooled machines for industrial refrigeration applications.

In the water/LiBr machine water is the refrigerant and cooling is based on the evaporation of water at very low pressures. Since water freezes below 0 °C, at this temperature the chilling temperature meets a physical limit. LiBr is soluble in water if the LiBr mass fraction of the mixture is less than about 70%, see Figure 4.18.

Crystallisation of the LiBr solution will occur at higher concentrations which will block the solution circuit, resulting in a failure of the refrigeration process and possible damage to the plant. This sets a limit for the temperature of the absorber. Poor control of temperature or a fast change of conditions may cause crystallisation, but appropriate controls, such as monitoring by level transducers, will minimise problems (see also IEA Heat Pump Programme Annex 24[(70)]). In order to supply sufficiently low temperatures to the absorber at high outside air temperatures evaporative water cooling is usually used.

Corrosion inhibitors are essential in LiBr machines and, without their use, long life will not be achieved. Additives such as lithium chromate, lithium molybdate and lithium nitrate have been used but generally this depends on the manufacturer.

In ammonia/water machines, ammonia is the refrigerant. This offers opportunities to provide refrigeration at temperatures down to –60 °C. Unlike LiBr, which is a salt, water has a vapour pressure of itself. This means that in

Figure 4.17 Fundamental concept of the GAX cycle-temperature overlap.

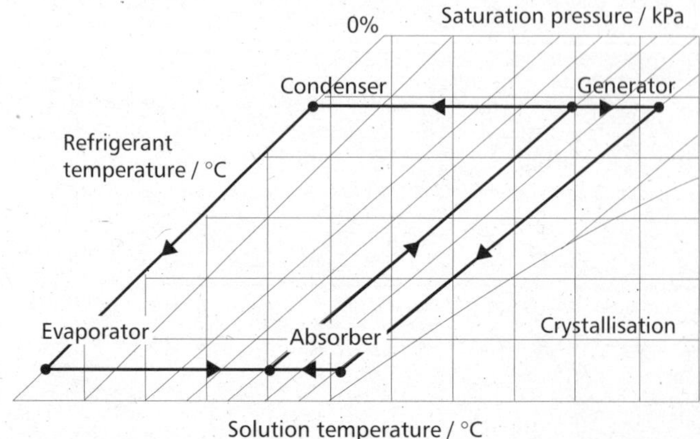

Figure 4.18 Pressure–temperature concentration diagram (PTX) for a water/LiBr system (single effect)

the generator, besides ammonia vapour, a certain amount of water vapour will also be present. In the evaporator, this will lead to problems because the ammonia will evaporate more easily than the water. This results in an accumulation of water in the evaporator, undermining the chilling process. To prevent this, an extra device known as a rectifier is incorporated in the system to separate the water content from the vapour flow coming from the generator. The rectifier cools the vapour produced in the generator, therefore demanding more heat, and therefore reducing the COP. Despite rectification, a small fraction of water will still remain in the vapour. To minimise accumulation in the evaporator, there always has to be a flow of non-evaporated fluid (i.e. liquid) from the evaporator to the absorber.

Ammonia is soluble in water at all operating conditions so crystallisation will not occur. Consequently, at equal chilling temperatures, a higher absorber temperature is possible with water/ammonia compared to water–LiBr chillers. This allows the selection of dry coolers (see section 4.4.2) if required. It should be noted however that air cooling is less efficient than evaporative cooling and consequently uses more energy.

4.4.5.2 Safety

The designer has a responsibility to ensure that the design of the refrigeration system takes into account all the necessary provisions for safe installation, commissing operation, maintenance and decommisioning of the system. The requirements of relevant UK health and safety related legislation are outlined in section 4.3.2.1.

Ammonia–water absorption chillers require special consideration as the refrigerant is ammonia and precautions are required in case of leakage. Ammonia detectors and alarms should be installed in chiller plant rooms. Ammonia–water solutions should be treated as special waste when being disposed of.

Skin contact with lithium bromide should be avoided and operators should wear appropriate personnel protection when charging or decommissioning lithium bromide/water chillers. Lithium bromide is highly corrosive to steel in the presence of oxygen. Corrosion is minimised by the addition of inhibitors such as lithium nitrate and other additives such as n-octanol. These chemicals are toxic and can cause chemical burns. Full protective clothing should be worn when handling, in accordance with manufacturers instructions.

4.4.5.3 Environmental impacts

Absorption chillers do not use refrigerants or other substances that can cause ozone depletion or contribute to global warming. However, many of the substances are toxic and safe handling and disposal procedures should be complied with in accordance with manufacturers instructions, see section 4.4.5.2.

4.4.5.4 Refrigerant leakage

LiBr–water absorption chillers operate below atmospheric pressure and therefore refrigerant leakage is not an issue. However, the ingress of air is a problem and purge units are normally provided to remove such non-condensables from the system. Ammonia–water systems operate at positive pressure and precautions must therefore be made to prevent leakage. Small leaks are readily detectable by the characteristic pungent smell of ammonia. Detectors and alarms should be provided in plant rooms to prevent exposure to toxic concentrations.

4.4.5.5 Coefficient of performance

Table 4.17 gives typical COPs for a some common commercially available absorption chiller types.

The coefficient of performance (COP) of absorption chillers is considerably lower than for vapour compression refrigeration systems. This means that absorption chillers have to reject considerably more heat than vapour compression systems, resulting in a requirement for larger or a greater number of dry air coolers or cooling towers. The heat dissipation ratio (see section 4.4.6) is a useful practical method of comparing heat rejection requirements for competing systems.

Table 4.17 Commercially available absorption chiller types[70] and COPs

Working pair	System	Driven/fired by (not direct)	Cooling capacity / kW	COP
H_2O/LiBr	Single-effect absorption	Steam, water	40–6000	0.7
		Gas, oil	40–6000	0.6
H_2O/LiBr	Double-effect absorption	Steam	70–6000	1.2
		Gas, oil	5–6000	1.0
NH_3/H_2O	Single-effect absorbtion	Gas	10–100	0.5
	Generator absorber heat exchanger (GAX)	Gas	10–100	0.68
H_2O/silica gel	Double-alternating absorption	Water	70–350	≤ 0.6
		Gas	70–350	≤ 0.5

4.4.6 Heat dissipation ratio

The heat dissipation ration (HDR) is a useful index for analysing condenser cooling water requirements. HDR is defined as the ratio of heat dissipated from the condenser and absorber with respect to the evaporator cooling duty:

$$\mathrm{HDR} = \frac{Q_{\mathrm{rej}}}{Q_{\mathrm{cooled}}} = 1 + \frac{1}{\mathrm{COP}} \qquad (4.5)$$

where Q_{rej} is the heat rejected at the condenser (W), Q_{cooled} is the heat absorbed in the evaporator (refrigerating effect) (W).

Table 4.18 shows the HDR for a range of chillers. For example, a single effect absorption chiller requires condensers that at least 1.9 times larger than those required for a vapour compression chiller with the same cooling capacity.

4.4.7 Secondary coolants

Secondary coolants (sometimes also known as heat transfer fluids, brines or secondary refrigerants) such as

Table 4.18 Heat dissipation ratios for absorption chillers and vapour compression chillers

Type of chiller	Lithium bromide absorption		Vapour compression	
	Single effect steam/hot water	Double effect steam	Double effect gas fired	Electric reciprocating
COP	0.7	1.2	1.0	>4
HDR	2.5	1.8	2.0	<1.3
Ratio of absorption chiller HDR to vapour compression HDR	>1.9	>1.4	>1.5	1.0

chilled water, brine or glycol mixes are generally used on larger plant where the volume of the primary refrigerant would be too large for environmental and/or cost reasons. The use of a secondary coolant involves an additional heat transfer process and therefore greater temperature difference, hence these systems are inherently less energy efficient than direct refrigeration systems.

Secondary coolants should ideally be non-toxic liquid with a high thermal conductivity, a high specific heat capacity and a low viscosity. For good heat transfer it is also desirable that the coolant velocity is high enough for turbulent flow. Table 4.19 summarises some of the key properties of a range of common secondary refrigerants. Water has good heat transfer and transport properties and is the most widely used secondary coolant for applications above 0 °C, especially for air conditioning systems. For low temperature applications calcium chloride, sodium chloride, ethylene glycol or propylene glycol are commonly used. Most of these substances require corrosion inhibitors to prevent damage to metal pipes and other components. Propylene glycol is often used in food industries on account of its low toxicity, despite its high viscosity which results in relatively poor energy efficiency compared to other potential secondary coolants.

Two-phase secondary coolants

The performance of secondary systems can be improved by using two-phase secondary coolants. Systems using carbon dioxide (CO_2) as a volatile secondary refrigerant are under development[74]. The advantages of using CO_2 as a volatile secondary include improved heat transfer coefficients and high latent cooling effect which reduces the mass circulated and the size of pipework.

Other forms of two-phase secondary coolants include pumpable ice slurries[75,76], using ice crystals that have been formed on the surface of a scraped evaporator. Some commercial systems use an orbiting rod as the ice scraper. The addition of an antifreeze allows ice slurries to be stored and pumped at low temperatures. Applications include food storage and processing and as an alternative to traditional ice storage systems (see section 4.4.10). Pumpable ice slurry systems could also be used for district cooling systems incorporating 'coolth' storage.

4.4.8 Evaporative cooling

Evaporative cooling uses the evaporation of water to decrease the dry bulb temperature of air. There are two main categories of evaporative cooling:

— *Direct evaporative cooling*: water is evaporated directly into the supply air stream, adiabatically reducing the air stream's dry bulb temperature but increasing its absolute humidity. Direct coolers may use wetted media or air washers.

— *Indirect evaporative cooling*: two air streams are used. A secondary air stream (either exhaust air or outdoor air) is cooled directly using evaporation. The cooled secondary air stream is then used to cool the primary supply air indirectly through an air-to-air heat exchanger before being exhausted. The supply air is therefore sensibly cooled without increasing its absolute humidity.

Evaporative cooling works best in hot dry climates, such as Arizona, and are not particularly suited to the UK's relatively damp climate. Evaporative cooling systems generally require much higher air flow rates than conventional air conditioning systems because of their relatively high air supply temperatures, and therefore require larger fans and ducts. They also cannot deal with latent cooling loads which is a major disadvantage in the UK. For these reasons evaporative cooling is often used in the UK in conjunction with a conventional refrigeration system or with a desiccant stage, see section 4.4.9.

Further information and guidance on evaporative cooling is given section 2.

Table 4.19 Properties of common secondary refrigerants

Substance	Concentration by weight / %	Viscosity / centipoise	Freezing point / °C	Flow rate per 100 kW for 5 K temp. rise
Water	100	1.55	0	4.8
NaCl	12	1.75	−8.0	5.1
$CaCl_2$	12	2.01	−7.2	5.2
Ethylene glycol	25	2.7	−10.6	5.1
Propylene glycol	30	5.0	−10.6	4.9
Polydimethylsiloxane	100	1.91	−111.0	14.5

4.4.9 Desiccant enhanced cooling

Desiccants are hygroscopic materials that readily absorb or adsorb moisture from the surrounding air. They can be solids or liquids, although application of desiccant technology in the UK is currently based on the use of solid materials. They may be natural or synthetic substances. Desiccants can either be used as part of stand-alone dehumidification systems or as an additional stage in evaporative cooling systems to improve their performance.

Desiccants attract moisture from the air because of a difference between the lower water vapour pressure at their surface and that of the surrounding air. This will happen when the desiccant is cool and dry. As the water content of a desiccant increases so does the water vapour pressure at its surface. When the surface vapour pressure exceeds that of the surrounding air, moisture leaves the desiccant. Heating will then dry the desiccant, its vapour pressure remaining high so that it has little ability to absorb moisture. Cooling the desiccant then reduces its vapour pressure so that it can absorb moisture once again. This is referred to as 'regeneration'.

The above process takes place in a typical air conditioning plant with a desiccant wheel and a thermal wheel working in conjunction with a refrigerated coil(s), see section 2.4.10.

The process may be summarised as follows:

- outside air passes through a filter before entering the desiccant wheel where moisture is removed; during this absorption process the temperature of the air rises
- the air is then cooled by the thermal wheel; the drier and cooler air may be further cooled by either evaporative cooling or mechanical cooling, dependent on the required final condition
- the cooler, dehumidified air is then delivered to the space to be air conditioned.

It is important that the designer calculates the optimum balance of desiccant dehumidification with refrigeration plant to meet the target requirements for cost and energy efficiency. High humidity climates such as the UK or applications where high latent heat loads are present (e.g. supermarkets) are possible candidates for desiccant systems. They are also particularly effective with radiant cooling, either by chilled ceilings or fabric thermal storage

The efficiency of the system is variable since it is dependent on the humidity of the air leaving the desiccant wheel. Designers should be aware, however, of the relatively high temperature (e.g. 18 °C) of the cooled air, compared to, say, a VAV system (e.g. 12 °C) requiring much higher air volumes and hence larger ducts, air handling units and increased fan energy. Several packaged desiccant cooling systems are now available.

For more detailed information, see section 2.

4.4.10 Ice storage systems

Ice storage allows 'load shifting' or the manipulation of energy demand profiles. Some of the potential benefits of this include:

- reduced energy costs by moving peak demand to times when energy may be cheaper (for example overnight)
- reduced power generation greenhouse gas emissions by moving peak demand to times when less polluting power plant is operated
- reduced chiller size and cost (and refrigerant charge) from reducing peak chiller loads by spreading operation over a longer period
- overcoming building or local area power supply limitations by reducing peak chiller electrical power consumption
- overcoming local regulatory restrictions in some countries e.g. the USA (California) on the construction of additional power generation plant; in these countries supply companies may positively encourage ice storage systems
- reduced space requirement for 'coolth' storage compared with chilled water storage systems.

A significant disadvantage of ice storage is that the production and melting of ice for building cooling systems is inherently inefficient and causes a reduction in chiller COP due to the lower evaporating temperatures (see section 4.4.4.5). The increase in chiller energy consumption may as high as 15–20%[76].

It has been established that, in the UK, that electricity grid power station CO_2 emissions per kW·h delivered electricity are lower overnight than during the day. Appropriately designed and controlled chillers with ice storage systems can therefore reduce the overall CO_2 emissions arising from the daytime operation of building cooling systems[77]. In particular it is important that chillers are controlled such that their condensing pressure is allowed to 'float' to follow the reduced ambient air temperature at night time. This may require the use of electronic expansion valves instead of conventional thermostatic expansion valves (TEVs). By maximising the benefit of lower night time condensing pressure and temperature on COP the negative effect of reduced evaporating temperature necessary to produce ice is minimised. Where daytime air temperatures are high the effect may even be to reduce overall chiller energy consumption. The designer should establish the overall impact on energy consumption and greenhouse gas emissions by carrying out a thorough energy and TEWI analysis.

There are a wide range of ice storage systems and control strategies. Control strategies should ideally ensure that the stored 'coolth' is used effectively and is not depleted prematurely. Some forms of ice storage, such as the ice on coil (ice builder) system, suffer a significant reduction in energy efficiency if the ice is only partially consumed during the day.

Further information and guidance on the selection and design of suitable ice storage systems and control strategies is given in CIBSE TM18: *Ice storage*[76].

4.4.11 Other refrigeration technology

At the time of writing vapour compression and absorption refrigeration systems are the dominant forms of refrigeration used for building refrigeration and air conditioning systems. However, a number of alternative forms of cooling do exist or are being developed. There is considerable interest in these alternatives due to the environmental impact of many current refrigerants, especially those that can cause ozone depletion and/or are greenhouse gases.

4.4.11.1 Solid adsorption systems

The solid adsorbent process differs from standard absorption chillers in that the process is essentially intermittent in nature, see Figure 4.19. The process starts (a) with an input of high temperature heat to bring about de-sorption of the working fluid from the adsorbent accompanied by the rejection of heat as the working fluid condenses. When this process is complete the adsorbent is cooled (rejecting a further quantity of heat) which leads to the total pressure falling (b). This, in turn, causes the working fluid in the right hand vessel to evaporate thus producing the desired refrigerating effect (c). For continuous cooling two such systems are necessary operating out of phase with one another.

The coefficient of performance of this system appears to be rather low due to heat being consumed in heating the bed to its desorbing temperature followed by rejection as the bed is cooled. Furthermore, the poor thermal diffusivity of porous or packed beds causes the process of heating or cooling to be an extremely slow one, lengthening the cycle time and reducing the power per unit mass of the bed. Solid absorption systems are currently the focus of university research. It is not know whether further development could overcome the many problems.

4.4.11.2 Thermoelectric (Peltier) cooling

The thermoelectric effect was discovered by Peltier in the 1830s. When a direct voltage is applied to an electrical circuit consisting of dissimilar metals and a current flows one junction tends to be cooled whilst the other is heated, see Figure 4.20. With pure metals the cooling effect becomes swamped by the ohmic heating so that in reality one junction becomes hot whilst the other becomes less hot, and no useful cooling is produced. However, the development of semiconductor materials has led to the development of practical thermoelectric cooling devices.

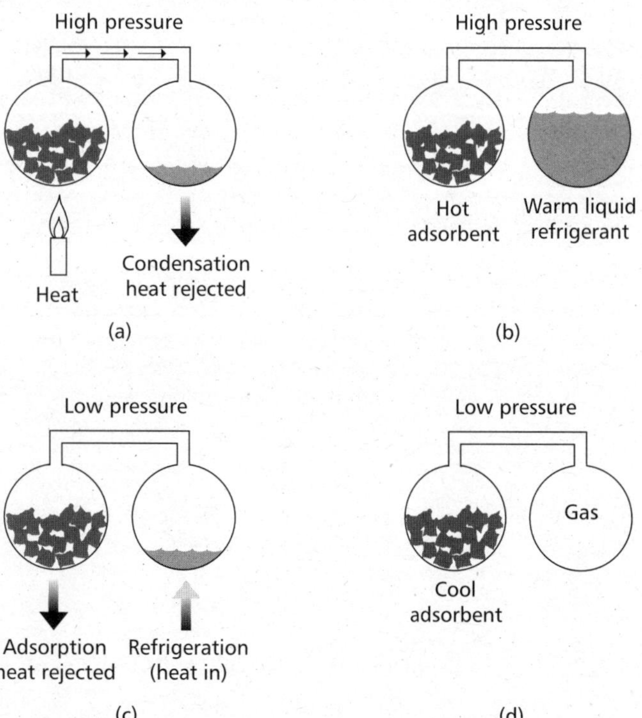

Figure 4.19 Processes within a simple low efficiency adsorption cycle.

Commercially available thermoelectric cooling units tend to be relatively small capacity devices such as electronic equipment coolers but units up to 3.5 kW have been used in submarines. COP is around 1.0 to 1.5 for typical air conditioning temperature ranges and therefore cannot compete with vapour compression machines.

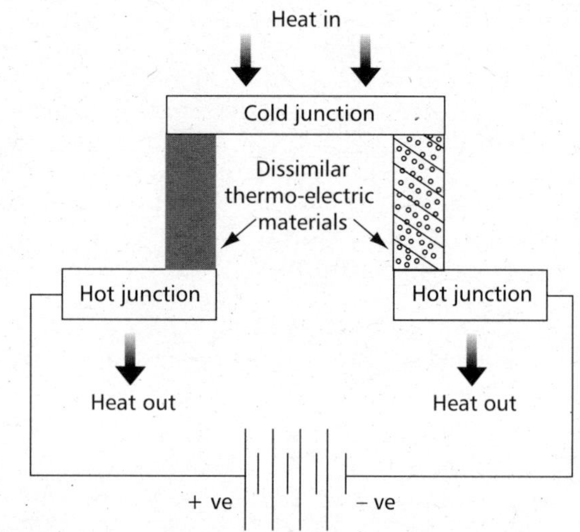

Figure 4.20 Principle of thermoelectric refrigeration

4.4.11.3 Steam jet (ejector) refrigeration

Steam jet refrigeration uses a primary flow of high pressure steam passing through an ejector to entrain water vapour from an evaporator and causes it to be compressed. The simplest form of steam jet refrigeration system is shown schematically in Figure 4.21. The temperature of the chilled water is reduced by evaporation at low pressure, the water vapour thus formed being induced continuously into the ejector by the injection of steam, so maintaining the low evaporating pressure.

The steam jet refrigeration system has a COP in the region of 0.2 to 0.3, around half that of a single effect absorption chiller. The advantage of the system is its simplicity and reliability. Research is currently being undertaken[78] to develop improved ejector-based refrigeration systems

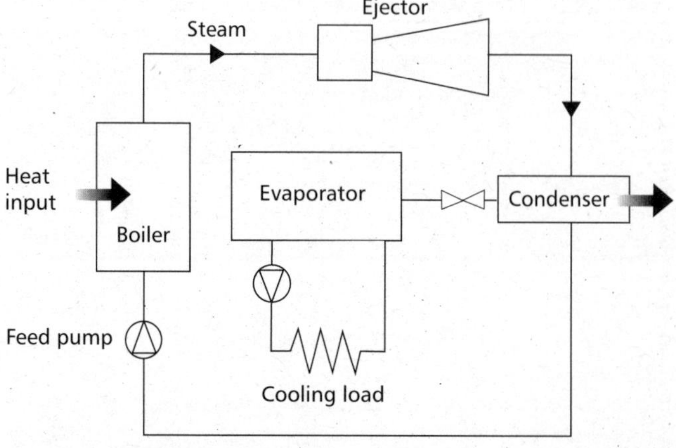

Figure 4.21 Steam jet refrigeration

using methanol as the working fluid that can make use of low grade heat such as that available from solar panels or waste heat from vehicle engines.

4.4.11.4 Stirling Cycle

The Stirling cycle is based on a closed thermodynamic cycle with regeneration. It is quite often used as a benchmark for assessing other systems. The operation of a reversed Stirling cycle is shown in Figure 4.22, although this does not represent a practical arrangement. Figure 4.21 shows the pressure and volume changes to the working fluid throughout the cycle.

The Stirling cycle involves the following process steps:

Process 1–2: The displacer remains stationary and the piston descends. The gas expands and its pressure falls. The gas temperature is cold but it remains constant because of heat transfer from the cold space.

Process 2–3: The displacer descends and the piston rises. The gas is maintained at constant volume and it passes through the regenerator which is hotter than the gas. The gas heats up due to heat transfer from the regenerator and its pressure rises; the regenerator cools.

Process 3–4: The displacer remains stationary and the piston rises. The gas is compressed and its pressure rises. The gas is hot and remains at constant temperature because of heat transfer to a heat sink.

Process 4–1: The displacer rises and the piston descends. The gas is maintained at constant volume and it passes through the regenerator which is colder than the gas. The gas cools due to heat transfer to the regenerator and its pressure falls; the regenerator heats up.

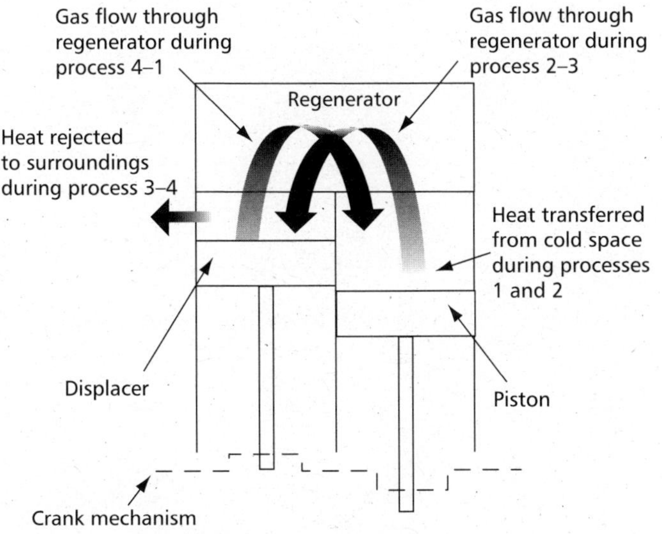

Figure 4.22 Reversed Stirling cycle: schematic

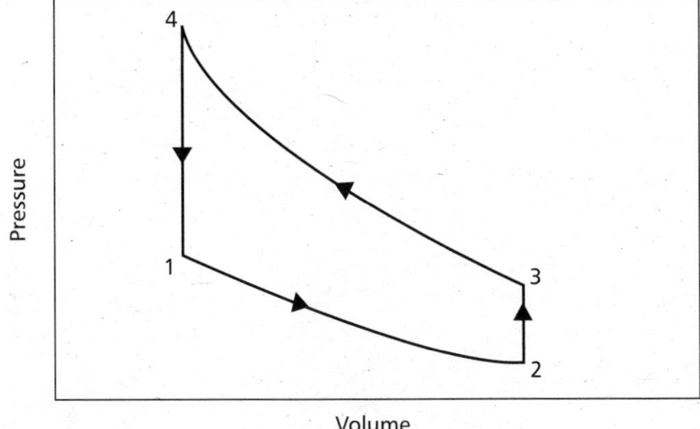

Figure 4.23 Stirling cycle: pressure–volume diagram

A variety of practical configurations have been devised including a piston and displacer in the same cylinder, a piston and displacer in separate cylinders and two pistons. The resulting designs are typically quite complex. A further area of design complexity is the heat transfer arrangements since only relatively small areas are available for both the external and regenerative heat transfers. Consequently, rather complex heat exchanger designs tend to be required.

At the time of writing no commercial Stirling cycle machines are available although various prototype domestic refrigerators based on the Stirling cycle have been built. The higher complexity would be expected to result in a cost higher than conventional vapour compression systems. Initial estimates of efficiency suggest that COP could be between 14% and 40% higher than equivalent vapour compression machines[(79)].

4.4.11.5 Gas cycle (air cycle) refrigeration

Gas cycle refrigeration is sometimes known as air cycle or reversed Brayton cycle and the Brayton cycle is sometimes known as the Joule cycle. Strictly, the reversed Brayton (or Joule) cycle and the air cycle are simply types of gas cycle refrigeration. The working fluid is normally but not necessarily air. Brayton cycles are closed cycle devices; although in practice many air cycle systems are open cycle. The air cycle is the basis of most aircraft air conditioning and cooling systems and some recent high speed trains.

The temperature of a gas decreases when it expands adiabatically (without external heat transfer) and does external work. Figure 4.24 shows a basic cycle and Figure 4.25 shows the associated pressure and volume changes. The processes are as follows:

Process 1–2: air is compressed causing its temperature and pressure to increase

Process 2–3: the air is cooled by transferring the heat of compression to a cooling medium, normally atmospheric air

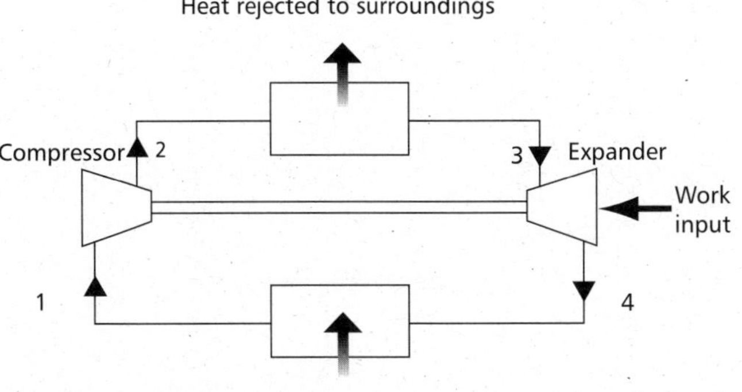

Figure 4.24 Reversed Brayton cycle: schematic

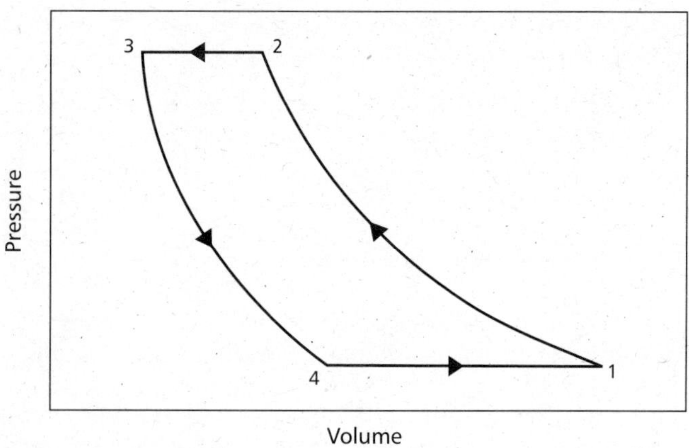

Figure 4.25 Reversed Brayton cycle: pressure–volume diagram

Process 3–4: the air is expanded by passing it through a turbine or expander, doing work on the surroundings, causing its temperature to decrease.

Process 4-1: the resultant cold air is reheated by absorbing heat from the load requiring cooling.

Some of the work required to compress the gas (process 1–2) is recovered in the expander (process 3–4) and used to help drive the compressor (a 'bootstrap' process). Additional work from an external source must also be supplied.

The system can work as an open cycle using air as the working fluid and this would reduce costs by minimising heat exchanger requirements. Input to the compressor would be from ambient air and the output from the expander would be supplied to the space to be cooled. This is the normal configuration for aircraft air conditioning systems(80).

Gas cycle systems using air have generally been designed for air conditioning applications although temperatures approaching –100 °C can be achieved. The gas cycle is inherently less efficient than a vapour compression system but in practice at low temperatures, less than –70 °C, their energy efficiencies are about equal. A closed air cycle system has been demonstrated in a building supplying chilled water at 6 °C to a conventional fan coil unit with a COSP of around 0.7 and with heat recovery from the rejected heat to heat water to 80 °C with a COSP of around 1.6(81).

4.4.11.6 Thermionic refrigeration

Thermionic cooling occurs when electrons pass across a semiconductor junction that has the junction electrodes separated by a vacuum. Although patents have been filed no practical device has yet been demonstrated. It is claimed that 30 kW of cooling should be produced per square metre of chip. The COP is predicted to be higher than vapour compression systems and the cost could be comparable to mass produced microchips(82). If a thermionic cooling chip becomes available, its incorporation into equipment such as refrigerators and air conditioning units should be straightforward.

4.4.11.7 Magnetic refrigeration

Magnetic refrigeration is based on the magneto-calorific effect. This is the heating or cooling of certain materials which occurs when they are magnetised or demagnetised respectively. The effect was identified more than 100 years ago and it has been used in cryogenic applications to produce temperatures of less than 1 K for more than 50 years. Recent developments(83) offer the possibility of effective devices working at normal refrigeration temperatures.

The process requires an input of work to move the magnetic material through the magnetisation/demagnetisation sequence. COPs around 5.0 have been reported(83) from tests with early prototypes. However, current devices rely on the use of a rare-earth element, gadolinium, for its good magneto-calorific effect which makes magnetic refrigeration devices very expensive. The development of commercial systems depend on identifying suitable alternative low cost materials.

4.4.11.8 Pulse tube refrigeration

The pulse tube refrigerator is based on the heating and cooling effect produced in a gas being compressed and expanded. For a pulse tube refrigeration device intended to cool a room, high pressure gas at room temperature would be injected at one end of the tube which contains gas at a lower pressure but also at room temperature. This would cause the initial charge to be compressed and displaced to the closed end. The compression process would cause the temperature of the initial charge to rise with a consequent temperature gradient along the tube. However, the gas can be cooled close to its original value by heat transfer to the environment. Releasing the pressure at this stage would cause the gas to expand and, consequently, cool. This produces a refrigeration effect since its temperature at the start of the expansion process was close to room temperature. The process is very similar to a reversed Stirling cycle and has been used for spacecraft cryogenic applications(84). Preliminary indications suggest that the efficiency and cost of pulse tube refrigeration devices needs to be improved for them to be competitive with vapour compression systems for normal building applications.

4.4.11.9 Thermoacoustic refrigeration

Thermoacoustic refrigeration uses acoustic generators and resonance effects to cause compression and expansion of a gas in a tube. In some respects it is similar to the pulse tube device.

An acoustic driver, which could be a loudspeaker-type device, in conjunction with the resonator, sets up standing waves in the tube which is packed with parallel plates known as the stack, see Figure 4.26. Helium or a helium-based mixture is normally the working fluid. Compressions and expansions in the acoustic wave cause localised heating and cooling of the gas which results in heat transfer into and out of the plates along their length. The overall effect is a temperature gradient along the length of the tube with the hot end near the acoustic generator. This gradient drives heat transfer from the cold space to the environment through suitable 'hot' and 'cold' heat exchangers.

Temperatures ranging from about –120 °C to –13 °C have been demonstrated by various thermoacoustic refrigerator designs with refrigeration capacities varying from tens of watts to several kilowatts(85). The main limitation of prototypes tested to date has been low COP which must be improved if the technology is to compete with vapour compression systems.

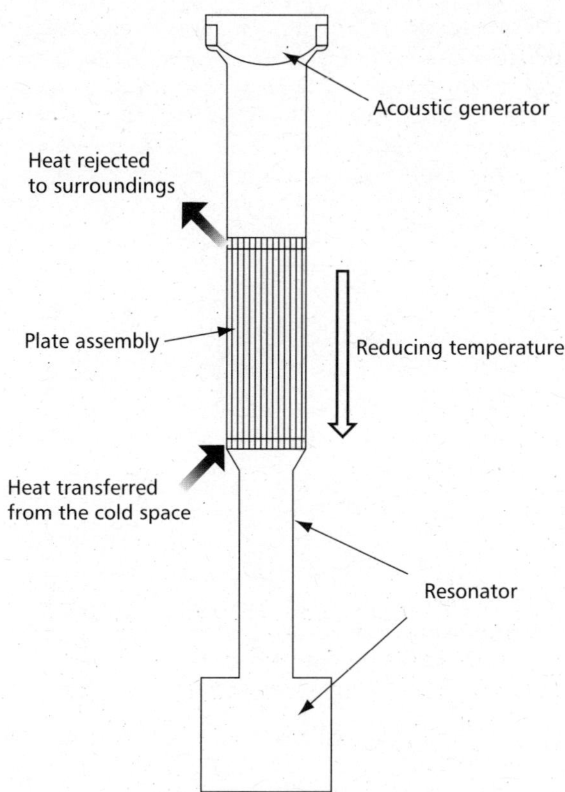

Figure 4.26 Thermoacoustic refrigerator: schematic

4.4.11.10 Optical cooling

Optical cooling involves the cooling of solids by the promotion of electro-magnetic radiation in the optical frequency range by similar incident radiation such that mean energy of the emitted photons is greater than that of those received. This results in a reduction of the solid's internal energy and, hence, cooling occurs. The principle was first proposed in 1929 but it took until the mid-1990s before any practical device was built. The main interest is in the development of optical cooling devices for cooling onboard spacecraft where compactness, low weight and reliability are important.

4.4.11.11 Vortex tube cooling

A vortex tube is an unusual device which can convert a stream of compressed air into two outlet streams, one of which is hotter and the other colder than the inlet. It was invented by Ranque in 1933 but it only received attention after publicity by Hilsch in 1947. The heating/cooling phenomenon is known as the Ranque-Hilsch effect.

A schematic of the tube is shown in Figure 4.27. Compressed air is the normal working fluid but other gases could be used. The compressed air is injected tangentially and this causes a screw-like, swirling motion around the circumference of the tube and it is discharged through the valve. If the valve is fully open, the tube acts as an injector; air is drawn in through the cold outlet port and becomes entrained in the drive air. However, at some point as the valve is closed, the direction of flow through the cold port reverses. The reversed flow through the cold port is found to have a much lower temperature than the drive air whilst the flow through the valve is hotter. There is no simple explanation for this effect but it is known that the valve and cold port must be about 50 and 0.5 tube diameters respectively from the injection point and the hole in the cold port must be also be about 0.5 tube diameters[86].

The cooling effect can be substantial; temperature reductions between the cold flow and drive air of 50–60 K are possible. Drive pressures are typically 10–15 bar and about 30% of the drive air is cooled under optimum conditions. However, the overall efficiency is very low with a COP around 0.2[87] and as a consequence their use in building services appears unlikely.

Despite their low efficiency and the need for a supply of clean, dry compressed air, vortex tubes are used for cooling specialised clothing used in hot environments such as mines or steelworks and the cooling of machine tool bits when liquid coolants would be inappropriate. In these applications their lack of moving parts, EMC fields or electrical supply are important advantages.

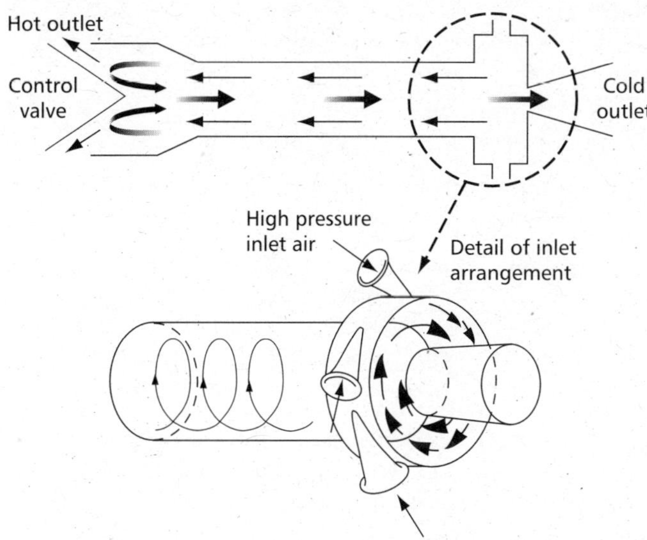

Figure 4.27 Vortex tube: schematic

4.5 Equipment

4.5.1 Introduction

This section provides information on a wide range of the equipment required for refrigeration and heat rejection systems. It sets out critical design issues relating to specific items of equipment and the key points to be considered in the selection of equipment. Where relevant, it provides references to statutory/mandatory regulations and guidance relating specifically to the design, installation or use of the equipment.

4.5.2 Refrigeration system components

This section gives the designer information on the components used in typical vapour compression refrigeration systems. Where appropriate information is given on the advantages and disadvantages of alternatives types of component.

4.5.2.1 Evaporators

Shell and tube direct expansion (DX) evaporators

A shell and tube DX evaporator comprises a steel vessel (shell) containing straight tubes, located between end tube plates, and having removable end covers. The refrigerant flows through the tubes. Water or another secondary coolant passes through the shell and over the tubes. A series of baffles within the shell improves heat transfer between the tubes and the secondary coolant.

Shell and tube DX evaporators are generally used for water temperatures down to 4 °C, or at lower temperatures for cooling secondary coolants such as brine or glycol. Refrigerant is distributed through the tubes in single or multiple pass, and control is either by thermostatic or electronic expansion valve. The latter allows more effective use of evaporating surface accommodating greater fluctuations in load (see section 4.5.2.3). Shell and tube DX evaporators are sometimes referred to as 'chillers'.

Advantages:

— small refrigerant charge inside the tubes;

— direct system (only one heat transfer operation).

Disadvantages:

— coolant side is generally inaccessible (chemical cleaning can be employed but caution is necessary)

— load fluctuations are more difficult to control than with flooded evaporators (see also section 4.5.2.3)

— prone to freezing when used as a water chiller.

Flooded refrigerant evaporators

The construction is similar to a shell and tube evaporator but the refrigerant is contained in the shell and the water or secondary coolant flows through the tubes. However, the shell incorporates a larger space at the top to allow expansion from liquid to vapour. These evaporators are suitable for water temperatures down to 4 °C and lower for secondary coolants such as brines and other fluids.

Advantages:

— large fluctuations in load are accommodated without risk of freezing (an expansion device which is sensitive to liquid level is normally used)

— direct system with higher rate of heat transfer than DX types.

Disadvantages:

— large refrigerant charge

— higher cost than DX evaporators.

Gasketed plate heat exchangers

A gasketed plate heat exchanger consists of a pack of corrugated metal plates with portholes for the passage of the two fluids between which heat transfer will take place. The plate pack is compressed between a frame plate and a pressure plate by means of tightening bolts. The plates are fitted with a gasket which seals the channel and directs the fluids into alternate channels. This arrangement allows additional plates to be easily added to increase the duty of the heat exchanger. The channels formed between the plates are arranged so that the refrigerant flows in one channel and the coolant in the other. Very low coolant and refrigerant temperature differences are possible (less than 2 K) making plate heat exchangers very suitable for systems that employ 'free cooling' techniques.

Advantages:

— very low refrigerant charge (internal volume is only about 10% of that for flooded evaporators)

— heat transfer coefficients can be three to four times greater than that of a shell and tube heat exchanger.

Disadvantages:

— oil fouling can occur affecting heat transfer (careful attention should be given to the type of refrigerant and oil used in the circuit and the manufacturer's approval should be obtained with regard to compatibility of refrigerants and oils)

— prone to freezing due to low mass of coolant inside the heat exchager (but less susceptible to permanent damage than shell and tube evaporators.

Brazed plate heat exchangers

The brazed plate heat exchanger is a variant of the gasketed plate heat exchanger except that it cannot be dismantled for cleaning. It is composed of a number of 'herringbone' corrugated plates brazed together. The plates are normally stainless steel coated with copper on one side. The assembly is clamped together with end plates and heated in a vacuum oven until the copper melts and forms a brazed joint. The channels between the two plates can be varied in their cross sectional dimensions to achieve the optimum heat transfer coefficient for the required application.

The advantages and disadvantages of brazed plate heat exchangers are the same as for gasketed plate heat exchangers.

Air blown DX evaporators

An air blown DX evaporator is basically the same in construction as an air cooled condenser and is used as an 'open unit' in cold rooms. It is usually enclosed within a fan coil or similar unit for air conditioning applications.

4.5.2.2 Condensers

Air cooled condensers

Air cooled condensers consist of copper tubes, in which the refrigerant is condensed, with aluminium cooling fins. They are usually constructed in single units or banks. Copper fins are sometimes employed in corrosive atmospheres.

The condensing temperature is related to the dry bulb temperature of the cooling air and is higher than the condensing temperature of systems that use evaporative heat rejection. The condensing temperature and pressure should be kept as low as possible by using a large condenser surface area, although there are practical and cost limits to this. In practice the temperature difference between the cooling airsteam and the condensing temperature is around 20 °C, increasing the overall inefficiency of the refrigeration process. There is also increased risk of the system high pressure cut-out tripping in hot weather causing a loss of cooling capacity.

Air cooled condensers are particularly well suited to small packaged systems but due to their size and relative inefficiency are seldom used for systems greater than about 1000 kW of cooling, especially in hot climates.

Many systems require that the condensing pressure is controlled to maintain it above a certain minimum value to ensure satisfactory operation of the expansion device (see section 4.5.2.3). Condensing pressure is commonly controlled by speed control or staging of the condenser cooling fans, although sometimes motorised dampers are used. To minimise noise levels low speed propellor or centrifugal fans are often used and discharge is directed upwards. The location and layout of condensers should follow the guidance given in section 4.5.5.4 to minimise short cycling and consequent head pressure difficulties.

Water cooled shell and tube condensers

Water cooled shell and tube type condensers comprise a welded pressure vessel containing the condensing surface in the form of plain or finned straight tubes located between end tube plates with removable end covers for access to the water tubes. These condensers are frequently used with cooling towers or dry air coolers.

For refrigerants other than ammonia, the water tubes are normally copper with special alternatives for sea water or polluted water conditions, such as rivers, pond or lakes. For ammonia the tubes have to be steel or stainless steel.

Gasketed/brazed plate heat exchangers

When used as a condenser the same considerations as noted above for gasketed heat exchangers and brazed plate heat exchangers apply, particularly the significant reduction in size compared with a shell and tube vessel but, due to the higher temperatures, the entrained oil will have a lower viscosity and therefore oil fouling should be less of a problem.

Evaporative condensers

Evaporative condensers are similar in operation to induced (or forced) draught water cooling towers (see section 4.5.5.4). The main difference is that the refrigerant vapour is condensed and is circulated inside the tubes of the condensing coil, which is continuously wetted on the outside by means of a recirculated water system. Air is simultaneously blown upwards over the coil, causing a small portion of the recirculated water to evaporate. The coil section consists of the closely nested pipes, water distribution system, and moisture eliminators, enclosed in a galvanized steel or plastic casing. Eliminators are preferably constructed from UV-resistant PVC.

Evaporative condensers are the most energy efficient method of heat rejection from a refrigeration system to ambient air because the surface temperature of the condenser tubes approaches the air wet bulb temperature and there is no other intermediate heat exchange process required. The ambient wet bulb temperature is often 8–12 °C lower than the dry bulb temperature, resulting in power savings of around 30% compared with an equivalent air cooled condenser system. Water pumping requirements are also less than for a cooling tower because the outside of the tubes only need to be kept wetted. Evaporative condensers are particularly effective with refrigerant migration (thermosyphon) chillers as they extend the time that thermosyphoning can occur.

Evaporative condensers have the following disadvantages:

— They normally need to be located close to the compressors in order to avoid long refrigerant pipe runs that would otherwise cause oil return difficulties, excess pressure drop and excessive refrigerant charge.

— A good water treatment and cleaning programme is essential to minimise the risk of *Legionella* and the formation of scale, corrosion and fouling

It is essential that the guidance on controlling *Legionella* bacteria given in the HSC Approved Code of Practice L8[(40)] and CIBSE TM13[(41)] are followed, see section 4.3.2.3. However, the risk of *Legionella* is lower than with cooling towers because the water volume is lower and restricted to the unit itself without extensive water circulation pipes and the risks associated with dead legs. It is important that manufacturers' recommendations for biocide dosing concentrations are adhered to as excessive usage can cause rapid corrosion of galvanised coil tubes and other metalwork. Scale control is also important as even small scale levels can significantly reduce heat transfer efficiency. Scale formation is minimised if the tubes are kept uniformally and totally wetted.

Practical guidance on water treatment for cooling towers and evaporative condensers is given by Eurovent[(88)].

Low pressure receiver

A low pressure receiver is a pressure vessel which incorporates a heat exchanger and is used in vapour compression systems between the evaporator and the compressor, see Figure 4.28. Integral heat exchange with the liquid line coming out of the condenser increases the level of subcooling and prevents liquid refrigerant from

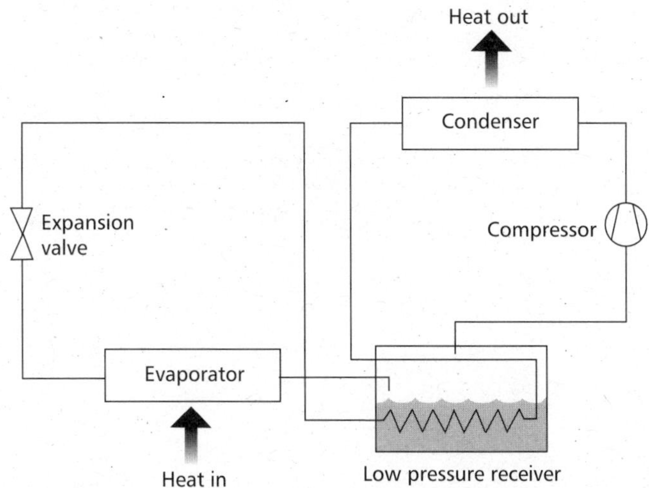

Figure 4.28 Vapour compression system with low pressure receiver

flooding back to the compressor. This allows the evaporator to be operated more efficiency in a fully flooded mode with no superheating at the exit and full wetting of all heat exchange surfaces. The evaporator can be controlled using a simple liquid level device on the high side instead of an expansion valve (see section 4.5.2.3).

4.5.2.3 Expansion devices

Expansion devices are used to reduce the pressure and temperature of the liquid refrigerant leaving the condenser to a level at which evaporation can take place in the evaporator. Expansion devices also serve a secondary function to meter the mass flow of refrigerant pumped by the compressor to equal that fed through the evaporator.

Capillary tube

A long small-bore capillary tube is used in domestic refrigerators and freezers and some other small direct refrigeration and air conditioning systems. This device has a fixed restriction usually in the form of a small-bore tube, the drop in pressure being determined by the length and diameter of the tube. These devices can be surprisingly effective and do not require potentially inefficient superheating in the evaporator. However, they are prone to blockage and do not allow for any adjustment of superheat levels.

Thermostatic expansion valve (TEV)

This is an automatic valve that controls the rate of liquid refrigerant flow to the evaporator whilst maintaining a predetermined degree of superheat at the evaporator outlet. Although this may result in increased system inefficiency and reduced evaporator effectiveness it does ensure that only gas is pumped and that no liquid enters the compressor, which for many compressor types would cause serious mechanical damage. There are two types of thermostatic expansion valve: 'externally equalised' and 'internally equalised'. Externally equalised types are normally used where an accurate flow rate of liquid refrigerant together with good modulation is required; a typical application is in air conditioning systems.

A TEV attempts to maintain a constant superheat at all times. It does not directly maintain the correct evaporating temperature. When there is less heat input to the evaporator less superheat is generated. This calls for the valve to close bringing about an increase in superheat back to the design value with a corresponding decrease in pressure, leading to a decrease in the evaporating temperature. With greater heat input to the evaporator greater superheat is generated, bringing about a decrease in superheat back to the design value with a corresponding increase in evaporating pressure leading to an increase in evaporating temperature.

A major disadvantage of TEVs is that they require a certain minimum refrigerant pressure difference across them. In cold weather the condensing temperature often has to be held artificially high (termed 'head pressure' control) to ensure correct operation of the TEV, resulting in higher than necessary compressor pressure ratio and increased system inefficiency (see sections 4.4.3.5 and 4.4.4.5). In typical systems with air cooled condensers this is usually achieved by modulating the condenser cooling fans. Slightly modified and more expensive balanced port TEVs can alleviate but not totally overcome the requirement for a high minimum pressure drop across the valve.

Electronic expansion valve

Electronic expansion valves rely on an external electronic signal rather than a thermostat and provide much closer control of superheat by virtue of the more accurate sensing of the superheat temperature in relation to the saturation temperature. They can operate with a wider range of evaporating and condensing temperatures than TEVs and do not require the condensing temperature to be held artificially high in cold weather (head pressure can 'float'). This allows input power savings at low ambient temperatures (see section 4.4.4.5).

The disadvantage of these valves is that they are more expensive and more difficult to set up than TEVs. Failure to commission them properly may lead to damaging liquid slugging of compressors. Electronic expansion valves should always be considered for large direct systems and chillers where the energy savings may easily outweigh the extra cost. Electronic expansion valves may also be integrated into an electronic or microprocessor control system.

Float valve regulators

There are two types of float valve depending on whether they are fitted to the high pressure side of the system or the low pressure side.

A high-side float valve controls the flow of liquid refrigerant passing from the condenser to the evaporator. It is used with systems with 'flooded' evaporators which are normally chillers with cooling capacities greater than about 400 kW. Careful attention is necessary with regard to the correct charge of refrigerant. Overcharging will result in liquid refrigerant returning to the compressor with subsequent damage. Undercharging will result in insufficient refrigerant in the evaporator, causing erratic and inefficient operation.

A low-side float valve directly controls the level of refrigerant in the evaporator or in a vessel feeding the evaporator. It is important that a minimum liquid level is maintained under all load conditions.

4.5.3 Direct expansion (DX) systems

4.5.3.1 General

The term 'direct expansion' describes an evaporator in which all the refrigerant supplied completely evaporates producing superheated vapour at the exit. This is in contrast to a flooded evaporator in which only partial evaporation takes place, producing saturated vapour at the exit. However, the use of this term is rather imprecise because it is also commonly used to describe a direct refrigeration or air conditioning system. The classification of direct and indirect refrigeration systems is defined in section 4.4.2. Direct systems usually use a direct expansion evaporator but so do many indirect systems including water chillers. For the purposes of this Guide, the term 'direct expansion' (DX) covers single room units, multi-split, ducted and variable refrigerant flow (VRF) systems. Direct expansion cooling may also be used for close control applications.

In general direct (DX) systems are thermodynamically more efficient (i.e. they have a higher COP) than indirect systems because they directly cool the substance or space being cooled without the use of an intermediate coolant and additional heat exchangers. However, in practice other factors such as the surface area of evaporators and condensers, compressor and fan efficiencies can significantly affect efficiency and large well engineered chillers can be more efficient than some direct systems.

4.5.3.2 Through-the-wall DX units

Also known as window mounted units, these are packaged fan coil units (FCUs) that incorporate a room-air side DX evaporator and outside facing condenser coil, with all the other components including fans, filters, compressor and an expansion device in the same casing. The unit is installed in a wall or window with the unit protruding outside. The units are intended for single rooms and have built-in self-contained controls. Many units can operate in a heat pump mode to provide heating as well as cooling.

Through-the-wall units are less suitable for large buildings due to the high maintenance overhead of many individual units, potential control difficulties and limited air-throw into deep rooms. Because of the need to keep the units compact the evaporator and condenser are often quite small. This requires low off-coil air temperatures on the room side when in cooling mode which can cause nuisance cold draughts and excessive dehumidification.

4.5.3.3 Single split DX units

These are similar to through-the-wall units except that the indoor and outdoor units are separate and connected by refrigerant pipes, which avoids the need for a large hole to be cut in the wall or window. The outdoor unit contains the compressor and condenser coil and can be roof or wall mounted. Indoor units offer considerable flexibility and may be wall or ceiling mounted. Some units are supplied with pre-charged flexible refrigerant pipes which simplifies installation for situations where the indoor and outdoor units are very close together. Where the separation distance is greater rigid pipework has to be installed onsite and particular care is required to prevent internal contamination or poor pipe layout if reliability problems are to be avoided (see section 4.5.3.7). The maximum pipe length is often around 100 m.

4.5.3.4 Multi-split DX units

These are similar to single-split units except that many indoor units can be connected to a single outdoor unit. They are very similar to variable refrigerant flow (VRF) units (see section 4.5.3.5) and most of the comments for VRF units apply to multi-split units.

4.5.3.5 Variable refrigerant flow (VRF) units

VRF units are basically multi-split system units with a refrigerant flow distributor control device. This device controls the refrigerant flow proportionally to the commands received from local automatic control sensors. The need to minimise the potential for refrigerant leakage (by reducing the extent and length of the refrigeration system pipework) is paramount, hence careful consideration should be given to the choice of this system as opposed to an indirect type.

Some manufacturers allow as many as 32 indoor units to be connected to a single outdoor unit although 8–16 units is more typical. Individual indoor units can provide heating or cooling as required using either a three- or two-pipe system. Two-pipe systems employ special refrigerant distribution units with vapour and fluid separation and flow control. Simultaneous heating and cooling can be provided with scope for heat recovery from units providing cooling to units requiring heating. The systems are suitable for larger buildings and offer considerable installation flexibility and choice of indoor units and are alternatives to individual room units and chilled water based systems. Applications include commercial and retail premises. (See section 2 for more details on split systems.)

The design and installation of the interconnecting pipework is crucial for reliable operation and it is vital that the manufacturers' instructions are fully complied with. Because of the extensive pipework these systems have greater potential for refrigerant leakage although manufacturers supply special ready-made branch and distributor fittings for brazing directly to the pipework which minimises the number of joints that could leak. However, the quality of on-site brazing and care to prevent dirt ingress and poor layout is crucial.

There is normally a 100 m limitation on the length of pipe between the external unit and the most remote room unit. This is to ensure that the pressure drop in the pipeline is minimised and that oil return to the compressor(s) is adequate. The requirements of BS EN 378[22] should be complied with, in particular with respect to the maximum refrigerant charge of the system. The maximum refrigerant charge is related to the practical limit of the refrigerant used and the volume of the smallest room served by the system, see section 5.4.4.2. Particular care is needed where VRF systems are installed in rooms where people may sleep, such as hotel bedrooms. The use of refrigerant detectors and alarms should be considered in these situations.

4.5.3.6 Ducted DX units

DX evaporator coils may be mounted in a duct or a central station air handling unit (AHU) for small commercial or residential buildings. The coils use copper tubes with aluminium fins for improved heat transfer. AHU systems typically provide up to 100 kW of cooling. As with multi-split DX systems the requirements of BS EN 378[22] should be complied with, in particular with respect to the maximum refrigerant charge of the system. The maximum refrigerant charge is related to the practical limit of the refrigerant used and the volume of the smallest room served by the system, see section 5.4.4.2.

4.5.3.7 Refrigerant pipework

The design and installation of refrigerant pipework can critically affect the system performance and reliability and requires particular care for split and multi-split systems and any other site erected system.

— *Liquid line pressure drop*: should be kept to a minimum to ensure that there is no flash gas at the expansion device as this can significantly reduce the cooling capacity of the system. In liquid lines the liquid temperature is close to the refrigerant saturation temperature and the effect of pressure drop is to reduce the temperature difference increasing the risk of flash gas forming at the expansion valve.

— *Suction line pressure drop*: a balance has to be made between the effect on compressor performance and the minimum velocity required for oil return from the evaporator. Where the direction of refrigerant flow is upwards then the velocity must be high enough to entrain the oil. One way of accomplishing this is to use a double riser. One riser is fitted with an oil trap which will gradually accumulate oil until the line is completely blocked off. The suction gas is then taken by the second (smaller) line resulting in a temporary pressure drop which will suck the oil from the trap.

— *Cleanliness*: it is vital that ingress of dirt is avoided as this could lead to internal blockages, especially in systems with capillary tube expansion devices.

— *Refrigerant leakage*: demountable flare and screwed joints should be avoided wherever possible to minimise the risk of leakage. The number of joints should be minimised and where necessary should be brazed using competent personnel following industry good practice working methods. Pipework should not be installed where mechanical damage is likely.

4.5.4 Water chillers

Factory built packaged chillers are generally preferable to site erected systems. Site erected systems increase the risk of refrigerant leakage and generally have longer runs of pipework which increases the refrigerant charge. There are considerable differences between chillers supplied by different manufacturers and the designer must make careful comparisons before choosing a supplier.

4.5.4.1 Vapour compression

Table 4.20 gives an overview of the four basic types of compressor currently used in the refrigeration industry:

— reciprocating (piston cylinder)

— scroll

— screw

— centrifugal.

These compressor types are described in detail below. The type of compressor used in an installation depends on the application and cooling capacity required.

Current practice on very large installations is to use centrifugal or screw compressors. On medium to large plant scroll, reciprocating or screw semi-hermetic multi-compressors are used. These can be either equal or unequally sized. For example, four compressors are often employed in a packaged unit, each compressor representing one step of capacity. This arrangement, whilst energy saving compared to other methods of capacity control, can result in frequent compressor cycling when small variations in load occur. A combination of this arrangement using one compressor with cylinder unloading or inverter control may provide a more reliable, cost effective and energy efficient alternative. Another option is the application of four unequal sized compressors which could also have the addition of individual capacity control or variable speed motors with inverter control.

Most compressors are driven by an electric motor and are either hermetic, semi-hermetic or open. Hermetic compressors are built into a welded shell with no access to internal parts for servicing or repair. Semi-hermetic compressors have removable covers which allow limited access to internal components for servicing repair. Hermetic and most semi-hermetic compressors are suction gas cooled, which means that the motor is cooled by the refrigerant vapour before it is compressed which reduces the capacity of the compressor. Open compressors

Table 4.20 Overview of vapour compression chillers

Type	Cooling range / kW	Refrigerant type and typical operating range	Capacity control*
Semi-hermetic:			
— reciprocating (2, 4, 6, 8, 10 and 12 cylinders)	20–1000	All types (–25 °C to +10 °C)	Cylinder, unloading
— single screw	200–2000	HCFC and HFC	Moving plate
— twin screw	200–3000	HCFC and HFC	Slider system
Hermetic:			
— twin screw	200–600	HCFC and HFC	Slider system, variable speed
— scroll	5–250	HCFC and HFC	—
— reciprocating (single-stage)	2–400	All types (–25 °C to +10 °C)	100%
— reciprocating (two-stage)	2–150	All types (–25 °C to +10 °C)	50/100% speed control
Centrifugal (multi-stage)	300–15000	HFC	Inlet guide vanes (all cases); variable speed (some cases)
Open-type reciprocating (2, 4, 6, 8, 10 and 12 cylinders)	100–1000	HFC and ammonia	Cylinder unloading
Open-type screw	200–3000	HFC and ammonia	Slider system, variable speed

* See section 4.5.6

have an external motor which drives the compressor via a drive shaft which passes through a vapour seal. This seal is a common cause of refrigerant leaks.

Reciprocating compressors

Reciprocating compressors are positive displacement machines with the refrigerant vapour compressed by pistons moving in a close fitting bore. Each cylinder has a suction and a discharge valve and the bearings are oil lubricated. Reciprocating compressors are available in a very wide range of sizes ranging from a single-cylinder type to eight cylinder or more compressors.

Screw compressors

Screw compressors are high-speed positive displacement machines, compression being obtained by the interaction of two screw-cut rotors or a single rotor meshing with two toothed wheels. They can generally operate over a wider pressure ratio range than reciprocating compressors.

Most screw compressors can be optionally equipped with an economiser which allows an additional charge of refrigerant gas to be pumped (a form of supercharging). A port positioned in the compressor casing is connected to an intermediate heat exchanger/liquid sub-cooler vessel. The higher pressure in this vessel allows the additional charge to flow into the port and be compressed together with the gas induced by the normal suction process.

This arrangement provides an increase in cooling capacity which is significantly higher than the extra power consumption thus improving the COP. The additional gas is provided by evaporating some liquid from the liquid line in the heat exchanger. This sub-cools the main liquid, passing through a coil to the expansion device. A larger capacity per kilogram flow is achieved whilst the compressor pumps only the same weight of gas.

Screw compressors are cooled by oil injected into the machine to seal the running clearances between the rotors and casing. Oil separators are generally included in packaged units and in the case of hermetic machines within the hermetic housing. Although the design is specific to the particular manufacturer, it is important that the specifier understands that some machines rely on a pressure differential across the compressor for lubrication, and that head pressure control will be necessary to maintain minimum oil pressure.

Centrifugal compressors

Centrifugal machines are 'dynamic'-type compression devices and can be single or multi-stage. The centrifugal action on the refrigerant gas allows large volumes to be compressed over low compression ratios with a relatively compact machine. They range in size from approximately 300 kW to 15 MW. Centrifugal compressors can be either hermetic or open. They are also available with economisers.

Hermetic units incorporate an induction motor and an internal gear which allows the impellers to run at speeds between 8000 and 10 000 revolutions per minute. Open-type machines can be driven by electric motors, steam turbines, gas turbines and gas engines. For capacities larger than about 7000 kW all machines are of the open type.

Scroll compressors

Scroll compressors are hermetically sealed rotary positive displacement machines with one fixed and one orbiting scroll which progressively compresses refrigerant with a constant volume ratio. They have comparable or slightly higher efficiencies than reciprocating machines at typical air conditioning application temperatures. Some types of scroll compressor are compliant in that they allow some radial or axial movement of the scroll which allows them to cope with some liquid returned to the compressor. Noise and vibration levels are less than for reciprocating compressors.

4.5.4.2 Absorption machines

Absorption machines are heat driven machines and do not have a compressor. They are larger and heavier than their vapour compression equivalents, hence the designer must confirm the weight and dimensions with the manufacturer.

Various types of absorption chiller are available but generally the choice of chiller type is determined by the temperature level of the available heat source and the temperature level of the load. Further information is given in section 4.4.5.

4.5.4.3 Multiple chillers

In large air conditioning systems, it is a common practice to split the refrigeration capacity between multiple machines in parallel with chilled water control. Unless careful attention is given to low load balance calculations, frequent compressor cycling can occur, exceeding the manufacturer's limits. It is also essential to co-ordinate the design of the control of the air handling equipment with that of the refrigerating machines, the choice being between a constant flow and a variable-flow chilled water system

Large systems may require the use of several chillers, either to meet the required capacity and/or to provide plant redundancy. In these cases the following circuit arrangements should be considered (see Figure 4.29):

(*a*) *Parallel evaporators*: parallel circuits allow multi-pass heat exchangers at a relatively low water pressure drop, consequently a lower pump power is required than for a series circuit. However, a slightly higher compressor power is required than for a series circuit, due to both machines having the same evaporating temperature. The designer should design the controls carefully to avoid short cycling under partial load conditions. There is also a danger of freezing one evaporator when the other is switched off and control is by a common thermostat downstream of the evaporators.

(*b*) *Series evaporators*: compared to the parallel arrangement, systems of this type use a higher chilled water pressure drop and, therefore, a higher pump power is required. Consequently, a single pass evaporator may well be necessary, hence component design could suffer. The compressor power is slightly lower than for a parallel arrangement, as the upstream machine will have a higher evaporating temperature

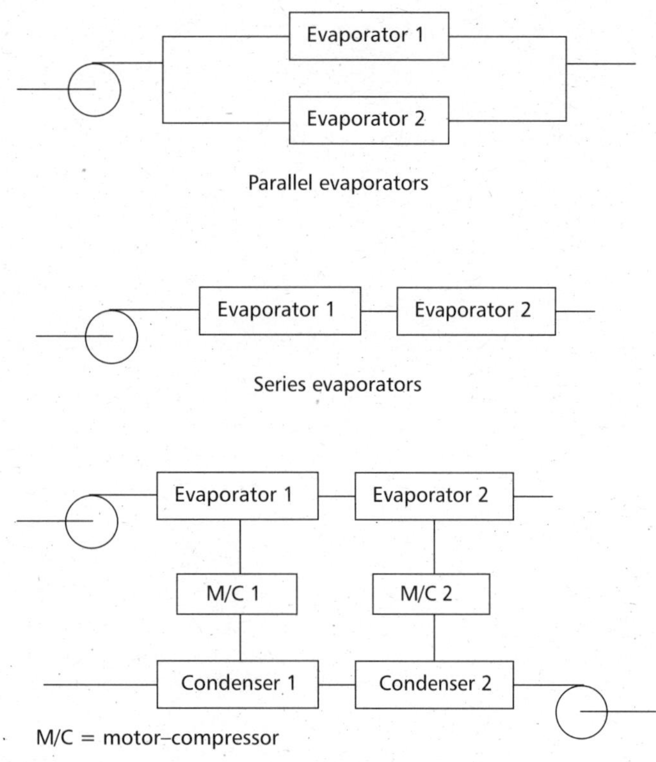

Figure 4.29 Chilled water systems: evaporator/condenser arrangements

than the downstream machine. Chilled water temperature is generally easier to control than with the parallel arrangement.

(*c*) *Parallel condensers*: parallel condenser water-cooling circuits are sometimes an advantage if more than one cooling tower is to be used. Generally, where a parallel arrangement is used, the compressor power will be greater but the water pump power will be lower, based on a similar argument to that used for the evaporators.

(*d*) *Series counterflow*: although having a higher pressure drop, this arrangement of evaporators and condensers can result in a lower compressor power than either parallel or series arrangements for multiple machine installations, particularly for heat reclaim schemes.

(*e*) *Steam turbine with centrifugal and absorption chillers*: this system is suitable for total energy installations where steam is available at pressures above 10 bar; it is used to obtain maximum economy in the use of steam to operate refrigeration machines. Steam passes in series through a back-pressure steam turbine driving a centrifugal water chiller and then, at the back-pressure, into a pair of absorption machines, each equal in capacity to the centrifugal unit. The evaporators are connected in series–parallel, the chilled water passing through the pair of parallel connected absorption machines and then through the centrifugal machine. The three condensers are usually, though not necessarily, connected in parallel. Double-effect steam-driven absorption chillers should also be considered, see section 4.4.5 and IEA Annex 24[(70)] for further details.

Of the above options (*a*) and (*b*) are the most popular, (*c*) and (*d*) are not popular and (*e*) is very seldom used.

Variable flow pumping

Where building cooling loads are variable significant energy savings can be achieved from the use of variable speed pumps. Figure 4.30 shows a constant primary variable secondary flow system. A conventional decoupled primary and secondary arrangement is used to maintain constant flow rate through the chiller evaporators and provide near failsafe operation.

The variable speed secondary pump is controlled to maintain constant differential pressure in the system to ensure a minimum flow rate is achieved through any coil. Flow rate through each individual coil is variable according to load by the position of its two-way control valve.

Modern chillers allow variation in the chilled water flow rate according to the load as long as a minimum flow rate value is maintained. This allows a variable primary variable secondary flow system to be used, shown in Figure 4.31. As well as reducing the number of pumps this approach can result in even greater energy savings than the constant primary variable secondary flow system[(89,90)]. The primary pump speed may be controlled according to the pressure drop across the chillers. Alternatively the primary circuit flow rate may be measured directly using a flow meter although the designer should be aware of the need to install the flow meter in strict accordance with the manufacturer's recommendations with respect to length of straight pipe upstream and down of the flow meter and the need for regular recailbration.

The disadvantage of the variable primary variable secondary flow system is greater complexity both for the designer and the operator and a greater risk of control failure. Particular care is needed in the control of chiller sequencing and it is recommended that the designer seeks the advice of the chiller manufacturer. It is recommended that these systems are only installed in buildings with competent on-site staff who have been trained to under-

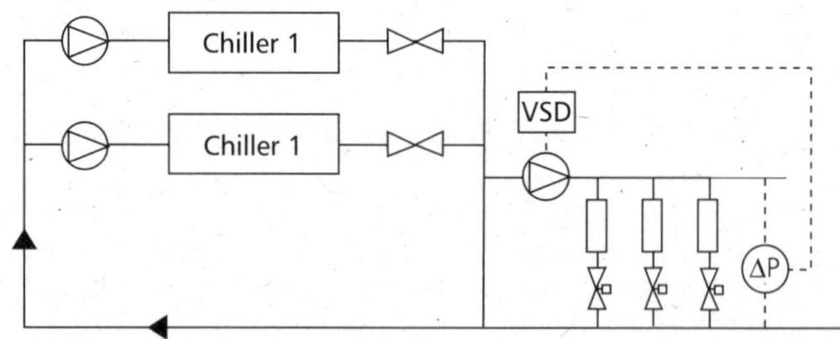

Figure 4.30 Constant primary variable secondary system

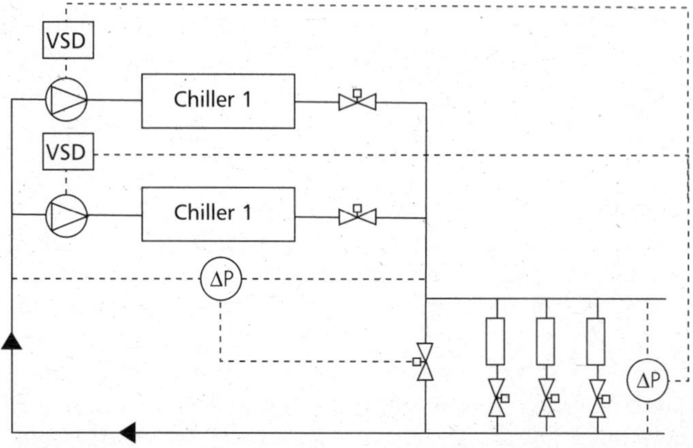

Figure 4.31 Variable primary variable secondary flow system

stand the system design and operation. The effect of variable flow rate on the chiller evaporator water-side heat transfer coefficient also needs to be considered. In general plate evaporators are less sensitive than shell and tube evaporators which may require design changes to the water-side baffling. The chiller manufacturer should be consulted about the suitability for variable flow rate operation and to confirm the safe minimum flow rate.

4.5.5 Heat rejection and cooling water equipment

Heat rejection plant is required to cool the condenser; the efficiency of this process will affect the system COSP. Overall seasonal efficiencies are therefore influenced by energy efficient design of heat rejection systems. Where ever possible opportunities for free cooling should be sought, especially for systems that are operated throughout the year, see section 4.4.3.

The basic types of condenser (see Table 4.10) are:

— *direct*: air-cooled, direct water-cooled, or evaporative

— *indirect*: condenser heat is rejected via a water system by using cooling towers or dry air coolers or some other form of environmental cooling (see section 4.4.3).

Information and guidance on the cost considerations of alternative forms of condenser cooling system are given in BSRIA TM 1/90[91] and BSRIA Technical Appraisal 1/93[92].

Table 4.21 gives a comparison of machine COPs together with the heat rejection which may be expected when evaporating at 5.0 °C and condensing at 35–40 °C. These are for water cooled systems; the COP would be lower for air cooled systems. The COPs are approximate and are for comparative purposes only.

4.5.5.1 Sources of water cooling

In most air conditioning applications where water is used, the water is recirculated and cooled by an evaporative process; make-up losses are catered for by the use of a storage tank connected to the mains supply via a ballcock or similar device.

Environmental cooling may be used directly for cooling a building. If it is not cold enough then it may be used as a heat sink for heat rejected from the condensers. Examples of environmental cooling include:

Table 4.21 Approximate cops and heat rejection

Type	COP*	Heat rejection/ cooling† / kW
Reciprocating compressor	4	1.25
Scroll compressor	4	1.25
Centrifugal compressor	5.5	1.18
Screw compressor	5.5	1.18
Absorption machine (single effect)	0.68	2.47

Note: COP = cooling power (kW) / input power (kW)
* Evaporator temperature: 5 °C
† Condenser temperature: 35–40 °C

— ambient air

— ground water

— rivers or lakes

— sea water.

Further information on these sources of cooling is given in section 4.4.3.1.

4.5.5.2 Air cooled condensers

Air cooled condensers are the simplest form of condenser heat rejection plant, in which air is blown over finned tubes containing the condensed refrigerant. They are generally found on stand-alone plant such as packaged air conditioners, split systems or some packaged air handling plant. They lose efficiency by having to operate at a relatively high condensing temperature, since they do not have the benefit of evaporative water cooling on the outside of the coil. See section 4.5.2.2 for further information.

4.5.5.3 Dry air coolers

Dry air coolers are heat exchangers of construction similar to that of an air cooled condenser. They are designed for cooling liquids (generally glycol–water) in a closed circuit. The freezing point of the liquid must usually be at least 5 K below the minimum winter ambient temperature of the site of installation. The cooling effect from night time sky radiation should also be considered where pipework is exposed.

Selection is normally to suit each individual case specifying maximum noise level, type of liquid, ambient temperature, liquid inlet temperature, liquid outlet temperature, maximum allowed pressure drop etc. They are simple in construction and operation with low installation and maintenance costs.

As the water distribution system is closed, atmospheric contamination cannot occur and microbiological control of water quality is simplified. Ambient air contamination could be a hazard and precautions similar to those for air-cooled condensers should be observed.

On some installations dry coolers have been used with sprayed water which improves their efficiency due to the evaporative cooling. These units are referred to as 'wet and dry coolers' or 'adiabatically enhanced' dry coolers. Local regulations regarding water treatment must be complied with.

4.5.5.4 Wet cooling towers

A cooling tower cools the condenser water by evaporative cooling. There are two types of wet cooling tower:

— *Open circuit*: water from the condenser is pumped to the cooling tower and is cooled by the evaporation of some of the condenser water. This requires all the water passing through the condenser to be treated and results in increased water consumption due to drift losses.

— *Closed circuit*: condenser water is circulated in a closed loop and a separate water circuit is pumped through the cooling tower, cooling the condenser water by transferring heat through a heat exchanger. This minimises water treatment costs but it also reduces energy efficiency due to the temperature difference across the heat exchanger, although this effect can be minimised by specifying a high efficiency heat exchanger.

In a mechanical draught tower (see Table 4.22) the entering water is sprayed into the plastic fill packing and one or more fans force air through the packing to enhance evaporation and, hence, the cooling effect. The cooled water falls to the base reservoir and is pumped back to the condenser. Natural draught cooling towers are rarely used for building air conditioning applications due to their much greater height and high approach temperature.

General

Various European standards for cooling towers have been produced by the Eurovent/CECOMAF Cooling Towers Working Group, upon which all the major manufacturers are represented. The standard for testing is Eurovent 9-2[93]. This standard forms the basis of a draft European standard[94].

Specification

Table 4.22 describes the main types of mechanical draught cooling towers. Mechanical draught cooling towers use fans to move the air through the tower, thus providing absolute control over the air supply, as opposed to 'atmospheric' or 'natural draught' types. With the use of efficient eliminators, drift losses have been reduced to as little as 0.001% of water flow rate. The advantages of mechanical draught towers compared to natural draught towers include the following:

- compact (i.e. small plan area)
- close control over water temperature
- small static lift
- siting of tower is independent of prevailing wind direction (refer to HSE Approved Code of Practice L8: *Legionnaires' disease: the control of Legionella in water systems*)[40]
- with efficient heat transfer packing, approach temperatures of 2–3 K are achievable, though 3–7 K is usually preferred.

The disadvantages include:

- fan powers can be higher than air cooled condenser equivalent (see Table 4.22 *a* and *b*)
- recirculation of discharged air back into the air intake must be avoided or performance will suffer.

Centrifugal fans are generally used to achieve low operating noise levels but variable fan speed motors should be considered for very noise sensitive locations.

The basic information required by the equipment manufacturer is as follows:

- design water flow rate
- design temperature range through which the water is to be cooled
- design ambient wet bulb temperature
- operational height above sea level
- any limitations on height, floor plan, weight, noise or appearance
- features which may affect the free flow of air to and from the unit
- preferably a drawing showing the tower location on site.

Selection of cooling tower site

The location of the cooling tower should receive careful consideration. There should be sufficient free space around the tower to allow free flow of air both to the inlet and from the discharge outlet.

Recirculation of the hot discharge back into the inlet must be avoided as it will substantially reduce performance. Discharge ducting or extended fan casings may be necessary to minimise recirculation risk and the effect of these components on fan power should be taken into account. The siting of the cooling tower should be such that the discharge air is not close to fresh air inlets and does not produce condensation upon nearby buildings and in the surrounding area.

The presence of exhaust heat from other equipment or of contaminated air from process plant (especially kitchen extract with high grease content), will reduce tower performance and may produce corrosive conditions. The tower should be sited as far away as possible, upwind of smoke stacks and other sources of pollution. Where local atmospheric air pollution is unavoidable, filters may be provided for cooling tower air inlets. The tower location should be carefully studied in relation to the noise created by the air and water.

The local authorities should always be consulted on the connection of mains water supplies to tanks and pumping circuits. In general it will be found that it is not permissible to connect pumps directly to the main and that a break tank must be interposed. Local fire regulations should be consulted when a tower is to be installed, particularly if any hazard or opportunity for ignition of the tower is present.

Water treatment

Every water cooling tower requires an appropriate water quality management regime. This is essential to minimise the risk of legionellosis and to control corrosion and fouling (e.g. by bacterial growth, such as *Pseudomonous*). Biological contamination, however, can be controlled only through the use of biocides and such treatment should be initiated at system start-up and continued regularly thereafter. Poor water treatment can greatly increase energy and water costs. *Legionella* can be controlled if the tower is designed and operated in accordance with CIBSE TM13[41]. The designer and owner/operator should ensure compliance with relevant UK regulations, see section 4.3.2.3. Compliance with the HSC's Approved Code of Practice (ACOP) L8[40] is mandatory. For information on corrosion and further information on water treatment see CIBSE Guide G: *Public health engineering*[95].

Table 4.22 Mechanical draught cooling towers

Type	Description
(*a*) Forced draught 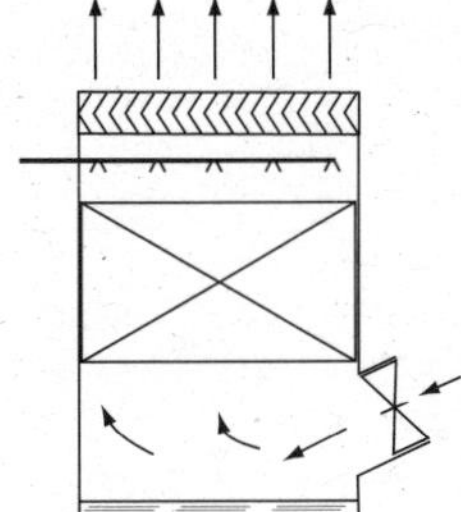	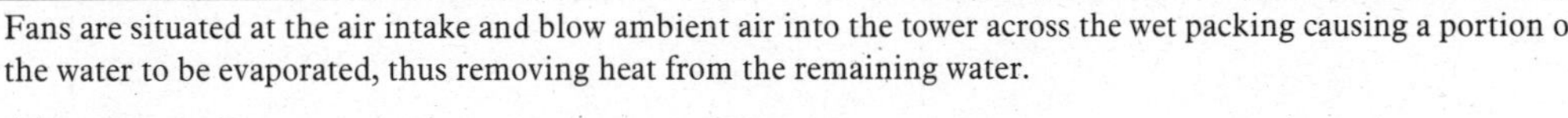Fans are situated at the air intake and blow ambient air into the tower across the wet packing causing a portion of the water to be evaporated, thus removing heat from the remaining water. Advantages: — Fans located close to the ground, thus vibration is kept to a minimum. — Fractionally more efficient than induced draught since velocity pressure converted to static pressure does useful work, while the fan handles inlet cold air, and thus the weight of air per unit volume is greater than in the induced draught arrangement. — Fans and motors are situated in a comparatively dry air stream and are more easily accessible for maintenance. Disadvantages: — Limited fan size, thus a larger number of smaller fans of higher speed are needed compared with induced. draught arrangement, resulting in more noise (but tower itself provides some attenuation). — Tendency for ice to form on the fans in winter and block or throttle the intake. — Some types can be prone to recirculation of used air into the accessible low pressure fan inlet and resulting reduction in performance may be substantial; this occurs if outlet air velocities are low. The air may be ducted away at high velocity but at the expense of greater resistance and increased fan power requirements.
(*b*) Induced draught	Fans are situated in the air outlet from the tower, usually on the top, but sometimes in the side or in the ducting. Advantages: — Large fans possible (hence low speed and low noise). — Recirculation of air unlikely due to higher outlet velocity. — More compact plan area than (*a*) due to absence of fans on side. Disadvantages: — More prone to vibration since fan is mounted on superstructure. — Mechanical parts less readily accessible for maintenance. — Mechanical parts located in a hot, humid air stream. — High inlet velocities can draw in rubbish; air filters can be fitted. There are two types of induced drught cooling tower: 'counterflow' and 'cross draught'.
Counterflow	(*i*) Counterflow Fans create vertical air movement up the tower across the packing in opposition to the water flow. Advantages: — Maximum performance arrangement as the coldest water is in contact with the driest air. — Up to three sides of the tower can be obstructed by adjacent buildings, provided that the remaining air inlet(s) are suitably increased in size. Disadvantages: — Mechanical parts and water distribution are not always easily accessible for maintenance.
Cross draught	(*ii*) Cross draught Fans create horizontal air flow as the water falls across the air stream. Some types have a greater plan area than (*c*), but the air intakes can be full height of tower which is consequently of low silhouette, blending well with the architectural requirements. Rain ingress should be taken into account when considering water treatment dosage. Advantages: — Low silhouette. Disadvantages: — Some risk of recirculation of saturated vapour if sited in a confined space. — If uncovered, distribution basin will collect rubbish; a cover should be provided unless installation is indoors. — Location demands unobstructed air flow towards each end of tower.

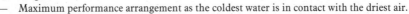

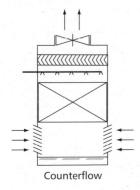

Testing

Where cooling towers need to be site performance tested for confirmation of compliance with design conditions the relevant standard for the UK is BS 4485: Part 2[96].

4.5.5.6 Evaporative condensers

An evaporative condenser is an extension of an air cooled condenser. As well as air being blown over the tubes, the tubes themselves are continuously wetted by a recirculating water system. They are able to achieve a similar performance to water cooled condensers and open-circuit cooling towers, but eliminate the condenser water pumps. See section 4.5.2.2 for further details.

4.5.6 Controls

Appropriate and properly commissioned controls are essential to maintain the desired levels of performance and safety with good energy efficiency. Guidance on control systems is given by CIBSE Guide H: *Building control systems*[11].

4.5.6.1 Capacity controls for mechanical refrigeration

Reciprocating compressors

Capacity control of reciprocating equipment is achieved in one of five ways, as follows:

— *Multi-modular*: several compressors are incorporated in a chiller package, each compressor representing a step of capacity (see also section 4.5.4.1). It is important that the chiller control system is compatible with the compressor safety controls, which should be set to avoid frequent cycling (see also section 4.5.6.4).

— *Cylinder unloading*: several methods are available but it is most common for the suction valve on one or more cylinders to be maintained in a raised position by hydraulic pressure, so allowing the refrigerant gas to pass back and forth without check and thereby reducing the mass flow through the compressor. A minimum gas flow must be maintained to minimise overheating and ensure adequate oil return. Insufficient oil return will adversely affect the operation of compressors or contribute to nuisance tripping of the oil safety switch. It is recommended that long hours operation with unloaded cylinders is avoided.

— *Speed variation*: the output of a reciprocating compressor is directly proportional to the speed of shaft rotation, which may be changed by varying the speed of the prime mover. A certain minimum speed must be maintained for lubrication to be effective. Two-speed compressors have been used in the past but variable speed utilising inverter control is becoming more common. Whilst accepting that the majority of compressors used will be semi-hermetic or hermetic, and thus the responsibility of the manufacturer, it is important to note that with multi-speed and inverter control applications, there may be problems with damage to windings during operation. This may be due to fluctuations ('spikes') in the electricity supply or to the compressor power requirement during speed changes. It is important that the designer gives careful consideration to this issue.

— *Hot gas bypass*: the load on the compressor is maintained while the evaporator capacity is varied. The most effective arrangement is to arrange for the hot refrigerant gas to by-pass the condenser and inject the refrigerant into the system downstream of the expansion valve and upstream of the evaporator. It should be noted that this method of capacity control offers no energy economies at part load and, depending on method chosen, can result in high discharge temperatures and therefore should be avoided. Extensive operation can cause compressor damage.

— *Evaporator pressure regulator*: this is a means of maintaining the evaporator pressure by throttling the flow of gas to the suction of the compressor. Energy efficiency is impaired and therefore this method should be avoided.

Cylinder unloading and speed variation are more economical due to the greater reduction in power consumption arising at part load compared with the small or zero reduction arising from using hot gas or evaporator pressure regulation.

Centrifugal compressors

In most centrifugal applications, the machine must respond to two basic variables:

— refrigeration load

— entering condensing water temperature.

A centrifugal compressor is, for a given speed, a relatively constant volume device compared with a multi-cylinder reciprocating compressor where cylinders can be deactivated progressively to accommodate load changes.

The control system must be able to alter both the head and flow output of the compressor in response to load changes. This is possible by using one of the following methods:

— refrigerant flow control by variable inlet guide vanes

— variable speed control.

Speed control is generally the most efficient method. However, its use is limited to drives whose speed can be economically and efficiently varied and to applications where the discharge pressure (head requirement) falls with a decrease in load (this restriction only applies to centrifugal compressors).

The most generally accepted method of flow control, particularly for hermetic centrifugal compressors, is that of variable inlet guide vanes. The vanes are usually located just before the inlet to the impeller wheel (or first impellor wheel in multi-stage compressors) of the compressor and are controlled by the temperature of the water leaving the evaporator. This method offers good efficiency over a wide range of capacity. At half load condition, for example, the power required may be only 45% of the full load power.

Hot gas bypass is useful to extend the control range of a machine to very low loads, particularly where the system head requirements (condenser pressure) remain high, thereby avoiding compressor surge. Instead of discharging gas into the compressor inlet, which can cause high temperature problems, the hot condenser gas is passed through a pipe and valve to the bottom of the cooler, thereby providing a 'false' load on the cooler. In this manner the compressor experiences a constant load. However, this technique should not be used continuously but only for occasional part-load conditions.

Designers should be aware that centrifugal compressor manufacturers often quote a time limit for continuous part load operation.

Surge is caused by flow breakdown in the impeller passageways; the impeller can no longer maintain the required system pressure and a periodic partial or complete flow reversal through the impeller occurs. Surge is characterised by a marked increased in the operating noise level and by wide fluctuations in discharge pressure eventually leading to shut-down. For this reason it is often not practical to run a centrifugal compressor at part-load under high summer condenser temperature conditions. Designers should be aware that for the same cooling capacity, different sizes of compressor have different surge lines.

Screw compressors

Capacity control is normally obtained by varying the compressor displacement using a sliding valve to retard the point at which compression begins and, at the same time, reducing the size of the discharge port to obtain the desired volume ratio (see also section 4.5.4.1). This typically allows 10% to 100% capacity control although below 60% of full load the compressor efficiency is very low. Variable motor speed control using an inverter is also increasingly used and at low loads offers higher efficiency than the slide valve method. Another form of capacity control is the use of multiple compressors.

Scroll compressors

Capacity control can be obtained using two-speed motors or multiple compressors. Although variable motor speed has been used it is not ideally suited for scroll compressors because it is not compatible with the method of radial compliance usually employed in scroll compressors which prevents damage by small quantities of liquid refrigerant or solid particles passing through the compressor. Speed control also creates difficulties with the compressor lubrication system. A relatively new form of capacity control uses an electronic modulating system that momentarily separates the scrolls axially and can provide between 10% and 100% capacity variation. Because the shaft continues to rotate at full speed the compressor lubrication system is not affected.

4.5.6.2 Capacity controls for absorption chillers

The capacity of centrifugal compressors is controlled by regulating the amount of heat supplied to the generator as hot water, steam or natural gas. This varies the ability of the solution to absorb the refrigerant and therefore the evaporation rate in the evaporator.

Some manufacturers also offer a variable flow solution pump which can significantly improve COP at part load.

4.5.6.3 Operational controls

The inclusion of a building management system provides the designer with a number of additional ways to maximise the operating efficiency of the refrigeration plant by precise control of the plant items to exactly match the system requirements. One such example is the ability to vary the chilled water flow temperature to match exactly the cooling requirements of the system, rather than allowing the plant to control to a single set-point temperature. In order that the benefits of the controls system are maximised, it is important that the control system communicates correctly with the refrigeration plant and vice versa. Failure to address this at the design stage can result in problems with final commissioning on-site or, at worst, the controls system failing to control the refrigeration plant to the level specified by the designer.

Control methods that may improve the energy efficiency of refrigeration plant include the following:

— *Variable set-point temperature on chilled water systems*: at periods of low cooling load it might be possible to raise the chilled water set-point temperature to a value higher than the normal value of around 6 °C. This simple measure could be controlled by a BMS. The flow temperature is slowly decreased until the space cooling requirement is matched, usually monitored by the position of the cooling valves on the cooling coils. If any valve is 100% open then demand is not met in all areas; if all are below 100% open then demand is exceeded and chilled water flow temperature need not be reduced any further. The compatibility of this particular method with the chiller should be confirmed with the chiller manufacturer.

— *Staging the operation of multiple refrigeration plant to meet the required demand*: this depends on the system design. For example, with constant speed primary pumping it is generally more efficient to run one chiller at full load than two at partial load, see CIBSE Guide H[11].

— *Variable chilled water flow rate, either on the secondary side only or on the primary and secondary sides*: further details of these techniques are given in section 4.5.4.3. The suitability of primary chilled water flow rate must be confirmed with the chiller manufacturer.

— *Reduced condenser water temperature*: the condenser water temperature should ideally be kept as low as possible although it is essential that the chiller manufacturer's specifications are adhered to.

4.5.6.4 Safety devices

It is essential that safety devices should not be used to operate the plant under normal conditions. Safety devices are provided to ensure that, in the event of a fault developing, the plant shuts down in such a way that there is no risk of injury to personnel and equipment is protected from damage. Where particular operational conditions may result in frequent recycling, safety devices should be of the manual reset type. Table 4.23 lists types of safety devices and their function.

Although safety devices are usually dealt with by the equipment manufacturer, the designer should ensure that the provisions of BS EN 378-1[22] and the IoR Safety Codes[37–39], are complied with, e.g. refrigerant pressure relief devices should discharge to a safe place, and all cut-outs and switches should be tested during commissioning. It is recommended that, if the compressor/machine is fitted with capacity control, these tests be carried out with the compressor/machine at minimum capacity.

References

1 *Energy efficiency in buildings* CIBSE Guide F (London: Chartered Institution of Building Services Engineers) (2003)

2 *Purchasing efficient refrigeration — the value for money option* Good Practice Guide GPG 278 (Action Energy) (2000) (www.actionenergy.org.uk)

3 *Running refrigeration plant efficiently — a cost saving guide for owners* Good Practice Guide GPG 279 (Action Energy) (2000) (www.actionenergy.org.uk)

4 *Energy efficient refrigeration technology — the fundamentals* Good Practice Guide GPG 280 (Action Energy) (2000) (www.actionenergy.org.uk)

Table 4.23 Type and function of safety devices

Safety device	Function
Mechanical refrigeration:	
— high refrigerant pressure cut-out	Breaks circuit on excessive refrigerant pressure rise
— low refrigerant pressure cut-out	Breaks circuit on fall in refrigerant pressure
— low oil pressure cut-out	Protects against failure of lubricating system
— high oil temperature cut-out	Protects against failure of lubricating system or if bearing failure occurs
— low refrigerant temperature cut-out	Protects against low evaporating temperatures
— fusible plug	Protects against high refrigerant temperatures
— pressure relief device	Protects against high refrigerant pressure (static)
— low water temperature cut-out	Protects against evaporator freezing (in water chillers)
— flow switches	Protects against reduced fluid flow through evaporator or condenser
Absorption refrigeration:	
— low refrigerant temperature cut-out	Protects against evaporator freezing
— low chilled water temperature cut-out	Protects against evaporator freezing
— high solution temperature cut-out	Protects against over-concentration of the solution and consequent crystallisation
— low cooling water temperature cut-out	Protects against over-concentration of the solution and consequent crystallisation
— flow switches	Protects against reduced fluid flow through evaporator or condenser

5 *Designing energy efficient refrigeration plant* Good Practice Guide GPG 283 (Action Energy) (2000) (www.actionenergy.org.uk)

6 *An introduction to absorption cooling* Good Practice Guide GPG 256 (Action Energy) (1999) (www.actionenergy.org.uk)

7 *Cutting the cost of refrigerant leakage — an introductory guide for users of small to medium-sized refrigeration systems* Good Practice Guide GPG 178 (Action Energy) (1997) (www.actionenergy.org.uk)

8 *Energy use in offices* Energy Consumption Guide ECG 19 (Action Energy) (2000) (www.actionenergy.org.uk)

9 Hayden G W and Parsloe C J *Value engineering of building services* BSRIA Applications Guide AG15/96 (Bracknell: Building Services Research and Information Association) (1996)

10 *Refrigeration and heat rejection* CIBSE Guide B14 (London: Chartered Institution of Building Services Engineers) (1986) (withdrawn)

11 *Building control systems* CIBSE Guide H (London: Chartered Institution of Building Services Engineers) (2000)

12 *CFCs HCFCs and halons: professional and practical guidance on substances that deplete the ozone layer* CIBSE Guidance Note GN1 (London: Chartered Institution of Building Services Engineers) (2000)

13 Parsloe C and Wild L J *Project management handbook for building services* BSRIA Application Guide AG 11/98 (Bracknell: Building Services Research and Information Association) (1998)

14 *Conservation of fuel and power* Building Regulations 2000 Approved Document L2 (London: The Stationery Office) (2002) (www.safety.dtlr.gov.uk/bregs/brads.htm)

15 *Energy Assessment and Reporting Methodology* CIBSE TM22 (London: Chartered Institution of Building Services Engineers) (1999)

16 *Energy use in offices* (ECG019); *Energy efficiency in hotels* (ECG036); *Energy consumption in hospitals* (ECON 72); *Energy consumption guide for nursing and residential homes* (ECG057) Action Energy Energy Consumption Guides (Action Energy) (various dates)

17 *BREEAM for offices*; *BREEAM — new industrial units*; *BREEAM — retail* (Garston: Building Research Establishment) (updated periodically) (www.breeam.org)

18 *Environmental design* CIBSE Guide A (London: Chartered Institution of Building Services Engineers) (1999)

19 *Testing buildings for air leakage* CIBSE TM23 (London: Chartered Institution of Building Services Engineers) (2000)

20 *Daylighting and window design* CIBSE Lighting Guide LG10 (London: Chartered Institution of Building Services Engineers) (1999)

21 Tozer R M Reliability engineering for internet site providers (ISPs) and financial institutions *Proc. Ibero-American Conf. Refrigeration and Air Conditioning (CIAR 2001)* (London: Waterman Gore) (2001)

22 BS EN 378: *Specification for refrigerating systems and heat pumps. Safety and environmental requirements*: Part 1: 2000: *Basic requirements, definitions, classification and selection criteria*; Part 2: 2000: *Design, construction, testing, marking and documentation*: Part 3: 2000: *Installation, site and personal protection*; Part 4: 2000: *Operation, maintenance, repair and recovery* (London: British Standards Institution) (2000)

23 *Whole life costs construction procurement* Guidance No. 7 (London: Office of Government Commerce) 2000 (available in electronic format only from www.ogc.gov.uk)

24 Allen G *The Private Finance Initiative* (PFI) House of Commons Research Paper 01/117 (London : House of Commons Library) (2001)

25 *Building Services Component Life Manual* (Oxford: Blackwell Science) (2001)

26 BS ISO 15686: *Buildings and constructed assets. Service life planning*: Part 1: 2000: *General principles*; Part 2: 2001: *Service life prediction procedures* (London: British Standards Institution) (dates as indicated)

27 Building Performance Group *The BPG Building Fabric Component Life Manual* (London: Spon Press) (1999)

28 *Guide to ownership, operation and maintenance of building services* (London: Chartered Institution of Building Services Engineers) (2000)

29 *Building log books* CIBSE TM31 (London: Chartered Institution of Building Services Engineers) (2003)

30 The Construction (Design and Management) Regulations 1994. Statutory Instrument 1994 No. 3140 (London: Her Majesty's Stationery Office) (1994)

31 Directive 2002/91/EC Of The European Parliament and of The Council of 16 December 2002 on the energy performance of buildings *Official J. of the European Communities* L001 65–71 EN (4 January 2003)

32 The Management of Health and Safety at Work Regulations 1999 Statutory Instrument 1999 No. 3242 (London: The Stationery Office) (1999)

33 The Pressure Systems Safety Regulations 2000 Statutory Instrument 2000 No. 128 (London: The Stationery Office) (2000)

34 The Pressure Equipment Regulations 1999 Statutory Instrument 1999 No. 2001 (London: The Stationery Office) (1999)

35 Control of Substances Hazardous to Health Regulations 1999 (London: The Stationery Office) (1999)

36 The Notification of Cooling Towers and Evaporative Condensers Regulations 1992 Statutory Instrument 1992 No. 2225 (London: Her Majesty's Stationery Office) (1994)

37 *Safety code for refrigerating systems utilizing group A1 and A2 refrigerants* (Carshalton: Institute of Refrigeration) (1999)

38 *Safety code for refrigerating systems utilizing group A3 refrigerants* (Carshalton: Institute of Refrigeration) (2001)

39 *Safety code for refrigerating systems utilizing ammonia refrigerant* (Carshalton: Institute of Refrigeration) (2002)

40 *Legionnaires' disease: The control of legionella bacteria in water systems* Approved Code of Practice and Guidance L8. (London: The Stationery Office) (2000)

41 *Minimising the risk of Legionnaires' disease* CIBSE TM13 (London: Chartered Institution of Building Services Engineers) (2000)

42 *Safe management of ammonia refrigeration systems* Health and Safety Executive Guidance Note PM 81 (London; HSE) (1995)

43 The Noise at Work Regulations 1989 Statutory Instrument 1989 No. 1790 (London: The Stationery Office) (1989)

44 Regulation (EC) No 2037/2000 of the European Parliament and of the Council of 29 June 2000 on substances that deplete the ozone layer *Official J. of the European Communities* L244 1–24 (29 June 2000)

45 Environmental Protection Act 1990 (London: Her Majesty's Stationery Office) (1990)

46 *Montreal Protocol on substances that deplete the ozone layer, Montreal, 16 September 1987* (London: Her Majesty's Stationery Office) (1988)

47 *Kyoto protocol to the United Nations framework convention on climate change* (New York, NY: United Nations Organisation) (1997)

48 The Environmental Protection (Controls on Ozone-Depleting Substances) Regulations 2002 Statutory Instrument 2002 No. 528 (London: Her Majesty's Stationery Office) (2002)

49 *Climate Change. The UK Programme* (London: The Stationery Office) (2000)

50 *Guideline methods of calculating TEWI* (Medmemham: British Refrigeration Association) (1996).

51 *Technical standards for compliance with the Building Standards (Scotland) Regulations 1990 (as amended)* (Edinburgh: Scottish Executive) (2001)

52 *Conservation of fuel and power* The Building Regulations (Northern Ireland) 1994 Technical booklet F (London: The Stationery Office) (1999)

53 *Guidance for the use of the carbon emissions calculation method* CIBSE TM32 (London: Chartered Institution of Building Services Engineers) (2003)

54 *Standard specification for the commissioning of mechanical engineering services installations for buildings* CSA Technical Memorandum No. 1 (Horsham: Commissioning Specialists Association) (1999)57 Health and Safety at Work etc. Act 1974 (London: Her Majesty's Stationery Office) (1974)

55 *Refrigeration systems* CIBSE Commissioning Code R (London: Chartered Institution of Building Services Engineers) (2002)

56 *Commissioning of water systems in building* BSRIA Application Guide AG 02/89 (Bracknell: Building Services Research and Information Association) (1989)

57 *Sub-metering new build non-domestic buildings* General Information Leaflet GIL 65 (ActionEnergy) (2001) (www.actionenergy.org.uk)

58 *New ways of cooling — information for building designers* General Information Leaflet GIL 85 (ActionEnergy) (2002) (www.actionenergy.org.uk)

59 De Saulles T *Free cooling systems — design and application guide* BSRIA Research Report RR 16/96 (Bracknell: Building Services Research and information Association) (1996)

60 Tozer R Private communication (2003)

61 Blackhurst D R Recent developments in thermosyphon cooling for air conditioning *Proc. Inst. Refrigeration* **95** 44–59 (1999)

62 Dunsdon K H Thermosysphon in air conditioning *Proc. Conf. Efficient Air Conditioning — the Role of Refrigeration, London, 2001* (Carshalton: Institute of Refrigeration) (2001)

63 *Occupational exposure limits* HSE EH40 (Bootle: Health and Safety Executive (published annually)

64 *Working with ammonia* Guidance Note 10 (Carshalton: Institute of Refrigeration) (2002)

65 Butler D J G and D J Hall *Ammonia refrigerant in buildings: minimising the hazards* BRE Information Paper IP18/00 (Garston: Building Research Establishment) (2000)

66 *Guidelines for the use of hydrocarbon refrigerants in static refrigeration and air conditioning systems* (Carshalton: Air Conditioning and refrigeration Industry Board) (2001)

67 *Code of practice for the minimisation of refrigerant emissions from refrigerating systems* (Carshalton: Institute of Refrigeration) (1995)

68 *Cutting the cost of refrigerant leakage* Good Practice Guide GPG 178 (Action Energy) (1997) (www.actionenergy.org.uk)

69 Butler D J G *Minimising refrigerant emissions from air conditioning systems in buildings* BRE Information Paper IP1/94 (Garston: Building Research Establishment) (1994)

70 *Absorption machines for heating and cooling in future energy systems* IEA Heat Pump Programme Annex 24 (Novem, Netherlands: IEA Heat Pump Centre) (2001) (available from: www.heatpumpcentre.org)

71 Tozer R and R W James Theory and application of absorption refrigeration systems *Proc. Inst. Refrigeration* 1995-96 (1-1) (Carshalton: Institute of Refrigeration) (1996)

72 *An introduction to absorption cooling* Good Practice Guide GPG 256 (Action Energy) (1999) (www.actionenergy.org.uk)

73 IEA Heat Pump Centre Newsletter **17** (2/1999) (Novem, Netherlands: IEA Heat Pump Centre) (1999) (available from: www.heatpumpcentre.org)

74 Pearson S F Development of improved secondary refrigerants *Proc. Inst. Refrigeration* 1992-93 (7-1) (Carshalton: Institute of Refrigeration) (1993)

75 Paul J Innovative applications of pumpable ice slurry *Proc. Inst. Refrigeration* 2001-02 (5-1) (Carshalton: Institute of Refrigeration) (2001)

76 *Ice storage* CIBSE TM18 (London: Chartered Institution of Building Services Engineers) (1994)

77 Beggs C B Ice thermal storage: theoretical study of environmental benefits *Building Serv. Eng. Res. Technol.* **18** (3) 157–160 (1997)

78 Riffat S B, S A Omer and P S Doherty Experimental performance of an ejector refrigeration using ethanol as a working fluid *Int. J. Ambient Energy* **21** (1) 310 (2000)

79 Green R H et al. The design and testing of a Stirling cycle domestic freezer *Proc Int. Inst. Refrigeration Conf., Aarhus, Denmark, 1996* (Paris: International Institute of Refrigeration) (1996)

80 Rogers B H Cooling in aircraft *Proc. Inst. Refrigeration* 1994-95 (4-1) (Carshalton: Institute of Refrigeration) (1995)

81 Gigiel A, Russell S and Butler D J G Heating and cooling of buildings with air cycles *Proc. Inst. Refrigeration* 1999-00 (6-1) (Carshalton: Institute of Refrigeration) (2000)

82 Hishinuma Y et al. Refrigeration by combined tunnelling and thermionic emission in vacuum: use of nanometer scale design *Appl. Phys. Lett.* **78** 2752–2754 (2001)

83 Zimm C et al. Description of a near-room temperature magnetic refrigerator *Advances in Cryogenic Eng.* **43** (New York: Plenum Press) (1998)

84 Dean W and Westra G *Pulse tube refrigeration for spacecraft and commercial applications* Report for the SBIR Contract for the Marshall Flight Centre, Contract No. NAS8-39917

85 Swift G Thermoacoustic engines and refrigerators *Physics Today* (July 1995)

86 Haselden G *Cryogenic fundamentals* (London: Academic Press) (1971)

87 Althouse A, Turnquist C and Bracciano A *Modern refrigeration and air conditioning* (Tinley Park, IL: Goodheart-Willcox Co) (1988)

88 *Guidelines for the prevention of uncontrolled bacteriological contamination, including Legionella Pneumophila, in cooling towers and evaporative condenser* Eurovent 9/2. (Paris: Eurovent) (2002)

89 Taylor S T Primary-only versus primary–secondary flow systems *ASHRAE J.* (February 2002) 125–129 (Atlanta GA: American Society of Heating Refrigeration and Air Conditioning Engineers) (2002)

90 Avery G Improving the efficiency of chilled water plants *ASHRAE J.* (May 2001) 14–18 (Atlanta GA: American Society of Heating Refrigeration and Air Conditioning Engineers) (2001)

91 *Air conditioning condenser cooling systems. Cost considerations* BSRIA Technical Memorandum 1/90. (Bracknell: Building Services research and Information Association) (1990)

92 *Heat rejection systems — some methods and their operating costs* BSRIA Technical Appraisal 1/93. (Bracknell: Building Services research and Information Association) (1993)

93 *Thermal performance acceptance testing of mechanical draught standardized water cooling towers* Eurovent 9-2 (Brussels: European Committee of Air Handling and Refrigeration Equipment Manufacturers (Eurovent/Cecomaf)) (1992) (available from: www.eurovent-cecomaf.org)

94 prEN 13741: *Thermal performance acceptance testing of mechanical draught series wet cooling towers* (draft) BSI document number 99/716219DC (London: British Standards Institution) (1999)

95 *Public health engineering* CIBSE Guide G (London: Chartered Institution of Building Services Engineers) (1999)

96 BS 4485: *Water cooling towers*: Part 2: 1988: *Methods for performance testing* (London: British Standards Institution) (1988)

Appendix 4.A1: Summary data for refrigerants

Group	Safety group	Refrigerant number	Description (composition = % weight)	Chemical formula	Practical limit / kg·m^{-3}	Flammability (lower limit), concentration in air		GWP	ODP
						/ kg·m^{-3}	/ % (vol.)		
L1	A1	R22	HCFC	$CHClF_2$	0.3	—	—	1700	0.055
L1	A1	R125	HFC	CF_3CHF_2	0.39	—	—	3200	0
L1	A1	R134a	HFC	CF_3CH_2F	0.25	—	—	1300	0
L1	A1/A1	R404A	R125/143a/134a (44/52/4)	CF_3CHF_2 + CF3CH$_3$ + CF_3CH_2F	0.48	—	—	3800	0
L1	A1/A1	R407C	R32/125/134a (23/25/52)	CH_2F_2 + CF_3CHF_2 + CF_3CH_2F	0.31	—	—	1600	0
L1	A1/A1	R410A	R32/125 (50/50)	CH_2F_2 + CF_3CHF_2	0.44	—	—	1900	0
L1	A1/A2	R413A	R134a/218/600a (88/9/3)	CF_3CH_2F + C_3F_8 + CH $(CH_3)_3$	0.25	—	—	1760	0
L1	A1/A1	R417A	R125/134a/600a (46.5/50/3.5)	CF_3CHF_2 + CF_3CH_2F + $CH_3CH_2CH_2CH_3$	0.31	—	—	1950	0
L2	B2	R123	HCFC	CF_3CHCl_2	0.1	—	—	93	0.02
L2	B2	R717	Ammonia	NH_3	0.00035	0.104	15	0	0
L3	A3	R290	Propane	$CH_3CH_2CH_3$	0.008	0.038	2.1	3	0
L3	A3	R600	Butane	$CH_3CH_2CH_2CH_3$	0.008	0.036	1.5	3	0
L3	A3	R600a	Isobutane	$CH(CH_3)_3$	0.008	0.043	1.8	3	0
L3	A3	R1270	Propylene	C_3H_6	0.008	0.043	2.5	3	0

Appendix 4.A2: Pressure–enthalpy charts for refrigerants

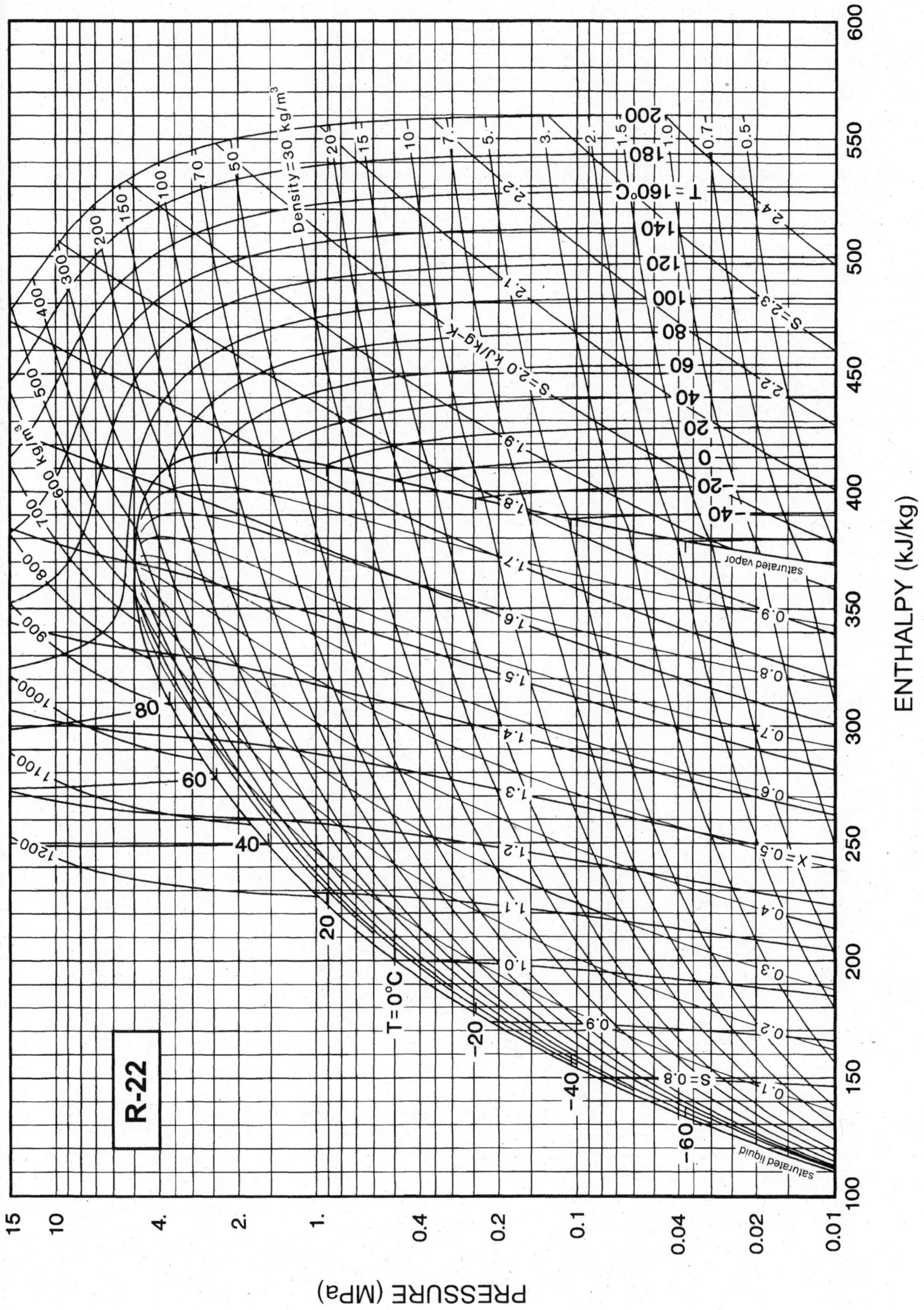

Figure 4.A2.1 Enthalpy–pressure chart for R22 (reproduced with permission from 2001 ASHRAE Handbook: *Fundamentals* © American Society of Heating, Refrigerating and Air-Conditioning Engineers Inc.)

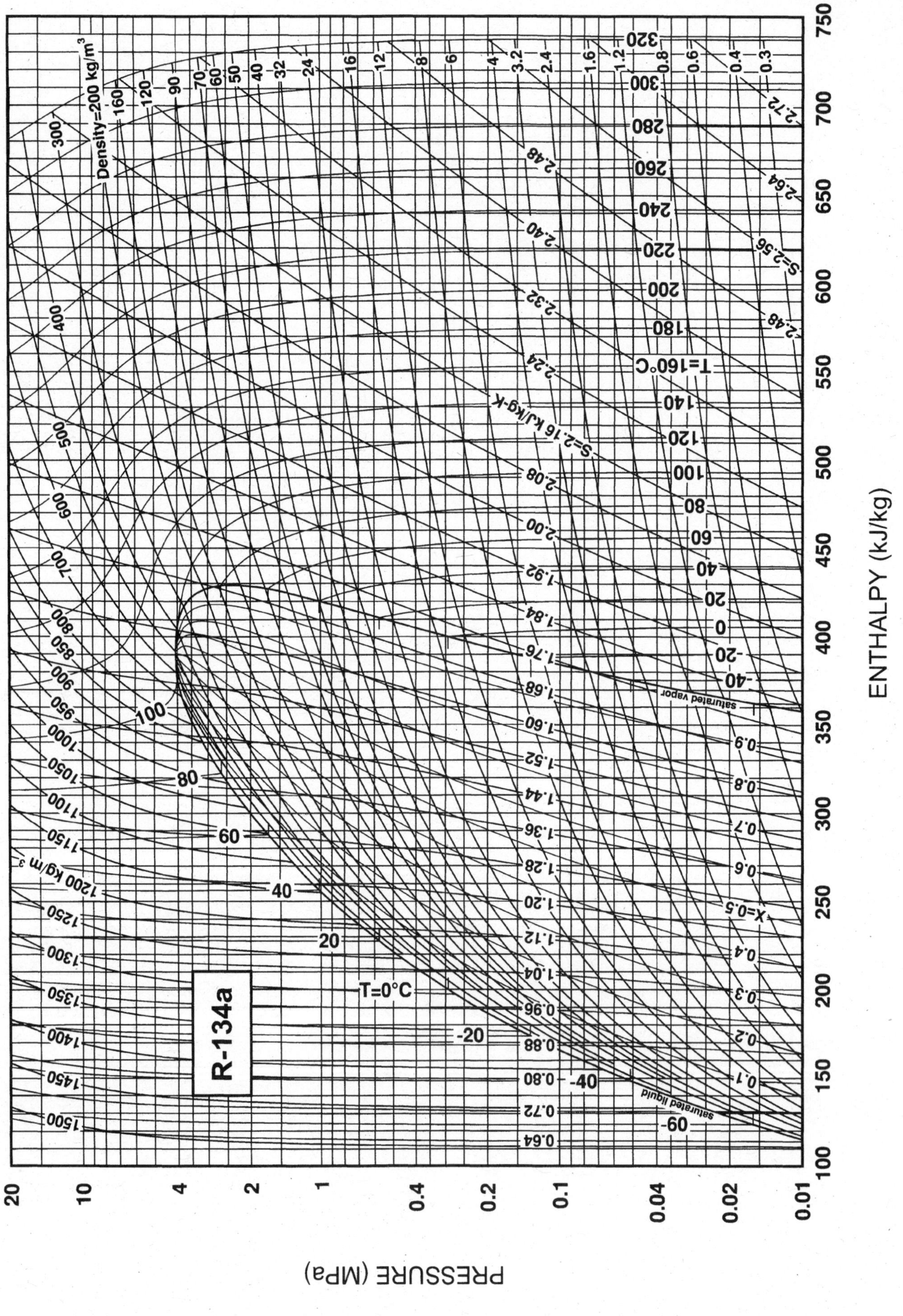

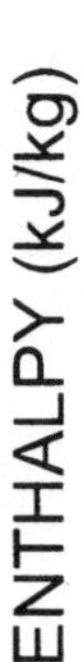

Figure 4.A2.2 Enthalpy–pressure chart for R134a (reproduced with permission from 2001 ASHRAE Handbook: *Fundamentals* © American Society of Heating, Refrigerating and Air-Conditioning Engineers Inc.)

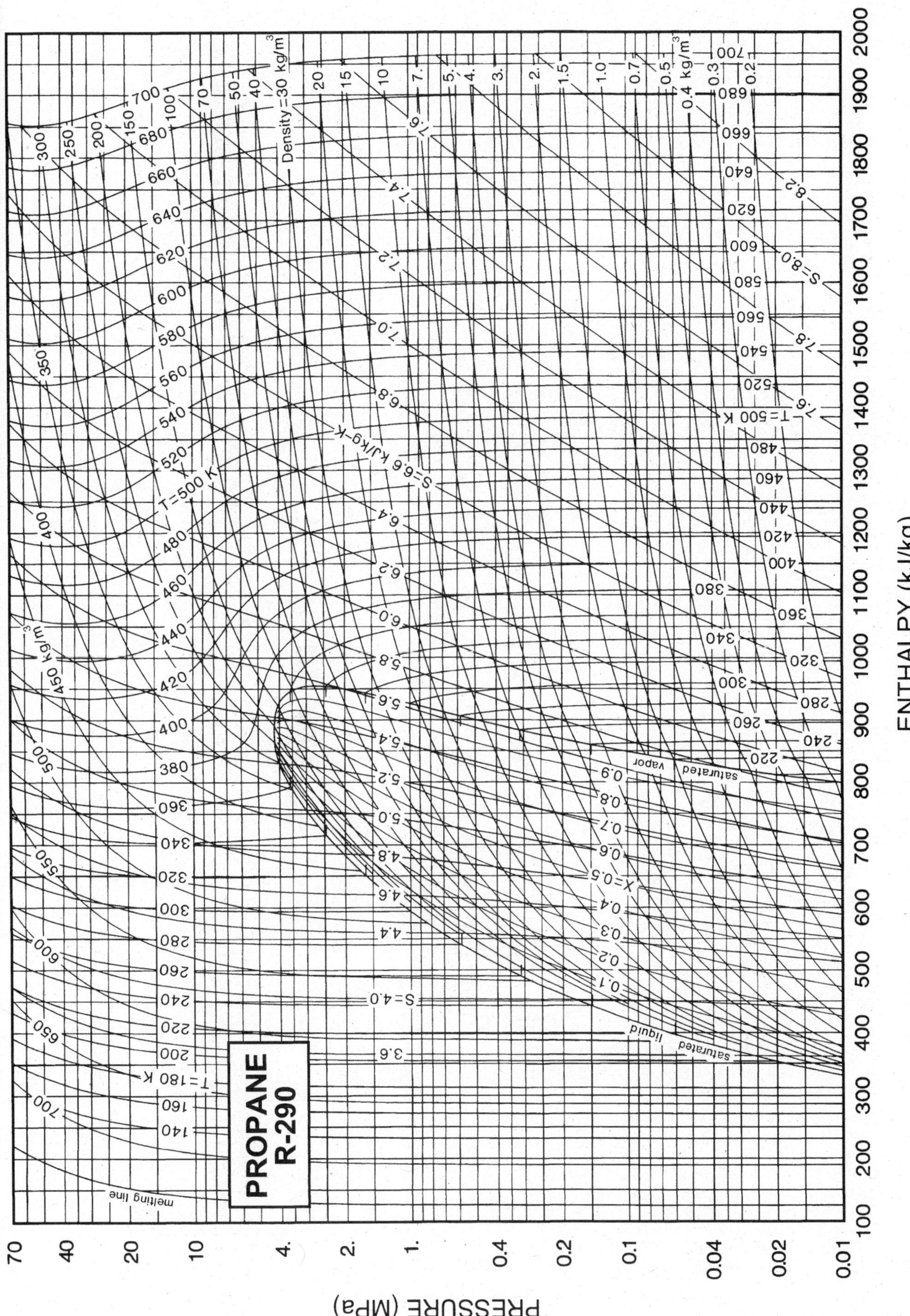

Figure 4.A2.3 Enthalpy–pressure chart for R290 (propane) (reproduced with permission from 2001 ASHRAE Handbook: *Fundamentals* © American Society of Heating, Refrigerating and Air-Conditioning Engineers Inc.)

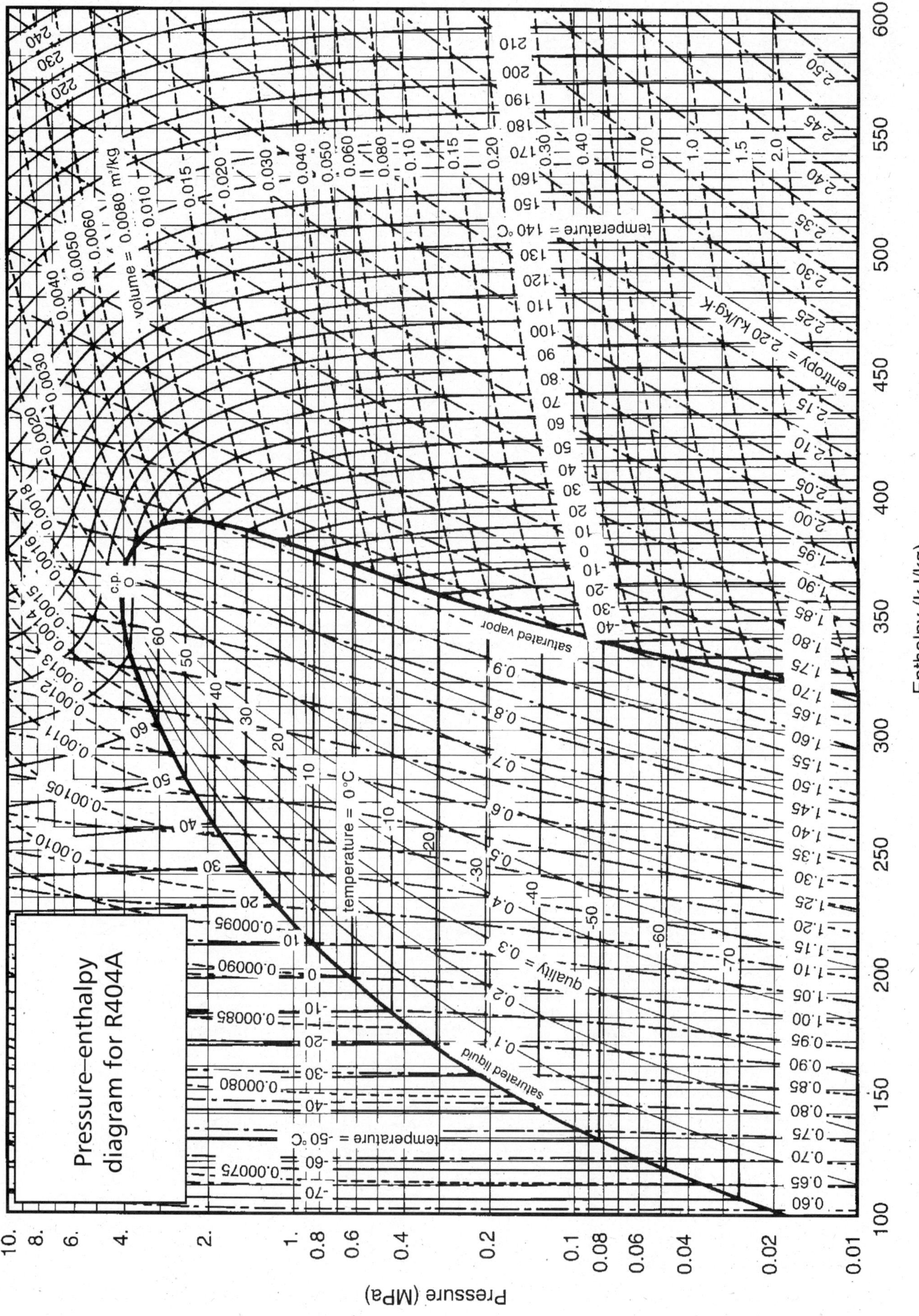

Figure 4.A2.4 Enthalpy–pressure chart for R404A (reproduced with permission from E. I. duPont de Nemours & Co. Inc.)

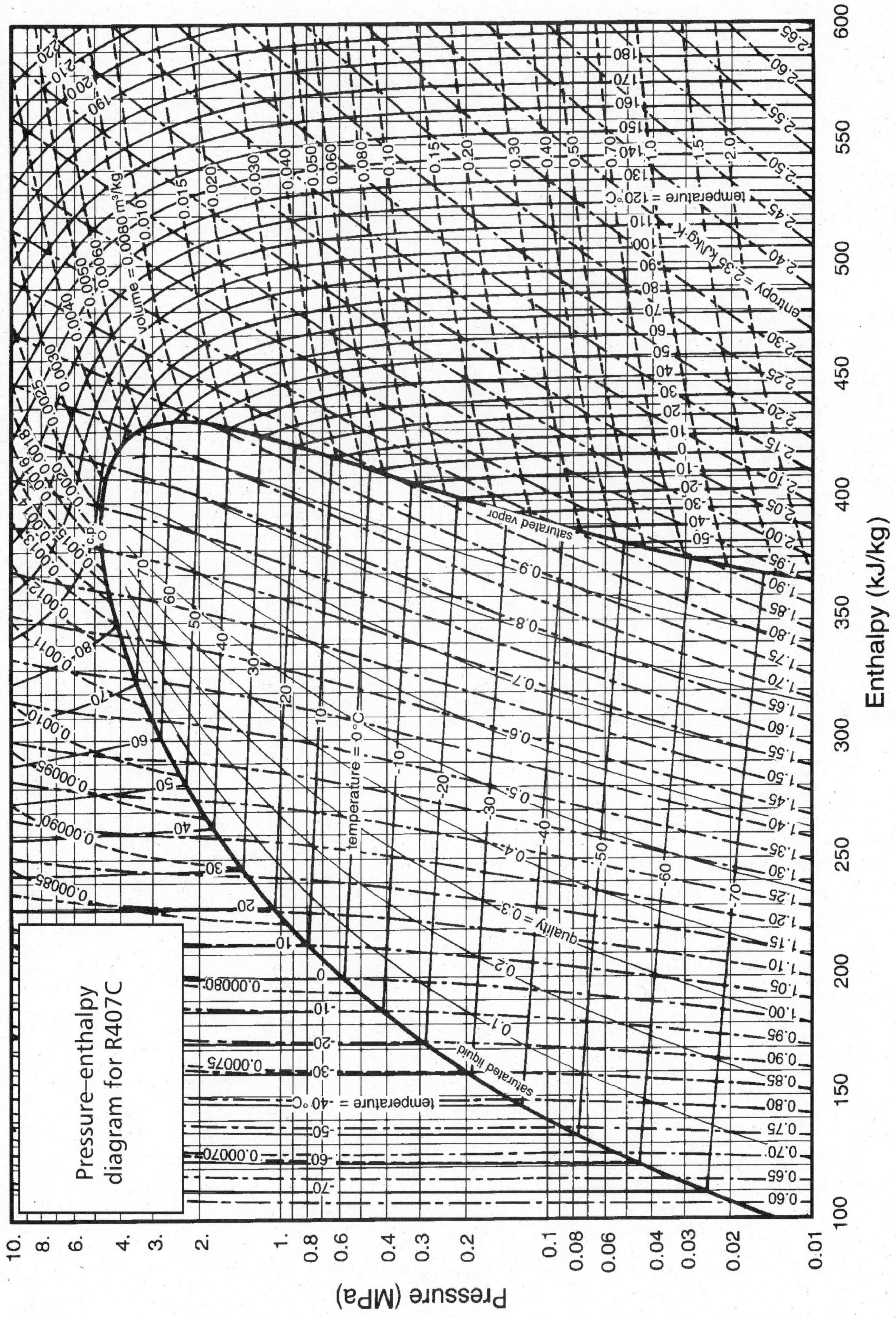

Figure 4.A2.5 Enthalpy–pressure chart for R407C (reproduced with permission from E. I. duPont de Nemours & Co. Inc.)

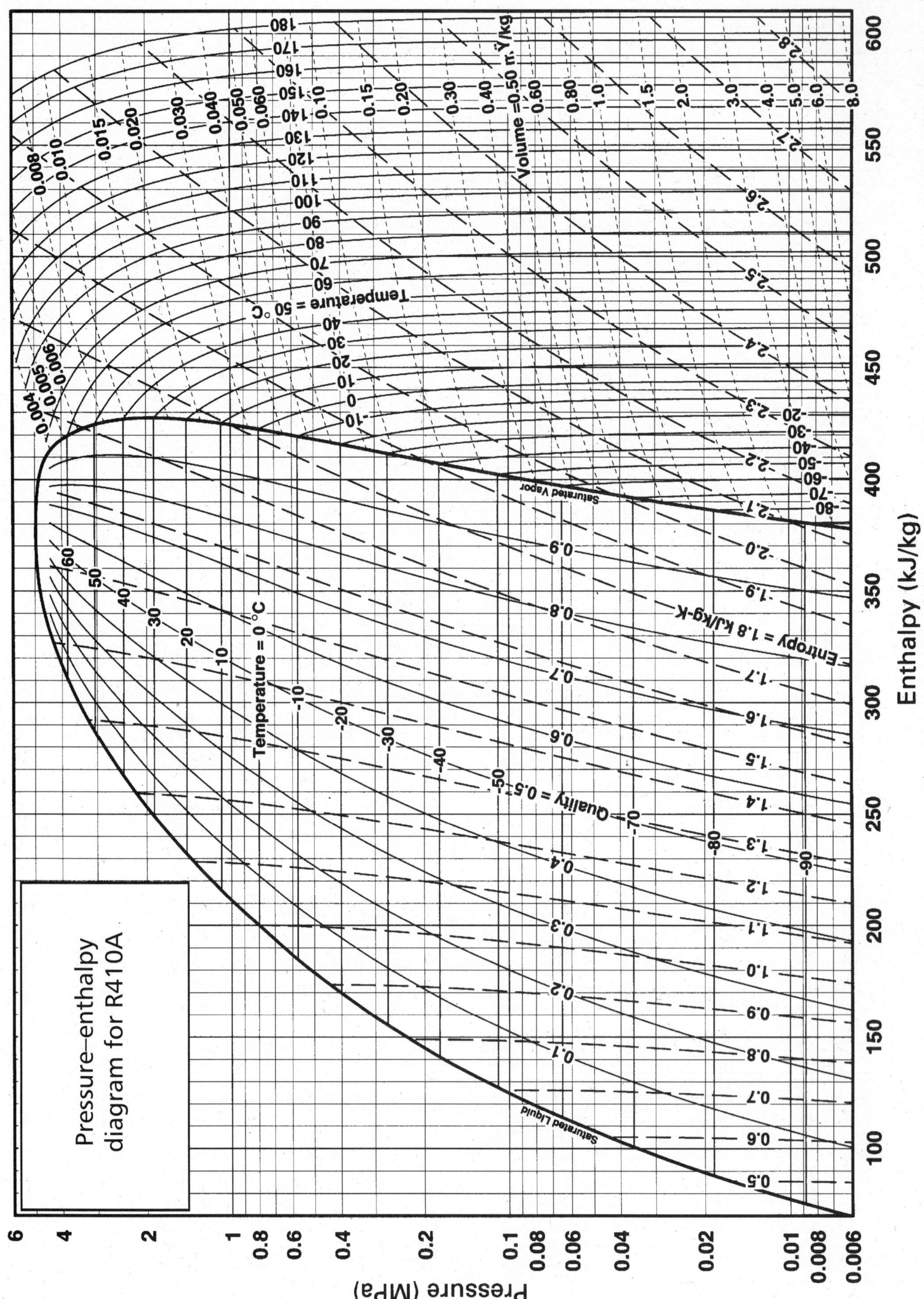

Figure 4.A2.6 Enthalpy–pressure chart for R410A (reproduced with permission from E.I. duPont de Nemours & Co. Inc.)

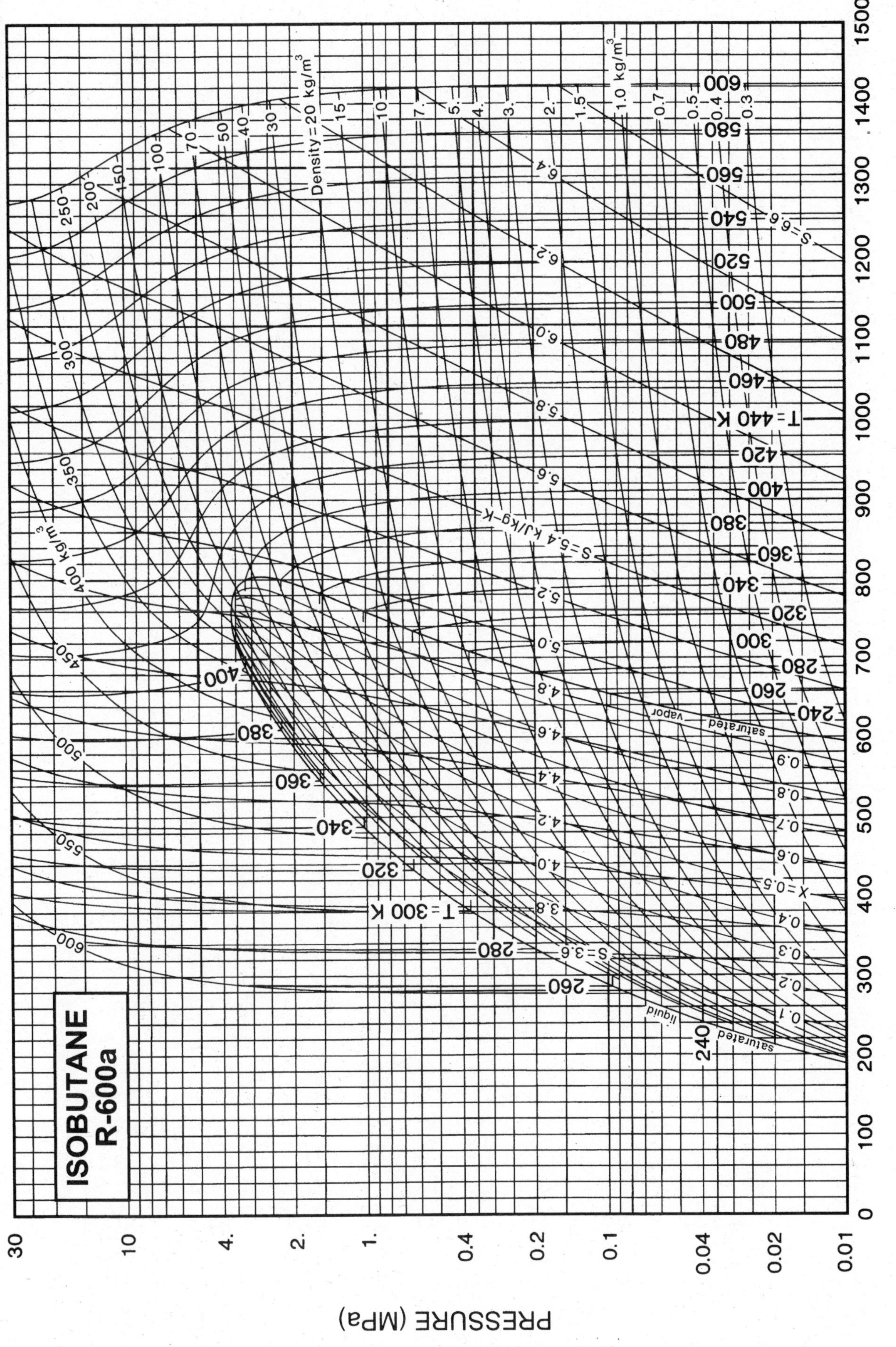

Figure 4.A2.7 Enthalpy–pressure chart for R600a (isobutane) (reproduced with permission from 2001 ASHRAE Handbook: *Fundamentals* © American Society of Heating, Refrigerating and Air-Conditioning Engineers Inc.)

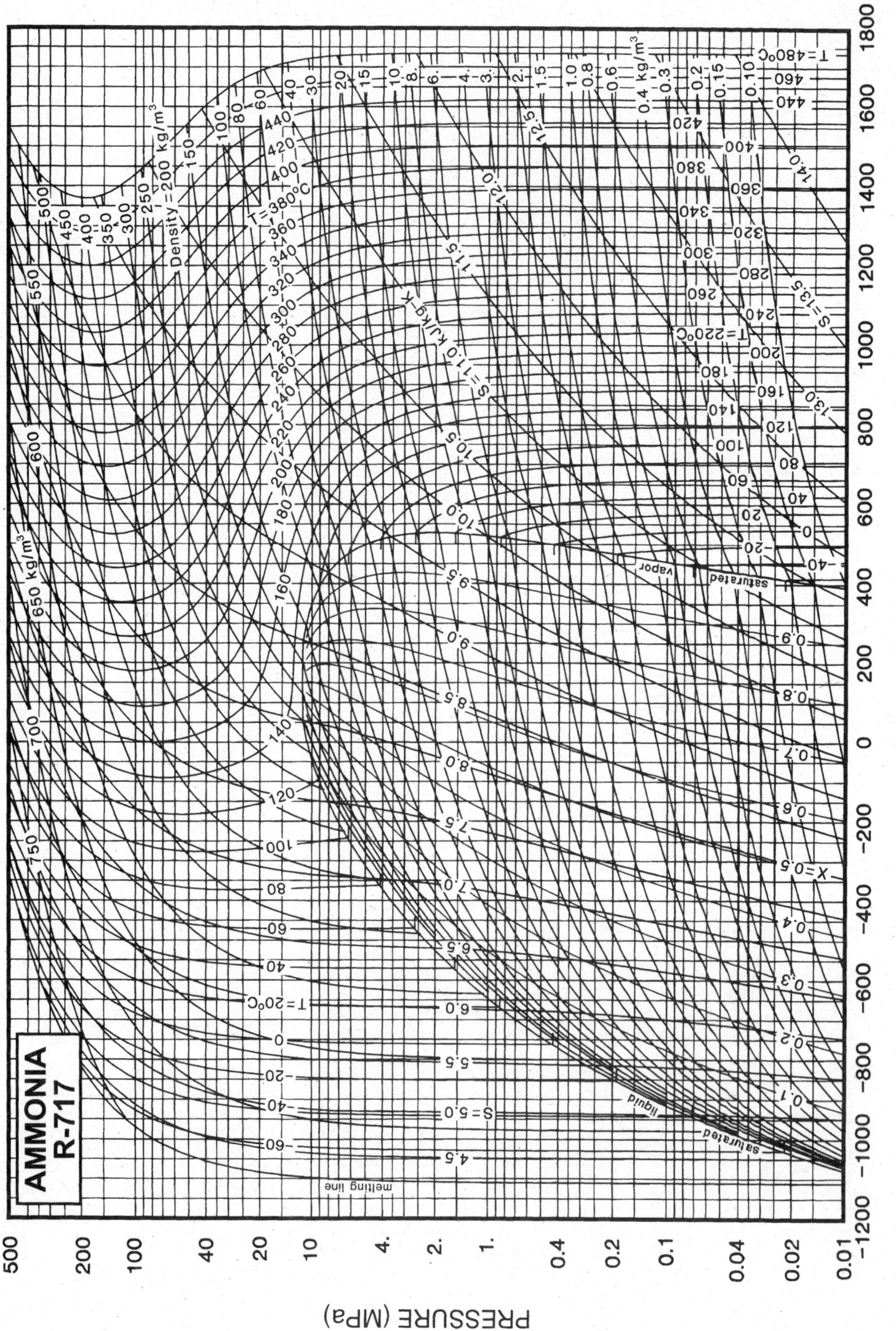

Figure 4.A2.8 Enthalpy–pressure chart for R717 (ammonia) (reproduced with permission from 2001 ASHRAE Handbook: *Fundamentals* © American Society of Heating, Refrigerating and Air-Conditioning Engineers Inc.)

5 Noise and vibration control for HVAC

5.1 Introduction

5.1.1 General

Ventilation and air conditioning of buildings are the subject of increasing interest both because of their contribution to effective building performance and occupant satisfaction, and the increasing focus on energy consumption and carbon emissions from buildings. A particular cause of interest is Part L[1] of the Building Regulations for England and Wales (and its equivalent Part J of the Building Standards (Scotland) Regulations[2]). Part L and its equivalent sets challenging new targets for energy efficiency of buildings in general and of mechanical ventilation systems in particular.

5.1.2 Overview of section 5

CIBSE Guide section 5 is the replacement for section B12 of the 1986 edition of CIBSE Guide B[3]. It has been comprehensively rewritten to take account of developments in the subject in the intervening years. It is intended for use by practising designers who hold a basic knowledge of the fundamentals of building physics and building services engineering.

Although the structure of section 5 does not follow the pattern of the other four sections, it is still intended to be used by engineers during the design of ventilation systems. Figure 5.1 sets out the outline design process for the various systems, and indicates those stages at which reference to this section will be most appropriate.

5.1.3 Noise from HVAC systems

Noise from heating, ventilation and air conditioning (HVAC) systems is one of the problems of air conditioned and mechanically ventilated buildings. Naturally ventilated buildings require convected air currents which, originating in apertures to the exterior, may transmit unacceptable levels of external noise. Excessive noise contributes to discomfort, uneasiness, difficult communication and loss of productivity, since those who are not comfortable in their surroundings are not fully effective. However, some noise is useful in masking the sounds from colleagues and other sources. Masking noise is especially important in multi-occupied offices in order to provide privacy.

For these and other reasons, criteria have been developed for controlling the levels of noise in buildings. Criteria are normally intended as 'levels not to be exceeded', aiming to produce noise levels which are comfortable and provide masking, whilst not being too difficult to achieve. However, they may become downgraded to 'design targets'. An important element of HVAC design is to control the noise to meet the specified criterion, whilst having minimum effect on the cost and aerodynamic performance of the fan/duct installation.

The building services engineer must take responsibility for the control of noise, whether it originates in the mechanical plant, or is external noise transmitted through the system. Where the noise is related to the design of the building, such as apertures for natural ventilation, the engineer must ensure that the architect, or other responsible person, is aware of potential problems and is advised on preferred locations for air inlets. Air inlets for natural ventilation systems are normally chosen to be on a part of the building remote from sources of air pollution and so remote from noise sources such as traffic, but they may be exposed to other noise sources.

The engineer may be required to take responsibility for all the services noise in a building, including pumps, lifts and escalators, as discussed in section 5.3.

Most services components in a building interact with each other, or with the building through their attachments to it. The HVAC installation should be treated as a complete system, the separate parts of which influence other parts, see Figure 5.2. The system components are duct sections, bends, take-offs, fittings, silencers etc. The termination of the complete system is at the occupants.

In the system shown in Figure 5.2, the air and noise travel from the fan through a number of components of the system, being affected by each one until they finally reach the occupants. During this process, one system may influence the performance of the preceding system. For example, the entry conditions into system 1 may modify the performance and noise generation of the fan. Other noise sources in the services in a building, considered in section 5.3, include chillers, compressors, pumps etc. Any equipment which is designed to move air or water, or to provide heating or cooling, must be considered as a potential noise source.

The mechanical equipment data should include noise, but the method by which this has been obtained is not always clear. Data may be measured, interpolated or unavailable. There are standardised procedures to be followed[5,6,7] and, unless it is stated that this has been done, the data should be treated with caution. The client, or other person responsible for approving equipment, should be clearly advised to consider the risks in the use of any component for which relevant octave band noise data, obtained under British, European, International or equivalent Standards procedures, is not available.

One factor, which the designer should be aware of, is that standardised noise measurement procedures are generally carried out in idealised situations, in which there is an attempt to prevent extraneous factors, e.g. turbulent

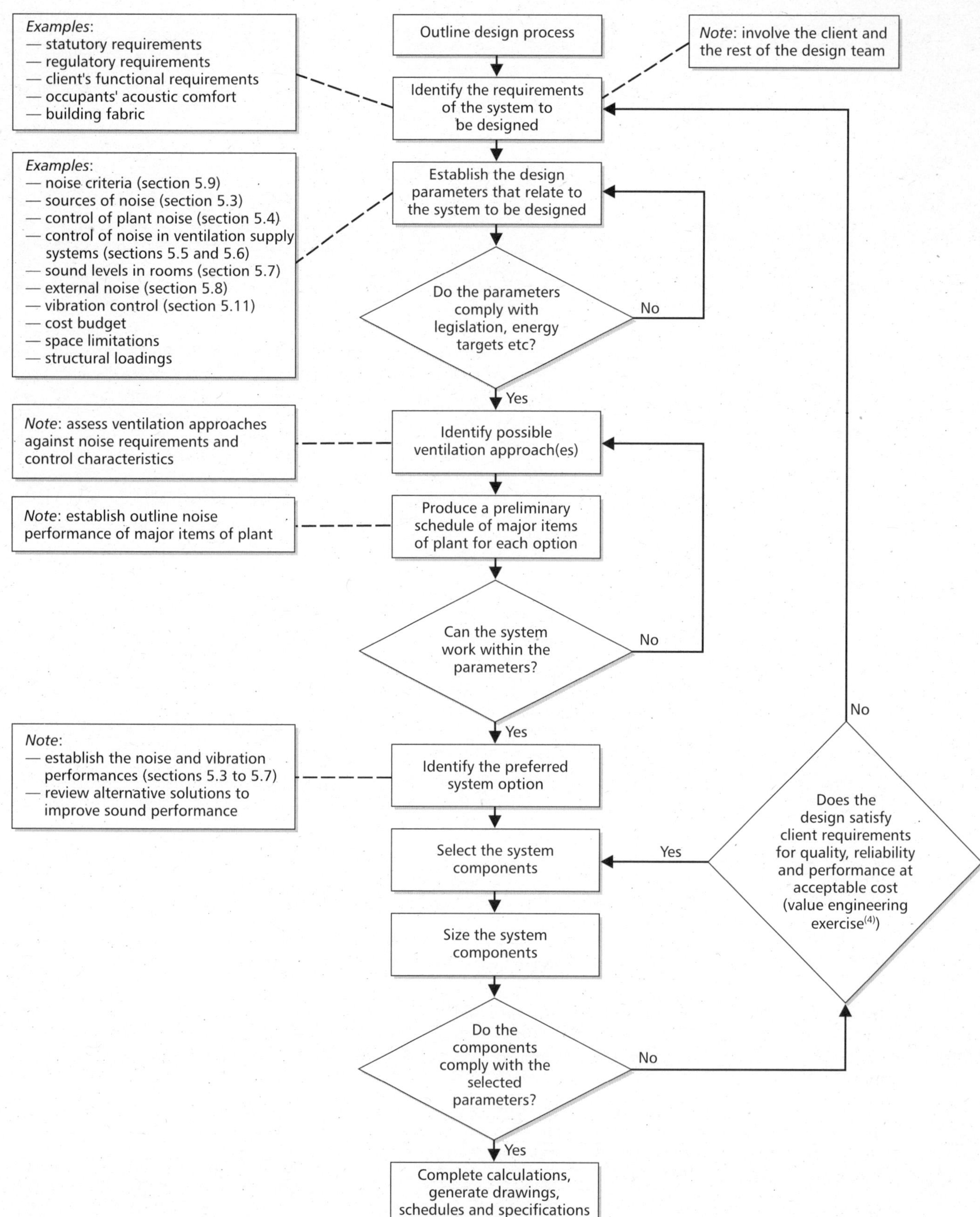

Figure 5.1 Outline design process

airflow, affecting the measurements. Thus, the performance on site may be different from the data supplied with the item of equipment and it is important to ensure that the duct design, and other factors, are such as to minimise adverse interactions. This is broadly achieved by limiting air speeds and ensuring good flow conditions, which also contributes to energy conservation.

The complete system, as shown in Figure 5.2, originates in the fan inlet and continues through coil, filter, humidifiers and duct components to the duct termination and from there to the occupants, for whom the system is intended to provide a comfortable environment. Each component in the system either produces or reduces noise. The final noise level in the room is the summation of all these separate effects. The fan is the primary noise source, whilst airflow over duct fittings may generate aerodynamic noise. When the noise level exceeds criterion values additional noise control is required. Poor airflow conditions may cause duct components to have noise

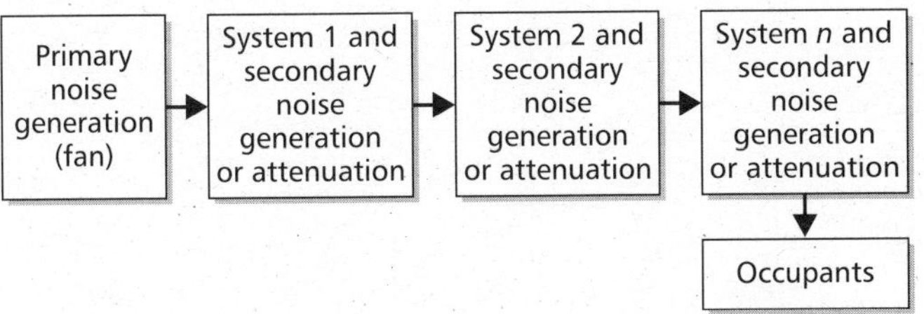

Figure 5.2 HVAC system in which the primary noise source is a fan

characteristics that differ from those given in the manufacturer's data. However, on the positive side, many duct components, such as bends and take-offs, contribute to attenuation of noise. The major noise-reducing component is normally a duct attenuator (silencer), but the operation of this is sensitive to airflow conditions and to its inlet and outlet duct connections. It may act as a source of additional noise, particularly at low frequencies.

Some noise is beneficial as an aid to masking the sounds of colleagues or to assist exclusion of external noise. This is known as 'masking noise', which may occasionally need to be added artificially. Background noise from the HVAC system is a useful masking noise, but should not be so high as to be distracting or to affect speech intelligibility. For a well designed office, background noise of 35 to 45 dBA (approximating to room noise criterion levels of 30–40) usually permits communication by normal voice with colleagues in close proximity. During early formulation of room noise criteria, it was considered that good speech intelligibility between colleagues was a primary factor in office design. Whilst speech is still a factor to be considered, changes in working practices have modified the manner in which many people work. Most workers now have a local noise source provided by the cooling fan in their computer, and the increasing use of the telephone and e-mail means that speech is, perhaps, becoming less important for communication between colleagues in the same office. An improved understanding of workers' interaction with their environment has focussed attention on general comfort within the environment, of which noise is one factor, and the relation of comfort to productivity.

Noise in HVAC systems can be divided into three frequency ranges:

— low frequencies, characterised by 'rumble' noise, from about 31.5 Hz to 125 Hz on the octave band scale of measurement (see Appendix 5.A5); rumble is typically, but not exclusively, from large central plant fans

— mid frequencies, from about 125 Hz to 500 Hz, lead to 'roar', which might be from small fans located close to the occupied space

— higher frequencies contribute to hiss and whistle, which are often a result of diffuser noise.

An excess in any range leads to an unbalanced noise spectrum and the potential for complaints[8]. A simple A-weighted noise measurement (see Appendix 5.A5) does not give sufficient information on these three frequency ranges and is of only limited use.

The primary path by which HVAC noise reaches occupants of the space being served is directly down the duct and out into the room, but this is not the only path. Other paths include the following:

— *Breakout noise from a duct*: occurs mostly near to the fan and is perceived as a throbbing, rumbly noise, or as a tonal noise if there is tone generation by the fan. Breakout noise often reduces downstream, because the noise has already broken out through the sides of the duct. Breakout can be a problem to occupants when a duct passes over their space.

— *Structure-borne noise*: results from poor vibration isolation of machinery, resulting in fluctuating forces acting directly into the structure and transmitting vibration through the building. The consequent vibration of surfaces radiates 'structure-borne' noise.

It is unlikely that structure-borne vibration will be perceived directly by touching walls or floors (i.e. a 'feelable' vibration) for surfaces outside the plant room, but pipe vibration may still be detectable at a distance from sources such as pumps, compressors etc. However, vibrating surfaces, including those which cannot be felt as vibrating, still radiate noise, which is perceived by the listener as 'machinery hum', which may be fluctuating or steady. Fluctuating noise (throb) is more objectionable than a steady noise.

5.2 Summary of noise and vibration problems from HVAC

5.2.1 Typical sources of HVAC noise and their characteristics

Noise is produced by vibrating surfaces and by moving air streams. Sometimes the two interact, as in the case of fan blades. The primary source of the noise normally lies in the rotation of a machine, such as a motor, pump or fan. However, energy imparted to air or water can be converted into noise through interaction of fluid flow with solid objects, e.g. louvres in a duct termination. A very broad generalisation is that the 'noise conversion efficiency' of a machine is around 10^{-7} of its input power, but there are wide variations above and below this figure, whilst aerodynamic noise increases rapidly with air velocity. A fan, which contains both drive motor and fan wheel, is more likely to convert around 10^{-6} of its input power to noise. Sound powers are low in terms of wattage but, because of the sensitivity of the ear, only milliwatts of acoustic power are required to produce a loud noise (see Appendix 5.A1).

Different types of mechanical equipment produce noise over different frequency ranges. This is illustrated in Figure 5.3, which shows the frequencies most likely to be produced by equipment and gives a typical subjective terminology by which listeners might describe the noises.

Figure 5.3 indicates that central plant (fans and pumps) is likely to cause noise up to about 500 Hz, whilst the very lowest frequencies are a result of defective installation. VAV units lead to noise from about 125 Hz to 3000 Hz, fan powered units being responsible for the lower end of this range. Chillers lead to noise in the 250 Hz to 1000 Hz

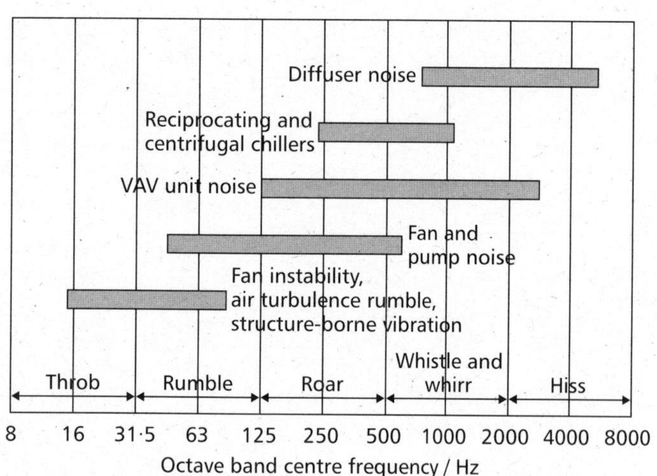

Figure 5.3 Frequencies at which different types of mechanical equipment generally control sound spectra (reproduced from ASHRAE *HVAC Applications Handbook* by permission of the American Society of Heating, Refrigerating and Air-Conditioning Engineers)

range whilst higher frequencies are due to diffuser noise. These system components are considered in more detail in section 5.3.

5.2.2 Transmission paths

Figure 5.4 shows transmission paths for roof-top and ground level plant rooms and are summarised as follows:

— noise radiates to atmosphere from the air inlet (path 1)

— vibration from the fan transmits to the structure (path 5)

— noise from the plant breaks out of the plant room (path 3)

— noise may break out of the supply duct to adjacent spaces (path 2)

— incorrect duct or pipe anchoring may put vibration into the structure (path 5)

— duct borne noise is emitted from the room units (path 4)

— vibration from ground level plant gets into the structure (path 5)

— noise from plant transmits through walls or windows to adjacent spaces (path 2).

In controlling the noise of the HVAC plant, all transmission paths must be assessed for their contribution to the final noise in occupied spaces and the paths controlled accordingly.

5.2.3 Control of the transmission paths

This section considers some general principles of good practice in noise and vibration control in HVAC. More details are given in sections 5.4, 5.5, 5.6 and 5.11. The preferred way to control noise is to prevent it occurring in the first place, but some noise generation is unavoidable from realistic airflow velocities. In HVAC systems, controlling noise means:

— choosing the operating condition of the fan so that it is at a high efficiency point on its characteristic; this minimises fan noise

— ensuring good flow conditions for the air stream; the consequent benefits include components behaving more nearly as described in the manufacturer's data and reduced pressure losses, conserving energy and saving operating costs

— isolating vibrating components, including all machinery, ducts and pipework from the structure

— choosing an in-duct silencer or other means to control airborne noise in ducts[9]; a full silencer may not be required, as lining bends with acoustic absorbent may be adequate, but this depends on the results of noise predictions (see section 5.10).

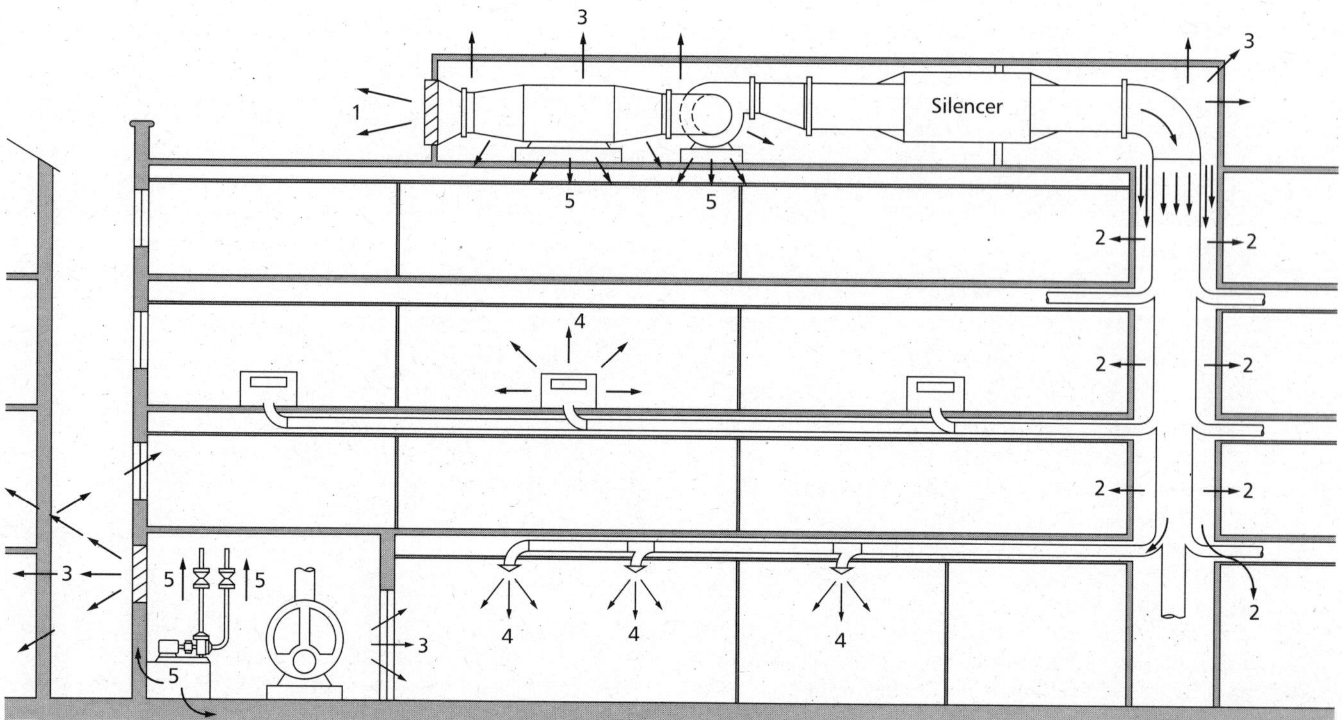

Figure 5.4 Transmission paths for roof-top and ground level plant rooms

Noise control relies on attention to detail, both in the design and the implementation. It depends on choosing the correct components and ensuring that they are installed correctly.

There are many instances of problems which have resulted from inadequacies in design and installation, including:

- undersized fans, which could not accept the pressure loss of retrofit silencers
- oversized fans, which were working on an undesirable part of their characteristic
- vibration isolators which were by-passed by solid connections
- unsealed gaps left between spaces.

5.3 Noise sources in building services

There are a large number of potential noise sources in a building services installation including fans, duct components, grilles and diffusers, plant such as chillers, boilers, compressors, cooling towers, condensers, pumps, stand-by generators, lifts and escalators. The tendency away from central plant to local systems in the ceiling space has brought noise sources closer to occupants and increased the problems of noise reaching occupied rooms. Noise from a plant room, especially large central plant, may break out to the exterior and be a source of annoyance to neighbours. Nuisance to neighbours comes under the responsibility of the local environmental health department, which may require the noise to be abated. Local authorities often apply conditions to planning consents in order to protect neighbours from nuisance caused by building services plant. Such conditions must be complied with.

Prediction formulae have been established for some items of plant by measurements on a sample of the plant. Much of this work was carried out many years ago, when information was not available from manufacturers. Since that time designs have changed. There have been efforts by the larger manufacturers of plant to reduce plant noise, whilst most manufacturers have also become aware of the need to provide data on the noise of their plant. The main source of information on noise is now the manufacturer. Inability, or reluctance, to provide such information might influence the choice of manufacturer.

The measurement conditions for plant noise must be specified along with the relation of the measurement procedure to standardised methods. It should be remembered that the installation conditions may not be the same as the measurement conditions and that there are uncertainties in measurement, especially at low frequencies.

In the very early stages of a project, plant may not have been fully specified and, only under these temporary circumstances, generic information on noise may be used to give an initial overview of the noise of the project and to indicate space requirements for noise control, e.g. how much space to allow for in-duct silencers. Generic prediction information is given in Appendix 5.A2, which must be regarded as for temporary use only, until equipment-specific information is available. The uncertainties of generic information are at least ±5 dB, and often greater.

5.3.1 Fans

Control of fan noise depends on:

- choosing an efficient operating point for the fan
- design of good flow conditions
- ensuring that the fan is vibration isolated from the structure
- ensuring that the fan is flexibly connected to the duct.

Where fan noise will be a problem, an in-duct attenuator should be used; these are described in detail in section 5.6.

5.3.2 Variable air volume (VAV) systems

Noise from VAV systems depends on the method of control. Where the flow is adjusted by means of a damper or throttle valve, noise is mainly generated by turbulence at the obstruction to flow. Where control is by a fan, either cycled or modulated, the fan is the source of the noise, but modulation may affect the noise by changing the operating point of the fan. Improper air balancing must be avoided to ensure that the fan does not deliver at an unnecessarily high static pressure.

Manufacturers' noise data for a VAV system will not be achieved in practice unless careful attention is given to the support of the box and to the airflow conditions both into and out of the box. There should be straight duct runs at both sides of the box in order to minimise turbulent flows and the resulting potential for enhanced noise. Break-out noise from the box should also be taken into account.

5.3.3 Grilles and diffusers

Control of air velocity and flow conditions is the key to reducing this noise. Manufacturers' data should be consulted. Grilles and diffusers are the last stage in noise control because, once the sound has escaped into the room, there is no further attenuation other than by room surface absorption. Grilles and diffusers are considered in Appendix 5.A2.

5.3.4 Roof-top units

Roof-top units have three main noise paths into the building space:

- through the duct
- breakout from the casing of the unit, which then transmits through the roof; this is most likely to occur underneath the unit, where the noise levels will be highest
- vibration transmission from the unit to the roof and consequent re-radiation of noise.

Noise through the duct is treated by absorptive material in the unit or by a silencer in the duct. Both supply and return may require treatment. Breakout, if a problem, is controlled by strengthening the underside of the casing or by adding sound attenuating material underneath the unit. Vibration transmission is reduced by well designed anti-vibration mounts.

5.3.5 Fan coil units

These are an example of how noise sources are brought close to the occupants. Room perimeter units must be chosen for their low noise, by reference to manufacturers' information. Ceiling void units must be carefully mounted with inlet and discharge ducts designed to minimise the external resistance and with an adequate return air path ensured. A discharge silencer, or lined duct, may be required. Noise breakout through the casing must not be neglected. The sound power of the units will be provided by the manufacturer.

5.3.6 Chillers, compressors and condensers

These produce both tonal and broadband noise. The tonal noise is typical of that from rotating or reciprocating machinery, linked to the rotational frequency. The broadband noise is from fluid flows, either liquid or gas. The tonal noise is often dominant, perceived as a whine or whirr, but the frequency range depends on the mode of operation. Reciprocating compressors have a relatively low-frequency fundamental tone, related to the oscillation frequency of the pistons. Screw compressors have strong tones in the octave bands between 250 Hz and 2000 Hz, and may require special attention to noise and vibration control, especially when they are located externally.

5.3.7 Pumps

Pumps produce external noise from the motor, fluid-borne noise from the impeller and vibration into both the structure and the pipes. Noise problems may arise from the airborne noise, controlled by choosing a non-sensitive location or by an enclosure for the pump. If the pipes make solid contact with a radiating surface, there is the potential for both fluid-borne noise and pipe vibration to reappear as airborne noise at a distance from the pump. It is necessary to:

— use vibration isolators to isolate the pump from the building

— use a flexible connection from pump to pipes

— use resilient mountings for supporting the pipe to the structure.

5.3.8 Stand-by generators

This noisy plant, which requires to be tested at regular intervals, is often housed in a separate generator room. A flow of fresh air is required both for the engine intake and for cooling. Noise problems arise from:

— the fresh air inlet

— the warm air discharge

— the engine exhaust

— the structure, due to vibration transmission.

The air inlet and discharge may require to be silenced by use of duct silencers, acoustic louvres or equivalent measures. The engine exhaust silencer will need to be selected to satisfy local requirements for environmental noise. Vibration isolation must be discussed with the supplier of the generator. It is common practice to line the generator room with acoustic absorbent in order to reduce the build-up of reverberant sound.

5.3.9 Boilers

Hot water boilers may vary in size from a few hundred kilowatts, or lower, up to megawatts, depending on the heating requirement. Noise sources within the boiler room are from the air supply fan and the combustion. External noise is from the flue. A small boiler of about 200 kW capacity may have a spectrum peak at around 125 Hz and overall sound power level of 90 dBA. In general, the frequency of the peak drops with increasing boiler capacity so that, in the megawatt range, the spectrum peak is at 63 Hz or below. A large boiler, of several megawatt capacity, may have an overall sound power in excess of 100 dBA. Manufacturers' information should be consulted for octave band data. The presence of low frequencies leads to the total sound power being greater than the A-weighted sound power.

5.3.10 Cooling towers

Cooling tower noise is mainly noise from the fan, details of which should be available from the manufacturer. See also Appendix 5.A2 for fan noise prediction.

5.3.11 Lifts

The intermittent operation of lifts, including door opening and closing, motor surges and operation of brakes, may cause disturbance in adjacent occupied spaces. Most of the noise is structure borne, for example impacts on door stops and lift machinery vibration. It is possible to reduce each of the noise sources by design and correct installation. Advice should be sought from the manufacturer.

5.3.12 Escalators

Escalators are a source of noise and vibration from the motor and drive mechanism. This is not normally a problem provided that the equipment has been installed correctly. However, there is a possibility that vibration input from the motor will couple with a resonance on a surrounding floor or wall to produce a noticeable effect, which will then require correction.

5.4 Noise control in plant rooms

5.4.1 Health and safety

Plant rooms may have noise levels which exceed the limits for worker protection. If, for example, a maintenance engineer spends long periods in a very noisy plant room it will be necessary to wear hearing protection as noise exposure may exceed the permitted daily 'noise dose'.

The Health and Safety Executive has defined three 'action levels' in the Noise at Work Regulations[10]. (See Appendices 5.A1 and 5.A5 for definitions of acoustical terms.) These action levels are as follows:

(*a*) *First action level*: daily personal noise exposure ($L_{EP,d}$) of 85 dBA.

(*b*) *Second action level*: daily personal noise exposure ($L_{EP,d}$) of 90 dBA.

(*c*) *Peak action level*: peak sound pressure level of 200 Pa (which is equivalent to a peak sound pressure level of 140 dB re 20 μPa).

The peak action level refers to impulsive noise. A useful guide for steady noise is that, if it is necessary to raise one's voice to shouting level in order to communicate clearly with someone standing about 2 m away, the first action level has been exceeded, but this must be checked by measurement. If measurements show that the first action level has been reached, it is a requirement of the Noise at Work Regulations to make hearing protection available for employees who request it. When the second or peak action levels have been reached, there is an obligation to provide hearing protection for all exposed employees and to ensure that these are worn. Further details are given in the HSE's *Guidance on the Noise at Work Regulations*[11].

It is, of course, advisable to put some effort into design of a plant room in order to prevent breaching the action levels. This is not only healthier for employees, but exceeding the second action level places additional legal obligations on management for enforcement, regular checks, record keeping etc.

(An agreement within the European Union will lead to reduction of the action levels by the year 2004. The first action level will then be a daily exposure of 80 dBA, the second action level will be 85 dBA and the peak action level will be 112 Pa[12]).

5.4.2 Breakout noise from plant rooms

Figure 5.4 indicates how noise breaks out from plant rooms, either to atmosphere or to adjacent occupied space. In order to reduce breakout noise the following steps must be taken:

— Isolate the equipment from the structural floor. This can be either by individual vibration isolation of each piece of equipment or by using a floating floor (see section 5.11).

— Ensure that the separating walls give sufficient attenuation (see section 5.7.4). This requires information on the sound power outputs of each item of plant, so that the overall level and spectrum of the plant room noise can be estimated. The levels are then related to the noise criterion for the adjacent space and the requirements for wall attenuation determined. Many plant rooms have hard walls, which contribute to build-up of reverberant noise. This results in a higher internal level than might be anticipated, but the effect is reduced by lining some of the plant room surfaces with sound absorbent. Reverberation must be included as a factor in predicting plant room noise levels (see section 5.7.6). It may be necessary to design special noise attenuating double isolating walls to protect sensitive locations adjacent to plant rooms, and to make sure that pipes and other components are not fixed directly to these walls.

— Ensure that all penetrations of the plant room walls, floor or ceiling are carefully sealed.

— Pay proper attention to noise transmission through the plant room external walls and silencing of air inlets and outlets, louvres etc. in order to prevent noise to atmosphere which, as a potential for disturbance in neighbouring buildings, should not be neglected in the design. It may be necessary to include a silencer in the air inlet to the fan.

5.4.3 Break-in noise in plant rooms

This refers to high levels of plant room noise entering the ducts and then being transmitted to occupied spaces. The problem is controlled by correct location of a duct silencer. The silencer should be placed to penetrate the plant room wall, so that all break-in noise to the duct is reduced along with other duct-borne noise.

5.4.4 Estimation of noise levels in plant rooms

In a cramped plant room, the direct sound from the nearest item of plant is likely to control the local noise. However in a large uncrowded plant room, where a reverberant sound field may be assumed, the reverberant field is approximated by equation 5.A7.2, see Appendix 5.A7, used with the sound power levels of each item of plant. A reverberation time of 2 seconds should be assumed. The contributions of each item to the reverberant field are added, as in Appendix 5.A1. The direct sound of nearby plant must also be included.

5.5 Regeneration of noise in ducts

5.5.1 Airflow generated noise

This noise, also known as regenerated noise, is produced by turbulence in the airflow. It is reduced by ensuring streamline flow and minimising obstructions or abrupt changes in the flow. Airflow noise increases as approximately the sixth power of flow velocity and is generally broad band. Sometimes a tone is perceptible with a frequency of about $f = 0.2\ u/d$, where u is the flow velocity (m·s^{-1}) and d the dimension of an obstruction in the flow (m). In general, the regenerated sound power of a duct fitting is given approximately by:

$$L_W = C + 10 \lg A + 60 \lg u \tag{5.1}$$

where L_W is the airflow generated noise power level (dB), C is a constant, which varies with the fitting, A is the minimum flow area of the fitting (m^2) and u is the maximum flow velocity in the fitting (m·s^{-1}). (*Note*: lg = $\log_{10}$.)

Equation 5.1 illustrates the importance of limiting the velocity, since a doubling of velocity gives an 18 dB increase in regenerated sound power. Reduction of velocity is achieved by increasing the duct size or, for example, running two parallel ducts. Where it is anticipated that velocity generated noise will be a problem, silencing must be installed after the final in-duct noise source. For typical fittings and flow velocities, the overall regenerated power level is likely to be in the region of 50–70 dB, but the levels vary with frequency. The maximum level is at $f = 0.2\ u/d$, as above. A more detailed determination of regenerated noise is given in Appendix 5.A2.

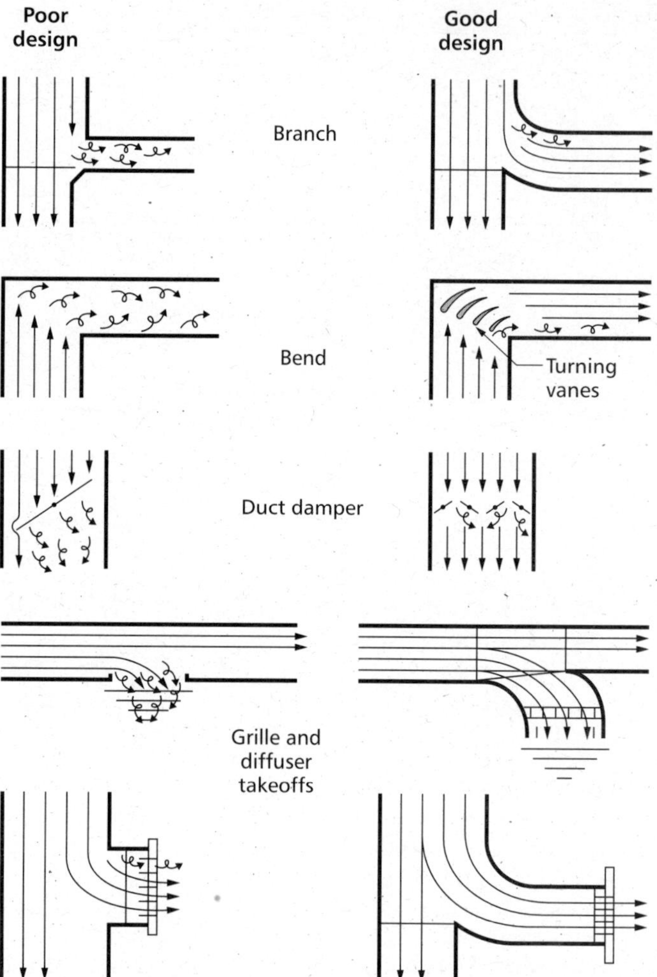

Figure 5.5 Principles of good duct design to avoid turbulence[12] (reproduced from *Control of Noise in Ventilation Systems* by M A Iqbal, T K Willson and R J Thomas, by permission of E & F N Spon)

5.5.2 System effects on regeneration of noise

Figure 5.5[13] illustrates good principles of duct design in order to avoid turbulence and its associated pressure loss and noise. Some obstructions, such as dampers, are necessary, but multiple dampers are preferred to single dampers in a noise-sensitive system. Dampers should be fitted at least 1.5 to 2.0 meters back from a duct termination in order to reduce damper noise escaping into occupied space. Manufacturers' literature on damper noise should be consulted and the levels assessed in relation to other noise in the duct, in order to determine whether secondary silencing is required after the damper.

A detailed prediction method for duct termination regenerated sound power is given in *Sound and vibration design and analysis*[14] and is considered further in Appendix 5.A2, section 5.A2.5. An estimate of regenerated noise is also given by equation 5.1 and Table 5.1, which is for well designed systems as illustrated in Figure 5.5, where regenerated noise is unlikely to be a problem.

Damper manufacturers can supply information from which the regenerated noise of their products may be estimated. The information is often provided in terms of air velocity, resulting pressure drop and a reference overall regenerated sound power level. Spectrum corrections are

Table 5.1 Corrections to equation 5.1 for low turbulence duct fittings

Duct fitting	Value of C / dB	Notes	Octave band power level correction / dB for stated octave band / Hz							
			63	125	250	500	1000	2000	4000	8000
Straight duct	−10	No internal projections	0	−2	−7	−8	−10	−12	−15	−19
90° radiused bend	0	Aspect ratio 2:1, throat radius $w/2$	0	−2	−7	−8	−10	−12	−15	−19
90° square bend with turning vanes	+10	Close spaced, short radius single skin vanes	0	−2	−7	−8	−10	−12	−15	−19
Gradual contraction	+1	Area ratio 3:1, A and u as for smaller duct	0	0	−10	−16	−20	−22	−25	−30
Sudden contraction	+4	Area ratio 3:1, A and u as for smaller duct	+3	0	−10	−16	−20	−22	−25	−30
Butterfly damper	−5	A and u apply to minimum area free damper	0	−3	−9	−9	−10	−17	−20	−24

Table 5.2 Guide to maximum duct velocities for final runs to outlets*

Duct location	Duct type	Maximum air velocity for stated type of space / m·s^{-1}		
		Critical	Normal	Non-critical
Riser or above plasterboard ceiling	Rectangular	5	7.5	10
	Circular	7	10	15
Above suspended ceiling	Rectangular	3	5	6
	Circular	5	7	10

* Velocities can be increased by about 50% in main ducts

Table 5.3 Maximum free air velocity for supply and return air openings

Type of opening	Permitted air velocity for stated type of space / m·s^{-1}		
	Critical	Normal	Non-critical
Supply	1.5	2.5	3
Return	2	3	4

applied to the reference level. The spectrum corrections will be different for different blade settings.

The aim should be for system design and construction which ensures that regenerated noise in the duct is not a problem. A guide to maximum permitted air velocities is given in Table 5.2 for different types of space. A 'critical' space is, for example, a private office or similar. A 'normal' space is a general office, whilst a 'non-critical' space might be for circulation or storage. These spaces may typically have rating criteria of 25, 35 and 45. Note that the doubling of air velocity between critical and non-critical spaces represents a sound level difference of up to 20 dB.

Similar velocity limits for grilles and diffusers are given in Table 5.3 for general guidance, but manufacturers' information should be consulted. Note that multiple grilles in a room may require a reduction in the velocity through each grille

5.5.3 Silencers

Silencers are considered in section 5.6.7. They are an obstruction in the flow and therefore generate turbulence noise. This noise, which is dependent on flow velocity, is sometimes referred to as the 'self-noise sound power level' of the silencer. Self-noise is likely to be from 50 to 80 dB overall sound power level. Manufacturers' data must be consulted.

5.6 Control of noise transmission in ducts

5.6.1 Duct components

Duct components may include:

— straight ducts of various lengths, rectangular or circular in cross-section

— silencers

— bends (elbows), right angled or curved

— branches, which may have one or more take-offs

— distribution boxes (plenums)

— terminal units, grilles, diffusers, registers.

Additionally, transition pieces connect the fan or silencer to the duct. Most ducts are of sheet metal construction but short flexible lengths of other material may be used, e.g. to connect a ceiling void fan coil unit to a terminal. There are specialist duct systems for on-site duct manufacture from sheets of stiff resin-bonded fibreglass or similar.

5.6.2 Unlined straight ducts

Attenuation of noise in straight unlined ducts is mainly through transfer of energy from the sound wave to the duct wall. This energy then appears as either breakout noise from the duct or as duct vibration. A duct with stiff walls will vibrate less than one with flexible walls, and will therefore have both lower attenuation and lower breakout noise. Duct attenuation is expressed as decibels per metre (dB·m^{-1}) and is lower for circular ducts than for rectangular, as circular ducts have greater wall stiffness than rectangular ducts. Circular ducts might require additional attenuation to be added into the system. Duct flexibility varies with the duct dimensions and frequency of excitation, so that attenuation depends on these quantities. The attenuation in straight sheet metal ducts is given in Table 5.4.

5.6.3 Lined straight ducts

Lined ducts are an effective way of reducing noise, but refer to section 5.6.9 on the use of fibrous materials in ducts. Published data on absorption coefficients for acoustic lining materials shows a continuous rise with increasing frequency, often up to the maximum of unity (total absorption). Absorption coefficients are measured either at normal incidence or random incidence, following standard procedures. However, these values do not apply to absorbent duct linings, since when the material is used

Table 5.4 Approximate attenuation of unlined sheet metal ducts at octave frequencies

Duct section	Mean dimension or diameter / mm	Attenuation (/ dB·m^{-1}) for stated octave band / Hz			
		63	125	250	500 and above
Rectangular	≤300	1.0	0.7	0.3	0.3
	300–450	1.0	0.7	0.3	0.2
	450–900	0.6	0.4	0.3	0.1
	>900	0.5	0.3	0.2	0.1
Circular	<900	0.1	0.1	0.1	0.1
	>900	0.03	0.03	0.03	0.06

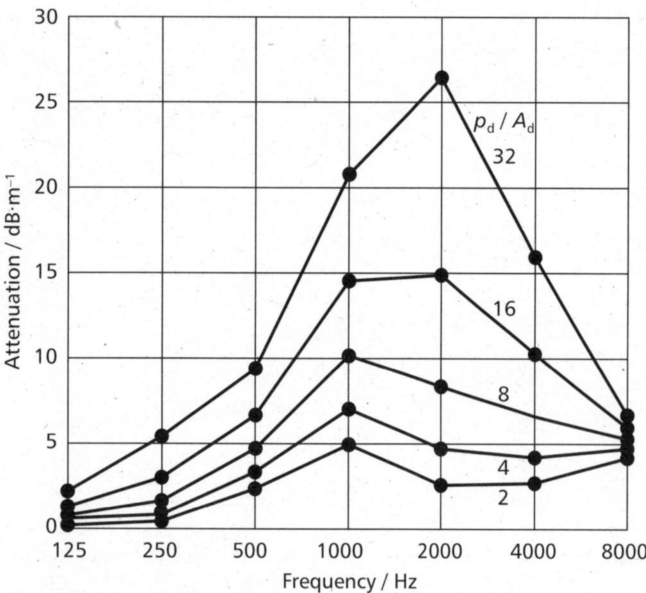

Figure 5.6 Attenuation of lined duct; 25 mm lining

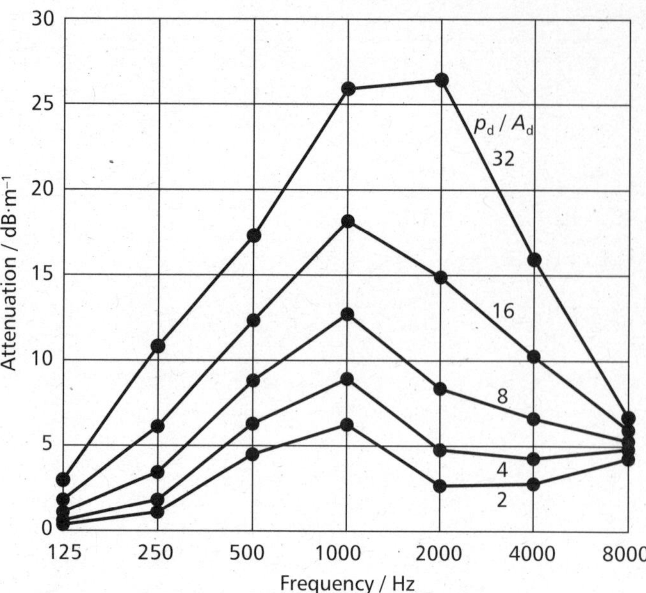

Figure 5.7 Attenuation of lined duct; 50 mm lining

as a duct liner, high frequencies do not interact with it in the same way as for the absorption coefficient measurement, but propagate down the duct with reduced effect from the absorbent lining. This is particularly so at high frequencies, where the attenuation in the lined duct reduces from its maximum at mid frequencies. Physically, at high frequencies the sound propagates down the centre of the duct and has reduced interaction with the lining. For a given lining material and thickness, the smaller the duct widths or diameters, the greater the attenuation.

For a lined plenum, the published absorption properties of a material should be used where the plenum is large enough for the sound to reflect within it; that is, when the plenum dimensions are greater than the wavelength of the sound to be controlled. Prediction formulae for lined ducts are considered in Appendix 5.A2, section 5.A2.6. An important parameter is the ratio p_d/A_d, where p_d is the duct perimeter (m) and A_d is the cross sectional area of the duct (m^2).

Results of the prediction formulae are presented in Figures 5.6 and 5.7, where the insertion loss is shown against frequency with p_d/A_d as the variable. Figure 5.6 is for 25 mm lining and Figure 5.7 for 50 mm lining. Thus, from Figure 5.6 for a 600 mm by 700 mm duct, $p_d/A_d = 6$ and the insertion loss at 500 Hz, for example, is interpolated as about 4 dB·m^{-1}. The basis of Figures 5.6 and 5.7 is an extensive series of measurements on rectangular ducts, using the substitution method, in which the lined duct is replaced by a similar unlined section.

The attenuation of lined circular ducts is shown in Table 5.5 for a 25 mm lining[14]. Increasing the lining thickness to 50 mm increases the attenuation by only a small amount. Short lengths of lined circular ducts, as connections to diffusers, may be the final opportunity for noise control.

Table 5.5 Approximate attenuation of lined circular ducts[14] (reproduced from *Sound and Vibration Design and Analysis* by permission of the National Environmental Balancing Bureau, Gaithersburg, MD)

Duct diameter / mm	Attenuation / dB·m^{-1} for stated octave band / Hz							
	63	125	250	500	1000	2000	4000	8000
150–300	1	2	3	5	7	6	5	4
300–600	0.5	1	2	4	6	5	4	3
600–900	0	0.5	1	3	4	3	2	2
900–1200	0	0	1	2	2	2	2	2

5.6.4 Duct bends

A bend, lined or unlined, has greater attenuation than a similar length of lined or unlined duct, since some of the sound energy impinges at right angles on the facing part of the bend. The attenuation of straight lined ducts is limited at low and high frequencies, but the attenuation of a lined bend increases with frequency, before falling slightly at the highest frequencies. The controlling factors for a particular bend are the duct width and the frequency. To gain maximum benefit from a lined bend, the lining should be installed both before and after the bend for a distance of at least two duct widths or diameters.

5.6.4.1 Square elbows

Tables 5.6 and 5.7, based on information published by the (US) National Environmental Balancing Bureau[14], compare lined and unlined elbows in terms of the numerical value of the product of frequency f (kHz) and width w (mm). Thus, for a 300 mm duct at 2 kHz, $(f \times w) = 600$.

Table 5.6 Approximate attenuation of unlined and lined square elbows without turning vanes[14] (reproduced from *Sound and Vibration Design and Analysis* by permission of the National Environmental Balancing Bureau, Gaithersburg, MD)

Frequency × width / kHz·mm	Attenuation / dB	
	Unlined	Lined
<50	0	0
50–100	1	1
100–200	5	6
200–400	8	11
400–800	4	10
>800	3	10

Table 5.7 Approximate attenuation of unlined and lined square elbows with turning vanes[14] (reproduced from *Sound and Vibration Design and Analysis* by permission of the National Environmental Balancing Bureau, Gaithersburg, MD)

Frequency × width / kHz·mm	Attenuation / dB	
	Unlined	Lined
<50	0	0
50–100	1	1
100–200	4	4
200–400	6	7
> 400	4	7

5.6.4.2 Round elbows

The insertion loss values for round elbows are not as well known as for square elbows, but an approximation of the attenuation is given in Table 5.8 for unlined round elbows[14].

Lined round elbows have greatest attenuation for smaller ducts, with a gradual decrease in attenuation for a given frequency as the duct dimension increases with constant lining thickness. As an approximation, lined elbows of all sizes with 25 mm lining achieve at least 10 dB reduction at 1000 Hz and above, about 7 dB at 500 Hz, 5 dB at 250 Hz, 2 dB at 125 Hz and zero at 63 Hz. Increasing the lining thickness to 50 mm gives additional attenuation of 3 dB, except at 63 Hz. These figures are very approximate and intended as a qualitative guide. More precise values should be available in a computer prediction program.

Table 5.8 Approximate attenuation of unlined round elbows[14] (reproduced from *Sound and Vibration Design and Analysis* by permission of the National Environmental Balancing Bureau, Gaithersburg, MD)

Frequency × width / kHz·mm	Attenuation / dB
<25	0
25–50	1
50–100	2
>100	3

5.6.5 Duct take-offs

When airflow is taken from the main duct by a junction or side branch, it is assumed that the sound power divides as the areas of the ducts as in Figure 5.8. The attenuation is given by equation 5.2.

$$\Delta L = 10 \lg \frac{A_1 + A_2}{A_1} \qquad (5.2)$$

where ΔL is the attenuation (dB), A_1 is the cross sectional area of the take-off branch (m^2) and A_2 is the cross sectional area of the main duct after the branch (m^2).

Changes in total cross-section may also cause reflection of sound back up the duct, but equation 5.2 represents the major effect.

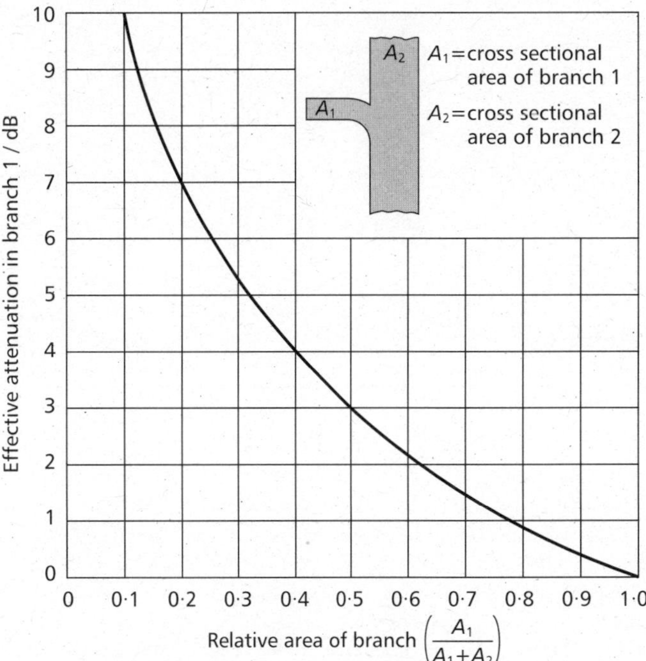

Figure 5.8 Effective attenuation of a duct branch

5.6.6 End reflection loss

The change in propagation medium, as sound travels from a duct termination into a room, results in reflection of sound back up the duct. The effect is greatest at long wavelengths (i.e. low frequencies) and is a contribution to the control of low frequency noise from the system. When a high level of low frequency noise is anticipated, it can be useful to reduce the sizes of ducts feeding a space and increase their number proportionately.

The end reflection loss of a duct terminated flush with a wall is given as[14]:

$$\Delta L_R = 10 \lg [1 + (0.8\,\lambda / \pi\, d)^{1.88}] \qquad (5.3)$$

where ΔL_R is the reflection loss (dB), λ is the wavelength of the sound (m) and d is the diameter of a circular termination (m). Wavelength is determined from $c = \lambda f$, see Appendix 5.A1. The effective diameter of a rectangular termination is:

$$d = \sqrt{(4\,A / \pi)} \qquad (5.4)$$

where A is the area of the termination.

Equation 5.3 shows that the relation between wavelength and duct dimension (λ/d) is the controlling factor. The equation is to be used for end reflection losses for terminations having aspect ratios (i.e. height/width) of the order of unity. Slot diffusers were not investigated in the work which led to equation 5.3 and manufacturers' data should be consulted for these components. Values of end reflection loss are given in Table 5.9.

5.6.7 Passive silencers and plenums

5.6.7.1 Passive silencers

A passive silencer, see Figure 5.9, contains localised sound absorbent, normally associated with narrowed air pas-

Table 5.9 End reflection loss at octave band frequencies(14) (reproduced from *Sound and Vibration Design and Analysis* by permission of the National Environmental Balancing Bureau, Gaithersburg, MD)

Duct dimension, *D* / mm	End reflection loss / dB at stated octave band / Hz				
	63	125	250	500	1000
150	18	13	8	4	1
300	13	8	4	1	0
450	10	6	2	1	0
600	8	4	1	0	0
750	6	2	1	0	0
1000	5	2	1	0	0
1200	4	1	0	0	0

sages. Both rectangular and circular silencers are used. The rectangular silencer is built up from an assembly of absorbent splitter modules. Its acoustic performance is determined largely by that of one of its single assemblies, which approximates to a narrow, lined duct. The parallel assemblies give increased capacity to carry the required air volume without increase of velocity. The cross section of the silencer is often significantly greater than that of the duct in which it is located. Changes in shape or cross section affect the operation of the silencer. Attenuation and pressure loss increase as the airways are narrowed. Another important variable is the length of the silencer. Longer silencers have increased attenuation and some additional pressure loss. Silencer pressure loss is not proportional to the length of the silencer, since significant pressure loss occurs at the entry and exit. A circular silencer is normally either open ('unpodded') or contains an inner assembly, the absorbent 'pod' or 'bullet'. Special systems may have concentric absorbent layers with airways between.

The static insertion loss of a silencer is measured without airflow, using noise from a loudspeaker. The dynamic insertion loss includes effects of airflow and may give lower results.

Care must be taken in the location of silencers in order to prevent interaction with other components. The attenuation values of two silencers placed close together in series are not necessarily additive, since interactions and poor airflows may affect their operation.

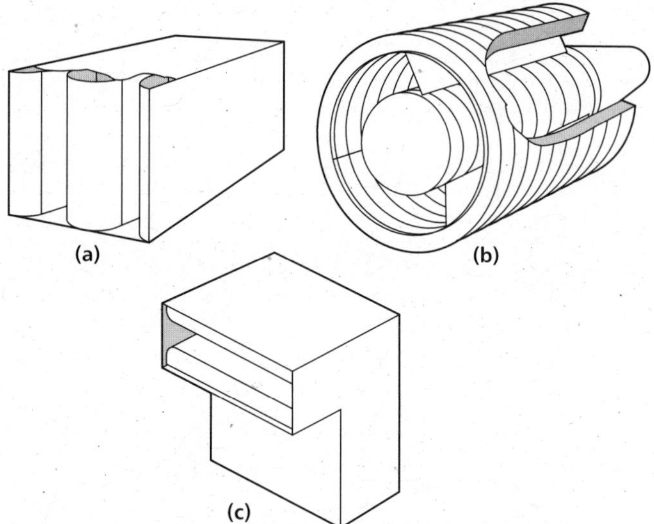

Figure 5.9 Dissipative duct silencers; (a) rectangular, (b) circular, (c) rectangular elbow (reproduced from ASHRAE Handbook: *HVAC Applications*, by permission of the American Society of Heating, Refrigerating and Air-Conditioning Engineers)

Silencers are included in the design when an analysis of the system has shown that the room criteria will not be met. The attenuation of passive silencers is low at low frequencies, rises to a maximum in the middle frequencies (1–2 kHz) and drops at higher frequencies. Manufacturers' silencer data should be backed by a statement of the standards by which it was measured. Factors to be considered in selecting a silencer include its attenuation at different frequencies and its pressure loss. Duct designs leading to poor entry and exit flow conditions increase the pressure loss and may generate additional low frequency noise. Particular attention should be given to the exit conditions.

It is advisable to locate silencers several duct widths or diameters clear of bends, in order to maintain good airflow. Commercial packaged silencers are available in a wide range of configurations giving some control over dimensions, pressure loss and attenuation, in order to optimise the choice for a particular application. In general, higher attenuation is obtained by reducing the distance across the airway and by increasing the length of the silencer. Reduced pressure loss is given by increasing the airway area whilst keeping the cross dimension constant. That is, by either increasing the height of the silencer or by adding additional airways to increase its width. Both these measures give a greater area for the airflow and so reduce the velocity in the airways, although too rapid a transition from a duct to a silencer of greater cross-section than the duct, will not produce the full benefit. For a given airway, the pressure loss increases as the square of the air velocity and it is seen that, in specifying a silencer, various requirements of insertion loss, pressure loss, space and cost must be balanced.

Location of a silencer should be between the major noise source and the occupied space, preferably between straight duct runs in order to give good flow conditions at the entrance and exit to the silencer. Often the major noise source is the plant room fan, but fan coil units, for example, introduce noise sources closer to the occupied space. A length of lined duct, between a ceiling space fan coil and the duct termination, may be adequate to deal with fan coils.

5.6.7.2 Plenums

Plenums are analysed by considering the inlet duct as a source of sound power into the plenum. The sound reflects within the plenum, as in a room, and a proportion of the sound energy passes into the outlet duct. The factors to be considered are then the dimensions, relative positions of the inlet and outlet and the absorption coefficient of the plenum lining.

For the plenum shown in Figure 5.10, it can be shown that the insertion loss is given by:

$$\mathrm{IL} = 10 \lg \left(A_{\mathrm{out}} \left(\frac{Q \cos \theta}{4 \pi r^2} + \frac{1 - \bar{\alpha}}{A \bar{\alpha}} \right) \right) \tag{5.5}$$

where IL is the insertion loss (dB), A_{out} is the outlet area of the plenum (m^2), Q is a directivity factor depending on the location of the inlet (normally taken as 4 for plenums, see section 5.7.3), θ is the angle between the slant distance (r) and the plane containing the axis of the inlet duct (see Figure 5.10) (degree), r is the slant distance from entry to

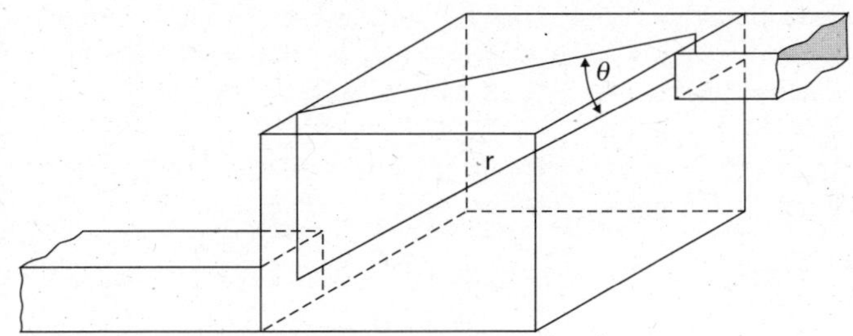

Figure 5.10 Schematic of a plenum chamber

exit (see Figure 5.10) (m), A is the total inside surface area minus the areas of the inlet and outlet (m^2) and $\overline{\alpha}$ is the average absorption coefficient of the lining.

Equation 5.5 assumes that the wavelength of the sound is small compared with the dimensions of the plenum. That is, it assumes that sound in the plenum behaves like sound in a room. (*Note*: there are similarities between equation 5.5 for a plenum and equation 5.A7.1 for a room.)

Equation 5.5 gives best results when the areas of the inlet and outlet are small compared with the total surface area. The positioning of the plenum may affect its performance, as duct lengths into and out of the plenum may resonate with components in the noise.

5.6.8 Active silencers

Active silencers detect the noise travelling in the duct and generate an opposing noise, which is added in with the travelling noise in order to produce cancellation. They are most effective in the low frequencies, where passive silencers have limited performance.

There are two main configurations of active silencer in which the active components are mounted either externally on the duct or in a central pod. The first type, illustrated in Figure 5.11(a), has some advantages for ease of retrofitting, whilst the second type, Figure 5.11(b), has technical advantages in the way in which the cancelling sound couples with the travelling sound. It also permits multiple units to be stacked to control noise in a large duct. Multiple units have been used, for example, to control noise breakout to atmosphere from air inlet or outlet openings. Active silencers have an application in natural ventilation, in order to give silenced, low pressure loss penetrations into the building.

Figure 5.11 shows how the upstream signal microphone picks up the travelling noise and sends it to a digital controller which outputs the cancelling noise to the loudspeaker. The downstream control microphone supplies performance information back to the controller to modify its parameters, and minimise the remaining downstream noise. Absorptive material round the perimeter and in the pod control high frequency noise, whilst the active components control lower frequency noise.

Active silencers have developed well beyond the laboratory demonstration and are now produced commercially by several companies, generally in a hybrid configuration incorporating both passive and active absorption, which can give wide-band noise control. The main advantage of an active silencer is that it gives good low frequency attenuation with lower pressure loss and in smaller space than an equivalent low frequency passive silencer. There are a number of factors such as air velocity, frequency range, duct dimensions etc., which need to be considered in the selection of an active silencer. Expert advice should be sought.

5.6.9 Use of fibrous sound absorbing materials in ducts

Although fibrous materials are excellent and inexpensive sound absorbers, there have been concerns over their use in ducts. Specifically, fibrous duct linings:

— may contribute to mould growth

— degrade with time

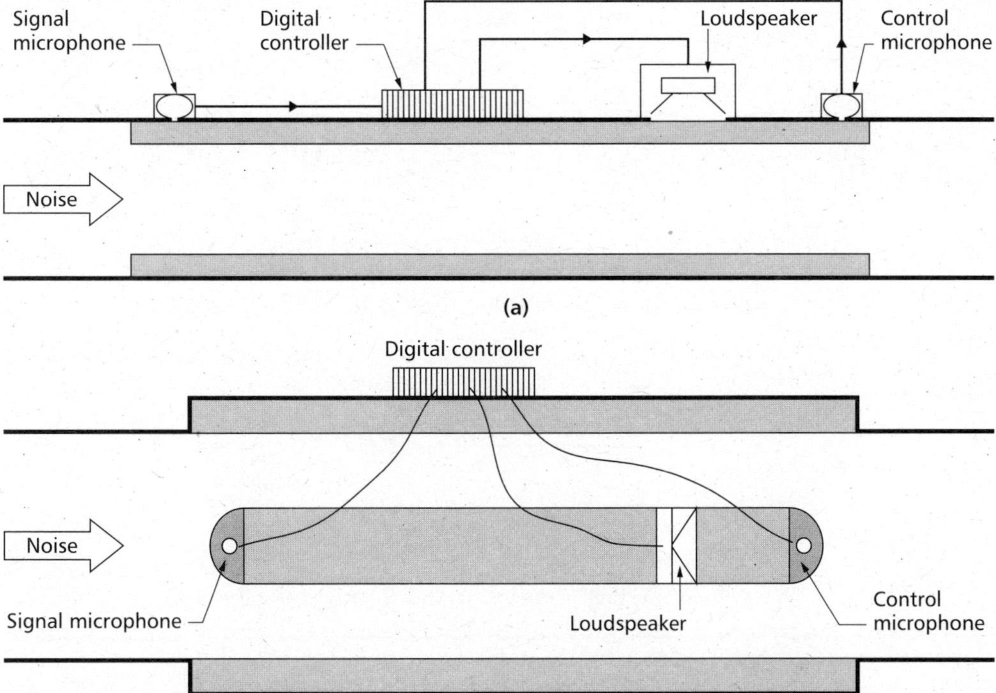

Figure 5.11 Active silencers; (a) mounted externally, (b) in a central pod

— erode from the surface and become carried in the air

— are difficult to clean.

In order to satisfy these concerns some general provisions that may be taken include the following:

— Fibrous linings should be kept at least 3 m away from wet sections as mould growth may occur if they become wet.

— Care should be taken in the installation, especially to seal raw edges.

— Linings are available with toughened surfaces, treated for mould control.

— In sensitive locations, the lining may be covered with a Mylar, or similar, facing although this reduces the absorption at high frequencies.

— If the lining might be damaged it should be protected with a perforated metal sheet having at least 25% open area, in order to maintain the absorption properties of the lining material.

— The material should be kept dry and undamaged prior to installation.

Unprotected fibrous material is sometimes used as a layer above suspended ceilings, for both noise control and thermal insulation. This results in a poor atmosphere for maintenance work above the ceiling and, if the ceiling tiles are moved, may result in fibres entering the space below.

5.6.10 Duct breakout noise

As duct materials are lightweight and thin, they transmit sound through the duct walls. This is known as breakout noise, which is a particular problem when long runs of duct pass over an occupied space. Breakout of noise leads to the noise in the duct reducing with distance, but breakout should never be used as a method of in-duct noise reduction unless the duct passes over non-sensitive spaces, such as storage areas. Break-in noise may also occur. For example, if the high noise level in a plant room breaks into a duct, the noise is then transmitted down the duct. The duct silencer for the main fan should be fitted to penetrate the plant room wall, so attenuating any noise which breaks into the duct within the plant room.

In estimating duct breakout, the procedure is as follows:

— determine the sound power in the duct

— determine the acoustic intensity in the duct

— obtain the sound transmission loss of the duct material

— determine the resulting external noise power.

The sound power in a duct is given in Appendix 5.A1 as:

$$P = I A_d \tag{5.6}$$

where P is the sound power (W), I is the in-duct sound intensity (W·m^{-2}) and A_d is the duct cross sectional area (m^2).

However, breakout is associated with a gradual reduction in the internal sound intensity in the duct. This was considered as duct attenuation in section 5.6.2.

It can be shown[15] that the sound power radiated from a length of duct is given by:

$$P_{(breakout)} = P_{(duct)} - R + 10 \lg (S_d / A_d) \tag{5.7}$$

where $P_{(breakout)}$ is the sound power radiated from the duct (W), $P_{(duct)}$ is the sound power in the duct (W), R is the sound reduction index of the duct wall material, S_d is the surface area of the section of duct wall (i.e. duct perimeter × duct length) (m^2) and A_d is the cross sectional area of the duct (m^2).

Equation 5.7 has limited application for the following reasons:

— The in-duct power level is not constant, but reduces with distance down the duct as the sound breaks out.

— The term (S_d / A_d) does not have a limit and could be so large that the breakout sound power exceeds the in-duct sound power, which is an unrealistic situation. The equation should be limited to ducts lengths of 5–10 m or the maximum breakout sound power limited to 3 dB below the in-duct sound power level.

— The sound reduction index (R) is normally measured under standard reverberant laboratory conditions, which differ from the sound fields in ducts. However, measurements of R have been made in different types of ducts and these should be consulted for further information[16,17]. As an approximation, the R values can be taken as the values for the sheet material from which the duct is constructed.

— The ceiling void and ceiling attenuation influences transmission of casing breakout noise from ceiling units into the occupied space below[17]. Thus, the location of the ducts and units within the void may affect noise radiation into the occupied apace.

5.7 Room sound levels

A duct system noise calculation gives the noise levels in the duct immediately before the conditioned space. Both the effect of the termination and the propagation from the termination into the room to the occupiers must be taken into account. This section deals with propagation in the room and with determination of room sound levels when the sound power issuing from the terminations is known. Duct terminations are considered in Appendix 5.A2, section 5.A2.5.

5.7.1 Behaviour of sound in rooms

When a source of sound operates in a room, energy travels from the source to the room boundaries, where some is absorbed and some of it is reflected back into the room. There are a number of subsequent reflections before the sound is reduced to such a low level that, in effect, it no

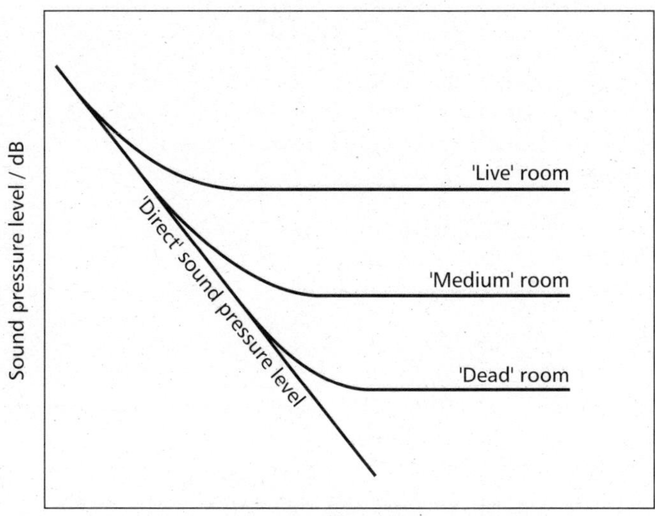

Figure 5.12 Variation of sound pressure level with distance from source

longer contributes to the total energy in the space. In a large absorbent and furnished room, particularly where the height is small compared with the other dimensions, the sound may be reflected by the furniture and absorbed by the floor and ceiling materials, so reducing the significance of the perimeter walls.

At any point in a room there are two contributions to the total sound:

— *direct sound*: that which comes directly from the source to the listener

— *reverberant sound*: that which has been reflected before it reaches the listener.

The balance between these contributions depends on the distance from the source and on the reflectiveness of the room perimeter, see Figure 5.12. This is considered further in Appendix 5.A7.

5.7.2 Determination of sound level at a receiver point

The conclusions from a series of measurements by Shultz[18] were that the relation between sound pressure level and sound power level in real rooms was of the form:

$$L_p = L_W - (10 \lg r) - (5 \lg V) - (3 \lg f) + 12 \quad (5.8)$$

where L_p is the sound pressure level (dB), L_W is the sound power level (dB), r is the distance from a source (m), V is the volume of the room (m^2) and f is the frequency (Hz)*.

If there are a number of sources, their effects at a point must be added.

* Although equation 5.8 appears to differ from equation 5.A7.1[17] in Appendix 5.A7, they are connected. The term (10 log r) means that, in real rooms, the level of the direct sound falls as 3 dB per doubling of distance, rather than 6 dB as in equation 5.A7.3 in Appendix 5.A7. The terms (5 log V) and (3 log f) together embody the acoustical characteristics of the space, as does the term $(4 / R_R)$ in equation 5.A7.2 (Appendix 5.A7), since R_R depends on the surface areas in the room and their absorption coefficients, which vary with frequency. Work following up on Shultz has produced complex empirical equations by curve fitting a range of measurements[14], but other methods use simple equations with tabulated correction factors for both single and multiple sound sources.

For a normally furnished room with regular proportions and acoustical characteristics which are between 'average' and 'medium-dead', as defined below, equation 5.8 leads to the following equations.

For a room volume less than 430 m^3, for a point source of sound:

$$L_P = L_W + A - B \quad (5.9)$$

where L_P is the sound pressure level at a specified distance (dB), L_W is the sound power level of the source (dB), A is a constant depending on the room volume and the sound frequency (dB) and B is a constant depending on the distance from the source (dB).

Values of A and B are given in Tables 5.10 and 5.11, which are derived from information contained in the ASHRAE *HVAC Applications Handbook*[17]. It will be seen that A incorporates the volume and frequency terms of the Schultz equation (equation 5.8) whilst B incorporates the distance term and falls off at 3 dB per doubling of distance.

For room volumes from 430 m^3 to 4250 m^3 the influence of room volume is less and the ASHRAE recommendation[17] is:

$$L_p = L_W - C - 5 \quad (5.10)$$

where C is a constant depending on the sound frequency and the distance from the source (dB). Values of C are given in Table 5.12.

In many rooms there is an array of ceiling sources, each one of which has an associated volume for which it is the major noise source. One way of proceeding is to calculate the effect of each source at a reception point and add these levels. However, ASHRAE[17] gives a simplified procedure for determining the noise at a reception height of 1.5 m,

Table 5.10 Values of constant A for equation 5.9

Room vol.* / m^3	Value of A (/ dB) for stated octave band / Hz						
	63	125	250	500	1000	2000	4000
42	4	3	2	1	0	–1	–2
71	3	2	1	0	–1	–2	–3
113	2	1	0	–1	–2	–3	–4
170	1	0	–1	–2	–3	–4	–5
283	0	–1	–2	–3	–4	–5	–6
425	–1	–2	–3	–4	–5	–6	–7

* Irregular values of volume arise from metric conversion from cubic feet

Table 5.11 Values for constant B for equation 5.9

Distance from point source / m	Value of B / dB
0.9	5
1.2	6
1.5	7
1.8	8
2.4	9
3.0	10
4.0	11
4.9	12
6.1	13

Table 5.12 Values for constant C for equation 5.10

Distance from source / m	Value of C / dB for stated octave band / Hz						
	63	125	250	500	1000	2000	4000
0.9	5	5	6	6	6	7	10
1.2	6	7	7	7	8	9	12
1.5	7	8	8	8	9	11	14
1.8	8	9	9	9	10	12	16
2.4	9	10	10	11	12	14	18
3.0	10	11	12	12	13	16	20
4.0	11	12	13	13	15	18	22
4.9	12	13	14	15	16	19	24
6.1	13	15	15	16	17	20	26
7.6	14	16	16	17	19	22	28
9.8	15	17	17	18	20	23	30

incorporating the height of the ceiling and the floor area served by each diffuser:

$$L_{p1.5} = L_{W(s)} - D \tag{5.11}$$

where $L_{p1.5}$ is the sound pressure level 1.5 m above the floor (dB), $L_{W(s)}$ is the sound power level of a single diffuser (dB) and D is a constant depending on the sound frequency, the floor-to-ceiling height and the floor area served by a single diffuser (dB). Values of D are given in Table 5.13.

Equations 5.8, 5.9, 5.10 and 5.11 are valid only for office types of rooms of 'average' to 'medium-dead' (see below) acoustical characteristics. Large reverberant spaces such as sports halls, where there are long unobstructed sound paths, may be analysed using the approach described in Appendix 5.A7. The accuracy of equations 5.9, 5.10 and 5.11 is 2–5 dB.

For the purposes of the above equations, the characteristics of room spaces are defined as follows:

— *Live*: hard surfaced rooms with no furnishing or absorbent material. These rooms echo or 'ring' when stimulated by a source. Typical reverberation time greater than 2 s.

— *Medium-live*: hard surfaced rooms with no specific attempts at adding absorption other than through the occupants and their furniture. Typical reverberation time around 1.5 s.

— *Average*: rooms with suspended ceilings or soft furnishings, carpeted and with drapes, e.g. typical office spaces. Typical reverberation time 0.7–1 s.

— *Medium-dead*: rooms with suspended ceilings, carpets and soft furnishings, e.g. executive offices. Typical reverberation time around 0.5 s.

— *Dead*: rooms which have been designed to be sound absorbent. Typical reverberation time less than 0.3 s.

Table 5.13 Values of constant D for equation 5.11

Floor-to-ceiling height / m	Floor area / m²	Value of D / dB for stated octave band / Hz						
		63	125	250	500	1000	2000	4000
2.4–2.7	9.3–14	2	3	4	5	6	7	8
	18–23	3	4	5	6	7	8	9
3.0–3.7	14–18.5	4	5	6	7	8	9	10
	23–28	5	6	7	8	9	10	11
4.3–4.9	23–28	7	8	9	10	11	12	13
	32.5–37	8	9	10	11	12	13	14

5.7.3 Source directivity

When the sound power of the duct termination has been calculated, a further step is required to assess whether the room influences the radiation from the termination. If the adjacent surfaces are acoustically non-absorbing, the influence depends on the location of the termination within the room, and affects only the direct sound. The reverberant sound is not changed by the location. A general consideration for sources is as follows.

If the source is located in free space, a situation which could be approximated by a duct projecting into the centre of a room, the energy from the duct outlet spreads uniformly and, for the direct sound, the relevant relation for intensity is given by (see Appendix 5.A1):

$$I = P / 4 \pi r^2 \tag{5.12}$$

where I is the sound intensity (W·m^{-2}), P is the sound power (W) and r is the distance from the source (m).

Figure 5.13 shows a further three basic locations for an outlet. If the termination is in the centre of a reflecting surface (position A), the sound propagates into half space due to reflections from the wall, so that, at any point, there is twice as much direct energy as before. This is an apparent doubling of the directly radiated source power, caused by reflections from one surface before the sound first reaches a listener. The result is a 3 dB increase in direct sound level.

If the termination is at one edge of the room (Figure 5.13, position B), where two reflecting surfaces meet, propagation is into a quarter space. There is an apparent quadrupling of the directly radiated sound caused by reflections from two surfaces before the sound reaches a listener, leading to a 6 dB increase in the direct sound over the source located in free space.

If the termination is in a corner (Figure 5.13, position C), where three reflecting surfaces meet, propagation is into one-eighth space. This is an apparent eight-fold increase

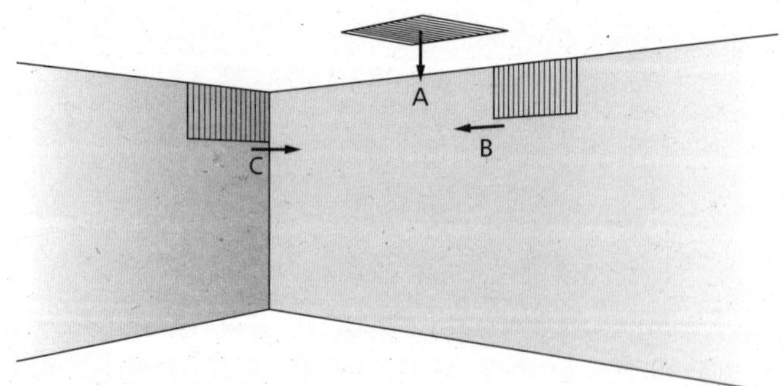

Figure 5.13 Outlet locations

in the directly radiated source power, caused by reflections from three surfaces before the sound reaches a listener. This leads to a 9 dB increase in the direct sound over the source located in space.

These initial reflections from surfaces adjacent to the source do not affect the reverberant sound levels.

A general relation for effective sound power of the source is:

$$L_W = (10 \lg P) + (10 \lg Q) + 120 \quad (5.13)$$

where L_W is the sound power level (dB), P is the sound power (W) and Q is a directivity factor. The directivity factor indicates how much more energy is received due to reflection of the sound by the adjacent surfaces. Under the conditions of reflective surfaces, as in Figure 5.13, Q takes values of 1 for a source in free space, and 2, 4 or 8 for positions A, B and C respectively.

If the adjacent surface is very absorbing, e.g. a suspended ceiling at higher frequencies, the sound will not be reflected from it and there will not be the simple theoretical interaction described above. Use of these directivity concepts is approximate. (There are parallels with reflection of light from reflective or dull adjacent surfaces).

Directivity is also an inherent property of some noise sources, which radiate preferentially in certain directions, irrespective of their location in a room. If a source is inherently highly directional, it will not be influenced by those adjacent surfaces which do not intercept its radiation. In general, when the dimensions of a source are large compared with the wavelength of the radiated sound, it becomes directional. See *Noise control in building services*[15] for further information.

5.7.4 Sound transmission between rooms

There are a number of paths by which sound may transmit between rooms, as shown in Figure 5.14. These are as follows:

— *Directly through the wall*: the mechanism is that sound impinging on the wall in the source room causes the wall to vibrate; for example, a sound level of 94 dB gives an oscillating pressure of 1 Pa on the wall. The vibration of the wall then causes it to act as a radiator of sound on the other side, into the receiving room.

— *Through gaps between the rooms*: often due to insufficient sealing of joints or penetrations. Gaps hidden by lightweight components such as skirtings, wall coverings, dry lined walls and electrical sockets can be significant and difficult to locate at a later stage. These gaps may cause a big reduction in the insulation of the wall.

— *By various flanking paths*: these are indirect paths due to vibration of room surfaces other than the partition wall.

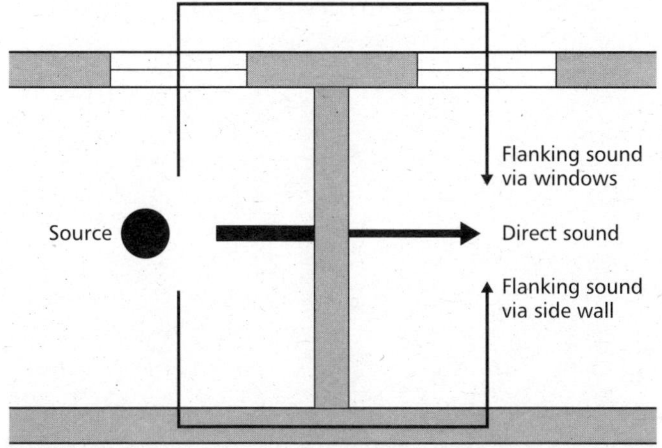

Figure 5.14 Sound transmission paths between rooms

The acoustical conditions in the receiving room influence the sound level within it. If the room is very absorbing, the level is lower than if it is very reverberant.

Problems of sound transmission between rooms may arise from poor design or installation of partitions and ceilings, which is not directly the responsibility of the building services engineer. However, a flanking path between rooms via ducts is the responsibility of the building services engineer. It should be noted that Building Regulations Part E[19], which previously covered only domestic housing, now includes all residential buildings. This includes hotels, student halls of residence etc.

Inadequate attenuation by plant room walls may also be a problem. The building services engineer must provide expected plant room noise levels for the architect or building designer. The attenuation required depends on the total sound power of the machinery in the plant room, although in a crowded plant room, if the nearest plant to a sensitive wall is noisy, this plant may be the main influence on the noise at the wall. Installation practices are also important, see section 5.4.

There are a number of ways of expressing the room-to-room airborne sound insulation, as follows.

5.7.4.1 Level difference

The level difference is simply the difference, as measured on site, of the average levels in the source room and in the receiving room, i.e:

$$D = L_1 - L_2 \quad (5.14)$$

where D is level difference (dB), L_1 is the average sound level in the source room (dB) and L_2 is the average sound level in the receiving room (dB).

The level in the receiving room depends on the properties of the partition wall, the flanking paths and on the reverberant build-up of sound in the room. Furnishing a receiving room in heavily absorbent material will tend to increase the measured level difference by decreasing the reverberant build-up of sound in the room.

5.7.4.2 Sound reduction index

The properties of the wall itself are given by the sound reduction index (R) which is measured by standardised procedures in a test room[20]. The reverberation time in the receiving room is standardised to $T_o = 0.5$ s, in order to allow for the effects in different rooms. A receiving room reverberation time, T, of 1 second will cause the level difference to be 3 dB higher than in a room having $T = 0.5$ s, i.e. $10 \lg (T/0.5) = 3$ dB when $T = 1$ s.

The sound reduction index is a property of the separating wall material for samples measured in a laboratory according to current standards[20] and this is the quantity which may be quoted in manufacturers' literature. Some examples of sound reduction index are given in Table 5.14, where the values are shown in decibels at octave band frequencies from 63 Hz to 4000 Hz. Although most laboratory measurements have traditionally been made in third octave bands from 100 Hz to 3150 Hz, as required in the older standards, measurement procedures now recommend extending the range from 50 Hz to 5000 Hz third octave bands. This recognises that the limited band of measurements from 100 Hz to 3150 Hz does not provide sufficient information for a full assessment of subjective effects of noise.

Sound reduction index and level difference are related by the reverberation time (see Appendix 5.A7, equation 5.A7.7), giving:

$$R = L_1 - L_2 + 10 \lg (T) + 10 \lg (S / 0.16\, V) \tag{5.15}$$

where R is the sound reduction index, L_1 and L_2 are the average sound levels in the source room and receiving room respectively (dB), T is the reverberation time (s), S is the total surface area of the room (m^2) and V is the room volume (m^3).

However, the validity of equation 5.15 reduces for short reverberation times.

5.7.4.3 Weighted sound reduction index

A single number representation of sound reduction is given by the weighted sound reduction index, R_w. This is obtained by comparing the measured attenuation–frequency curve with standardised curves, moderated by certain conditions. The value of the curve at 500 Hz then gives R_w[21].

There are differences between sound transmission under laboratory conditions and sound transmission in field conditions. The field measurement is often influenced by factors that are controlled in the laboratory, particularly flanking transmission and leakage through gaps. Table 5.14 gives typical values of sound reduction indices. Manufacturers' data should be consulted for standard prefabricated office partitions.

5.7.5 Privacy and cross talk

Privacy describes the ability to talk within one space without being overheard in another space. In an open plan office, privacy is related to background noise and distance. Privacy between adjacent private offices depends on the level of the sound transmitted between the spaces and the background noise in the 'listening' room. The level should be below the criterion level of the second space. Transmission is determined by the efficiency of the dividing wall and suspended ceiling. Office partition walls should preferably go up to the structural ceiling in order to prevent leakage from one office into the ceiling void and then down into the adjoining office. Where there is an unbroken space in the ceiling void, inclusion of absorption may help to reduce sound transmission.

However, the best acoustical design can be undone by cross-talk between rooms through common ducts. Figure 5.15 illustrates how sound enters a duct and travels to an adjoining room. Prediction is by estimating the sound pressure at the termination leading into the duct. This can be converted to sound power into the duct using equation 5.A1.13, see Appendix 5.A1, which may then be dealt with as described in section 5.6 and Appendix 5.A4 in order to determine the sound power that enters the second room. The sound level of the intruding speech should be 5–10 dB below the sound level in the second room. Alternatively, the sound power from the first room in the duct should be 5–10 dB below the HVAC sound transmitted into the duct that feeds the second room.

Approximate values for speech sound powers for loud voices are given in Table 5.15[15].

These figures are used to calculate the direct and reverberant sound at the duct termination responsible for the cross-talk. Direct sound is given by (see Appendix 5.A1):

Table 5.14 Typical values of sound reduction index

Material	Sound reduction index, R, for stated octave band / Hz						
	63†	125	250	500	1000	2000	4000
6 mm glass	15	18	23	30	35	27	32
Sealed double glazed window (6 mm outer, 12 mm air gap, 6 mm inner)	18	20	18	28	38	34	38
Separate window panes (5 mm outer, 150 mm air gap, 4 mm inner)	20	26	34	44	54	53	51
Acoustic double glazing (10 mm outer, 200 mm air gap, 6 mm inner)	26	37	46	45	47	57	64
Lightweight block (100 mm thick) e.g. 'Thermalite'	20	27	32	37	40	41	45
Galvanised steel sheet:							
— 22 gauge (0.55 mm thick)	3	8	14	20	23	26	27
— 16 gauge (1.6 mm thick)	9	14	21	27	32	37	43
200 mm reinforced concrete	36	42	41	50	57	60	65
Stud partition (9 mm plasterboard on 50 mm × 100 mm studs at 400 mm centres, 12 mm plaster both sides)	20	25	28	34	47	39	50

† Some of the values at 63 Hz are estimated

Table 5.15 Sound powers for loud voices

Frequency / Hz	Sound power level, L_W / dB
63	69
125	72
250	77
500	80
1000	80
2000	75
4000	76

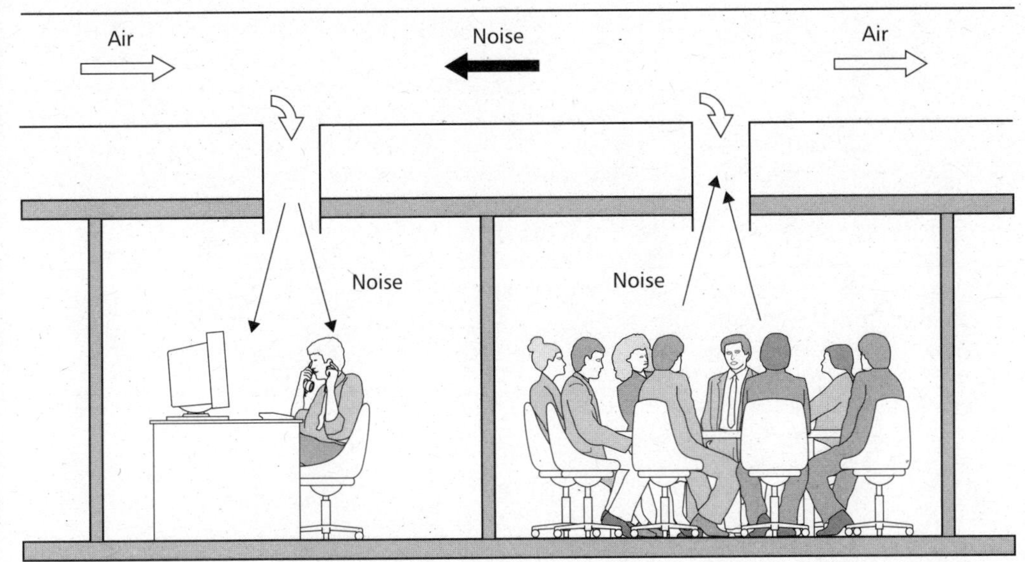

Figure 5.15 Cross talk between rooms

$$L_{p(direct)} = L_W - (20 \lg r) - 11 \qquad (5.16)$$

where $L_{p(direct)}$ is the direct sound pressure level (dB), L_W is the sound power level (dB) and r is the distance to the source (m).

Reverberant sound is obtained from equation 5.23 (see section 5.7.6) by assuming a reverberation time, T, of 0.5 s, typical of offices.

Hence:

$$L_{p(reverb)} = L_W - (10 \lg V) + 11 \qquad (5.17)$$

where $L_{p(reverb)}$ is the reverberant sound pressure level (dB), and V is room volume (m^3).

The sound powers into the duct are then given by:

$$L_{W(direct)} = L_{p(direct)} + 10 \lg A_d \qquad (5.18)$$

$$L_{W(reverb)} = L_{p(reverb)} + (10 \lg A_d) - 6 \qquad (5.19)$$

where $L_{W(direct)}$ is the direct sound power level (dB), $L_{W(reverb)}$ is the reverberant sound power level (dB) and A_d is the cross sectional area of the duct (m^2).

The –6 term in the reverberant power into the duct in equation 5.19 arises because of the random directions of arrival of the reverberant sound.

The total power into the duct is then the decibel summation of the two powers as described in Appendix 5.A1 and the calculation proceeds as in Appendix 5.A4.

Control of cross talk is achieved by lining the duct, as described in section 6, by splitting the duct into two or more runs, so that adjacent rooms are fed from different lines or by using 'cross talk silencers' in the duct between rooms.

5.7.6 Sound in large reverberant spaces

These spaces are typically assembly halls with hard surfaces, sports halls, swimming pool halls and churches. Multi-purpose halls may be used, as required, for sports, music performances and speech, but the design criteria will be to satisfy the most critical use. There will normally be an amplification system when used for speech. When used for sports or as a swimming pool, the requirement is to keep down the level of reverberant noise by use of absorbing material.

In these large spaces, sound propagation and reverberation is described by equation 5.A7.1, see Appendix 5.A7, in which the direct and reverberant sound can be separated. If the air supply is from a high level in the hall, the reverberant sound is likely to predominate at the level of the occupants and equation 5.A7.2 gives:

$$L_{pR} = L_W + 10 \lg (4 / R_R) \qquad (5.20)$$

where L_{pR} is the reverberant sound pressure level (dB), L_W is the sound power level (dB) and R_R is the room constant.

The room constant is defined as (see Appendix 5.A7):

$$R_R = \frac{S\,\bar{\alpha}}{1 - \bar{\alpha}} \qquad (5.21)$$

where R_R is the room constant (m^2), S is the total room surface area (m^2) and $\bar{\alpha}$ is the average absorption coefficient for the room surfaces.

But from Appendix 5.A7, equation 5.A7.8 gives:

$$T = 0.16\, V / R_R \qquad (5.22)$$

where T is the reverberation time (s) and V is the room volume (m^3).

Equations 5.20 and 5.22 lead to the reverberant sound level as:

$$L_p = L_W + (10 \lg T) - (10 \lg V) + 14 \qquad (5.23)$$

Therefore, the reverberant sound level produced by the ventilation system is estimated either by equation 5.20 if the room constant R_R is first calculated from knowledge of the room surfaces, or by equation 5.23 from the reverberation time. The information for these predictions should be obtained from the acoustics consultant.

5.8 Transmission of noise to and from the outside

Transmission of noise into or out of buildings has important implications for the building services engineer, whether the noise is from building services within the building or because the building services themselves alter the sound insulation of a building, e.g. by creating a new aperture and thereby admitting external noise. Building services noise may also be transmitted to another area of the same building or to an adjacent building. Some building services equipment is located outside and its noise may affect the building it serves or neighbouring buildings. Reflection of noise from adjacent building surfaces should be taken into account, see section 5.7.3 and *Noise control in building services*(15).

5.8.1 Transmission of noise to the outside and to other rooms

Noise from building services travels to the outside in a number of ways. It might be created outside from a roof-mounted air handling unit or condenser, or inside, such as from a fan or boiler plant. It then travels through louvres, ducts or the fabric of the building to the outside. It will be necessary to design the system to ensure that specified criteria are met outside the building. It is usual for the local authority to stipulate the criterion in such situations, to protect public open space or limit noise into nearby buildings.

Estimation of noise passing through the fabric of the building to the outside or to other parts of the building will generally require specialist knowledge of the sound insulation of materials, which is beyond the scope of this Guide, although general principles are given in section 5.7.4. If the building services engineer concludes that estimation is required, this should be brought to the attention of the project manager.

5.8.2 Transmission of external noise to the inside

For the building services engineer, the transmission of noise from the outside into a room should be considered from two distinct aspects. The first is that considered in section 5.8.1 above, where noise from the plant, occurring or created outside a building, travels into the building through windows, the roof or any other element, including the services themselves. Generally, but not always, the building services engineer will have no control over the sound insulation of the building against external noise and it will be necessary to ensure that criteria are met solely by appropriate design of the plant. The second aspect is that of noise from other sources, such as road or rail traffic, aircraft or industrial noise, entering a building via its own services, an inlet or exhaust duct or perhaps an extract fan. The opening for the fan or duct, or any gap around a duct, will have little insulation against noise from the outside and could seriously compromise the sound insulation of a building. Careful thought must be given to the sound insulation of the combined system.

5.8.3 Naturally ventilated buildings

Natural ventilation generally requires far more apertures in the building fabric with potential for external noise to enter the building. The low pressure drops required for natural ventilation imply the use of large and, probably, unattenuated ducts. These allow noise from the inside to get out and noise from the outside to get in. Generally, natural ventilation is difficult to apply to those buildings that require special levels of sound insulation against external noises, since apertures for intake and exhaust are also sites of acoustical weakness. Care must be taken in:

— *choice of the location of the apertures*: this may also be influenced by concerns over the quality of the incoming air

— *estimation of the noise leakage through the apertures*: a silencer may be required; the relatively low pressure loss of active silencers makes them suitable for noise control in natural ventilation.

5.9 Criteria for noise in HVAC systems

5.9.1 Objective

The objective of an acoustical criterion is to guide the design of an occupied space, so that it meets a specified acoustical standard. There are two components to be considered in complying with acoustical criteria:

— limiting the noise emission into the space

— designing the acoustics of the space.

The dimensions, perimeter materials and furnishings determine the acoustics of the space. These are not normally under the control of the building services designer, who has to make assumptions about typical spaces, as in section 5.7.2. In addition to HVAC noise, an office has activity noise related to the work in progress, e.g. office machines, telephones, conversation. The HVAC designer has responsibility for the HVAC noise, which must comply with the agreed criteria at specified locations. Compliance with acoustical criteria for HVAC is normally considered in the absence of activity noise.

Naturally ventilated buildings must also fulfil the design criteria, although the noise sources may be external to the building and not under the control of the designer.

In developing a criterion, the needs of work efficiency have to be balanced against costs of silencing. The term 'work efficiency' includes worker health, comfort, concentration, absence of errors etc., when working on their own and additionally includes communication with colleagues, when working with others. Communication may be by either telephone or direct speech over a neighbouring area.

5.9.2 Approaches

At the present time there are conflicting approaches to criteria. The widespread use of A-weighted decibels for environmental noise assessments is influencing room noise criteria, especially in the countries of mainland Europe. This is attractive for its simplicity and the ability it gives to compare noises, although it is difficult to relate, say, a 40 dBA steady services noise with a continuously fluctuating, intruding traffic noise, which averages as 40 dBA, but may have much higher peak levels. Reliance on the A-weighting may be unsafe, as a wide range of different noises could have the same A-weighted value. Some will be subjectively acceptable and some will not be. In particular, it has been found that the A-weighted measure is inadequate for noises which have high levels at low frequencies, as may occur with services noise(22). Countries which have adopted the A-weighting for general use are now placing additional restrictions on low frequency noise, summarised by Mirowska(23), covering the range from about 10 Hz to 200 Hz. This is mainly to protect people in their homes, although Denmark includes a low frequency restriction for noise in offices at a level about 10 dB higher than for homes(24).

5.9.3 ASHRAE approach

The American Society of Heating, Refrigerating and Air-Conditioning Engineers (ASHRAE) treats differences in noise spectra by considering the noise 'quality', as determined by the relative values of three frequency ranges (low, medium and high) within the noise(17). The frequencies considered are as follows:

- *low frequencies*: 16 Hz, 32 Hz and 63 Hz octave bands
- *mid frequencies*: 125 Hz, 250 Hz and 500 Hz octave bands
- *high frequencies*: 1 kHz, 2 kHz and 4 kHz octave bands.

There is normally little problem from duct-borne high frequency noise, although it may be generated by airflow over grilles. Middle-to-low frequencies include fan blade noise from a central fan or noise from a nearby fan coil unit. Low frequency noise often originates in a central fan and is the most difficult to control. It is recognised as an annoying rumble, but is not adequately recorded by an A-weighted measurement.

5.9.4 Review

The historical difficulty of developing a satisfactory criterion is illustrated by the large number of criteria that have been developed. The ones used most are:

- dBA level: first published in 1936
- NC (noise criterion): first published 1957
- NR (noise rating): first published 1962
- PNC (preferred noise criterion) first published 1971
- RC (room criterion) Mark I: first published 1982
- NCB (balanced noise criterion): first published 1988
- RC (room criterion) Mark II: first published 1995

Descriptions of these criteria are given in Appendix 5.A8.

NR and NC are currently used in the UK. The RC, NC and NCB are used in the USA, but RC Mark II is ASHRAE's current recommendation. PNC is rarely used. The main criteria (NR, NC, RC, NCB) are very similar in the frequency range 125–2000 Hz and there is little to choose between them. There is some divergence at higher frequencies and considerable divergence at lower frequencies. For example, NR is 19 dB more lenient at 31.5 Hz than RC.

The trend in the development of criteria over the past 30 years has been to extend criteria into the lower frequencies, whilst also placing greater limitations on the levels permitted at these low frequencies, as it has become recognised that they may have a particularly disturbing effect(22). For example, comparing the 35 rating at 31.5 Hz, NR35 is at 79 dB, NC35 (originally defined only down to 63 Hz, but commonly extended to 31.5 Hz) is at 68 dB (11 dB lower than NR), the RC is at 60 dB (19 dB lower than NR). However, NCB35 is at 71 dB, (8 dB lower than NR). The NCB assessment includes noise from all sources in the office, not just HVAC, so that each source, including HVAC systems, office machines, human activity etc., must be lower than the criterion limit.

The NR is an old criterion, which is satisfactory at low frequencies only when those frequencies do not occur. It has the weakness that it will permit high, potentially disturbing, low frequency levels to slip beneath its envelope. The NR is not satisfactory in those circumstances where the HVAC noise contains relatively high levels at low frequencies. ASHRAE approves the use of NC only in non-critical applications, but recommends RC Mark II for offices. Whilst it may be felt that the RC is very stringent in comparison with NR, it must be remembered that:

- a number of criteria for comfort in domestic premises place limitations on the levels of low frequency noise(23,24)
- there is a greater likelihood of disturbance by fluctuating levels at low frequencies(25)
- a sound level meter measurement averages the fluctuations and so does not indicate the peak levels in the fluctuations.

5.9.5 Criteria for design and commissioning

A design criterion must specify its requirements on a frequency basis, normally at octave bands. However, there is a problem with availability of design data, since it is only recently that 63 Hz data have become more readily available, whilst there are very few at 31.5 Hz and none at 16 Hz. The dimensions of test laboratories in relation to the wavelength determine the frequency limit and it is useful that new laboratories have been built with dimensions that give reliable readings down to 31.5 Hz. Some criteria, although used in design, were developed for troubleshooting, where the full range of octave band measurements are made on site. At the present time, the engineer is constrained to design with data down to 63 Hz and ensure that:

- the fan is used on an efficient part of its characteristic, in order to avoid low frequency instabilities

— the ductwork and airflows are designed to prevent low frequency turbulence

— fans, pumps and similar equipment are vibration isolated from the structure.

Since commissioning checks whether the design criteria have been met, the same criteria must be used for both design and commissioning.

5.10 Noise prediction

5.10.1 System noise

System noise prediction follows a simple logical process, but this is sometimes lost in the complexities of real systems. The prediction process for the HVAC system is as follows:

(1) Obtain the noise power of the source in octave frequency bands from manufacturers' data.

(2) Determine the successive effects of system components on the noise as it propagates in the duct, adding the effects, which may be negative (noise reduction) or positive (noise regeneration). Data on component effects should be provided by manufacturers. The end result is the sound powers at the duct terminations, see Appendix 5.A2, section 5.A2.5.

(3) Determine breakout noise from ducts and central devices etc. above a room, see section 5.6.10 and manufacturers' data.

(4) Determine the total sound power input to the room.

(5) Finally obtain the sound level at the occupant, see section 5.7.2.

These steps are to be carried out at all frequencies required for the criterion used.

5.10.2 Noise to atmosphere

This is most likely to occur from:

— a fan intake

— ventilation louvres in a plant room

— breakout through plant room roof or walls.

For the fan intake, the sound power at the opening is determined from the fan sound power and the attenuation that occurs between the fan and intake. Propagation effects to the outside are then included as in Appendix 5.A1, including directional radiation as appropriate.

The louvres in a plant room are treated similarly, but first the noise level in the plant room is estimated and this is assumed to be the level at the inside of the louvres. Louvre attenuation, as defined by the manufacturer, is then subtracted and the resulting propagation predicted.

Breakout through walls is treated similarly to louvres.

Directivity of the sources should be included.

These predictions are approximate and a more detailed analysis is given in BS EN 12354-4[26].

5.11 Vibration problems and control

5.11.1 Introduction

Some noise problems, which appear to be of airborne origin, actually originate in structure-borne vibration from poorly isolated machinery and services. Excessive vibration threatens the stability and service life of structures, may interfere with proper functioning of plant and equipment, will shorten (or, in extreme cases, destroy) plant working life, and will also interfere with human comfort. Even allowing for the most ideal design/selection/location conditions likely to be encountered by the building services engineer, vibration control may still be necessary for all of the plant that has been discussed earlier, e.g. boilers, chillers, air handling units, condensers, fans, compressors, generators, lift machinery, cooling towers, pumps, pipes, ducts etc.

The best form of vibration control is avoidance, by careful location of plant rooms and selection and location of low vibration equipment within them such that vibration does not become a concern. Some basic control measures are frequently included within packaged equipment, e.g. rubber bushes, but additional, external vibration control is often required. Vibration isolation, or control, normally refers to the reduction of vibration input through the mounting points of the plant to the building. However, the same mounting system works in reverse and isolates the plant from vibration of the building.

On a large scale, whole buildings are vibration isolated from their foundations in order to reduce problems encountered from building vibration originating in external sources, e.g. underground railways, road traffic, earthquake, ordnance shock etc., and the building services engineer may be involved in these problems, if only to assist in ascertaining the fragility level that services plant and associated control systems can withstand. Here, fragility level is defined as the maximum shock in units of acceleration due to gravity which a piece of equipment can withstand without suffering damage sufficient to cause it to become inoperable. For example, a fragility level of '3 g' means that the equipment can withstand an acceleration of about 30 $m \cdot s^{-2}$. The design for earthquake and ordnance shock is beyond the scope of this Guide but a useful reference is *A Practical Guide to Seismic Restraint*[27].

The two principal divisions of vibration control can be considered as:

— *architectural/structural*: floating floor systems, building isolation bearings, seismic restraints

— *mechanical*: sprung inertia bases, pads, elastomeric mounts, helical spring pedestal mounts, helical spring/elastomeric hangers, pipe/duct flexible connectors.

The building services engineer may be involved in the design of a floating floor for a plant room, but mounting whole buildings on springs is very specialised and should be left to others.

In this Guide, the word 'spring' is generally used in a very wide sense to describe a range of components which compress under load, including pad materials, elastomeric blocks, elastomers-in-shear arrangements, helical steel springs, pneumatic springs, and other arrangements incorporating hydraulic and mechanical damping.

5.11.2 Fundamentals of vibration and vibration control

5.11.2.1 Acceleration, velocity, displacement and frequency

Vibratory force has four convenient physical quantities:

— displacement, x (mm)

— velocity, v (mm·s^{-1})

— acceleration, a (mm·s^{-2})

— frequency, f (Hz).

(In practical vibration isolation work, it is usually, more convenient to use millimetres for the unit of length than meters.)

At a given frequency, f, the quantities are related by the following equations:

$$v = 2\,\pi f x \qquad (5.24)$$

$$a = 2\,\pi f v \qquad (5.25)$$

Then:

$$a = 4\,\pi^2 f^2 x \qquad (5.26)$$

Figure 5.16 and the associated Table 5.16 show the relationship, using a simple sine wave for illustration. The symbols X, V and A represent the maximum values of displacement, velocity and acceleration, respectively. Two complete cycles of the wave occur in 135 ms, giving a frequency of 14.8 Hz. The amplitude scale, which has a maximum of 1.0, could be displacement, velocity or acceleration, but for the purposes of illustration it may be taken to represent a displacement of 1 mm, as in Table 5.16. Given the frequency and any one attribute, values of the remaining ones can be calculated for that frequency, see Appendix 5.A6.1.

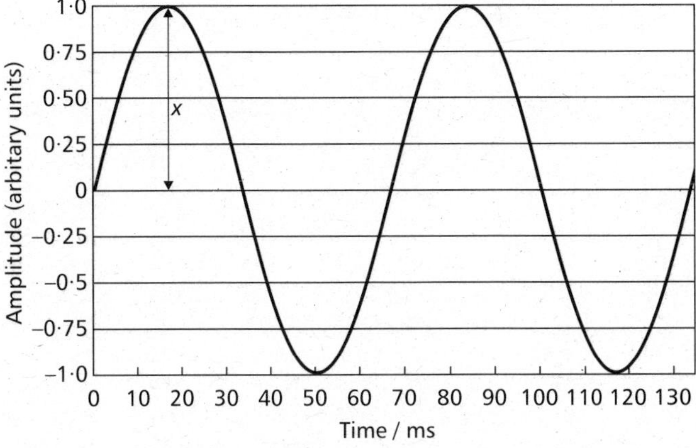

Figure 5.16 Vibration quantities

Table 5.16 Relation between vibration quantities

Quantity	Angular relationship	Maximum value at frequency 14.8 Hz
Displacement, x	$x = X \sin(2\,\pi f t)$	$X = 1$ mm
Velocity, v	$v = V \cos(2\,\pi f t)$	$V = 2\,\pi f X = 93$ mm·s^{-1}
Acceleration, a	$a = -A \sin(2\,\pi f t)$	$A = 2\,\pi f V = 8443$ mm·s^{-2}

The acceleration is nearly 1 g (= 9.81 m·s^{-2}). Excessive vibration has an adverse effect, for which there are some objective data, on structures and on service or process equipment. The frequency is important in assessing such an effect. An acceleration of, say, 1 g at 3 Hz (typical earthquake condition) is a totally different proposition to the same 1 g at 30 Hz, which might be encountered with ordnance or even common mechanical shock problems. The effect of vibrations on human comfort is more subjective, see CIBSE Guide A, section 1[(28)].

5.11.2.2 Natural frequency, static deflection, disturbing frequency, damping, vibration isolation efficiency

Natural frequency (f_n) is the constant frequency at which an object vibrates when set into motion and left to vibrate freely, e.g. when it is struck. It can be seen physically that, if the mass suspended on a spring is increased, the resonant frequency is lowered, whilst if the stiffness of the suspension is increased, the frequency increases.

Since the deflection under load depends on the stiffness and the mass, a simple prediction formula for resonant frequency is obtained in terms of the length, d, which the loaded spring deflects:

$$f_n \approx \frac{15.8}{\sqrt{d}} \qquad (5.27)$$

where f_n is the natural frequency (Hz) and d is the static vertical deflection of an isolated load on its springs (mm).

In practical vibration isolation, the spring stiffness is expressed as the spring rate (kg·mm^{-1}), which describes the load in kilogrammes required to deflect a spring by 1 mm.

Figure 5.17 shows how the displacement of the system changes if it is driven by a force that varies over a range of frequencies above and below resonance. There is a peak of response at resonance and a fall-off on either side of this peak. The disturbing frequency, f_d (Hz), is considered to be the frequency of the most probable vibratory force to require attenuation. Usually, satisfactory treatment of the disturbing (or forcing) frequency will produce 'bonus' treatment of all higher frequencies, and some lesser degree of attenuation at lower frequencies. The disturbing frequency may represent the most dangerous or annoying frequency and/or the most difficult frequency to attenuate. For the building services engineer it is usually the lowest speed of rotation/reciprocation present on an item of

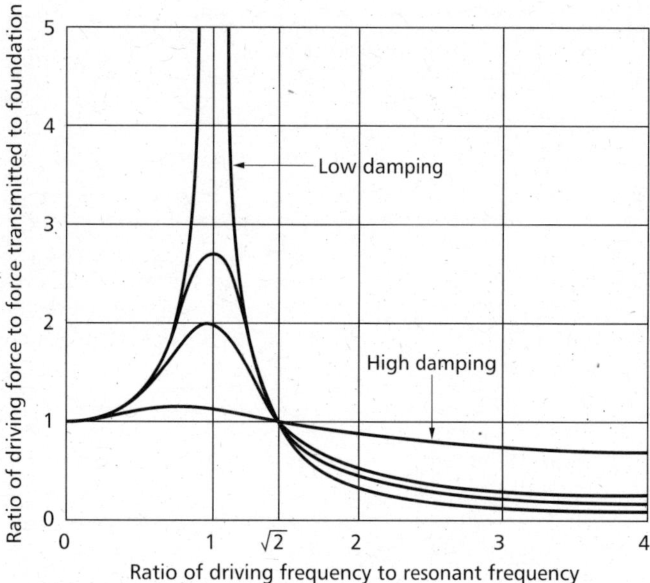

Figure 5.17 Vibration transmissibility

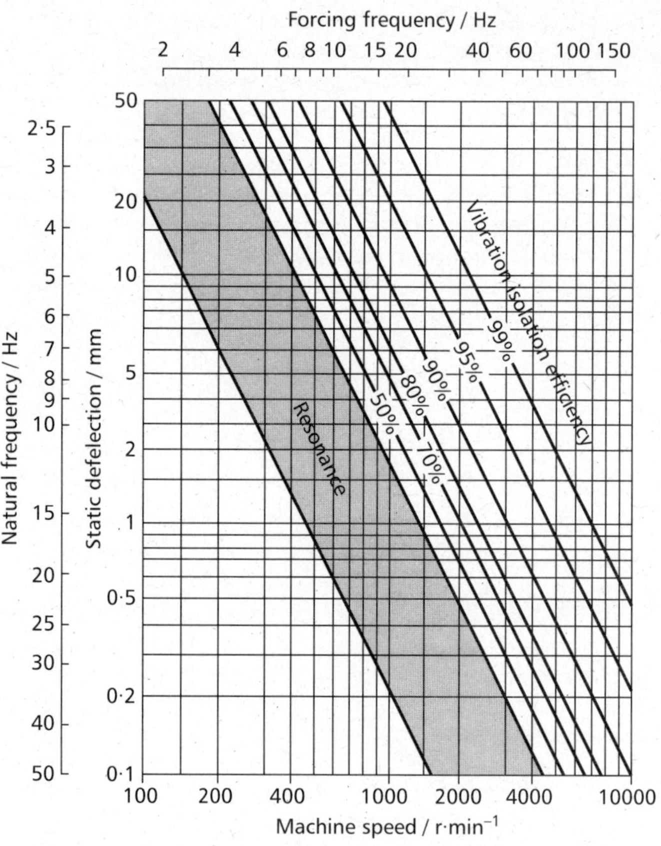

Figure 5.18 Relation between frequency, static deflection and vibration isolation efficiency (reproduced by courtesy of Eurovib (Acoustic Products) Ltd.)

equipment, but other factors such as amplitude also affect the full assessment. Figure 5.17 also shows that, when the disturbing frequency is in the region of the resonance of the mass/spring system, there is amplification. The attenuation region is for frequencies above about 1.4 f_n for all values of damping, but the attenuation reduces as the damping increases.

Damping relates to the dissipation of energy within the isolator during vibration. Low damping means that vibration continues for a relatively long time after impulsive stimulation. High damping results in more rapid decay. When damping is greater than some 'critical' value, oscillations cannot take place and, after displacement, an object slowly returns to its equilibrium position, e.g. like a pendulum suspended in treacle. Helical spring vibration isolators have very small inherent damping, whilst elastomer materials have a greater level. It may be necessary to add damping to a helical spring isolator. This might affect the resonant frequency of the system if the added stiffness of the damping material is high.

Vibration isolation efficiency (VIE) is the term used to give the amount of the disturbing frequency that is not transferred to the structure. It is sometimes expressed as the opposite, transmissibility (T) where T gives the amount transferred.

Isolation efficiency and transmissibility are related by (VIE+T)=1, although VIE is usually expressed as a percentage.

The equation for VIE when the system has no damping is:

$$\text{VIE} = 100\left(1 - \left(\frac{1}{\left(\frac{f_d}{f_n}\right)^2 - 1}\right)\right) \tag{5.28}$$

where VIE is the vibration isolation efficiency (%), f_d is the disturbing frequency (Hz) and f_n is the natural frequency (Hz).

Equation 5.28 gives the undamped response in Figure 5.17.

Figure 5.18 shows the relationship between disturbing frequency, the natural frequency and the vibration isolation efficiency. As with equation 5.25, note that a single degree of freedom (vertical vibration) is assumed and that the support structure is infinitely stiff. Mountings on flexible support structures are considered in section 5.11.4.2. As an example of the use of Figure 5.18, if the supported system has a natural frequency of 2.5 Hz and a forcing frequency of 5 Hz, the VIE is about 70%. In general, a forcing frequency of twice the system resonance frequency always gives 67%. A forcing frequency of three times the resonance frequency gives 87.5% whilst four times gives 93%, five times gives 96% and six times gives 97%. These figures are in the absence of damping.

Equation 5.28 applies when there is no damping (energy dissipation) in the system. This is never so in practice. The effects of damping include both limiting the maximum amplitude when the driving frequency is equal to the resonant frequency and reducing the isolation in the attenuation region.

5.11.3 Rating equipment for vibration emission

The degree of out-of-balance force transmitted by mechanical/electrical equipment in its normal operating mode (i.e. without specific, other than nominal, vibration isolation provision) is obviously critical to the evaluation of the vibration isolation requirement of a given machine in a given location. It is very difficult to obtain manufacturers' data for vibration emission and the conclusion is that very few have such data available. In the same way that it is now a requirement for manufacturers to provide acoustic data, they must be pressed to provide vibration levels. Data may be provided in various formats, but preference should be given to peak velocity, acceleration or displacement (any one or more of these) plus the frequency. The absence of such data has led to the adoption of various rules-of-thumb for treatment, resulting in degrees of under and over provision of isolation, and leading to wide variations of opinion and confidence in specialist advice. There are some areas of activity e.g. fine wine storage, electron microscopy, life science study, semi-conductor production, where such input data is essential, failing which over-design is inevitable.

5.11.4 Vibration limits

It is rare for clients or building services engineers to specify vibration limits for human comfort, e.g. an upper acceleration level at a specific frequency or frequencies. It is presently customary for engineers to use either the project's acoustical criterion as the limit for structure-borne noise or refer to limiting vibration via 'good practice' or other subjective terms, or perhaps by stating the percentage vibration isolation efficiency (VIE) required from any of the rotating/reciprocating equipment which puts energy into the structure. Any one of these methods might be augmented by specific reference to required treatments, e.g. pumps to be mounted on 25 mm static deflection spring inertia bases (perhaps with a minimum inertia ratio, see section 5.11.5). However, a distinction must be drawn between the selection/definition of a criterion and the individual isolation product/technique required to achieve it.

A noise criterion is effective only down to its lower frequency, say 31.5 Hz. It follows that a supplementary criterion is required for those frequencies lower than this which have their source in vibration. Exhortation to use good practice in selecting, installing, and isolating equipment is unsatisfactory. Specifying percentage vibration isolation efficiency (VIE) or its opposite, transmissibility, is an attempt to be objective. However the terms are widely misunderstood, in that they are very much frequency and amplitude dependent.

By this is meant that a given VIE level, say 90% (a common criterion), is demanding for high plant power at low frequencies, as the low frequencies call for high deflection of the isolation spring. However, 90% VIE is wholly inadequate for low plant power and high frequencies, since these frequencies easily become audible as radiation from the building surfaces. The satisfaction of the VIE requirement will also vary with the type of machine. Some machines, by their basic nature, emit greater degrees of out-of-balance force than others. Interaction with the structure, e.g. due to resonances in the structure, introduces further variability.

5.11.4.1 Vibration control to ensure comfort for occupants of buildings

BS 6472[29] gives limiting curves for vibration in buildings (acceleration/frequency and velocity/frequency) in terms of both x/y and z axes, and makes tentative suggestions as to which curves are likely to cause different degrees of human discomfort, see CIBSE Guide A[28]. However, BS 6472 is intended for diagnosis in existing situations rather than for prediction in the design of new buildings. A different approach is required for design, as described in the following paragraph.

A vibration criterion for general use may be obtained by setting VIE percentage limits in terms of the disturbing frequencies and machine powers. Table 5.17 relates the lowest disturbing frequency of interest to the spring static deflection (d) in order to produce the appropriate mounting resonance frequency which gives the vibration isolation efficiency stated in the table. Thus, for a disturbing frequency of 3.3 Hz and a VIE of about 40%, equation 5.28 shows that a mounting resonance frequency of 2 Hz is required. Equation 5.27 relates this frequency to the static deflection, d, of the mounts, giving 65 mm. To specify a VIE of 90% for a disturbing frequency of 3.3 Hz requires a resonance of about 1.1 Hz and a deflection of over 200 m, which is impracticable. Thus, Table 5.17 sets realistic, experience-based criteria. The required increase in VIE with machine power is linked to the greater force input of larger machines. The VIE values shown are for control of the lowest disturbing frequency given in the table.

Table 5.17 Illustrating practical expectations for vibration isolation

Machine power / kW	Vibration isolation efficiency (VIE) static deflection (d) and mounting resonance frequency (f_n) for stated lowest disturbing frequency (f_d)								
	f_d = 3.3 Hz			f_d = 7.5 Hz			f_d = 12 Hz		
	VIE / %	d / mm	f_n / Hz	VIE / %	d / mm	f_n / Hz	VIE / %	d / mm	f_n / Hz
0–0.9	42	65	2	72	20	3.5	83	12	4.6
1–9.9	42	65	2	88	40	2.5	83	12	4.6
10–49.9	64	85	1.7	92	65	2	93	25	3
50–99.9	74	105	1.5	95	85	1.7	97	65	2
>100	78	125	1.4	96	105	1.5	98	85	1.7
	f_d = 15 Hz			f_d = 25 Hz			f_d = 33 Hz		
0–0.9	84	8	5.5	96	12	4.6	94	4	7.9
1–9.9	90	12	4.5	96	12	4.6	97	8	5.6
10–49.9	95	25	3.2	98	20	3.5	98	12	4.6
50–99.9	97	40	2.5	98	25	3.2	99	20	3.5
>100	98	65	2	99	40	2.5	99	25	3.2

Notes: (1) the disturbing frequency, f_d, is usually the lowest speed of rotation, (2) the machine power is the absorbed power at the given speed of rotation, not the nominal rating or the absorbed power at a different speed, (3) d is the minimum vibration isolator static deflection under a given static load; where the input data is of doubtful provenance, it is frequently necessary to select, say, a 75 mm static deflection isolator to give a minimum static deflection of, say, 60 mm, (4) f_n is the natural frequency of the isolator/mounted machinery as installed and levelled, and assuming the support structure and the machine base frame are of infinite stiffness and the minimum isolator static deflection is obtained.

It will be noted that this method of setting a criterion has the advantage of stating the required natural frequency and static deflection, as well as the resulting vibration isolation efficiency.

Its disadvantage is that it makes no allowance for variations in structural natural frequency (largely controlled by slab deflection) and it does not discriminate between sensitive buildings, e.g. studios, and less sensitive buildings such as retail stores. It is, nonetheless, a good general purpose guide for most common structures and is relatively easily understood and therefore enforced.

5.11.4.2 Relation between vibration at source and the associated structure

Simple vibration theory, as used above, assumes that the isolator is mounted on a solid foundation, a condition that might be approached in a basement. However, where plant is at a higher level in the building, the natural vibrations of the support structure, e.g. the plant room floor, might interact with the vibrations of the plant. In order to avoid such interaction, the resonant frequency of the mass on its isolators should be about one tenth of the fundamental resonance frequency of the floor slab. As the resonant frequency of the floor reduces for wider slabs, the mounting resonance of the vibration isolation system must also be reduced for these slabs. That is, in order to lower the mounting frequency, the static deflection should be increased as the slab width between columns increases. The structural engineer will be able to provide information on slab resonances.

Vibration isolation manufacturers have their own recommendations, which might typically be, say, for a disturbing frequency of 25 Hz and 95% vibration isolation efficiency:

— *installed in basement*: static deflection = 8.6 mm
— *on 10 m floor span*: static deflection = 9.9 mm
— *on 15 m floor span*: static deflection = 11.2 mm.

5.11.4.3 Criteria for equipment

Criteria for equipment can refer to emission levels which must not be exceeded, in which case an appropriate standard must be selected for that equipment, taking care to ensure that power, velocity/acceleration and frequency are included in the maximum permissible levels.

Criteria for fragility levels is best given as the maximum acceleration that is to be withstood at the critical frequency (usually the lowest), without resulting in machine malfunction.

5.11.5 Common types of vibration isolator

Figure 5.19 illustrates common types of vibration isolator[30,31].

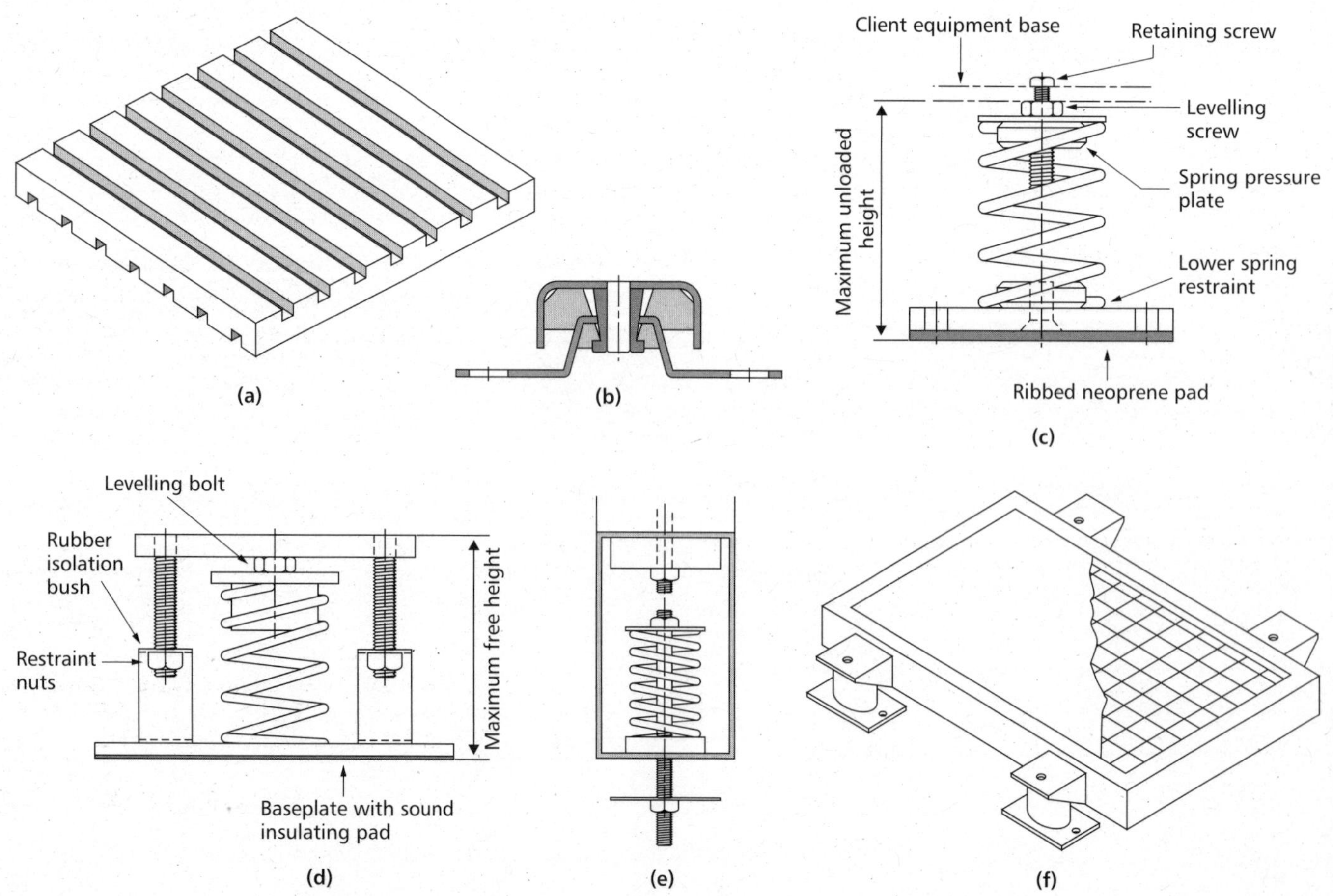

Figure 5.19 Typical vibration isolators; (a) ribbed mat, (b) elastomer in shear, (c) open spring isolator, (d) restrained spring isolator, (e) pipe/duct hanger, (f) formwork for inertia base (reproduced by courtesy of Eurovib (Acoustic Products) Ltd)

5.11.5.1 General

A number of difficulties arise in the selection of vibration isolators. In particular, static deflection depends on vertical load, but this load is not always known accurately. The vertical load from the plant is either given by the equipment manufacturer or calculated from input data supplied by the manufacturer. Either way it is subject to error, often an underestimate. Additionally, anti-vibration mount (AVM) suppliers add safety factors over and above any safety limit built-in to the isolator design. The AVM supplier will not normally produce a bespoke mount, but offer the nearest standard one above the required carrying capacity. It is therefore important to make a distinction between minimum required static deflection and the nominal static deflection that a mount gives when accurately loaded. A common example is the selection of nominal 30 mm deflection helical spring mounts to give not less than 25 mm static deflection.

5.11.5.2 Pad materials: flat, laminated and contoured

With some exceptions, pad materials are too unpredictable and limited in performance to be regarded as reliable vibration isolators. Their most popular, convenient, and successful role is as cheap and easily fitted sound separators, rather than vibration isolators. Elastomeric materials have inherent variability of elastic properties, which affect their performance. A column of elastomer will not compress uniformly, and will only deflect in proportion to its ability to bulge or distort under load, determined by the 'shape factor', which is given by:

$$\text{Shape factor} = \frac{\text{Area under load}}{\text{Area free to bulge}} \tag{5.29}$$

Thus, a circular disc of elastomer will deflect somewhat less than a rectangular strip of equal thickness and equal surface area. Generally, a high shape factor produces a stiff mount.

In order to avoid over-stress, a deflection limit on pads is 10–15% of the thickness. Reliable deflection is also compromised by the wide manufacturing tolerance, presently ±5%, allowed for moulded stiffness (related to Shore hardness). Further, the static and dynamic stiffnesses of a given elastomer differ, due to non-linear deflection. The mounted resonance frequency should not be determined from equation 5.27, although an approximation may be obtained by multiplying the result by 1.5. For preference, refer to individual manufacturers for information, but a distinction should be drawn between standard catalogue information and certified data. Much catalogue data will assume equation 5.27 is valid for elastomers, which can be misleading. Trial design exercises will quickly demonstrate the limitations of pads as isolators. They are best regarded as low frequency noise separators, i.e. vibration breaks rather than vibration isolators.

Pad materials are available either as single units or in sheet form, from which the desired size may be cut. The material is often ribbed or similarly profiled, in order to increase its flexibility, or stacked in multiple vertical layers with a stiff diaphragm material between layers to improve 'shape factor' effects. It will be recognised that a doubling of pad thickness will result in approximately twice the deflection at equal load, and a doubling of surface area will result in a doubling of load capacity at constant deflection. However, these approximations ignore the dynamic factors referred to above. Pads must be uniformly loaded to prevent excessive localised compression and, because of their high stiffness, it may be difficult to load pads uniformly with sufficient weight for the required deflection. They cannot be mechanically fastened down to the structure without compromising isolation unless they are incorporated in suitable housings or between plates.

Polychloroprene (neoprene) is considered to have the best all round properties, but a wide range of materials are available, all of which have various advantages and limitations. A distinction should be drawn between a properly specified material and 'commercial grade', where quality can be distinctly variable. Bearings for critical applications are always subject to batch test approval. For example, when elastomeric blocks are used in building bearings, all of the static and dynamic variables are taken into account, as a guaranteed maximum resonant frequency is required. Manufacturing techniques include compression moulding, injection moulding, extrusion and calendering.

5.11.5.3 Elastomer-in-shear

These mounts suffer from the same fundamental limitations and unpredictable variables as do pads, but to a lesser degree. However, to achieve significant deflections without excessive column height, it has been common practice for some 50 years to install elastomers at least partly in shear. An example is turret mounts, with static deflections up to 10 mm. There is greater flexibility in shear than in compression, although most isolators use a combination of shear and compression. The most commonly claimed upper deflection limit is 12 mm, but 10 mm is regarded as the practical maximum.

For the approximate determination of resonant frequency, in the absence of manufacturers' certified data, equation 5.27 may be used and the result multiplied by 1.2. As with pads and blocks, elastomer-in-shear mounts are most commonly associated with lighter loads and higher disturbing frequencies, but there are exceptions. These mounts are also available in hanger form, both on their own and in conjunction with helical springs. Unlike pads, elastomer-in-shear mounts can be fixed down without compromising the isolation. They are very commonly incorporated into fan and pump products by the manufacturer.

11.5.4 Helical springs

The helical spring is the most commonly used, most reliable and most predictable device employed in vibration isolation. Springs differ from elastomer materials in that they deflect uniformly under increasing load and have equal static and dynamic stiffness, as required for equation 5.27. There are various mounting configurations including open, caged, enclosed and restrained. They are also available as pipe or duct hangers. When supplied in other than 'open' mode they can be damped or undamped. They are available in a wide range of load carrying capacities from kilograms to tonnes per isolator.

Typical deflections are 30 mm, giving a mounting frequency of about 3 Hz and a vibration isolation efficiency (VIE) of over 90% but they are readily available in deflections up to 150 mm. Helical springs occasionally fail at higher machine frequencies due to wave propagation through the spring (especially in hanger mode) and this has led to the incorporation of elastomeric pads as vibration breaks. When in 'open' format it is good practice for the ratio between spring diameter and spring deflected height to be no less than 0.8:1.0 in order to promote spring stability. When enclosed, caged or restrained this relationship is clearly less important, although good spring design should always preclude buckling and other forms of instability.

If springs are to be fixed at their upper or lower ends, methods other than welding, which affects temper, should be sought. Springs are generally designed with up to 50% overload potential, but the overload percentage will diminish as the rated load increases, otherwise the spring will reach unreasonable dimensions. Load range can be increased by ganging springs in parallel, leading to restrained spring mounts of up to 8 tonnes load at up to 150 mm static deflection.

5.11.5.5 Inertia bases

Any spring mounted base which is used to support mechanical equipment is referred to as an inertia base. A steel base frame without spring support is a known as a skid, and concrete bases without springs underneath are referred to as plinths or 'housekeeping pads'. Displacement forces from the mechanical 'driver' have to overcome the additional inertia provided by the base. This is very effective where there are two or more drivers, perhaps at differing speeds of rotation, as with a motor and a fan or a motor and a pump. The base may be a bolted or welded steel frame, a bolted or welded steel concrete pouring frame, or a cast concrete base on a timber or metal former, the former having first been fitted on the underside with pads or mounts. Inertia bases can be used to provide additional mass per spring, thus increasing static deflection and reducing the resonant frequency of a supported system. However, care should be taken that the additional mass does not cause problems to the structure. The additional mass is useful in lowering the centre of gravity of the supported system and in providing resistance to lateral and axial forces. A typical inertia base consists of a steel form, which is filled with concrete to give the mass.

Support brackets for vibration isolators are usually attached to the base. A larger base is used to provide a platform for a number of items of equipment e.g. run and stand-by pumps, which cannot conveniently be supported individually. Most pumps are very conveniently mountable on inertia bases, which also gives the advantages of improved vibration isolation. Spring mounted concrete pouring frames are available in flat pack form for bolted on-site assembly. These have the advantage of lightweight shipping and site handling and their final location in the plant room can be chosen and adjusted before pouring the concrete. Advice should be sought before finalising the design of an inertia base.

The rule of thumb for the ratio of masses of the base and the supported equipment is 1.5:1.0 for most conventional equipment, including pumps, but could rise to 5:1 for equipment with large lateral out-of-balance forces such as high pressure blowers, where there are high static and velocity pressures.

It has become common for the fan and motor section of air handling units (AHUs) to be internally isolated using a lightweight steel inertia base, spring mounts and one or more flexible duct connectors. Whilst this arrangement can work effectively, it is a generalised optimisation and for more critical applications it is preferable to have the fan/motor section mounted rigidly and to isolate the whole AHU from the structure, if necessary incorporating steel rails to tie the whole assembly together. This has the added advantage of presenting the whole of the unit as inertia to the 'driver'.

11.5.6 Flexible pipe connectors

Although quite short, typically 150 mm flange-to-flange, these give flexibility to prevent anchored pipes by-passing the isolators and also take up strains from minor misalignments. They are not to be confused with expansion joints, which are specialist products employed for different purposes. They are available in a range of reinforced elastomers, and with flanged or screwed connections. For high pressures or risk of displacement they are available with isolated restraint rods. Reliable data for their isolation efficiency are not available but it is generally believed to be good practice to install them, for example, on any pump flow and return. Spring hangers will still be required, especially where pipework is fixed to structures directly adjacent to occupied areas. They are not to be confused with hoses, some of which are properly rated for noise and vibration isolation(32). A typical pump installation reflecting good vibration isolation practice will consist of a spring inertia base, a flow and return flexible pipe connector, and perhaps four spring hangers.

5.11.5.7 Flexible duct connectors

Used as a vibration break, particularly between the fan and its duct, they can be of circular or rectangular section. The recommended length is sufficient to allow 150 mm of slack between the two coupled ducts. They are normally made from organic or synthetic canvas impregnated with neoprene or another sealing elastomer, but are also available in a range of alternative materials with varying acoustic and fire ratings. The better models are provided with their own integral fabric flanges and a matching metal flange. They can also be fitted directly to coupling ductwork by jubilee clips. Reliable data for vibration isolation performance are not available but their use signifies good practice, although duct isolation hangers may still be necessary.

5.11.5.8 Isolation hangers

These are used for ducts and pipes. Where plant rooms directly adjoin occupied areas and especially where 'weak' structures are present, it is essential that pipework and ductwork are isolated from the structure The flexible element may be either helical spring or elastomer or a combination of these. A good design of hanger will have a spring diameter to height ratio of 0.8:1.0, large clearance holes which are grommet and bush protected, an elastomeric element to preclude high frequency bypass, and a restraint cross-bar to enable the load to be taken and pipes to be levelled prior to the spring being actually loaded. This last feature prevents spring overload and obviates erratic pipe levelling. Where detailed pipe and duct co-ordinated services drawings are available, together with adequate architectural and structural detail, hangers can be selected and located in advance. Current practice is for pipework to be installed 'rigid' on standard studding, but leaving enough vertical room for the hangers to be cut-in later, thus ensuring their accurate selection from a site survey. Increasing machine powers, weaker slabs and developing environmental awareness, are putting greater emphasis on the inclusion of spring hangers in plant rooms. Spring hangers are essential where acoustic ceilings are installed.

5.11.5.9 Air springs

The use of helical steel springs requires increasing amounts of static deflection as the required mounted natural frequency is reduced. Assuming a rigid structure, from equation 5.27, a natural frequency of 1.4 Hz requires a static deflection of 125 mm. To achieve an actual static deflection of 125 mm, helical springs would be designed for 150 mm static deflection, due to the input variables, which probably represents the upper limit for convenient helical spring mount design, especially where very light or very heavy loads are concerned. Air springs operate in a different way and achieve natural frequencies of 1 Hz (equivalent to 250 mm of static deflection). They are basically air-filled reinforced rubber cushions with a valve controlling the internal air pressure, giving variation of the load carrying capacity and natural frequency. They require regular inspection and maintenance, including a constant air supply. Some types of machinery, such as electron microscopes, require a very high degree of isolation. Air springs serve this purpose, taking up much less space than their helical spring counterparts. They are not generally as convenient or competitive as elastomers and helical springs, which are for the general range of equipment encountered by the building services engineer.

5.11.5.10 Floating floors

The maximum difference in noise level obtainable from a homogenous construction is about 50 dB, particularly at lower frequencies. No matter how much design input and installation care is taken to optimise the mass, the quality of the construction and avoidance of leaks through air gaps, the level difference is controlled by flanking paths. The purpose of floating floors is the minimisation of flanking paths and the introduction of an isolating air space

Whilst there is no reason why floating floors should not be designed for vibration isolation, this can lead to difficulties, particularly from differential plant loading and it is for this reason that the floating floor is more often considered as an acoustical treatment. Floating floors are designed with natural frequencies down to, say, 6 Hz, which is in the range of elastomer in shear isolators, whilst for higher resonant frequencies, say 10–15 Hz, pads and quilts can be used. The simplest floating floor is concrete laid onto a resin bonded mineral wool mat, such that the mat has only a small deflection. More complex systems use an array of pads covered by formwork, onto which the concrete is poured. Some spring systems may be jacked up after the floor is laid.

Design of a floating floor must take the following into consideration:

- the additional mass of floor and plant on the structural floor
- the appropriate load bearing points on the structural floor
- the number and distribution of mounts.

Specialist advice must be sought in the design of a floating floor.

5.11.5.11 Structural bearings

These are used to isolate whole buildings from earthquake or shock. Construction of the bearings is often elastomeric pads or blocks, sometimes built up as a multiple sandwich construction between steel plates although springs may be used. This is a very specialised area for which expert help must be sought.

5.11.6 Practical examples of vibration isolation

5.11.6.1 General observations

Degrees of freedom

The simple one-dimensional approach is to consider a spring-mounted body constrained to move in one direction, normally vertical. This is a good approximation to what occurs in most installations, but other movement, generally undesired, may occur. A mounted body has the potential to move in three linear directions, X, Y and Z, whilst also turning on its mounts in three rotational modes about these axes. The non-vertical movements occur when forces acting from the isolators on to the body exercise a turning moment through its centre of gravity. This is avoided when the top supports of the isolators are in the horizontal plane through the centre of gravity but, in practice, this idealised design may not be possible. The design will be to keep the centre of gravity at a low level.

Number and location of mounts

Knowledge of the position of the centre of gravity enables moments to be taken in order to determine the load at each mounting point. Where the number and location of mounts is pre-determined by the equipment manufacturer, it is reasonable to expect that the equipment and base design has, as far as possible, centralised the centre of gravity in the horizontal plane and positioned it as low as practicable. Additionally, the mounts should be located for equal loading. Optimally, they will also be located at equal centres and the manufacturers' skid or base will have been designed to be sufficiently stiff for minimal deflection between mounting points. This is the ideal situation and will usually position the mounts at a maximum of 2000 mm centres.

When a beam has its centre of gravity dead centre, and is supported by a number of mounts at equal centres, the actual load on the mounts at the extremities of the beam are half the load on the intermediate mounts. The solution here is to centre the mounts at equal centres such that the span between mounts is twice the span between the end mounts and the ends of the beam. Where this is not possible, the end mounts should be rated at half the load of the intermediate mounts. When equipment is mounted on a very stiff beam and mounts are selected for equal loads, the deflection of the mounts will be equal, despite uneven load distribution along the beam. Bending of the supporting beam could occur where large loads and lighter skids are involved. Many computer programmes for selection of anti-vibration mounts only work in two dimensions and assume that the beam is stiff enough to resist bending. Where the centre of gravity is not geometric dead centre, the same practical approach can be taken, except that, where a load is obviously biased toward one end of the beam, 'tipping' will occur unless the load capacity of the mount is increased at that end.

The rule of thumb for skid design is that the beam should have a depth not less than 1/10th. of the span between mounts, whilst beam deflection may be up to 1/250th. of this span. It is reasonable for the building services engineer to require equipment manufacturers to mount their equipment on adequately stiff skids, and to give the location of the centre of gravity. Where the manufacturer has pre-determined the mount positions, they should also be able to state the loads for each mount. There will be occasions, however, when the equipment supplier will have only partial information, e.g. the total weight plus individual component weights. A specialist will then have to determine the position of the centre of gravity and calculate individual mounting point loads. Further, there will be occasions when it will be necessary to supplement the manufacturer's skid with an additional base frame, or perhaps an inertia base. For a rectangular base, four or eight mounts are preferable to six, in order to inhibit rocking modes.

Where mount location points are not pre-determined the vibration specialist will endeavour to locate mounts at equal centres and at equal loading. Subject to the maximum span between mounts and to skid stiffness, it is probably better to have mounts at equal loading but different centres, than differential loading at equal centres. Another factor that will affect the number of mounts is load. Most anti-vibration mount manufacturers produce a range of standard, single-spring mounts at 'standard' deflections up to about 1200 kg vertical load. Higher load mounts are produced with load sharing, multiple spring elements arranged in parallel. When selecting a mount for a given application, the specialist will usually choose a standard product with standard load/deflection characteristics. This will be the mount that carries the nearest standard load above the specific design load.

Types of mount

Pads and elastomer-in-shear mounts are normally used for light loads and small machine power. Pads and blocks are useful 'sound separators' but are not an effective vibration isolator, other than when specially designed and selected, e.g. bearings, floating floors. Elastomer-in-shear has its lowest dynamic natural frequencies in the region of 6 Hz which will give adequate vibration isolation efficiency (VIE) for disturbing frequencies down to about 1000 r·min^{-1} (17 Hz), depending upon machine power and location. A maximum power of 3 kW and a minimum speed of 1000 r·min^{-1} is a reasonable guide. Although such mounts are available for high loads, the maximum load per mount should be less than 180 kg. These mounts should never be exposed to loads in extension, nor any significant lateral load without the approval of the manufacturer.

Commercial grade neoprene is a good all-round choice of pad material for plant room use. These mounts are sometimes designated 'single deflection', meaning deflections up to 6 mm maximum, and 'double deflection' for up to 12 mm deflection. Elastomer-in-shear mounts, particularly the cheaper ones, do not normally incorporate levelling devices but, because of the limited deflection, any differential loading will not result in undue out-of-level problems. As with all plant mounting operations, however, one should ensure that the initial plant base location is levelled before installation.

For applications involving machinery in excess of 3 kW and/or below 1000 r·min^{-1} (17 Hz), helical steel spring mounts are normally selected. The simplest of these is the open spring, which is typically restricted to operations where there are no significant fluid loads or excessive wind or other lateral loads. They are available in small sizes for light duty, up to 25 mm maximum deflection where lateral stability is not critical, and in larger sizes for 25 mm and higher deflections, where the geometry of the spring design will be much more stable and capable of higher loads. The smaller springs are typically used in the fan and motor section of small air handling units and the larger springs on a wide range of equipment. Springs that might otherwise be unstable are caged or enclosed. A cage will usually offer a means of lateral restraint and guidance, perhaps also being damped by elastomeric side shields.

The principal difference between caged and enclosed springs is that caged mounts allow visual access to the spring, whereas totally enclosed mounts do not. However, the totally enclosed spring is better protected, which is considered essential in some adverse environments, such as off-shore installations. Where significant fluid loads or lateral loads are concerned, restrained spring mounts should always be selected. These mounts are also preferred for high deflection applications above 50 mm. Differential loading or deflection on mounts, whether accidental, or unavoidable, can lead to a variation in mounted height. Obviously, the minimum height available is that set by the mount which is least deflected and all other mounts must be levelled up (in progressive rotation) at least to that point. (It is always possible to level up, but never to level down.) If it is necessary to predict a levelled height prior to mounting and commissioning a machine, a safety factor should always be added to take account of such variations.

5.11.6.2 Determination of loads for a mounted system

The following example demonstrates how to calculate loads for a system mounted at four points. It is treated in a step-by-step manner for clarity. Other procedures, generalised formulae and computer programs may also be used.

The methods given are applicable to determination of the springs required for a variety of isolated systems such as pumps, fans, air handling units etc. Large systems, e.g. floating floors, cooling towers and whole buildings, require special techniques, some of which are discussed later.

Example 5.1: fan and motor combination

The data for an air handling unit consisting of a single fan and motor mounted on a rigid frame are as follows:

- weight of fan: 21 kg
- weight of motor: 38 kg
- weight of frame: 12 kg
- frame dimensions: 1000 mm × 550 mm
- operating speed: 900 r·min^{-1} (= 15 Hz)
- vibration isolation efficiency: 95%

The positions of the centres of gravity of the fan and motor will have been provided by the manufacturer, or determined separately, and are as shown in Figure 5.20.

The centre of gravity of the combination is on the line joining their separate centres of gravity (CG_1 and CG_2). The length of this line (T) is given by:

$$T = \sqrt{(L_2^2 + W_2^2)} = \sqrt{(600^2 + 220^2)} = 639 \text{ mm}$$

The position of the centre of gravity of the combination on the line joining their separate centres of gravity is then given by moments around B as in Figure 5.21.

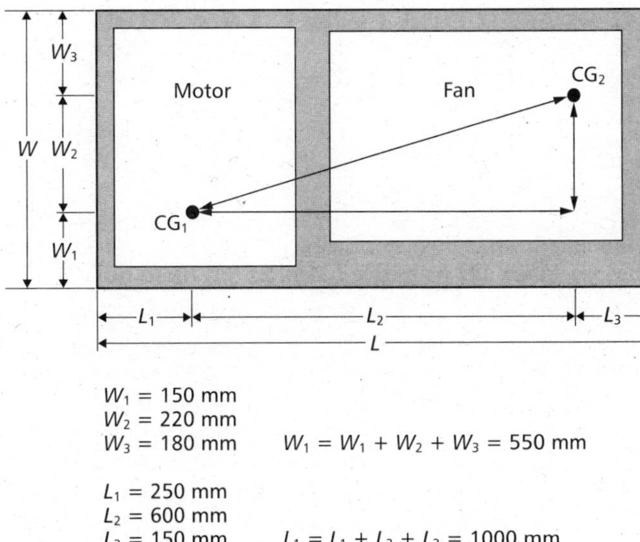

Figure 5.20 Example 5.1: Plan dimensions and location of centres of gravity of fan and motor

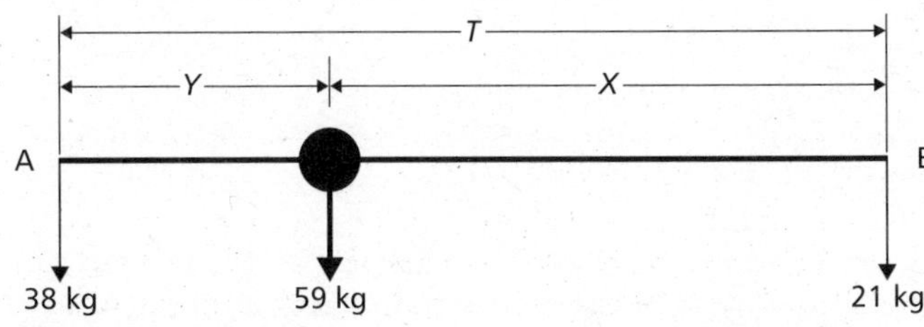

Figure 5.21 Example 5.1: Position of centre of gravity of combination on line joining centres of gravity of fan and motor

Hence:

$$59\,X = 38\,(X + Y) = 38 \times 639$$

Leading to:

$$X = 411.6 \text{ mm and } Y = 227.4 \text{ mm}$$

It is now necessary to determine the weight distribution of the fan and motor at the corners of the frame, where the mountings will be located. The weight of the frame itself is divided equally between the corner supports.

The position of the fan/motor centre of gravity with respect to the edges of the frame is obtained by first determining distances L_2' and W_2' as in Figure 5.22. From consideration of the triangles it follows that $L_2' = 214$ mm and $W_2' = 78.3$ mm.

The centre of gravity of the combination in the horizontal plane is then determined as shown in Figure 5.23, i.e:

- distance from side AD of frame = $L_1 + L_2'$ = 250 + 214 = 464 mm
- distance from side BC of frame = 536 mm
- distance from side DC = $W_1 + W_2'$ = 150 + 78 = 228 mm
- distance from side AB = 322 mm

(As vertical motion only is assumed, the height of the centre of gravity is not considered).

The load sharing between sides AD and BC is obtained by a similar process to that shown in Figure 5.21. Hence:

- load carried on side BC = (464/1000) × 59 = 27.4 kg
- giving load carried on side AD = 31.6 kg.

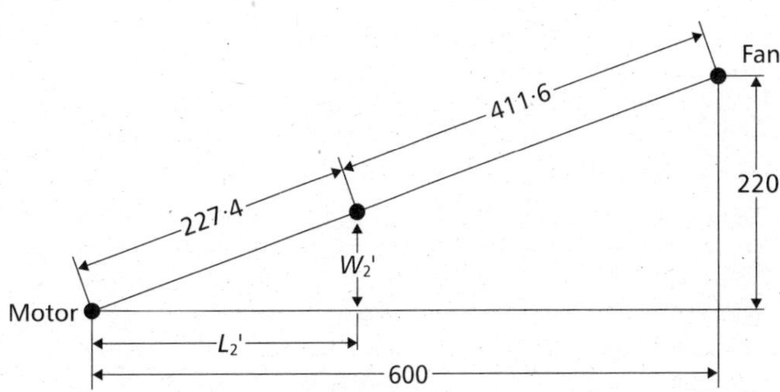

Figure 5.22 Example 5.1: Location of centre of gravity of combination

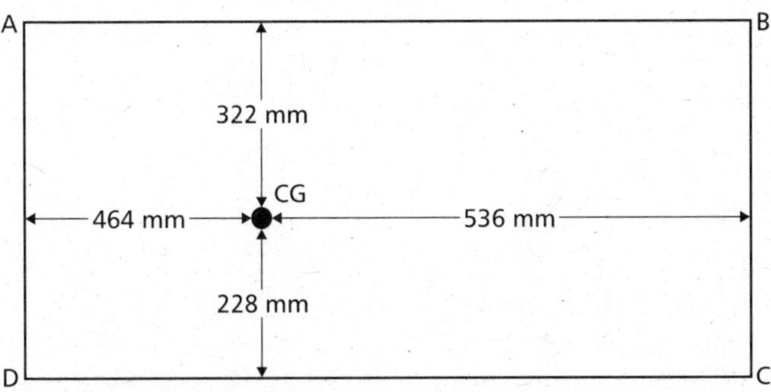

Figure 5.23 Example 5.1: Position of centre of gravity of combination with respect to frame

In a similar manner, the distribution of load between points B and C is given by:

— load at B = (228/550) × 27.4 = 11.4 kg

— giving load at C = 16 kg

— load at D = (322/550) × 31.6 = 18.5 kg

— giving load at A = 13.1 kg

In addition to these loads, each support point carries one quarter of the 12 kg weight of the frame.

Therefore, total loads are 16.1 kg at A, 14.4 kg at B, 19 kg at C and 21.5 kg at D. However, it is advisable to add a safety margin of 15–20% to the calculated loads.

The isolation efficiency required is 95%. From Table 5.17, standard 25 mm deflection mounts, chosen for appropriate load carrying, will be suitable.

5.11.6.3 Mounting specific plant items

The above example is applicable to many items encountered by the building services engineer. Large plant may require additional mounting points which, for very heavy plant, may need to be chosen in relation to positions of support columns in the building. The following sections considers some specific problems.

Mounting heavy plant on isolator rails

Cooling towers are considered, by way of example, but the principles are applicable to mounting any large item of plant on isolator rails, e.g. high capacity air handling units.

Traditionally, cooling towers were located either unmounted in non-critical locations or sound-separated by pad/strip isolators. In some cases the fan section alone would be vibration isolated. As requirements became more demanding, isolated rail systems were developed for these and other large plant, whereby a pair of toe-down support channels were fitted along the length of the base of the tower with a nest of helical isolation springs. Isolation for equipment connected to the tower was provided by flexible pipe connectors, flexible connectors on forced draught fan discharges and, perhaps, some on-board isolation for the pump. The deflection limit was generally 25 mm, which worked well and, in many instances, is still effective.

The use of cooling towers has declined but they are still encountered in both closed- and open-circuit form, especially where very large condenser water loads are required.

A large office block may have one or more cooling towers located at roof level, served by induced draught axial flow or centrifugal forced draught fans. Multiple fans with a total absorbed power of 30 kW, and with a pump at perhaps a further 5 kW may be used. The power (thermal) rating for these towers can be as high as 3 MW and the operating weight 15 tonnes. Complications typically arise from:

— inverter speed control, typically 800 rev·min^{-1} or less

— a weak roof with a critical space, e.g. directors' suite, immediately beneath

— cooling towers of modern construction that do not allow direct mounting but require some form of base frame with mounts located below.

The static deflection will be determined by the required VIE at the optimum duty (usually the highest speed) plus any additional static deflection to avoid coupling with the natural frequency of a weak roof. The highest speed is the most critical, because at lower speeds there is a reduction in absorbed power due to reduced rotational forces. Table 5.17 indicates isolation on a rigid slab to at least 95% VIE, which requires a static deflection of 30 mm. The spring natural frequency is 2.75 Hz and the forcing frequency is 13.33 Hz (i.e. 800 rev·min^{-1}). The importance of the slab stiffness is not so much a function of its deflection under its own load, but rather any additional deflection created by the equipment load.

The floor spring rate is compared with the mount spring rate, where the mount spring rate needs to be not more than 1/10th. of the slab spring rate in order to separate the two resonant frequencies. A short cut to obtain the total mount deflection is to add the additional floor deflection under the load of the machine to the static deflection of the mount. As a final check, ensure that the natural frequency of the mount does not coincide with the natural frequency of the slab (information obtained from the structural engineer) and that a vibrational mode of the slab does not coincide with the disturbing frequency. The most obvious measure, if either should occur, is to further increase the mount static deflection and hence the VIE. For the present example, assuming an additional slab deflection under load of, say, 10 mm, the design static deflection of the mounts is increased from 30 mm to 40 mm, giving a spring natural frequency of 2.5 Hz.

If the floor deflects an additional 10 mm under a load of, say, 15 tonnes, the floor spring rate is 1500 kg·mm^{-1} and the mount spring rate needs to be not more than 150 kg·mm^{-1}. In practice, because of the input variables and spring selection and optimisation, the spring selection is preferred as nominal 50 mm static deflection mounts to achieve in situ deflection of not less than 40 mm. Current rooftop applications indicate that static deflections of nominal 75 mm are common and up to 125 mm is not unusual as a result of the combinations of high machine power, low rotational speeds, critical locations and weak roofs.

It is usual to arrange two or three vibration isolated parallel steel rails, laid on the roof or other flat surface, on which to support the plant. The rails should extend to the full dimensions of the base and have small deflection under the load of the plant. The rails are drilled to allow the plant to be mechanically fixed and to accept the requisite number of restrained spring mounts. Because of difficulty in accessing levelling screws and also in providing a clear landing ground on the mounts, internal levelling mounts are usually provided. Depending upon rail profile the rails may have to be cut out to allow access to the levelling screws. The number of mounts is determined by the total load required and the permitted maximum span between mounts, which in turn will be influenced by structural column centres and the structural engineer's proposals for supporting point loads from the mounts. Typical rail sections are 200 mm × 75 mm parallel channel or 203 mm × 203 mm universal column. The total and sectional static operating loads are generally available from the cooling tower manufacturer and will vary from rail to rail and at various points along the rail. The vibration isolation specialist has the choice to select mounts for individual point loads, or to equalise the loads and allow the beam to accept any stress differentials. The mounts are held-down to the sub-structure and incorporate restraint devices to deter lateral and vertical lift. The mounts are factory-fixed to the upper rail and the upper rail is site-fixed to the tower. Rail-end 'tip-potential' loads should be allowed for in the choice of isolators.

The pump set, if mounted on a tower, is indirectly isolated by the rail system but generally also incorporates some pad or bush sound separation. Flexible connectors are installed on forced draught fan discharges, and pipework connections are isolated via restrained flexible pipe connectors and spring hangers or floor supports. The natural frequency of the pipework isolators is best matched to the springs supporting the rails. Any nearby structural pipe penetrations must be resiliently sealed through the structure to control noise and vibration transmission.

Simple rail isolation systems are available as standard from suppliers. For more complex applications, advice must be sought from a vibration specialist directly, or via the plant manufacturer, and the design criteria and compliance must be clearly understood by all parties.

Vibration isolation of pipework or ductwork

Vibration transmission occurs along pipes and ducts, despite the use of flexible connectors. In pumped systems, pump vibration is carried by the liquid and may reappear as noise at any location where there is a hard contact between the pipe and the structure. Similarly, duct vibration arises from the fan and from turbulence in the air stream. A vibration isolation pipe hanger is shown in Figure 5.19(e). Rubber bushes are used in pipe clamps but these act in a similar manner to pad materials and are sound breaks, rather than vibration isolators.

The hanger is chosen to compress appropriately under the load being carried. There are considerations of permitted length of unsupported pipe or duct and of correct alignment. If the hanger is misaligned, the lower rod might contact with the hanger assembly, so bypassing the spring. A trapeze support might be used, where the pipe is carried by a length of steel, which is itself supported by a hanger at each end. Trapeze supports are often used to hang ducts.

The hanger itself is fixed back to the structure by a rod, or a wire for small capacity hangers used with light loads. Hangers are available with single or multiple parallel springs to carry loads from about 5 kg up to 1000 kg.

Floating floors

Floating floors are used both to provide vibration isolation and to increase sound transmission loss. Flanking paths limit noise isolation to about 50 dB, and normally less at lower frequencies. It follows that where high level differences are required, e.g. plant rooms immediately adjacent to conference suites, then floating floors, and possibly floating rooms are a solution. Also, where there is a risk that outside noise and vibration will penetrate a building, floating design for a section might be preferred to the option of isolating a whole building.

Whilst it is possible to design floating floors strengthened locally to accept plant loads, this is not a preferred technique unless disturbing frequencies are high, and loads are low (in which case floating floor requirement is doubtful). The reasons for this include:

— floor fracture during plant installation

— requirement for higher deflection floors than would otherwise be the case

— problem of coupling between vibration characteristics of the plant and those of the floor, leading to the plant driving the floor into vibration.

Therefore there is not a good case for floating plant rooms in their entirety and relying on this measure for total vibration isolation.

The technique is to cast housekeeping pads to the main structural slab to a depth where they will project above the proposed floating floor. The plant can then be mounted on high deflection, high efficiency anti-vibration mounts and, if necessary, on spring inertia bases. This method has the advantage that the local mass increases the efficiency of the vibration isolators and that the floating floor does not cast up to the perimeter of the housekeeping pad using closed cell foam edging strip, or similar, to give resilient separation. In order to complete the isolation of the plant room, walls can be built up on the floating floor and the ceiling hung by springs from the structural slab above. The effect is one of a room within a room with complete separation from the enclosing structure.

Floating floors may be 'wet' or 'dry'. Dry construction is usually used in studios and multiplex cinemas where the anti-vibration mounts, which could be pads, quilts, blocks, or mounts are secured to the bottom of a suitable rigid board (e.g. 25 mm thick marine plywood). Partitions and perimeter walls are in turn erected from the floating floor and various kinds of floor finish are applied in the usual way. The same technique can be applied to wet construction where a polythene membrane is firstly installed above the plywood formers, following which the upper concrete floor is cast. Alternative constructions are available, including 'jack-up' mounts, which are incorporated into a floor cast on polythene sheet and used to raise the floor after it has set. It is unusual for floating floor elements to be installed at greater than 900 mm centres and 600 mm is more usual. Floating floors are better described as sound separators than vibration isolators and when installed with care work extremely well. Bad installations are virtually irretrievable

5.12 Summary

5.12.1 Noise in HVAC systems

Noise in HVAC systems is controlled by following the advice given in this section. In particular:

— Choose a quiet fan, which is sized to operate at an efficient point on its characteristic.

— Design for good airflow. Aim to minimise turbulence and pressure loss, both of which produce noise.

— Include all sources in predictions, e.g. breakout, in addition to duct borne noise.

— Do not forget that building services systems might affect the sound insulation between neighbouring areas.

— Seal all wall penetration with flexible material. This reduces both noise and vibration.

— Choose the location and selection of external plant and air grilles to avoid noise disturbance to nearby properties.

5.12.2 Vibration in HVAC systems

Vibration in HVAC systems is controlled by the following the advice given in this section. In particular:

— Choose a good location for the plant, remote from sensitive areas. This also helps with noise control.

— Ensure that vibration isolation is properly installed with no bridging material across the flexible mountings.

— Ensure that vibration isolators are loaded to give equal deflections and installed to maintain vertical alignment of their springs and other components.

— Remember that misaligned isolators are a source of many problems.

— Check support bolts for integrity and free movement.

— Do not neglect vibration from pipes and ducts. Use flexible attachments to the structure.

Further advice is given by Schaffer(33).

References

1 *The Building Regulations 2000 — Conservation of fuel and power in dwellings* Approved Document L1 (2002 edition) and *The Building Regulations 2000 — Conservation of fuel and power in buildings other than dwellings* Approved Document L2 (2002 edition) (London: The Stationery Office) (2001)

2 *Technical Standards for compliance with the Building Standards (Scotland) Regulations 1990 (as amended)* (Edinburgh: The Stationery Office) (1990 with subsequent amendments)

3 *Installation and equipment data* CIBSE Guide B (London: Chartered Institution of Building Services Engineers) (1986) (out of print)

4 Hayden G W and Parsloe C J *Value engineering of building services* BSRIA Applications Guide AG 15/96 (Bracknell: Building Services Research and Information Association) (1996)

5 BS EN 25136: 1994: *Determination of sound power radiated into a duct by fans — In-duct method* (London: British Standards Institution) (1994)

6 BS EN ISO 7325: 1996: *Acoustics — Measurement procedures for ducted silencers — Insertion loss, flow noise and total pressure loss* (London: British Standards Institution) (1996)

7 BS EN ISO 11691: 1997: *Measurement of insertion loss of ducted silencers without flow — laboratory survey method* (London: British Standards Institution) (1997)

8 Blazier W E Sound quality considerations in rating noise from heating, ventilating and air conditioning (HVAC) systems in buildings *Noise Control Eng.* **43** (3) 53–63 (1995)

9 BS EN ISO 14163: 1998: *Acoustics. Guidelines for noise control by silencers* (London: British Standards Institution) (1998)

10 The Noise at Work Regulations 1989 Statutory Instrument 1989 No. 1790 (London: The Stationery Office) (1989)

11 *Reducing Noise at Work. Guidance on the Noise at Work Regulations 1989* HSE L108 (London: Health and Safety Executive) (1998)

12 Revision of the EU Noise at Work Directive — latest developments *Noise and Vibration Worldwide* **32** (8) 20–21 (September 2001) (Brentwood: Multi-Science Publishing) (2001)

13 Iqbal M A, Willson T K and Thomas R J *The Control of Noise in Ventilation Systems* (London: E & F N Spon) (1977)

14 *Sound and vibration design and analysis* (Gaithersburg MD: National Environmental Balancing Bureau) (1994)

15 *Noise control in building services* (Colchester: Sound Research Laboratories) (1988)

16 Cummings A Acoustic noise transmission through duct walls *ASHRAE Trans.* **91** (2A) 48–61 (1985)

17 *Sound and vibration control* Chapter 46 in ASHRAE Handbook: *HVAC Applications* (Atlanta GA: American Society of Heating, Refrigerating and Air-conditioning Engineers) (1999)

18 Schultz T J Relation between sound power level and sound pressure level in dwellings and offices *ASHRAE Trans.* **91** (1A) 124–153 (1985)

19 *The Building Regulations 2000 — Resistance to the passage of sound Approved Document E* (second impression with amendments) (London: The Stationery Office) (2001)

20 BS EN ISO 140-3: 1995: *Laboratory measurements of sound insulation of building elements* (London: British Standards Institution) (1995)

21 BS EN ISO 717-1: 1997: *Rating of sound insulation in buildings and of building elements. Airborne sound insulation* (London: British Standards Institution) (1997)

22 *Guidelines for community noise* (Copenhagen: World Health Organisation) (2000)

23 Mirowska M Evaluation of low frequency noise in dwellings *Proc. 9th. Internat. Meeting on Low Frequency Noise and Vibration, Aalborg, May 2000* (Aalborg, Denmark: Aalborg University, Department of Acoustics) (2000)

24 Jakobson J Danish guidelines on environmental low frequency noise, infrasound and vibration *Proc. 9th. Internat. Meeting on Low Frequency Noise and Vibration, Aalborg, May 2000* (Aalborg, Denmark: Aalborg University, Department of Acoustics) (2000)

25 Bradley J S Annoyance caused by constant amplitude and amplitude–modulated sounds containing rumble *Noise Control Eng.* **42** (6) 203–208 (1994)

26 BS EN 12354-4: 2000: *Building acoustics — Estimation of acoustic performance of buildings from performance of elements. Part 4: transmission of indoor sound to the outside* (London: British Standards Institution) (2000)

27 *A practical guide to seismic restraint* (Atlanta GA: American Society of Heating, Refrigerating and Air-conditioning Engineers) (1999)

28 *Environmental criteria for design* Section 1 in *Environmental design* CIBSE Guide A (London: Chartered Institution of Building Services Engineers) (1999)

29 BS 6472: 1992: *Guide to evaluation of human exposure to vibration in buildings (1 Hz to 80 Hz)* (London: British Standards Institution) (1992)

30 BS 6414: 1983: *Method for specifying characteristics of vibration and shock isolators* (London: British Standards Institution) (1983)

31 BS EN 1299: 1997: *Mechanical vibration and shock. Vibration isolation of machines. Information applicable to source isolation* (London: British Standards Institution) (1997)

32 BS EN 1736: 2000: *Refrigerating systems and heat pumps. Flexible pipe elements, vibration isolators and expansion joints. Requirements, design and installation* (London: British Standards Institution) (2000)

33 Schaffer M *A practical guide to noise and vibration control for HVAC systems* (Atlanta GA: American Society of Heating, Refrigerating and Air-Conditioning Engineers) (1992)

Appendix 5.A1: Acoustic terminology

5.A1.1 Basic parameters

5.A1.1.1 Frequency, wavelength and velocity

Sound is produced by rapid pressure fluctuations in the air. The fluctuating pressure is about one hundred thousandth of the static atmospheric pressure for what would appear to us to be a 'very loud' noise of 94 dB. The frequency of the fluctuations may be between 20 times a second (20 Hz), or lower for some fan instabilities, and up to 20 000 times a second for audible noise. However, for HVAC, we are not normally concerned with frequencies above 4000 Hz or, occasionally, 8000 Hz.

In addition to frequency, the quantities that define a sound wave include:

— wavelength, λ

— velocity, c = 345 m·s^{-1} (approx., depending on temperature).

Wavelength, frequency and velocity are related by the following equation:

$$c = \lambda f \qquad (5.A1.1)$$

where c is the velocity (m·s^{-1}), λ is the wavelength (m) and f is the frequency (Hz).

Thus we can relate frequency and wavelength by velocity, see Table 5.A1.1.

It is useful to develop an appreciation of frequencies and related wavelengths, since this helps an understanding of the operation of noise control.

Noise frequencies are obtained from a frequency analyser which, in the case of simple analysis requirements, can be incorporated into a sound level meter (see Appendix 5.A4).

Table 5.A1.1 Relation between frequency and wavelength of sound

Frequency / Hz	Wavelength / m
63	5.5
125	2.8
250	1.4
500	0.69
1000	0.35
2000	0.17
4000	0.086

5.A1.1.2 Sound pressure

The sound pressure in a wave is force per unit of area for the wave and has units of pascals (Pa) (i.e. N·m^{-2}). The sound pressure fluctuates above and below atmospheric pressure by a small amount and a time average may be zero. The sound pressure is therefore quantified by the square root of the square of the fluctuations, giving the root mean square (rms) value. (Squaring the pressure fluctuations makes all values positive.)

5.A1.1.3 Sound intensity

The sound intensity is a measure of the rate of flow of sound energy in watts per square metre (W·m^{-2}). This is analogous to illumination.

5.A1.1.4 Sound power

The sound power is a characteristic of the source, expressed in watts (W). The sound power is a fundamental quantity associated with the source alone. Intensity and pressure depend on the transmission path from source to receiver.

5.A1.1.5 Noise level

Noise levels are generally expressed in decibels (see below, section 5.A1.2) and are measured with a sound level meter (see Appendix 5.A5).

5.A1.2 Noise levels and the decibel

The decibel is the logarithm of the ratio between two values of some characteristic quantity such as power, pressure or intensity, with a multiplying constant to give convenient numerical factors. Logarithms are useful for compressing a wide range of quantities into a smaller range. For example:

— lg 10 = 1

— lg 100 = 2

— lg 1000 = 3

Hence the ratio 1000:10 is compressed into a ratio of 3:1.

This approach is advantageous for handling sound levels, where the ratio of the highest to the lowest sound likely to be encountered, is as high as 1 000 000:1. A useful development, many years ago, was to take the ratios with respect to the quietest sound which can be heard. This is the threshold of hearing, which is at about 20 μPa (i.e. 2×10^{-5} Pa) of pressure or 10^{-12} W·m^{-2} of intensity for the average person.

When the word 'level' is added to the word for a physical quantity, decibel levels are implied, denoted by L_X, where the subscript 'X' is the symbol for the quantity.

All intensity levels are expressed as follows:

$$L_I = 10 \lg (I / I_0) \qquad (5.A1.2)$$

where L_I is the intensity level (dB), I is the measured intensity (W·m^{-2}) and I_0 is the reference intensity (i.e. 10^{-12}) (W·m^{-2}).

However, it can be shown that intensity is proportional to the square of pressure, giving the pressure level, as follows:

$$L_p = 10 \lg (p / p_0)^2 = 20 \lg (p / p_0) \qquad (5.A1.3)$$

where L_p is the pressure level (dB), p is the measured pressure (Pa) and p_0 is the reference pressure (i.e. 2×10^{-5}) (Pa).

This is the formulation most commonly used and, by substituting the numerical value of p_0 (i.e. 2×10^{-5} Pa) and taking logarithms, leads to the decibel level as:

$$L_p = (20 \lg p) + 94 \qquad (5.A1.4)$$

Thus if $p = 1$ Pa, the sound pressure level is 94 dB.

Similarly, equation A1.2 leads to:

$$L_I = (10 \lg I) + 120 \qquad (5.A1.5)$$

Note that if the sound pressure is doubled, that is $p \rightarrow 2\,p$, L_p increases by 6 dB. If the sound intensity is doubled, that is $I \rightarrow 2\,I$, L_I increases by 3 dB. This is because $I \propto p^2$.

Although the sound pressure is the quantity most frequently measured (see Appendix 5.A5) it is not the most fundamental property of the source. Sound represents a flow of energy propagated from the source. The source acts as a reservoir of power (rate of production of energy, i.e. J·s^{-1} or watts). At a distance from the source we detect the flow of energy at our location. This flow is the acoustic intensity, the energy flow in watts per square meter.

The intensity can be measured directly, but we normally measure sound pressure. The reason for this is that measuring instruments, such as microphones, employ a diaphragm which, deflecting under the fluctuating force of the sound wave, converts its deflection to an electrical signal. Since pressure = force/area, it is the sound pressure which applies a force to the diaphragm.

The reference levels for pressure and intensity are close to normal thresholds of hearing, so that the threshold is approximately 0 dB. A big advantage of these choices of reference level is that the decibel values of sound pressure level and sound intensity level are the same for the same sound, to within about 0.5 dB.

Both intensity and pressure define what is occurring at a point in space. The more fundamental quantity is the sound power of the source, expressed in watts (i.e. joules per second). Acoustic power levels are very low wattage and are given in decibels as:

$$L_W = 10 \lg (P / P_0) \qquad (5.A1.6)$$

where L_W is the sound power level (dB), P is the sound power (W) and P_0 is the reference power (i.e. 10^{-12}) (W).

Then:

$$L_W = (10 \lg P) + 120 \qquad (5.A1.7)$$

(Some earlier texts used 10^{-13} W as the reference pressure, as it resulted in more convenient formulae when using older systems of units, but this was changed to 10^{-12} W for use with SI units.)

Equation 5.A1.7 shows that an acoustic power of 1 W is a sound power level of 120 dB. Note that if the sound power is doubled, that is $P \rightarrow 2\,P$, L_W increases by 3 dB.

If the source is small compared with the wavelength, it approximates to a point source. The inverse square law of radiation then applies, similar to sources of light, and at a distance r the intensity is:

$$I = P / (4\,\pi\,r^2) \qquad (5.A1.8)$$

where I is the intensity (W·m^{-2}), P is the sound power (W) and r is the distance from the source (m).

By substituting numerical values, the intensity can be expressed as an intensity level in decibels as:

$$L_I = L_W - (20 \lg r) - 11 \qquad (5.A1.9)$$

where L_I is the sound intensity level (dB), L_W the sound power level (dB) and r is the distance from the source (m).

But, as the decibel sound pressure levels and sound intensity levels are numerically the same, this can immediately be written in the more familiar pressure terms as:

$$L_p = L_W - (20 \lg r) - 11 \qquad (5.A1.10)$$

If the sound is constrained into a hemisphere by reflecting surfaces, the surface area for radiation changes from $(4\,\pi\,r^2)$ to $(2\,\pi\,r^2)$ and the sound pressure level becomes:

$$L_p = L_W - (20 \lg r) - 8 \qquad (A1.11)$$

The $(20 \lg r)$ term for free propagation, either spherical or hemispherical, means that if distance r is doubled or halved the pressure level change is 6 dB (i.e. $20 \lg 2 = 6$).

These equations illustrate the importance of the sound power of the source as the fundamental quantity. Sound power is in watts (or sound power level, see equation 5.A1.6) whilst the sound pressure at a point is what we perceive after the sound travelling from the source has been modified by propagation effects.

If the sound is constrained in a duct it does not spread out and so does not reduce in intensity as the distance increases. The intensity ($W \cdot m^{-2}$) in a duct of constant cross-section will remain constant in the absence of losses. However, losses always occur by breakout, energy transfer to duct wall vibration, absorption etc. The internal noise level in a duct section near to the fan is typically 90–100 dB and proper design reduces it to around 35 dB in the room. By using the equations for sound intensity and sound power, it follows that a sound pressure level/sound intensity level of 96 dB in a duct of 0.5 m^2 cross sectional area, equates to the sound power into the duct of (2×10^{-3}) W (i.e. two milliwatts). A general relation for sound intensity, area and sound power is:

$$L_W = L_I + 10 \lg A_d \qquad (5.A1.12)$$

where A_d is the cross sectional area of the duct (m^2).

Then for the example above, where the area is 0.5 m^2, sound power in the duct is:

$$L_W = 96 + 10 \lg 0.5 = 93 \text{ dB}$$

Working backwards and converting sound power level (dB) to sound power (W) using equation 5.A1.6:

$$P = 10^{-12} \text{ antilg } 9.3 = 2 \times 10^{-3} \text{ W}$$

However, as the decibel levels for pressure and intensity are equal, equation 5.A1.12 can also be written as:

$$L_W = L_p + 10 \lg A_d \qquad (5.A1.13)$$

The sound power level is not numerically the same as the sound pressure or intensity level (except for ducts having a cross sectional area of 1 m^2, since 10 lg A_d is then zero). Pressure and intensity levels are affected by the propagation path.

When calculating duct system noise, the fundamental quantity is the sound power entering or leaving a duct element. This continues up to the duct termination, which acts as a source of power into the room, from which the room sound level is predicted, see section 5.7.

Equation 5.A1.12 is also useful for estimating the level at a distance from an extended source, such as boiler house louvres or an opening in a wall. If the sound pressure level averaged over the extended source is known, combining this with the area gives the sound power level, which can then be used with equation 5.A1.11 to determine the level at a distance. However, large sources are directional, so that equation 5.A1.11 will underestimate at higher frequencies in directions to the front of the source.

5.A1.3 Addition and subtraction of decibels

As decibels are logarithmic ratios they do not add arithmetically. It is necessary to convert back to the original physical units, add or subtract values of intensity or (pressure)^2 and then re-convert the result back to decibels. This means first converting the decibel levels, N, using antilogs (i.e. $10^{N/10}$), summing (or subtracting, as appropriate), and then taking the logarithm of the sum (or difference) (i.e. 10 lg (sum or difference)).

Example 5.A1.1

(*a*) Add 55 dB and 57 dB sound pressure levels

From equation 5.A1.3:

$$55 \text{ dB} = 20 \lg (p_1 / p_0) = 10 \lg (p_1 / p_0)^2$$

Then:

$$(p_1 / p_0)^2 = \text{antilg } 5.5 = 10^{5.5}$$

Similarly:

$$(p_2 / p_0)^2 = \text{antilg } 5.7 = 10^{5.7}$$

The sum of the sound pressure levels is:

$$10^{5.5} + 10^{5.7} = 316228 + 501187 = 817415$$

Hence, the sum of the two levels, in dB, is:

$$10 \lg (817415) = 59.1 \text{ dB}$$

which would normally be rounded to 59 dB.

(*b*) Subtract 60 dB from 61 dB

The difference is:

$$10^{6.1} - 10^6 = 1\,258\,925 - 1\,000\,000 = 258\,925$$

Hence:

$$10 \lg (258\,925) = 54 \text{ dB}$$

This shows that if a noise of level 60 dB has one of level 54 dB added to it, the resulting level is 61 dB.

It is necessary to work back to the original quantities, e.g. (sound pressure)^2, which is a measure of the energy in the sound wave, add them, and then work forward to determine the total decibel level.

To simplify addition and subtraction Figure 5.A1.1 can be used. For addition, the scales are used as shown. For subtraction, enter the difference between the two levels on the upper scale. The amount to be subtracted from the smaller decibel level is given on the bottom scale.

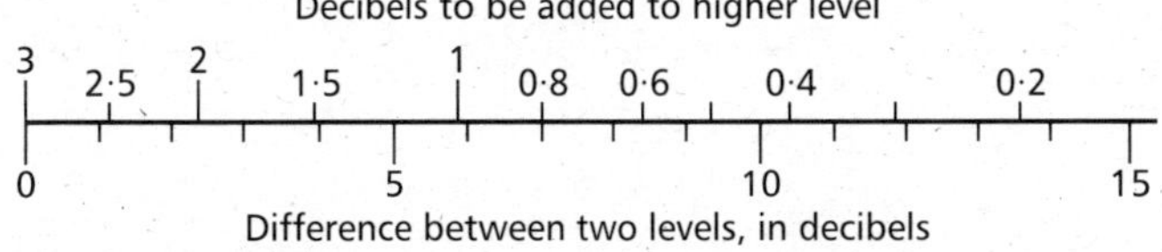

Figure 5.A1.1 Line chart for addition of sound pressure levels in dB

Example 5.A1.2

The calculations performed in Example 5.A1.1 are carried out using Figure 5.A1.1, as follows.

(*a*) Add 55 dB and 57 dB sound pressure levels:

— bottom scale: difference between levels to be added is (57 – 55) = 2 dB

— top scale: corresponding value to be added to the higher level is 2.1 dB

— sum is (57 + 2.1) = 59.1 dB.

(*b*) Subtract 60 dB from 61 dB:

— top scale: difference between levels to be subtracted is (61 – 60) = 1 dB

— bottom scale: corresponding value to be subtracted from the smaller level is 6 dB

— difference is (60 – 6) = 54 dB.

Appendix 5.A2: Generic formulae for predicting noise from building services plant

5.A2.1 Fans

There have been many investigations of fan noise, but a generally satisfactory prediction formula has not been found. It is known that fan noise depends on the air volume flow rate, fan pressure and fan operating point. An approximate prediction formula which may be used for initial work is:

$$L_W = K_W + 10 \lg Q + 10 \lg p_f + C \quad (5.A2.1)$$

where L_W is the estimated fan sound power level (dB re. 10^{-12} W), K_W is a constant (see Table 5.A2.1) (dB), Q is the volume flow rate ($m^3 \cdot s^{-1}$), p_f is the fan pressure (Pa), C is a correction factor for the fan operating point (see Table 5.A2.2) (dB).

Although equation 5.A2.1 was formerly recommended by ASHRAE, it has since been withdrawn because of its inaccuracies. It is provided here for initial guidance only. Once the fan has been selected, the manufacturer's noise data should be used.

5.A2.2 Chillers and compressors

The primary sources of noise are the compressors and drive motors. The following relations give the overall A-weighted sound pressure level (see Appendix 5.A5, section 5.A5.2) at 1 m(5.A2.1).

For centrifugal compressors:

$$L_{pA} = 54 + 11 \lg P_c \quad (5.A2.2)$$

For reciprocating compressors:

$$L_{pA} = 66 + 9 \lg P_c \quad (5.A2.3)$$

where L_{pA} is the A-weighted sound pressure level at 1 m (dB) and P_c is the electrical power input to the compressor (kW).

5.A2.3 Cooling towers

The overall sound power level is given by:

$$L_W \approx 12 + 10 \lg P \quad (5.A2.3)$$

where L_W is the sound power level (dB) and P is the fan sound power (W).

Octave band levels are given approximately by allocating the 63 Hz band a level 4 dB below the overall level and reducing each successive octave band by 2 dB.

5.A2.4 Regeneration of noise by duct components

This method, which is based on recent work at Liverpool University(5.A2.2), is applicable to in-duct components such

Table 5.A2.1 Values of K_W in equation 5.A2.1

Fan type	Correction factor, K_W / dB, for stated octave band / Hz							Blade frequency increment* / dB
	63	125	250	500	1000	2000	4000	
Centrifugal:								
— forward curved	38	38	28	30	20	15	10	3
— all other types	30	30	28	24	19	13	10	3
Propeller	33	36	43	41	40	37	30	5
Vane axial for stated hub ratio:								
— 0.3 to 0.4	34	28	28	33	32	30	23	6
— 0.4 to 0.6	34	28	31	28	26	21	15	6
— 0.6 to 0.8	38	37	36	36	34	32	28	6
Tube axial for stated wheel diameter:								
— over 1000 mm	36	31	32	34	32	31	24	7
— under 1000 mm	33	32	34	38	37	36	28	7

* The blade frequency increment is added into the octave band that contains the blade passage frequency, which is given by multiplying the number of blades by fan speed.

Table 5.A2.2 Values of C in equation 5.A2.1

Fan efficiency / %	C / dB
Peak	0
80	6
70	9
50	15

as bends, transition pieces and take-offs, but is not applicable to termination devices. It is based upon a theoretical model for rectangular ductwork but is also applicable to circular section ductwork.

For a particular element, the required information is pressure loss factor, ζ, obtained from section 4 of CIBSE Guide C[(5.A2.3)] or other data source, duct cross sectional dimensions and air velocity. It is necessary to determine an approximate value of the clear area ratio (σ) and a characteristic dimension (d).

These can be estimated from pressure loss factor as follows.

The clear area ratio is given by:

$$\sigma = \frac{\zeta^{1/2} - 1}{\zeta - 1} \qquad (5.A2.5)$$

where σ is the clear air ratio and ζ is the pressure loss factor.

The characteristic dimension is given by:

$$d = b\,(1 - \sigma) \qquad (5.A2.6)$$

where d is the characteristic dimension (m) and b is the duct dimension in the direction of flow constriction (see Figure 5.A2.1) (m).

Figure 5.A2.1 illustrates how the flow of air is constrained in one direction when it encounters a mitred bend. Similar effects are observed for other in-duct elements.

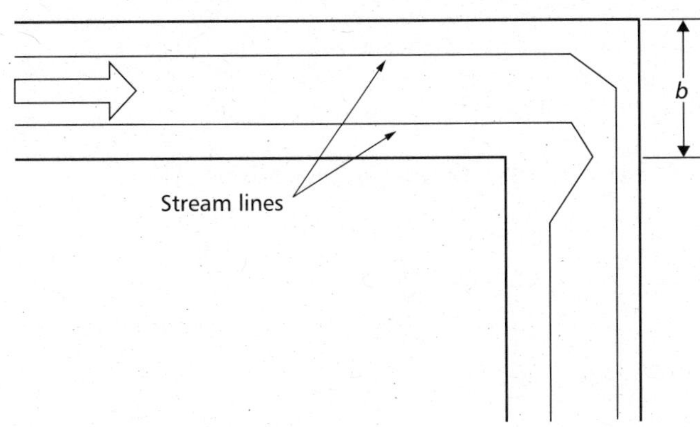

Figure 5.A2.1 Constriction in a duct

A graph giving σ in terms of ζ is shown in Figure 5.A2.2. There are different expressions for noise regeneration below and above the duct 'cut-on' frequency, which is the frequency above which complex acoustic modes are propagated in the duct; propagation is as a plane wave below the cut-on frequency.

The cut-on frequency is given by:

$$f_c = \frac{c}{2\,l} \qquad (5.A2.7)$$

where f_c is the cut-on frequency (Hz), c is the velocity of sound (m·s^{-1}) and l is the longest duct cross sectional dimension (m).

Where the required octave band frequency, f_o, is below cut-on (i.e. $f_c > f_o$), the sound power generated by the fitting is:

$$L_W = -37 + 20 \lg (K(St)) + 20 \lg \zeta + 10 \lg A + 40 \lg u \qquad (5.A2.8)$$

where L_W is the sound power level (dB), $K(St)$ is an experimentally determined factor related to the Strouhal number, ζ is the pressure loss factor, A is the cross sectional area of the duct and u is the air velocity in the duct (m·s^{-1}).

For $f_c < f_o$, where the required octave band frequency, f_o, is above the cut-on frequency:

$$L_W = -84 + 20 \lg (K(St)) + 20 \lg (St) + 10 \lg \zeta - 40 \lg \sigma + 10 \lg A + 60 \lg u \qquad (5.A2.9)$$

where (St) is the Strouhal number.

The term 20 lg ($K(St)$) is determined as follows. $K(St)$ is an experimentally determined factor, see Figure 5.A2.3, where the vertical axis on the curve is 20 lg ($K(St)$) and the horizontal axis is the Strouhal number, (St).

So, a value for 20 lg ($K(St)$) may be obtained if the Strouhal number is known. (*Note*: Figure 5.A2.3 is based on data for a variety of air velocities in two different duct sizes and has an accuracy of around ± 2 dB. Similar curves have been obtained for other elements.)

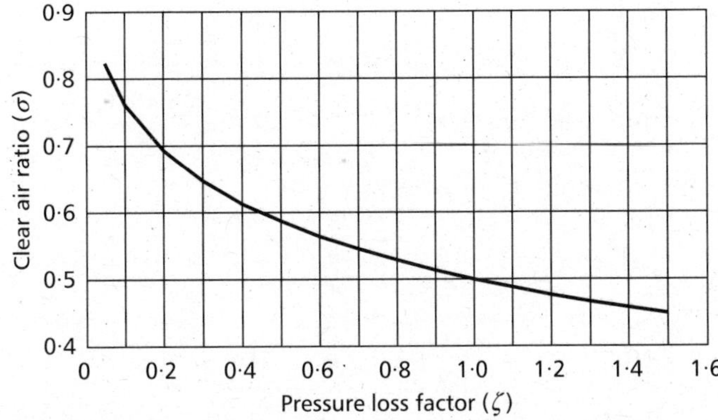

Figure 5.A2.2 Determination of clear air ratio from pressure loss factor

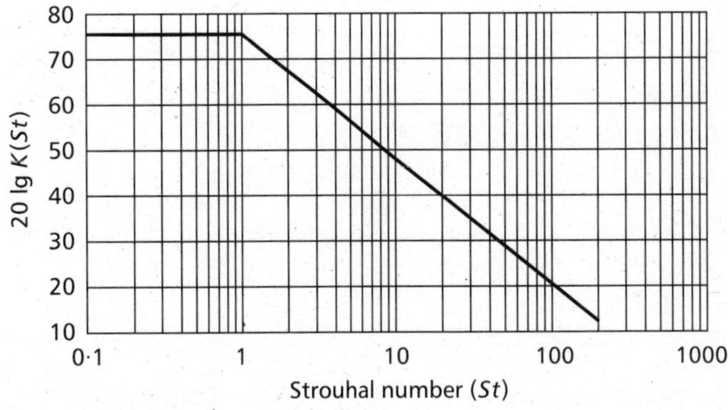

Figure 5.A2.3 Determination of term 20 lg (K(St)) from Strouhal number (accuracy approx. ± 2 dB)

The Strouhal number is given by the equation:

$$(St) = f\,d\,/\,v_c \quad (5.A2.10)$$

where (St) is the Strouhal number, f is the frequency, d is the characteristic dimension (m) (see equation 5.A2.6) and v_c is the constriction velocity (m·s^{-1}).

The constriction velocity is given by:

$$v_c = u\,/\,\sigma \quad (5.A2.11)$$

where u is the air velocity in the duct (m·s^{-1}) and σ is the clear air ratio (see equation 5.A2.5).

The procedure for determining the regenerated noise level for a given octave band frequency is as follows:

- calculate (St) from d and σ (both functions of ζ) and air velocity u
- read off appropriate value of 20 lg $(K(St))$ from Figure 5.A2.3
- insert values in the above equations depending on whether the octave band frequency, f_o, is below or above duct higher mode cut-on, $f_c = c/(2\,l)$ (equation 5.A2.7).

Other terms in the equations are physical constants or duct dimensions.

Thus, from knowledge of pressure loss coefficient, duct dimensions and air velocity one can calculate the sound power level for any chosen octave band centre frequency.

Example 5.A2.1

A duct element of 600 mm by 400 mm, where the 400 mm dimension is in the direction of the constricted flow, has pressure loss factor (ζ) of 1.25, and a clear air ratio (σ) of 0.47.

Given the duct dimension in the direction of constricted flow as 400 mm, from equation 5.A2.6 the characteristic dimension is:

$$d = 0.4\,(1 - 0.47) = 0.21 \text{ m}$$

For an air velocity (u) of 15 m·s^{-1}, the constriction velocity is obtained from equation 5.A2.11:

$$v_c = 15\,/\,0.47 = 31.9 \text{ m·s}^{-1}$$

From equation 5.A2.7, the duct cut-on frequency for higher modes is:

$$f_c = 345\,/\,(2 \times 0.6) = 288 \text{ Hz}$$

Then, from equation 5.A2.10, for f_o = 125 Hz, the Strouhal number is:

$$(St) = 125 \times 0.21\,/\,31.9 = 0.82$$

Estimating from Figure 5.A2.3, a Strouhal number of 0.82 gives 20 lg $(K(St))$ = 75. Then, as the frequency is below cut-on, equation 5.A2.8 applies, i.e:

$$L_W = -37 + 75 + 20 \lg 1.25 + 10 \lg 0.24 + 40 \lg 15$$

$$= -37 + 75 + 2 - 6 + 47 = 81 \text{ dB}$$

The octave band sound pressure level for the 125 Hz octave band is thus 81 dB.

At 1000 Hz, which is above the duct cut-on frequency, the Strouhal number is 6.6, leading to 20 lg $(K(St)) \approx 53$.

Equation 5.A2.9 then applies, i.e:

$$L_W = -84 + 53 + 20 \lg 6.6 + 10 \lg 1.25 - 40 \lg 0.47 + 10 \lg 0.24 + 60 \lg 15$$

$$= -84 + 53 + 16 + 1 + 13 - 6 + 71 = 64 \text{ dB}$$

The octave band sound pressure level for the 1000 Hz octave band is thus 64 dB.

Similar calculations may be carried out at other frequencies. A spreadsheet can also be developed.

5.A2.5 Duct terminations

These are airflow noise sources situated on the room boundary and could result in an audible hissing noise.

The preferred source of noise data is the manufacturer, relating the air velocity and diffuser configuration to the sound power generated by the flow. In the absence of such data an initial estimate of the noise may be obtained from a detailed study of noise from diffusers, summarised by Beranek and Ver[(5.A2.4)], and calculation algorithms in *Sound and vibration design and analysis*[(5.A2.1)].

Overall sound power is determined as:

$$L_W = 10 + 10 \lg A_d + 30 \lg \xi + 60 \lg u \quad (5.A2.12)$$

where L_W is the sound power level (dB), A_d is the area of the duct cross-section prior to the diffuser, ξ is a normalised pressure drop coefficient (see equation 5.A2.13) and u is the air velocity upstream of the diffuser (m·s^{-1}).

The normalised pressure drop coefficient (ξ) is given by:

$$\xi = 2\,\Delta p\,/\,\rho\,u^2 \quad (5.A2.13)$$

where Δp is the pressure drop across the diffuser (Pa).

Pressure drop increases with constriction in the diffuser, such that pressure drop coefficients from about 3 to 20 cover a wide range of diffusers.

The diffuser spectrum is typically a broad band with a peak which spans an octave band and falls off at about 3 dB/octave at lower frequencies than the peak and 5 dB/octave at higher frequencies. The frequency of the peak is the air velocity in the duct multiplied by 160 and is shown in Table 5.A2.2 for the octave band in which the peak will be located.

Table 5.A2.2 Peak frequencies for diffuser noise

Velocity u / m·s^{-1}	Peak octave band / Hz
10	2000
9	2000
8	1000
7	1000
6	1000
5	1000
4	500
3	500
2	250
1	125

Table 5.A2.3 Coefficients for equation 5.A2.16 (reproduced from ARI Standard 885-1998[5.A2.6] by permission of the Air-Conditioning and Refrigeration Institute)

Octave band centre frequency / Hz	A	B	C
125	–0.865	0.723	0.375
250	–0.582	0.826	0.975
500	–0.0121	0.487	0.868
1000	0.298	0.513	0.317
2000	0.089	0.862	0
4000	0.0649	0.629	0
8000	0.150	0.166	0

Expanding the pressure drop coefficient and inserting numerical data enables equation 5.A2.12 to be written as:

$$L_W = 10 + 10 \lg A_d + (30 \lg \Delta p) + 5 \qquad (5.A2.14)$$

where the pressure loss is obtained from manufacturers' information for the air velocity.

The octave band level at the peak frequency is lower than the total level and given approximately by:

$$L_{W(peak)} \approx 10 + 10 \lg A_d + 30 \lg \Delta p \qquad (5.A2.15)$$

Diffuser noise is then obtained by determining the level of the peak using equation 5.A2.15 whilst Table 5.A2.2 gives the octave band in which this occurs. Octave band levels at frequencies higher and lower than the peak frequency are given approximately by deducting 3 dB/octave at lower frequencies and deducting 5 dB/octave at higher frequencies.

This is a simplified approach to the fuller treatment[5.A2.1] and Beranek and Ver[5.A2.4] and is less accurate than these, which claim to give the level to within 5 dB of measurement.

Excessive noise is controlled by increasing the diffuser area or by using a greater number of diffusers, which also reduces the velocity and pressure drop.

5.A2.6 Lined ducts

Prediction formulae for attenuation in lined rectangular ducts include the ratio p_d / A_d, where p_d is the duct perimeter and A_d is its cross sectional area. Other factors are the frequency of the sound and the thickness of the lining. Detailed studies have been made of insertion loss of lined ducts[5.A2.5]. An empirical prediction equation[5.A2.1,5.A2.6] is:

$$\text{IL} = 3.28\, 10^A\, (0.305\, p_d / A_d)^B\, (0.039\, t)^C \qquad (5.A2.16)$$

where IL is the insertion loss (dB), A, B and C are coefficients (see Table 5.A2.3), p_d is the duct perimeter (m), A_d is the duct cross-sectional area (m^2) and t is the lining thickness (mm).

The information on which this equation is based was for a limited range of variables. For example, the ratio p_d / A_d varied between about 2 and 30 and t may be either 25 mm or 50 mm, with a density between 24 and 48 kg·m^{-3}. (It was found that insertion loss is not sensitive to lining density.)

References (Appendix 5.A2)

5.A2.1 *Sound and vibration design and analysis* (Gaithersburg MD: National Environmental Balancing Bureau) (1994)

5.A2.2 Waddington D C and Oldham D J Generalized flow noise prediction curves for air duct elements *J. Sound and Vibration* 222 163–169 (1999)

5.A2.3 *Flow of fluids in pipes and ducts* Section 4 in *Reference data* CIBSE Guide C (London: Chartered Institution of Building Services Engineers) (2001)

5.A2.4 Beranek L L and Ver I L (eds.) Noise and Vibration Control Engineering (Chichester: Wiley Interscience) (1992)

5.A2.5 Kuntz H L and Hoover R M The interrelationships between the physical properties of fibrous duct lining materials and the lined duct sound attenuation *ASHRAE Trans.* **93** (2) 449-470 (1987)

5.A2.6 *Procedure for estimating occupied space sound levels in the application of air terminal units* ARI Standard 885: 1998 (Arlington VA: Air-Conditioning and Refrigeration Institute) (1998)

Appendix 5.A3: Interpreting manufacturers' noise data

Manufacturers' noise data should be available for fans, silencers, fan coil units, dampers, VAV boxes etc. Interpretation of the data requires close reading of accompanying information, in order to discover which standards were used in the measurements, and to understand the symbols and subscripts employed. Noise data are required from the 63 Hz octave band to the 4000 Hz band. However, some data do not yet go below 125 Hz. Generally, if a manufacturer cannot supply noise data, certified as measured according to accepted standardised procedures, an alternative supplier should be considered.

The data available may be expressed in a number of forms, e.g. as 'A-weighted' (dBA), as 'unweighted octave band' or as 'A-weighted octave band'. Additionally, a single decibel level might be allocated, e.g. to a fan, and corrections in tabular or graphical form given in order to derive the octave band levels.

Each statement of noise might be expressed as either 'sound pressure' or 'sound power' (see Appendix 5.A1). The distinction between pressure and power is often shown as a subscript. For example, L_p is sound pressure, whilst L_W is sound power. Some manufacturers give A-weighted levels, shown as L_{pA} or L_{WA}, which might be either the total level or A-weighted octave band levels. Propeller fans, which could be located on the perimeter of an occupied space, may be given as an A-weighted sound pressure level at 1 m, 3 m or 4 m, and shown, for example, as L_{pA4m}. Some American manufacturers express the noise as a loudness level in 'sones', but this is limited to fans which discharge directly into occupied areas.

The inlet and discharge noise should be identified separately. Formerly it was assumed that the noise split equally between inlet and discharge but it is now known that the discharge sound power may be several decibels greater than the inlet. The casing sound power breakout should also be known.

Practices differ between countries. UK manufacturers are likely to give unweighted octave band levels, whilst some Continental companies give A-weighted octave band levels, which is permitted in their national standards. Silencer attenuation may be given as an overall A-weighted reduction. This must be viewed cautiously, since the frequency dependence of silencer attenuation leads to its A-weighted performance being input spectrum dependent. Therefore, do not make, or accept, assumptions, but read the data carefully.

Standard measurement methods attempt to remove extraneous factors, of which poor airflow is the most likely to occur in an installation. Consequently fans and silencers are measured under ideal conditions[5.A3.1,5.A3.2], with care taken to ensure good airflow. Different conditions in field installations may affect the noise attenuation of a silencer and the noise generation of a fan and duct fittings.

Despite careful measurements, there are uncertainties in the published data of about ±5 dB at 63 Hz for fans and less than this for silencers. Uncertainties reduce at higher frequencies. Not all published data are directly measured; some are extrapolated from measurements on representatives of a family of equipment types.

A full discussion of manufacturers' data is given in *Application of Manufacturers' Sound Data*[5.A3.3].

References (Appendix 5.A3)

5.A3.1 BS EN 25136: 1994: *Determination of sound power radiated into a duct by fans — In-duct method* (London: British Standards Institution) (1994)

5.A3.2 BS EN ISO 7325: 1996: *Acoustics — Measurement procedures for ducted silencers — Insertion loss, flow noise and total pressure loss* (London: British Standards Institution) (1996)

5.A3.3 Ebbing C and Blazier W E *Application of Manufacturers' Sound Data* (Atlanta GA: American Society of Heating, Refrigerating and Air-conditioning Engineers) (1998)

Appendix 5.A4: Basic technique for prediction of room noise levels from HVAC systems

5.A4.1 Prediction

In the prediction, each component of the HVAC system is considered separately. Components of interest might be the fan, plenum, duct, branch, elbow etc., finally leading to the duct termination at the room. Additionally, there may be breakout and regenerated noise. Figure 5.A4.1 is used to illustrate the prediction, where it is required to predict the noise in the room at a distance of 2 m from the duct termination.

The inlet (A) goes to the fan (B), which discharges into a 900 mm by 750 mm duct, 10 m long, between (B) and the first branch at (C), supplying a 600 mm by 600 mm branch serving other parts of the building. The main duct continues as 600 mm by 600 mm for 5 m to a second branch at (D). The branch at (D) is a 3 m run of 600 mm by 450 mm duct to elbow (E), whilst the main duct continues at 600 mm by 600 mm to (G) and beyond. At (E), a further 600 mm by 450 mm run, 3 m long, leads to a 600 mm by 450 mm duct termination at (F), to supply a room 10 m × 8 m × 3 m. All ducts, branches and the elbow are unlined.

This hand calculation has been given to illustrate the procedures, but use of a computer program is recommended. The results from different programs may differ by one or two decibels, depending on the data and calculation processes built into the program. In selecting a program, make sure that it has been rigorously validated and is guaranteed to conform to a recognised calculation procedure

Table 5.A4.1 shows the calculation, in which breakout noise is not included because there is no breakout path into the room.

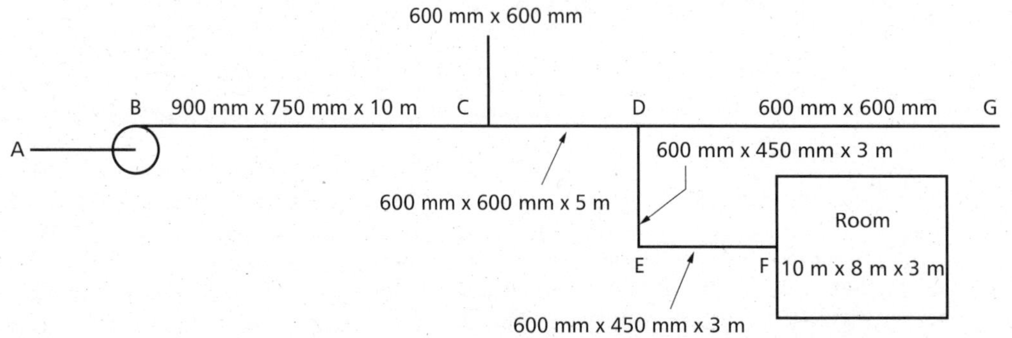

Figure 5.A4.1 Example 5.A4.1: ductwork system schematic

Table 5.A4.1 Room noise prediction for example calculation

Item		Sound power level / dB for stated octave band / Hz							
		63	125	250	500	1000	2000	4000	8000
1	Fan	97	94	99	93	85	74	68	60
2	Rectangular duct (900 mm × 750 mm × 10 m)	−6	−4	−3	−1	−1	−1	−1	−1
3	Branch duct (50% continuation)	−3	−3	−3	−3	−3	−3	−3	−3
4	Rectangular duct (600 mm × 600 mm × 5 m)	−3	−2	−1	−1	−1	−1	−1	−1
5	Branch duct (42% continuation)	−4	−4	−4	−4	−4	−4	−4	−4
6	Rectangular duct (450 mm × 600 mm × 3 m)	−2	−1	−1	0	0	0	0	0
7	Rectangular mitred elbow (600 mm)	0	−1	−5	−8	−4	−3	−3	−3
8	Rectangular duct (450 mm × 600 mm × 3 m)	−2	−1	−1	0	0	0	0	0
9	End reflection (600 mm × 450 mm)	−8	−4	−1	0	0	0	0	0
10	Room (10 m × 8 m × 3 m); occupant 2 m from duct termination	−8	−9	−10	−11	− 12	−13	−14	−15
Sound level at occupier / dB		61	65	70	65	60	49	42	33

Table 5.A4.2 Room levels compared with various criteria

Criterion	Room level and attenuation / dB for stated octave band / Hz							
	63	125	250	500	1000	2000	4000	8000
Room (unsilenced)	61	65	70	65	60	49	42	33
NR35	63	52	45	39	35	32	30	28
NC35	60	52	45	40	36	34	33	32
RC35	55	50	45	40	35	30	25	—
Silencer attenuation	8	12	25	38	39	23	16	10
Silenced room level	53	53	45	27	21	26	26	23

Figure 5.A4.2 Example 5.A4.1: branch dimensions for noise calculation

The following points should be noted with respect to Table 5.A4.1:

(1) Fan (Table 5.A4.1, row 1): the fan sound power is not given at 31.5 Hz. It is rare for sound power at this frequency to be known. However, as 31.5 Hz is included in criteria, the duct design must avoid turbulence and pressure losses which might lead to generation of low frequencies.

(2) Straight duct between (B) and (C) (Table 5.A4.1, row 2): see Table 5.4.

(3) Branch at (C) (Table 5.A4.1, row 3): see Figure 5.A4.2.

The attenuation of noise power into the continuing main duct is then given by equation 5.2:

$$\Delta L = 10 \lg (0.72 / 0.36) = 3 \text{ dB}$$

Since $A_1 = A_2$, the attenuation of noise power into the branch will also be 3 dB. (See also Figure 5.8.) These branch attenuations are constant across the frequency range.

(4) Straight duct between (C) and (D) (Table 5.A4.1, row 4): see Table 5.4.

(5) Branch at (D) (Table 5.A4.1, row 5): the areas of the ducts after the branch are 0.36 m^2 and 0.27 m^2, giving an area ratio of (0.63 / 0.27) = 2.33; with the attenuation in the smaller duct required, equation 5.2 gives 3.7 dB attenuation, rounded to 4 dB (as in Table 5.A4.1, row 5).

(6) Straight duct between (D) and (E) (Table 5.A4.1, row 6): see Table 5.4.

(7) Elbow at E (Table 5.A4.1, row 7): see Table 5.6.

(8) Straight duct between (E) and (F) (Table 5.A4.1, row 8): see Table 5.4.

(9) Termination (Table 5.A4.1, row 9): for a rectangular duct 600 mm × 450 mm, equation 5.4 (see section 5.6.6) gives an effective diameter of 586 mm, rounded to 600 mm. Table 5.9 gives end reflection losses for various effective diameters.

(10) Room effect (Table 5.A4.1, row 10): room volume is 240 m^3; Table 5.10 (see section 5.7.2) gives values of attenuation for rooms of various volumes.

The final row in Table 5.A4.1 is the sound level at the occupier, which must be compared with the specified criterion.

Section 1 of CIBSE Guide A[(5.A4.1)] suggests a criterion of NR35 for a general office, but this rating will not be satisfactory for noises with a high content of low frequencies.

If the duct passes across the ventilated space, breakout noise should be calculated and the resulting levels in the room compared with those from the duct borne noise, in order to estimate whether extra attention has to be given to the breakout noise. Similarly, breakout noise from units above the ceiling must be considered as additional sources of noise into the room (see sections 5.6.10 and 5.A4.2).

Table 5.A4.2 compares the room levels obtained above with several criteria, where the attenuation required is the difference between the room level and the criterion. The criteria are described in Appendix 5.A8. Clearly, the RC criteria (both Mark I and Mark II) are the most stringent at low frequencies, but there are only small differences between all the criteria in the range from 125 Hz to 2000 Hz. Although lower frequencies than 63 Hz occur in the criteria, calculation data for these frequencies are not normally available.

The attenuation of a commercial silencer to generally meet the requirements is also shown in Table 5.A4.2. The resulting room levels are given in the final row of Table 5.A4.2. The silencer is a 2.1 m long absorptive silencer, with cross-sectional dimensions of 900 mm × 750 mm, which should be fitted into a straight section of the main duct, not too close to the fan discharge and preferably where the duct penetrates the plant room wall. The pressure loss is 70 Pa for a fan delivery of 5 $m^3 \cdot s^{-1}$. A silencer is often chosen to meet requirements at the most critical frequency, typically 125 Hz or 250 Hz. Satisfying the attenuation at this frequency may lead to over-attenuation at higher frequencies.

In addition to its attenuation, factors to be considered in the selection of a silencer include airflow, pressure loss and size. For example, when the fan in the example gives 5 $m^3 \cdot s^{-1}$, the air velocity in the main duct is 7.4 $m \cdot s^{-1}$, which is an acceptable velocity, resulting in 70 Pa pressure loss, as above. However, if the same silencer is used on a 10 $m^3 \cdot s^{-1}$ fan, the doubling of velocity leads to a quadrupling of pressure loss.

The main attenuation at low frequencies is from duct losses, including breakout, and end reflection loss. At 63 Hz these total 21 dB, which is greater than the silencer attenuation at this frequency. If breakout noise was a problem, requiring stiffening of the duct or change to a circular duct, the duct breakout attenuations might not be obtained, giving a potential room level of 66 dB. For example, compare Tables 5.4 and 5.5.

Table 5.A4.2 shows that the room levels comply closely with the NR35 and NC35 criterion levels. The A-weighted room level is 40 dBA. However, this is an example of how a criterion can be met but the room noise may not give an acceptable acoustic environment. The rapid fall in room level between 250 Hz and 500 Hz, due largely to the silencer attenuation at 500 Hz, unbalances the spectrum. In practice, office activity noise may fill in the levels at mid frequencies and help to balance the spectrum, but this cannot be relied upon, and will not be applicable to commissioning measurements. A problem with commissioning measurements is that, in practice, the noise level will vary over the room space. The measurement positions for commissioning should be specified in the contract.

Noise that is judged to be satisfactory by NR and NC criteria may have inherent problems exposed by the more detailed RC criterion and its application to quality assessment. See ASHRAE Handbook: *HVAC Applications*[5.A4.2] for further details.

5.A4.2 Breakout travelling through the ceiling

For breakout from ducts, the duct sound power is determined as in section 5.6.10, and the effect in the room is estimated as described in section 5.7, taking attenuation through the ceiling into account.

For casing breakout, the manufacturer of boxed equipment, such as a fan coil unit or similar, will supply information on casing breakout sound power. This is used to determine room noise levels as above.

5.A4.3 Regenerated noise

All duct sections, straight or with bends, are potential sources for regenerated noise, depending on the velocity. Manufacturers of in-duct components provide data to enable regenerated noise to be estimated. The data are often stated in terms of the product of velocity and pressure loss, leading to an overall sound power figure, which is then corrected in a specified way in order to give octave band sound power levels. The regenerated sound power levels must be compared with the in-duct sound power levels from the fan at the point of origin of the regenerated noise, in order to estimate their significance. Table 5.1 may also be used to give an estimate of regenerated noise from low turbulence duct fittings. The calculations in Appendix 5.A2, sections 5.A2.4 and 5.A2.5, may also be used.

5.A4.4 Multiple sources

A room will normally have more than one noise source from the HVAC systems, e.g. multiple duct outlets, breakout from a box or a duct in the ceiling void etc. It is the summation of the noise from these sources which must meet the criterion, where summation is carried out as in Appendix 5.A1.3. Consequently, where there are multiple sources, the noise from each must be lower than the criterion and, for example, the silencer attenuation derived above, may need to be increased. Return air ducts must be included

5.A4.5 Computer predictions

Many organisations have HVAC noise prediction software, either developed in-house or obtained from an outside supplier. Use of a proven system is recommended and it is advisable to carry out some checks on the software against manual calculations.

References (Appendix 5.A4)

5.A4.1 *Environmental criteria for design* Section 1 in *Environmental design* CIBSE Guide A (London: Chartered Institution of Building Services Engineers) (1999)

5.A4.2 *Sound and vibration control* Chapter 46 in ASHRAE Handbook: *HVAC Applications* (Atlanta GA: American Society of Heating, Refrigerating and Air-conditioning Engineers) (1999)

Appendix 5.A5: Noise instrumentation

5.A5.1 Sound level meter

This is the most widely used method of measuring noise. Whilst hand-held instruments appear to be easy to use, lack of understanding of their operation and limitations and of the meaning of the varied measurements which they can give, may result in misleading readings. For serious measurements, a sound level meter should only be used by those who have studied the instrument manual, become familiar with the meter and, preferably, had a course of instruction on the use and calibration of the instrument.

The operation of the sound level meter is indicated in Figure 5.A5.1. The microphone output is amplified and passed to weighting networks or electrical filters before being sent on to an indicating instrument.

The electrical filters are an important part of the sound level meter, as they give an indication of the frequency components of the sound. The filters are as follows:

- *A-weighting*: on all meters
- *C-weighting*: on most meters
- *linear (L-weighting)*: on some meters
- *octave filters*: on some meters
- *third octave filters*: on some meters.

The main classes of sound level meter are Type 1 (precision) or Type 2 (general purpose), in which Type 1 is the more accurate. (There is also Type 3 for survey work and preliminary investigations and Type 0 (high precision) mainly for laboratory measurements.)

5.A5.2 Sound level meter weighting networks

Weighting networks are shown in Figure 5.A5.2.

Originally, the A-weighting was intended for low levels of noise. B-weighting was intended for medium levels of noise. C-weighting was intended for higher levels of noise. The weighting networks were based on human hearing contours at low, medium and high levels and it was hoped that their use would mimic the response of the ear. This concept, which did not work out in practice, has now been lost. A- and C-weighting are used at all levels whilst B-weighting is rarely used. Linear weighting is used to detect low frequencies. A specialist G-weighting is used for infra-sound below 20 Hz.

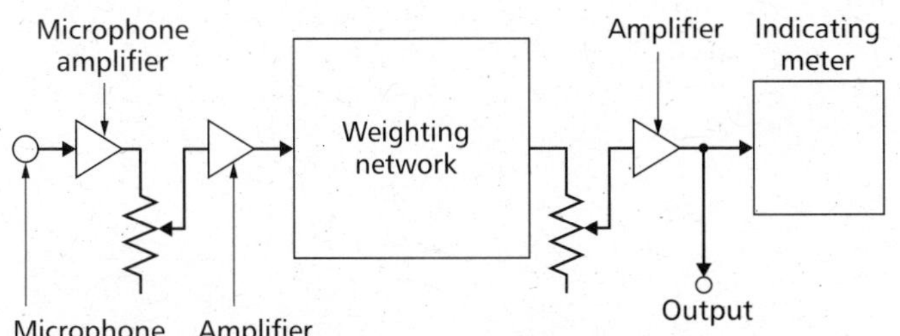

Figure 5.A5.1 Components of a typical sound level meter

The A-weighting depresses the levels of the low frequencies, as the ear is less sensitive to these. This is acceptable if there is largely middle and high frequency noise present, but if the noise is high at low frequencies, the A-weighting does not give a valid measure(5.A5.1). Low frequencies are often the residual problem in HVAC. A-weighting is adequate for placing noises of similar spectrum (frequency components) in order from worst to best. But, if the spectra are very different, the A-weighting is not reliable as an indicator of subjective response.

5.A5.3 Equivalent level (L_{eq})

This is the steady level over a period of time that has the same energy as that of the fluctuating level actually occurring during that time. A-weighted equivalent level, designated L_{Aeq}, is used for many legislative purposes.

Mathematically,

$$L_{\mathrm{Aeq}} = 10 \lg \left[\frac{1}{T_2 - T_1} \int_{T_1}^{T_2} \left(\frac{p_{\mathrm{A}}(t)}{p_0} \right)^2 \mathrm{d}t \right] \tag{5.A5.1}$$

where T_1 is the start time of the noise, T_2 is the end time of the noise, p_0 is the reference pressure of 20 μPa and $p_A(t)$ is the A-weighted instantaneous sound pressure (Pa).

Here we are averaging the fluctuations in the noise and converting to decibels.

Daily noise exposure, $L_{EP,d}$, is a form of equivalent level which is used to assess noise exposure with respect to hearing loss(A5.2). It is given by:

$$L_{\mathrm{EP,d}} = 10 \lg \left[\frac{1}{T_0} \int_{0}^{T_e} \left(\frac{p_{\mathrm{A}}(t)}{p_0} \right)^2 \mathrm{d}t \right] \tag{5.A5.2}$$

where T_e is the duration of the exposure to the noise (hours or seconds), T_0 is 8 hours (= 28 800 s), p_0 is the reference pressure of 20 μPa, $p_A(t)$ is the time weighted

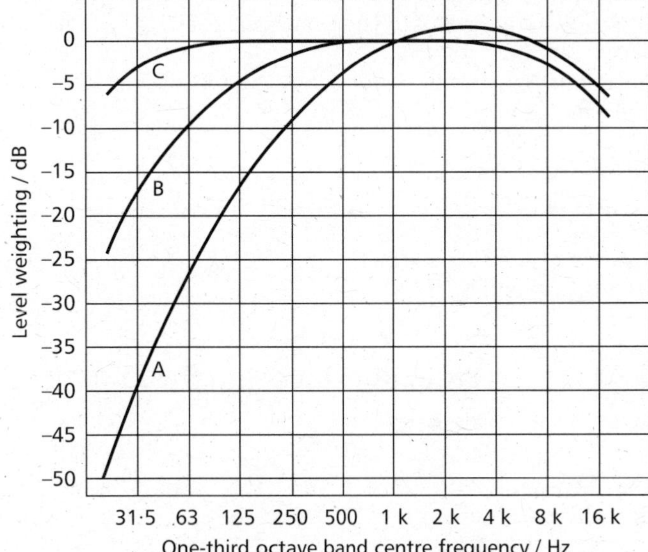

Figure 5.A5.2 Sound level meter weighting networks

variation of instantaneous sound pressure in the undisturbed field in air at atmospheric pressure to which the person is exposed, or the pressure in the disturbed field adjacent to the person's head, adjusted to provide the notional equivalent undisturbed field (Pa).

5.A5.4 Percentiles (L_N)

These are a statistical measure of the fluctuations in noise level, i.e. in the envelope of the noise, which is usually sampled a number of times per second. The most used percentiles are L_{90} and L_{10}. The L_{90} is the level exceeded for 90% of the time and represents a low level in the noise. It is often used to assess background noise. The L_{10} is the level exceeded for 10% of the time and is a measure of the higher levels in a noise. It is often used for assessment of traffic noise. Modern computing sound level meters give a range of percentiles. Note that the percentile is a statistical measure over a specified time interval. Percentiles cannot be combined like decibel levels without knowledge of the statistics of the noise.

5.A5.5 Frequency analysis

This gives more detail of the frequency components of a noise. Frequency analysis normally uses one of three approaches: octave band, one-third octave band or narrow band.

Octave and one-third octave band filters can be incorporated in sound level meters or be externally connected components. For an octave band filter, the higher limit is twice the lower limit. For a 1/3-octave band filter the higher limit is about 1.28 times the lower limit. A narrow band analysis can be in fractional octaves, such as 1/12-octave or in constant bandwidth analysis using, say, filters of constant bandwidth (e.g. 4 Hz) over the whole frequency range. Thus, for octave band centre frequency, f_c:

— lower limit $\approx 0.7 f_c$

— upper limit $\approx 1.4 f_c$.

For 1/3-octave band centre frequencies, f_c:

— lower limit $\approx 0.88 f_c$

— upper limit $\approx 1.12 f_c$.

Commonly used centre frequencies for octave band filters are 31.5 Hz, 63 Hz, 125 Hz, 250 Hz, 500 Hz, 1 kHz, 2 kHz, 4 kHz and 8 kHz but lower and higher bands are also defined.

Narrow band analysis is most useful for complex tonal noises. It could be used, for example, to give a precise numerical value of a fan tone frequency, to determine the frequencies of vibration transmission from machinery or to detect system resonances.

Criteria for assessment of noise are based on dBA, octave bands or 1/3-octave band measurements. These measures clearly give increasingly detailed information about the noise.

References (Appendix 5.A5)

A5.1 *Guidelines for community noise* (Copenhagen: World Health Organisation) (2000)

A5.2 *Reducing Noise at Work. Guidance on the Noise at Work Regulations 1989* HSE L108 (London: Health and Safety Executive) (1998)

Appendix 5.A6: Vibration instrumentation

5.A6.1 Vibration quantities

Vibration may be measured as acceleration (a), velocity (v) or displacement (x).

Velocity is the rate of change of displacement, i.e:

$$v = \frac{\mathrm{d}x}{\mathrm{d}t} \tag{5.A6.1}$$

Acceleration is the rate of change of velocity, i.e:

$$a = \frac{\mathrm{d}v}{\mathrm{d}t} = \frac{\mathrm{d}^2 x}{\mathrm{d}t^2} \tag{5.A6.2}$$

For the special case of a sinusoidal vibration, where:

$$x(t) = X \sin \omega t$$

the relationship is:

$$v = \omega X \cos \omega t \tag{5.A6.3}$$

$$a = -\omega^2 X \sin \omega t \tag{5.A6.4}$$

where ωt is the angular frequency (i.e. $2 \pi f$) (rad·s^{-1}) and X is the amplitude of the displacement

Acceleration is normally measured using a piezoelectric accelerometer and suitable preamplifier.

Acceleration levels in decibels are given by:

$$N = 20 \lg (a / a_0) \tag{5.A6.5}$$

where N is the acceleration level (dB) and a_0 is a reference acceleration of 10^{-6} m·s^{-2}.

The reference levels for velocity and displacement are 10^{-9} m·s^{-1} and 10^{-12} m. The decibel levels for acceleration, velocity and displacement are numerically equal at $\omega = 1000$ rad·s^{-1} (i.e. $f = 159$ Hz).

Vibration measurements are also expressed in the measured physical quantities, m·s^{-2}, m·s^{-1} and m, but sometimes millimetres are used as the unit of length, rather than metres. This depends on the magnitude of the vibration.

5.A6.2 Piezoelectric accelerometer

This is widely used, although other types of accelerometer are available. Operation is similar to a mass spring system, in which the piezoelectric element acts as the spring and carries a seismic mass. Vibration of the surface to which the accelerometer is attached then results in distortion of the piezoelectric element, leading to production of an electrical charge. Accelerometers have resonant frequencies, but because of the stiffness of the element, this is usually at a much higher frequency than the range of measurement. The charge sensitivity of an accelerometer is expressed in picocoulombs per unit of acceleration, or pC/(m·s^{-2}). The charge developed across a piezoelectric accelerometer can also be sensed as a voltage. The voltage sensitivity is expressed in mV/(m·s^{-2}).

5.A6.3 Amplifiers

The output of an accelerometer must first go to a preamplifier, which is designed to detect the output and convert the high electrical impedance of the accelerometer to a low output impedance, suitable for connection to a range of analysing instruments. The amplifier may also contain circuits to carry out the mathematical functions that convert acceleration into velocity and displacement by integration of acceleration. The final level indication is either the root mean square (rms) or peak value of the acceleration. Accelerometers may be connected directly into the microphone socket of some sound level meters, which then perform the measurement and analysis functions.

5.A6.4 Accelerometer fixings

Attachment of the accelerometer to a vibrating surface must be done with care. Magnetic fittings are a convenient method of fixing on flat magnetic surfaces. Alternatively, beeswax or similar temporary adhesive can be used. The accelerometer must be attached so that it is in intimate and secure contact with the surface, in order to ensure that the two vibrate together.

In general, vibration measurement is more specialised than sound measurement and fewer engineers are familiar with it, except in certain industries. Vibration measurement is one way of condition monitoring of equipment and it may be used for this purpose on rotating systems. Machinery vibration normally consists of a large number of discrete harmonic frequencies, which should be investigated with a narrow band analysing system.

Uses of vibration analysis in building services include:

- checking the efficiency of vibration isolators
- investigating pipe vibration
- investigating complaints of vibration of building surfaces
- looking for correlation between vibration and noise in a building.
- general diagnostic purposes.

These are successively more complex applications. The engineer should be aware of when to call on expert help.

Appendix 5.A7: Direct and reverberant sound in a room

Considering a point source in a room, the simple approach is that, as one moves away from the source, the direct sound pressure level, due to energy which travels straight from the source to the ear, falls at 6 dB per doubling of distance (see Appendix 5.A1). After a certain distance the summation of all the reflected sound in the room exceeds the direct level from the source. This is a region which is controlled by reverberant sound (see Figure 5.12). Thus, close to a source the total level is controlled by the source. Distant from a source the total level is controlled by the reverberant sound and, in this region, is constant over the room. This is expressed in equations 5.A7.1 to 5.A7.3:

$$L_p = L_W + 10 \lg \left(\frac{4}{R_R} + \frac{Q}{4 \pi r^2} \right) \qquad (5.A7.1)$$

The reverberant sound is given by:

$$L_{pR} = L_W + 10 \lg \left(\frac{4}{R_R} \right) \qquad (5.A7.2)$$

The direct sound is given by:

$$L_{pD} = L_W + 10 \lg \left(\frac{Q}{4 \pi r^2} \right) \qquad (5.A7.3)$$

where L_p is the total sound level at the receiver point (dB), L_W is the sound power level (dB), L_{pR} is the reverberant sound level at the receiver point (dB), L_{pD} is the direct sound level at the receiver point (dB), R_R is the room constant (m^2), Q is the directivity factor for the source and r is the distance from source to receiver (m).

The term $(4 / R_R)$ relates to the reverberant field and $(Q / 4 \pi r^2)$ to the direct sound field.

The room constant is defined as:

$$R_R = \frac{S \bar{\alpha}}{1 - S \bar{\alpha}} \qquad (5.A7.4)$$

and:

$$S = S_1 + S_2 + S_3 + \ldots.. + S_n \qquad (5.A7.5)$$

where S is the total room surface area (m^2), S_1 etc. are the surface areas of the room surfaces (m^2) and $\bar{\alpha}$ is the average absorption coefficient of the room surfaces.

The average absorption coefficient, $\bar{\alpha}$, is given by:

$$\bar{\alpha} = \frac{S_1 \alpha_1 + S_2 \alpha_2 + S_3 \alpha_3 + \ldots.\ S_n \alpha_n}{S} \qquad (5.A7.6)$$

The α terms are the random incidence absorption coefficients of the materials of the room surfaces. These coefficients vary with frequency and are usually smallest at low frequencies.

The room constant may also be obtained through measurement of the reverberation time, T, as follows:

$$T = \frac{0.16\,V}{S\,\bar{\alpha}} \qquad (5.A7.7)$$

If the average absorption coefficient, $\bar{\alpha}$, is small, equation 5.A7.4 reduces to $R_R \approx S\,\bar{\alpha}$.

Hence :

$$T \approx \frac{0.16\,V}{R_R} \qquad (5.A7.8)$$

Referring to equation 5.A7.1, the first term inside the brackets is controlled by the absorption in the room and represents the reverberant level (equation 5.A7.2). The second term represents the direct sound from the source according to the inverse square law, as if the room were not present (equation 5.A7.3). The directivity factor, Q, indicates how the noise is radiated preferentially in a direction of interest.

Equations 5.A7.2 and 5.A7.3 show that the direct and reverberant sound levels are equal when:

$$\frac{4}{R_R} = \frac{Q}{4\,\pi\,r_r^2} \qquad (5.A7.9)$$

or:

$$r_r = (Q\,R_R / 16\,\pi)^{1/2} \qquad (5.A7.10)$$

where r_r is the reverberation radius (m).

In reverberant rooms, the reverberation radius indicates distances at which either the direct or reverberant sound predominates. The direct sound is predominant at distances less than the reverberation radius, whilst the reverberant sound predominates at greater distances. The greater the value of room constant, R_R, the less reverberant the room and the greater the reverberation radius. However, most furnished offices do not fulfil the assumptions on which equation 5.A7.1 to 5.A7.3 are based.

This simple approach is reasonable for large rooms in which all three dimensions are of the same order, say 3:2:1, which are considered further in section 7. For many furnished rooms, and especially offices where the floor area is large compared to the height, the simple approach does not always hold. Furnished offices have reflections from furniture whilst the HVAC terminals are multiple sources. Although equation 5.A7.1 is useful due to its simplicity, it may give misleading results in real rooms. Recognition of this led to research sponsored by ASHRAE, summarised in the section 5.7, in order to determine what happens in real rooms.

Equations 5.A7.1 to 5.A7.3 may be used in large reverberant spaces such as sports halls.

Appendix 5.A8: Noise criteria

5.A8.1 Noise rating (NR)

Kosten and van Os[5.A8.1], developed octave band criteria for assessing the effects of external industrial and other noises on people in their homes. Whilst the resulting NR curves and criteria[5.A8.2] have become well known and widely used, it should be noted that the work was aimed at domestic premises, especially for night-time disturbance. Corrections were made for characteristics of both the noise and the residential district, although these were not included in the subsequent use for HVAC noise. NR is a tangent assessment, where the rating is given by the highest NR curve which is tangential to an octave band analysis of the noise. (A tangent method should also state the octave band that determines the highest criterion level, but this is not normally given.) NR criteria were included in a draft ISO Standard on environmental noise[5.A8.3] and are sometimes referred to as the 'ISO criteria', but they were removed from the final version of the standard and have no status within International Standards.

An examination of the evaluation spectra used by Kosten and van Os in their validation of the NR curves, shows that, for 'acceptable spectra' related to NR25–30, the low frequency levels of the test spectra are, on average, 10–15 dB below the 63 Hz criterion level. 31.5 Hz was not tested, as the initial definition of the NR curves did not go below 63 Hz. Thus, Kosten and van Os's data did not test the NR curves at the lower frequencies for which they are used. As a consequence, circumstances arise in HVAC applications in which an objectionable low frequency noise satisfies the NR design criterion.

Whilst it would be possible to modify NR in order to increase its stringency at low frequencies, there are other criteria, described below, which already do this and which should be used as an alternative to NR.

5.A8.2 Noise criterion (NC) curves

Beranek developed criteria to ensure good speech intelligibility. Much of the original work was carried out in engineering offices where speech communication between colleagues was required, but where the background noise sometimes interfered. Beranek determined the highest levels, with respect to the mid frequency speech interference bands, which could occur at both higher and lower frequencies and still give 'acceptable' conditions. This work led successively to the NC[5.A8.4], the

PNC[5.A8.5], and the NCB[5.A8.6,5.A8.7] criteria, as problems with the each version became apparent.

Beranek[5.A8.4] describes the development of NC curves, the forerunner of both PNC and NCB. The work was aimed at determining the maximum noise level under which office workers maintain efficiency.

A relationship for acceptability was obtained, as follows:

$$\text{LL} - \text{SIL} \leq 22 \text{ units}$$

where LL is the Stevens loudness level[5.A8.8] and SIL is the three-band speech interference level, i.e. the arithmetic average of levels at 500 Hz, 1000 Hz and 2000 Hz. The result is based on the responses of 300 office workers in executive offices/small conference rooms and steno-graphic/engineering drafting rooms, during actual and contrived noise exposures.

The NC curves are a representation of the SIL/LL criteria on an octave band basis, i.e. the number attributed to the curve is equal to its speech interference level, whilst the loudness level (phons) for a spectrum following the curve is 22 units greater than the SIL, in accord with the relationship above. This permits maximum low frequency levels, whilst still satisfying the criterion adopted. Beranek was also aware of the complaint potential of beats and fluctuations at low frequencies, but did not include these. Bradley[5.A8.9] has studied fluctuations in HVAC noise.

NC is described in section 1 of CIBSE Guide A[5.A8.2]. It has been widely used in the assessment of noise in buildings. NC is a 'tangent' approach similar to NR. It was found that a noise spectrum closely following an NC curve, and therefore satisfying the basis for the curves, does not itself give a pleasant sound, but rather has both throb (rumble) and hiss. In a similar manner, an environmental noise, which falls off rapidly with frequency, can be annoying even though it does not exhibit tonal characteristics. NC should not be used for assessment in spaces that are sensitive to noise, but could have an application in non-sensitive areas, such as busy lobbies, where there is considerable activity noise.

5.A8.3 Room criterion (RC) Mark I and II

Blazier[5.A8.10] developed the RC Mark I curves on the spectrum of noise from 68 offices, which were known to have good acoustics, and later developed a method for determining the 'noise quality' of a spectrum[5.A8.11].

It was found that a spectrum falling at 5 dB/octave represented the noise in the offices. The levels in the lowest octave bands (16 Hz and 31.5 Hz) indicate the possibility of noise-induced vibration of lightweight building components. The RC Mark I curves are described in section 1 of CIBSE Guide A[5.A8.2]. Recent work, leading to RC Mark II, has modified the 16 Hz band to lower it to the same level as the 31.5 Hz band[5.A8.12]. Large, low frequency fluctuations, which can occur from poor running of fans, are controlled more effectively by this lower 16 Hz limit.

The use of RC Mk II is to derive a noise quality assessment for the HVAC noise. This is the method currently recommended by ASHRAE[5.A8.12].

5.A8.4 Balanced noise criterion (NCB)

Beranek[5.A8.6,5.A8.7] further modified the NC curves to produce the NCB, which extends down to the 16 Hz octave band. Beranek again starts with the proposition that the most important acoustical requirement of working spaces is satisfactory speech communication. Thus each curve is based around, and has the rating number of, its (four-band) speech interference level (SIL). The four band SIL is the average of the 500 Hz, 1000 Hz, 2000 Hz and 4000 Hz bands.

The second most important requirement is spectrum balance, which is a determinant of the 'quality' of the noise. Balance is obtained by equalising the octave band loudness levels of each band. This assumes that 'balance' is a function of octave band loudness.

The NCB curves are intended for both occupied and unoccupied space, including activity noise, which may be 10–15 dB above air handling noise at mid-frequencies and above, but similar to air handling noise at the lowest frequencies. The procedure for using NCB curves is described by Beranek[5.A8.6,5.A8.7], although neither the PNC or NCB criteria have gained widespread acceptance.

5.A8.5 Comparison of criteria

Rating curves at the levels of NC35, PNC35, RC35 Mark I and II, NCB35, NR35 are compared in Table 5.A8.1.

All criterion curves are very similar from 125 to 1000 Hz and fairly similar at higher frequencies, but diverge at lower frequencies. The divergence is such that the difference between NR35 and RC35 is 19 dB at 31.5 Hz. This means that a noise, which just met the NR35 criterion at 31.5 Hz, would exceed RC35 by 19 dB. The difference between the criteria is of no consequence if there is no low frequency noise present, but the difference does mean that a low frequency HVAC rumble, which would exceed the RC criterion, could still pass the NR criterion whilst being subjectively objectionable.

5.A8.6 The dBA

The dBA is a single number measure of a noise (see Appendix 5.A5). Its effectiveness in preventing disturbance depends, however, on the spectrum of the HVAC noise, as a wide range of spectra will give the same dBA reading. Reduction of dBA will not necessarily lead to a

Table 5.A8.1 Comparison of noise criteria

Octave band/ Hz	Sound pressure level obtained for stated criterion / dB					
	NC35	PNC35	RC35 Mk I	RC35 Mk II	NCB35	NR35
16	—	—	65	60	84	—
31.5	—	62	60	60	71	79
63	60	55	55	55	58	63
125	52	50	50	50	50	52
250	45	45	45	45	44	45
500	40	40	40	40	40	39
1000	36	35	35	35	37	35
2000	34	30	30	30	32	32
4000	33	28	25	25	30	30
8000	32	28	20	20	27	28

more acceptable noise. For example, a reduction of, say, 5 dBA for a noise with an audible tone will be most effective if the tone is controlling the overall value of the dBA. 125 Hz is attenuated by 16 dB in the dBA weighting, so that a tone at this frequency will have to be more than 16 dB above the levels of the mid frequencies for it to influence the dBA strongly. If an attempt at reducing the dBA did this by reducing higher frequencies, a lower frequency tone would become more prominent and disturbing.

5.A8.7 Assessment of criteria

The two decades from 1980 to 2000 have seen considerable developments in North America, which have made new criteria available for high quality acoustic design of ventilated buildings. The newer criteria, in particular RC, are not yet well known in the UK, but should be given serious consideration for use[5.A8.2]. Compliance with them ensures a subjectively neutral and acceptable sound in the room.

The NR criterion (noise rating) is not safe to use under all circumstances, since it permits unacceptable levels of low frequency noise. It is recommended that use of the NR be phased out.

The NC criterion is an improvement on the NR, although it is no longer recommended by ASHRAE except for non-sensitive locations. Developments from the NC, that is, PNC and NCB have not been widely accepted. RC and NCB are both given in ANSI Standard S12.2: *Criteria for evaluating room noise*[5.A8.13] as alternative methods for assessing room noise.

RC Mark II[5.A8.11] is a recent criterion, which has been developed specifically for assessment of occupant satisfaction in the presence of HVAC noise. It is used to give an indication of the quality of a noise, based on relative levels at low, mid and high frequencies, so that any correction required is focussed on the appropriate frequency range.

References (Appendix 5.A8)

5.A8.1 Kosten C W and Van Os G J Community reaction criteria for external noises *NPL Symposium 12: The Control of Noise* (London: Her Majesty's Stationery Office) (1962)

5.A8.2 *Environmental criteria for design* Section 1 in *Environmental design* CIBSE Guide A (London: Chartered Institution of Building Services Engineers) (1999)

5.A8.3 *Assessment of noise with regard to community response* (draft) R1996 (Geneva: International Standards Organisation) (1971)

5.A8.4 Beranek L L Revised criteria for noise in buildings *Noise Control* 19–27 (January 1957)

5.A8.5 Beranek L L, Blazier W E and Figwer J J Preferred noise criterion (PNC) curves and their application to rooms *J. Acoustical Soc. America* **50** 1223–1228 (1971)

5.A8.6 Beranek L L Balanced noise criterion (NCB) curves *J. Acoustical Soc. America* **86** (2) 650–664 (1989)

5.A8.7 Beranek L L Application of NCB noise criterion curves *Noise Control Eng.* **33** (2) 45–56 (1989)

5.A8.8 Stevens S S Perceived level of noise by Mark VII and decibels (E) *J. Acoust. Soc. America* **51** 575-601 (1972)

5.A8.9 Bradley J S Annoyance caused by constant amplitude and amplitude–modulated sounds containing rumble *Noise Control Eng.* **42** (6) 203–208 (1994)

5.A8.10 Blazier W E Revised noise criteria for application in the acoustical design and rating of HVAC systems *Noise Control Eng.* **16** (2) 64–73 (1981)

5.A8.11 Blazier W E RC Mark II: A refined procedure for rating noise of heating ventilating and air conditioning (HVAC) systems in buildings *Noise Control Eng.* **45** (6) 243–250 (1997)

5.A8.12 *Sound and vibration control* Chapter 46 in ASHRAE Handbook: *HVAC Applications* (Atlanta GA: American Society of Heating, Refrigerating and Air-conditioning Engineers) (1999)

5.A8.13 *Criteria for evaluating room noise* ANSI Standard S12.2 (New York NY: American National Standards Institute) (1995)

Index